EGON RONAY'S

CELLNET GUIDE

HOTELS & RESTAURANTS

1989

HOTELS, RESTAURANTS AND INNS GREAT BRITAIN AND IRELAND

WITH COMPLIMENTS FROM CELLNET

EGON RONAY'S GUIDE

Egon Ronay's Guides
City Wall House,
Basing View,
Basingstoke,
Hampshire RG21 2AP

EDITORIAL CONTRIBUTORS
Roy Johnstone
Joy Langridge

DESIGN
Carole Thomas Design Associates

COVER DESIGN
Spero Communications Design Ltd

MARKETING AND SPONSORSHIP
CONSULTANTS
Spero Marketing Consultancy Ltd

Cartography revised by Intermap PS Ltd
All road maps are based on the Ordnance Survey Maps, with the permission of the Controller of HM Stationery Office. Crown copyright reserved. All town plans are based on aerial photographs.

The contents of this book are believed correct at the time of printing. Nevertheless, the publisher can accept no responsibility for errors or omissions or changes in the details given.

Distributed in the United Kingdom by the Publishing Division of The Automobile Association, Fanum House, Basingstoke, Hampshire RG21 2EA and overseas by the British Tourist Authority, Thames Tower, Black's Road, London W6 9EL.

ISBN 0 86145 781 1

AA Reference 58023

Typeset in Great Britain by William Clowes Limited, Beccles and London

Printed in Great Britain by Jarrold and Sons Ltd, Norwich

CONTENTS

PAGE

How to use this Guide 8
Explanation of symbols

Foreword 10
A word from our sponsor

Introduction 11
Egon Ronay sums up

Awards for Excellence 15
Unique Wedgwood plaques for Hotel and Restaurant of the Year

    Hotel of the Year 16
    The three finalists

    Restaurant of the Year 18
    The three finalists

Inspector for a day 39
The stars have their say

A Wheelchair's Eye View 48
How a new hotel measures up to the scrutiny of a disabled guest

Six of the Best 51
Profiles of six leading hotel managers

Cellar of the Year 57
Our panel chooses ten finalists for the annual Egon Ronay's Guides
Noilly Prat Award

Outstanding wine lists 61
Other distinguished cellars up and down the land

A Taste of Twenty Pinot Noirs 66
Our wine expert knows the score, plus vintage charts

Credit, Travel and Entertainment Cards 78

Just Desserts 104
A sweet selection from star chefs

Coffee Award of Excellence 109
The Story of Coffee
The three finalists for the first Egon Ronay's Guides Master Blend
Award. Also a list of the other award winners 113

Cheese Symbol of Excellence 116
Advertising feature from Dairy Crest

SPECIAL INVESTIGATION 140
Weekend activity breaks

The Fiat guide to successful motoring 158
Fiat main and service dealers

An offer for answers 893
A discount off next year's Guide

Reader's comments 925
Send us your reports

continued ...

Diners offer you a second Card. Free. What you do with it is your business.

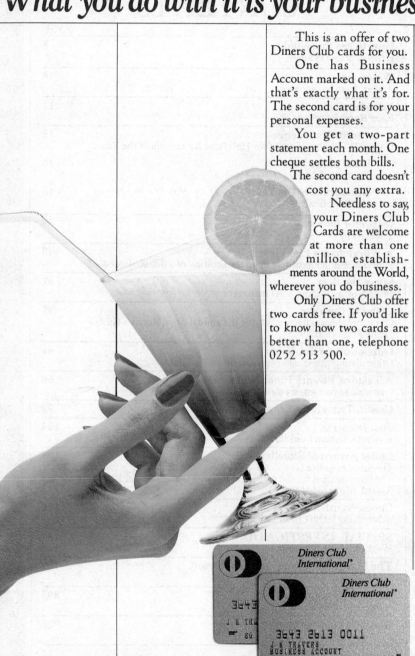

This is an offer of two Diners Club cards for you.

One has Business Account marked on it. And that's exactly what it's for. The second card is for your personal expenses.

You get a two-part statement each month. One cheque settles both bills.

The second card doesn't cost you any extra.

Needless to say, your Diners Club Cards are welcome at more than one million establishments around the World, wherever you do business.

Only Diners Club offer two cards free. If you'd like to know how two cards are better than one, telephone 0252 513 500.

Diners Club International®

Diners Club International®

3643 2613 0011
J H TRAVERS
BUSINESS ACCOUNT
86 DC UK 00/00 00/00 05

Diners means business (and pleasure)

QUICK REFERENCE LISTS

Starred restaurants   20
Elite eating
MAP

Fifteen minutes off the motorway   31
MAP and list of starred restaurants and high-grade hotels

De luxe and grade 1 hotels   74
The highest standards of accommodation

Town House hotels   81
Not all city hotels are faceless

Private House hotels   82
De luxe 'bed and breakfast' hotels

Country House hotels   83
Pastoral peace and personal service
MAP   84

Beautifully situated hotels   86
. . . where every prospect pleases
MAP   88

Hotels with sports facilities   92
Indulge in your favourite pastime: **swimming, fishing, riding, golf, squash, tennis.**

Restaurants with outstanding cheeseboards   114
We cream off the best

Restaurants with rooms   118
Meals are the main ingredient, but you can stay overnight

Seafood restaurants   119
There's a plaice for us

Sunday eating   121
In London and major cities

London restaurants with distinctly national cooking   130
First choose your country

Early evening eating in London   134
Before the curtain goes up . . .

Late night eating in London   137
. . . or after the last encore

Open-air eating   139
In and around London

A LOT FOR LESS – the budget section   165
LONDON RESTAURANTS under £30 for two   167
LONDON HOTELS under £60 for two   180
BED AND BREAKFAST under £38 for two   185
BARGAIN BREAKS   187

continued . . .

With a car like this who needs an office?

To find out why turn to pages 24–30.

Cellnet
THE CELLPHONE NETWORK

THE ENTRIES

HOTELS, RESTAURANTS AND INNS

LONDON	239
LONDON AIRPORTS	327
ENGLAND	333
SCOTLAND	721
WALES	799
CHANNEL ISLANDS	827
ISLE OF MAN	838
NORTHERN IRELAND	841
REPUBLIC OF IRELAND	849

THE MAPS

London and countrywide . . 897

TOWN PLANS
including sights and establishments

Bath	350	Manchester	560
Birmingham	362	Newcastle upon Tyne	582
Bournemouth	376	Oxford	598
Brighton	386	Stratford-upon-Avon	656
Bristol	394	York	716
Cambridge	408	Edinburgh	742
Canterbury	414	Glasgow	756
Chester	430	Cardiff	804
Harrogate	496	Belfast	842
Leeds	532	Cork	860
Liverpool	542	Dublin	864

SUMMARY OF COVERAGE
This guide includes the following number of establishments:

Hotels	1620
Inns	101
Restaurants	959
Total	2680

HOW TO USE THIS GUIDE

As well as our recommended establishments this Guide includes a wealth of interesting features and many useful quick reference lists designed to help you select the hotel or restaurant that best meets your requirements. These are to be found before the main gazetteer of listings which begins on page 239.

ORDER OF LISTINGS

London and London Airports appear first and are in alphabetical order by establishment name. Listings outside London are in alphabetical order by location within divisions of England, Scotland, Wales, Channel Islands, Isle of Man, Northern Ireland and the Republic. See contents page for specific page numbers.

MAP REFERENCES

Map references are to the map section at the back of the book or to a town plan printed with the entries. Use the map section to help select establishments in areas you wish to visit.

— ▲ —

HOTELS

Percentage ratings

According to their percentage rating, hotels are classified as:

De luxe	85–100%
Grade 1	70–84%
Grade 2	50–69%

Some entries are ungraded because of major construction or refurbishment programmes and therefore appear without a percentage rating in the gazetteer. See also Private House hotels below.

■ The percentage shown on a hotel entry is an individual rating arrived at after careful testing, inspection and calculation according to our unique grading system.

■ We assess hotels on 19 factors, which include the quality of service and the public rooms – their cleanliness, comfort, state of repair and general impression. Bedrooms are looked at for size, comfort, cleanliness and decor. The exterior of the building, efficiency of reception, conduct and appearance of the staff and room service are among other factors. The percentage is arrived at by comparing the total marks given for the 19 factors with the maximum the hotel could have achieved.

■ The size of the hotels and the prices charged are not considered in the grading, nor is the food. **If we recommend meals in a hotel or inn, a separate entry is made for its dining room.**

Price categories

These are based on the current price, including VAT (also service if applicable), for a double room for two occupants with private bath and cooked breakfast.

£A	over £130	£D	£58–£75
£B	£95–£130	£E	£40–£58
£C	£75–£95	£F	under £40

Where an entry states half-board only, the price also incudes dinner.

H Hotel entries are identified by the letter 'H'.

HR Hotels with restaurants that have a separate entry are identified by the letters 'HR'.

PH These hotels are categorised as Private House hotels and are not graded. They are de luxe 'bed and breakfast' hotels offering comfortable, often luxurious accommodation and personal service, but do not have a restaurant or public rooms, although some may have a drawing room (see page 82). This is a new classification this year especially created to highlight these fine establishments.

I Inns are identified by the letter 'I', and are not graded. We distinguish them from hotels by their more modest nature, usually with respect to the day rooms. For our purposes, an inn is normally either a pub with hotel-style accommodation or a small hotel with a bar and the atmosphere of a pub.

R (RR) Restaurants are identified by the letter 'R' or, if they also have accommodation, by the letters 'RR' (see also page 118).

Room service
If an establishment provides no room service, we print **None. All day** and **24 hours** give the hours during which room service is available. The exact nature of the service – whether you can get a sandwich or a full meal, whether at any time or only at mealtimes – will vary from one place to another.

♿ Considered by the management as suitable for wheelchairs.

Credit Credit cards accepted by the establishment.

Dogs Dogs are usually welcome unless an entry states specifically 'No dogs'.

RESTAURANTS

★ ★★ ★★★
We award one to three stars for excellence of cooking. One star represents cooking much above average, two outstanding cooking, and three the best in the land.

■ We only include restaurants where the cooking comes up to our minimum standards, however attractive the place may be in other respects. We take into account how well the restaurant achieves what it sets out to do as reflected in the menu, decor, prices, publicity, atmosphere – factors that add up to some sort of expectation.

♔ ♔♔ ♔♔♔
These refer to the degree of luxury in a restaurant and have nothing to do with the quality of the cooking.

♨ This shows that the cooking is done by the owner or a member of the family.

♗ We use the wine glass symbol to indicate a house wine that is judged well chosen by our inspectors.

♨ We use the coffee pot symbol to highlight those establishments selected for our Coffee Award of Excellence (see page 113).

▱ This symbol represents a wine list that is outstanding. *Also* see page 61.

▱ Indicates a restaurant with a good cheeseboard (see page 116).

About £..... for two
The approximate cost (except in the Budget Section—**A Lot for Less**) of a three-course meal including wine, coffee, service and VAT. This is based on a choice from average-priced dishes on the menu and includes one of the least expensive bottles of wine.

FOREWORD

Once again it is my pleasure to welcome you to *Egon Ronay's Cellnet Guide to Hotels and Restaurants.* Together our two organisations are entering the third year of our partnership and I hope that you are able to regard the Guide as an old friend, as I do – one who can be relied upon to give you the advice you need exactly when you need it. Over the years I have used the Guide many times to plan ahead for meetings and accommodation. It is because of this personal experience that I am more than happy to continue my company's support for an enterprise which maintains the standard of excellence which Cellnet has achieved in its own area of business.

To those of you who will be using the Guide for the first time I extend a special welcome. You will find that the inspectors who compile this reference work are meticulous in their attention to detail and bear the user of the Guide in mind at all times. In the same way Cellnet's philosophy is continuously to examine ways in which we might develop the system to cater for the particular needs of our customers.

Those readers who are already Cellnet customers will recognise Cellnet's influence on the Guide to ensure its utility for the business traveller. We are continuing the 'Off The Motorway' guide to hotels and restaurants within easy reach of a motorway junction.

Cellnet takes pride in every area of its operation and this includes the organisations and projects with which we are associated. *Egon Ronay's Cellnet Guide to Hotels and Restaurants* has always been a credit to us and I welcome our joint involvement for a third year. Armed with the Guide and a Cellnet cellphone you will never be at a loss for a meeting venue no matter how far away from the office you may be.

THE CELLPHONE NETWORK

Colin Davis
Managing Director, Cellnet

INTRODUCTION

Can you imagine?

3,000 nights a year in hotel beds!

It is not an exclamation meant to underline either the number of Guide inspectors going around testing hotels, or the thoroughness of hotel inspections. It is a heartfelt commiseration with the unfortunate men and women who have to spend most of their nights – you might be surprised to learn – in discomfort. Sagging beds; sloping beds; narrow beds; short beds; beds too soft; beds too hard; a rogue spring here, a hard button there; thin rubber mattresses that won't keep down the tucked-in sheets; unsavoury blankets, touched, coughed and sneezed on by dozens of guests before you, without freshly laundered top-covers, not to mention the un-cleaned duvets; and, of course, next morning's backache and stiff-ness even in the youngest testers.

Perhaps too many hoteliers have forgotten the obvious: the main objective of spending a night at a hotel is not to experience bur-nished lampshades and deep-pile carpets in the lounge, half a dozen varieties of malt whisky in the bar, nor the very rare smile at the reception desk. One's aim is an attractive bedroom with a really comfortable bed with a good, well-balanced mattress, preferably on a solid, well-sprung base. (It is not for nothing that the Savoy Hotel manufactures its own beds, and some Americans even have one shipped home after experiencing it.)

GAME OF MONOPOLY

The Guide, always useful for choosing a restaurant, has now be-come essential for choosing a hotel, too. Gone are the days when you could go by the name of the owning corporation, which is now often meaningless. The veritable game of Monopoly in the last decade is exemplified by this cir-cular: 'Please note that both the Ladbrokes in Basingstoke are now Hiltons.' There was a time when, for example, Crest hotels were owned by Crest Hotels. Now, as far as the general public is concerned, the question of who owns Crest hotels, i.e. what is the foun-tainhead of standards applying to them, is worthy of the Mastermind series. Are Holiday Inns really Crest Hotels, or vice versa? Or do they belong to Bass? Do Crest Hotels own Holiday Inns, or could they be a subsidiary of Grand Met-ropolitan? Or are the standards of both governed by a multinational conglomerate, or an Arab Emi-rate, or an Egyptian owner of department stores? Might the style have been set by Tiny Rowland himself?! On the whole, it strikes me as a change for the better: a hotel, once again, has to be judged not by its owning company, but by its management team. Forget about the chains and corporations (this is the only one of the leading guides that does not print their names and you can see why) – go by the write-up in the Guide.

Let me draw your attention to a new and important category of accommodation: *private house hotels*, not conventional hotels as they do not offer the full range of hotel services, particularly restaurants. But they can be every bit as pleasant and luxurious (and almost as expensive) as a top hotel, with as good – often better – service. Many people will prefer their more genteel ambience to the hurly-burly of a typical hotel.

CREDIT WHERE IT'S DUE

This Guide has done an enormous amount in its 30 years of existence to popularise chefs personally by giving them their due instead of ascribing the cuisine's merit to the proprietors, and by making the public conscious of their names, personalities and record. Yet there are those who brazenly take guides and critics to task for criticising caterers while – allegedly – gaining their living from them. The boot is, of course, on the other foot. The business of restaurants has benefited very substantially from guide recommendations for decades. Plays can be made successful by drama critics, but not the other way round. The practice of giving recognition to chefs has greatly contributed to the social recognition of their profession, to the point of its prac-

titioners being lionised and with the result of attracting more English youngsters into a hitherto overwhelmingly foreign domain.

YOU GET WHAT YOU PAY FOR

Have these young British stars been successful – not only in gaining laurels but also a well-deserved bank balance? One has to admire the talent, imagination, let alone the enthusiasm, near-manic dedication and inhumanly long hours of an increasing number of young British chefs and the surprising originality of some. There would be no difficulty in naming 30 or 40, some of whom have 'arrived' or have every hope of becoming truly great chefs. But there is a worrying question mark hanging over their heads. These young giants can only develop their ideas and style, and go from strength to strength to the glory of English cooking and the benefit of Britain's reputation if the public is prepared to pay for it. If it isn't, frustration and stagnation will set in and we shall slowly slide back towards the meat-and-two-veg scenario. You cannot be creative, let alone achieve perfection, on a shoestring. The public has to rethink what a restaurant meal is worth, because in the end we get the food we are prepared to pay for.

It would perhaps be exaggerated, as far as the past 12-18 months are concerned, to spotlight any particular development in restaurant food trends. But there is one exception: the proliferation of very high quality, traditional, British farmhouse cheeses, now competitive with the best French cheeseboards. Who would have thought it ten years ago?

PRESTIGE OF WAITING

'Hello Nick! Hello Jean! I am Fred, your waiter for tonight' – sounds fanciful and repugnant, but if we are not careful, informality of service, covering a total lack of skill, might go over the top before long. The reason why the British shun this highly skilled occupation is not the confusion between service and servility, but the lack of social acceptance of waiting as a profession. The industry and the catering colleges should do infinitely more to bring about a radical change. 'I am a *chef*' sounds good. But there are not many who would want to say: 'I am a *waiter*.' For years now I have advocated the introduction of an educational system that would result in a diploma combined with letters a candidate can affix to his/her name on achieving some standard proved by examination. Trade Associations should turn some of their attention to finding the best young waiters, and to promotional drives to improve the image of the skilled waiter. As for proprietors, how many send their wine waiters on regular wine-tasting courses so that they can, in time, give us reliable advice from their own experience? There is no doubt that skilled attention is half the pleasure of dining out. I look forward to the day when young British waiters will understand and appreciate the satisfaction they can get from making other people happy and satisfied.

In fact the same idea motivates the Publisher of this Guide. It is also the best guarantee to keep the gap between its circulation and that of its competitors as wide as it is at present. That is why every letter received from readers is seriously considered: be it a complaint or praise or suggestion of any kind, it is acted upon.

AN IRISH STORY, BUT TRUE

This continuous effort to give satisfaction can sometimes be reciprocated in the most unexpected circumstances, such as when an inspector got lost in Dublin on the night of the Eurovision Song Contest. Worried about being late for his test dinner, he flagged down a passing Garda motorbike rider. Too honest to invent an emergency situation, he explained his predicament and identity, confessing that he was simply late for dinner. The Garda, fully aware of the importance of the matter and perhaps with an eye on the reputation of Irish hospitality, reassured him: 'Leave it to us, sir!' and the startled but grateful inspector found his car led, at frightening speed, through all the red lights, by the dutiful Irishman, and flanked by the other motorbikes with flashing lights, to be delivered on time to his dinner table. **'Céad míle fáilte!'** (a hundred thousand welcomes) indeed.

EGON RONAY

AWARDS FOR EXCELLENCE

Each year the Guide selects a Hotel and a Restaurant of the Year, chosen on the basis of consistent excellence and/or outstanding enterprise. There are three finalists for each award, and the winners for 1989 will be announced in November 1988 at the Guide's celebrity launch, where they will be presented with unique Wedgwood plates which will be theirs to keep. Made of Queensware, these plaques will feature a handpainted view of each winning establishment.

The most recent winners, starting with 1988, have been:

HOTEL OF THE YEAR

Park Hotel Kenmare,
Kenmare

Homewood Park,
Freshford

Inn on the Park,
London W1

Hambleton Hall,
Oakham

Cromlix House,
Dunblane

RESTAURANT OF THE YEAR

Morels,
Haslemere

Walnut Tree Inn,
Abergavenny

Le Manoir aux Quat' Saisons,
Great Milton

Chez Nico,
London SW8

Dorchester Grill Room,
London W1

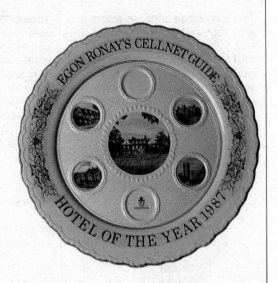

See overleaf for our 1989 finalists ▶

CARLYON BAY HOTEL

Carlyon Bay, Cornwall

The clifftop setting is spectacular, and the whole place is well groomed, friendly and most inviting, with fresh flowers a feature throughout. The grounds include an 18-hole golf course, and guests will find almost endless possibilities for leisure and relaxation. Bedrooms have a pleasant, restful appeal, enhanced in many cases by wonderful views. Full marks to keen manager David London and his smart, hard-working team.

HUNSTRETE HOUSE

Hunstrete, Nr Bristol, Avon

An outstanding country house hotel set in quite beautiful surroundings created by John and Thea Dupays and reflecting their interests – antiques, paintings (many by Thea herself), pottery and porcelain, as well as the magnificent gardens and deer-grazed parkland. Elegant public rooms, lovely bedrooms with discreet service – a haven of peace and tranquillity, yet just a short drive from Bath and Bristol.

HOTEL OF THE YEAR 1989

Our finalists for 1989
are as follows,
listed alphabetically:

★ **CARLYON BAY HOTEL**
  Carlyon Bay, Cornwall

★ **HUNSTRETE HOUSE**
  Hunstrete, nr Bristol, Avon

★ **THE SAVOY**
  London, WC2

THE SAVOY

London, WC2

A hundred years after first opening its doors, the Savoy is still a very special hotel, and a stay here remains a unique experience. Timeless style and elegance combine with superb service, tip-top comfort and the latest in technology. Willy Bauer has few peers among hotel managers, and his immaculately uniformed staff do him great credit.

EGON
RONAY'S
GUIDE

L'ARLEQUIN

London, SW8

Quality is stamped on every dish that charming, modest Christian Delteil produces, and his talent and Gallic flair have made his elegant Battersea restaurant a must for discriminating eaters of the eighties. The lunchtime set menu provides what must surely be the best value for money in town. Service matches the cooking, and Christian's wife Geneviève is a delightful and well-informed *patronne*.

L'ORTOLAN

Shinfield, Berkshire

Stylish perfection in a converted vicarage. John Burton-Race's menus make mouth-watering reading, and choosing is a delicious dilemma, with every dish seeming to be the right one. Maybe every dish *is* the right one, as results on the plate exceed even their seductive descriptions. Service is discreet and well timed, and the improved cellar now does justice to the cooking.

RESTAURANT OF THE YEAR 1989

Our finalists for 1989
are as follows,
listed alphabetically:

★ **L'ARLEQUIN**
London, SW8

★ **L'ORTOLAN**
Shinfield, Berkshire

★ **RAMORE**
Portrush, Co Antrim

RAMORE

Portrush, Co Antrim

Huge picture windows overlook the harbour, making a fine backdrop for an attractive restaurant with highly professional family owners. Joy Caithness provides the warmest of welcomes, and son-in-law George McAlpin produces surprise after surprise from the kitchen, applying his brand of magic to the freshest of produce. Flavours are always in happy harmony, sauces classical, presentation a delight.

EGON
RONAY'S
GUIDE

STARRED RESTAURANTS

★★★
THREE STAR RESTAURANTS

LONDON

La Tante Claire, **SW3**

ENGLAND

Great Milton: Le Manoir aux Quat' Saisons
Shinfield: L'Ortolan

★★
TWO STAR RESTAURANTS

LONDON

L'Arlequin, **SW8**
Le Gavroche, **W1**
Harvey's, **SW17**
Inter-Continental Hotel, Le Soufflé, **W1**
Simply Nico, **SW1**

ENGLAND

Bray-on-Thames: Waterside Inn
Staddle Bridge: McCoy's

SCOTLAND

Peat Inn: The Peat Inn

★
ONE STAR RESTAURANTS

LONDON

Clarke's, **W8**
The Connaught Restaurant, **W1**
Hyatt Carlton Tower, Chelsea Room, **SW1**
Inigo Jones, **WC2**
Le Mazarin, **SW1**
Le Meridien Piccadilly, Oak Room, **W1**
Odins, **W1**
Le Poulbot, **EC2**
Rue St Jacques, **W1**
Savoy Restaurant, **WC2**
Sutherlands, **W1**
Tiger Lee, **SW5**

Continued overleaf

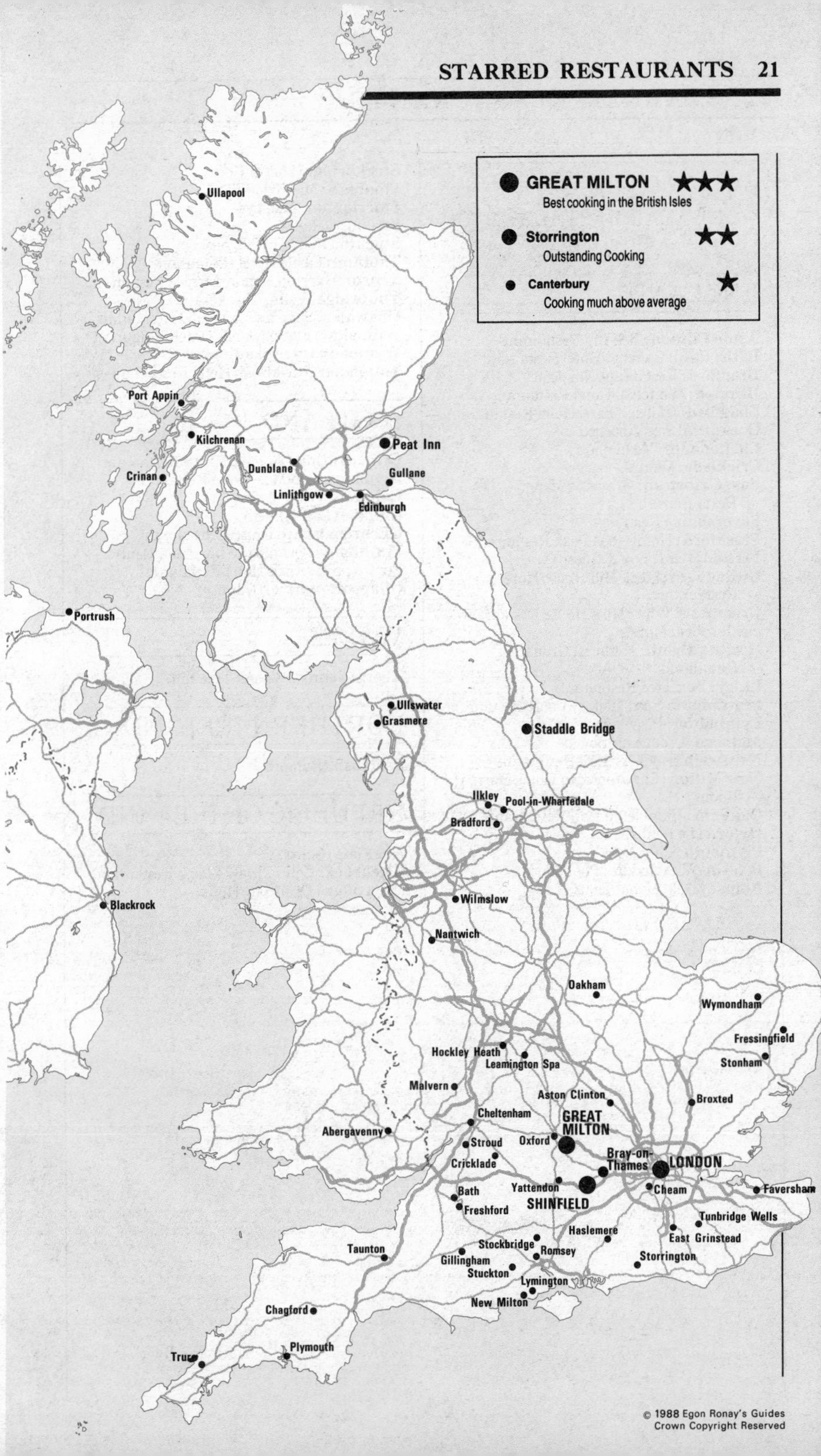

GREAT MILTON ★★★
Best cooking in the British Isles

Storrington ★★
Outstanding Cooking

Canterbury ★
Cooking much above average

Ullapool

Port Appin
Kilchrenan
Crinan
Dunblane
Linlithgow
Edinburgh
Peat Inn
Gullane

Portrush

Ullswater
Grasmere
Staddle Bridge

Ilkley
Pool-in-Wharfedale
Bradford

Blackrock

Wilmslow
Nantwich

Oakham
Wymondham
Fressingfield
Stonham

Hockley Heath
Leamington Spa
Malvern
Aston Clinton
Broxted

Abergavenny
Cheltenham
Stroud
Cricklade
Bath
Freshford

Oxford
GREAT MILTON
Bray-on-Thames
Yattendon
SHINFIELD
LONDON
Cheam
Faversham
Tunbridge Wells
East Grinstead
Storrington

Taunton
Stockbridge
Gillingham
Stuckton
Romsey
Haslemere
Lymington
New Milton

Chagford
Plymouth
Truro

★
ONE STAR RESTAURANTS
continued

ENGLAND

Aston Clinton: Bell Inn Restaurant
Bath: Royal Crescent Hotel Restaurant
Bradford: Restaurant Nineteen
Broxted: Whitehall Hotel Restaurant
Chagford: Gidleigh Park Hotel Restaurant
Cheam: Al San Vincenzo
Cheltenham: Redmond's
Cricklade: Whites
East Grinstead: Gravetye Manor Restaurant
Faversham: Read's
Freshford: Homewood Park Restaurant
Fressingfield: Fox & Goose
Gillingham: Stock Hill House Hotel Restaurant
Grasmere: White Moss House Restaurant
Haslemere: Morels
Hockley Heath: Nuthurst Grange Restaurant
Ilkley: Box Tree Restaurant
Leamington Spa: Mallory Court Restaurant
Lymington: Provence
Malvern: Croque-en-Bouche
Nantwich: Rookery Hall Restaurant
New Milton: Chewton Glen Hotel, Marryat Room
Oakham: Hambleton Hall Restaurant
Oxford: Le Petit Blanc
Plymouth: Chez Nous
Pool-in-Wharfedale: Pool Court
Romsey: Old Manor House

Stockbridge: Sheriff House
Stonham: Mr Underhill's
Storrington: Manleys
Stroud: Oakes
Stuckton: The Three Lions
Taunton: Castle Hotel Restaurant
Truro: Alverton Manor, Terrace Restaurant
Tunbridge Wells: Thackeray's House
Ullswater: Sharrow Bay Hotel Restaurant
Wilmslow: Stanneylands Hotel Restaurant
Wymondham: Adlard's
Yattendon: Royal Oak Hotel Restaurant

SCOTLAND

Crinan: Crinan Hotel, Lock 16 Restaurant
Dunblane: Cromlix House Restaurant
Edinburgh: Handsel's
Gullane: La Potinière
Kilchrenan: Ardanaiseig Restaurant
Linlithgow: Champany Inn Restaurant
Port Appin: Airds Hotel Restaurant
Ullapool: Altnaharrie Inn

WALES

Abergavenny: Walnut Tree Inn

NORTHERN IRELAND

Portrush: Ramore

REPUBLIC OF IRELAND

Ahakista: Shiro
Blackrock: Colin O'Daly's Park Restaurant
Moycullen: Drimcong House

If you have an enquiry about cellphones, ask us. The Japanese did.

When anyone wants advice on electronics they think of the Japanese. When the Japanese wanted advice on cellphones, they thought of Cellnet. Which is why they asked us to act as consultants when they decided to set up a new cellular phone system.

It had to be the best in the world.

It will function on a similar specification as the one used in the Cellnet UK network. They couldn't find a more perfect model.

We now cover over 94% of the country and no one has more experience of cellular communications. We have divided the country into a large number of small cells.

Each one is controlled by a transmitter.

This connects the cellphone calls made in its area to a digital exchange, which is purpose built to our own design.

These exchanges switch the call either to another cellphone or to the landline phone system as necessary which enables you to contact any phone in the world.

In densely populated areas such as city centres, extra capacity and quality are guaranteed.

This is achieved by dividing up each cell into smaller sectors. Each of these can perform like a single cell.

This special four cell repeat pattern is another example of Cellnet's advanced technology. And another reason why we are the acknowledged world leaders.

Whatever type of cellphone you're considering – a car phone, a pocket mobile phone or self-contained transportable – Cellnet provides a host of additional advanced services. Including taking and sending messages. Personal operator services. Direct links with your office extension. Mobile transmission of data. Faxes and a full 24 hour information service.

Post the coupon on page 30 or phone us now on 0800 424 323.

It's what the Japanese would suggest.

Cellnet
THE CELLPHONE NETWORK

With a car like this who needs an office?

Thanks to Cellnet a car can be a better equipped office than most offices. You can send facsimile documents and plans. Tap into a computer system for placing orders, receiving information or leaving and receiving messages. Using the same Cellnet network that is used for ordinary cellphones and with its special sectorisation system, provides the highest capacity cellular system available. Even in the heart of London Cellnet's advanced cellular technology can increase the capacity of the system fourfold.

Ensuring the clearest possible reception on all types of cellphone.

With data transmission, the need for accuracy is of special

concern. A decimal point in the wrong place or a missing word can be crucial mistakes in business. For this reason special techniques for eliminating mistakes before they happen are built into the Cellnet system. Because the same Cellnet network is used as for cellphones, you can make or receive data calls from your car or briefcase. And be connected to another telephone anywhere in the world. The choice of equipment is wide. Almost all types of BABT approved equipment are compatible. You can use whatever is most suited to your normal business needs.

Many other services are available. The 24 hour personal operator service. Direct connection with your own office extension, so that you remain part of the normal switchboard service. And of course the special service for leaving messages on your own voice mailbox. As well as special alerters to tell you when there are messages awaiting your attention.

So when you choose a cellphone make sure you specify the Cellnet system. Whether you need a carphone, a pocket size portable or a self-contained transportable for site use, you will have not just the most advanced system. But the most advanced backing to go with it. The 'office car' takes on a new meaning. Post the coupon on page 30 or phone us now on 0800 424 323.

Cellnet
THE CELLPHONE NETWORK

*H*e takes his secretary on every trip.

With the Cellnet system you need never be without the facilities of a secretary, even though you are miles away from the office.
Working men and women can work whatever hours they want.

And working husbands need never be without the approval of their wives.

The Cellnet 24 hour operators give you help and advice
whatever the time of day or night.

Our operators will find numbers and make connections just
as your secretary does. We even have operators who will organise
flowers or champagne for you before you arrive for an anniversary

that slipped your memory.

Cellnet are pledged to provide the best possible service to all their subscribers wherever they are. And Cellnet cover over 94% of the UK including the Channel Isles and the Isle of Man.

We provide the communication services you need in running a business, in keeping with our position as the world leaders in cellular phone technology.

Apart from constant communication with customers wherever you travel, there are the benefits of the 600 messaging service. This will alert you when messages are received and store them until you've finished and are ready to deal with them. Just as your secretary does.

And equipment has also been developed so that you can fax plans or documents, use computers, and plug into data systems. As easily as if you were in the office.

When you choose a cellphone be sure to specify the Cellnet system. It's revolutionised business and you can be sure you are not just getting the most advanced system but you will be kept up-to-date with all the latest developments as they happen.

Which is why all working men and women should post the coupon, on page 30 or phone us now on 0800 424 323.

29

Cellnet

THE CELLPHONE NETWORK

Free information and guide updates

To be sure of receiving free updates of Egon Ronay's Cellnet Guide recommendations, and, or information about Cellnet, please complete and return the coupon below or, if you prefer, ring 0800 424 323 giving the necessary details.

The updates are published exclusively in Cellnet's customer magazine Selection and your name will be added to our distribution list for future issues.

Please cut along the perforation and send to;

Cellnet, Dept. ERGZ,
Freepost, Conrad House, Birmingham Road,
Stratford-Upon-Avon, Warwickshire, CV73 0BR.

Please tick the appropriate box

☐ Please send me information about Cellnet.

☐ Please send me information about Cellnet and future copies of Selection with free updates to the Guide.

☐ I am an existing Cellnet user but do not receive copies of Selection. Please add my name to your distribution list. My cellphone number is 0860_____

Name _____
Position/Title _____
Company _____
Nature of Business _____
Address _____
_____
Postcode _____ Business Tel _____

15 MINUTES OFF THE MOTORWAY

Eating in the motorway service areas may cut out extra travelling time, but it also cuts out any possibility of pleasing the discerning palate.

Yet throughout the land outstanding eating is available just a short drive from the motorway network, and the map and list that follow pinpoint starred restaurants that need no more than a 15-minute detour. And if you're looking for somewhere to spend the night in style, we also feature de luxe and grade 1 hotels within a similar range.

So even when time is important, you don't have to leave out the good things—just leave the motorway!

For further details of these establishments, see individual entries in the main section of the Guide.

ENGLAND

M1

JUNCTION 7
St Albans, Noke Thistle Hotel
JUNCTION 12
Flitwick, Flitwick Manor
JUNCTION 13
Aspley Guise, Moore Place Hotel
JUNCTION 16
Northampton, Swallow Hotel
JUNCTION 22
Leicester, Holiday Inn
JUNCTION 23
Quorn, Quorn Country Hotel
JUNCTION 24
Castle Donington, Donington Thistle Hotel
JUNCTION 25
Nottingham, Albany Hotel
Nottingham, Royal Moat House International Hotel
JUNCTION 28
South Normanton, Swallow Hotel
JUNCTION 34
Rotherham, Rotherham Moat House
JUNCTION 47
Leeds, Hilton International

M2

JUNCTION 7
Canterbury, County Hotel
Canterbury, Howfield Manor

M3

JUNCTION 2
Egham, Great Fosters
Egham, Runnymede Hotel
JUNCTION 3
Ascot, Royal Berkshire Hotel
Bagshot, Pennyhill Park Hotel
JUNCTION 5
Rotherwick, Tylney Hall
JUNCTION 8
Winchester, Lainston House
JUNCTION 10
Turners Hill, Alexander House

M4

JUNCTION 4
Heathrow Airport (West Drayton), Excelsior Hotel
Heathrow Airport (West Drayton), Holiday Inn
Heathrow Airport, Sheraton-Heathrow
Heathrow Airport (Hayes), Sheraton Skyline

JUNCTION 6
　Slough, Holiday Inn
　Windsor, Oakley Court Hotel
JUNCTION 8/9
　Bray-on-Thames, Waterside Inn
　Maidenhead, Fredrick's Hotel
　Taplow, Cliveden
JUNCTION 11
　Reading, Caversham Hotel
　Reading, Ramada Hotel
　Shinfield, L'Ortolan
JUNCTION 13
　Yattendon, Royal Oak Hotel Restaurant
JUNCTION 15
　Swindon, Blunsdon House Hotel
JUNCTION 16
　Swindon, Pear Tree Hotel
JUNCTION 17
　Beanacre, Beechfield House
　Castle Combe, Manor House
　Easton Grey, Whatley Manor Hotel
JUNCTION 18
　Bath, Aspley House Hotel
　Bath, Francis Hotel
　Bath, Priory Hotel
　Bath, Royal Crescent Hotel & Restaurant
　Colerne, Lucknam Park Hotel
JUNCTION 19
　Bristol, Grand Hotel
　Bristol, Holiday Inn
　Bristol, Ladbroke Dragonara Hotel

M5

JUNCTION 4
　Bromsgrove, Grafton Manor
　Chaddesley Corbett, Brockencote Hall
JUNCTION 5
　Abberley, Elms Hotel
　Droitwich Spa, Château Impney Hotel
JUNCTION 7
　Worcester, Fownes Hotel
JUNCTION 8
　Malvern, Croque-en-Bouche
JUNCTION 9
　Corse Lawn, Corse Lawn House
JUNCTION 10
　Cheltenham, The Greenway
　Cheltenham, Redmond's
JUNCTION 11
　Gloucester, Hatton Court
JUNCTION 13
　Stroud, Oakes
JUNCTION 14
　Thornbury, Thornbury Castle
JUNCTION 25
　Hatch Beauchamp, Farthings Country
　　House Hotel
　Taunton, Castle Hotel & Restaurant
JUNCTION 29
　Whimple, Woodhayes

M6

JUNCTION 2/3
　Coventry, Ansty Hall
　Coventry, De Vere Hotel

JUNCTION 6
　Birmingham, Albany Hotel
　Birmingham, Copthorne Hotel
　Birmingham, Holiday Inn
　Birmingham, Metropole & Warwick
　　Hotel
　Birmingham, Plough & Harrow Hotel
　Sutton Coldfield, New Hall
JUNCTION 17
　Congleton, Great Moreton Hall Hotel
　Nantwich, Rookery Hall & Restaurant
JUNCTION 40
　Penrith, North Lake Gateway Hotel
　Ullswater, Leeming House Hotel
　Ullswater, Sharrow Bay Hotel &
　　Restaurant
JUNCTION 42
　Wetheral, Crown Hotel
JUNCTION 43
　Brampton, Farlam Hall Hotel

M11

JUNCTION 8
　Broxted, Whitehall Hotel & Restaurant
　Hatfield Heath, Down Hall Hotel

M18

JUNCTION 2
　Doncaster, Doncaster Moat House

M20

JUNCTION 3
　Wrotham Heath, Post House Hotel
JUNCTION 8
　Hollingbourne, Great Danes Hotel
　Lenham, Chilston Park
JUNCTION 9
　Ashford, Eastwell Manor
JUNCTION 11
　Hythe, Hythe Imperial Hotel
JUNCTION 13
　Dover, Dover Moat House

M23

JUNCTION 10
　East Grinstead, Gravetye Manor &
　　Restaurant
　Gatwick Airport, Gatwick Hilton
　　International
　Gatwick Airport (Horley), Gatwick
　　Penta Hotel
JUNCTION 11
　Cuckfield, Ockenden Manor Hotel
　Lower Beeding, South Lodge
　Rusper, Ghyll Manor

M25

JUNCTION 7
　Croydon, Holiday Inn
　Croydon, Selsdon Park Hotel
JUNCTION 9
　Dorking, Burford Bridge Hotel

M27

JUNCTION 2/3
Romsey, Old Manor House
JUNCTION 12
Portsmouth, Holiday Inn

M40

JUNCTION 4
Marlow, Compleat Angler Hotel
JUNCTION 7
Great Milton, Le Manoir aux Quat'
    Saisons & Restaurant
Oxford, Le Petit Blanc
Oxford, Randolph Hotel

M42

JUNCTION 5
Solihull, Regency Hotel
JUNCTION 9
Wishaw, Belfry Hotel

M50

JUNCTION 2
Ledbury, Hope End Country House

M53

JUNCTION 5
Puddington, Craxton Wood Hotel
JUNCTION 12
Chester, Chester Grosvenor
Chester, Crabwall Manor

M54

JUNCTION 4
Shifnal, Park House Hotel

M56

JUNCTION 5
Manchester Airport, Ladbroke
    International
JUNCTION 6
Handforth, Belfry Hotel
Wilmslow, Stanneylands Hotel &
    Restaurant

M62

JUNCTION 4
Liverpool, Atlantic Tower Thistle Hotel
JUNCTION 26
Halifax, Holdsworth House Hotel

M63

JUNCTION 9
Manchester, Holiday Inn Crown Plaza
    Midland
Manchester, Hotel Piccadilly
Manchester, Portland Thistle Hotel
Manchester, Ramada Renaissance

A1(M)   Northern Section

JUNCTION A
Kirkby Fleetham, Kirkby Fleetham
    Hall
JUNCTION E
Stockton on Tees, Swallow Hotel
JUNCTION N
Newcastle upon Tyne, County Thistle
    Hotel
Newcastle upon Tyne, Gosforth Park
    Thistle Hotel
Newcastle upon Tyne, Holiday Inn

SCOTLAND

M8

JUNCTION 2
Edinburgh, Caledonian Hotel
Edinburgh, Carlton Highland Hotel
Edinburgh, Edinburgh Sheraton
Edinburgh, George Hotel
Edinburgh, Handsel's
Edinburgh, King James Thistle Hotel
Edinburgh, Ladbroke Dragonara
JUNCTION 16
Glasgow, Hospitality Inn
JUNCTION 17
Glasgow, One Devonshire Gardens
Glasgow, Stakis Grosvenor Hotel
JUNCTION 17/18
Glasgow, Albany Hotel
JUNCTION 18
Glasgow, Holiday Inn
JUNCTION 31
Langbank, Gleddoch House Hotel

M9

JUNCTION 3
Linlithgow, Champany Inn Restaurant
JUNCTION 9
Dunblane, Cromlix House & Restaurant

WALES

M4

JUNCTION 25
Llangybi, Cwrt Bleddyn Hotel
JUNCTION 26
Newport, Celtic Manor Hotel
JUNCTION 32
Cardiff, Holiday Inn
Cardiff, Park Hotel
Cardiff, Stakis Inn on the Avenue
JUNCTION 34
Miskin, Miskin Manor

NORTHERN IRELAND

M2

JUNCTION 1
Holywood, Culloden Hotel

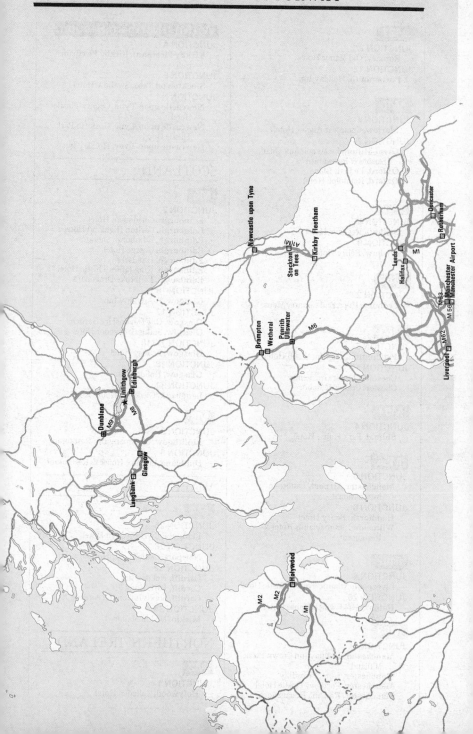

Hotel □
Restaurant ★
Hotel and Restaurant ⊞

M4 Junction 6   □ Slough
                 □ Windsor

M4 Junction 8/9 ★ Bray-on-Thames
                 ⊞ Maidenhead
                 ⊞ Taplow

THE *Cellnet* THEATRE GUIDE

A theatre visit can be easy to arrange with your cellphone. A call to the box office will usually reserve your tickets - or you can pay for them right away over the phone with your credit card.

Here is a list of most major theatres throughout Britain - compliments of Cellnet!

LONDON THEATRES	Box Office
ADELPHI Strand WC2E 7NH	01-836 7611
ALBERY St Martin's Lane WC2	01-836 3878
ALDWYCH Aldwych WC2	01-836 6404
AMBASSADORS West St WC2	01-836 6111
APOLLO Shaftesbury Ave W1	01-437 2663
APOLLO VICTORIA Wilton Rd SW1	01-630 6262
ARTS 6-7 Gt Newport St WC2	01-836 3334
ASTORIA Charing Cross Road WC2	01-434 0403
BARBICAN Barbican EC2Y 8BQ	01-628 8795
BLOOMSBURY Gordon St WC1H 0AH	01-387 9629
COLISEUM (English National Opera) St Martin's Lane WC2	01-836 3161
COMEDY Panton ST SW1	01-930 2578
COVENT GARDEN (Royal Opera House) WC2	01-240 1066
CRITERION Piccadilly Circus W1	01-930 3216
DRURY LANE (Theatre Royal) WC2	01-836 8108
DUCHESS Catherine St WC2	01-836 8243
DUKE OF YORK'S St Martin's Lane WC2	01-836 5122
FORTUNE Russell St WC2B 5HH	01-836 2238
GARRICK Charing Cross Rd WC2	01-836 4601
GLOBE Shaftesbury Ave W1	01-437 3667
HAYMARKET (Theatre Royal) SW1	01-930 9832
HER MAJESTY'S Haymarket SW1Y 4QL	01-930 4025
LYRIC King St Hammersmith W6 0QL	01-741 2311
LYRIC Shaftesbury Ave W1	01-437 3686
MAYFAIR Stratton St W1	01-629 3036
MERMAID Puddle Dock Blackfriars EC4	01-236 5568
NATIONAL Upper Ground South Bank SE1 9PX	01-928 2252
NEW LONDON Drury Lane WC2	01-405 0072
OLD VIC Waterloo Rd SE1 8NB	01-928 7616
PALACE Shaftesbury Ave W1	01-434 0909
PALLADIUM 8 Argyll St W1	01-437 7373
PHOENIX Charing Cross Rd WC2	01-836 2294
PICCADILLY Denman St W1	01-437 4506
PRINCE EDWARD Old Compton St W1	01-734 8951
PRINCE OF WALES Coventry St W1	01-839 5987
QUEEN'S Shaftesbury Ave WC2	01-734 1166
REGENT'S PARK (Open Air)	01-486 2431
ROYAL COURT Sloane Sq SW1	01-730 1745
SADLER'S WELLS Rosebery Ave EC1	01-278 8916
ST MARTIN'S West St WC2	01-836 1443
SAVOY Strand WC2	01-836 8888
SHAFTESBURY Shaftesbury Ave WC2	01-379 5399
SHAW 100 Euston Rd NW1 2AJ	01-388 1394
STRAND Aldwych WC2	01-836 2660

VAUDEVILLE Strand WC2	01-836 9987
VICTORIA PALACE Victoria St SW1	01-834 1317
WESTMINSTER Palace St SW1	01-834 0283
WHITEHALL Whitehall SW1	01-930 7765
WYNDHAM'S Charing Cross Rd WC2	01-836 3028
YOUNG VIC 66 The Cut SE1	01-928 6363

REGIONAL THEATRES

BELFAST "Lyric" 55 Ridgeway St Stranmillis Rd Belfast 9	0232 660081
BIRMINGHAM "Repertory" & "Studio" Broad St Birmingham B1 2EP	021-236 4455
BRISTOL "Theatre Royal & New Vic Studio" King St Bristol BS1 4ED	0272 264388
CHELTENHAM "Everyman" Regent St Cheltenham Glos GL5 1HQ	0242 512515
CHESTER "Gateway" Hamilton Pl Chester Cheshire CH1 2BH	0244 40393
COVENTRY "Belgrade" Belgrade Sq Coventry Warwickshire CV1 1GS	0203 553055
CREWE "Lyceum" 10 Heath St Crewe Cheshire CW1 2DA	0270 211149
DERBY "Playhouse" Theatre Walk Eagle Centre Derby Derbyshire DE1 2NF	0332 363275
DUNDEE "Repertory" Tay Square Dundee DD1 1PB	0382 23530
EASTBOURNE "Devonshire Park" Compton St Eastbourne Sussex	0323 36363
EDINBURGH "Royal Lyceum" Grindlay St Edinburgh EH3 9AX	031-229 9697
EXETER "Northcott' Stocker Rd Exeter Devon EX4 4QB	0392 54853
GLASGOW "Citizens" 119 Gorbals St Glasgow G5 9DS	041-429 0022
IPSWICH "Wolsey Theatre" Civic Dr Ipswich Suffolk IP1 2AS	0473 53725
LANCASTER "Duke's Playhouse" Moor La Lancaster Lancs LA1 1QE	0524 66645
LEEDS "Playhouse" Calverley St Leeds W Yorks LS2 3AJ	0532 442111
LEICESTER "Phoenix Arts" 11 Newarke St Leicester Leics LE1 5TA	0533 554854
LIVERPOOL "Playhouse" Williamson Sq Liverpool L2 1EL	051-709 8363
MANCHESTER "Royal Exchange" Cross St Manchester M2 7DH	061-833 9833
MILFORD HAVEN "Torch Theatre" St Peter's Rd Milford Haven SA73 2BU	064-62 5267
NEWCASTLE UPON TYNE "Playhouse" Barras Bridge Newcastle upon Tyne NE1 7RH	091-232 3421
NORTHAMPTON "Royal Theatre" & "Opera House" 19-21 Guildhall Rd Northampton Northants NN1 1DP	0604 32533
NOTTINGHAM "Playhouse" (Theatre Trust Ltd) Wellington Circus Nottingham NG1 5AF	0602 419419
OXFORD "Playhouse" Beaumont St Oxford OX1 2LW	0865 247134
PLYMOUTH "Theatre Royal" Royal Parade Plymouth Devon PL1 2TR	0752 669595
SALISBURY "Playhouse & Studio" Malthouse La Salisbury Wilts SP2 7RA	0722 20333
SHEFFIELD "Crucible" & "Studio" 55 Norfolk St Sheffield S1 1DA	0742 769922
SWANSEA "Grand" Singleton St Swansea SA1 3QJ	0792 475715
WINDSOR "Theatre Royal" Thames St Windsor Berks S14 1PS	0753 853888
YORK "Theatre Royal" St Leonard's Pl York YO1 2HD	0904 23568

You can tell a lot about a Hotel by the jam it serves.

You'll find Baxters Jams and Marmalades on the breakfast tables in some of the finest Hotels in the World.

They wouldn't settle for anything but the best for their guests.

Another nice thing about the Baxters Scottish range, is that it isn't only the preserve of Hotels.

You can have your own Baxters on your own breakfast table, at home.

You wouldn't serve anything but the best to *your* guests (or yourself) now would you?

BY APPOINTMENT TO
HER MAJESTY THE QUEEN

FRUIT CANNERS
W. A. BAXTER & SONS LTD

Baxters

BAXTERS OF SPEYSIDE LTD., SCOTLAND

INSPECTOR FOR A DAY

NANETTE NEWMAN AND BRYAN FORBES   PETER AND VIRGINIA BOTTOMLEY

RONNIE CORBETT   CLARE FRANCIS   SIR DAVID NAPLEY   STEVE CRAM

'Oh goody!' said a real inspector, tucking his toes under the table and consulting the bill of fare. 'Tonight I can eat what I please *and* I don't have to write a report about it!' It says much for the dedication of the Home Team that they can be relied on, year after year, to inspect hotels and restaurants, picking dishes that test the expertise of the kitchen regardless of personal preference. And the compilation of detailed reports – often to the strictest of deadlines – is not everyone's cup of tea. So our 'regulars' welcome the year's intake of guest celebrities, brief them thoroughly, then see to it that no plate is left unturned in the course of duty.

This year, we asked our guest inspectors to pick a venue, if possible, out of London. 'Is Newcastle far enough?' asked Steve Cram. It was, of course, but no-one could have known that the brasserie he chose would change hands a few days after his inspection. Things move fast in the restaurant business.

A quick glimpse at the diary of the Minister for Roads and Traffic (engagements in Lambeth, Carlisle, the City of London and Yorkshire – maybe two or more the same day), plus the fact that his wife is also a minister with similarly long-standing prior commitments, convinced us that, for Peter and Virginia Bottomley, London it would have to be. Even so, duty called – once – during the meal, in the form of the Commons' division bell.

Ronnie Corbett is a connoisseur, often to be found in the capital's best eating houses, but we persuaded him – good sport that he is – to choose a new venue. This time, *we* nearly didn't make it: foul weather, traffic jams and instant-sprouting roadworks ruined our carefully co-ordinated arrival. By the time we found the only usable telephone on the route from London to Haslemere, Ronnie was deciding the whole thing must be a hoax. As we catapulted into Morels, red-faced and distinctly *un*cool, straight for the loos, Ronnie and Anne collapsed in giggles: 'I've not seen an entrance like that for *quite* some time!' he chortled.

Nanette Newman, award-winning film actress (**The Raging Moon**, **International Velvet**), presenter of TV's popular **The Fun Food Factory,** and best-selling author (her third cookbook, **Nanette Newman Entertains**, is just published), is a wonderfully inventive cook. She credits television cooking series for widening our awareness of food, but finds it in her heart to 'wish we were more joyous and *relaxed* about eating – as they are in France'. Wherever Bryan eats, he 'must be made to feel welcome.' So turn the page and see how they fared.

NANETTE NEWMAN & BRIAN FORBES

VISIT

LE MANOIR AUX QUAT' SAISONS
Great Milton

For Nanette, ambience and décor are important ingredients in any meal. Bryan is 'interested in food, but not obsessively so'. About once every ten years, when not directing a film, finishing a novel (latest titles include **The Rewrite Man** and **The Endless Game**) or running his bookshop, he'll stray into the kitchen and surprise his wife with 'a wonderful soufflé or langoustines flambées'. ('I just follow a recipe and use the very best cognac,' he confides impishly.) At our behest, Nanette Newman and Bryan Forbes tackled one of Britain's premier eating establishments: **The Manoir aux Quat' Saisons.**

Nanette's report:

❝ Having to comment on this restaurant makes one feel like an inexperienced actor who's asked to pass judgement on Lord Olivier. Raymond Blanc is held in awe by many, such as myself, for his self-taught culinary genius and for developing a restaurant that is regarded as one of the best in England. On a sunny Sunday in early spring, one could not wish for a better setting: spring flowers, log fires and an ambience of understated confidence. The young waiters are excellent – charming and attentive in the best possible way. The service is smooth and unruffled and the presentation of the food is a delight to the eye. I chose the soufflé de sole et tourteau à la citronelle et gingembre (soufflé of crab nestled in a fillet of sole, served with a lemon barley and ginger-scented juice), having seen it in Raymond Blanc's magnificent cookbook. The sauce was excellent – a lovely hint of ginger and, rising out of the sole, a perfect creamy soufflé; although, if I'm honest, the sole was a bit tough. My main course was turbot: deliciously simple, a dish that – if you'd been ill – would soon tempt you back to food again. The pommes soufflées au sabayon de cidre (Calvados soufflé nestled in apple, baked, served with a cider sabayon sauce) was faultless – light and refreshing. I immediately wished I'd chosen the assiette du chef (minute portions of six desserts), a masterpiece of artistic decoration placed round an exquisite biscuit swan. Lovely coffee – constantly refilled. All in all, a very special Sunday lunch – possibly not *quite* as amazing as I had expected, but then with such a reputation preceding it, I doubt that any restaurant could quite live up to it. Superb though, nevertheless. ❞

Bryan adds:

❝ An outpost of France in rural England, and the perfect setting for those travellers prepared to make a detour in search of culinary delights. There's a welcoming atmosphere the moment one steps over the threshold and a superb wine list – even if some of the vintages require a second mortgage! The main dining room is intimate (perhaps a shade too intimate for my taste, for tables are cheek-by-jowl and conversations can be overheard). Bottled water is served the moment one sits down, which is sufficiently unusual in an English restaurant to merit a mention. My first course was inspired – an asparagus mousse presented like a Monet watercolour and totally delicious; I followed this with sea bass, living in great expectations, and, to be honest, I was marginally disappointed. However the Calvados soufflé served in a scooped-out apple shell was mouth-watering (being a lover of Calvados, I could have wished for a more generous taste . . .). All in all, a rich experience – for the rich! ❞

RONNIE CORBETT

V I S I T S

MORELS
Haslemere

Loved by millions of viewers for his appearances on **The Frost Report**, his many roles in the long-running comedy series **The Two Ronnies** (with friend and colleague Ronnie Barker) and his characterisation of the hapless Timothy in **Sorry!**, Ronnie Corbett readily admits to 'a consuming interest in food'. Though his popularity as a performer keeps him constantly on the go – filming, recording, appearing in pantomime and cabaret – he and his wife, Anne, eat out as often as they can and both appreciate fine cuisine. Cooking runs in the Corbett family: 'My father was a professional baker, confectioner and pâtissier and I used to love watching him stirring sauces, preparing, rolling and folding the different pastries . . .'. At home, Ronnie bakes his own bread, makes an excellent ragoût, boeuf bourguignon or coq au vin, and though Anne's enthusiasm for the kitchen is tempered by years of cooking for the family (the Corbetts have two daughters), they are both quick to re-create dishes they have enjoyed in a restaurant 'before the enthusiasm goes!' Ronnie loves fish, eats a great deal of fruit, but is not a man for carbohydrate. His idea of a baked potato, Anne tells us, 'is to scoop out the centre and eat the skin with a little salt – no butter'. In a restaurant, he looks for attention to detail, *'thinly* sliced brown bread with the smoked salmon, fresh *warm* toast with the pâté'. His spare time is spent on the golf course, where Ronnie is as keen as any professional. He plays for the Variety Club of Great Britain and describes his handicap as 'a warm 16 – getting hotter'. He has developed a taste for 'big Australian wines' and for the cuisine 'down under'. They both recommend the Bangkok in Bute Street for Thai cooking, Langan's Brasserie for atmosphere and sheer tastiness, would choose Harveys or Tante Claire for a very special occasion, and remember a truly memorable meal at L'Oustaù de Baumanière in Provence. Where, in the nearer Home Counties, would he choose . . .? **Morels.**

See overleaf for Ronnie's report.

Ronnie's report:

❝ Lucky Haslemere to have a restaurant of this calibre on its doorstep! If you had told me we were dining in Belgravia, I wouldn't have been surprised. There's an air of confidence here which makes you feel they'd cope well with any hiccups, and their standard of attention to detail augurs well for the quality of the cooking. The ambience is welcoming, with an understated elegance which doesn't detract from the food (I dislike fussy décor). The warm savoury croustade we were offered as we sat down was crisp and light; the menu was enterprising. My starter of terrine of calf's brain cooked in port jelly was smooth and delicious; Anne's grilled scallops and langoustines with basil butter was (and it has to be said) very disappointing – the scallops thin, with a distinct lack of sauce. However, I gave full marks to my fillet of halibut with a light mustard sauce and my wife enjoyed her char-grilled pigeon breast with juices of langoustine. Our vegetables were fresh, seasonal and lightly cooked and neither of us had ever seen a finer cheeseboard either in or out of France. I'm not a 'sweet' man, but I was not allowed to escape without at least a taste, so we settled for the assiette du chef with a 'batterie' of spoons! It was a feast for the eye. I sampled a strawberry in glistening spun sugar, approved of the tart fruit sauces and am told the chocolate marquise, biscuit glacé, almond soufflé and tea sorbet can be recommended without reserve. Lovely almond tuiles accompanied the coffee and the well-balanced wine list produced an excellent Hermitage and a fragrant, full-bodied Gewürztraminer. We shall certainly go again. ❞

PETER & VIRGINIA BOTTOMLEY

VISIT

KUNDAN
London SW1

'I'm not at all sure it's me you want,' said Peter Bottomley mildly, when approached in the middle of a busy Parliamentary term. 'Virginia's the foodie in the family.' Both are MPs, and in addition to Party and constituency duties, Virginia is Parliamentary Undersecretary of State for the Environment, while Peter, as Parliamentary Under-Secretary of State at the Department of Transport, is Minister for Roads and Traffic. They first met at a party 'over a prehistoric form of Trivial Pursuit', and together they beat all comers. Five times Parliamentary Swimming Champion and Captain of 'The Wobblers' (the Party Football Team), Peter Bottomley describes his attitude to food as 'somewhere halfway between Mahatma Gandhi and a Philistine'. He loves fruit, approves of muesli 'because you don't have to *do* anything to it', drinks Bovril (or is it Marmite?) in the office, and has never been fond of meat – though he's 'happy to eat anything on a plate that's not likely to bite back'. ('I'd be very surprised,' smiled Virginia, 'if at the end of a meal he could identify *what* he's eaten!') He remembers with delight a crossing to the US on the first *Queen Elizabeth* when, as an eleven-year-old, he negotiated a truce with his mother on the subject of meat and, for the duration of the trip, was allowed five puddings for breakfast, five for lunch and five for supper. In a restaurant, Peter will always take the set menu or ask for the special of the day: 'Forty minutes is quite long enough to demolish two courses'. Virginia, however, loves meat: 'Our household works very well on the Jack Sprat principle.' She finds a meal out with family or friends 'a pleasant way of "switching off" for a while', enjoys reading a menu and sampling new dishes: 'I go out to *eat* and not just guzzle.' Peter wishes that restaurants would serve a wider selection of non-alcoholic drinks for drivers and enjoys a Wimpy chilli beanburger as much as a more elaborate meal. They both like Browns in Cambridge (in the **Just A Bite** Guide) and speak well of the Inn on the Lake in Godalming. Since they both 'eat Indian when electioneering' we were not surprised they chose to inspect **Kundan**.

Peter and Virginia Bottomley share a quiet moment together during a conference break.

Peter's report:

❝ When we eat out, we enjoy 'eating Indian'. The food is well balanced and filling; there's meat on the menu for Virginia and a variety of vegetarian alternatives for me. Kundan is conveniently near the House (of Commons) and the atmosphere is relaxing. We were only summoned back once to vote on this occasion, which was lucky. Sometimes the Whips' demands can play havoc with the digestion! The restaurant is spacious, so you never feel 'crowded' and I like the feeling that it appeals across the board: to Cabinet Ministers who recognise good food and to families who bring the children out to eat. I also like the feeling that one could turn up here unannounced and not be disappointed. I approve of restaurants that deal courteously with the 'carriage trade'. Virginia has eaten here several times and has always found the food good. She ordered the set menu, starting with 'meaty kebabs with spicy sauces' – ground beef, chicken and lamb – all very tasty. Her main course, also good, was rogan josh (more tasty and tender lamb, cooked with spices, browned onions, ginger and garlic and simmered in yoghurt), served with the dhal of the day and appropriate vegetables. The freshly baked breads deserve a mention, as does the fact that they serve non-alcoholic beer. I chose mulligatawny soup – which I enjoyed – followed by (and without being an expert) the best lightly cooked mixed nut cutlet I have ever eaten. The dessert (a traditional homemade carrot halva) was served warm; it was delicious. The service here is friendly and competent – you'd never feel afraid of asking for information about the dishes, or for something not on the menu. (They went out to fetch me a Pepsi Cola.) And in the evenings, it's easy to park. ❞

CLARE FRANCIS

VISITS

THE COMPLEAT ANGLER
Marlow

'Well now,' mused Clare Francis, when asked to pick a restaurant to inspect for this year's Guide, 'I love eating in a beautiful location, somewhere where the atmosphere's not *too* quiet.' Inevitably associated with her successful sailing exploits of the 1970s (her single-handed transatlantic crossings; skippering in the Whitbread Round-the-World Race), Clare is now firmly established as a best-selling thriller writer. Her three novels, **Night Sky, Red Crystal** and **Wolf Winter,** appeared at two-yearly intervals to critical acclaim, and Clare is currently working on her fourth. A writer's world can be a solitary one and she enjoys eating out with friends, especially after the opera or theatre. 'Obviously, I work alone, so I like to go to a restaurant where there's lots of life; the place must have a buzz.' In London, she favours Le Caprice, Orso and the Quai de St Pierre, where she particularly loves their soupe de poisson. A confirmed fish-eater, she remembers the days when, in restaurants, 'you had to make subtle enquiries. Now most places do it.' At home she cooks fresh pasta, especially tagliatelle with garlic and herbs – her ten-year-old son Tom's favourite, and daily invents 'sauce à la Clare' with whatever is to hand. When eating out, Clare Francis dislikes poor service, which she qualifies as 'over-intrusive – it puts me off my food – or conversely, having to "whistle-up" a waiter.' She wishes waiters didn't interrupt one's conversation after the starters, by asking: 'What did you order? Was it the fish?' before re-laying the cutlery. For Sunday lunch, Clare would go to the Pontevecchio in the Old Brompton Road. 'They love children, spoil them rotten and always slip them bits of food . . .' For her tour of inspection, Clare chose the **Valaisan Restaurant** at the **Compleat Angler Hotel.**

Clare's report:

❝ The situation is impressive – beside a weir with the Thames on two sides – and the ambience comfortable. The service was efficient, though cool. We gave high marks for the range and size of the menu; the aim is high French cuisine, and at these prices we expected the best. My starter – a crispy salad with morsels of poached lobster – was excellent and the ambitious champagne vinaigrette was a perfect complement. My companion's seafood sausage on a bed of puréed onion also got high marks. Next, I went for *lotte* (monkfish), one of my favourite fish; it was unusually presented in large, thin slices on noodles with a cream of saffron sauce, but the result was disappointing – the sauce was bland, and the noodles were tasteless and slightly overdone. The vegetables, though properly cooked, also lacked seasoning. My companion's saddle of rabbit ran into similar difficulties, with unseasoned noodles and a cream of garlic sauce that lacked both verve and flavour. But the wines (a Sancerre and a Nuits St Georges) were delicious and moderately priced. The cheeses, too, were excellent. For dessert, I chose a tarte aux pommes from the sweet trolley, and it compared well with the many I have had in France, although the pastry was a little chewy round the edges. This place aims high but, on this occasion at least, did not quite achieve its ambitions. ❞

STEVE CRAM

VISITS

MICHAEL'S BRASSERIE
Newcastle-on-Tyne

Many would envy Steve Cram; tall and slender as a string bean, he eats what he likes without putting on an ounce. 'As long as I can run, I'll be all right,' he grins. A world-class athlete and middle-distance runner, Steve has (to date) five gold medals from the European Championships and the Common-wealth Games; he brought home the Silver for the 1500 metres from the 1984 Olympics and, in 1985, broke three world records. He holds a Bachelor's degree in Sports Studies from Newcastle Univer-sity, was BBC Sports Personality of the Year in 1983 and, in 1980, spent twelve months as mascot for the Red Arrows. He loves his food and has definite tastes – his German mother taught him to appreciate vegetables 'cooked well, with spices and herbs. I'm not keen on potatoes, salads or raw vegetables and I detest cheese! This can cause problems if eating out. Fish, yes, well . . . I'll eat my way around the world, but always come back to meat – especially liver. It's not unknown for me to order chicken livers, followed by calf's liver.' His wife, Karen, enjoys cooking and says that Steve will also 'experiment in the kitchen – even bake bread when in the mood. He makes good soups, delicious stir-fries . . .' 'And *the best* chocolate fudge,' adds Steve. He'll choose a hotel abroad for its culinary reputation and happily sample local fare. In Colorado it's venison, buffalo and elk. A hotel must also provide 'a good strong shower, a large bed so my feet don't hang over the edge' (he's over 6ft) 'and reliable 24-hour service'. He and Karen nip over to the Lake District to eat at the Miller Howe Hotel and at Sharrow Bay (Steve's training runs of 90 miles a week soon burn up the calories), but wherever they travel, they always return to Newcastle – and home. Accordingly, Steve chose **Michael's Brasserie**.

Steve's report:

❝ As far as eating establishments are concerned, Newcastle may be renowned more for quantity than quality. Michael's Brasserie, in High Bridge Street, is brave enough to set itself apart from the crowd, to provide a classy alternative to the usual 'fayre'. Managed by Michael Powney and his sister Kim, it has become a firm favourite with my wife Karen and me. On first entering the restaurant, it may seem a little small, but don't be put off by the apparent intimacy of the tables. The décor is simple and unfussy, which helps to provide a very relaxed and friendly atmosphere – equally appropriate for a romantic, candle-lit dinner for two, or a more lively night out with friends. The menu is not large, but is imaginative enough to provide the diner with some interesting choices (for starters, for example, there was a mousseline of sole dressed with prawns in a wine and cream sauce, or pigeon breasts, gently fried and served warm on a crisp, tossed green salad with a herb vinaigrette). Local produce is used and the dishes are well presented; they provide a genuine taste

Continued overleaf

of the North-East and categorically prove we don't all eat stottie cake and chips! Karen chose Loch Fyne scallops cooked with saffron, white wine and cream, while I enjoyed my saddle of local venison with a port wine sauce. You could have had a seafood ragoût (all local fish and shellfish) or calf's liver with a sauce made from root vegetables and red wine. We have found the food never less than excellent and it is presented in a way seldom seen in this part of the world. It would be wrong to describe it as 'nouvelle cuisine' as the servings are large enough to satisfy the heartiest of Geordie appetites. However, Clive Imber, the head chef, obviously takes great care that his food looks as good as it tastes. Many dishes – main courses as well as desserts – are finished off with exquisite sauces, which add to the blend of wonderful flavours on offer. For dessert, I couldn't resist the chocolate truffle gâteau. Karen approved of her fruit sorbet, while you could have chosen an orange bavarois or superb rhubarb parfait. By the way, *don't* miss the fudge at coffee time! **"**

UNDER NEW MANAGEMENT

Shortly after Steve Cram's report came in, **Michael's Brasserie** changed hands. We are told that the style of cooking will remain the same 'for the foreseeable future' but have not yet inspected the new team. As we go to press, Michael Powney is negotiating for new (and bigger) premises in Newcastle. Watch this space!

SIR DAVID NAPLEY

V I S I T S

WHITES
Cricklade

One of the country's leading lawyers and senior partner in a busy London practice, Sir David Napley is often found 'on the front bench' when legal questions are debated on radio and television. A former President of the Law Society, Director of the British Academy of Forensic Sciences, a long-standing member of the Home Office Law Reform Committee and President of the West Ham Boys' Club, Sir David stills finds time to write, paint and eat. He enjoys restaurants, although (and here we have an expert witness) Lady Napley's home cooking is of the best. 'Cooking is a great accomplishment,' says Sir David gravely. 'I have never cooked.' Lady Napley always judges the probable cleanliness of restaurant kitchens by the loos, and 'in hotel rooms, I always inspect the insides of kettles and take my own *clean* cups.'

Sir David regrets the decline of the freshly cooked English breakfast: 'I always check with the hotel beforehand. If breakfast is served buffet-style, with infra-red eggs and chewed-up bits of bacon – I don't book.' He disapproves of 'rip-off wine lists', feels that a good cigar should be allowed with the coffee, ('For me, it's part of the meal,') and wishes restaurants would offer a wider choice of half bottles. (Lady Napley is allergic to alcohol and only occasionally allows herself a small glass of claret.) He loves English dishes when they can be found on menus, recommends Le Coq Hardi just outside Paris, likes eating at Santini in Ebury Street, 'I feel I'm back in Venice,' and can mostly be found at L'Ortolan in Shinfield, which he promoted. He chose to inspect **Whites.**

Sir David's Report:

" Since one is taught that a guest never criticises the food, wine or hospitality provided by one's host, it was with some apprehension that one approached the task of guest Inspector. Indeed, it is difficult to determine which is the more formidable: to act in defiance of the former or to succeed in the performance of the latter. My wife and I, however, felt considerably reassured when we arrived at Whites in Cricklade. The house, some 300 years old, has been tastefully, yet simply, decorated and furnished by Gwen White, who rules over the front of the house, whilst her husband Colin performs his feats of cooking at the rear. Whites suffers the disadvantage that its size – as with so many restaurants – precludes the possibility of pre-prandial drinks in a lounge whilst one studies the menu, but as soon as it was handed to us we became sufficiently engrossed to forget this minor inconvenience. Five starters included such delicacies as a clear broth of scallops with saffron, lemon or chervil, or a more prosaic fresh crab salad with a fresh herb mayonnaise. The main dishes were six in number, ranging from 'escalope of free-range pork with a Meaux mustard sauce and a julienne of pork, kidney and calf's tongue', to 'salmis of pigeon breasts with a rich red wine and orange sauce'. My wife chose and spoke well of a feuilleté of calf's sweetbreads with a cucumber and shallot sauce, whilst I took Jerusalem artichoke mousse with fresh watercress sauce. I enjoyed it, although the ingredients were rather too bland for my palate (perhaps, if my wife is right, because it has been impaired by smoking cigars). I much enjoyed the Dart salmon with a sorrel beurre blanc. The new season's lamb, which my wife chose, was the right shade of pink, and its flavour, she said, was well balanced by the timbale of wild rice, apricots and pine kernels, served with a Sauternes and raisin sauce. The meal was rounded off by a choice of good puddings, followed by coffee.

My host chose from the adequate wine list a 1985 Condrieu, which I was happy to feel was worth every penny of the £25 it cost him, and the atmosphere was pleasant and relaxed. Our conversation obscured the delay which preceded the main course. I can confer on Whites the accolade the restaurateur ever needs: I shall return. "

A WHEELCHAIR'S • EYE VIEW •

MONG our hefty readers' correspondence, we recently had a letter from 17-year-old Jason Awbery-Taylor, bemoaning the fact that we did not recommend sufficient restaurants in his home area near to Blackpool. Although he is disabled and has to use a wheelchair to get about, this does not deter him from enjoying gastronomic delights throughout the UK.

Jason is one of 1·1 million disabled persons according to estimated government figures. Obviously degrees of disability vary. For instance, there are an estimated 20,000 disabled people who actively take part in sport – anything from archery to water skiing! Jason, who suffers from a muscular wasting disease known as Friedreich's Ataxia, impressed us so much with his openness we decided to invite him and his parents to join us as guests on an inspection visit and see what we could learn at first hand from the experience.

For our test we chose a new hotel and restaurant at Sutton Coldfield. **New Hall**, owned by the hotel group Thistle Hotels, had been open just a month at the time of our visit. This 12th-century house has recently undergone a £4 million refurbishment and an extra 53 bedrooms have been built in similar architectural style. We requested a room suitable for a disabled guest in a wheelchair.

While Jason approved of the room's decorative order, he and his parents pointed out some design faults that made the room quite impractical for an unaided wheelchair user. In the bathroom, the floor tiles were slippery, but more frustrating than that was the boxed-in vanity unit that made it quite impossible for Jason to get close to the basin to wash.

Jason did remark that at least New Hall had a very comfortable bed and so he was more than pleased at being assured of a good night's sleep. Items such as thick shag-pile carpets and gravel-covered car parks are other features that make life for a wheelchair user that much more difficult.

Jason, eager to carry out his inspectoral duties to the full, gave the room service a spot check. He phoned down for a drink which arrived very promptly, but the porter arrived without a pass key and, as Jason politely pointed out, he was unable to open the door. The mistake was quickly realised and soon rectified, and full marks next morning when early morning coffee was delivered without a hitch; it seemed they had learnt their lesson from the previous day.

It was also obvious that the nature of Jason's disability made his co-ordination difficult, and serving his soft drink in a long-stemmed glass, while looking stylish, was totally impractical in his case. Equally impractical were the pretty porcelain

coffee and tea cups – another example of how disabled or infirm guests could easily be aided by greater attention being paid to their needs. As Jason's mother pointed out, perhaps just a small checklist of items available to disabled guests, such as a two-handled cup or special cutlery along with perhaps more specialised equipment, could be supplied – a small, but useful attention to detail.

Our test of the restaurant proved highly successful and enjoyable. Jason was especially impressed by Head Chef Allan Garth's chicken liver parfait studded with prunes, and at breakfast the next day gave top marks to the home-made fresh croissants. Both Jason and his parents were quick to point out that the tables were not only on the small side but much too close together.

As we discussed further Jason's thoughts and observations on his visit, it became obvious to me that the life of the disabled guest in a hotel (be it top-class or a simpler establishment) is not an easy one. Staff can be eager to please but equally can often be very patronising and unreceptive to their needs. Mrs Awbery related the story of how, when communicating with the blind, many people shout or speak to them in a loud voice, totally misunderstanding their disability. This certainly seems to sum up the need for us to have a greater understanding of the disabled person's requirements.

It is essential that a proportion of newly built hotel rooms should be designed to a standard that allows the most severely disabled guest to use the facilities an able-bodied person can use. It *can* be done, as is shown by the **London Tara Hotel**, where six of their 800-plus rooms are designed to a very high specification, including automatic door opening and closing, electric hoists over the beds and baths, interconnecting rooms, intercoms and emergency call buttons. They even mark the room numbers in Braille, and such attention to detail more than merits the little effort it requires.

Jason is like many other seventeen-year-olds, and the fact that he is confined to a wheelchair should not prevent him from enjoying the pleasures able-bodied people take for granted. It is time for a greater effort to be made to ensure that poorly and inadequately designed facilities are replaced. 1·1 million disabled people are certainly getting a raw deal.

PETER CHAPMAN

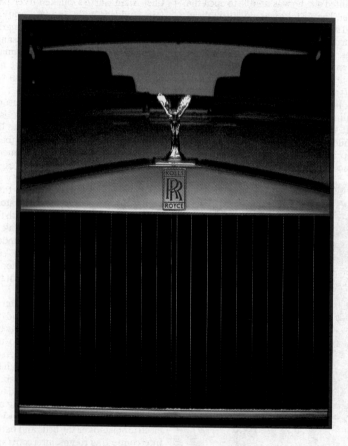

For demanding excellence in everything you do.

Rolls-Royce Motor Cars Limited

P·R·O·F·I·L·E·S
OF THE
6 BEST
OF · SIX · LEADING
HOTEL · MANAGERS

Over the past few years, it seems to me that all the media attention within the hotel and catering industry has been focused on chefs. Nothing wrong with that, but what about hotel managers? A hotel, after all, is only as good as its manager. So what makes an outstanding manager? I believe it is the qualities of the six managers we are profiling on the following pages.

Every year our inspectors stay in and visit hundreds of hotels, and between us we have selected the following managers, who, we felt, had made their mark on the hotels they run. It is not insignificant that among our six favourites there are two women, more and more of whom are likely to achieve managerial status in the future. Given the chance, women can manage and motivate every bit as well as their male counterparts.

I am indebted to spouses, personal assistants and secretaries who provided, in confidence, the necessary background material and photographs.

In alphabetical order (and let's hope they are still at the hotels as stated when we went to press) here they are; remember, it is the individual, and not necessarily the hotel, that we are presenting. . . . ►

ANDREW O. ELIEL
PUBLISHER

WILLY BAUER
THE SAVOY
LONDON

As the Savoy celebrates its centenary in 1989, it is appropriate that Mr Bauer should feature here, for, since becoming General Manager in 1982, he has been the major factor behind the hotel's success. Having studied at the Heidelberg Hotel School, Willy has done everything in the hotel industry, from learning about wine in Eastbourne in the sixties to managing a hotel in Liverpool in the seventies. Willy attaches great importance to selecting the right person for the job, particularly in hiring department head managers. He's a 'visible' manager, greeting guests, and seeing for himself that everything is running smoothly. A smile is important to Willy, and as he frequently says, 'You're only as good as your staff'.

DOREEN BOULDING
BELGRAVIA-SHERATON
LONDON

Unlike many of her colleagues, Doreen's background is mostly in sales, but she is no less outstanding a General Manager for that. Outside the United States, she is the only woman manager in Sheraton, and has been in her present position for some years, having previously been involved with the hotel's £4 million transformation. She believes that little things are important – flowers, hairdryers in rooms, tie racks in wardrobes and large soft bathrobes. The Belgravia-Sheraton is a smallish hotel by London standards with a club-like atmosphere, where guests like to return. Doreen has stamped her individuality throughout, motivating staff to provide comfort, style and service in good measure.

MARIE-BEATRICE LALLEMAND
RAMADA RENAISSANCE
BRIGHTON

From Strasbourg Hotel School, via a spell with Holiday Inns, to managing a new luxury hotel in the comparatively brief period of ten years is testimony to Miss Lallemand's ability. Soon after this hotel had opened we were impressed with its atmosphere, style and service. It is perhaps less easy to generate warmth and hospitality within a corporate image, yet this hotel positively exudes exuberance! Staff go about their tasks with smiles and panache, reflecting the qualities that Marie-B instils in all personnel. She combines Gallic charm with British calm in an American fashion, thoroughly justifying the word 'international'.

RORY MURPHY
ASHFORD CASTLE
CONG, ÉIRE

For 15 years Rory has been looking after this magnificent hotel, having previously worked for the Great Southern Group in Ireland. After graduating from the Shannon Hotel School, he spent some time working in Switzerland and has reached the position of Managing Director via a reliable route. Always immaculately dressed himself, it is no wonder that his staff are similarly attired, but above all he is a man of great charm with a twinkle in his eye and a ready smile. His attention to detail, his insistence on quality, and a genuine desire that all guests receive as personal a service as possible, are reflected in the atmosphere of the hotel. It's an old cliché but, at its best, you can't better Irish hospitality.

ROBIN SHEPPARD
ELCOT PARK
NEWBURY

In little over ten years, Robin has risen from a trainee with the then British Transport Hotels to his present position as Managing Director of this improving hotel. As passionate about the hotel industry as anyone, he does more than most in instituting better and far-reaching training programmes, not only for his own staff, but equally importantly for those entering the industry. A born leader and motivator, he is both creative and innovative, with the ability to make every individual guest feel special. He takes an active interest in all his members of staff, realising that each is an integral part of the team. In short, he is a professional, a man of great wit and understanding, determined to provide a better service for the public.

PIETER VAN DIJK
PEEBLES HOTEL HYDRO
PEEBLES, SCOTLAND

Trained initially in Holland and France, Pieter has spent more than 25 years in Scotland, having had the good sense to marry a Scottish girl! Apart from a gap of six years, he has spent all this time at Peebles, not only managing and continually improving this imposing hotel, but also involving himself in many aspects of the Scottish tourist industry and the local community. A man of boundless energy, enthusiasm and charm, he leads by example and has a genuine concern for the comforts and enjoyment of all guests, whether a lone businessman, conference visitor or delegate, or the holiday family. When one thinks of the Peebles Hotel Hydro, one automatically thinks of Pieter (and vice versa); the two just seem inexorably linked.

Do you really hold the best card?

More restaurants and hotels throughout Britain accept Access than any other credit, charge or dining card. Surprising isn't it?

So if you really want the best choice of the best food, perhaps you should find out more about Britain's leading credit card.

For further details write to us at Access, Southend-on-Sea, SS99 0BB.

Access.

THE DEFINITIVE APERITIF.

CELLAR OF THE YEAR

T HE PERFECT WINE LIST may not exist because it is practically impossible to apply absolute standards to a subject redolent of personal preference and prejudice.

However, here are a few pointers of style and content that we look for in an 'outstanding' wine list. Such a list should offer a well-balanced selection of exciting wines, the main criterion being the excellence of each choice: close your eyes, stick a pin at random in any wine on the list and it should be a fine example of its kind.

Quality of selection is more important than comprehensive coverage, a small list of exquisitely chosen wines being of more interest than a 'bible' of 400 famous clarets, many of which may be too young or from duff vintages.

A serious list must have a balance of good and lesser vintages. Burgundies should include a majority of growers' wines with perhaps a handful of good examples from the best *négociants*. The names of the Burgundy grower or *négociant* and of both vineyard and commune must be shown.

There should be a sensible spread between the numbers of great wines – always priced reasonably, relative to their quality – and of well-chosen wines at modest prices.

THE PANEL DECIDES
Left to right: Michael Edwards, Wine Writer, and Andrew Eliel, Publisher and Chief Inspector, both of Egon Ronay's Guides; Jill Goolden, Wine Writer and Presenter of BBC's 'Food and Drink'; David Rutherford OBE, Chairman, Wine and Spirit Association; Mark Elliott, Product Group Manager, Noilly Prat.

EGON RONAY'S **NOILLY PRAT**

Cellar of the Year

Our wine experts nosed their way through hundreds of lists to arrive at a selection of ten contenders for the 'Cellar of the Year' award. Here are the regional finalists.

LONDON

PAVILION RESTAURANT
FINSBURY CIRCUS
GARDENS, LONDON EC2

One of the least pretentious of the great wine lists, just a faultless selection of exquisite wines from the best (though not always the best-known) growers: Riesling, Clos Häuserer (Humbrecht) '85; Balgownie Cabernet Sauvignon '83; and the ambrosial Château Gilette, Crème de Tête (Sauternes) '55.

SOUTH OF ENGLAND

DUNDAS ARMS
KINTBURY, BERKSHIRE

This pub restaurant's cellar is remarkable for exceptional house wines (Vouvray Sec from Huet, Passetoutgrain from Henri Jayer) and keen pricing of outstanding Bordeaux and Burgundy: Ch. Figeac '79 (£21·00); Vieux Château Certan '71 (£20·00!); Pommard Domaine Mussy '82 (£18·50).

HEART OF ENGLAND

CHERWELL BOAT HOUSE
OXFORD

An informal atmospheric restaurant with simple food but a stunning wine list with especially fine clarets in magnums and double magnums. Delectable champagnes too.

EAST OF ENGLAND

OLD BRIDGE HOTEL
HUNTINGDON,
CAMBRIDGESHIRE

Excellent and unusual wines by the glass from the Canadian 'Wine Machine' and a marvellously judged selection of classic and New World Wines. Chianti Classico Isole e Olena '82 (£8·75); Delatite Rhine Riesling (Victoria) '86 (£12·75); Chambertin Clos de Bèze (Armand Rousseau) '78 (£48·00).

WEST COUNTRY

MEADOW HOUSE
KILVE, SOMERSET

The painstaking collection of wine enthusiast David MacAuslan. Excellent Californian Pinot Noir from Saintsbury, big fat burgundies from Robert Ampeau, Penfold's Grange Hermitage 1979 and seven Gran Coronas Reservas from Miguel Torres catch the eye.

MIDLANDS

NUTHURST GRANGE
HOCKLEY HEATH,
WARWICKSHIRE

A well-balanced thoughtfully laid out list with helpful unsnobbish comments. Some very fine burgundies: Bourgogne Blanc Les Clous (de Villaine) '85; Puligny Montrachet Les Combettes (Sauzet) '83; Corton (Domaine Paul Chanson) '69.

NORTH OF ENGLAND

BOX TREE COTTAGE
ILKLEY, WEST YORKSHIRE

Finely balanced cellar with some lovely bottles: Châteauneuf du Pape Blanc (Ch. de Beaucastel) 1982; Gevrey Chambertin Les Cazetiers (Faiveley) 1980; Kaseler Nieschen Riesling Auslese (Bischoft Priesterseminar) 1983.

WALES

THE WALNUT TREE
ABERGAVENNY, GWENT

As always, a universally splendid list, the wine comments a model of helpful brevity. Very strong in beautifully preserved mature wines: Vougeot La Perrière (Bertagna) '76; Châteauneuf du Pape, Clos L'Oratoire des Papes '62; Joseph Phelps Cabernet Sauvignon '78.

SCOTLAND

LA POTINIÈRE
GULLANE, LOTHIAN

For quality, depth, flair of selection and unequalled value for money, this is the finest list of French wines in the country: Chablis Grand Cru Vaudésir (Reynier) '78 (£23·00); Ch. Lynch Bages '61 (£65·00); Chambolle Musigny 1er Cru (Faiveley) '69 (£20·00); Ch. Suduirant 1962 (£45·00).

REPUBLIC OF IRELAND

ARBUTUS LODGE
CORK, CO CORK

Superb cellar with a strong leaning towards France. Wonderful clarets, burgundies and Rhônes: four vintages of Ch. Léoville Barton back to 1929; La Romanée (Belin) 1937; Côte Rôtie La Landonne 1980.

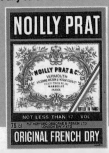

OUTSTANDING WINE LISTS

LONDON

Au Jardin des Gourmets, **W1**
Boulestin, **WC2**
The Capital Restaurant, **SW3**
Le Gavroche, **W1**
Hilaire, **SW7**
Hyatt Carlton Tower, Chelsea Room, **SW1**
Inigo Jones, **WC2**
Inn on the Park, Four Seasons & Lanes
    Restaurants, **W1**
Inter-Continental Hotel, Le Soufflé, **W1**
Ménage à Trois, **SW3**
Mijanou, **SW1**
Ninety Park Lane, **W1**
Pavilion, **EC2**
Pollyanna's, **SW11**
The Ritz Restaurant, **W1**
RSJ, **SE1**
Rue St Jacques, **W1**
Scotts, **W1**
La Tante Claire, **SW3**

ENGLAND

Alfriston: Moonrakers Restaurant
Aston Clinton: Bell Inn Restaurant
Bath: Priory Hotel Restaurant
Beanacre: Beechfield House Restaurant
Bray-on-Thames: Waterside Inn
Buckland: Buckland Manor Restaurant
Chagford: Gidleigh Park Hotel Restaurant
Chilgrove: White Horse Inn
Coggeshall: White Hart Hotel Restaurant
Dartmouth: Carved Angel
East Grinstead: Gravetye Manor
    Restaurant
Faversham: Read's
Fressingfield: Fox & Goose
Great Dunmow: Starr
Great Milton: Le Manoir aux Quat' Saisons
    Restaurant
Harrogate: Russell Hotel, Hodgson's
    Restaurant
Herstmonceux: Sundial
Hintlesham: Hintlesham Hall Restaurant
Hockley Heath: Nuthurst Grange
    Restaurant
Hungerford: Bear at
    Hungerford
    Restaurant
Hunstrete: Hunstrete
    House Restaurant
Huntingdon: Old
    Bridge Hotel
    Restaurant

Ilkley: Box Tree Restaurant
Kilve: Meadow House Restaurant
Kintbury: Dundas Arms
Ledbury: Hope End Country House Hotel
    Restaurant
Malvern: Croque-en-Bouche
Nantwich: Rookery Hall Restaurant
New Milton: Chewton Glen Hotel, Marryat
    Room
North Huish: Brookdale House
Oakham: Hambleton Hall Restaurant
Oxford: Cherwell Boathouse
Oxford: Restaurant Elizabeth
Pool-in-Wharfedale: Pool Court
Ridgeway: The Old Vicarage
Shepton Mallet: Bowlish House Restaurant
Shinfield: L'Ortolan
Southwold: Crown Restaurant
Speldhurst: George & Dragon, Oak Room
Stamford: George of Stamford Restaurant
Ston Easton: Ston Easton Park Restaurant
Taunton: Castle Hotel Restaurant
Thornbury: Thornbury Castle Hotel
    Restaurant
Waterhouses: Old Beams

SCOTLAND

Dunblane: Cromlix House Restaurant
Edinburgh: Handsel's
Fort William: Inverlochy Castle Restaurant
Gullane: Greywalls Restaurant
Gullane: La Potinière
Linlithgow: Champany Inn Restaurant
Peat Inn: The Peat Inn
Port Appin: Airds Hotel Restaurant

WALES

Abergavenny: Walnut Tree Inn
Llanrwst: Meadowsweet Hotel Restaurant

REPUBLIC OF IRELAND

Bray: Tree of Idleness

Cork: Arbutus Lodge
    Hotel Restaurant
Dublin: Le Coq Hardi
Dun Laoghaire: Res-
    taurant Mirabeau
Kenmare: Park Hotel
    Kenmare
    Restaurant

Champagne

THE REGION & THE WINE

THE CHAMPAGNE REGION lying almost 100 miles north east of Paris and covers an area of about 35,000 hectares, of which three quarters are vineyards. This is the only area in the world from which true champagne can originate. The region consists of two separate districts, the Marne and the lesser (both in size and quality rating) Aube.

EVERY VINEYARD HAS A QUALITY RATING (known as the echelle rating) derived from the excellence of its site and soil. The three areas of the Marne have ratings from 100 % down to 80 % ; the Aube's span is narrower, from only 87 % down to 80 % .

CHAMPAGNE LANSON, one of the very oldest of the Grande Marque houses, has extensive vineyard holdings totalling in excess of 200 hectares, located in some of the finest villages in the Marne, with an average echelle rating of 98.6 % .

ONLY THREE GRAPE VARIETIES are permitted in Champagne. The Pinot Noir is a classic black variety producing great length of flavour; the Pinot Meunier, a coarser black variety, is not now allowed to be replanted in vineyards of 95 % quality and above; the Chardonnay is a particularly fine white variety which has the highest intensity of flavour of the three and is grown especially, but not exclusively, on the Côte des Blancs. Only the Chardonnay and the Pinot Noir are used by Champagne Lanson for their Vintage wines.

VINTAGES ARE PRODUCED only in those years when the weather has been particularly favourable to the vines and every vintage therefore has its own personality, reflecting its year.

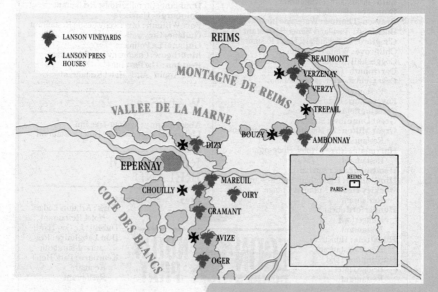

LANSON VINEYARDS

LANSON PRESS HOUSES

REIMS

BEAUMONT

VERZENAY

VERZY

MONTAGNE DE REIMS

TREPAIL

VALLÉE DE LA MARNE

BOUZY

AMBONNAY

DIZY

EPERNAY

MAREUIL

OIRY

CHOUILLY

CRAMANT

AVIZE

OGER

CÔTE DES BLANCS

REIMS

PARIS

MANY FEATURES MAKE CHAMPAGNE the highest quality sparkling wine in the world. The very strict laws of appellation under which champagne is produced not only delimit the area in which its decreed grape varieties are grown, but also such things as planting, pruning, picking, pressing, volumes and age. At harvest time, the grapes are brought in large baskets to the press houses around the region. The origin of each load is carefully marked and kept with similar grapes from the same vineyard.

THE PRESSED JUICES are taken to the cellars for fermentation and those emanating from the same vineyards are brought together — this is known as the 'assemblage' — to form the basis for making the final blends or 'cuvées'.

PRIOR TO BOTTLING, the proprietors build their cuvées to their own particular style. This is a unique art requiring the most sensitive palates, great experience and the ability to retain subtle nuances of bouquet and flavour in the memory. Dozens of samples from the assembled wines will be tasted time and again to determine the exact proportions required for the ideal cuvée.

AT COURLANCY, Lanson's headquarters, this unique champagne technique is headed up by Pierre Lanson, representing the sixth consecutive generation of the family to acquire this expertise and skill.

THE WINE IS THEN BOTTLED, having had added a little sugar and yeast, to create a secondary fermentation in bottle, the result of which is a little more alcohol and most importantly carbon dioxide gas which remains in solution because the bottle is sealed: it is this gas that produces the sparkle when the cork is removed years later.

THE FERMENTATION in bottle creates a sediment which is eventually removed, after the wine has matured. At this stage, the champagne is

completely dry and requires a 'liqueur d'expédition' or 'dosage' made up of a little of the same wine and sugar to adjust the level of dryness required for different styles. At Lanson all this happens after about three year's maturation for non vintage qualities, and five to six years for vintage wines.

THE WINE IS NOW READY to receive its final cork and a six month wait for the dosage to marry with the wine before being sent to the many markets of the world.

CHAMPAGNE LANSON

ESTABLISHED IN 1760, Champagne Lanson is one of the oldest of the Grande Marque houses led by six generations of the family from the first Jean Baptiste through to Pierre and his younger brother Jean Baptiste today.

IT IS THIS CONTINUITY that ensures the tradition and quality of Champagne Lanson. In fact, Pierre and Jean Baptiste Lanson are fortunate to be able to benefit from the wise and often bold decisions of their ancestors.

FIRST WAS THEIR DETERMINATION to establish Champagne Lanson on the world market and especially in the United Kingdom, where it is today the second biggest selling marque. Travelling in those days was often difficult and tedious but the reward for such hard work is that Champagne Lanson is now established in over 100 export markets.

SECOND, THE PURCHASE OF SUBSTANTIAL NUMBERS of first rate vineyards, mainly between the two World Wars, has guaranteed them about 30 % of their grape requirements as well as good relations with other growers. The majority of their vineyards have a 95 %-100 % échelle rating which produces the best grapes. Sixty-five hectares are in the Vallée de la Marne, mostly at Dizy and Mareuil (95 % and 99 % respectively) with 66 hectares and 43 hectares in the Côte des Blancs and Montagne de Reims respectively, each rated at 100 %.

THIRDLY, ALTHOUGH THEIR DECISIONS have often been bold they have not been made in haste. Such a decision was to introduce temperature controlled stainless steel vats during the 1960s and 1970s and more recently, in 1983, a massive extension to their cellar capacity which now permits a total stock holding of 26 million bottles and approaching 100,000 hectolitres in vats.

CAN THE SUCCESS OF CHAMPAGNE LANSON be sustained? Much will depend on the present leaders. Prior to joining the family company, Pierre was twice decorated in service with the crack French Parachute Corps before joining the CIVC, the governing body of the champagne industry, which suggests his ability to make bold decisions based on essential experience. Jean Baptiste, before joining the family firm, worked with Rolls Royce in the South of France and so should have an eye for quality. As to the future, there is already another generation of Lansons waiting in the wings.

FOR MORE INFORMATION ABOUT VINTAGE YEARS, send off the Champagne Lanson reply card opposite page 64. Champagne Lanson will send you their Vintage Tasting Notes and a copy of 'Why Not?', a booklet illustrated by Patrick Lichfield, which takes an irreverent look at champagne styles and occasions as well as covering more serious information on the Champagne region and its wine.

THE VINTAGE YEARS

VINTAGES ARE PRODUCED only in those years when the weather has been particularly favourable to the vines and every vintage therefore has its own personality, reflecting the year.

CHAMPAGNE LANSON, one of the oldest of the Grande Marque houses, will send you a free copy of their Vintage Tasting Notes, together with a booklet, illustrated by Patrick Lichfield which takes an irreverent look at champagne style and occasions, as well as covering more serious information on the Champagne region and its wine.

Why not?

Please send me Champagne Lanson's Vintage tasting notes and a copy of your *'Why Not'* book.

Name _____

Address _____

_____

_____

_____ Telephone _____

Please
Affix
Postage
Stamp.

CHAMPAGNE LANSON
MULBERRY HOUSE
WILTSHIRE ROAD
WOKINGHAM
BERKSHIRE RG11 1TN

I don't see why people make
such a to-do about choosing a new cook.
There is only one thing that is absolutely essential.
I always ask at once, 'Do you drink?',
and if she says 'No!', I bow politely and say that I am
very sorry but I fear she will not suit.
All *good* cooks drink.

J. A. McNEILL WHISTLER 1834-1903
Attributed in
LIFE WAS WORTH LIVING

Some people have a foolish way of
not minding, or pretending not to mind what they eat.
For my part, I mind my belly very studiously,
and very carefully; for I look upon it, that he who does not
mind his belly, will hardly mind anything else.

SAMUEL JOHNSON 1709-84
Boswell's
LIFE OF JOHNSON

A TALE OF TWENTY PINOT NOIRS

Great red Burgundy is difficult to make and difficult to buy. So when a true enthusiast discovers a really fine example of this most hedonistic red wine, combining sensual aromas with rich and subtle flavours, it's a cause for celebration.

The Pinot Noir grape grown on the limestone soil of Burgundy's Côte d'Or *can* produce the most exciting red wines in the world; but it is also a very temperamental grape, slow to ripen and prone to disease. The Burgundian climate is fickle and mercurial: heavy summer rainfall may cause rot and mildew to form quickly on the delicate Pinot grapes; conversely too little rain and too much sun may result in wines so fiercely tannic and alcoholic that the fascinating smell of Pinot Noir – Burgundy's special gift to the red wine drinker – is lost in the process, or at least locked away for years. Above all, classic red Burgundy of the highest class is only made in very small quantities from low-yielding vines which bear as few as eight grapes per plant.

Hence the real stuff can never be cheap. But if you are prepared to be open-minded by opting for well-made wines from less fashionable villages (Mercurey, Monthélie, Marsannay come to mind) you will find delicious affordable bottles which make the claim that Burgundy is overpriced look very hollow. Follow the winemaker and not the appellation in today's market. Deal with specialist merchants (the firms mentioned below are impeccable sources) who know Burgundy well and who buy exclusively from the best growers.

Main picture: the village of Monthélie, Côte de Beaune. Inset: Aubert de Villaine in his Bouzeron cellar, one of the coldest in Burgundy.

The main aim of this feature is to test the conventional wisdom that only in the soil and climate of Burgundy does the Pinot Noir achieve real distinction. To do this as methodically as possible, I have tasted well over 100 Pinot Noirs from around the world to arrive at a final selection of 20 good wines for detailed appraisal.

As Burgundy remains the richest source of the best Pinot Noir, it seemed sensible to compare ten Burgundies with ten wines of the same grape from as far afield as Alsace and South Africa, Italy and Oregon, Germany and Australia. The results are an eye-opener, not least to those pundits who maintain that great Pinot Noir cannot be made in California.

To help the reader assess the wines, I have employed a flexible five-star rating system in preference to the more fashionable, but rigid, numerical scale (0–20 or 50–100). I greatly prefer the 'broad brush' star system because it is inherently fairer to the wines, which by their nature are constantly changing and evolving.

The sensible wine writer should heed the wise advice of that great French authority Jacques Puisais: 'when it comes to wine tasting you should accept that you will be mistaken at least one time in three'.

Thus:

★★★★★ = **Outstanding**
★★★★ = **Excellent**
★★★ = **Good**
★★ = **Quite good**
★ = **Average**

A very approximate retail price per bottle is quoted after each wine, followed by suppliers' names listed by coded abbreviation. Their telephone numbers are at the end of the feature.

Michael Edwards
WINE WRITER, EGON RONAY'S GUIDES

RED BURGUNDY

Recent visits to the Côte d'Or confirm the impression that an increasing number of growers are making red Burgundy worthy of the name. Yields are down to sensible levels, wine-making is more meticulous and there has been an uninterrupted run of good vintages. The red wines of 1985 are very fine, in some cases as spectacular as those of the very great 1969 vintage. These ten wines are a genuine expression of the Pinot Noir grape at its most elegant and subtle.

1985 BOURGOGNE ROUGE 'LA DIGOINE'
A et P de Villaine
£5.98 ADN ★★★★

An unpretentious wine but one that captures all the charm of the Pinot Noir grape. Aubert de Villaine believes that his 1985 is the best red wine he has ever made at Bouzeron. Lovely scent of soft fruits enhanced by a flavour which combines elegance with vigour. Perfectionist wine-making at a gentle price.

1985 MARSANNAY ROUGE
Domaine Fougeray de Beauclair
£6.30 HW ★★★

Marsannay is a new appellation touching the suburbs of Dijon. The red wines of this village can be aggressively earthy, but here is a fine example of skilful wine-making with great depths of fruit the dominant characteristic.

1986 COTES DE NUITS VILLAGES
Domaine Robert Dubois
£7.17 WW ★★★

Régis Dubois is a highly competent wine-maker who prices his product most reasonably. Brilliant ruby colour, pure Pinot aromas, lively fruit, new oak tannins.

1984 MERCUREY CHAMP MARTIN
Michel Juillot
£7.35 DD ★★★★

A good Mercurey can offer the best value of any red Burgundy, and Michel Juillot is an excellent wine-maker. He has managed to draw some splendid aromas (blackcurrant leaves?) from this fine deep-coloured wine, which also has great character on the palate. Will age very well. Excellent with game.

1985 MONTHELIE
Domaine Laroche
£9.99 H LAR ★★★

Monthelie is a little-known village between Meursault and Volnay. The red wines are subtle and stylish, akin to Volnay but with less concentration of flavour; this one has better structure than many; immaculate wine-making.

1985 SANTENAY
Olivier Leflaive
£10.85 HHN ★★★★

Olivier Leflaive has quickly established himself as a *negociant-éleveur* of the first rank. His policy is to buy in the best possible grapes, which are then transformed into wines of rare distinction by his brilliant wine-maker Jean Marc Boillot. This Santenay is vastly superior to any I have previously tasted – sensuously rich yet exquisitely elegant, given added complexity by the use of new oak.

1983 SAVIGNY LES BEAUNE 'AUX GRANDS LIARDS' Domaine Simon Bize
£10.70   ADN   ★★★

1983 was a difficult year in which to make well-balanced red Burgundy: very careful selection and a lot of patience are essential. Patrick Bize has produced a delicious bottle where clear, ripe fruit holds the strong tannin in check.

1985 CORTON GRAND CRU Roland Rapet
About £22.00 HEY ★★★★★

Corton is the longest-lived red wine of the Côte de Beaune, sometimes rivalling Le Chambertin for majestic power. As good an example as you will find from a wonderful vintage which may well prove as great as the superlative 1969.

1986 CLOS VOUGEOT Jean et Etienne Grivot
About £24.00   HEY HHN
★★★★★

Some 1986 red Burgundies will be as spectacular as the 1985, as in this copybook Clos Vougeot. Wonderful animal smells, explosive fruit, glorious ripe tannins, a very long finish. Don't touch till 1996.

1986 VOLNAY CLOS DU CHATEAU DES DUCS Michel Lafarge
About £23.00 HHN ★★★★★

If I had to name a Burgundy grower whose every wine is memorable, it would have to be Michel Lafarge. No one makes better wine in Volnay (a village of outstanding domaines) and this is his greatest Cru made from *very* old vines. I hesitate to describe its splendour except to say it needs about 15 years to really show its paces. Rather a case of this wine in your cellar than anything of comparable price from Bordeaux!

ALSACE, BADEN, FRIULI

Three fine European Pinot Noirs. They don't taste a bit like Burgundy, but all are deftly made wines with seductive Pinot aromas and sprightly fruit. Serve them cool as summer partners to a plate of cold meats; and the open-minded may like to try them with richly flavoured fish like salmon.

1986 PINOT NOIR HERRENWEG (Turckheim) Domaine Zind Humbrecht
Price on application   PAV
★★★★

Léonard Humbrecht is probably Alsace's greatest grower, his superb Tokay on a level with finest white Burgundy. Here he shows he is no slouch at making red wine. From Pinot Tordhu vines (20 years old), a stylish wine of luminous ruby colour, lovely floral bouquet, and a flavour that exudes class and refinement; at once fine drawn and well structured, alluringly fruity yet with a real taste of its *terroir*. The master on top form.

1985 PINOT NOIR VOGTSBURG-BISCHOFFINGEN
Karl Heinz Johner
Price on application   UC   ★★★

Who says the Germans can't make red wine? Not in the same class as the Alsace maybe, but a fat broad Pinot of great crowd appeal. Thank you, Barry Ralph, for your last bottle.

1985 PINOT NERO FRIULI-VENEZIA GIULIA
Vinicolu Udinese
£5.00   REC   ★★★

Between the Alps and the Adriatic, Friuli is the least hide-bound of Italian wine regions. Brilliant youthful ruby, delightful nose of flowers and spices, 'sweeter' flavour than Burgundy but packed with gorgeous fruit; slight prickle on the tongue.

AUSTRALIA, NEW ZEALAND, SOUTH AFRICA

A mixed bunch. The sun-baked vineyards of Australia have real problems producing a refined Pinot Noir; New Zealand *are* refined but lack roundness; only South Africa seems to be successful here.

1984 NOBILO'S PINOT NOIR
Huapai Valley, Auckland
£6.50   AV   ★★

The smell is right, recalling a Côte Challonaise, but the taste is hollow and weak, maybe because the wine just reaches 11.5° alcohol. A less purist approach might have made for a better wine.

1985 PINOT NOIR HEATHCOTE WINERY
Victoria
About £9.00   BM   ★★(★)

At least an Australian Pinot Noir that does not assault the taster with head-

spinning alcohol. Limpid purple/ruby colour, pretty bouquet of red fruits (cherries?); soft supple flavour, a restrained use of oak, but lacking structure. Quite attractive.

1984 GRAND VIN NOIR HAMILTON RUSSELL
About £9.00   UC   ★★★

From the most southerly vineyard in Africa, a 100% Pinot Noir grown on soil of aranaceous shale. A real mouthful of wine with healthy fruit and long complex flavours. Draw the cork one hour in advance. Will live for years.

CALIFORNIA & OREGON

Most wine pundits maintain that Oregon in the Pacific North-West is the perfect spot for growing Pinot Noir; certainly the climate is cool and the wines possess good natural acidity and refinement. But my own feeling is that Carneros, the coolest area of Napa Valley in California, can now produce just as good Pinot Noir with the added bonus of generous balanced fruit.

1985 PINOT NOIR EYRIE VINEYARD
£11.31   WW   ★★★

David Lett is the guru of Oregon winemakers, his Pinot Noir the most complex and long-lived of any. This wine has a good deep colour but it's closed in and dumb at the moment (May 1988); needs plenty of time. Is it as good as his very fine 1983?

1985 PINOT NOIR ALPINE VINEYARD

£9.20 WW ★★(★)

A lighter fine-drawn wine with a very elegant bouquet; the flavour is delicate but rather too lean to my taste.

1983 CARNEROS PINOT NOIR CLOS DU VAL

£9.37 REID ★★★

Fine crimson colour, brick-red at rim. Rich vinous nose of extrovert Californian character; velvet palate confirms. It lacks the subtle nuances of good red Burgundy yet is an impeccably crafted wine which will give a lot of pleasure.

1986 CARNEROS PINOT NOIR SAINTSBURY

£8.65 HHN ★★★★

Awake, gentle reader, the best-made Pinot Noir outside Burgundy: the one wine that bears serious comparison with a fine Côte d'Or; lovely purple/red colour, splendidly pure smell and taste of top-flight Pinot Noir with superb fruit and a proper structure. Exceptional promise.

CONCLUSIONS

★ The best red Burgundies are still the finest Pinot Noirs; good value among the lesser appellations.

★ CARNEROS PINOT NOIR SAINTSBURY the most interesting discovery.

★ Plenty of fine Pinot Noir from Alsace, South Africa and Oregon.

★ For everyday drinking, PINOT NERO DEL FRIULI exceptional value.

CODE to wine suppliers

ADN	ADNAMS, Southwold (0502) 74222
AV	AVERY'S OF BRISTOL (0272) 214141
BM	BRIAN MORRIS, Sittingbourne (0795) 70730
DD	DOMAINE DIRECT, London 01-837 3521
HEY	HEYMAN BROTHERS, London 01-730 0324
HHN	HAYNES HANSON & CLARK, London 01-736 7878
H LAR	HENRI LAROCHE, London 01-735 0865
HW	HEDLEY WRIGHT, Sawbridgeworth (0279) 723344
PAV	PAVILION WINE CO. London 01-628 8224
REC	RECOUNT WINES, London 01-730 6377
REID	REID WINES, Bristol (0272) 52645
UC	UPPER CRUST, East Horsley (04865) 3280
WW	WINDRUSH WINES, Cirencester (0285) 67121

VINTAGE CHART

Ratings in bold indicate that the lesser wines may be fading, but the great ones may be at their best. These ratings are a rough 'rule of thumb' with many exceptions.

Where we print a dash, you are unlikely to find this particular vintage available.

	0 = NO GOOD		RED WINES		7 = THE BEST		
Vintage	Beaujolais	Burgundy	Bordeaux	Rhône	California	Rioja	Port
1945	–	6	7	5	–	–	7
1947	–	5	5	5	–	–	5
1948	–	3	5	–	–	–	7
1949	–	6	7	4	–	–	–
1952	–	5	5	5	–	–	–
1953	–	3	6	4	–	–	–
1955	–	3	6	5	–	–	6
1957	–	3	2	5	–	–	–
1959	–	6	6	6	–	5	–
1960	–	–	1	3	–	–	6
1961	–	5	7	6	–	–	–
1962	–	5	5	5	–	4	–
1963	–	1	0	–	–	4	6–7
1964	–	3	3–6	6	–	7	–
1966	–	5	6	5	–	–	5
1967	–	6	4	6	–	–	5
1968	–	2	0	–	7	5	–
1969	–	7	2	6	5	–	–
1970	–	4	6	5	7	6	5
1971	–	6	3–5	6	2	2	–
1972	–	5	1	4–6	3	1	4
1973	–	4	4	4	5	5	–
1974	–	2	3	3	7	3	–
1975	–	0	3–6	1	6	4	3
1976	5	1–5	4–5	5–6	–	4	–
1977	0	3	3	3	6	1	7
1978	6	6	5	7	5	6	–
1979	4	5	4–6	5	4	3	–
1980	2	2–5	3	4	6	3	4
1981	5	1–4	4	1–5	2	5	–
1982	3	4	7	4	3–4	–	3
1983	4	2–6	4–6	4–6	3	4	4–5
1984	2	4	3	3–4	4	2	–
1985	7	6	5	4–6	6	3	6

Ratings in bold indicate that the lesser wines may be fading, but the
great ones may be at their best. These ratings are a rough
'rule of thumb' with many exceptions.

Where we print a dash, you are unlikely to find this particular
vintage available.

	0 = NO GOOD		WHITE WINES			7 = THE BEST	
Vintage	Burgundy	Alsace	Sweet Bordeaux	Dry Loire	Germany	California	Champagne
1945	–	–	6	–	6	–	6
1947	–	–	5	–	5	–	6
1948	–	–	4	–	–	–	–
1949	–	–	5	–	5	–	6
1952	–	–	4	–	–	–	4
1953	–	–	5	–	3	–	5
1955	–	–	6	–	–	–	5
1957	–	–	3	–	–	–	–
1959	–	–	4	–	5	–	5
1960	–	–	–	–	–	–	–
1961	2	–	4	–	2	–	6
1962	5	–	6	–	–	–	5
1963	–	–	–	–	–	–	–
1964	2	–	0	–	5	–	5
1966	4	–	3	–	2	–	6
1967	4	6	7	–	4		–
1968	–	–	–	–	–	6	–
1969	5	–	3	–	3	3	5
1970	4	–	6	–	2	5	5
1971	5	6	6	–	6	6	5
1972	2	–	0	–	–	4	–
1973	3	3	4	–	3	6	6
1974	2	–	1	–	1	6	–
1975	2	5	6	–	4–6	6	5
1976	4	7	6	–	7	5	5
1977	2	2	0	–	3	6	–
1978	7	4	4	–	2	5	4
1979	5	5	2	–	5	5	4
1980	3	3	2	–	3	5	–
1981	4	4	4	–	4	5	–
1982	4	4	3	–	4	5	6
1983	3–5	7	6–7	3	6	2–4	–
1984	4	4	3	4	–	2–4	–
1985	5	6	4	5	3	6	–

DE LUXE AND GRADE 1 HOTELS

LONDON

■ **91%**
The Connaught, **W1**
The Savoy, **WC2**
■ **90%**
The Berkeley, **SW1**
Claridges, **W1**
■ **89%**
Hyatt Carlton Tower, **SW1**
Inn on the Park, **W1**
■ **87%**
The Ritz, **W1**
■ **86%**
Inter-Continental Hotel, **W1**
■ **85%**
Hyde Park Hotel, **SW1**
■ **84%**
Grosvenor House, **W1**
Howard Hotel, **WC2**
London Hilton on Park Lane, **W1**
Londonderry Hotel, **W1**
May Fair Inter-Continental Hotel, **W1**
Le Meridien Piccadilly, **W1**
■ **83%**
Sheraton Park Tower, **SW1**
■ **81%**
Dukes Hotel, **SW1**
Royal Garden Hotel, **W8**
■ **80%**
Athenaeum Hotel, **W1**
Hotel Britannia Inter-Continental, **W1**
Cannizaro House, **SW19**
The Capital, **SW3**
Churchill Hotel, **W1**
The Halcyon, **W11**
London Marriott Hotel, **W1**
Park Lane Hotel, **W1**
Royal Lancaster Hotel, **W2**
The Selfridge, **W1**
Whites Hotel, **W2**
■ **79%**
Belgravia-Sheraton, **SW1**
Holiday Inn (Swiss Cottage), **NW3**
The Lowndes, **SW1**
Portman Inter-Continental Hotel, **W1**
The Westbury, **W1**
■ **78%**
The Gloucester, **SW7**
■ **77%**
Blakes Hotel, **SW7**
Brown's Hotel, **W1**
The Goring Hotel, **SW1**
The Montcalm, **W1**
The Waldorf, **WC2**
■ **76%**
The Berkshire Hotel, **W1**
Dorset Square Hotel, **NW1**

■ **75%**
St James Court Hotel, **SW1**
■ **74%**
Mountbatten Hotel, **WC2**
■ **73%**
Hilton International Regent's Park, **NW8**
Holiday Inn (Mayfair), **W1**
Stakis St Ermin's Hotel, **SW1**
Tower Thistle Hotel, **E1**
White House, **NW1**
■ **72%**
Chelsea Hotel, **SW1**
Chesterfield Hotel, **W1**
Holiday Inn (Swiss Cottage), **NW3**
Royal Horseguards Thistle Hotel, **SW1**
Royal Westminster Thistle Hotel, **SW1**
■ **71%**
Cadogan Thistle Hotel, **SW1**
The Clifton-Ford, **W1**
Hilton Mews at Park Lane, **W1**
Holiday Inn (Marble Arch), **W1**
Ramada Hotel, **W1**
■ **70%**
Basil Street Hotel, **SW3**
Green Park Hotel, **W1**
Marlborough Crest, **WC1**
Royal Court Hotel, **SW1**

LONDON AIRPORTS

GATWICK
■ **76%**
Gatwick Hilton International,
■ **71%**
Gatwick Penta Hotel,

HEATHROW
■ **77%**
Sheraton Skyline,
■ **73%**
Holiday Inn,
■ **72%**
Excelsior Hotel,
■ **70%**
Sheraton-Heathrow Hotel,

ENGLAND

■ **89%**
Taplow: Cliveden
■ **88%**
New Milton: Chewton Glen Hotel
Ston Easton: Ston Easton Park
■ **87%**
Bath: Royal Crescent Hotel
Warminster: Bishopstrow House

■ 86%
Great Milton: Le Manoir aux Quat' Saisons
Melton Mowbray: Stapleford Park

■ 85%
Nantwich: Rookery Hall
Stratford-upon-Avon: Ettington Park Hotel

■ 84%
Torquay: Imperial Hotel

■ 83%
Brighton: Ramada Renaissance Hotel
Buckland: Buckland Manor
Hunstrete: Hunstrete House

■ 82%
Ashford: Eastwell Manor
Bath: Priory Hotel
Chester: Chester Grosvenor
Hintlesham: Hintlesham Hall
Linton: Wood Hall
Oakham: Hambleton Hall
Thornbury: Thornbury Castle Hotel
Windsor: Oakley Court Hotel

■ 81%
Birmingham: Birmingham Metropole
Chagford: Gidleigh Park Hotel
Colerne: Lucknam Park Hotel
East Grinstead: Gravetye Manor
Leamington Spa: Mallory Court
Longhorsley: Linden Hall Hotel
Rotherwick: Tylney Hall Hotel
Ullswater: Sharrow Bay Hotel

■ 80%
Freshford: Homewood Park
Turners Hill: Alexander House
Uckfield: Horsted Place
Winchester: Lainston House

■ 79%
Broadway: Lygon Arms
Cheltenham: The Greenway
Flitwick: Flitwick Manor
Grasmere: Michael's Nook
Taunton: Castle Hotel

■ 78%
Aston Clinton: Bell Inn
Bagshot: Pennyhill Park Hotel
Bournemouth: Carlton Hotel
Bournemouth: Royal Bath Hotel
Brighton: The Grand
Dedham: Maison Talbooth
Manchester: Holiday Inn, Crown Plaza Midland
Manchester: Ramada Renaissance Hotel
Storrington: Little Thakeham
York: Middlethorpe Hall

■ 77%
Ascot: Royal Berkshire
Bakewell: Hassop Hall Hotel
Battle: Netherfield Place
Beanacre: Beechfield House
Bilbrough: Bilbrough Manor Hotel
Maidenhead: Fredrick's Hotel
Marlow: Compleat Angler Hotel
Portsmouth: Holiday Inn
Reading: Caversham Hotel
Stratford-upon-Avon: Billesley Manor

■ 76%
Bath: Apsley House Hotel
Birmingham: Plough & Harrow Hotel

Broxted: Whitehall Hotel
Chaddesley Corbett: Brockencote Hall
Droitwich Spa: Château Impney Hotel
Gloucester: Hatton Court
Lower Beeding: South Lodge
Reading: Ramada Hotel
Six Mile Bottom: Swynford Paddocks
Slough: Holiday Inn
Sutton Coldfield: New Hall

■ 75%
Bolton Abbey: Devonshire Arms
Charingworth: Charingworth Manor
Chester: Crabwall Manor Hotel
Climping: Bailiffscourt
Easton Grey: Whatley Manor
Gittisham: Combe House Hotel
Grimston: Congham Hall
Kirkby Fleetham: Kirkby Fleetham Hall
Leicester: Holiday Inn
Lenham: Chilston Park
Manchester: Hotel Piccadilly
Newcastle upon Tyne: Gosforth Park Thistle Hotel
North Stoke: Springs Hotel
St Albans: Noke Thistle Hotel
Shifnal: Park House Hotel
South Molton: Whitechapel Manor
Stow-on-the-Wold: Wyck Hill House
Stratford-upon-Avon: Welcombe Hotel
Tetbury: Calcot Manor
Truro: Alverton Manor
Ullswater: Leeming House Hotel

■ 74%
Abberley: Elms Hotel
Baslow: Cavendish Hotel
Birmingham: Copthorne Hotel
Coventry: Ansty Hall
Great Ayton: Ayton Hall
Hockley Heath: Nuthurst Grange
Liskeard: The Well House
Northampton: Swallow Hotel
Penrith: North Lakes Gateway Hotel
Poole: Mansion House
Quorn: Quorn Country Hotel
Whimple: Woodhayes
Wrotham Heath: Post House Hotel

■ 73%
Borrowdale: Stakis Lodore Swiss Hotel
Brampton: Farlam Hall Hotel
Bristol: Hilton International Bristol
Castle Donington: Donington Thistle Hotel
Crathorne: Crathorne Hall Hotel
Croydon: Holiday Inn
Eastbourne: Cavendish Hotel
Holbeton: Alston Hall Hotel
Hythe: Hythe Imperial Hotel
Lower Slaughter: Lower Slaughter Manor
Maiden Newton: Maiden Newton House
Manchester: Portland Thistle Hotel
Rotherham: Rotherham Moat House
Wareham: Priory Hotel
Windermere: Miller Howe Hotel
Wishaw: Belfry Hotel
Woodstock: Bear Hotel
Woodstock: Feathers Hotel

■ **72%**
Aspley Guise: Moore Place
Bedford: Woodlands Manor Hotel
Birmingham: Albany Hotel
Birmingham: Holiday Inn
Bournemouth: Highcliff Hotel
Castle Combe: Manor House Hotel
Chelmsford: Pontlands Park Country Hotel
Congleton: Great Moreton Hall Hotel
Dover: Dover Moat House
Eastbourne: Grand Hotel
Grasmere: Wordsworth Hotel
Hatfield Heath: Down Hall Hotel
Hurstbourne Tarrant: Esseborne Manor
Kilve: Meadow House
Langdale: Langdale Hotel
Manchester Airport: The Hilton International Hotel
North Huish: Brookdale House
Oakham: The Whipper-In Hotel
Salcombe: Tides Reach Hotel
Scarborough: Royal Hotel
Solihull: Regency Hotel
Stamford: George of Stamford
Tunbridge Wells: Spa Hotel
■ **71%**
Ambleside: Rothay Manor
Bristol: Grand Hotel
Broadway: Dormy House
Bury St Edmunds: Angel Hotel
Corse Lawn: Corse Lawn House Hotel
Cuckfield: Ockenden Manor Hotel
Doncaster: Doncaster Moat House
Eastbourne: Queen's Hotel
Evershot: Summer Lodge
Ferndown: Dormy Hotel
Halifax: Holdsworth House
Handforth: Belfry Hotel
Jervaulx: Jervaulx Hall Hotel
Lavenham: Swan Hotel
Leeds: Hilton International
Loftus: Grinkle Park Hotel
Ludlow: Feathers Hotel
Markington: Hob Green Hotel
Matlock: Riber Hall
Mawnan Smith: Nansidwell Country
Newcastle upon Tyne: County Thistle Hotel
Nottingham: Albany Hotel
Nottingham: Royal Moat House International
Plymouth: Copthorne Hotel
Rusper: Ghyll Manor
Stratford-upon-Avon: Moat House International
Streatley-on-Thames: Swan at Streatley
Swindon: The Pear Tree at Purton
Tetbury: Close Hotel
Tetbury: Snooty Fox Hotel
Upper Slaughter: Lords of the Manor Hotel
Woodbridge: Seckford Hall Hotel
■ **70%**
Bath: Francis Hotel
Brighton: Brighton Metropole Hotel
Bristol: Holiday Inn

Bromsgrove: Grafton Manor
Canterbury: County Hotel
Canterbury: Howfield Manor
Chipping Campden: Cotswold House Hotel
Coventry: De Vere Hotel
Croydon: Selsdon Park Hotel
Dorking: Burford Bridge Hotel
Egham: Great Fosters
Egham: Runnymede Hotel
Gillingham: Stock Hill House Hotel
Hatch Beauchamp: Farthings Country House Hotel
Helmsley: Black Swan Hotel
Hollingbourne: Great Danes Hotel
Huntingdon: Old Bridge Hotel
Huntsham: Huntsham Court
Kingsbridge: Buckland-Tout-Saints Hotel
Ledbury: Hope End Country House Hotel
Liverpool: Atlantic Tower Hotel
Lymington: Passford House Hotel
Mottram St Andrew: Mottram Hall Hotel
Newcastle upon Tyne: Holiday Inn
Oxford: Randolph Hotel
Plymouth: Holiday Inn
Poole: Hospitality Inn
Puddington: Craxton Wood Hotel
South Normanton: Swallow Hotel
Staddle Bridge: McCoy's at the Tontine
Stockton-on-Tees: Swallow Hotel
Storrington: Abingworth Hall
Stratford-upon-Avon: Shakespeare Hotel
Swindon: Blunsdon House Hotel
Warwick: Hilton Inn
Wetheral: Crown Hotel
Wilmslow: Stanneylands Hotel
Worcester: Fownes Hotel
York: Mount Royale Hotel
York: Viking Hotel

SCOTLAND

■ **91%**
Fort William: Inverlochy Castle
■ **88%**
Auchterarder: Gleneagles Hotel
■ **83%**
Dunblane: Cromlix House
■ **82%**
Advie: Tulchan Lodge
■ **81%**
Turnberry: Turnberry Hotel
■ **80%**
Edinburgh: Caledonian Hotel
■ **79%**
Banchory: Invery House
■ **78%**
Edinburgh: Edinburgh Sheraton
Edinburgh: George Hotel
Glasgow: Holiday Inn
Kilchrenan: Ardanaiseig
■ **77%**
Gullane: Greywalls
St Andrews: The Rusack's
■ **76%**
Glasgow: One Devonshire Gardens

Inverness: Culloden House
St Andrews: Old Course Golf & Country Club
■ **75%**
Arisaig: Arisaig House
Glasgow: Albany
Newton Stewart: Kirroughtree Hotel
■ **74%**
Aberdeen: Holiday Inn
Auchterarder: Auchterarder House
Ballater: Craigendarroch Hotel
Edinburgh: Hilton National
Kelso: Sunlaws House Hotel
Kilwinning: Montgreenan Mansion House
Old Meldrum: Meldrum House Hotel
Stewarton: Chapeltoun House
■ **73%**
Eriska: Isle of Eriska
Kinclaven By Stanley: Ballathie House
Port Appin: Airds Hotel
■ **72%**
Bonnyrigg: Dalhousie Castle Hotel
Callander: Roman Camp Hotel
Glasgow: Stakis Grosvenor Hotel
Glenborrodale: Glenborrodale Castle
Humbie: Johnstounburn House Hotel
Oban: Knipoch Hotel
Portpatrick: Knockinaam Lodge Hotel
■ **71%**
Aberdeen: Bucksburn Moat House
Aberdeen: Copthorne Hotel
Aviemore: Stakis Four Seasons Hotel
Banchory: Raemoir House Hotel
Edinburgh: Carlton Highland Hotel
Kildrummy: Kildrummy Castle Hotel
Peebles: Peebles Hotel Hydro
■ **70%**
Ballater: Tullich Lodge
Crinan: Crinan Hotel
Edinburgh: King James Thistle Hotel
Glasgow: Hospitality Inn
Kilmore: Glenfeochan House
Langbank: Gleddoch House Hotel
Nairn: Clifton Hotel
Tiroran: Tiroran House

WALES

■ **78%**
Northop: Soughton Hall
Portmeirion: Hotel Portmeirion
■ **76%**
Newport: Celtic Manor Hotel
■ **75%**
Cardiff: Holiday Inn
Llandudno: Bodysgallen Hall
■ **74%**
Llandderfel: Palé Hall
Llangybi: Cwrt Bleddyn Hotel
■ **72%**
Cardiff: Stakis Inn on the Avenue
■ **71%**
Cardiff: Park Hotel
Miskin: Miskin Manor
Rossett: Llyndir Hall
■ **70%**
Abergwesyn: Llwynderw Hotel

CHANNEL ISLANDS

■ **81%**
St Saviour: Longueville Manor Hotel
■ **77%**
St Brelade's Bay: Hotel l'Horizon
■ **74%**
St Peter Port: St Pierre Park Hotel
■ **73%**
Rozel Bay: Chateau la Chaire
St Brelade: Atlantic Hotel
St Lawrence: Little Grove Hotel
■ **70%**
Bouley Bay: Water's Edge Hotel
St Brelade's Bay: St Brelade's Bay Hotel

NORTHERN IRELAND

■ **72%**
Holywood: Culloden Hotel

REPUBLIC OF IRELAND

■ **87%**
Cong: Ashford Castle
■ **86%**
Kenmare: Park Hotel Kenmare
■ **79%**
Dublin: Berkeley Court
Gorey: Marlfield House
■ **78%**
Dublin: Shelbourne Hotel
Newmarket-on-Fergus: Dromoland Castle
■ **77%**
Dublin: Jurys Hotel
Maynooth: Moyglare Manor
■ **76%**
Dublin: The Westbury
■ **75%**
Cashel (Co Tipperary): Cashel Palace Hotel
Parknasilla: Parknasilla Great Southern Hotel
■ **74%**
Killarney: Hotel Europe
■ **73%**
Cashel (Co Galway): Cashel House Hotel
■ **72%**
Ballynahinch: Ballynahinch Castle
Beaufort: Hotel Dunloe Castle
Mallow: Longueville House
Rosslare: Kelly's Strand Hotel
■ **71%**
Dublin: Burlington Hotel
Killiney: Fitzpatrick's Castle Hotel
Newbridge: Hotel Keadeen
■ **70%**
Ballyvaughan: Gregans Castle Hotel
Newmarket-on-Fergus: Clare Inn
Poulaphouca: Tulfarris
Rathnew: Tinakilly House Hotel

CREDIT, TRAVEL AND ENTERTAINMENT CARDS

Have you ever gone into a restaurant with a wallet full of notes and still given yourself heartburn worrying if you have enough to pay the bill? Or reached for your cheque book, found you've forgotten your chequecard and then worried about whether you can afford to write the cheque in the first place? Or if the bill is more than £50, agonised about whether they'll take more than one cheque?

When you carry a credit card into the great majority of establishments you also carry peace of mind, with none of the risks of carrying a lot of cash; no fretting about whether your guest will order a fat cigar with his brandy; no reaching for the calculator before calling for a bottle of birthday bubbly; no public counting out of notes when the bill comes; none of the bother of writing a cheque.

In hotels, too, where items like telephone calls cannot always be calculated in advance; credit cards are a boon: who wants to spend a sleepless night wondering if that last long-distance call was the one that broke the bank or drained the ready cash?

And when the credit card bill comes in, the payment is as simple and painless as the rest of the transaction.

DINERS CLUB INTERNATIONAL

Head Office Address: Diners Club House, Kingsmead, Farnborough, Hants. GU14 7SR. Tel: (0252) 516261. *Eire Address:* Russell Court, St. Stephens Green, Dublin 2. Tel: (0001) 779444. The Diners Club Card was the first card without a pre-set spending limit and is warmly accepted wherever you do business around the world. The Diners Club is the only charge or credit card to offer its members a second card free, to separate personal expenditure from business expenses, as well as lounges at international airports, including Heathrow.

ACCESS

Headquarters Address: Joint Credit Card Co. Ltd (a credit broker) 200 Priory Crescent, Southend on Sea, Essex SS2 6QQ. Tel: Southend (0702) 352211. For written details about Access cards apply at any bank displaying the Access sign or write to the above address. MasterCard and Eurocard are accepted at all Access retail and service establishments.

VISA

Address: Barclaycard Centre, Northampton NN1 1SG. Tel: Northampton (0604) 21100. Holders of all Visa cards are welcome wherever they see the familiar blue, white and gold badge. Most of the best-known hotels and restaurants in the United Kingdom welcome Visa.

AMERICAN EXPRESS

Around the world and around the corner, you'll find the American Express Card is warmly welcomed by leading Hotels, Restaurants, Travel Companies and Shops. As a Cardmember you have the freedom of *no pre-set spending limit,* and all the benefits and privileges the Card confers. Apply today!
Membership Application: American Express Europe Ltd, Amex House, P.O. Box 63, Edward Street, Brighton BN2 1YE. Or phone (0273) 696933.

TOWN HOUSE HOTELS

This exclusive category highlights a small number of hotels of distinctive personality. Most are conversions of town residences which retain not only their period facades but also interior character and, to some extent, the feel of a private house. None of them has more than 50 bedrooms, and very few are owned by groups. Excellent personal service is another attribute.

LONDON

Alexander Hotel, **SW7**
Coburg Hotel, **W2**
Dorset Square Hotel, **NW1**
The Fenja, **SW3**
The Halcyon, **W11**
Portobello Hotel, **W11**

ENGLAND

Bath: Number Nine
Bath: Priory Hotel
Bath: Queensberry Hotel
Bath: Royal Crescent Hotel
Birmingham: Plough & Harrow Hotel
Brighton: Granville Hotel
Brighton: Topps Hotel
Bury St Edmunds: Angel Hotel
Chipping Campden: Cotswold House Hotel
Harrogate: Studley Hotel
Poole: Mansion House
Sherborne: Eastbury Hotel

Tetbury: Close Hotel
Truro: Alverton Manor
Wareham: Priory Hotel
Wickham: Old House Hotel
Woodstock: Feathers Hotel
York: Mount Royale Hotel

SCOTLAND

Edinburgh: Howard Hotel
Elgin: Mansion House Hotel
Glasgow: One Devonshire Gardens
Glasgow: White House
Nairn: Clifton Hotel

WALES

Llandudno: St Tudno Hotel

REPUBLIC OF IRELAND

Cashel: Cashel Palace Hotel
Cork: Arbutus Lodge Hotel

PRIVATE HOUSE HOTELS

Some ten years ago we detected a trend towards country house hotels – there were 23 in our 1980 Guide, now there are around 100.

This year we detect a trend towards de luxe 'bed and breakfast' hotels which we are categorising as Private House hotels, symbolised by the letters PH in the gazetteer section. This handful of hotels offers guests comfortable, often luxurious accommodation and personal service, but do not have restaurants or public rooms, though some have perhaps a drawing room. Under our usual percentage rating, they would have suffered by not having normal hotel facilities, so rather than classifying them lower we are creating a new section specially for these fine establishments.

LONDON

Abbey Court Hotel, **W2**
Beaufort, **SW3**
The Fenja, **SW3**
Fortyseven Park Street, **W1**
L'Hotel, **SW3**
Knightsbridge Green, **SW1**
Number Sixteen, **SW7**

BATH

Fountain House
The Queensberry

LINCOLN

D'Isney

GLASGOW

White House

COUNTRY HOUSE HOTELS

This is a select category of small hotels offering civilised comfort, good service and fine food in an attractive and peaceful rural setting. Most of them are imposing country mansions, converted and run with loving care by dedicated owners, often a husband-and-wife team. Generally they have no more than 35 bedrooms; all have recommended in-house restaurants, many of star standard.

ENGLAND

Battle: Netherfield Place
Beanacre: Beechfield House
Bilbrough: Bilbrough Manor Hotel
Brampton: Farlam Hall Hotel
Bromsgrove: Grafton Manor
Broxted: Whitehall Hotel
Buckland: Buckland Manor
Chaddesley Corbett: Brockencote Hall
Chagford: Gidleigh Park Hotel
Chagford: Teignworthy
Charingworth: Charingworth Manor
Cheltenham: The Greenway
Colerne: Lucknam Court
Corse Lawn: Corse Lawn House Hotel
Dulverton: Ashwick Country House Hotel
East Grinstead: Gravetye Manor
Easton Grey: Whatley Manor
Ettington: Chase Country House Hotel
Evershot: Summer Lodge
Flitwick: Flitwick Manor
Freshford: Homewood Park
Gillingham: Stock Hill House Hotel
Grasmere: Michael's Nook
Grasmere: Wordsworth Hotel
Great Milton: Le Manoir aux Quat' Saisons
Hintlesham: Hintlesham Hall
Hockley Heath: Nuthurst Grange
Hunstrete: Hunstrete House
Hurstbourne Tarrant: Esseborne Manor
Kilve: Meadow House
Kingsbridge: Buckland-Tout-Saints Hotel
Kirkby Fleetham: Kirkby Fleetham Hall
Leamington Spa: Mallory Court
Ledbury: Hope End Country House Hotel
Linton: Wood Hall
Liskeard: The Well House
Lynton: Hewitt's
Maiden Newton: Maiden Newton House
Matlock: Riber Hall
Middlecombe: Periton Park
Nantwich: Rookery Hall
New Milton: Chewton Glen Hotel
North Huish: Brookdale House
Oakham: Hambleton Hall

Porlock: The Oaks Hotel
Puddington: Craxton Wood Hotel
South Molton: Whitechapel Manor
Ston Easton: Ston Easton Park
Storrington: Abingworth Hall
Storrington: Little Thakeham
Stow-on-the-Wold: Wyck Hill House
Swindon: The Pear Tree at Purton
Taplow: Cliveden
Tetbury: Calcot Manor
Thornbury: Thornbury Castle Hotel
Turners Hill: Alexander House
Uckfield: Horsted Place
Ullswater: Leeming House Hotel
Ullswater: Sharrow Bay Hotel
Upper Slaughter: Lords of the Manor Hotel
Warminster: Bishopstrow House
Whimple: Woodhayes
Windermere: Miller Howe Hotel
Worfield: Old Vicarage Hotel
York: Middlethorpe Hall

SCOTLAND

Arisaig: Arisaig House
Auchterarder: Auchterarder House
Ballater: Tullich Lodge
Banchory: Invery House
Drumnadrochit: Polmaily House Hotel
Dunblane: Cromlix House
Eriska: Isle of Eriska
Glenborrodale: Glenborrodale Castle
Gullane: Greywalls
Inverness: Culloden House
Kilchrenan: Ardanaiseig
Kilmore: Glenfeochan House
Newton Stewart: Kirroughtree Hotel
Oban: Knipoch Hotel
Old Meldrum: Meldrum House Hotel
Port Appin: Airds Hotel
Portpatrick: Knockinaam Lodge Hotel
Scarista: Scarista House
Tiroran: Tiroran House

Continued overleaf

Continued

WALES

Abergwesyn: Llwynderw Hotel
Llandudno: Bodysgallen Hall
Northop: Soughton Hall
Rossett: Llyndir Hall
Talsarnau: Maes-y-Neuadd Hotel

CHANNEL ISLANDS

Rozel Bay: Château La Chaire
St Saviour: Longueville Manor Hotel

REPUBLIC OF IRELAND

Ballyvaughan: Gregans Castle Hotel
Cashel: Cashel House Hotel
Kenmare: Park Hotel Kenmare
Mallow: Longueville House
Maynooth: Moyglare Manor
Rathnew: Tinakilly House Hotel
Wicklow: Old Rectory

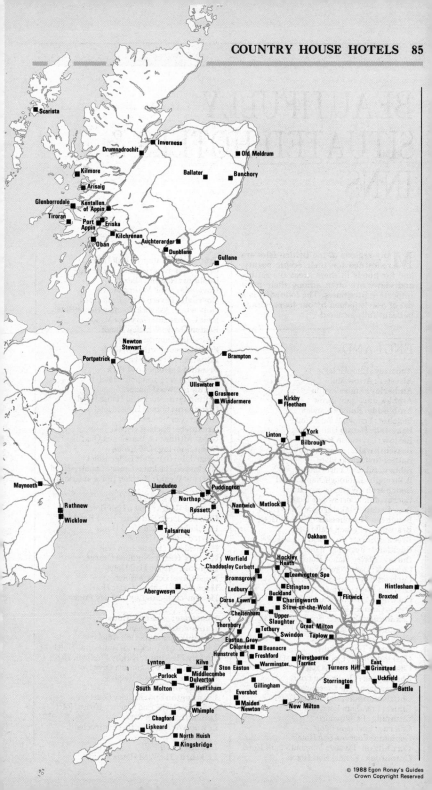

BEAUTIFULLY SITUATED HOTELS & INNS

Many regions of the British Isles are renowned for their scenic beauty, and for hotels in these areas the setting and views are often among their most important attributes. The following is a list of hotels judged by our inspectors to be beautifully situated

ENGLAND

Abberley: Elms Hotel
Alcester: Arrow Mill
Amberley: Amberley Inn
Ambleside: Nanny Brow
Ambleside: Rothay Manor
Bagshot: Pennyhill Park Hotel
Bakewell: Hassop Hall Hotel
Baslow: Cavendish Hotel
Bassenthwaite: Armathwaite Hall
Battle: Netherfield Place
Bibury: Bibury Court Hotel
Bilbrough: Bilbrough Manor Hotel
Bonchurch: Winterbourne Hotel
Borrowdale: Borrowdale Hotel
Borrowdale: Stakis Lodore Swiss Hotel
Boughton Monchelsea: Tanyard Hotel
Brampton: Farlam Hall Hotel
Brockenhurst: Rhinefield House Hotel
Buckland: Buckland Manor
Burley: Burley Manor Hotel
Calstock: Danescombe Valley Hotel
Carlyon Bay: Carlyon Bay Hotel
Carlyon Bay: Porth Avallen Hotel
Cartmel: Aynsome Manor Hotel
Castle Combe: Manor House Hotel
Chaddesley Corbett: Brockencote Hall
Chagford: Gidleigh Park Hotel
Chagford: Mill End Hotel
Chagford: Teignworthy
Charingworth: Charingworth Manor
Chartham: Thruxted Oast
Chedington: Chedington Court
Cheltenham: The Greenway
Chittlehamholt: Highbullen Hotel
Churt: Frensham Pond Hotel
Climping: Bailiffscourt
Colerne: Lucknam Court
Coniston: Coniston Sun Hotel
Cornhill-on-Tweed: Tillmouth Park Hotel
Cranbrook: Kennel Holt Hotel

Crathorne: Crathorne Hall Hotel
Crosby-on-Eden: Crosby Lodge Hotel
Dedham: Maison Talbooth
Dovedale: Izaak Walton Hotel
Dovedale: Peveril of the Peak Hotel
Dulverton: Ashwick Country House Hotel
East Grinstead: Gravetye Manor
Easton Grey: Whatley Manor
Evershot: Summer Lodge
Fairy Cross: Portledge Hotel
Flitwick: Flitwick Manor
Freshford: Homewood Park
Freshwater: Faringford Hotel
Frome: Selwood Manor
Gillingham: Stock Hill House Hotel
Gittisham: Combe House Hotel
Golant: Cormorant Hotel
Grasmere: Michael's Nook
Great Milton: Le Manoir aux Quat' Saisons
Great Snoring: Old Rectory
Grizedale: Grizedale Lodge Hotel
Hackness: Hackness Grange Country Hotel
Harrow Weald: Mansion House at Grim's Dyke
Haslemere: Lythe Hill Hotel
Hatfield Heath: Down Hall Hotel
Hawkchurch: Fairwater Head Hotel
Hawkshead: Field Head House
Haytor: Bel Alp House
Hintlesham: Hintlesham Hall
Hockley Heath: Nuthurst Grange
Holbeton: Alston Hall Hotel
Hope Cove: Cottage Hotel
Hope Cove: Lantern Lodge Hotel
Horton-cum-Studley: Studley Priory Hotel
Hunstrete: Hunstrete House
Huntsham: Huntsham Court
Jervaulx: Jervaulx Hall Hotel
Kingsbridge: Buckland-Tout-Saints Hotel
Kirkby Fleetham: Kirkby Fleetham Hall
Lamorna Cove: Lamorna Cove Hotel
Langdale: Langdale Hotel
Langley-on-Tyne: Langley Castle
Leamington Spa: Mallory Court
Ledbury: Hope End Country House Hotel
Lenham: Chilston Park
Lewdown: Fox's Earth, Lewtrenchard Manor
Linton: Wood Hall
Liskeard: The Well House

Loftus: Grinkle Park Hotel
Longhorsley: Linden Hall Hotel
Looe: Talland Bay Hotel
Lower Beeding: South Lodge
Maidencombe: Orestone Manor House
Malvern: Cottage in the Wood Hotel
Markington: Hob Green Hotel
Marlow: Compleat Angler Hotel
Matlock: Riber Hall
Mawnan Smith: Meudon Hotel
Mawnan Smith: Nansidwell Country House
Melton Mowbray: Stapleford Park
Moretonhampstead: Manor House Hotel
Mullion: Polurrian Hotel
Nantwich: Rookery Hall
New Milton: Chewton Glen Hotel
Newton Solney: Newton Park Hotel
Oakham: Hambleton Hall
Otley: Chevin Lodge
Portloe: Lugger Hotel
Richmond: Petersham Hotel
Ross-on-Wye: Pengethley Manor Hotel
Rotherwick: Tylney Hall Hotel
Rothley: Rothley Court
Ruckhall: The Ancient Camp Inn
St Mawes: Hotel Tresanton
Salcombe: Soar Mill Cove Hotel
Saunton: Saunton Sands Hotel
South Molton: Whitechapel Manor
South Walsham: South Walsham Hall Hotel
Ston Easton: Ston Easton Park
Storrington: Abingworth Hall
Storrington: Little Thakeham
Stow-on-the-Wold: Wyck Hill House
Stratford-upon-Avon: Billesley Manor
Stratford-upon-Avon: Ettington Park Hotel
Sutton Coldfield: New Hall
Taplow: Cliveden
Thornbury: Thornbury Castle Hotel
Thornton-le-Fylde: River House
Torquay: Imperial Hotel
Torquay: Osborne Hotel
Tresco: Island Hotel
Troutbeck: Mortal Man Hotel
Ullswater: Leeming House Hotel
Ullswater: Old Church Hotel
Ullswater: Rampsbeck Hotel
Ullswater: Sharrow Bay Hotel
Underbarrow: Greenriggs Country House
Upper Slaughter: Lords of the Manor Hotel
Veryan: Nare Hotel
Wadhurst: Spindlewood Country House Hotel
Warminster: Bishopstrow House
West Bexington: Manor House
Whitewell: Inn at Whitewell
Whitwell-on-the-Hill: Whitwell Hall Country
Winchester: Lainston House
Windermere: Langdale Chase Hotel
Windermere: Miller Howe Hotel
Windsor: Oakley Court Hotel
Woodbridge: Seckford Hall Hotel
Woody Bay: Woody Bay Hotel
York: Middlethorpe Hall

SCOTLAND

Aberdeen: Ardoe House Hotel
Achiltibuie: Summer Isles Hotel
Advie: Tulchan Lodge
Airth: Airth Castle Hotel
Altnaharra: Altnaharra Hotel
Annan: Warmanbie Hotel
Ardentinny: Ardentinny Hotel
Arduaine: Loch Melfort Hotel
Arisaig: Arisaig House
Auchterarder: Auchterarder House
Auchterarder: Gleneagles Hotel
Auchterhouse: Old Mansion House Hotel
Ballater: Tullich Lodge
Banchory: Invery House
Banchory: Raemoir House Hotel
Barrhill: Kildonan Hotel
Beattock: Auchen Castle Hotel
Bonnyrigg: Dalhousie Castle Hotel
Brae: Busta House Hotel
Crinan: Crinan Hotel
Drumnadrochit: Polmaily House Hotel
Dryburgh: Dryburgh Abbey Hotel
Dunblane: Cromlix House
Dunkeld: Hillhead of Dunkeld
Duror: Stewart Hotel
Eriska: Isle of Eriska
Ettrickbridge: Ettrickshaws Hotel
Fort William: Mercury Hotel
Garve: Inchbae Lodge Hotel
Gatehouse of Fleet: Cally Palace Hotel
Glenborrodale: Glenborrodale Castle
Gullane: Greywalls
Harray Loch: Merkister Hotel
Helmsdale: Navidale House Hotel
Humbie: Johnstounburn House Hotel
Inverness: Bunchrew House Hotel
Inverness: Culloden House
Inverness: Dunain Park Hotel
Isle of Gigha: Gigha Hotel
Isle of Raasay: Isle of Raasay Hotel
Kelso: Ednam House Hotel
Kelso: Sunlaws House Hotel
Kenmore: Kenmore Hotel
Kentallen of Appin: Ardsheal House
Kentallen of Appin: Holly Tree Hotel
Kilchrenan: Ardanaiseig
Kilchrenan: Taychreggan Hotel
Kildrummy: Kildrummy Castle Hotel
Killiecrankie: Killiecrankie Hotel
Kilmore: Glenfeochan House
Kilwinning: Montgreenan Mansion House
Kinclaven By Stanley: Ballathie House
Kinloch Rannoch: Loch Rannoch Hotel
Kirkmichael: Log Cabin Hotel
Langbank: Gleddoch House Hotel
Newton Stewart: Kirroughtree Hotel
North Middleton: Borthwick Castle
Oban: Knipoch Hotel
Old Meldrum: Meldrum House Hotel
Onich: Onich Hotel
Peebles: Cringletie House Hotel
Peebles: Peebles Hotel Hydro
Pitcaple: Pittodrie House Hotel

continued . . .

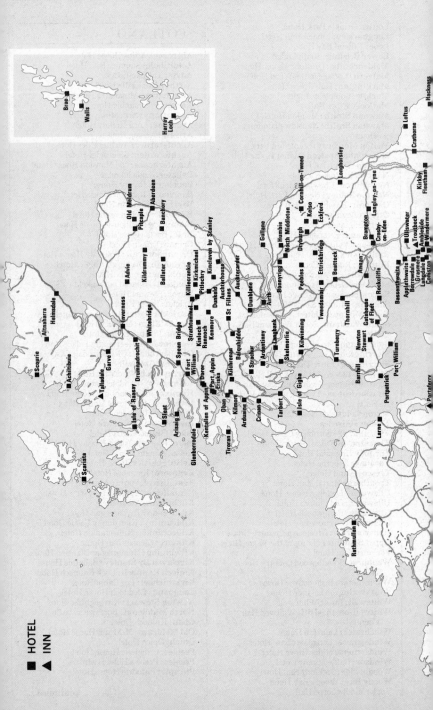

HOTEL
▲ INN

continued . . .
Pitlochry: Green Park Hotel
Port Appin: Airds Hotel
Port William: Corsemalzie House Hotel
Portpatrick: Knockinaam Lodge Hotel
Rockcliffe: Baron's Craig Hotel
St Fillans: Four Seasons Hotel
Scarista: Scarista House
Scourie: Eddrachilles Hotel
Skelmorlie: Manor Park Hotel
Sleat: Kinloch Lodge
Spean Bridge: Letterfinlay Lodge Hotel
Strachur: Creggans Inn
Strathtummel: Port-an-Eilean Hotel
Talladale: Loch Maree Hotel
Tarbert: Stonefield Castle Hotel
Thornhill: Barjarg Tower
Tiroran: Tiroran House
Turnberry: Turnberry Hotel
Tweedsmuir: Crook Inn
Walls: Burrastow House
Whitebridge: Knockie Lodge Hotel

WALES

Aberdovey: Hotel Plas Penhelig
Aberdovey: Trefeddian Hotel
Abergwesyn: Llwynderw Hotel
Abersoch: Porth Tocyn Hotel
Aberystwyth: Conrah Country Hotel
Beaumaris: Bulkeley Arms Hotel
Beddgelert: Royal Goat Hotel
Bontddu: Bontddu Hall Hotel
Conwy: Sychnant Pass Hotel
Crickhowell: Gliffaes Hotel
Eglwysfach: Ynyshir Hall Hotel
Gwbert-on-Sea: Cliff Hotel
Lake Vyrnwy: Lake Vyrnwy Hotel
Lamphey: Court Hotel
Llanarmon Dyffryn Ceiriog: Hand Hotel
Llandderfel: Palé Hall
Llandudno: Bodysgallen Hall
Northop: Soughton Hall
Pantmawr: Glansevern Arms
Penmaenpool: George III Hotel
Portmeirion: Hotel Portmeirion
Pwllheli: Plas Bodegroes
Reynoldston: Fairyhill
Ruthin: Ruthin Castle
St David's: Warpool Court Hotel
Talsarnau: Maes-y-Neuadd Hotel
Tal-y-Llyn: Ty'n-y-Cornel Hotel

CHANNEL ISLANDS

Bouley Bay: Water's Edge Hotel
St Brelade's Bay: Hotel l'Horizon

Sark: Hotel Petit Champ
Sark: Stocks Hotel

NORTHERN IRELAND

Larne: Magheramorne House Hotel
Portaferry: Portaferry Hotel

REPUBLIC OF IRELAND

Ballylickey: Ballylickey Manor House
Ballylickey: Sea View House Hotel
Ballynahinch: Ballynahinch Castle
Ballyvaughan: Gregans Castle Hotel
Beaufort: Hotel Dunloe Castle
Caragh Lake: Ard-na-Sidhe
Caragh Lake: Caragh Lodge
Cashel (Co Galway): Cashel House Hotel
Cashel (Co Galway): Zetland House Hotel
Clifden: Abbeyglen Castle Hotel
Clifden: Hotel Ardagh
Clifden: Rock Glen Hotel
Cong: Ashford Castle
Crossmolina: Enniscoe House
Delgany: Glenview Hotel
Dundrum: Dundrum House Hotel
Ferrycarrig Bridge: Ferrycarrig Hotel
Glen of Aherlow: Aherlow House Hotel
Gorey: Marlfield House
Kanturk: Assolas Country House
Killarney: Aghadoe Heights Hotel
Killarney: Cahernane Hotel
Killarney: Castlerosse Hotel
Killarney: Hotel Europe
Killiney: Court Hotel
Killiney: Fitzpatrick's Castle Hotel
Knocklofty: Knocklofty House Hotel
Letterfrack: Rosleague Manor Hotel
Mallow: Longueville House
Maynooth: Moyglare Manor
Newmarket-on-Fergus: Dromoland Castle
Oughterard: Connemara Gateway Hotel
Oughterard: Currarevagh House
Parknasilla: Parknasilla Great Southern
    Hotel
Poulaphouca: Tulfarris
Rathmullan: Rathmullan House
Rathnew: Tinakilly House Hotel
Renvyle: Renvyle House Hotel
Riverstown: Coopershill
Scotshouse: Hilton Park
Shanagarry: Ballymaloe House
Waterville: Waterville Lake Hotel

The perfect Master Blend.

HOTELS WITH SPORTS FACILITIES

INDOOR SWIMMING

LONDON

The Berkeley, **SW1**
Grosvenor House, **W1**
Holiday Inn (Marble Arch), **W1**
Holiday Inn (Swiss Cottage), **NW3**
Kensington Close Hotel, **W8**
Le Meridien Piccadilly, **W1**
Rembrandt Hotel, **SW7**

LONDON AIRPORTS

GATWICK
Gatwick Hilton International
Gatwick Penta Hotel

HEATHROW
Excelsior Hotel
Heathrow Penta Hotel
Holiday Inn
Sheraton-Heathrow Hotel
Sheraton Skyline

ENGLAND

Ascot: Royal Berkshire
Barnham Broom: Barnham Broom Hotel
Basingstoke: Hilton Lodge
Basingstoke: Hilton National
Bassenthwaite: Armathwaite Hall
Birmingham: Albany Hotel
Birmingham: Cobden Hotel
Birmingham: Copthorne Hotel
Birmingham: Holiday Inn
Blackpool: Imperial Hotel
Blackpool: Pembroke Hotel
Blakeney: Blakeney Hotel
Bolton: Last Drop Village Hotel
Borrowdale: Stakis Lodore Swiss Hotel
Bournemouth: Norfolk Royale Hotel
Bournemouth: Royal Bath Hotel
Bowness on Windermere: Belsfield Hotel
Bradford: Baron Hotel
Bramhope: Post House Hotel
Brentwood: Post House Hotel
Brighton: Brighton Metropole Hotel
Brighton (Hove): Courtlands Hotel
Brighton: The Grand
Brighton: Ramada Renaissance Hotel
Bristol: Crest Hotel
Bristol: Holiday Inn
Bristol: Redwood Lodge Hotel
Brockenhurst: Balmer Lawn Hotel
Brockenhurst: Careys Manor Hotel
Brockenhurst: Rhinefield House Hotel
Broughton: Broughton Park Hotel
Burnham: Burnham Beeches Hotel
Calbourne: Swainston Manor Hotel
Cambridge: Cambridgeshire Moat House
Cambridge: Post House Hotel
Canterbury: Ebury Hotel
Carlisle: Crown & Mitre Hotel
Carlisle: Swallow Hilltop Hotel
Carlyon Bay: Carlyon Bay Hotel
Castle Donington: Donington Thistle Hotel
Chelmsford: Pontlands Park Country Hotel
Chester: Mollington Banastre Hotel
Chittlehamholt: Highbullen Hotel
Chollerford: George Hotel
Churt: Frensham Pond Hotel
Cobham: Hilton National
Colerne: Lucknam Park
Constantine Bay: Treglos Hotel
Cooden: Cooden Resort Hotel
Coventry: Crest Hotel
Croydon: Holiday Inn
Croydon: Selsdon Park Hotel
Dover: Crest House
Driffield: Bell Hotel
Eastbourne: Grand Hotel
Farnborough: Queen's Hotel
Fawkham: Brandshatch Place
Ferndown: Dormy Hotel
Garforth: Hilton National
Gateshead: Swallow Hotel Gateshead
Gillingham: Stock Hill House Hotel
Gloucester: Crest Hotel
Golant: Cormorant Hotel
Grasmere: Wordsworth Hotel
Guildford: University Post House Hotel
Hackness: Hackness Grange Country Hotel
Harrogate: Majestic
Harrogate: Hotel St George
Hatfield Heath: Down Hall Hotel
Havant: Post House Hotel
Haydock: Post House Hotel
Hethersett: Park Farm Hotel
Hollingbourne: Great Danes Hotel
Hope Cove: Lantern Lodge Hotel
Hull: Marina Post House Hotel
Hythe: Hythe Imperial Hotel
Knutsford: The Cottons Hotel

Lancaster: Post House Hotel
Langdale: Langdale Hotel
Leicester: Holiday Inn
Linton: Wood Hall
Liverpool: Britannia Adelphi Hotel
Liverpool: Liverpool Moat House
Lower Slaughter: Lower Slaughter Manor
Lymington: Passford House Hotel
Maidenhead: Crest Hotel
Manchester: Britannia Hotel
Manchester: Copthorne Hotel
Manchester: Holiday Inn
Manchester: Portland Thistle Hotel
Manchester Airport: Excelsior Hotel
Manchester Airport: The Hilton International Hotel
Matlock Bath: New Bath Hotel
Mawnan Smith: Budock Vean Hotel
Milton Damerel: Woodford Bridge Hotel
Moreton-in-Marsh: Manor House Hotel
Mottram St Andrew: Mottram Hall Hotel
Mullion: Polurrian Hotel
Newcastle upon Tyne: Gosforth Park Thistle Hotel
Newcastle upon Tyne: Holiday Inn
Newquay: Atlantic Hotel
Newquay: Hotel Bristol
Northampton: Swallow Hotel
Norwich: Post House Hotel
Oxford: Oxford Moat House
Penrith: North Lakes Gateway Hotel
Peterborough: Peterborough Moat House
Plymouth: Copthorne Hotel
Plymouth: Holiday Inn
Portsmouth: Holiday Inn
Reading: Caversham Hotel
Reading: Post House Hotel
Reading: Ramada Hotel
Rotherwick: Tylney Hall Hotel
St Ives: Garrack Hotel
Salcombe: Marine Hotel
Salcombe: Soar Mill Cove Hotel
Salcombe: South Sands Hotel
Salcombe: Tides Reach Hotel
Samlesbury: Swallow Trafalgar Hotel
Samlesbury: Tickled Trout Hotel
Saunton: Saunton Sands Hotel
Scarborough: Palm Court Hotel
Scarborough: Royal Hotel
Shaftesbury: Royal Chase Hotel
Shanklin: Cliff Tops Hotel
Shedfield: Meon Valley Hotel
Sheffield: Hallam Tower Post House Hotel
Sheffield: Hotel St George
Shifnal: Park House Hotel
Sidmouth: Fortfield Hotel
Sidmouth: Victoria Hotel
Slough: Holiday Inn
Solihull: St John's Swallow Hotel
South Marston: South Marston Hotel
South Milford: Selby Fork Hotel
South Mimms: Crest Hotel
South Normanton: Swallow Hotel
Southampton: Post House Hotel
Stoke Fleming: Stoke Lodge Hotel
Stratford-upon-Avon: Billesley Manor
Stratford-upon-Avon: Ettington Park Hotel

Streatley-on-Thames: Swan at Streatley
Swindon: Blunsdon House Hotel
Swindon: Post House Hotel
Telford: Telford Hotel, Golf & Country Club
Telford: Telford Moat House
Tewkesbury: Tewkesbury Park Hotel
Thurlestone: Thurlestone Hotel
Torquay: Grand Hotel
Torquay: Imperial Hotel
Torquay: Kistor Hotel
Torquay: Palace Hotel
Tunbridge Wells: Spa Hotel
Uckfield: Horsted Place
Walberton: Avisford Park Hotel
Walsall: Barons Court Hotel
Wareham: Springfield Country Hotel
Warminster: Bishopstrow House
Warrington: Lord Daresbury Hotel
Warwick: Hilton Inn
Washington: George Washington Hotel
West Runton: Links Country Park Hotel
West Stoughton: Burnt House Farm
Wetheral: Crown Hotel
Whitwell-on-the-Hill: Whitwell Hall Country House Hotel
Willerby: Grange Park Hotel
Wilmslow: Valley Lodge Hotel
Wishaw: Belfry Hotel
Woolacombe: Woolacombe Bay Hotel
Wrotham Heath: Post House Hotel
York: Swallow Chase Hotel

SCOTLAND

Aberdeen: Bucksburn Moat House
Aberdeen: Holiday Inn
Aberdeen: Stakis Tree Tops Hotel
Airth: Airth Castle Hotel
Auchterarder: Gleneagles Hotel
Aviemore: Stakis Coylumbridge Resort Hotel
Aviemore: Stakis Four Seasons Hotel
Ayr: Caledonian Hotel
Ballater: Craigendarroch Hotel
Barrhill: Kildonan Hotel
Dunblane: Stakis Dunblane Hydro
Edinburgh: Carlton Highland Hotel
Edinburgh: Edinburgh Sheraton
Edinburgh: Royal Scot Hotel
Forfar: Royal Hotel
Glasgow: Holiday Inn
Glasgow: Stakis Pond Hotel
Glasgow: Swallow Hotel
Inverness: Caledonian Hotel
Inverness: Kingsmills Hotel
Irvine: Hospitality Inn
Kinloch Rannoch: Loch Rannoch Hotel
Lerwick: Shetland Hotel
Peebles: Peebles Hotel Hydro
Peterhead: Waterside Inn
St Andrews: Old Course Golf & Country Club
South Queensferry: Forth Bridges Moat House
Stranraer: North West Castle Hotel
Troon: Marine Highland Hotel
Turnberry: Turnberry Hotel

WALES

Aberdovey: Trefeddian Hotel
Abersoch: Riverside Hotel
Aberystwyth: Conrah Country Hotel
Cardiff: Holiday Inn
Cardiff: Post House Hotel
Cardiff: Stakis Inn on the Avenue
Chepstow: St Pierre Hotel
Lamphey: Court Hotel
Llandudno: Empire Hotel
Llandudno: St Tudno Hotel
Llangybi: Cwrt Bleddyn Hotel
Miskin: Miskin Manor
Newport: Celtic Manor Hotel
St David's: Warpool Court Hotel
Swansea: Hilton National

CHANNEL ISLANDS

St Peter Port: St Pierre Park Hotel
St Brelade's Bay: Hotel l'Horizon
St Helier: Apollo Hotel
St Helier: Beaufort Hotel
St Helier: Grand Hotel
St Peter: Mermaid Hotel

ISLE OF MAN

Douglas: Sefton Hotel
Ramsey: Grand Island Hotel

NORTHERN IRELAND

Comber: La Mon House Hotel

REPUBLIC OF IRELAND

Ballina: Downhill Hotel
Beaufort: Hotel Dunloe Castle
Bunratty: Fitzpatrick's Shannon Shamrock Hotel
Carrickmacross: Nuremore Hotel
Cork: Jurys Hotel
Dublin: Berkeley Court
Dublin: Jurys Hotel
Dublin Airport: Dublin International Hotel
Dundalk: Ballymascanlon Hotel
Galway: Corrib Great Southern Hotel
Galway: Great Southern Hotel
Kilkenny: Newpark Hotel
Killarney: Hotel Europe
Killarney: Killarney Great Southern Hotel
Killarney: Torc Great Southern Hotel
Killiney: Fitzpatrick's Castle Hotel
Kinsale: Actons Hotel
Knocklofty: Knocklofty House Hotel
Limerick: Limerick Inn Hotel
Rosslare: Kelly's Strand Hotel
Waterford: Waterford Castle
Waterville: Waterville Lake Hotel

OUTDOOR SWIMMING

LONDON AIRPORTS

GATWICK
Chequers Thistle Hotel
Post House Hotel

HEATHROW
Skyway Hotel

ENGLAND

Alveston: Post House Hotel
Ascot: Berystede Hotel
Bagshot: Pennyhill Park Hotel
Barnham Broom: Barnham Broom Hotel
Bath: Priory Hotel
Beanacre: Beechfield House
Bembridge: Highbury Hotel
Birmingham: Post House Hotel
Bodymoor Heath: Marston Farm Hotel
Bognor Regis: Royal Norfolk Hotel
Bonchurch: Winterbourne Hotel
Borrowdale: Stakis Lodore Swiss Hotel
Bournemouth: Carlton Hotel
Bournemouth: East Cliff Court Hotel
Bournemouth: Highcliff Hotel
Bowness-on-Windermere: Old England Hotel
Bradford: Novotel
Brentwood: Post House Hotel
Bristol: Redwood Lodge Hotel
Broadway: Collin House Hotel
Brockenhurst: Balmer Lawn Hotel
Brockenhurst: Rhinefield House Hotel
Broxted: Whitehall Hotel
Buckland: Buckland Manor
Burley: Burley Manor Hotel
Carlyon Bay: Carlyon Bay Hotel
Castle Combe: Manor House Hotel
Charlecote: The Charlecote Pheasant
Cheltenham: Hotel de la Bere
Chittlehamholt: Highbullen Hotel
Climping: Bailiffscourt
Coatham Mundeville: Hall Garth
Cooden: Cooden Resort Hotel
Coventry: Novotel Coventry
Croydon: Selsdon Park Hotel
Dorking: Burford Bridge Hotel
Dorking: White Horse Hotel
Dulverton: Carnarvon Arms Hotel
East Horsley: Thatchers Hotel
Eastbourne: Grand Hotel
Easton Grey: Whatley Manor
Egham: Great Fosters
Evershot: Summer Lodge
Exmouth: Imperial Hotel
Fairy Cross: Portledge Hotel
Falmouth: Falmouth Hotel
Farnham: Trevena House Hotel

Faugh: String of Horses
Freshwater: Farringford Hotel
Frome: Selwood Manor
Gloucester: Hatton Court
Great Milton: Le Manoir aux Quat' Saisons
Grimston: Congham Hall
Hatherleigh: George Hotel
Helland Bridge: Tredethy Country Hotel
Helmsley: Feversham Arms Hotel
Holbeton: Alston Hall Hotel
Hunstrete: Hunstrete House
Ipswich: Post House Hotel
Kidderminster: Stone Manor Hotel
Kirkby Fleetham: Kirkby Fleetham Hall
Knapton: Knapton Hall
Lamorna Cove: Lamorna Cove Hotel
Leamington Spa: Mallory Court
Liskeard: The Well House
Looe: Talland Bay Hotel
Lostwithiel: Carotel Motel
Lymington: Passford House Hotel
Lyndhurst: Lyndhurst Park Hotel
Lyndhurst: Parkhill Hotel
Lynmouth: Tors Hotel
Maidencombe: Orestone Manor House
Maidstone: Boxley House Hotel
Manchester: Novotel Manchester West
Matlock Bath: New Bath Hotel
Meriden: Manor Hotel
Mudeford: Avonmouth Hotel
Mullion: Polurrian Hotel
New Milton: Chewton Glen Hotel
Newlyn: Higher Faugan Hotel
Newquay: Atlantic Hotel
Newquay: Hotel Riviera
North Stoke: Springs Hotel
Nottingham: Novotel
Ormesby St Margaret: Ormesby Lodge Hotel
Oxford: Welcome Lodge
Paignton: Palace Hotel
Paignton: Redcliffe Hotel
Plymouth: Mayflower Post House Hotel
Plymouth: Novotel
Preston: Novotel
Redbourn: Aubrey Park Hotel
Ross-on-Wye: Pengethley Manor Hotel
Rotherwick: Tylney Hall Hotel
Rusper: Ghyll Manor
St Ives: Boskerris Hotel
St Ives: Tregenna Castle Hotel
Salcombe: Soar Mill Cove Hotel
Sandown: Melville Hall Hotel
Sedlescombe: Brickwall Hotel
Sidmouth: Victoria Hotel
Silchester: Romans Hotel
Somerton: The Lynch Country House Hotel
South Marston: South Marston Hotel
South Walsham: South Walsham Hall Hotel
Steyning: Springwells Hotel
Stoke Fleming: Stoke Lodge Hotel
Stoke Mandeville: Belmore Hotel
Storrington: Abingworth Hall
Storrington: Little Thakeham
Studland Bay: Knoll House Hotel
Taplow: Cliveden
Tetbury: Calcot Manor

Tewkesbury: Bredon Manor
Thurlestone: Thurlestone Hotel
Torquay: Grand Hotel
Torquay: Imperial Hotel
Torquay: Livermead Cliff Hotel
Torquay: Livermead House Hotel
Torquay: Osborne Hotel
Torquay: Palace Hotel
Torquay: Toorak Hotel
Tresco: Island Hotel
Ventnor: Royal Hotel
Veryan: Nare Hotel
Walberton: Avisford Park Hotel
Wallingford: Shillingford Bridge Hotel
Ware: Briggens House Hotel
Wareham: Springfield Country Hotel
Warminster: Bishopstrow House
Wem: Hawkstone Park Hotel
Weston-on-the-Green: Weston Manor Hotel
Weston-super-Mare: Grand Atlantic Hotel
Wincanton: Holbrook House Hotel
Woolacombe: Woolacombe Bay Hotel
York: Mount Royale Hotel

SCOTLAND

Aberdeen Airport: Skean Dhu Hotel
Auchterhouse: Old Mansion House Hotel
Drumnadrochit: Polmaily House Hotel
Gatehouse of Fleet: Cally Palace Hotel
Nairn: Golf View Hotel
North Berwick: Marine Hotel
Pitlochry: Atholl Palace Hotel
Selkirk: Philipburn House Hotel
Tarbert: Stonefield Castle Hotel

WALES

Abersoch: Porth Tocyn Hotel
Caernarfon: Stables Hotel
Coychurch: Coed-y-Mwstwr Hotel
Fishguard: Fishguard Bay Hotel
Gwbert-on-Sea: Cliff Hotel
Llandudno: Empire Hotel
Portmeirion: Hotel Portmeirion
Tal-y-Llyn: Ty'n-y-Cornel Hotel

CHANNEL ISLANDS

Herm Island: White House Hotel
St Martin's: St Margaret's Lodge Hotel
St Martin's: La Trelade Hotel
St Peter Port: Duke of Richmond Hotel
St Peter Port: Flying Dutchman Hotel
St Peter Port: Old Government House Hotel
Bouley Bay: Water's Edge Hotel
Gorey: Old Court House Hotel
Petit Port: Sea Crest Hotel
Portelet Bay: Portelet Hotel
St Brelade: Atlantic Hotel
St Brelade: La Place Hotel
St Brelade's Bay: Hotel Château Valeuse
St Brelade's Bay: St Brelade's Bay Hotel
St Clement's Bay: Hotel Ambassadeur

Hotels with Swimming pools continued...
St Lawrence: Little Grove Hotel
St Saviour: Longueville Manor Hotel
Sark: Aval du Creux Hotel
Sark: Hotel Petit Champ
Sark: Stocks Hotel

ISLE OF MAN

Douglas: Palace Hotel

NORTHERN IRELAND

Dunmurry: Conway Hotel

REPUBLIC OF IRELAND

Ballylickey: Ballylickey Manor House
Clifden: Abbeyglen Castle Hotel
Cork: Jurys Hotel
Dublin: Jurys Hotel
Oughterard: Connemara Gateway Hotel
Renvyle: Renvyle House Hotel
Rosslare: Kelly's Strand Hotel
Shanagarry: Ballymaloe House

FISHING

ENGLAND

Alcester: Arrow Mill
Aldeburgh: Brudenell Hotel
Allendale: Bishopfield
Ambleside: Nanny Brow
Ambleside: Wateredge Hotel
Bagshot: Pennyhill Park Hotel
Baslow: Cavendish Hotel
Bassenthwaite: Armathwaite Hall
Bath: Bath Hotel
Beccles: Waveney House Hotel
Bibury: Bibury Court Hotel
Bibury: Swan Hotel
Bideford: Yeoldon House
Bigbury on Sea: Burgh Island
Bodymoor Heath: Marston Farm Hotel
Bolton Abbey: Devonshire Arms
Bristol: Crest Hotel
Bromsgrove: Grafton Manor
Burbage: Savernake Forest Hotel
Burley: Burley Manor Hotel
Burton upon Trent: Riverside Inn
Calbourne: Swainston Manor Hotel
Castle Combe: Manor House Hotel
Chagford: Mill End Hotel
Charlbury: The Bell
Chester: Penguin Hotel
Chittlehamholt: Highbullen Hotel
Chollerford: George Hotel

Churt: Frensham Pond Hotel
Clearwell: Clearwell Castle
Constantine Bay: Treglos Hotel
Cooden: Calahonda Hotel
Cornhill-on-Tweed: Tillmouth Park Hotel
Dovedale: Izaak Walton Hotel
Dulverton: Carnarvon Arms Hotel
East Grinstead: Gravetye Manor
Easton Grey: Whatley Manor
Egham: Runnymede Hotel
Fairford: Bull Hotel
Fairy Cross: Portledge Hotel
Falmouth: Greenbank Hotel
Fossebridge: Fossebridge Inn
Frome: Selwood Manor
Gittisham: Combe House Hotel
Grasmere: White Moss House
Great Milton: Le Manoir aux Quat' Saisons
Greta Bridge: Morritt Arms Hotel
Hackness: Hackness Grange Country Hotel
Harrogate: Russell Hotel
Hollingbourne: Great Danes Hotel
Huntingdon: Old Bridge Hotel
Huntsham: Huntsham Court
Kingham: Mill House Hotel
Lancaster: Post House Hotel
Langdale: Langdale Hotel
Lenham: Chilston Park
Lewdown: Fox's Earth, Lewtrenchard
  Manor
Lifton: Arundell Arms
Linton: Wood Hall
Loftus: Grinkle Park Hotel
Longham: The Bridge House
Lower Beeding: South Lodge
Lympsham: Batch Farm Country Hotel
Lyndhurst: Parkhill Hotel
Maiden Newton: Maiden Newton House
Marlborough: Ivy House
Marlow: Compleat Angler Hotel
Mawnan Smith: Budock Vean Hotel
Mawnan Smith: Meudon Hotel
Melton Mowbray: Stapleford Park
Milton Damerel: Woodford Bridge Hotel
Moretonhampstead: Manor House Hotel
Mousehole: Lobster Pot
Mullion: Polurrian Hotel
Needingworth: Pike & Eel
Newby Bridge: Swan Hotel
Otley: Chevin Lodge
Otterburn: Percy Arms Hotel
Paignton: Redcliffe Hotel
Portsmouth: Hospitality Inn
Quorn: Quorn Country Hotel
Ravenstonedale: Black Swan
Rotherwick: Tylney Hall Hotel
Rowsley: Peacock Hotel
Ruckhall: The Ancient Camp Inn
Salcombe: South Sands Hotel
Samlesbury: Tickled Trout Hotel
Sheffield: Hotel St George
Shorne: Inn on the Lake
Slaidburn: Hark To Bounty Inn
South Walsham: South Walsham Hall
  Hotel
Staddle Bridge: McCoy's at the Tontine
Stonehouse: Stonehouse Court Hotel
Stratfield Turgis: Wellington Arms Hotel

He takes his secretary on every trip.

To find out how turn to pages 24–30.

To find out how turn to pages 24–30.

Stratford-upon-Avon: Ettington Park Hotel
Stratford-upon-Avon: Welcombe Hotel
Sudbury: Mill
Sutton Coldfield: New Hall
Sutton Coldfield: Penns Hall Hotel
Taplow: Cliveden
Tewkesbury: Bredon Manor
Torquay: Livermead House Hotel
Tresco: Island Hotel
Ullswater: Leeming House Hotel
Ullswater: Old Church Hotel
Ullswater: Rampsbeck Hotel
Umberleigh: Rising Sun Hotel
Upper Slaughter: Lords of the Manor Hotel
Wallingford: Shillingford Bridge Hotel
Wansford-in-England: Haycock Hotel
Ware: Briggens House Hotel
Wareham: Priory Hotel
Warminster: Bishopstrow House
West Bexington: Manor Hotel
Weston-on-the-Green: Weston Manor Hotel
Whitewell: Inn at Whitewell
Windsor: Oakley Court Hotel
Winsford: Royal Oak Inn
Woodbridge: Seckford Hall Hotel
Woodstock: Bear Hotel

SCOTLAND

Aberdeen: Ardoe House Hotel
Achiltibuie: Summer Isles Hotel
Advie: Tulchan Lodge
Altnaharra: Altnaharra Hotel
Annan: Warmanbie Hotel
Ardentinny: Ardentinny Hotel
Auchterarder: Gleneagles Hotel
Ballachulish: Ballachulish Hotel
Banchory: Invery House
Banchory: Raemoir House Hotel
Barrhill: Kildonan Hotel
Beattock: Auchen Castle Hotel
Brae: Busta House Hotel
Bridge of Cally: Bridge of Cally Hotel
Callander: Roman Camp Hotel
Contin: Craigdarroch Lodge Hotel
Crinan: Crinan Hotel
Dryburgh: Dryburgh Abbey Hotel
Dunblane: Cromlix House
Eriska: Isle of Eriska
Ettrickbridge: Ettrickshaws Hotel
Fort William: Inverlochy Castle
Garve: Inchbae Lodge Hotel
Gatehouse of Fleet: Murray Arms
Glenlivet: Blairfindy Lodge Hotel
Harray Loch: Merkister Hotel
Helmsdale: Navidale House Hotel
Inverness: Bunchrew House Hotel
Isle of Gigha: Gigha Hotel
Isle of Raasay: Isle of Raasay Hotel
Kelso: Ednam House Hotel
Kelso: Sunlaws House Hotel
Kenmore: Kenmore Hotel
Kilchrenan: Ardanaiseig
Kilchrenan: Taychreggan Hotel
Kildrummy: Kildrummy Castle Hotel

Kilfinan: Kilfinan Hotel
Kilmore: Glenfeochan House
Kinclaven By Stanley: Ballathie House
Kinloch Rannoch: Loch Rannoch Hotel
Kirkmichael: Log Cabin Hotel
Lanark: Cartland Bridge Hotel
Letham: Fernie Castle Hotel
Onich: Onich Hotel
Pitlochry: Green Park Hotel
Port William: Corsemalzie House Hotel
Portpatrick: Knockinaam Lodge Hotel
Scourie: Eddrachilles Hotel
Scourie: Scourie Hotel
Skeabost Bridge: Skeabost House Hotel
Sleat: Kinloch Lodge
Spean Bridge: Letterfinlay Lodge Hotel
Strachur: Creggans Inn
Strathtummel: Port-an-Eilean Hotel
Talladale: Loch Maree Hotel
Thornhill: Barjarg Tower
Tiroran: Tiroran House
Tobermory: The Tobermory Hotel
Walls: Burrastow House
Whitebridge: Knockie Lodge Hotel

WALES

Beddgelert: Royal Goat Hotel
Criccieth: Bron Eifion Hotel
Crickhowell: Gliffaes Hotel
Gwbert-on-Sea: Cliff Hotel
Lake Vyrnwy: Lake Vyrnwy Hotel
Llanarmon Dyffryn Ceiriog: Hand Hotel
Llandderfel: Palé Hall
Llangollen: Hand Hotel
Llangollen: Royal Hotel
Pantmawr: Glansevern Arms
Penmaenpool: George III Hotel
Portmeirion: Hotel Portmeirion
Ruthin: Ruthin Castle
Tal-y-Llyn: Ty'n-y-Cornel Hotel
Tintern Abbey: Beaufort Hotel

CHANNEL ISLANDS

Herm Island: White House Hotel

ISLE OF MAN

Ramsey: Grand Island Hotel

NORTHERN IRELAND

Dunadry: Dunadry Inn

REPUBLIC OF IRELAND

Ballina: Mount Falcon Castle
Ballylickey: Ballylickey Manor House
Ballynahinch: Ballynahinch Castle
Beaufort: Hotel Dunloe Castle
Caragh Lake: Ard-na-Sidhe
Caragh Lake: Caragh Lodge
Carrickmacross: Nuremore Hotel
Cashel: Zetland House Hotel

Cashel: Cashel Palace Hotel
Clifden: Hotel Ardagh
Cong: Ashford Castle
Crossmolina: Enniscoe House
Dundrum: Dundrum House Hotel
Kanturk: Assolas Country House
Kilcoran: Kilcoran Lodge Hotel
Killarney: Aghadoe Heights Hotel
Killarney: Cahernane Hotel
Killarney: Castlerosse Hotel
Killarney: Hotel Europe
Kinsale: Blue Haven Hotel
Knocklofty: Knocklofty House Hotel
Letterfrack: Rosleague Manor Hotel
Mallow: Longueville House
Newmarket-on-Fergus: Dromoland Castle
Newport: Newport House
Oughterard: Currarevagh House
Parknasilla: Parknasilla Great Southern
   Hotel
Poulaphouca: Tulfarris
Rathmullan: Rathmullan House
Renvyle: Renvyle House Hotel
Riverstown: Coopershill
Rossnowlagh: Sand House Hotel
Scotshouse: Hilton Park
Waterford: Waterford Castle
Waterville: Waterville Lake Hotel

RIDING

ENGLAND

Allendale: Bishopfield
Bagshot: Pennyhill Park Hotel
Bromsgrove: Grafton Manor
Buckland: Buckland Manor
Exford: Crown Hotel
Great Milton: Le Manoir aux Quat' Saisons
Hintlesham: Hintlesham Hall
Melton Mowbray: Stapleford Park
Middlecombe: Periton Park
Rusper: Ghyll Manor
South Walsham: South Walsham Hall
   Hotel
Stratford-upon-Avon: Ettington Park
   Hotel
Taplow: Cliveden
Wareham: Springfield Country Hotel

SCOTLAND

Auchterarder: Gleneagles Hotel
Dunblane: Cromlix House
Eriska: Isle of Eriska
Langbank: Gleddoch House Hotel
Peebles: Peebles Hotel Hydro

Tarbert: Stonefield Castle Hotel
Turnberry: Turnberry Hotel
Uig: Uig Hotel

WALES

Glyn Ceiriog: Golden Pheasant Hotel

NORTHERN IRELAND

Comber: La Mon House Hotel

REPUBLIC OF IRELAND

Beaufort: Hotel Dunloe Castle
Cashel: Cashel Palace Hotel
Dundrum: Dundrum House Hotel
Killarney: Hotel Europe
Renvyle: Renvyle House Hotel
Waterford: Waterford Castle

GOLF

LONDON AIRPORTS

HEATHROW
Holiday Inn

ENGLAND

Bagshot: Pennyhill Park Hotel
Barnham Broom: Barnham Broom Hotel
Cambridge: Cambridgeshire Moat House
Carlyon Bay: Carlyon Bay Hotel
Chittlehamholt: Highbullen Hotel
Freshwater: Farringford Hotel
Grimsby: Humber Royal Crest Hotel
Hythe: Hythe Imperial Hotel
Mawnan Smith: Budock Vean Hotel
Moretonhampstead: Manor House Hotel
New Milton: Chewton Glen Hotel
St Ives: Tregenna Castle Hotel
Shedfield: Meon Valley Hotel
Stratford-upon-Avon: Welcombe Hotel
Studland Bay: Knoll House Hotel
Telford: Telford Hotel, Golf & Country Club
Tewkesbury: Tewkesbury Park Hotel
Thurlestone: Thurlestone Hotel
Torquay: Palace Hotel
Walberton: Avisford Park Hotel
Ware: Briggens House Hotel
Washington: George Washington Hotel
Wem: Hawkstone Park Hotel
West Runton: Links Country Park Hotel
Wishaw: Belfry Hotel

Hotels with Golf continued ...

SCOTLAND

Auchterarder: Gleneagles Hotel
Gatehouse of Fleet: Murray Arms
Kenmore: Kenmore Hotel
Langbank: Gleddoch House Hotel
Old Meldrum: Meldrum House Hotel
Skeabost Bridge: Skeabost House Hotel
Turnberry: Turnberry Hotel

WALES

Chepstow: St Pierre Hotel
Gwbert-on-Sea: Cliff Hotel
Portmeirion: Hotel Portmeirion

CHANNEL ISLANDS

St Peter Port: St Pierre Park Hotel

REPUBLIC OF IRELAND

Carrickmacross: Nuremore Hotel
Clifden: Abbeyglen Castle Hotel
Cong: Ashford Castle
Kenmare: Park Hotel Kenmare
Newmarket-on-Fergus: Clare Inn
Newmarket-on-Fergus: Dromoland Castle
Renvyle: Renvyle House Hotel
Scotshouse: Hilton Park
Waterville: Waterville Lake Hotel

SQUASH

LONDON

Kensington Close Hotel, **W8**

LONDON AIRPORTS

GATWICK
Copthorne Hotel
Gatwick Penta Hotel

ENGLAND

Ascot: Royal Berkshire
Barnham Broom: Barnham Broom Hotel
Bassenthwaite: Armathwaite Hall
Birmingham: Albany Hotel
Birmingham: Birmingham Metropole
Bolton: Last Drop Village Hotel
Borrowdale: Stakis Lodore Swiss Hotel

Brandon: Brandon Hall Hotel
Bristol: Redwood Lodge Hotel
Brockenhurst: Balmer Lawn Hotel
Cambridge: Cambridgeshire Moat House
Cheltenham: Hotel de la Bere
Chester: Mollington Banastre Hotel
Chittlehamholt: Highbullen Hotel
Churt: Frensham Pond Hotel
Clayton-le-Woods: Pines Hotel
Cobham: Hilton National
Coventry: Novotel Coventry
Croydon: Holiday Inn
Croydon: Selsdon Park Hotel
Driffield: Bell Hotel
Fawkham: Brandshatch Place
Ferndown: Dormy Hotel
Harrogate: Majestic
Hythe: Hythe Imperial Hotel
Langdale: Langdale Hotel
Leamington Spa: Mallory Court
Ledbury: Feathers Hotel
Liverpool: Britannia Adelphi Hotel
Maidenhead: Crest Hotel
Manchester: Holiday Inn
Milton Damerel: Woodford Bridge Hotel
Moretonhampstead: Manor House Hotel
Mottram St Andrew: Mottram Hall Hotel
Mullion: Polurrian Hotel
Newcastle upon Tyne: Gosforth Park
  Thistle Hotel
Newquay: Atlantic Hotel
Newquay: Hotel Riviera
Nottingham: Royal Moat House
  International
Oxford: Oxford Moat House
Paignton: Palace Hotel
Penrith: North Lakes Gateway Hotel
Portsmouth: Holiday Inn
St Ives: Tregenna Castle Hotel
Salcombe: Tides Reach Hotel
Samlesbury: Swallow Trafalgar Hotel
Saunton: Saunton Sands Hotel
Shedfield: Meon Valley Hotel
South Marston: South Marston Hotel
South Walsham: South Walsham Hall
  Hotel
Swindon: Blunsdon House Hotel
Taplow: Cliveden
Telford: Telford Hotel, Golf & Country Club
Tewkesbury: Tewkesbury Park Hotel
Thurlestone: Thurlestone Hotel
Torquay: Imperial Hotel
Torquay: Livermead House Hotel
Torquay: Palace Hotel
Walberton: Avisford Park Hotel
Wallingford: Shillingford Bridge Hotel
Wareham: Springfield Country Hotel
Warrington: Lord Daresbury Hotel
Washington: George Washington Hotel
Weston-on-the-Green: Weston Manor
  Hotel
Westonbirt: Hare & Hounds Hotel
Wetheral: Crown Hotel
Weybridge: Oatlands Park Hotel
Wilmslow: Valley Lodge Hotel
Wincanton: Holbrook House Hotel
Wishaw: Belfry Hotel
Woolacombe: Woolacombe Bay Hotel

SCOTLAND

Auchterarder: Gleneagles Hotel
Auchterhouse: Old Mansion House Hotel
Ballater: Craigendarroch Hotel
Banchory: Tor-na-Coille Hotel
Barrhill: Kildonan Hotel
Edinburgh: Carlton Highland Hotel
Glasgow: Holiday Inn
Inverness: Kingsmills Hotel
Kinloch Rannoch: Loch Rannoch Hotel
Langbank: Gleddoch House Hotel
North Berwick: Marine Hotel
Peebles: Peebles Hotel Hydro
Pitcaple: Pittodrie House Hotel
South Queensferry: Forth Bridges Moat House
Tarbert: Stonefield Castle Hotel
Troon: Marine Highland Hotel
Troon: Sun Court Hotel

WALES

Cardiff: Holiday Inn
Chepstow: St Pierre Hotel
Gwbert-on-Sea: Cliff Hotel
Llangybi: Cwrt Bleddyn Hotel
Miskin: Miskin Manor
Portmeirion: Hotel Portmeirion
Wolf's Castle: Wolfscastle Country Hotel

NORTHERN IRELAND

Dunmurry: Conway Hotel
Holywood: Culloden Hotel

REPUBLIC OF IRELAND

Ballina: Downhill Hotel
Carrickmacross: Nuremore Hotel
Cork: Jurys Hotel
Dundalk: Ballymascanlon Hotel
Killiney: Fitzpatrick's Castle Hotel
Knocklofty: Knocklofty House Hotel
Rosslare: Kelly's Strand Hotel

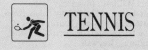

LONDON

Cadogan Thistle Hotel, **SW1**
Hyatt Carlton Tower, **SW1**
Portman Inter-Continental Hotel, **W1**

LONDON AIRPORTS

HEATHROW
Holiday Inn

ENGLAND

Abberley: Elms Hotel
Ascot: Royal Berkshire
Ashford: Eastwell Manor
Bagshot: Pennyhill Park Hotel
Bakewell: Hassop Hall Hotel
Barnham Broom: Barnham Broom Hotel
Bassenthwaite: Armathwaite Hall
Beanacre: Beechfield House
Bigbury on Sea: Burgh Island
Bodymoor Heath: Marston Farm Hotel
Bognor Regis: Royal Norfolk Hotel
Borrowdale: Stakis Lodore Swiss Hotel
Bournemouth: Highcliff Hotel
Bowness on Windermere: Belsfield Hotel
Bramley: Bramley Grange Hotel
Bristol: Redwood Lodge Hotel
Broadway: Lygon Arms
Brockenhurst: Balmer Lawn Hotel
Brockenhurst: Rhinefield House Hotel
Broxted: Whitehall Hotel
Buckland: Buckland Manor
Burnham: Burnham Beeches Hotel
Cambridge: Cambridgeshire Moat House
Carlisle: Swallow Hilltop Hotel
Carlyon Bay: Carlyon Bay Hotel
Castle Combe: Manor House Hotel
Chagford: Gidleigh Park Hotel
Chagford: Teignworthy
Charlecote: The Charlecote Pheasant
Cheltenham: Hotel de la Bere
Chittlehamholt: Highbullen Hotel
Climping: Bailiffscourt
Coatham Mundeville: Hall Garth
Cobham: Hilton National
Cobham: Woodlands Park Hotel
Colchester: Marks Tey Hotel
Croydon: Selsdon Park Hotel
Dane End: Green End Park Hotel
Darlington: Blackwell Grange Moat House
Dovedale: Peveril of the Peak Hotel
Droitwich Spa: Château Impney Hotel
Dulverton: Carnarvon Arms Hotel
East Dereham: King's Head Hotel
Easton Grey: Whatley Manor
Egham: Great Fosters
Evershot: Summer Lodge
Exmouth: Imperial Hotel
Fairy Cross: Portledge Hotel
Farnham: Trevena House Hotel
Fawkham: Brandshatch Place
Ferndown: Dormy Hotel
Flitwick: Flitwick Manor
Freshford: Homewood Park
Great Ayton: Ayton Hall
Great Milton: Le Manoir aux Quat' Saisons
Grimston: Congham Hall
Hackness: Hackness Grange Country Hotel
Harrogate: Majestic
Harrogate: Old Swan Hotel

Haslemere: Lythe Hill Hotel
Hatfield Heath: Down Hall Hotel
Helmsley: Feversham Arms Hotel
Hethersett: Park Farm Hotel
Hintlesham: Hintlesham Hall
Holbeton: Alston Hall Hotel
Hollingbourne: Great Danes Hotel
Horton-cum-Studley: Studley Priory Hotel
Hunstrete: Hunstrete House
Huntsham: Huntsham Court
Hurstbourne Tarrant: Esseborne Manor
Hythe: Hythe Imperial Hotel
Ilkley: Craiglands Hotel
Kidderminster: Stone Manor Hotel
Knutsford: The Cottons Hotel
Leamington Spa: Mallory Court
Lenham: Chilston Park
Liskeard: The Well House
Loftus: Grinkle Park Hotel
Longhorsley: Linden Hall Hotel
Lower Beeding: South Lodge
Lower Slaughter: Lower Slaughter Manor
Lymington: Passford House Hotel
Lyndhurst: Lyndhurst Park Hotel
Marlow: Compleat Angler Hotel
Matlock: Riber Hall
Matlock Bath: New Bath Hotel
Mawnan Smith: Budock Vean Hotel
Mawnan Smith: Nansidwell Country House
Melton Mowbray: Stapleford Park
Milton Damerel: Woodford Bridge Hotel
Moreton-in-Marsh: Manor House Hotel
Moretonhampstead: Manor House Hotel
Mottram St Andrew: Mottram Hall Hotel
Mullion: Polurrian Hotel
Nantwich: Rookery Hall
Newbury: Elcot Park Hotel
Newcastle upon Tyne: Gosforth Park Thistle Hotel
Newlyn: Higher Faugan Hotel
Newquay: Atlantic Hotel
North Stifford: Stifford Moat House
North Stoke: Springs Hotel
Oakham: Hambleton Hall
Paignton: Palace Hotel
Rotherwick: Tylney Hall Hotel
Rusper: Ghyll Manor
St Ives: Tregenna Castle Hotel
Salcombe: Soar Mill Cove Hotel
Saunton: Saunton Sands Hotel
Shedfield: Meon Valley Hotel
Sidmouth: Victoria Hotel
Silchester: Romans Hotel
Six Mile Bottom: Swynford Paddocks
Slough: Holiday Inn
South Milford: Selby Fork Hotel
South Walsham: South Walsham Hall Hotel
Stafford: Tillington Hall Hotel
Storrington: Abingworth Hall
Storrington: Little Thakeham
Stratford-upon-Avon: Billesley Manor
Stratford-upon-Avon: Ettington Park Hotel
Studland Bay: Knoll House Hotel
Taplow: Cliveden

Tewkesbury: Bredon Manor
Tewkesbury: Tewkesbury Park Hotel
Thurlestone: Thurlestone Hotel
Torquay: Grand Hotel
Torquay: Imperial Hotel
Torquay: Livermead House Hotel
Torquay: Osborne Hotel
Torquay: Palace Hotel
Torquay: Toorak Hotel
Tunbridge Wells: Spa Hotel
Turners Hill: Alexander House
Uckfield: Horsted Place
Veryan: Nare Hotel
Wadhurst: Spindlewood Country House Hotel
Walberton: Avisford Park Hotel
Ware: Briggens House Hotel
Wareham: Springfield Country Hotel
Warminster: Bishopstrow House
Weedon: Crossroads Hotel
Wem: Hawkstone Park Hotel
Weston-on-the-Green: Weston Manor Hotel
Weston-super-Mare: Grand Atlantic Hotel
Westonbirt: Hare & Hounds Hotel
Weybridge: Oatlands Park Hotel
Whimple: Woodhayes
Whitwell-on-the-Hill: Whitwell Hall Country House Hotel
Wincanton: Holbrook House Hotel
Winchester: Lainston House
Windermere: Langdale Chase Hotel
Wishaw: Belfry Hotel
Woolacombe: Woolacombe Bay Hotel
Yelverton: Moorland Links Hotel
York: Swallow Chase Hotel

SCOTLAND

Aberdeen: Stakis Tree Tops Hotel
Advie: Tulchan Lodge
Auchterarder: Gleneagles Hotel
Auchterhouse: Old Mansion House Hotel
Aviemore: Stakis Coylumbridge Resort Hotel
Banchory: Raemoir House Hotel
Contin: Craigdarroch Lodge Hotel
Drumnadrochit: Polmaily House Hotel
Drymen: Buchanan Arms Hotel
Dunblane: Cromlix House
Dunblane: Stakis Dunblane Hydro
Dunkeld: Hillhead of Dunkeld
Eriska: Isle of Eriska
Fort William: Inverlochy Castle
Gatehouse of Fleet: Cally Palace Hotel
Gatehouse of Fleet: Murray Arms
Glenborrodale: Glenborrodale Castle
Gullane: Greywalls
Inverness: Culloden House
Kelso: Sunlaws House Hotel
Kentallen of Appin: Ardsheal House
Kilchrenan: Ardanaiseig
Kilwinning: Montgreenan Mansion House
Kinclaven By Stanley: Ballathie House
Kinloch Rannoch: Loch Rannoch Hotel

Nairn: Golf View Hotel
Nairn: Newton Hotel
North Berwick: Marine Hotel
Peebles: Cringletie House Hotel
Peebles: Peebles Hotel Hydro
Pitcaple: Pittodrie House Hotel
Pitlochry: Atholl Palace Hotel
Pitlochry: Pitlochry Hydro Hotel
Tarbert: Stonefield Castle Hotel
Troon: Sun Court Hotel
Turnberry: Turnberry Hotel

WALES

Aberdovey: Hotel Plas Penhelig
Aberdovey: Trefeddian Hotel
Abersoch: Porth Tocyn Hotel
Chepstow: St Pierre Hotel
Coychurch: Coed-y-Mwstwr Hotel
Crickhowell: Gliffaes Hotel
Lake Vyrnwy: Lake Vyrnwy Hotel
Llanarmon Dyffryn Ceiriog: Hand Hotel
Llandudno: Bodysgallen Hall
Llangybi: Cwrt Bleddyn Hotel
Northop: Soughton Hall
Portmeirion: Hotel Portmeirion
St David's: Warpool Court Hotel
Wolf's Castle: Wolfscastle Country Hotel

CHANNEL ISLANDS

Herm Island: White House Hotel
St Peter Port: St Pierre Park Hotel
St Brelade: Atlantic Hotel
St Brelade's Bay: St Brelade's Bay Hotel

NORTHERN IRELAND

Holywood: Culloden Hotel

REPUBLIC OF IRELAND

Ballina: Downhill Hotel
Ballina: Mount Falcon Castle
Ballynahinch: Ballynahinch Castle
Beaufort: Hotel Dunloe Castle
Blessington: Downshire House Hotel
Caragh Lake: Caragh Lodge
Carrickmacross: Nuremore Hotel
Cashel: Cashel House Hotel
Clifden: Abbeyglen Castle Hotel
Clifden: Rock Glen Hotel
Cong: Ashford Castle
Cork: Jurys Hotel
Dundalk: Ballymascanlon Hotel
Dundrum: Dundrum House Hotel
Ferrycarrig Bridge: Ferrycarrig Hotel
Gorey: Marlfield House
Kanturk: Assolas Country House
Kenmare: Park Hotel Kenmare
Kilkenny: Newpark Hotel
Killarney: Aghadoe Heights Hotel
Killarney: Cahernane Hotel
Killarney: Castlerosse Hotel
Killarney: Killarney Great Southern Hotel
Killarney: Torc Great Southern Hotel
Killiney: Fitzpatrick's Castle Hotel
Knocklofty: Knocklofty House Hotel
Letterfrack: Rosleague Manor Hotel
Limerick: Limerick Inn Hotel
Maynooth: Moyglare Manor
Newmarket-on-Fergus: Dromoland Castle
Oughterard: Connemara Gateway Hotel
Oughterard: Currarevagh House
Parknasilla: Parknasilla Great Southern Hotel
Rathmullan: Rathmullan House
Renvyle: Renvyle House Hotel
Rosslare: Kelly's Strand Hotel
Rossnowlagh: Sand House Hotel
Shanagarry: Ballymaloe House
Waterford: Ardree Hotel
Waterford: Waterford Castle
Waterville: Waterville Lake Hotel

JUST DESSERTS

For many the sweet course is the high point of a meal.
As the hors d'oeuvre are sampled and the main course savoured, there is often concern to 'save room for dessert'. Everyone deserves the occasional indulgence and for those who find sumptuous sweets irresistible we present a selection of recipes contributed by chefs from some of our starred restaurants.

On these pages you will find just a hint of the variety that can be introduced – gloriously fresh fruit desserts or smooth and rich chocolate specialities.

Remember, sugar is a natural product and it comes in many forms, so use it to create quite different results – fine icing sugar to flavour creams, sparkling caster sugar to enhance light sponges and rich brown soft sugar to complement full-flavoured mixtures.

Other forms that are useful are golden syrup, demerara and versatile granulated sugar. Whichever type you choose it will provide a valuable source of energy and, like all other foods, it can form part of a healthy diet.

So go on – succumb to temptation!

CHOC-O-BLOC STANLEY

Tom McCoy ■ McCOYS RESTAURANT ■ Staddle Bridge

INGREDIENTS
Serves 6

150 g/5 oz plain dessert chocolate	14 boudoir biscuits (sponge fingers)
7 egg yolks	about 150 ml/$\frac{1}{4}$ pint unsweetened strong black coffee, cooled
225 g/8 oz caster sugar	whipped cream to decorate
300 g/11 oz unsalted butter, softened	
150 g/5 oz cocoa	**Coffee bean sauce:**
600 ml/1 pint whipping cream	300 ml/$\frac{1}{2}$ pint milk
50 g/2 oz icing sugar	75 g/3 oz sugar
	5 ml/1 tsp freshly ground coffee
	3 egg yolks

METHOD

Break the chocolate into a bowl and place over a saucepan of hot water; do not allow the water to boil. While the chocolate is melting, beat the egg yolks with the sugar until pale and creamy. Add the melted chocolate, folding it in well. Work the butter until very soft, then slowly add the cocoa, working it in until well blended. Add this cocoa and butter mixture to the yolks and chocolate, and whisk together. Whip the cream with the icing sugar until it stands in soft peaks, then lightly stir this into the chocolate mixture until well blended.

Brush the boudoir biscuits with the coffee and use to line the sides of a 16.5 cm/

6½ in charlotte mould (or straight-sided, deep cake tin). Pour in the chocolate mixture and chill for 2–3 hours or until firm.

To make the sauce, bring the milk to the boil with 40 g/1½ oz of the sugar. Add the coffee and remove from the heat. Leave for 15 minutes. Whisk the remaining sugar and egg yolks together until pale. Whisk the coffee mixture into the yolks, then pour it back into the saucepan and heat gently over low heat, stirring continuously, until thickened – about 6 minutes. Do not overcook the sauce or it will curdle. Stir frequently until cool.

Turn out the charlotte and decorate with whipped cream. Serve with the coffee bean sauce.

BROCHETTE DE FRUITS TROPICAUX
sa Sauce aux Figues et Poivres Roses

Jean-Yves Morel ■ MORELS ■ Haslemere

INGREDIENTS
Serves 4

1 mango
1 paw-paw
3 kiwi fruit
2 bananas
8 strawberries
juice of 1 lemon
30 ml/2 tbsp caster sugar
30 ml/2 tbsp butter

Fig and pink peppercorn sauce:

300 g/11 oz fresh figs, peeled
30–45 ml/2–3 tbsp Sauternes
30 ml/2 tbsp sugar syrup (see note)
15 ml/1 tbsp lemon juice
15 ml/1 tbsp preserved pink peppercorns, chopped (not dried)

METHOD

Peel the fruit (except the strawberries) and cut into even, bite-sized chunks. You will have to cut the mango flesh off the stone and remove the seeds from the middle of the paw-paw. Toss the prepared fruit in the lemon juice and sugar to prevent it discolouring. Thread the pieces of fruit on to 4 skewers and set aside.

Make the sauce as follows: peel the figs and purée them in a liquidiser. Pour in the Sauternes. Heat the sugar syrup with the lemon juice and chopped peppercorns, then leave to cool. Mix the fig purée and syrup together.

Take a large frying pan to cook the brochettes. Heat the butter in the pan and, when it stops sizzling, add the brochettes. Fry rapidly until lightly brown on both sides, turning once. Do not overcook the fruit – it should be ready in about 2 minutes.

Arrange the brochettes on a warmed serving dish and pour the sauce over them. Serve at once.

NOTE: to make a sugar syrup, dissolve 100 g/ 4 oz caster sugar in 100 ml/4 fl oz water and bring to the boil. Allow to cool, then use as required.

REINETTE EN CHAUSSON BEURRE AU CALVADOS

Anton Edelmann ■ SAVOY RESTAURANT ■ London

INGREDIENTS
Serves 4

| 75 g/3 oz sultanas |
| 30 ml/2 tbsp Calvados |
| pinch of ground cinnamon |
| 4 Reinette apples (or other dessert apples) |
| 350 g/12 oz puff pastry (defrosted if frozen) |
| 1 egg yolk, lightly whisked |
| 25 g/1 oz icing sugar |
| 50 g/2 oz granulated sugar |
| 50 ml/2 fl oz water |
| 10 ml/2 tsp glucose |
| 50 g/2 oz butter |
| 150 ml/¼ pint single cream |

Decoration (optional):
30–45 ml/2–3 tbsp single cream

METHOD

Soak the sultanas in the Calvados for 20–30 minutes and sprinkle with the cinnamon.

Peel and core the apples right through the centre. Top and tail them so that they stand well. Roll out the puff pastry to 3 mm/ ⅛ in thick and cut out four ovals measuring about 17 × 12 cm/6½ × 4½ in. Brush the pastry edges with a little of the egg yolk and place an apple at one end of each oval. Fill the apples with the soaked sultanas and reserve the Calvados. Fold over the longest end of the pastry to enclose the apple completely. Seal the edges and crimp them with a knife. Brush the pastry with egg yolk and make a small slit in the top of each.

Bake the apples at 220°C, 425°F, Gas 7 for 20 minutes. Remove from the oven and dust well with icing sugar. Place under a hot grill to produce a shiny glaze on the pastry.

Mix the granulated sugar, water and glucose in a saucepan and heat until the sugar dissolves. Bring to the boil, then boil until a pale amber caramel is formed. Remove the pan from the heat, add the butter and cream, and stir until the butter has melted and the cream has combined with the caramel. Stir in the reserved Calvados, then pass the sauce through a fine sieve.

Place an apple on each serving plate and pour sauce round it. Feather the sauce with cream. Serve at once.

AN
EGON RONAY'S
GUIDE
ONLY INCLUDES
THE BEST.

NOTHING FEELS LIKE BACARDI® AND COKE

COFFEE

An Award for Excellence

FRESH ground coffee is one of the most delicious drinks today. But the way it is served is crucial.

Master Blend – the premium range of fresh ground coffees, has joined with Egon Ronay's Hotels and Restaurants Cellnet Guide to encourage high standards and draw attention to the coffee service as a course in its own right.

The Egon Ronay's Guide Coffee Award of Excellence will be presented to establishments for the quality and style of their coffee service, which must include decaffeinated coffee, fresh milk and cream, petits fours or mints and liqueurs.

Coffee drinking is part of our everyday life. Master Blend together with Egon Ronay's Guide aims to ensure it is a memorable and enjoyable experience both at home as well as in catering establishments.

The Story of Coffee

*T*HERE *are two main varieties of coffee plant – Coffee Arabica and Coffee Robusta. The best quality beans are those produced by the Arabica plants. Master Blend uses Arabica beans in its fine quality range of ground coffees.*

The quality of coffee depends on a number of factors – its parent plant, the climate, soil and amount of care taken during processing. The flavour of coffee is finally determined by the blending and roasting of the beans by the roaster.

Most coffees are blends. Blending is an art in itself, but the basic principle is to mix together coffees from different regions or countries which display a range of characteristics, with the aim of creating a well-balanced cup of coffee.

Simple blends may be just two types of coffee and described as a blend of two. Others may be named after a country, the beans of which provide the characteristics of the blend, or they may be described by the appropriateness for different occasions.

Breakfast blend, for example, is usually based on Kenyan coffee, which provides a light acidity described as tangy; after dinner coffee is generally darker roasted and provides a more bitter but richer and full bodied coffee.

M ASTER Blend – like any superior coffee house has specially developed blend recipes. As with any jealously guarded secret they will never be revealed!

BREWING coffee is the final link in the chain from the coffee plant to the customer's cup. The first rule is to use a top quality coffee made from the finest beans, such as the Master Blend range. Fine ground coffee should be used for the filter method of preparation, and a medium ground coffee for the jug and cafetiere methods.

Always use freshly drawn cold water and the softer the water the better, although artificially softened water should not be used.

Ideally, coffee should be made with water just below boiling point, at 96° C/204° F. Do not allow coffee to boil as this damages the flavour, resulting in a bitter taste.

WHEN it comes to presentation and imaginative styles of serving coffee, some adventurous European habits have become part of the British coffee drinking culture. Examples include Café Royale – strong, black coffee sweetened with sugar and laced with a generous measure of Cognac brandy. Just as popular are Irish and Gaelic coffees; hot, black coffees served in a tall glass with sugar and either Irish or Scotch whiskies, topped with cream.

Many coffee buffs regard Espresso as the ultimate coffee, because instead of water slowly soaking up the flavour, water is forced quickly through the coffee under pressure to extract the maximum flavour. Espresso coffee is served black in small cups which can be decorated with a twist of lemon.

Alternatively, cappuccino coffee is made by topping a cup of Espresso coffee with frothy milk. A little cocoa, chocolate powder or cinnamon should be sprinkled on top.

Photographs courtesy International Coffee Organisation

THERE'S no mystery to making delicious coffee at home; Master Blend's extensive range has a blend to suit all methods.

For those with filter machines simply measure the correct quantities of filter coffee and fresh water into the machine, switch it on and moments later you can enjoy the luxury of Master Blend – in light, medium or dark roast.

For cafetieres, Master Blend produces a medium roasted, medium ground coffee best suited for this method. Measure out the coffee into a warmed jug, pour on the water, which should be just off the boil and leave it to stand for three minutes. Then, slowly depress the plunger and serve.

You can use this same aromatic blend of coffee for use in a percolator. Pour in cold water, measure the coffee into the basket, replacing it together with the lid to heat up, and enjoy fresh roast and ground coffee with ease.

Espresso machines are perhaps the most modern method of making coffee in the home. Instructions depend on the type of equipment but Master Blend Espresso coffee will guarantee a strong, dark, delicious authentic continental taste.

SO whether you enjoy your coffee mild and smooth or strong and full-bodied, Master Blend offers the perfect choice.

COFFEE AWARD OF EXCELLENCE

AWARD WINNERS

LONDON
Blakes Hotel Restaurant, SW17
Crowthers, SW14
Four Seasons Restaurant, Inn on the Park, W1
Harvey's, SW17
Oak Room, Le Meridien, Piccadilly, W1
Neal Street Restaurant, WC2
Ninety Park Lane, W1
The Savoy Restaurant, WC2
Simply Nico, SW1
Sutherlands, W1
La Tante Claire, SW3

ENGLAND
CHAGFORD, Devon: **Gidleigh Park Hotel Restaurant**
CHELTENHAM, Gloucestershire: **Redmond's**
CRICKLADE, Wiltshire: **Whites**
DEDHAM, Essex: **Le Talbooth, Maison Talbooth**
GREAT MILTON, Oxfordshire: **Le Manoir Restaurant**
MATLOCK, Derbyshire: **Riber Hall**
NEWCASTLE UPON TYNE, Tyne & Wear: **Fisherman's Lodge**
OAKHAM, Leicestershire: **Hambleton Hall Restaurant**
ROADE, Northamptonshire: **Road House**
SHINFIELD, Berkshire: **L'Ortolan**
TWICKENHAM, Middlesex: **McClements**
ULLSWATER, Cumbria: **Sharrow Bay Restaurant**
WYMONDHAM, Norfolk: **Adlard's**
YATTENDON, Berkshire: **Royal Oak**

SCOTLAND
EDINBURGH, Lothian: **Handsel's**
PEAT INN, Fife: **The Peat Inn**

WALES
TRELLECK, Gwent: **Village Green**

NORTHERN IRELAND
HOLYWOOD, Co Down: **Iona**
PORTRUSH, Co Antrim: **Ramore**

REPUBLIC OF IRELAND
CONG, Co Mayo: **Ashford Castle**
DUBLIN, Co Dublin: **Patrick Guilbaud**

FINALISTS

From the list of award winners we have selected the following three finalists from which to choose our overall winner.

L'ORTOLAN
SHINFIELD, BERKSHIRE

The excellent expresso and filter coffee served here are both strong and aromatic, and is accompanied by a tiered tray of pastry petits-fours, followed by a cigar-box case crafted in chocolate, containing the most delicate handmade chocolates – divine!

RIBER HALL
MATLOCK, DERBYSHIRE

We were impressed with the super aroma of the coffee, even before the first sip. Strength and flavour are perfectly balanced, giving a satisfying full and delicious aftertaste. It is accompanied by stunning bitter chocolate truffles – moist, full flavoured, extremely rich – quite wonderful!

IONA
HOLYWOOD, CO DOWN, NORTHERN IRELAND

A simple restaurant whose fairly basic style and design is followed through in the presentation of its excellent coffee. Chunky pottery cups are served with no frills, except for the exceptionally good strong aromatic coffee and a few beautifully made 'tuile' biscuits. No licence, so take your own choice of after-dinner drinks!

OUTSTANDING CHEESEBOARDS

The following is a list of restaurants considered by our inspectors to have noteworthy cheeseboards. The range of cheeses offered need not always be large, but in all cases the selection is interesting and well kept.

LONDON

Le Bistroquet, **NW1**
Cavaliers', **SW8**
Claridge's Restaurant, **W1**
Clarke's, **W8**
Corney & Barrow, **EC2**
Le Gavroche, **W1**
Inn on the Park, Four Seasons Restaurant, **W1**
Leith's, **W11**
Le Marmiton, **EC2**
Le Meridien Piccadilly, Oak Room, **W1**
Le Muscadet, **W1**
Ninety Park Lane, **W1**
Quincy's 84, **NW2**
Rue St Jacques, **W1**
Savoy Restaurant, **WC2**
Simply Nico, **SW1**
La Tante Claire, **SW3**
Thomas de Quincey's, **WC2**
Westbury Hotel, The Polo Restaurant, **W1**

ENGLAND

Ambleside: Kirkstone Foot Hotel Restaurant
Aylesbury: Pebbles
Bath: Priory Hotel Restaurant
Boughton Monchelsea: Tanyard Hotel Restaurant
Bray-on-Thames: Waterside Inn
Bristol: Restaurant Lettonie
Calstock: Danescombe Valley Hotel Restaurant
Chagford: Gidleigh Park Hotel Restaurant
Chagford: Mill End Hotel Restaurant
Cheltenham: Redmond's
Chester: Arkle Restaurant
Clun: Old Post Office
Corse Lawn: Corse Lawn House Restaurant
Cricklade: Whites
Dedham: Le Talbooth
Edburton: Tottington Manor Hotel Restaurant
Edenbridge: Honours Mill
Ettington: Chase Hotel Restaurant
Evershot: Summer Lodge Restaurant

Grasmere: Michael's Nook Restaurant
Great Milton: Le Manoir aux Quat' Saisons
Hockley Heath: Nuthurst Grange Restaurant
Hungerford: Bear at Hungerford Restaurant
Hurstbourne Tarrant: Esseborne Manor Restaurant
Kilve: Meadow House Restaurant
Kingsbridge: Queen Anne Restaurant
Knutsford: La Belle Epoque
Lavenham: The Great House
Lymington: Provence
Maiden Newton: Maiden Newton House Restaurant
Malvern: Croque-en-Bouche
Nantwich: Rookery Hall Restaurant
New Milton: Chewton Glen Hotel, Marryat Room
Oakham: Hambleton Hall Restaurant
Plumtree: Perkins Bar Bistro
Ramsbottom: Village Restaurant
Richmond: Lichfields
Ridgeway: The Old Vicarage
Romsey: Old Manor House
Shinfield: L'Ortolan
Stamford: George of Stamford Restaurant
Ston Easton: Ston Easton Park Restaurant
Stonham: Mr Underhill's
Storrington: Abingworth Hall Restaurant
Stroud: Oakes
Sutton: Partners 23
Swindon: Pear Tree Hotel Restaurant
Taplow: Cliveden Dining Room
Tetbury: Calcot Manor Restaurant
Thornbury: Thornbury Castle Hotel Restaurant
Tresco: Island Hotel Restaurant
Truro: Alverton Manor, Terrace Restaurant
Tunbridge Wells: Thackeray's House
Wareham: Priory Hotel Restaurant
Warminster: Bishopstrow House Restaurant
Waterhouses: Old Beams
Wisbech: Rose & Crown Hotel, Marais Restaurant
Witherslack: Old Vicarage Hotel Restaurant
Worcester: Brown's Restaurant

SCOTLAND

Canonbie: Riverside Inn
Colbost: Three Chimneys
Edinburgh: Martins

Knipoch: Knipoch Hotel Restaurant
Port Appin: Airds Hotel Restaurant

WALES

Abergwesyn: Llwynderw Hotel Restaurant
Abersoch: Porth Tocyn Hotel Restaurant
Felingwm Uchaf: Plough Inn, Hickman's
Restaurant
Llandudno: Bodysgallen Hall Restaurant
Llandudno: St Tudno Hotel Restaurant
Llanrwst: Meadowsweet Hotel Restaurant

REPUBLIC OF IRELAND

Cashel: Cashel House Hotel Restaurant
Cork: Arbutus Lodge Hotel Restaurant
Cork: Lovetts Restaurant
Dublin: Locks
Dublin: Patrick Guilbaud
Dun Laoghaire: Restaurant Mirabeau
Oughterard: Currarevagh House
Restaurant
Rosses Point: Reveries

The Dairy Crest Symbol of Excellence

Wherever you see this sign, you will be entering an establishment where the quality and presentation of cheeses is excellent.

The Dairy Crest Symbol of Excellence is only awarded by the Egon Ronay's Guides' team of inspectors where they find a high standard of cheese available — whether presented on a cheeseboard or included in a meal or snack.

Now in its third year, the Award is an on-going sign of commitment from Britain's leading cheese manufacturer, Dairy Crest Foods, to the improvement of cheese quality, variety and presentation.

The Symbol is recognised nationally by caterers who strive to reach its high standards, and by the ever more discerning public who are seeking nothing but the best when eating in hotels, restaurants, pubs and cafes.

So, wherever you see the Egon Ronay's Guide Dairy Crest Symbol of Excellence, you will enjoy guaranteed quality of:

TASTE — through expert selection, handling and storage

VARIETY — through imaginative use of traditional, new and local cheeses

PRESENTATION — through the use of colour, texture and shape to give a mouth-watering display

INFORMATION — through the caterer's knowledge and understanding

Where you find English cheeses at their best, you will be sure to find Dairy Crest's own excellent cheeses, such as the famous Lymeswold range, the reduced-fat Tendale range and the full selection of English and Welsh traditional cheeses and prize-winning Cheddars and Stilton.

DAIRY CREST

RESTAURANTS WITH ROOMS

'**R**estaurants with rooms' is a category based on 'restaurants avec chambres' in France. We give relevant information about accommodation in the restaurant entry.

ENGLAND

Ashbourne: Callow Hall
Barnstaple: Lynwood House
Baslow: Fischer's at Baslow Hall
Beaminster: Bridge House
Blandford Forum: La Belle Alliance
Bradford: Restaurant Nineteen
Brampton: Tarn End
Brockenhurst: Le Poussin
Caldbeck: Park End Restaurant
Campsea Ashe: Old Rectory
Cartmel: Uplands
Cawston: Grey Gables
Clun: Old Post Office
East Buckland: Lower Pitt
Farrington Gurney: Old Parsonage
Glastonbury: No 3
Grantham: Barkston House
Great Dunmow: Starr
Gulworthy: Horn of Plenty
Harwich: Pier at Harwich
Hastingleigh: Woodmans Arms Auberge
Helford: Riverside
Horndon on the Hill: Hill House
Knutsford: La Belle Epoque
Lavenham: The Great House
Lymington: Provence
Lympstone: River House
Newgate Street: Gable House
Oakhill: Oakhill House
Ockley: King's Arms Restaurant
Padstow: Seafood Restaurant

Pool-in-Wharfedale: Pool Court
Shepton Mallet: Bowlish House Restaurant
Shipdham: Shipdham Place
Stockbridge: Sheriff House
Stonham: Mr Underhill's
Storrington: Manleys
Sturminster Newton: Plumber Manor Restaurant
Thame: Thatchers
Trebarwith Strand: Old Millfloor
Uppingham: Lake Isle
Waterhouses: Old Beams
Wootton Common: Lugleys Restaurant
Yeovil: Little Barwick House

SCOTLAND

Canonbie: Riverside Inn
Fort William: The Factor's House
Kingussie: The Cross
Peat Inn: The Peat Inn
Ullapool: Altnaharrie Inn

WALES

Felingwm Uchaf: Plough Inn, Hickman's Restaurant
Harlech: Cemlyn Restaurant
Pwllheli: Plas Bodegroes
Swanbridge: Sully House
Trelleck: Village Green
Welsh Hook: Stone Hall

REPUBLIC OF IRELAND

Dingle: Doyle's Seafood Bar
Dublin: Le Coq Hardi
Waterville: Huntsman

SEAFOOD RESTAURANTS

The following is a selection of restaurants where seafood is a major feature on the menu. For more details see the individual entries in the main section.

LONDON

Bentley's, **W1**
Bill Bentley's, **EC2**
La Bouillabaisse, **SW10**
La Croisette, **SW10**
Frère Jacques, **WC2**
Grimes, **WC2**
Lou Pescadou, **SW5**
Manzi's, **WC2**
Le Quai St Pierre, **W8**
Scotts, **W1**
Le Suquet, **SW3**
Sutherlands, **W1**
Tiger Lee, **SW5**
Yung's, **W1**

RESTAURANTS UNDER £30 FOR TWO (See A Lot for Less)

Faulkners, **E8**
Seashell, **NW1**

ENGLAND

Birmingham: Biarritz
Burnham Market: Fishes
Burnham-on-Crouch: Contented Sole
Constantine Bay: Treglos Hotel
Dartmouth: Carved Angel
East Langton: Bell Inn
Great Yarmouth: Seafood Restaurant
Harrogate: Drum & Monkey
Harwich: Pier at Harwich
Helford: Riverside
Hull: Ceruttis
Looe: Talland Bay Hotel
Lympstone: River House
Newcastle upon Tyne: Fishermans Lodge
Newcastle upon Tyne: Fishermans Wharf
Norwich: Green's Seafood
Padstow: Seafood Restaurant
Penzance: Harris's

Salisbury: Crustaceans
Stokesley: Chapters
Tresco: Island Hotel
Waltham Abbey: Blunk's

SCOTLAND

Aberdeen: Atlantis
Anstruther: Cellar Restaurant
Colbost: Three Chimneys
Crinan: Crinan Hotel, Lock 16 Restaurant
Edinburgh: L'Auberge
Glasgow: Rogano
Kinlochbervie: Kinlochbervie Hotel
Linlithgow: Champany Inn Restaurant
Port Appin: Airds Hotel

WALES

Llandudno: Lanterns

CHANNEL ISLANDS

St Anne: Nellie Gray's
St Peter Port: Le Nautique
St Aubin's Harbour: Old Court House Inn Restaurant
St Brelade's Bay: Hotel L'Horizon, Star Grill
Sark: Aval du Creux Hotel

NORTHERN IRELAND

Holywood: Schooner
Portrush: Ramore

REPUBLIC OF IRELAND

Baltimore: Chez Youen
Cashel: Cashel House Hotel
Cashel: Chez Hans
Clifden: Abbeyglen Castle Hotel
Clifden: Hotel Ardagh
Cork: Lovetts Restaurant
Dingle: Doyle's Seafood Bar
Dun Laoghaire: Restaurant Na Mara
Howth: King Sitric
Killarney: Gaby's
Waterville: Huntsman
Youghal: Aherne's Seafood Restaurant

WHAT PEOPLE WHO EAT OUT EAT IN.

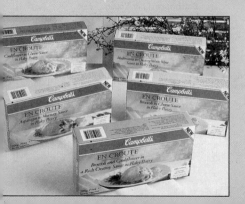

SUNDAY EATING IN AND AROUND BRITAIN'S MAJOR CENTRES

LONDON

Ajimura, **WC2 (D)**
Al Gallo d'Oro, **W8**
Al Hamra, **W1**
Athenaeum Hotel Restaurant, **W1**
L'Aventure, **NW8**
Bahn Thai, **W1**
Basil Street Hotel, The Dining Room, **SW3**
Benihana, **NW3**
The Berkeley Restaurant, **SW1**
Berkshire Hotel, Ascot Restaurant, **W1**
Le Bistroquet, **NW1**
Bitter Lemons Taverna, **SW6**
Blakes Hotel Restaurant, **SW7**
Bloom's, **NW11 & E1**
Bombay Bicycle Club, **SW12 (L)**
Bombay Brasserie, **SW7**
Boucha's, **W14 (D)**
Buzkash, **SW15 (D)**
Café Flo, **NW3**
The Capital Restaurant, **SW3**
Le Caprice, **SW1**
Caravan Serai, **W1**
Cheng-du, **NW1**
Chuen Cheng Ku, **W1**
Churchill Hotel, The Arboury, **W1**
Claridge's Restaurant & Causerie, **W1**
The Connaught Restaurant, **W1**
La Croisette, **SW10**
Crowthers, **SW14**
Cumberland Hotel, Wyvern Restaurant, **W1**
Delhi Brasserie, **SW7 & W1**
Don Pepe, **NW8**
Drakes, **SW3**
Dukes Hotel Restaurant, **SW1**
Dynasty of Hampstead, **NW3**
Ebury Court Hotel Restaurant, **SW1**
English Garden, **SW3**
English House, **SW3**
La Famiglia, **SW10**
Fifty-One Fifty-One, **SW3**
Frère Jacques, **WC2**
Fulham Diner, **SW6**
Fung-Shing, **WC2**
Good Earth, **NW7 & SW3**
Good Friends, **E14**

The Grafton, **SW4 (L)**
Green's Restaurant, **SW1 (L)**
The Halcyon, Kingfisher Restaurant, **W11**
Halepi, **W2**
Hiroko of Kensington Hilton, **W11**
Hokkai, **W1 (D)**
Howard Hotel, Quai D'or Restaurant, **WC2**
Hyatt Carlton Tower, Chelsea Room &Rib
  Room, **SW1**
Ikkyu, **W1 (D)**
L'Incontro, **SW1**
Inn on the Park, Four Seasons Restaurant &
  Lanes, **W1**
Inter-Continental Hotel, Le Soufflé , **W1**
Jacques, **N4**
Joe's Café, **SW3 (L)**
Kaya, **W1 (D)**
Ken Lo's Memories of China Chelsea, **SW10**
  (L)
Kensington Place, **W8**
Kensington Tandoori, **W8**
Koto, **NW1 (D)**
Lal Qila, **W1**
Last Days of the Empire, **W1**
Last Days of the Raj, **WC2 (D)**
Left Bank, **SW10 (L)**
Leith's, **W11**
Lena's Thai Restaurant, **SW11 (D)**
Lindsay House, **W1**
Lok-Zen, **N10**
Lou Pescadou, **SW5**
Majlis, **SW7**
Mandarin, **W8**
Mandarin Kitchen, **W2**
Manzi's, **WC2 (D)**
Martin's, **NW1**
May Fair Inter-Continental, Le Château, **W1**
Memories of India, **SW7**
Ménage à Trois, **SW3 (D)**
Ming, **W1**
Mr Kai, **W1**
Mr Kong, **WC2**
Monkeys, **SW3**
Nanyang, **SW7 (D)**
New Diamond, **WC2**
New Leaf, **W5 (D)**
New Shu Shan, **WC2**
192, **W11 (L)**

Otters, **SW6 (L)**
Peking Duck, **NW11**
Peter's, **NW6 (L)**
Phoenicia, **W8**
Pollyanna's, **SW11 (L)**
Princess Garden, **W1**
Pun, **SW7**
Quincy's 84, **NW2**
Read's, **SW5 (L)**
Red Fort, **W1**
The Ritz Restaurant, **W1**
St James Court Hotel, Inn of Happiness, **SW1**
San Lorenzo Fuoriporta, **SW19**
San Martino, **SW3**
Santini, **SW1 (D)**
Savoy Restaurant, **WC2**
Scotts, **W1 (D)**
Shanghai, **W8**
Shogun, **W1**
Sinar Matahari, **W13**
Singapore Garden, **NW6**
Stafford Hotel Restaurant, **SW1**
Le Suquet, **SW3**
Swiss Centre, The Chesa, **W1**
Tiger Lee , **SW5 (D)**
Treasure of China, **SE10**
Tui, **SW7**
Turner's, **SW3**
The Veeraswamy, **W1**
Waltons, **SW3**
Weng Wah House, **NW3**
Westbury Hotel, The Polo Restaurant, **W1**
Yours Faithfully, **SW12 (L)**
Yung's, **W1**
Ziani, **SW3**

RESTAURANTS UNDER £30 FOR TWO
(See A Lot for Less)

Ajanta Tandoori, **W12**
Le Bistroquet, **NW1**
La Brasserie, **SW3**
Break for the Border, **WC2 (D)**
Café des Fleurs, **NW6**
Caffe Mamma, **Richmond**
Camden Brasserie, **NW1**
La Cloche, **NW6**
Criterion Brasserie, **W1**
Daquise, **SW7**
Diwana Bhel-Poori House, **NW1 & W2**
Ebury Wine Bar, **SW1**
La Fin de La Chasse, **N16 (L)**
Foxtrot Oscar, **SW3**
Gachon's, **SW10**
Gavins, **SW15**
Green Cottage, **NW3**
Grill St Quentin, **SW3**
Gurkhas Tandoori, **W1**
Harry Morgan's, **NW8**
Hung Toa, **W2**
Indian Inn, **N3**
Joe Allen, **WC2**
Khyber Pass, **SW7**

Lantern, **NW6**
Malabar, **W8**
Manna, **NW3**
Maxies Wine Bar, **W7**
Le Mercury, **N1**
Mother Huff's, **NW3**
Moti Mahal, **SW7**
Noor Jahan, **SW5**
Oliver's, **W14**
Ormes, **SW4**
Orso, **WC2**
Penang, **W2**
Le Petit Prince, **NW5 (D)**
La Preferita, **SW11**
Punters Pie, **SW11**
Ravi Shankar, **NW1**
Sabras, **NW10**
Sagarmatha, **NW1**
Sofra, **W1**
Tiger under the Table, **NW11**
Topkapi, **W1**
Villa Estense, **SW6 (L)**
Welcome Inn, **SW16**
Woodlands, **W1, SW1 & Wembley**

LONDON AIRPORTS

Sheraton Skyline, Colony Room **(D)**

AROUND LONDON

BERKSHIRE
Ascot : Royal Berkshire Restaurant
Bray on Thames : Waterside Inn
Cookham : Peking Inn
Maidenhead : Fredrick's Hotel Restaurant
Taplow : Cliveden Dining Room
Windsor : Oakley Court Hotel, Oak Leaf Room

BUCKINGHAMSHIRE
Marlow : Compleat Angler Hotel, Valaisan Restaurant
Speen : Old Plow Inn, Atkins Restaurant **(L)**

ESSEX
Waltham Abbey : Blunk's

HERTFORDSHIRE
Welwyn : Heath Lodge Hotel Restaurant

SURREY
Cobham : Il Giardino
Croydon : Tung Kum
East Molesey : Hampton Court Brasserie
East Molesey : Vecchia Roma
Egham : La Bonne Franquette
Esher : Good Earth
Guildford : Rumwong
Hersham : The Dining Room **(L)**
Richmond : Lichfields **(L)**
Ripley : Michels **(L)**
South Godstone : La Bonne Auberge **(L)**

ENGLAND

BATH

Hole in the Wall **(D)**
Popjoy's
Priory Hotel Restaurant
Royal Crescent Hotel Restaurant

AROUND BATH

AVON
Farrington Gurney: Old Parsonage **(L)**
Freshford: Homewood Park Restaurant
Hunstrete: Hunstrete House Restaurant

SOMERSET
Oakhill: Oakhill House **(L)**
Shepton Mallet: Bowlish House Restaurant
Ston Easton: Ston Easton Park Restaurant

WILTSHIRE
Lacock: Sign of the Angel Restaurant **(L)**
Warminster: Bishopstrow House
    Restaurant

BIRMINGHAM
Chung Ying
Dynasty
New Happy Gathering
Plough & Harrow Hotel Restaurant
Rajdoot **(D)**
Sloans **(L)**

AROUND BIRMINGHAM

HEREFORD & WORCESTER
Bromsgrove: Grafton Manor Restaurant
Chaddesley Corbett: Brockencote Hall
    Restaurant **(L)**

WARWICKSHIRE
Hockley Heath: Nuthurst Grange
    Restaurant **(L)**

WEST MIDLANDS
Sutton Coldfield: New Hall Restaurant

BRIGHTON
China Garden Restaurant
Eaton Garden **(L)**
Lum Thai **(D)**
La Marinade **(L)**
Old Ship Hotel Restaurant
Peking
Whitehaven Hotel, Rolling Clock Restaurant

AROUND BRIGHTON

EAST SUSSEX
Jevington: Hungry Monk

Lewes: Light of Bengal
Lewes: Trumps

WEST SUSSEX
Lower Beeding: South Lodge Restaurant
Storrington: Abingworth Hall Restaurant
Storrington: Little Thakeham Restaurant
    (L)
Storrington: Manley's **(L)**

BRISTOL

Restaurant Lettonie **(L)**
Rajdoot **(D)**

AROUND BRISTOL

AVON
Thornbury: Thornbury Castle Hotel
    Restaurant

WILTSHIRE
Castle Combe: Manor House Hotel
    Restaurant
Easton Grey: Whatley Manor Restaurant

AROUND BOURNEMOUTH

DORSET
Corfe Castle: Morton's House Hotel
    Restaurant
Poole: Mansion House Restaurant
Tarrant Monkton: Langtons
Wareham: Priory Hotel Restaurant

CAMBRIDGE

Angeline **(L)**
Charlie Chan
Midsummer House **(L)**
Shao Tao

AROUND CAMBRIDGE

Duxford: Duxford Lodge Hotel Restaurant
Huntingdon: Old Bridge Hotel Restaurant

CANTERBURY

County Hotel, Sully's Restaurant
Ristorante Tuo e Mio

AROUND CANTERBURY

Ashford: Eastwell Manor Restaurant
Hastingleigh: Woodmans Arms Auberge **(D)**
Herne Bay: L'Escargot **(D)**
Hythe: Fredericks Hotel Restaurant **(L)**

CHESTER

Abbey Green Restaurant **(L)**
Crabwell Manor Restaurant

MANCHESTER

Rajdoot **(D)**
Siam Orchid **(D)**
Yang Sing

AROUND MANCHESTER

CHESHIRE
Handforth: Belfry Hotel Restaurant
Heaton Moor: Jade Garden

OXFORD

Café Français
Cherwell Boathouse **(L)**
Restaurant Elizabeth
Le Petit Blanc
La Sorbonne

AROUND OXFORD

Cumnor: Bear & Ragged Staff **(L)**
Great Milton: Le Manoir aux Quat' Saisons
Stanton Harcourt: Harcourt Arms
Woodstock: Feathers Hotel Restaurant

STRATFORD-UPON-AVON

Billesley Manor Restaurant
Bunbury's
Ettington Park Hotel Restaurant
Hussain's
Welcome Hotel Restaurant

AROUND STRATFORD-UPON-AVON

GLOUCESTERSHIRE
Buckland: Buckland Manor Restaurant
Chipping Camden: Cotswold House Hotel Restaurant

HEREFORD & WORCESTER
Broadway: Collin House Hotel Restaurant **(L)**
Broadway: Dormy House Restaurant
Broadway: Hunter's Lodge **(L)**
Broadway: Lygon Arms Restaurant
Evesham: Hussains

WARWICKSHIRE
Ettington: Chase Hotel Restaurant **(L)**
Leamington: Mallory Court Restaurant
Studley: Peppers **(D)**

SCOTLAND

EDINBURGH

L'Auberge
Caledonian Hotel, Pompadour Restaurant **(D)**

AROUND EDINBURGH

Gullane: Greywalls Restaurant
Gullane: La Potinière **(L)**

GLASGOW

Amber **(D)**
One Devonshire Gardens Restaurant

AROUND GLASGOW

Langbank: Gleddoch House Hotel Restaurant

WALES

CARDIFF

La Chaumière **(L)**

AROUND CARDIFF

Coychurch: Coed-y-Mwstwr Hotel
  Restaurant

NORTHERN IRELAND

BELFAST

Manor House

AROUND BELFAST

Holywood: Schooner **(L)**
Waringstown: The Grange **(L)**

(L) = lunch only
(D) = dinner only

REPUBLIC OF IRELAND

AROUND CORK

Mallow: Longueville House, President's
  Restaurant
Shanagarry: Ballymaloe House Restaurant
Youghal: Aherne's Seafood Restaurant **(D)**

AROUND DUBLIN

Dun Laoghaire: Digby's
Maynooth: Moyglare Manor Restaurant

CO WICKLOW
Bray: Tree of Idleness

Cellnet
THE CELLPHONE NETWORK

Your System for the Future

How cellular telephones work

Cellular telephones use new technology which enables you to make and receive telephone calls from a phone in your car, your briefcase or your pocket, or a remote site – for example a construction site.

Your cellphone works just as easily as your home and office phone and enables you to talk to any phone, anywhere in the world. Your Cellnet system cellphone can also perform tasks your home and office phone cannot.

Cellular works by dividing the total coverage area into many very small areas called 'cells'. Each cell is covered by a <u>low</u> power radio

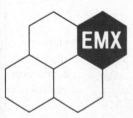

transmitter and receiver. As the cellphone user moves from one cell to another the system automatically switches control of the call from the cell the user is leaving to the cell the user is entering. This process is called 'Hand-off' and takes no more than 300 milli-seconds – making it imperceptible in speech. Each cell links into a digital exchange (EMX) connected directly into the worldwide telephone system.

How cellular telephones work

No matter what business or profession you are in, you cannot afford to miss calls, or be out of touch with colleagues, clients or suppliers. With a cellphone you can turn unproductive time into constructive time.

You needn't waste time in traffic jams – you can talk to a colleague or client while on the way to see another. You can confirm appointments or change travel plans on route. And you are readily available when others need to reach you.

83% of Cellnet subscribers who were questioned in a Gallup Poll, said that a cellphone was essential to their business. Some of the phones had paid for themselves with one call, with 12% of subscribers reporting orders of £50,000 or more being taken over the cellphone.

When you choose Cellnet, you are selecting a system. A world leading system. Cellnet does not retail phones. Or manufacture phones. Cellnet provides the major network which cellphones require to operate.

What kind of cellphone should you have?

Your dealer will recommend the most appropriate phone for your purpose. Essentially there are three types and four grades of cellphone. The three types of cellphone are car, portable and transportable. Car cellphones are hands-free in operation and function best with a roof-mounted aerial. A portable cellphone goes in your briefcase or pocket. A transportable cellphone employs a heavy-duty battery and can be used on construction sites and other locations not connected to the telephone exchange.

Cellphones are graded according to their power output. Class 1 being the most powerful and Class 4 being the least powerful. You can expect a carphone to be Class 1 or 2 and a portable to be Class 4.

Of equal importance to the choice of phone is the choice of facility. Your cellphone can be turned into what is virtually an answering service or otherwise perform a number of functions no ordinary telephone can manage.

What a cellphone can do that an ordinary phone cannot

All the facilities described below are available with Cellnet at no extra charge.

Call Forwarding: If you know that you are not going to be in your car, when visiting a client or when you've gone home, calls to your cellphone can be directed to any other telephone (eg your office or home) so that you don't miss an important call.

No-Answer Transfer: Alternatively, if you're going to be away from the phone for a few minutes, your calls can automatically be re-directed after 5 rings when there is no answer.

Divert on Busy: Equally, even if your cellphone is engaged, the system can re-direct calls after 5 rings to your office or wherever you wish.

Call Waiting: If you are expecting an important call there is no need to worry that you will miss it by using the phone while you are waiting. An incoming call to your cellphone can be put 'on hold' if your phone is already in use. You will receive a warning tone to let you know that a call is waiting. You can then, if you wish, put the existing call on hold, whilst you deal with the new one.

<u>Three Party Conference:</u> This facility enables you to set up a call between yourself and two other people, allowing you for instance to bring another colleague in on a critical discussion even though he may also be 'out on the road'.

<u>Selective Calling:</u>
Certain categories
of outgoing calls
can be barred on the
cellphone, for instance,
if you wish, International
access may not be allowed
to certain users.

Turning your cellphone into an Answering Service

The Cellnet 600 Plus Messaging Service guarantees that you are never out of touch, wherever you are. It works with any type of cellphone on the Cellnet system. When a caller rings your cellphone number he can leave a message for you which you can retrieve as soon as you return to your cellphone. At the same time your Pocket Alerter (included in the service) 'beeps' to warn you that someone is leaving a message.

Suppose, you think the message may be urgent. Perhaps, you are in a meeting in someone else's office. Simply phone and quote your unique confidential PIN (Personal Identification Number) – immediately your cellphone has become the equivalent to an answering service.

Cellnet
THE CELLPHONE NETWORK

For further information see pages 24-30

LONDON RESTAURANTS WITH DISTINCTLY NATIONAL COOKING

(†) for full details of these restaurants see Restaurants under £30 for two (A lot for less).

AFGHAN

Buzkash, **SW15**
Caravan Serai, **W1**

AMERICAN

Fifty-one Fifty-one, **SW3**
Jams, **W1**

CHINESE

Cheng-du, **NW1**
China China, **SW1** (†)
Chuen Cheng Ku, **W1**
Dynasty of Hampstead, **NW3**
Fulham Diner, **SW6**
Fung-Shing, **WC2**
Good Earth, **NW7 & SW3**
Good Friends, **E14**
Green Cottage, **NW3** (†)
Hung Toa, **W2** (†)
Ken Lo's Memories of China, **SW1**
Ken Lo's Memories of China Chelsea, **SW10**
Lok-Zen, **N10**
Mandarin, **W8**
Mandarin Kitchen, **W2**
Maxies Wine Bar, **W7** (†)
Ming, **W1**
Mr Kai, **W1**
Mr Kong, **WC2**
Nanyang, **SW7**
New Diamond, **WC2**
New Leaf, **W5**
New Shu Shan, **WC2**
Peking Duck, **NW11**
Poons, **WC2**
Poons of Covent Garden, **WC2**
Princess Garden, **W1**
Pun, **SW7**
St James Court Hotel, Inn of Happiness, **SW1**
Shanghai, **W8**
Tiger Lee, **SW5**
Treasure of China, **SE10**
Welcome Inn, **SW16** (†)
Weng Wah House, **NW3**
Yung's, **W1**

ENGLISH

Drakes, **SW3**
English Garden, **SW3**
English House, **SW3**
Green's Restaurant, **SW1**
Lindsay House, **W1**
Wiltons, **SW1**

FRENCH

L'Arlequin, **SW8**
Au Jardin des Gourmets, **W1**
L'Aventure, **NW8**
Barnaby's, **SW13**
Bubb's, **EC1**
Café Flo, **NW3**
Café Royal Grill Room, **W1**
Capital Hotel Restaurant, **SW3**
Chez Moi, **W11**
Ciboure, **SW1**
City Brasserie, **EC3**
Claridge's Restaurant, **W1**
Criterion Brasserie, **W1** (†)
Daphne's, **SW3**
La Dordogne, **W4**
L'Etoile, **W1**
La Fantaisie Brasserie, **SW1**
Le Gamin, **EC4**
Le Gavroche, **W1**
Gavvers, **SW1**
The Grafton, **SW4**
Grill St Quentin, **SW3** (†)
Inter-Continental Hotel, Le Soufflé, **W1**
Interlude, **WC2**
Langan's Bistro, **W1**
Le Marmiton, **EC2**
Le Mazarin, **SW1**
Le Meridien Piccadilly, Oak Room, **W1**
Mijanou, **SW1**
Monsieur Thompsons, **W11**
Le Muscadet, **W1**
Ninety Park Lane, **W1**
Oscar's Brasserie, **EC4**
Pavilion, **EC2**
Le Plat du Jour, **NW1** (†)

Le Poulbot, **EC2**
Rue St Jacques, **W1**
St James Court Hotel, Auberge de Provence,
 SW1
Simply Nico, **SW1**
La Tante Claire, **SW3**
Les Trois Plats, **SW3**

GREEK & CYPRIOT

Andreas, **W1** (†)
Bitter Lemons Taverna, **SW6**
Costas Grill, **W8** (†)
Halepi, **W2**
Lemonia, **NW1** (†)
Little Akropolis, **W1** (†)
White Tower, **W1**
Wine & Mousaka, **W5** (†)
Wine & Mousaka, **Richmond** (†)

HUNGARIAN

Gay Hussar, **W1**

INDIAN & PAKISTANI

Ajanta, **W12** (†)
Bombay Bicycle Club, **SW12**
Bombay Brasserie, **SW7**
Delhi Brasserie, **SW7 & W1**
Diwana Bhel-Poori House, **NW1 & W2** (†)
Gurkhas Tandoori, **W1** (†)
Indian Inn, **N3**
Kensington Tandoori, **W8**
Khyber Pass, **SW7** (†)
Kundan, **SW1**
Lal Qila, **W1**
Last Days of the Empire, **W1**
Last Days of the Raj, **WC2**
Majlis, **SW7**
Malabar, **W8** (†)
Memories of India, **SW7**
Moti Mahal, **SW7** (†)
Noor Jahan, **SW5** (†)
Ravi Shankar, **NW1** (†)
Red Fort, **W1**
Sabras, **NW10** (†)
Saloo's, **SW1**
The Veeraswamy, **W1**
Woodlands, **SW1** (†)
Woodlands, **W1** (†)
Woodlands, **Wembley** (†)

INDONESIAN

Sinar Matahari, **W13**

ITALIAN

Al Gallo d'Oro, **W8**
Caffe Mamma, **Richmond** (†)
Casa Cominetti, **SE6**
La Famiglia, **SW10**
Flavio, **SW10** (†)

Gavins, **SW15** (†)
Giovanni's, **WC2**
Gran Paradiso, **SW1**
Il Barbino, **W8** (†)
L'Incontro, **SW1**
Luigi, **SE19**
Orso, **WC2** (†)
La Perla, **W1** (†)
Piccadilly Restaurant, **W1**
La Preferita, **SW11** (†)
San Frediano, **SW3**
San Lorenzo, **SW3**
San Lorenzo Fuoriporta, **SW19**
Santini, **SW1**
Villa Estense, **SW6** (†)
Zia Teresa, **SW3** (†)
Ziani, **SW3**

JAPANESE

Ajimura, **WC2**
Asuka, **NW1**
Benihana, **NW3**
City Miyama, **EC4**
Defune, **W1**
Fuji, **W1**
Ginnan, **EC4**
Gonbei, **WC1**
Hana-Guruma, **EC4**
Hiroko of Kensington, **W11**
Hokkai, **W1**
Ikeda, **W1**
Ikkyu, **W1**
Kitchen Yakitori, **W1** (†)
Koto, **NW1**
Masako, **W1**
Miyama, **W1**
Nakamura, **W1**
Ninjin Club, **W1**
One Two Three, **W1**
Saga, **W1**
Shogun, **W1**
Suntory, **SW1**
Wakaba, **NW3**
Yumi, **W1**

JEWISH

Bloom's, **NW11 & E1**

KOREAN

Arirang House, **SW1**
Arirang Korean Restaurant, **W1**
Kaya, **W1**

LEBANESE

Al Hamra, **W1**
Phoenicia, **W8**

MALAYSIAN

Penang, **W2** (†)

If you have an inquiry about
Cellphones, ask us. The Japanese did.

To find out why turn to pages 24–30.

Cellnet
THE CELLPHONE NETWORK

MEXICAN

Break for the Border, **WC2** (†)

NEPALESE

Gurkhas Tandoori, **W1** (†)
Sagarmatha, **NW1** (†)

POLISH & RUSSIAN

Daquise, **SW7** (†)

PORTUGUESE

Ports, **SW3**

SINGAPOREAN

Tiger under the Table, **NW1** (†)

SOUTH-EAST ASIAN

Penang, **W2**
Singapore Garden, **NW6**
T'ang, **SW10** (†)

SPANISH

Don Pepe, **NW8**

SWEDISH

Anna's Place, **N1**

THAI

Bahn Thai, **W1**
Bangkok, **SW7**
Chaopraya Restaurant, **W1**
Chiang Mai, **W1** (†)
Lena's Thai Restaurant, **SW11**
Tui, **SW7**

TURKISH

Efes Kebab House, **W1** (†)
Sofra, **W1** (†)
Topkapi, **W1** (†)

VIETNAMESE

Lindas, **W9** (†)

EARLY EVENING EATING IN LONDON

Restaurants listed below open for dinner at 6pm or earlier.

LONDON

Ajimura, **WC2**
Al Hamra, **W1**
Arirang Korean Restaurant, **W1**
Arirang House, **SW1**
Asuka, **NW1**
Athenaeum Hotel Restaurant, **W1**
Bahn Thai, **W1**
Bentley's, **W1**
Berkshire Hotel, Ascot Restaurant, **W1**
Bitter Lemons Taverna, **SW6**
Bloom's, **E1 & NW11**
Buzkash, **SW15**
Café Flo, **NW3**
Café Royal Grill Room, **W1**
Le Caprice, **SW1**
Caravan Serai, **W1**
Chuen Cheng Ku, **W1**
City Miyama, **EC4**
Claridges, The Causerie, **W1**
Defune, **W1**
Delhi Brasserie, **SW7 & W1**
Dukes Hotel Restaurant, **SW1**
Dynasty of Hampstead, **NW3**
Frère Jacques, **WC2**
Fuji, **W1**
Fulham Diner, **SW6**
Fung-Shing, **WC2**
Gay Hussar, **W1**
Ginnan, **EC4**
Gonbei, **WC1**
Good Earth, **NW7 & SW3**
Good Friends, **E14**
Gran Paradiso, **SW1**
Grimes, **WC2**
The Halcyon, Kingfisher Restaurant, **W11**
Halepi, **W2**
Hana-Guruma, **EC4**
Hiroko of Kensington Hilton, **W11**
Hokkai, **W1**
Ikkyu, **W1**
Inigo Jones, **WC2**
Inn on the Park, Lanes, **W1**
Kaya, **W1**
Kensington Tandoori, **W8**
Koto, **NW1**
Lal Qila, **W1**
Last Days of the Empire, **W1**
Last Days of the Raj, **WC2**
Lindsay House, **W1**
Lok-Zen, **N10**
Majlis, **SW7**
Mandarin, **W8**

Mandarin Kitchen, **W2**
Manzi's, **WC2**
Masako, **W1**
Memories of India, **SW7**
Ming, **W1**
Mr Kong, **WC2**
Nakamura, **W1**
Nanyang, **SW7**
New Diamond, **WC2**
New Leaf, **W5**
New Shu Shan, **WC2**
Peking Duck, **NW11**
Phoenicia, **W8**
Piccadilly Restaurant, **W1**
Poons, **WC2**
Poons of Covent Garden, **WC2**
Pun, **SW7**
Red Fort, **W1**
RSJ, **SE1**
Savoy Grill Room, **WC2**
Scotts, **W1**
Shogun, **W1**
Si Cheun, **W1**
Sinar Matahari, **W13**
Singapore Garden, **NW6**
Stafford Hotel Restaurant, **SW1**
Swiss Centre, The Chesa, **W1**
Thomas de Quincey's, **WC2**
Tiger Lee, **SW5**
Treasure of China, **SE10**
The Veeraswamy, **W1**
Weng Wah House, **NW3**
Westbury Hotel, The Polo Restaurant, **W1**
Yumi, **W1**
Yung's, **W1**

RESTAURANTS UNDER £30 FOR TWO
(See A Lot for Less)

Ajanta Tandoori, **W12**
Andreas, **W1**
La Brasserie, **SW3**
Break for the Border, **WC2**
Café des Fleurs, **NW6**
Caffe Mamma, **Richmond**
Chiang Mai, **W1**
China China, **SW1**
Costas Grill, **W8**
Cranks, **W1**
Criterion Brasserie, **W1**
Daquise, **SW7**
Diwana Bhel-Poori House, **NW1 & W2**
Ebury Wine Bar, **SW1**
Efes Kebab House, **W1**
Faulkners, **E8**
Flavio, **SW10**

Geale's, **W8**
Green Cottage, **NW3**
Grill St Quentin, **SW3**
Gurkhas Tandoori, **W1**
Harry Morgan's, **NW8**
Hung Toa, **W2**
Indian Inn, **N3**
Joe Allen, **WC2**
Khyber Pass, **SW7**
Kitchen Yakitori, **W1**
Laurent, **NW2**
Lemonia, **NW1**
Little Akropolis, **W1**
Maxies Wine Bar, **W7**
Mélange, **WC2**
Le Mercury, **N1**
Moti Mahal, **SW7**
Noor Jahan, **SW5**
Oasis in the City, **EC1**
Oliver's, **W14**

Orso, **WC2**
Penang, **W2**
La Perla, **W1**
Plat du Jour, **NW1**
Punters Pie, **SW11**
Ravi Shankar, **NW1**
Sabras, **NW10**
Sagarmatha, **NW1**
Seashell, **NW1**
Sofra, **W1**
Soho Brasserie, **W1**
Tiger under the Table, **NW11**
Topkapi, **W1**
Welcome Inn, **SW16**
Wine & Mousaka, **W5**
Wine & Mousaka, **Richmond**
Wolfe's, **SW3**
Woodlands, **W1, SW1 & Wembley**
Zazou Brasserie, **W1**
Zia Teresa, **SW3**

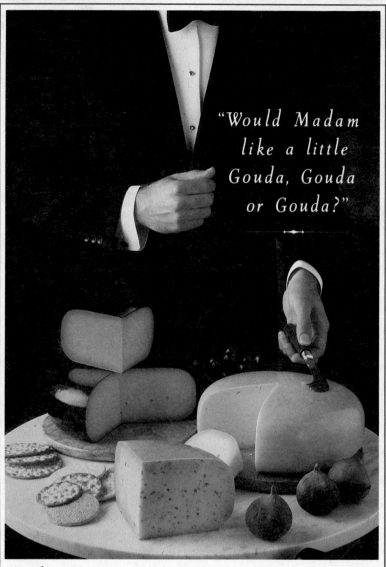

"Would Madam like a little Gouda, Gouda or Gouda?"

*A*sk for Gouda and you'll be pleasantly surprised. In more ways than one. For, as well as young Gouda, there's the full flavoured mature in the black wax, and the delicately spiced Gouda with cumin seeds. Also keep an eye out for other Gouda specialities such as cream Gouda and Gouda with fine herbs. Together, they make Gouda the Dutch cheese that goes right across the board.

LATE NIGHT EATING IN LONDON

Restaurants listed below serve dinner at 11pm or later

LONDON

Ajimura, **WC2**
Al Gallo d'Oro, **W8**
Al Hamra, **W1**
Alastair Little, **W1**
Anna's Place, **N1**
Arirang Korean Restaurant, **W1**
Au Jardin des Gourmets, **W1**
L'Aventure, **NW8**
Bahn Thai, **W1**
Bangkok, **SW7**
Benihana, **NW3**
Berkshire Hotel, Ascot Restaurant, **W1**
Bibendum, **SW3**
Le Bistroquet, **NW1**
Bitter Lemons Taverna, **SW6**
Blakes Hotel Restaurant, **SW7**
Bombay Bicycle Club, **SW12**
Bombay Brasserie, **SW7**
Boucha's, **W14**
La Bouillabaisse, **SW10**
Boulestin, **WC2**
Buzkash, **SW15**
Café Flo, **NW3**
Café Royal Grill Room, **W1**
Le Caprice, **SW1**
Caravan Serai, **W1**
Chaopraya Restaurant, **W1**
Cheng-du, **NW1**
Chez Moi, **W11**
Chinon, **W14**
Chuen Cheng Ku, **W1**
Churchill Hotel, The Arboury, **W1**
Ciboure, **SW1**
Claridge's Restaurant, The Causerie, **W1**
Clarke's, **W8**
La Croisette, **SW10**
Dan's, **SW3**
Daphne's, **SW3**
Delhi Brasserie, **SW7 & W1**
Don Pepe, **NW8**
La Dordogne, **W4**
Drakes, **SW3**
Dynasty of Hampstead, **NW3**
Eatons, **SW1**
English Garden, **SW3**
English House, **SW3**
L'Escargot, **W1**

La Famiglia, **SW10**
Fifty-One Fifty-One, **SW3**
Frère Jacques, **WC2**
Frith's, **W1**
Fulham Diner, **SW6**
Fung-Shing, **WC2**
Gay Hussar, **W1**
Giovanni's, **WC2**
Good Earth, **NW7 & SW3**
Good Friends, **E14**
The Grafton, **SW4**
Gran Paradiso, **SW1**
Greenhouse, **W1**
Grimes, **WC2**
The Guinea, **W1**
Guinea Grill, **W1**
Kingfisher Restaurant, **W11**
Halepi, **W2**
Harvey's, **SW17**
Hiders, **SW6**
Hilaire, **SW7**
Howard Hotel, Quai D'or Restaurant, **WC2**
Hyatt Carlton Tower, Chelsea Room & Rib Room, **SW1**
L'Incontro, **SW1**
Inigo Jones, **WC2**
Inn on the Park, Four Seasons Restaurant & Lanes, **W1**
Inter-Continental Hotel, Le Soufflé, **W1**
Interlude, **WC2**
Jams, **W1**
Joe's Café, **SW3**
Kaya, **W1**
Kensington Place, **W8**
Kensington Tandoori, **W8**
Kundan, **SW1**
Lal Qila, **W1**
Langan's Bistro, **W1**
Langan's Brasserie, **W1**
Last Days of the Empire, **W1**
Last Days of the Raj, **WC2**
Left Bank, **SW10**
Leith's, **W11**
Lena's Thai Restaurant, **SW11**
Lindsay House, **W1**
Lok-Zen, **N10**
Lou Pescadou, **SW5**
Luigi's, **SE19**
Majlis, **SW7**
Mandarin, **W8**
Mandarin Kitchen, **W2**
Manzi's, **WC2**
Martin's, **NW1**
Le Mazarin, **SW1**

Memories of India, **SW7**
Ménage à Trois, **SW3**
Mijanou, **SW1**
Ming, **W1**
Mr Kai, **W1**
Mr Kong, **WC2**
Monkeys, **SW3**
Motcombs, **SW1**
Le Muscadet, **W1**
Nanyang, **SW7**
Neal Street Restaurant, **WC2**
New Diamond, **WC2**
New Leaf, **W5**
New Shu Shan, **WC2**
Odette's, **NW1**
Odins, **W1**
192, **W11**
Otters, **SW6**
Park Lane Hotel, Bracewells, **W1**
Peking Duck, **NW11**
Peter's, **NW6**
Phoenicia, **W8**
Piccadilly Restaurant, **W1**
Pollyanna's, **SW11**
Pomegranates, **SW1**
Poons, **WC2**
Poons of Covent Garden, **WC2**
Ports, **SW3**
Princess Garden, **W1**
Pun, **SW7**
Le Quai St Pierre, **W8**
Read's, **SW5**
Red Fort, **W1**
The Ritz Restaurant, **W1**
Royal Roof Restaurant, **W8**
RSJ, **SE1**
Rue St Jacques, **W1**
St James Court Hotel, Auberge de Provence
    & Inn of Happiness, **SW1**
Salloos, **SW1**
San Frediano, **SW3**
San Lorenzo, **SW3**
San Lorenzo Fuoriporta, **SW19**
San Martino, **SW3**
Santini, **SW1**
Savoy Restaurant & Grill Room, **WC2**
Shanghai, **W8**
Shogun, **W1**
Si Cheun, **W1**
Simply Nico, **SW1**
Singapore Garden, **NW6**
Le Suquet, **SW3**
Sutherlands, **W1**
Swiss Centre, The Chesa, **W1**
T'ang, **SW10**
La Tante Claire, **SW3**
Thomas de Quincey's, **WC2**
Tiger Lee , **SW5**
Treasure of China, **SE10**
Les Trois Plats, **SW3**
Tui, **SW7**
Turner's, **SW3**
The Veeraswamy, **W1**
Waltons, **SW3**
Weng Wah House, **NW3**
Yung's, **W1**
Zazou, **W1**
Ziani, **SW3**

LONDON AIRPORTS

HEATHROW
Sheraton Skyline, Colony Room

RESTAURANTS UNDER £30 FOR TWO
(See A Lot for Less)

Ajanta Tandoori, **W12**
Andreas, **W1**
Le Bistroquet, **NW1**
La Brasserie, **SW3**
Break for the Border, **WC2**
Café des Fleurs, **NW6**
Caffe Mamma, **Richmond**
Camden Brasserie, **NW1**
Chiang Mai, **W1**
China China, **SW1**
La Cloche, **NW6**
Cranks, **W1**
Criterion Brasserie, **W1**
Daquise, **SW7**
Diwana Bhel-Poori House, **NW1**
Efes Kebab House, **W1**
La Fin de la Chasse, **N16**
Flavio, **SW10**
Foxtrot Oscar, **SW3**
Gavins, **SW15**
Geale's, **W8**
Green Cottage, **NW3**
Grill St Quentin, **SW3**
Gurkhas Tandoori, **W1**
Hung Toa, **W2**
Il Barbino, **W8**
Indian Inn, **N3**
Joe Allen, **WC2**
Khyber Pass, **SW7**
Lantern, **NW6**
Laurent, **NW2**
Lemonia, **NW1**
Malabar, **W8**
Manna, **NW3**
Mélange, **WC2**
Le Mercury, **N1**
Mother Huff's, **NW3**
Moti Mahal, **SW7**
Noor Jahan, **SW5**
Oliver's, **W14**
Ormes, **SW4**
Orso, **WC2**
Penang, **W2**
La Perla, **W1**
Le Petit Prince, **NW5**
La Preferita, **SW11**
Punters Pie, **SW11**
Sagarmatha, **NW1**
Sofra, **W1**
Soho Brasserie, **W1**
Tiger under the Table, **NW11**

Topkapi, **W1**
Villa Estense, **SW6**
Welcome Inn, **SW16**
Wine & Mousaka, **W5**

Wine & Mousaka, **Richmond**
Woodlands Restaurant, **W1**
Zazou Brasserie, **W1**
Zia Teresa, **SW3**

OPEN AIR EATING IN AND AROUND LONDON

LONDON

Al Hamra, **W1**
Anna's Place, **N1**
L'Aventure, **NW8**
Bill Bentley's, **EC2**
Buzkash, **SW5**
Café Flo, **NW3**
Christian's, **W4**
Dan's, **SW3**
Delhi Brasserie, **SW7**
La Dordogne, **W4**
La Famiglia, **SW10**
Frith's, **W1**
Fuji, **W1**
Gran Paradiso, **SW1**
The Halcyon, Kingfisher Restaurant, **W11**
Ikeda, **W1**
Jacques, **N4**
Luigi's, **SE19**
Memories of India, **SW7**
Misanou, **SW1**
Le Muscadet, **W1**
Odette's, **NW1**
192, **W11**
Pollyanna's, **SW11**
Le Quai St Pierre, **W8**
Read's, **SW5**
The Ritz Restaurant, **W1**

St James Court (Inn of Happiness), **SW1**
San Lorenzo Fuoriporta, **SW19**
San Martino, **SW3**
Stafford Hotel Restaurant, **SW1**

RESTAURANTS UNDER £30 FOR TWO
(See A Lot for Less)

Le Bistroquet, **NW1**
La Brasserie, **SW3**
Café des Fleurs, **NW6**
Camden Brasserie, **NW1**
Costas Grill, **W8**
Efes Kebab House, **W1**
Le Fin de la Chasse, **N16**
Flavio, **SW10**
Little Akropolis, **W1**
Manna, **NW3**
Mélange, **WC2**
Mother Huff's, **NW3**
Oliver's, **W14**
La Preferita, **SW11**
Punters Pie, **SW11**
Sofra, **W1**
Topkapi, **W1**
Zazou Brasserie, **W1**

WEEKEND ACTIVITY BREAKS

— TWENTY YEARS ON —

NOBODY seems to know just who pioneered bargain weekend breaks in the UK – or when. A Trusthouse Forte spokesman, unable to confirm whether his company was actually the first as is popularly believed, was at least able to report that the THF chain had been offering them since the early 1970s.

As it happens, Trust House Hotels – as the company was known then – was advertising special discounts from Friday and Saturday evenings to Sunday afternoons and Monday mornings respectively in the winter of 1969.

Right from the start, it was a marketing ploy aimed at filling rooms on the two or three nights of the week when business travellers were off the road and relaxing in the comfort of their own homes.

The strategy worked – and how! Ever since, the short break has been the fastest growing sector in the British holiday industry; indeed for many years it has been the *only* area of expansion. So much so that, according to the latest figures, the short leisure break hotel market is worth more than £400m a year.

In a bid to attract even more people to the idea of spending a mini-holiday over and above their main summer vacation, an ever increasing number of hotels are today offering other types of weekend packages ... in the shape of theme and activity breaks.

Are they as good as the brochures make out? Or are they merely window-dressing, designed to part the public even more quickly from its hard-earned cash? Above all, do they give value for money? It's worth noting that the price in a couple of cases was the equivalent of a week's half-board holiday by air in mainland Greece, and, for the price of several other breaks, we could have taken a seven-days' self-catering vacation in Spain, also including the plane ticket.

In fact, on the evidence of a study by our inspectors of a good cross-section of these offerings, most of the activities and courses are extremely well run – in many cases much better than the hotels.

In almost three-quarters of the deals we checked out, the hotels, it seemed, were also having a weekend break and, measured against *Egon Ronay's Guides'* inspectors' evaluations at other times but mostly in midweek, it was hard to believe that they were the same establishments.

Could it be because business people are regular customers and tip more generously? Or that casual staff are farmed in to enable the permanent employees to have a day off? Or is it because weekends are also viewed as a time for relaxation by the workforce, and management is reluctant to read the riot act for fear of staff walking out?

Says Chief Inspector and Publisher Andrew Eliel: 'It is a combination of all these reasons. The one thing for certain, as the inspectorate's reports show, is that things can and do get sloppy. And the problem, it seems, is getting worse.

'Participants are enjoying themselves so much on the courses and the activity programmes that they are turning a blind eye to the hotels' shortcomings. But that won't always be the case. And already the danger signs are there, with more and more people taking short breaks in Europe and even the United States.'

Just how badly standards drop at weekends is shown by the number of points awarded by the inspectors for service. With the exception of four venues (the world-famous Gleneagles – the only establishment to score full marks; the Black Swan at Helmsley, N Yorks; the Sunlaws House Hotel at Kelso, Borders; and British Rail's special weekend Intercity 'travelling hotel'), customer care and attention ranged from average (five cases) to unsatisfactory (also five cases) to appalling (just the one example, but that's one too many).

Another big let-down was the cooking. The fare at just over half the hotels was considered well below average, even considering that none of them is recommended separately for its restaurant in the main body of the Guide.

In addition, only two hotels of the 15 assessed put out fresh milk (rather than UHT) on the beverage trays in visitors' rooms, while five still imposed a single room supplement. (British Rail was the biggest culprit here, charging a whacking £95 on top of the advertised £245 fare.)

Just how off-colour in general the hotels are is perhaps most clearly demonstrated when their points are measured against those of the courses and activities. In all but two cases, the attractions score better marks.

Of course, this could mean that the standard of the courses and activities is remarkably high. In truth, it is a reflection of both the hotels and the featured attractions.

Only one event's programme –

the steam railway weekend based at Basingstoke – was really below par, while, at the other end of the spectrum, the clay-pigeon shooting, horse-riding and walking with wildlife weekends earned particularly high marks.

As a means to fill bedspace, activity breaks, it seems, are proving a lucrative investment.

Here's how our inspectors fared on each of the 15 activity breaks tested ...

For £220 half-board (easily the most expensive short break sampled, and the equivalent of a two-weeks inclusive holiday in Greece if you add the air fare from London and the cost of a hire car at Edinburgh airport), you would expect the best. And the two-day horse-riding weekend based at GLENEAGLES HOTEL, Auchterarder, 40 miles north of the Scottish capital, proved to be precisely that.

But even here there were deficiencies: the radio, listed in the brochure, was missing from our inspector's room; two lamps failed to function; and she was erroneously billed for double instead of single accommodation (though in fairness it was the hotel that spotted the mistake).

Be that as it may, we are glad to record that, the service was impeccable. A kilted doorman genuinely seemed to enjoy greeting visitors and helping them with baggage, the receptionists were pleasant and friendly, the porters cheerful, and the chambermaids quietly efficient. At mealtimes, wine was poured regularly and unobtrusively, and plates cleared promptly.

The room, though on the small side, afforded good views of the impressive grounds and distant Ochil Hills. Mod cons included a mini-bar, colour TV, in-house movies, direct-dial telephone and trouser press while, in the bathroom, there were thick, fluffy white towels; a matching bathrobe; hairdryer; quality toiletries; and a shower that maintained pressure and temperature.

Mealtimes, too, were a pleasure – but then there are 75 chefs on the payroll! Even sticking to the set eight-day cycle menu is tempting. On the first night, for instance, we chose goose liver and truffle terrine with aspic and toasted brioche; lobster and apple brandy soup with fresh double cream; poached salmon stuffed with leeks and served with a white wine and cream sauce accompanied by cauliflower, French beans, baby sweetcorn, peppers, plus baked and roast potatoes; strawberries and cream; and filter coffee. Preparation, presentation and service were first class, the vegetables particularly deserving mention.

Dinner on the second night was equally impressive, while the full Scottish breakfasts (including Loch Fyne kippers) were both mouth-watering and just the right pick-me-up for the activity to come – the real reason for our being there. The hotel actually offers a number of options – among them golf, shooting, tennis, squash, bowls, croquet, fishing, and 'health and beauty.'

We had chosen riding, which is based in the grounds at the Mark Phillips Equestrian Centre, claimed to be among the best facilities of its kind in the world. We were not to be disappointed.

The complex is superb – for horses and riders alike. There is a spacious, carpeted reception and even a bar and restaurant overlooking the grand arena. The changing and shower facilities are immaculate, and liveried Land Rovers ferry you the half-mile to and from the hotel.

At no extra cost, you can also get full riding kit, breeches, hard hats, boots, etc on loan.

The grand arena and practice areas are laid with Fibresand, and great care has been taken in the selection of the horses. There is a mount to suit any size, weight and ability level, starting with a tiny woolly Shetland for tots on the leading rein.

A week before she travelled, our inspector was phoned by the hotel to agree an instructional and riding schedule. (Touches like these somehow make the previously mentioned room shortcomings stand out even more.) This timetable was adjusted at our inspector's request on the actual weekend, and, on her arrival on the Friday afternoon, she was taken on a guided tour of the centre.

Three riding sessions are included in the price. In fact, she was to ride four times during the weekend – once out on a trail and three 45-minute private lessons. The centre helpfully suggested that she counted the trail ride as the additional session as it was £15 cheaper than a lesson.

Tuition was of a high standard and, during one of the instructional periods in the grand arena, she rode a huge grey formerly owned and ridden by Captain Mark Phillips.

After a light lunch at the centre on the Saturday, she stayed to watch a showjumping competition in the grand arena, and later fitted in a swim and jacuzzi free of charge at the hotel's Country Club.

On Sunday she treated herself to a body scrub and massage (£20 including gratuity) before turning for home in the afternoon.

VERDICT: Memorable. Hotel first class, apart from the bedroom shortcomings. Equestrian centre extremely well designed; advertised activity instructive and a lot of fun. Expensive – but the cosseting and enjoyment made it worth every penny.

Although about half the price of Gleneagles, the **'Super Sleuth' weekend** at the **OLD SWAN HOTEL**, Harrogate, N Yorks, had a lot going for it – certainly sufficient to take the runner-up spot in our league table.

In common with all the other short breaks sampled, the hotel was not in the same league as Gleneagles, but the overall package was impressive nonetheless.

On arrival, guests were informed by reception that their instructions were in their rooms together with a notebook and pen. The first assignment proved to be a cocktail party where participants were split into teams of detectives, after which came dinner.

On both nights there was a set menu offering two choices per course and, with the emphasis on fresh ingredients, the banquet-style meals were surprisingly good and attractively presented. Table service was even better.

For good measure, the inspector's single room was of a good size, clean, nicely furnished and reasonably equipped.

During the weekend there were three 'mysterious deaths' and, on the Saturday morning, a real-life sleuth (Det Supt Robin Cooper) outlined the actual police investigations of three Yorkshire murders. After that, it was up to the groups to study the clues and post-mortem reports, and interview suspects (fellow guests) in a bid to unmask the 'killer' on the Sunday morning.

In fact, nobody did – at least not the right one. But several came pretty close.

VERDICT: Well-managed blend of socialising and crime-solving. There was a good mix of guests of all ages and, to add further variety, Saturday afternoon was kept free for exploring the lovely Victorian town. There was also a dance at the hotel on Saturday evening. In short, a good deal for a good price.

The brainchild of a retired farmer, the **Herriot Country weekend** at the **BLACK SWAN HOTEL**, Helmsley, N Yorks, is a comprehensive guided coach tour of the magnificent scenery and locations featured in the films of and various series on the experiences of the well-known veterinary surgeon.

It was obvious that an effective partnership existed between the hotel and the party leader, and it was most gratifying to see the staff involving themselves with the weekend-breakers. There was a personally addressed, signed letter of welcome and an itinerary from the Black Swan manager in each bedroom and, at the first get-together on the Friday evening, the assistant manageress took the time to introduce the guests to the tour leader.

In addition, the duty manager stayed throughout the first evening's illustrated talk on magnificent Swaledale.

It was all the more disappointing therefore to come across evidence of poor housekeeping. In our inspector's room, the bathrobes were stained and dirty-looking, there were fingermarks down the door, and dust and dirt in the corners of the bathroom floor. Maintenance could have been better, too – the shower control was stiff and one of the taps defective.

Service, though friendly, courteous and efficient, was obtrusive in the early evening, a chambermaid insisting on turning down the bedcovers at the very time people were getting ready for dinner. Quality and presentation of meals, though, were above average for hotel fare. That said, however, Friday's meal was spoiled by an overpowering sauce on the chicken dish and too much oil in the courgettes.

The coach tours on the two days were leisurely and well organised, taking in numerous historic sites, buildings, villages and landscapes. But the pub lunch on the Saturday drew widespread criticism – mass-produced roast chicken and tinned vegetables, soaked in a tasteless gravy, with sickly cheesecake for afters, and UHT milk in the coffee.

Other niggles included the £5 supplement for singles and having to find the £1.25 admission to Rievaulx Abbey. (After all, everything else was included in the price.)

VERDICT: Reasonable value for money. Hotel staff seemed genuinely concerned that guests should enjoy the tours. Leader and guide Ken Wiseman knew his stuff and encouraged a convivial mood in the party.

Up at the **CREST HOTEL,** Newcastle upon Tyne, you could be forgiven for thinking that the main attraction of the special weekend was visiting castles and islands in Northumbria. In fact, the secondary title – **a Crest Bird-watching Break** – is what it was really all about.

To anyone who has a keen interest in wildlife, fauna and birds, it is a mini-holiday to be recommended. That is, providing they're not too picky about the hotel.

Although everyone paid the same, some were allocated standard accommodation, others executive rooms and even the Lady Crest suites, which, as the name implies, are designed principally with women in mind. In such a tight-knit group, this is a policy virtually guaranteed to generate ill feeling among those who get the short straw and end up with the basics.

The non-executive offerings are inferior. There are no mini-bars or hairdryers, they are generally less comfortable, and the furnishings are of a lower quality.

Although the hotel set aside a room especially for the bird-watchers' first night pre-dinner get-together, and a senior member of staff briefly welcomed everybody, it was all rather formal. In addition, more effort could possibly have gone into the hospitality, which was limited to sherry and a few nuts.

Unfortunately, too, the quality of the meals and the presentation was to vary considerably. On one night the main course was served on cold plates and some of the food also turned out to be cold. Table service, into the bargain, was slow, with lengthy spells between courses.

The packed lunches – basically salads in plastic trays – were of variable quality. On the credit side, though, breakfast was something to look forward to, and the service at this time of day was on a different planet when compared with the evenings. Less than satisfactory, however, were the hotel's public areas which were rather tatty. The foyer was dingy and badly lit, and the third-floor reception desk badly signposted, while carpet in the bars and restaurant, for instance, looked decidedly tired.

It was the excellence of the activity element that was behind this break's comparatively high mark. As our inspector remarks: 'The leader, Tim Cleeves from the Royal Society for the Protection of Birds, was exactly the right choice. From the outset, he created a relaxed, friendly atmosphere, laced with good humour. And the way he put the subject across was very impressive – not too fundamental to insult your intelligence and not too technical, either.

'In the hands of somebody of this calibre, the programme couldn't help but be successful. Take the illustrated talks on Friday and Saturday night – they were not only enjoyable in their own right but they also whetted the appetite for the following day.

'The variety of habitat we were treated to was remarkable. And the Farne Islands, where we ended up, are probably the best place in Britain to view seabirds at very close quarters.'

The only hiccup on the travels turned out to be the hotel's fault, which perhaps wasn't altogether surprising – the ferry hadn't been paid for in advance.

VERDICT: The bird-watching was superb; the hotel a shade Crestfallen!

Two other forms of activity break came equal fifth: a treasure hunt based at the MOUNT HOTEL, Wolverhampton, and a spot of fly-fishing at the SUNLAWS HOUSE HOTEL, Kelso, in the Borders.

'A good idea, well carried through' was our inspector's comment on the **treasure hunt** at the **MOUNT HOTEL,** which was conceived at the

outset to show people that there is a lot more to the West Midlands than an industrial landscape.

At the end of both days, participants were invited to complete a questionnaire on the attractions visited. On this occasion there were joint winners, both of whom received a crystal vase worth £25 for their efforts.

The places of interest (all visited by coach) were: the Stuart crystal factory to see the art of glass-making, a narrow boat cruise into the Singing Cavern, a tour of the Black Country Museum, and trips to Bantock House to view displays of fine Worcester porcelain, the Lock Museum and an old-fashioned farm in Sandwell Valley.

Accommodation was reasonable, except that two elderly ladies in the party were obliged to share a single-sized room. There were half a dozen choices per course on the table d'hôte menu, but service problems were encountered in the dining room on the Saturday, making dinner a less pleasant experience compared with the previous evening.

The tour leader, according to our man, 'started poorly and seemed rather bored, but improved on acquaintance'. The tour guide, on the other hand, was 'a real poppet who went out of her way to please'.

The presentation of an item of Stuart crystal to all participants at the end of the break was a nice touch. Also impressive: the price included coach travel to and from London and Bristol.

VERDICT: Value for money and good fun.

When trying a new experience on a short break, it can pay you to do a little homework first. Consider the case of one of our inspectors who, out of the blue, booked a **fly-fishing weekend** at **SUNLAWS HOUSE HOTEL,**

Kelso. Little did he know that he would be the only person on the course.

What he hadn't realised and what the hotel failed to tell him when he made his reservation was that the high season for this particular activity is in March or October when parties of a dozen are catered for.

The first inkling that he had inadvertently opted for the low season and would be the only 'student' on the course wasn't apparent until he reported to reception on arrival, at which point he was introduced to the ghillie who was to show him the ropes.

Still, at least it meant that he would receive intensive individual tuition the following day, a Saturday. But with nothing to do in the evenings and no fellow novices to socialise and swap experiences with, it was not exactly a convivial weekend.

One consolation, though, was the hotel. The cost of the weekend (admittedly on a bed and breakfast basis) was the lowest in the survey yet, remarkably, the Sunlaws' score came second only to Gleneagles. Another unexpected treat was that, for the price of the single accommodation booking, our inspector was allocated a twin-bedded room on the ground floor. What is more, his baggage was taken there for him.

In our man's words, the room was 'attractive, comfortable, homely and pristinely clean. It was also prettily decorated, nicely furnished and overlooked the garden.'

In addition, he reported, there were some nice touches like complimentary mineral water, and 'a rarity this – a radio with good reception on Radio 3'.

The only let-down was the provision of UHT rather than fresh milk with the tea-making facilities.

The bathroom boasted a 'battery of toiletries and large generous towels, and the bed was properly turned down while I was out dining each night'.

The rest of the hotel was equally pleasing, the character of the day rooms 'a fine blend of elegant period personality with the emphasis ever on comfort'.

Service was excellent; nothing was too much trouble for the staff, from serving a bar lunch in the conservatory to cleaning shoes left outside the room overnight.

Meals, however, varied in quality. Breakfasts and packed lunches were good, but dinners were only fair – 'too complicated and ambitious for the talents of the kitchen'. The wine list was 'excellent', but puddings were 'mediocre'.

As for learning to fly-fish, it transpired that the ghillie was an accomplished teacher. 'All the tackle was provided,' our inspector reports, 'and, after six hours, I really felt I had learned to cast. Not only that, the course was fun and flexible.'

That it rated the second worst mark of the whole exercise was down to our inspector being bereft of the company of like-minded weekend breakers.

VERDICT: 'I shall certainly be returning, but not in the low season. To stand in the middle of a stream, suitably attired, must be one of the best ways to prevent a heart attack'.

The best-run course, as opposed to the hotel or total package with the highest score, was judged to be the **clay-pigeon shooting**, arranged by UK Field and Stream Ltd. This was based on a weekend break at the **CHEQUERS HOTEL**, a THF establishment at Newbury, Berks.

The hotel, sad to relate, just wasn't in the same class. Indeed, the weekend wasn't very old before it chalked up its first black mark: the special welcoming reception on the

Friday night began 30 minutes before the advertised time. But at least the wine was on the house and the function was attended by the Chequers' manager.

Regrettably, the dinner that followed was scarcely a good advertisement. 'There did not seem to be enough staff, and service was slow and somewhat disorganised.' Our representative was given and subsequently ordered à la carte, only to discover later that the price of the break restricted guests to table d'hôte. When he protested about being charged extra and explained what had happened, however, the bill was immediately reduced.

The meal on the following night was no better, and earlier in the day at breakfast, our man was obliged to send a hard egg and soggy toast back to the kitchen for replacement.

In addition, the packed lunch supplied by the Chequers on the Saturday was 'fairly dull'.

If the food wasn't off-putting enough, our inspector was disturbed by a plumbing noise in his room and, although he made a point of reporting this to reception at the first opportunity, he was not offered alternative accommodation.

Thankfully, the course was top-notch. There were two instructors to the 18 guests, most of whom had never picked up a gun before.

The course leaders went over the essentials and showed an instructional video on Friday night, and this was followed the next morning by a half-hour talk on gun safety and etiquette. The group then drove ten miles in convoy to Watership Down, the very location featured in the book and film of the same name. Not a single rabbit, though, was seen; they were presumably keeping their heads down on account of the gunfire.

At the site, a three-sided marquee provided some shelter from a cold wind, and there was a tented area

with a chemical loo. The shooting lesson lasted all day, each person firing some 70 or 80 cartridges, and once again the hotel manager did himself and his masters credit by putting in an appearance.

On Sunday morning there was a £12 optional extra in the form of a 25-shot competition, for which the hotel put up two bottles of wine. That virtually everyone turned up showed just how enjoyable the course was.

VERDICT: With the tutors so well in command of their subject and equally eager to share their enthusiasm for the sport, the course was quite excellent. Pity about the hotel, though.

The **hang-gliding course** offered by the **PENNINE HILTON NATIONAL HOTEL** (formerly the Ladbroke) at Huddersfield, W Yorks, proved remarkably similar to the Chequers' experience in Newbury.

Once again, food was the big disappointment – that and the fact that the reception staff, apart from not listening to the customer, clearly didn't know anything about the special weekend (see panel).

As our inspector was to comment: 'It was one long comedy of errors. The one saving grace was

THE CUSTOMER'S ALWAYS RIGHT

■ On the hang-gliding weekend at the Pennine Hilton National Hotel, Huddersfield, the itinerary requested guests to ask reception to check out the weather conditions with the course leader. Our inspector reports: 'This I did, only to be told by a receptionist that it was up to me to do this. I soon put her right!'

■ The following day the same inspector once again asked reception to phone the hang-gliding people. This time there was a different girl in charge who … a) insisted that she didn't know the number … b) had no knowledge of the course … and c) had no information about it, either. 'In the end,' says our man, 'she agreed to give them a ring if I went back to my room and got the number.'

■ Our man at Huddersfield (again!) calculated that he owed £112 when the time came to settle up. The accounts lady, presenting him with a statement for nearly £240, suggested that he might have made a mistake.

It turned out that she had charged him normal rate and was very surprised when told he was on a special activity break package. She eventually found the correct details and re-did her sums and, this time, came up with a total of … £30.

He could have left it at that, of course – but just to prove that Egon Ronay people are chivalrous and have a conscience, he suggested she plug her calculator back in. The outcome? A bill for £112.

---

the twin five-star room which was just fine.'

The most memorable aspect of all, though, was the course, held on a nearby moor and brilliantly organised by Keith Cockcroft, former captain of the British hang-gliding team. On average, there is one instructor to four students, and the early stages of tuition are devoted to craft assembly and, above all, safety.

After that, it was on to the learning slopes to practise take-offs and landings with, in between, tethered flights of around ten yards about six feet off the ground.

After lunch in the town (not included in the price), tuition continued until, at the end of the session, each novice progressed to a steeper slope for a 100ft tethered

flight at a height of around 20ft. The evening was spent in a local pub for a debriefing and general discussion of the day's events.

On Sunday, instruction continued on a steeper slope still, with the emphasis on turning. On the completion of each sortie, the 'pilot' is obliged to carry the hang-glider back to the starting-point – uphill, of course, and very tiring.

Apparently it takes around eight days to reach P1 free-flight certificate standard – 'so the course gives you a good insight'. It should also confirm whether you like it and it likes you!

VERDICT: The course is highly recommended and, note, you don't have to be a Hilton National Hotel customer to participate.

Country Walks, Walking With Wildlife was the attraction offered by the **KESWICK HOTEL**, a THF establishment at Keswick-on-Derwentwater, Cumbria.

On arrival, our inspector found in her room a letter from the establishment's general manager: 'Not all the staff behind the reception desk are hotel personnel and therefore cannot offer the service that our own receptionists and management can, so please bear with us...' It seemed to have something to do with the installation of a new computer earlier in the week but, as the last day of the temporary staff changes coincided with the first day of our stay, we were prepared to ignore it.

Poor service both at reception and especially in the dining room, however, was a general feature of the weekend, as was the lack of co-ordination between the hotel and the activity organiser.

Says our inspector: 'Take Sunday, when breakfast was squeezed between a dawn outing and a forest plantation walk. We were tired, hungry and on a tight schedule, so you would have thought that the management, who must have known the timetable, would have ensured that everything was laid on for us at 9am. It wasn't. In fact, we had to wait for 40 minutes and then rush our food!'

All in all, the manager tried hard (he joined the introduction party on the Friday night) but was let down by his staff.

The accommodation was bright and airy enough, but the decor was 'on the tatty side and the windows were filthy'. The food was passable if not very imaginative.

Once more, it was the activity programme and the standard of the course leader that saved the situation. It was a shame, though, that the hotel didn't hire the minibus transport by the day rather than for a certain number of hours each time. On Saturday, for instance, it meant a late afternoon rush to get back to the Keswick Hotel because the vehicle was needed elsewhere, which meant there wasn't time for the nice relaxing tea at the local tea shop as planned by the course leader.

Fortunately, all these negative aspects were more than compensated for by the expert planning and guidance of the course leader and by the walks themselves, luckily blessed with glorious weather. Two daytime walks took us through broad-leaved and coniferous woodland and our endurance was tested by a late evening badger watch, followed by a dawn foray to see red deer feeding.

Brand-new binoculars and a packed lunch on Saturday, which, though impractically packed for rucksacks, was of a high quality, were provided. Rooms were held until 2pm on Sunday.

VERDICT: Full marks for the course leader's choice of programme. But the hotel staff could have done better – and so could the brochure. There should have been more advice on footwear, and tips such as packing midge repellent.

Vying with the Gleneagles Hotel as the most expensive short break sampled was **THE WEST HIGHLANDER – a 1394¾-mile rail journey** over a long weekend, starting and finishing at London St Pancras. The fare per person when sharing a sleeping-car compartment was £245. Solo travellers, however, paid a hefty £95 on top because, argued British Rail Intercity, they 'upset the food costings'.

All told, singles got rather a rough deal. An absurd example of bureaucracy meant, for instance, that they could not convert their cabins to single occupancy and gain extra room by simply folding away the top bunk. The reason? The bunk was made up and, as an official explained: 'There's nowhere to put the bedding, sir. In any case, the supplement is for single-room occupancy – not a single cabin.'

The bunks, though on the narrow side, were reasonably comfortable; cabins were air-conditioned; and there was no shortage of hot water at the washbasins. In addition, there was a lavatory at each end of the carriage.

The package offered two main attractions – journeying through some of Britain's finest scenery, and

being hauled by a steam locomotive part of the way.

The views were seen from six day-cars which customers were obliged to use – from no later than 6.15am on the first morning! On the first full day, the train proceeded to Oban, where passengers transferred to a ferry for the island of Mull and subsequently to Iona and its famous abbey. Then, returning to the mainland, it was back on the train for dinner and the journey to Fort William where there was an overnight hotel stop. Facilities here were 'very basic, with production-line breakfasts, though not too bad for a tourist hotel'. Next day, it was the return steam ride to Mallaig over arguably the most scenic rail route in Britain, except on this occasion the steam engine was sidelined because of an environmental fire risk.

In the evening it was all aboard the main train again for dinner and the sleeping accommodation, and the last leg to London.

The food en route, for the most part, was prepared in 30-year-old kitchen cars. But though meals were well above the BR average, only one – a delicious coq au vin with new potatoes and peas, with treacle pudding and custard to finish – was judged to be up to *Egon Ronay's Guides'* standard. The remainder ranged from overcooked roast beef and lamb to soggy fish and chips.

There was an effort to use fresh produce, and traditional Scottish dishes were not forgotten, with both haggis and neeps and cock-a-leekie on the starters list.

VERDICT: Not a journey of high gastronomy and style. Though most travellers were elderly, no one seemed to want to socialise in groups or seek out alliances. Poor value for money for singles – but there can be few more civilised ways to see such dramatic landscapes.

A particular surprise, given the company's popularity and reputation, was the low placing of the Embassy Hotels' Leisure Learning package sampled. The break we chose was **Historic Houses of the Thames Valley** based at the **HOG'S BACK HOTEL**, Seale, near Farnham, Surrey.

The first indication our inspector had that the hotel was putting on anything out of the ordinary was when she came across the itinerary in her room. There was no initial ice-breaking – indeed, guests on the course didn't meet each other until dinner, after which their weekend host gave an illustrated talk on the houses that were to be visited.

Our representative, it turned out, was the only member of the predominantly elderly group not to have previously sampled a Leisure Learning event.

The dinner that night (and the following evening) was 'atrocious'. The cooking 'lacked talent and imagination and relied a great deal on what tasted like convenience foods'. The hors d'oeuvre buffet, for instance, consisted of cheap ham and salami, miserable-looking salads and various tinned items. The sweet trolley selection on the Saturday was 'pretty dreadful' too.

A packed lunch, also on Saturday, was a 'dull, listless ploughman's followed by a stodgy apple pie and coffee'. Without doubt, the best meal of the weekend was Sunday lunch, provided by the tea-shop staff at Stonor Park, one of four historic houses visited by coach.

The course itself seemed well organised and, in the absence of an advertised colleague, the leader had clearly done his research.

VERDICT: The course, it seemed, was designed for the elderly. But the weekend was badly let down by the hotel whose cooking staff could have learned a few things from their counterparts at Stonor Park. The view among the Leisure Learning regulars was that the Hog's Back was not one of the best hotels used.

Like the West Highlander the THF heritage tour, **Staffordshire Pots and Potters**, based at the **NORTH STAFFORD HOTEL**, Stoke-on-Trent, was of three nights' duration.

This got off to a bad start simply because the room was so unwelcoming – walls with badly cracked paintwork and carpets that had seen better days.

Dinner on the first night, following an introductory get-together, didn't do much to restore confidence. The salade niçoise turned out to be a 'very oily green bean salad with lots of anchovies and little else'. This was followed by roast beef – 'three slabs of tough, overcooked meat'.

For the sweet, our inspector chose raspberries from the trolley, 'naively believing them to be fresh. They were frozen and quite uneatable'.

Breakfast the next morning was 'moderately enjoyable', and lunch, a simple poached salmon salad, was fine. Not so the dinner, though – the lobster bisque with wild rice was tasteless (and the rice was the wrong sort). The main course of roast lamb and vegetables was reasonable, with fresh strawberries to follow.

The rest of the meals were just as uninspiring with the exception of a local breakfast speciality, Staffordshire oatcakes. These were 'more akin to pancakes than anything else, and were excellent – filled with cheese and served with grilled tomatoes and black pudding'.

The activity programme was very well organised, consisting of tours of the Spode and Mason's Ironstone china factories, visits to various museums, and a look around Cheddleton Flint Mill. A canal trip featured in the brochure was cancelled at the last minute. In addition, there was a film and an illustrated talk respectively on two nights, plus a special session on the Sunday morning in which group members were encouraged to show their own ceramic items for discussion and appraisal.

VERDICT: A good course, but the weekend would undoubtedly have been a greater success in a better hotel.

When we booked a **Lake District literary break** at the **WILD BOAR HOTEL,** Crook, near Windermere, Cumbria, we had expected to visit two residences with William Wordsworth connections, the home of John Ruskin and the Abbot Hall Art Gallery and Museum of Lakeland Life and Industry in Kendal.

What we weren't to realise at the time was that this package was about to be superseded. But it wasn't until after the booking was confirmed that the change was brought to our notice.

Unlike the other offerings in the survey, this hotel merely handed you the entry tickets to the places of interest and off you went under your own steam. The respective attractions were: Dove Cottage, Grasmere, Wordsworth's home from 1799 to 1808, and Rydal Mount near Ambleside, where he lived from 1813 until his death in 1850.

In addition to the tickets, we were given a book, *Wordsworth and the Lake District* – and for these we were charged an extra £15.50 for two people. In fact, by paying admission at the door and purchasing the book at one of the museums, we could have saved £2.95.

We would probably have got

them more quickly too. We had to prompt reception that we were on the Wordsworth Trail break, and it was evident that a special pack hadn't been made up for us. We not only had to wait for this to be done after a long, tiring journey, but also for the admission vouchers to be written out.

Apart from a blown main bulb, the room was impressive, with complimentary sherry awaiting the visitor on arrival and fresh fruit and half a dozen speciality teas provided.

However, Sunday at the hotel was best forgotten. Unlike the Saturday experience, the dinner was 'very poor' and the service 'distinctly lacking'. Our inspector also had to wait 20 minutes for coffee and mints – and was then served only after complaining.

VERDICT: The DIY pack did not prove a great success, and, as regards the hotel, it was a case of 'never on a Sunday'.

Most of the activity breaks sampled were let down by the performance of the hotels. With the exception of the two packages that came bottom of our table – in both these cases the advertised attractions were equally abysmal.

The weekend that was widely regarded as the pick of the bunch on our action shortlist – the **Reach For The Sky flying break** based at **BLACKWELL GRANGE MOAT HOUSE,** Darlington – turned out to be one of the most disappointing.

The abiding memory, says our inspector, is of a quite unsatisfactory experience at the hotel and discovering that acquiring a private pilot's licence can be expensive. For its part, the flying school seemed to assume (quite wrongly) that our man was a local and used the time as a sales pitch in a bid to persuade him to book lessons.

Teesside Aero Club was clearly competent and friendly enough for our embryonic aviator to recommend it, but, as he says: 'My appetite would have been better whetted if, during the 40 minutes' demonstration flight, I had been allowed to complete a manoeuvre rather than being given the job of de-icing the carburettor every quarter of an hour and being invited to put my hands on the controls briefly every now and again'.

As for the hotel, 'it is difficult to find anything complimentary to say about it. My arrival was not in the least welcoming and the check-in formalities were extremely slow – irksome, in fact, given that I had just driven 300 miles. Apparently the key to the room I had been allocated had gone missing. It was also pretty obvious that the reception staff knew nothing about the special weekend I had booked.'

The bedroom, on the ground floor and close to the car park, tended to be noisy. Indeed, with coach parties loading and unloading, there was a 'real cattle market atmosphere'.

The spoons with the room's tea-making facility hadn't been cleaned properly and, worse, the inspector caught the chambermaid washing the crockery in the bathroom and drying it with a used towel.

It wasn't until 10am on the Saturday that he was told to report to reception at 11.30am to catch the hotel's minibus to the airfield. After the flying session, he had to wait 20 minutes for transport back to Blackwell Grange.

On Saturday night, there was a dinner-dance featuring an amateurish band and a singer, a northern version of the late Elvis Presley, who also fancied himself as a comic. The music was far too loud; the service at the long banquet-style tables 'slow and disinterested.'

A run-down of the fare available shows that there was smoked chicken mousse with walnut mayonnaise ('a ready-plated starter, gradually becoming limp'), scallops and prawns gratin ('generally tasteless seafood and sloppy presentation'), venison medallions with blackcurrants ('exceedingly crude meat cooked to death, served with overcooked carrots and cauliflower and sauté potatoes that had been deep-fried in stale-oil'), roast beef ('thick slices with greasy gravy, tepid and chewy Yorkshire pudding and disappointing vegetables'), and desserts ('mainly synthetic-looking and commercially bought').

Breakfasts, too, were no more than greasy fry-ups, accompanied by weak, tepid tea in a poorly cleaned stainless-steel pot. On the second morning, a dropped doily was walked on by staff at least 20 times and not picked up, and a waitress, in order to open a window, stood on a newly laid tablecloth.

In addition, a request for two soft drinks in the garden terrace at 10.30am was turned down 'as the bar isn't open yet'. A request in advance to have everything put on one bill was ignored, and baggage which our man expressly asked to have brought from the room to the car was, after a ten minutes' wait in the car park, found dumped in reception.

VERDICT: The hotel seemed generally to be performing way below its best. We would have been better off and more likely to have enjoyed the weekend if we had dealt direct with the aero club.

Amazingly, our survey actually unearthed a short break that scored even fewer marks – **a steam railway weekend** based at the **HILTON LODGE,** at Basingstoke, Hants, (previously known as the Ladbroke Lodge), a hotel operated by Ladbroke Hotels, who recently took over the Hilton Chain.

The bald truth was that both the hotel and the activity programme were below par, a mix that inevitably put the package in bottom place.

The weekend got off on the wrong foot when reception, whose welcome 'wasn't very inspired', took at least 15 minutes to find the room key. If that wasn't a precursor, then the getting-to-know-everybody party certainly was; it was broken up almost as soon as it had begun and, with everybody being hurriedly ushered into dinner, the group rather split up.

The restaurant was a carvery, whose offerings had become boring by the second night. Quantity rather than quality seemed to be the maxim – *and* inconvenience, judging by the fact that two of the steam weekenders burned themselves on the plate stacker.

It turned out that the establishment did have a limited à la carte menu but we wouldn't have known unless we had asked. Not that it achieved much; although everything in the carvery was a set price, you were not given the opportunity to opt for the alternative menu and have your meal 'allowance' subtracted from it.

What service existed was restricted to serving bread rolls, wine, the sweet and the coffee. Not that you would have noticed on Saturday – our inspector had to ask for them. Mints and cream for the coffee, although on the menu, weren't forthcoming, while the promise of 'unlimited' coffee was restricted to one cup.

'Equally annoying,' says our man, 'was that you either got asked the same thing half a dozen times or you weren't asked at all.'

Certainly the staff weren't really aware of guests' needs. Once when our coach-lagged inspector ordered tea in the lounge, cleaners started vacuuming around him, and out of sheer frustration, he repaired to his room for some peace and quiet.

For a hotel that addresses itself to business people in the main on weekdays, it has to be said that the maintenance, repair and housekeeping in the public areas were rather poor. So, too, was room service…

Tea bags and milk were not replenished as a daily routine. Neither were toiletries, especially towels, which had been removed but not replaced, necessitating a rather wet walk to reception!

With the hotel such a bad advertisement, it was scarcely surprising that the 'steam' part of the weekend proved so disappointing. Being a bit of a steam buff, our inspector had been delighted to find Hollycombe Steam Fair on the list for a visit. It didn't usually operate on Saturdays, so he naturally assumed that a special arrangement had been made…

It hadn't. Someone, somewhere had dropped a clanger, and what eventually took place was a compromise and a very poor one. The group was subsequently shown round the fairground – a totally meaningless exercise since it was closed to the public and all the rides were covered up.

At least the morning's schedule was adhered to in the shape of a trip on the Watercress Line, a preserved railway running from nearby Alresford to Alton and featuring former British Railways carriages and steam locos. The one fortunate thing was that the group had been given an illustrated talk by someone from this railway the previous night,

BEWARE WHEN BOOKING...

Just because a short break is featured in a glossy brochure it doesn't necessarily mean that it will take place. In all, three other activity mini-holidays we hoped to include in this report were dropped by their organisers.

■ For instance, when we tried to make a reservation for an astrology weekend at the Crest Hotel, Walsall, West Midlands, just a week and a half in advance, it transpired that we were the first to enquire about it. It was withdrawn soon afterwards.

■ Anything to do with heritage usually finds several takers – but not, it seems, when it's to do with the castles of South Wales. We booked such a break at the Ladbroke Hotel, Swansea, only to have it cancelled through 'lack of interest' the week before the off. We also attempted to sample a Secret Nature weekend, offered in the Riviera Breaks' guide with a choice of 29 hotels in the Torbay area. But the complete brochure was scrapped almost as soon as it appeared.

■ And just because a particular offering is featured in a recent catalogue it doesn't mean that it will be repeated in the next 12-month period, as we discovered when we tried to book a Cambrian mountain bike-riding weekend at the Abernant Lake Hotel, Llanwrtyd Wells, Powys, part of the Mount Charlotte group.

■ It is also worth finding out all you can about an offering that takes your fancy. We liked the sound of a Best Western leisure and fitness getaway break at the Barnham Broom Hotel, Norfolk, where the attraction was a complete fitness assessment. But when we made enquiries, it became clear that the session itself lasted only 40 minutes.

because the weekend break leader was nowhere to be seen when the group alighted at Ropley to view the engine shed and workshops.

Neither was he on hand when most wanted the next day when the group was taken to the Great Western Society steam centre at Didcot. If only the organisers had known – they could have arranged for a guided tour by the Society.

And if only the organisers of the break had been a shade more knowledgeable about their subject – they might have considered giving Hollycombe a miss and taking the party instead to the Buckinghamshire steam centre near Aylesbury, or the railway museum at Swindon, or the Pendon museum near Didcot.

VERDICT: A weekend which could have been so good if only it had been properly organised and led, and based on a hotel that knows the real meaning of the word 'service'.

Over the page is a table showing how the sampled breaks fared. Marks were awarded for various aspects of the hotel and the activity, and percentages given for each. The total percentage does not necessarily equal the average of the hotel and activity percentages.

		EGON RONAY'S GUIDE %	HOTEL %	COURSE/ ACTIVITY %	TOTAL %
	BB = BED AND BREAKFAST HB = HALF-BOARD FB = FULL-BOARD *denotes additional single room supplement payable.				
1	GLENEAGLES HOTEL (Independent) Auchterarder, Tayside: £220 HB + 3 riding sessions	88	86	83	85
2	OLD SWAN HOTEL (Norfolk Capital Hotels) Harrogate, N Yorks: £122 FB + Super Sleuth weekend	68	74	78	75½
3	BLACK SWAN HOTEL (Trusthouse Forte Hotels) Helmsley, N Yorks: £135*HB + Herriot Country weekend	70	73	78	75
4	CREST HOTEL (Crest Hotels) Newcastle upon Tyne: £83 HB + Bird-watching Break	59	66½	78	71
5	MOUNT HOTEL (Independent) Wolverhampton, W Midlands: £75 BB + Treasure Hunt weekend + coach to & from London	60	67	74	70
5	SUNLAWS HOUSE HOTEL (Independent) Kelso, Borders: £74 BB + Fly-fishing break	74	77	58	70
7	CHEQUERS HOTEL (Trusthouse Forte Hotels) Newbury, Berks: £168 HB + Clay-pigeon shooting weekend	63	57	86½	68
8	PENNINE HILTON NATIONAL (Hilton International Hotels) Huddersfield, W Yorks: £112 BB + Hang-gliding weekend	62	58	78	65½
9	KESWICK HOTEL (Trusthouse Forte Hotels) Keswick, Cumbria: £132*HB + Walking With Wildlife weekend	62	52	84	64
10	THE WEST HIGHLANDER (British Rail Intercity) £245*FB (3 nights)	–	56½	75	63½
11	HOG'S BACK HOTEL (Embassy Hotels) Seale, Farnham, Surrey: £95 FB + Houses of the Thames Valley weekend (Leisure Learning)	64	55½	70	61
12	NORTH STAFFORD HOTEL (Trusthouse Forte Hotels) Stoke-on-Trent, Staffs: £172*FB (3 nights) + Staffordshire Pots and Potters short break	63	51	75½	60
13	WILD BOAR HOTEL (Best Western Hotels) Crook, Windermere, Cumbria: £90*HB + Wordsworth Trail weekend	60	60	–	59
14	BLACKWELL GRANGE MOAT HOUSE (Moat House Hotels) Darlington, Co Durham: £120 HB + Reach For The Sky flying weekend	62	49	74	58
15	HILTON LODGE (Hilton International Hotels) Basingstoke, Hants: £89.50 FB + Steam Railway Weekend	63	55½	57	56

Gastronomy...

the intelligent knowledge of whatever

concerns man's nourishment.

BRILLAT-SAVARIN 1755-1826
PHYSIOLOGIE DU GOÛT

'**C**uisine' means that

Things taste just like what they are!

CURNONSKY 1872-1956
' To Melanie Rouat '

Strange to say

how a good dinner and feasting

reconciles everybody.

SAMUEL PEPYS 1633-1703
DIARY

THE FIAT GUIDE TO SUCCESSFUL MOTORING

Fiat main and service dealers are strategically situated across the United Kingdom to offer comprehensive sales, servicing and repair facilities together with an abundant availability of spares and accessories.

At the time of going to press we have 344 dealerships, as shown in the list below, bringing the stylish Fiat range close to home and ensuring that you can easily contact us wherever you are.

To learn of any possible new appointments nearer to you please contact the Fiat Information Service, Dept ER88, Windsor, Berks SL4 3BA. Telephone: 01-897 0922.

★Denotes Service Only Dealer.

ENGLAND

AVON
BATH: **MOTOR SERVICES (BATH) LTD**
Locksbrook Rd. 0225 428000
BRISTOL: **AUTOTREND LTD**
724-726 Fishponds Rd. 0272 659491
BRISTOL: **BAWNS (BRISTOL) LTD**
168-176 Coronation Rd. 0272 631101
CLEVEDON: **JEFF BROWNS (CLEVEDON)**
Old Church Rd. 0272 871211
WESTON-SUPER-MARE: **JEFF BROWNS (LYMPSHAM)**
Bridgewater Rd. 0934 72300/72696
★THORNBURY BRISTOL: **SHIPPS OF THORNBURY**
Midland Way. 0454 413130

BEDFORDSHIRE
BEDFORD: **OUSE VALLEY MOTORS**
9 Kingsway. 0234 64491
BIGGLESWADE: **OWEN GODFREY LTD**
91-119 Shortmead St. 0767 313357
BILLINGTON: **D & J AUTOS LTD**
The Garage, Leighton Buzzard Rd.
0525 383068
LUTON: **BLACKABY & PEARCE (LUTON) LTD**
Poynters Rd. 0582 667742

BERKSHIRE
GORING-ON-THAMES: **COURTS GARAGE (GORING)**
42 Wallingford Rd. 0491 872006
MAIDENHEAD: **SOUTH BERKSHIRE MOTOR CO. LTD**
264-270 Windsor Rd. 0628 71628
NEWBURY: **BLACK AND WHITE GARAGE**
Hermitage Rd, Cold Ash. 0635 200444
READING: **JACK HILL (READING) LTD**
Chatham Street Multi-Storey Car Park.
0734 582521 ·
WINDSOR: **ANDREWS OF WINDSOR**
110 St Leonards Rd. 0753 866108

BUCKINGHAMSHIRE
★AMERSHAM: **AMERSHAM MOTORS LTD** Chesham Rd. 0494 722191
AYLESBURY: **AMERSHAM MOTORS**
Stoke Rd. 0296 81181

BEACONSFIELD: **MAURICE LEO LTD**
15 Gregories Rd. 04946 6171
BOURNE END: **CARCHOICE LTD**
Station Rd. 06285 22606
GERRARDS CROSS: **BURWOODS GARAGE LTD**
Oxford Rd, Tatling End. 0753 885216
HIGH WYCOMBE: **DESBOROUGH MOTOR CO LTD**
41 Desborough Ave. 0494 36331
MILTON KEYNES: **ELMDENE MOTORS LTD**
Townsend Thoresen Auto Centre, Unit 15, Erica Rd. 0908 320355

CAMBRIDGESHIRE
CAMBRIDGE: **HOLLAND FIAT CENTRE**
315-349 Mill Rd. 0223 242222
MARCH: **CARL PORTER LTD**
Causeway Garage, The Causeway.
0354 53340/55956
PETERBOROUGH: **PETERBOROUGH AUTOS**
Midland Rd. 0733 314431
St IVES: **OUSE VALLEY MOTORS**
Station Rd. 0480 62641

CHESHIRE
ALTRINCHAM: **S. DAVIS (ALTRINCHAM) LTD**
Dunham Rd. 061 928 4444
CHESTER: **COWIES OF CHESTER**
Mountview, Sealand Rd. 0244 374440
★CONGLETON: **ROBIN HOOD GARAGE**
West Heath. 0260 273219
CREWE: **COPPENHALL GARAGE**
Cross Green. 0270 500437
MACCLESFIELD: **D.C. COOK**
London Rd. 0625 28866
NORTHWICH: **STATION ROAD GARAGE (NORTHWICH) LTD**
Station Rd. 0606 49957
WARRINGTON: **WILLIAM MARTYN GARAGES LTD**
Wilderspool Causeway. 0925 50417

CLEVELAND
MIDDLESBROUGH: **REG VARDY LTD**
Trunk Rd (Opp Brambles Farm). 0642 244651

STOCKTON-ON-TEES: **WENTANE MOTORS LTD**
100 Yarm Lane. 0642 611544

CORNWALL
NEWQUAY: **TOWER OF NEWQUAY**
Tower Rd. 0637 872378/877332
TRURO: **W.H. COLLINS & SON (MOTORS) LTD**
Kenwyn Mews. 0872 74334

CUMBRIA
BARROW-IN-FURNESS: **COUNTY PARK MOTORS**
County Park Industrial Est., Park Rd.
0229 36888
CARLISLE: **GRIERSON & GRAHAM (CARLISLE) LTD**
33 Church St, Caldewgate. 0228 25092
FLIMBY: **DOBIE'S GARAGE**
Risehow. 0900 812332
★KENDAL: **CRAIGHILL & CO LTD**
113 Stricklandgate. 0539 20967/8
KESWICK: **KESWICK MOTOR CO LTD**
Lake Road Garage. Sales: 0596 72534

DEVON
BARNSTAPLE: **NORTH DEVON MOTOR CO**
Pottington Ind Est. 0271 76551
EXETER: **SIDWELL STREET MOTORS LTD**
85-88 Sidwell St. 0392 54923
★NEWTON ABBOT: **QUAY GARAGE**
The Avenue. 0626 52525/6
★OKEHAMPTON: **F. J. GLASS & CO (1981) LTD**
57 Exeter Rd. 0837 2255
PAIGNTON: **BABBACOMBE GARAGE LTD**
Totnes Rd. 0803 556796
PLYMOUTH: **MUMFORDS OF PLYMOUTH**
Plymouth Rd. 0752 261511
SIDMOUTH: **CENTRAL GARAGE (SIDFORD) LTD**
Crossways, Sidford. 03955 3595

DORSET
BOURNEMOUTH: **CAFFYNS PLC**
674-680 Wimborne Rd, Winton. 0202 512121
POOLE: **CAFFYNS PLC**
552-554 Ashley Rd, Parkstone. 0202 715394
WEYMOUTH: **OLDS**
172 Dorchester Rd. 0305 786311

CO DURHAM

CONSETT: **TRAVELWISE**
Delves La. 0207 502353
∗CROOK: **BROOKSIDE GARAGE LTD**
New Rd. 0388 762551
∗DARLINGTON: **E. WILLIAMSON (MOTORS) LTD**
1-7 Woodland Rd. 0325 483251
∗SACRISTON: **HUNTER & CHATER**
Woodside Garage, Wilton Rd. 091 371 0422

ESSEX

BASILDON: **H.W.S.**
Roundacre, Nethermayne. 0268 22261
BUCKHURST HILL: **MONTROE MOTORS**
Epping New Rd. 01-504 1171
CHELMSFORD: **M.M. AUTOS (CHELMSFORD) LTD**
Sheepen Rd. 0206 563311
Colchester Rd. 0245 361731
FRINTON-ON-SEA: **POLLENDINE MOTORS LTD**
132 Connaught Ave. 0255 679123/674341
HARLOW: **MOTORSALES (HARLOW) LTD**
Elizabeth Way, Burnt Mill. 0279 412161
HUTTON: **HUTTON GARAGES LTD**
661 Rayleigh Rd. 0277 210087
∗ROMFORD: **McQUIRE MOTORS LTD**
299-307 Collier Row La. 0708 766806
SOUTHEND-ON-SEA: **BELLE VUE MOTORS LTD**
460-464 Southchurch Rd. 0207 64945
WESTCLIFF-ON-SEA: **H.W.S.**
684 London Rd. 0702 470000

GLOUCESTERSHIRE

CHELTENHAM: **DANEWAY MOTOR CO LTD**
84 Bath Rd. 0242 523879
STROUD: **PAGANHILL SERVICE STATION LTD**
105 Stratford Rd. 04536 47181
GLOUCESTER: **WARNERS MOTORS LTD**
Quedgeley Garage, Quedgeley. 0452 720107
∗WOTTON-UNDER-EDGE: **WOTTON MOTOR CENTRE LTD**
Gloucester St. 0453 842240

GREATER MANCHESTER

ASHTON-UNDER-LYNE: **PREMIER MOTOR CO**
Manchester Rd, Mossley. 04575 67121
BOLTON: **D.C. COOK (BOLTON) LTD**
Kay St/Higher Bridge. 0204 362000
BURY: **BLACKFORD BRIDGE CAR SHOW LTD**
701 Manchester Rd, Blackford Bridge.
061-766 1346
LEIGH: **SMALLBROOK SERVICE STATION**
Smallbrook La. 0942 882201/891939
MANCHESTER: **D.C. COOK (MANCHESTER) LTD**
Midland Street Garage, Ashton Old Road.
061-273 4411
OLDHAM: **D.C. COOK (OLDHAM) LTD**
23-37 Lees Rd. 061-624 8046
ROCHDALE: **D.C. COOK (ROCHDALE) LTD**
Queensway. 0706 33222
STOCKPORT: **D.C. COOK (STOCKPORT) LTD**
West End Garage, Heaton La. 061-480 6661

HAMPSHIRE

ALDERSHOT: **CLEVELAND CARS LTD**
Ash St., Ash. 0252 334055
ANDOVER: **CLOVERLEAF CARS (ANDOVER)**
Salisbury Rd. 0264 61166
BASINGSTOKE: **CLOVERLEAF CARS (BASINGSTOKE)**
London Rd (A30). 0256 55221
BITTERNE **SEWARDS BITTERNE**
Bursledon Rd. 0703 422202
PORTSMOUTH: **CANNON GARAGES (PORTSMOUTH) LTD**
117 Copnor Rd. 0705 691621

RINGWOOD: **WELLS RINGWOOD**
Salisbury Rd. 04254 6111
SOUTHAMPTON: **SEWARDS**
Rushington Roundabout, Totton Bypass.
0703 861001
WINCHESTER: **GRAYSTONES**
12-14 City Road. 0962 62244

HEREFORD & WORCESTER

EVESHAM: **BRIGHTS GARAGE**
3 Cheltenham Rd. 0386 2301
HEREFORD: **GODSELL'S (HEREFORD) LTD**
BATH St. 0432 274134
KIDDERMINSTER: **STANLEY GOODWIN MOTORS LTD**
Worcester Rd. 0562 820202
WORCESTER: **BOWLING GREEN GARAGE (POWICK) LTD** Powick. 0905 830361
BROMSGROVE: **NEALE'S GARAGE (1985) LTD**
2-12 Station St. 0527 72071

HERTFORDSHIRE

CROXLEY GREEN: **CROXLEY GREEN MOTORS LTD**
185 Watford Rd. 0923 55511
HEMEL HEMPSTEAD: **SHAW & KILBURN**
Two Waters Rd. 0442 51212
HERTFORD: **PAMSONS MOTORS HERTFORD** 80 Ware Rd. 0992 584147
HITCHIN: **SERVAL (HITCHIN) LTD**
Ickleford. 0462 54526
KNEBWORTH: **LISLES MOTOR REPAIRS LTD**
London Rd, Woolmer Green. 0438 811011
ST. ALBANS: **LAP GROUP**
2 Beech Rd. Marshalswick. 0727 50871

HUMBERSIDE

BRIDLINGTON: **JORDANS**
248 Quay Rd. 0262 670331
DRIFFIELD: **GEORGE WILLIAMSON (GARAGES) LTD**
82-84 Middle St., South. 0377 43130
∗GRIMSBY: **ERIC C. BURTON & SONS LTD**
Station Garage, Wellowgate. 0472 355951
∗GOOLE: **J. WARDLE & SONS LTD**
Boothferry Rd., Howden. 0430 430388
HULL: **AB MOTOR CO OF HULL LTD**
96 Boothferry Rd. 0482 506976/54256
HULL: **JORDAN & JUBILEE GARAGE**
45-52 Witham. 0482 24131
SCUNTHORPE: **BRUMBY SERVICE GARAGE LTD**
The Fiat Centre, Normanby Rd. 0724 861191

ISLE OF WIGHT

SANDOWN: **HODGE & CHILDS LTD**
Station Ave. 0983 402552

KENT

ASHFORD: **ASHFORD MOTOR CO**
Chart Rd. 0233 22281
BECKENHAM: **BRUTONS OF BECKENHAM LTD**
181 Beckenham Rd. 01-650 3333
BEXLEYHEATH: **BELLWAY MOTORS KENT**
303/307 Broadway. 01-301 0420
BROMLEY: **THAMES**
96 Bromley Hill. 01-460 4646
DEAL: **CAMPBELLS OF DEAL LTD**
6 The Marina. 0304 363166
FARNBOROUGH: **FARNWAY SERVICE LTD**
2 Church Rd. 0689 50121
∗GILLINGHAM: **AUTOYACHTS LTD**
171 Pier Rd. 0634 2813333
∗GRAVESEND: **MARTINS GARAGE**
50 Singlewell Rd. 0474 66148
∗HAM STREET: **ANNINGS MARSH ROAD**
Nr Ashford. 023 373 2275
HYTHE: **RAMPART GARAGE**
15-17 Rampart Rd. 0303 67088
MAIDSTONE: **MCS GEORGE STREET LTD**
George St. 0622 677524/5/6

∗MARGATE: **S & S MOTORS**
10-12 Park La. 0843 227778
ORPINGTON: **GODDINGTON SERVICE STATION** 318 Court Rd. 0689 20337
RAMSGATE: **S & S MOTORS LEVERPOINT LTD**
Willsons Rd. 0843 593465
∗SITTINGBOURNE: **J G BURGESS & CO**
Ufton Lane Garage. 0795 23815
SWANLEY: **FOREMAN BROS LTD**
London Rd. 0322 68411
TUNBRIDGE WELLS: **G. E. TUNBRIDGE LTD** 319 St. John's Rd. 0892 511522

LANCASHIRE

BLACKBURN: **BARKERS**
King St. 0254 52981
BLACKPOOL: **DIXON AUTOMARKETS**
Rigby Rd. 0253 751212/401226
BURNLEY: **D. C. COOK (BURNLEY) LTD**
Parker St. Kingsway. 0282 58271
COLNE: **EAGLE SERVICE STATION**
Stonebridge Works, Windybank.
0282 863254
LANCASTER: **G & L CAR SERVICE LTD**
Wheatfield St. 0524 39857
PRESTON: **LOOKERS GROSVENOR MOTORS LTD**
306-310 Ribbleton La. 0772 792823
WIGAN: **WILLIAM MARTYN (WIGAN) LTD**
Great George St. 0942 826390

LEICESTERSHIRE

∗EARL SHILTON: **SWITHLAND MOTORS LTD** 42 Wood St. 0455 44111
LEICESTER: **TRINITY MOTORS (D. R. WATTAM) LTD**
47 Blackbird La. 0533 530137
∗MARKET HARBOROUGH: **BADGER BROTHERS**
109 Main St., Lubenham. 0858 66984
MELTON MOWBRAY: **ROCKINGHAM CARS LTD**
Manor Garage, Mill St. 0664 60141
WIGSTON: **KILBY BRIDGE MOTORS LTD**
Kilby Bridge. 0533 881109/886264

LINCOLNSHIRE

∗BOSTON: **LONDON ROAD GARAGE**
200 London Rd. 0205 55500
GRANTHAM: **WILLSONS OF GRANTHAM LTD**
Spittlegate Level. 0476 74117
LINCOLN: **MINSTER CARS**
316-322 Wragby Rd. 0522 34805
LOUTH: **BURTONS OF LOUTH**
Legbourne Rd. 0507 607555
∗RIPPINGALE: **WILLSONS OF RIPPINGALE** Windmill Garage,
Bourne. 077 835777
SKEGNESS: **DRM MOTORS**
Beresford Ave. 0754 67131
SLEAFORD: **RALPH DEAR**
Greyless Garage, Grantham Rd. 05298 674

LONDON

LONDON E4: **ALLEN BRIGGS (MOTORS) LTD**
47-59 Chingford Mount Rd. 01-527 5004/5
LONDON E14: **NORTH CITY AUTOS**
255-259 East India Dock Rd. 01-538 2121
LONDON N7: **CONTINENTAL MOTOR CENTRE LTD** Campdale Rd. 01-272 4762
LONDON N12: **LINDSAY BROTHERS LTD**
920 High Rd. 01-455 1022
LONDON N17: **BRUCE MOTOR GROUP**
127 Lordship La. 01-808 9291
∗LONDON NW10: **MARN SERVICE CENTRE**
854 Coronation Rd. 01-965 7001/2/3/4
LONDON NW11: **PAMSONS MOTORS**
761/3 Finchley Rd. 01-458 5968/8384
LONDON SE9: **CLIFFORDS OF ELTHAM**
Well Hall Rd. 01-850 3834
LONDON SE18: **WOOLWICH MOTOR CO**
160-170 Powis St. 01-854 2550

THE FIAT GUIDE TO SUCCESSFUL MOTORING

LONDON SE19: **SG SMITH MOTORS LTD**
Crown Point Service Station, Beulah Hill.
01-670 6266
LONDON SE23: **PREMIER MOTORS
(FOREST HILL) LTD**
163/167 Stanstead Rd. 01-291 1721
LONDON SW12: **BALHAM AUTOS**
147 Balham Hill SW12 9DL. 01-675 6744/5/6/7
★LONDON SW15: **AF TANN LTD**
51-57 Upper Richmond Rd. 01-870 8844
★LONDON SW19: **SPUR GARAGE LTD**
39 Hartfield Rd. 01-540 3325
LONDON W1: **FIAT MOTOR SALES LTD**
61-64 Baker St. 01-486 7555
LONDON W11: **RADBOURNE RACING LTD**
1a Clarendon Rd. 01-727 5066
LONDON W12: **MARN WEST LONDON**
370-376 Uxbridge Rd. 01-749 6058/9
★LONDON W13:
DICKENS & JOSE MOTORS LTD
145 Northfield Ave. 01-567 0430

MERSEYSIDE
BIRKENHEAD: **FIRS GARAGE
(WIRRAL) LTD**
Claughton Firs, Oxton. 051-653 8555
FORMBY: **ALTAR AUTOS LTD**
Altar Rd. 07048 73342
HESWALL: **HARDINGS (HESWALL)
AUTOS LTD** May Rd. 051-342 8471
★SOUTHPORT: **MILNER & MARSHAL LTD**
89-91 Bath St. North. 0704 35535
ST. HELENS: **FORWARD AUTOS**
Gaskell St. 0744 21961
LIVERPOOL: **STANLEY MOTORS
(LIVERPOOL) LTD**
243 East Prescot Rd. 051-228 9151
LIVERPOOL: **CROSBY PARK GARAGE LTD**
2 Coronation Rd, Crosby. 051-924 9101
LIVERPOOL: **LAMBERT AUTOS LTD**
Custom House, Brunswick Business Park.
051-708 8224

MIDDLESEX
HAMPTON HILL: **SUPREME AUTOS
(HAMPTON HILL) LTD**
7-11 Windmill Rd. 01-979 9061/2
NORWOOD GREEN: **FIRST COUNTY
GARAGES LTD** Norwood Rd. 01-571 2151
WEMBLEY: **FIAT MOTOR SALES LTD**
372 Ealing Rd. 01-998 8811
WEST DRAYTON: **PRIORS**
127 Station Rd. 0895 444672
WHITTON: **SPEEDWELL GARAGE
(WHITTON) LTD**
53/55 High St. 01-894 6893/4
WRAYSBURY: **CONCORDE GARAGE
(WRAYSBURY)**
31 Windsor Rd. 078481 2927/2815

NORFOLK
KING'S LYNN: **DENNIS MARSHALL**
Scania Way. 0533 771331
NORWICH: **POINTER MOTOR CO LTD**
Aylsham Rd. 0603 45345/6
★NORWICH: **WOODLAND CAR SALES LTD**
Salhouse Rd. 0603 70111
SCOLE: **DESIRA MOTOR CO LTD**
Diss Rd. 037 9740741
SHERINGHAM: **EARLGATE MOTORS LTD**
41 Cromer Rd. 0263 822782
GREAT YARMOUTH: **DESIRA MOTOR
CO LTD** North Quay. 0493 844266

NORTHAMPTONSHIRE
CORBY: **ROCKINGHAM CARS LTD**
Rockingham Rd. 0536 68991
KETTERING: **GRADY BROTHERS
(KETTERING) LTD**
Britannia Rd. 0536 513257
KILSBY (nr. Rugby): **HALFWAY GARAGE
(1986) LTD**
Crick Cross Rds. 0788 822226
NORTHAMPTON: **MOTORVOGUE LTD**
74 Kingsthorpe Rd. 0604 714555

RUSHDEN: **ROCKINGHAM CARS LTD**
John St. 0933 57500

NORTHUMBERLAND
HEXHAM: **MATT CLARK LTD**
Tyne Mills. 0434 603013/603236
STAKEFORD: **T. LIDDELL & SON**
Milburn Terrace. 0670 815038

NOTTINGHAMSHIRE
NEWARK-ON-TRENT: **ELLIOTS GARAGE
(NEWARK)** Sleaford Rd. 0636 703405
★NOTTINGHAM: **TECNICO**
81-85 Talbot St. 0602 473547
RUDDINGTON: **JCS GARAGES LTD**
Manor Park Garage, Wilford Rd.
0602 844114/844164
SUTTON-IN-ASHFIELD: **J.J. LEADLEY LTD**
Downing St. 0623 515222
★WORKSOP: **BARRATT MOTORS LTD**
7-15 Newcastle Ave. 0909 475124

OXFORDSHIRE
BANBURY: **WHITE HORSE GARAGE
(BANBURY) LTD**
21-27 Broad St. 0295 50733
CARTERTON: **BRIZE NORTON
GARAGES LTD**
Carterton Rd. 0993 844144
HENLEY-ON-THAMES: **BELL STREET
MOTORS (HENLEY) LTD**
66 Bell St. 0491 573077
OXFORD: **J.D. BARCLAY LTD**
Botley Rd. 0865 722444
WANTAGE: **MELLORS OF CHALLOW LTD**
Farringdon Rd. 023 572751

SHROPSHIRE
★LUDLOW: **PRL MOTORS**
Lower Galdeford Garage. 0584 4104
★SHREWSBURY: **WAVERLEY GARAGE LTD**
Featherbed La, Harlescott. 0743 236951
TELFORD: **T. J. VICKERS & SONS**
Trench Rd, Trench. 0952 605301

SOMERSET
BRIDGEWATER: **STACEY'S MOTORS**
48 St John St. 0278 423312
MINEHEAD: **MINEHEAD AUTOS LTD**
37-39 Alcombe Rd. 0643 3379/3238
STREET: **RIZZUTI BROTHERS**
West End Garage. 0458 42996
TAUNTON: **COUNTY GARAGE
(TAUNTON) LTD**
Priory Ave. 0823 337611
YEOVIL: **ABBEY HILL MOTOR SALES**
Boundary Rd. Lufton Trading Est. 0935 29115

STAFFORDSHIRE
CHASETOWN: **SPOT OF CHASETOWN**
Highfields Rd. 054 36 5544
NEWCASTLE-UNDER-LYME: **B.S. MARSON
& SONS**
Deansgate Garage, Keele Rd. 0782 622141
STAFFORD: **BOSTONS OF MILFORD**
16 The Green, Milford. 0785 661226
STOKE-ON-TRENT: **PLATT'S GARAGE
(LONGTON) LTD**
Lightwood Rd, Longton. 0782 319212/3/4
★UTTOXETER: **SMITHFIELD ROAD
GARAGE LTD** Smithfield Rd. 08893 3838

SUFFOLK
BECCLES: **BRAND (MOTOR)
ENGINEERS LTD**
Ringsfield Rd. 0502 716940
★BURY ST. EDMUNDS: **DESIRA MOTOR
CO. LTD** Mildenhall Rd. 0284 750001
IPSWICH: **STATION GARAGE**
Burrell Rd. 0473 690321
★LEISTON: **AVENUE SERVICE STATION**
King George's Avenue. 0728 830654
NEEDHAM MARKET: **TURNER'S
(NEEDHAM MARKET) LTD**
30 High St. 0449 721212

SURREY
CAMBERLEY: **MARN CAMBERLEY**
71 Frimley Rd. 0276 64672
CHEAM: **GODFREY'S (SUTTON &
CHEAM) LTD** 50 Malden Rd. 01-644 8877
CROYDON: **THAMES**
115 Addiscombe Rd. 01-655 1100
ENGLEFIELD GREEN: **SAVAGE & SONS
(MOTOR ENGINEERS) LTD**
Victoria St. 0784 39771
EPSOM: **H.F. EDWARDS & CO LTD**
4 Church St. 03727 44444
★FARNHAM: **FRENSHAM
ENGINEERING CO**
Shortfield, Frensham. 025125 3232
GUILDFORD: **ABC GUILDFORD**
Pilot Works, Walnut Tree Close. 04835 75251
KENLEY: **MARN KENLEY**
60 Godstone Rd. 01-660 4546
NEW MALDEN: **LAIDLER MOTOR CO LTD**
69 Kingstone Rd. 01-942 6075
REIGATE: **COLIN CRONK**
87/89 Bell St. 0737 223304
WALLINGTON: **BALHAM AUTOS
(WALLINGTON)**
268 London Rd. 01-647 5527/8

EAST & WEST SUSSEX
BRIGHTON: **TILLEYS (SUSSEX) LTD**
100 Lewes Rd. 0273 603244
BURGESS HILL: **TILLEYS (SUSSEX) LTD**
Chandlers Garage, London Rd. 04446 43431
★CHICHESTER: **TANGMERE GARAGE**
Tangmere-by-pass. 0243 782478
★EAST GRINSTEAD: **FELBRIDGE
GARAGE** Eastbourne Rd. 0342 24677
HORSHAM: **WILSON PURVES LTD**
Brighton Rd. 0403 61821/65637
HAILSHAM: **G.F. SHAW LTD**
Cowbeech. 0323 833321
★ISFIELD: **ROSEHILL GARAGE**
Isfield, Nr Uckfield. 082575 313/445
PULBOROUGH: **FLEET GARAGE
(FITTLEWORTH) LTD**
Fittleworth. 079 882 307/244
SHOREHAM-BY-SEA: **KEEN & BETTS
(SHOREHAM) LTD**
Adur Garage, Brighton Rd. 0273 461333
ST LEONARDS-ON-SEA: **ST LEONARDS
MOTORS LTD**
Church Wood Drive. 0424 53493
WADHURST: **EATON BROS.**
Forge Garage, Beech Hill. 089288 2126
WORTHING: **PDH (GARAGES) LTD**
Downlands Service Station,
Upper Brighton Rd. 0903 37487

TYNE & WEAR
GATESHEAD: **BENFIELD MOTORS**
Lobley Hill Rd. 091-490 0292
NEWCASTLE-UPON-TYNE: **BENFIELD
MOTORS LTD**
Railway St. 091-273 2131
SUNDERLAND: **REG VARDY LTD**
16-18 Villiers St. 091-510 0550
WHITLEY BAY: **WHITLEY LODGE
MOTOR Co** Claremont Rd. 091-252 3347

WARWICKSHIRE
BALSALL COMMON: **CARSTINS LTD**
324 Station Rd. 0676 33145
NUNEATON: **RESEARCH GARAGE
(NUNEATON) LTD**
Hunchwood Rd. 0203 382807
STRATFORD-UPON-AVON: **GM WYATT
GARAGES (STRATFORD) LTD**
Western Rd. 0789 67159
WARWICK: **GRAYS GARAGE LTD**
Wharf St. 0926 496231

WEST MIDLANDS
★BIRMINGHAM: **COLMORE DEPOT LTD**
35 Sutton New Rd, Erdington. 021-377 6533
BIRMINGHAM: **COLMORE DEPOT LTD**
979 Stratford Rd, Hall Green. 021-778 2323

CLENT: HOLY CROSS GARAGE LTD
Bromsgrove Rd. 0562 730557
COVENTRY: SMITH & SONS MOTORS LTD
Roland Ave, Holbrooks. 0203 667778
HARBOURNE: HARBOURNE AUTOMOBILES
50-52 High St. 021-427 3235
MARSTON GREEN: MARSTON GREEN GARAGE 32 Station Rd. 021-779 5140
SOLIHULL: TAMWORTH GARAGE LTD
The Green, Tamworth in Arden. 056 442218
TIPTON: CALDENE AUTOLAND
Burnt Treet. 021-520 2411
WALSALL: SPOT OF WALSALL
44a Ward St. 0922 32911
*WEST BROMWICH: **COLMORE DEPOT LTD** Birmingham Rd. 021-525 9408
WOLVERHAMPTON: A N BLOXHAM LTD
The Fiat Centre, Raby St. 0902 57116

WILTSHIRE
*CHIPPENHAM: **WADHAM STRINGER – CHIPPENHAM** 21 New Rd. 0249 655757
SWINDON: TARGET GARAGE LTD
Elgin Drive. 0793 512685

YORKSHIRE
*BARNSLEY: **S.A. SNELL (BARNSLEY) LTD** 436-440 Doncaster Rd. Stairfoot.
0226 731234
BRADFORD: WEST YORKSHIRE MOTOR GROUP Keighley Rd. Frizinghall. 0274 490031
BRADFORD: JCT 600
The Italian Car Centre, Sticker La.
0274 667234
CASTLEFORD: AIRE AUTOS LTD
Lock La. 0977 515806
*DONCASTER: **R ROODHOUSE LTD**
York Rd. 0302 390444
*HALIFAX: **MAYFIELD GARAGE (HALIFAX) LTD** Queens Rd. 0422 330800
HARROGATE: CROFT & BLACKBURN LTD
Leeds Rd, Pannal. 0423 879236
HUDDERSFIELD: WEST YORKSHIRE MOTOR GROUP
Lockwood Rd. 0484 537500
KEIGHLEY: WEST YORKSHIRE MOTOR GROUP Hardings Rd.
0535 603073/681121
LEEDS: JCT 600 (LEEDS) LTD
Spence La. 0532 431843
LEEDS: WHITEHEAD & HINCH LTD
South Broadgate La, Horsforth. 0532 585056
*MALTON: **BENTLEYS GARAGE**
Amotherby. 0653 3616
MIRFIELD: THORNTON MOTORS OF DEWSBURY LTD Calder Garage,
117 Huddersfield Rd. 0924 498316
*NORTHALLERTON: **TIM SWALES (CAR SALES) LTD**
Clock Lane Garage, Osmotherley.
060 983 263/666
ROTHERHAM: DEREK G. PIKE & CO
126 Fitzwilliam Rd. 0709 361666
RIPON: RICHARD CHESTER LTD
Dallamires La. 0765 4803
SCARBOROUGH: MISKIN & KNAGGS LTD
Manor Rd. 0723 364111/3
*SELBY: **PARKINSON'S GARAGE LTD**
Hambleton 0757 828181
SHEFFIELD: GT CARS
Suffolk Rd. 0742 721370/721378/722748
WAKEFIELD: PICCADILLY WAKEFIELD LTD
Bradford Rd. 0924 290220
YORK: PICCADILLY AUTO CENTRE
84 Piccadilly. 0904 34321

SCOTLAND
ABERDEEN: CALLANDERS GARAGE (AUTOPART) LTD
870 Great Northern Rd. 0224 695573
AYR: ROBERT McCALL LTD
Galloway Ave. 0292 260416
BATHGATE: J & A BROWNING LTD
11 East Main St. 0501 40536
BRECHIN: KAY'S AUTO CENTRE
18 Clerk St. 03562 2561
*COATBRIDGE: **R J CROSS LTD**
206 Bank St. 0236 35774

DOLLAR: STEWART BROTHERS
28-34 Bridge St. 025 942233/4
*DUMBARTON: **DUNCAN McFARLANE & SON**
96 Church St. 0389 63689
DUMFRIES: CENTRAL CAR SALES
77 Whitesands. 0387 61378
DUNDEE: MACALPINE MOTORS
Macalpine Rd. 0382 818004
DUNFERMLINE: FLEAR & THOMSON
128-138 Pittencrieff St. 0383 722565/6
EDINBURGH: CROALL & CROALL
Glenogle Rd. 031 556 6404/9
EDINBURGH: HAMILTON BROTHERS (EDINBURGH) LTD
162 St Johns Rd. 031 334 6248
FALKIRK: ARNOLD CLARK AUTOMOBILES LTD
Falkirk Rd, Grangemouth. 0324 474766
*FORRES: **DICKSON MOTORS (FORRES) LTD** Tytler St. 0309 72122/3
GLASGOW: RITCHIES
393 Shields Rd. 041 429 5611
GLASGOW: PEAT ROAD MOTORS (JORDAN HILL) LTD
120 Whittingehame Drive, Jordanhill.
041 357 1939
GOUROCK: MANOR VEHICLE (TURIN) LTD
92 Manor Crescent. 0475 32356
HAWICK: BORDER MOTOR CO
12 Havelock St. 0450 73881
INVERNESS: DONALD MACKENZIE LTD
62 Seafield Rd. 0463 235777/8,
IRVINE: HARRY FAIRBURN LTD
Ayr Rd. 0294 72121
KILMARNOCK: GEORGE BICKETT & CO LTD
67-79 Campbell St. Riccarton. 0563 22525/6
*LANARK: **J & J FERGUSON**
Wellgatehead. 0555 3106
LEVEN: LINKS GARAGE (LEVEN)
Scoonie Rd. 0333 27003
OBAN: HAZELBANK MOTORS LTD
Stevenson St. 0631 66476
PAISLEY: HAMILTON BROS LTD
Ralson Garage, 255 Glasgow Rd. 041 8829901
*PAISLEY: **LOCHFIELD GARAGE**
4-8 Lochfield Rd. 041 884 2281
PERTH: MACALPINE OF PERTH
St Leonards Bank. 0738 38511
PETERHEAD: CLYNE AUTOS
Seaview, St Fergus. 077 983 258
*PITSCOTTIE BY CUPER: **D.H. PATTERSON MOTOR ENGINEERS**
Burnbank Garage. 033482 200
*RUTHERGLEN: **McKECHNIE OF RUTHERGLEN** 77 Farmeloan Rd.
041 647 9722/5915
ST BOSWELLS: ST BOSWELLS GARAGE
St Boswells. 08352 2259/3475
STIRLING: HAMILTON BROTHERS LTD
44 Causeway Head Rd. 0786 62426
TRANENT: WILLIAM B COWAN LTD
The Garage Elphinstone. 0875 610492

ORKNEY ISLES
KIRKWALL: J & M SUTHERLAND
Junction Rd. 0856 2158

SHETLAND ISLES
AITH: AITH AUTOS LTD
Aith By Bixter. 059 581 230
LERWICK: AITH AUTOS LTD
9 Blackhill Industrial Estate. 0595 3385/4450

WALES
ABERDARE: WILSONS CAR SALES (ABERDARE) LTD
Canal Rd. Cwmbach. 0865 875577/883717
ABERGELE: SLATERS EUROCARS LTD
Marine Rd, Pensarn. 0745 822021/823387
ABERGAVENNY: CLYTHIA MOTOR CO
Merthyr Rd, Llanfoist. 0873 6888
ABERYSTWYTH: EVANS BROS
Royal Oak Garage, Llanfarian. 0970 61 2311/2
*BLACKWOOD: **A. J. STEVENS & SONS**
High Bank Garage, Fairview. 0443 831703

*BRIDGEND: **TS GRIMSHAW (BRIDGEND) LTD**
Tremains Rd. 0656 652984
BUILTH WELLS: PRYNNE'S SERVICE STATION LTD Garth. 059 12287
CARDIFF: T.S. GRIMSHAW LTD
Fiat House, 329 Cowbridge Road East.
0222 395322
CARDIGAN: B.V. REES
Abbey Garage, St Dogmaels. 0239 612025
CARMARTHEN: WILLIAM DAVIES & SONS Central Garage,
St Catherine St. 0267 236284
CHEPSTOW: TUTSHILL SERVICE STATION Gloucester Rd. 02912 3304/70062
CWMBRAN: C.K. MOTOR CO (SOUTH WALES) LTD
10/11 Court Road Industrial Estate.
06333 72711
KILGETTY: STEPASIDE GARAGE LTD
Camarthen Rd. 0834 813786
LLANISHEN CARDIFF: YAPP'S GARAGES LTD Fidlas Rd. 0222 751323
NEWPORT: L.C. MOTORS
121 Corporation Rd. 0633 212548/598892
PWLLHELI: PULROSE MOTOR SERVICES LTD Ala Rd. 0758 612827
SWANSEA: MOORCROFT MOTORS LTD
54 Sway Rd. Morriston. 0792 75271
*TONYREFAIL: **VALLEY MILL MOTORS**
Gilfach Rd. 0443 670742
WREXHAM: N & G DICKENS LTD
Border Service Station, Gresford.
097 883 6262

NORTHERN IRELAND
ARMAGH: ARMAGH GARAGES LTD
Portadown Rd. 0861 524252
BALLYMENA: YOUNGS (BROUGHSHANE) LTD
11 Raceview Rd. Broughshane.
0266 861380/861497
BALLYMONEY: MODEL CAR MART
Model Rd. 026 56 63275
BANBRIDGE: ANNAGH MOTORS (BANBRIDGE) LTD
51 Church St. 08206 24495
BANGOR: JAMES THOMPSON
135-141 Bryansburn Rd. 0247 463911
BELFAST: BAIRD CARS
7-9 Boucher Rd. 0232 247770
BELFAST: B.A.S. (MOTORS) LTD
45-47 Rosetta Rd. 0232 491049/491676
BELFAST: DICK & CO (BELFAST) LTD
43 Mallusk Rd, Newtownabbey. 0232 342511
BELFAST: W.J. BELL & SON
40-50 Townsend St. 0232 241394
*DOWNPATRICK: **DSC CARS**
10/12 Church Street, Downpatrick.
0396 612858/614322
DUNGANNON: FRANCIS NEILL MOTORS (DUNGANNON) LTD
1 Ranfurley Rd. 086 87 22552
ENNISKILLEN: T & T TOWN & COUNTRY CARS LTD Sligo Rd. 0365 22440
LISBURN: DORNAN'S SERVICE STATION (LISBURN) LTD 22 Market Pl. 08462 77412
*NEWRY: **N.W. KEHOE & SONS**
18 Patrick St. 0693 66500/63193
OMAGH: GLENPARK MOTORS
62 Gortin Rd. Co Tyrone. 0662 46521
PORTADOWN: ANNAGH MOTORS WORKS
Mahon Industrial Estate, Mahon Rd.
0762 332552

CHANNEL ISLANDS
GUERNSEY: GT CARS
Les Banques Garages, St Sampsons.
0481 47838
JERSEY: BEL ROYAL MOTOR WORKS LTD
Bel Royal, St. Lawrence. 0534 22556

EUROPE'S DRIVING FORCE

WHY TIPO'S C
EATING THEI

165 PCS

MPETITORS ARE
HEARTS OUT.

Just compare what the Tipo gives you with what the competition offers.

No contest.

Only the Tipo gives you 100% galvanised steel on all exposed bodywork.

The Tipo is more economical, more aerodynamically efficient and gives you more interior width than any car in its class.

And the Tipo offers a wealth of standard equipment that leaves the others standing.

Yet, incredibly, the Tipo's competitors charge you more.

But there's only one way to discover what a truly great car the Tipo really is.

Visit your nearest Fiat dealer and see one for yourself.

F I A T EUROPE'S DRIVING FORCE

What can bowl over any Casanova?

Steam Sponge Pudding Serves 4-6
Preparation and cooking time – 2 hours.

2 rounded tbsps. (60 ml) Lyle's Golden Syrup
4 oz (125 g) margarine   6 oz (175 g) self-raising flour
2 eggs   4 oz (125 g) Tate & Lyle Caster Sugar

Grease a large pudding basin and put the syrup in the bottom.   Cream the margarine and sugar until light and soft.   Add the beaten eggs gradually and mix well.   Fold in the sieved flour gently and add enough warm water to make a soft dropping consistency.   Spoon into the basin to cover the syrup.   Cover the basin with foil or greased greaseproof paper and steam for 1½ hours.   Turn out and pour over more warmed golden syrup.

Lyle's can.

"For any further advice and information about Lyle's Golden Syrup write to: Tate & Lyle, Enterprise House, 45 Homesdale Road, Bromley BR2 9TE."

A LOT FOR LESS

LONDON RESTAURANTS UNDER £30 FOR TWO

167

LONDON HOTELS UNDER £60 FOR TWO

180

BED & BREAKFAST UNDER £38 FOR TWO

185

BARGAIN BREAKS

187

He takes his secretary on every trip.

To find out how turn to pages 24–30.

Cellnet
THE CELLPHONE NETWORK

LONDON RESTAURANTS UNDER £30 FOR TWO

Two courses, half a carafe of wine, coffee, service, VAT – at time of going to press. Reasonable quality of food, although not always up to our usual restaurant standards. Restaurants with comparable prices in the main London section are listed separately at the end (note that prices there include three courses and a full bottle of wine).

Ajanta Tandoori

Map 21 A4
12 Goldhawk Road W12
01-743 5191
Credit Access, Amex, Visa
■ Simple, well-prepared food, pleasantly served in comfortable surroundings – that's Ajanta, a popular Indian restaurant at Shepherd's Bush. Chicken, prawns and lamb get excellent treatment in curries ranging from mild muglai to fierce phal. Very good tikkas and tandoori specialities, and a vegetarian pilao.
■ *L* 12–2.30 *D* 6–11.45
About £16 for two
Parking Difficult
Closed 25 & 26 Dec

Andreas

Map 27 A2
15 Frith Street W1
01-437 3911
Credit Access, Amex, Diners, Visa
■ A soho stalwart serving Greek specialities and dishes from the international repertoire. Lunchtime sees it at its busiest, with many regulars enjoying the dips with pitta bread, the spicy meatballs, the stuffed vine leaves and the hearty lamb stew. Mezedes a popular evening choice.
■ *L* 12–3 *D* 5.30–11
About £20 for two
Parking Difficult
Closed Sat, all Sun, Bank Hols & few days Xmas

Le Bistroquet

Map 20 C3
273 Camden High Street NW1
01-485 9607
Credit Access, Amex, Visa
■ Even the most familiar dishes have the stamp of originality and imagination in this really super wine bar: chicken satay with rice, marvellous fish cakes with parsley sauce, steak with shallots and matchstick chips, chocolate gâteau with a terrific expresso coffee sauce.
■ *L* 12–3, Sun 12–4 *D* 7–11.30
About £24 for two
Parking Ample
Closed 1 Jan & 3 days Xmas

Bon Ton Roulet

Map 21 D6
127 Dulwich Road SE24
01-733 8701
■ "Let the good times roll" is a very popular restaurant on two floors (ask for the much brighter upper room). The menu is short but not without interest: tempura vegetables with garlic mayonnaise, seafood au gratin, chicken supreme with peanuts, roast lamb with onion sauce.
■ *D* only 7–10.30
About £20 for two
Parking Limited
Closed Sun, Bank Hols except 1 May, 10 days Xmas & 1 wk Aug

La Brasserie

Map 23 C4
272 Brompton Road SW3
01-584 1668
Credit Access, Amex, Diners, Visa
■ A lively, long-hours brasserie with white-aproned waiters rushing to and fro providing splendid service. The decor is turn-of-the-century, the food authentic, traditional French; rillettes, fish soup, omelettes, moules marinière, chicken escalope princesse, veal provençale. Good simple sweets and excellent cafetière coffee. ♥ Well-chosen
■ *Meals* 8am–midnight
About £30 for two
Parking Difficult
Closed 25 & 26 Dec

Break for the Border

Map 27 A1
5 Goslett Yard, 125 Charing Cross Road WC2
01-437 8595
Credit Access, Visa
■ Wholesome Tex-Mex food served to the accompaniment of loud music (two live bands most evenings). Layered dip of beans, guacamole and cheese is a huge starter, best shared in anticipation of Texan ribs in a barbecue sauce, vegetable-filled enchiladas or brilliant marinaded chicken served in a corn basket with salad.
■ *Meals* 11.30am–11.45pm *D* Sun 5.30–10.45
About £25 for two Parking Difficult
Closed L Sun, all Bank Hols & few days Xmas

Café des Fleurs ♀

Map 20 B2
280 West End Lane, West Hampstead NW6
01-435 5290
Credit Access, Diners, Visa
■ Food and service are both commendable, the former being interesting and well prepared, the latter lively and cheerful. Charcoal grills are the mainstay, supplemented by specials like tagliatelle with tuna or duck with blackcurrant sauce. Delicious sweets. Breakfast served until noon. ♀ Well-chosen ☕
■ *Meals* 10.30am–midnight, Sun from noon
About £25 for two Parking Limited

Caffé Mamma

Map 7 A5
24 Hill Street, Richmond
01-940 1625
Credit Access, Amex, Visa
■ Cheerful decor represents a little corner of Italy and the menu gives priority to pasta. There's an abundant choice of sauced dishes, including tuna with peppers and carbonara (bacon, egg and onion). Start with minestrone, end with a splendid zabaglione. ☕
■ *Meals* noon–midnight
About £22 for two Parking Limited
Closed 25 & 26 Dec

Camden Brasserie

Map 20 C3
216 Camden High Street NW1
01-482 2114
■ A popular eating place with tables set outside in fine weather. The menu is short and simple, with very good grills as the main offering. There's also a daily pasta dish (starter or main course), plus merguez, spicy chicken wings, salads and simple sweets. ☕
■ *L* 12–3 *D* 6.30–11.30, Sun 6–10.30
About £28 for two Parking Difficult
Closed L Bank Hols & 1 wk Xmas

Chiang Mai

Map 27 A2
48 Frith Street W1
01-437 7444
Credit Access, Visa
■ Thailand in the heart of Soho – or at least Thai food, with its fresh flavours and subtle spicing. Curries are popular – try the chicken with coconut cream – and there's a wide choice of satays, hot and sour dishes, filled omelettes and dishes with chillis.
■ *L* 12–3 *D* 6–11.30
About £27 for two Parking Limited
Closed Sun & Bank Hols

China China ♀

Map 27 A3
38 Panton Street SW1
01-925 0311
Credit Access, Amex, Diners, Visa
■ A modern Chinese restaurant near many theatres and cinemas. The menu offers a pretty good choice that includes sesame prawns, barbecued spare ribs and beef with ginger and spring onions; lobster and crab as available, and grilled, steamed or sweet and sour fish.
■ *L* 12–3 *D* 5.30–11.45, Sat 12–11.45
About £25 for two Parking Difficult
Closed Sun, 25 & 26 Dec

La Cloche

Map 20 B3
304 Kilburn High Road NW6
01-328 0302
Credit Access, Visa
■ Casually dressed staff are bright, friendly and very efficient, adding to the fun of a meal in this delightful former butcher's shop. The short, imaginative menu is typified by deep-fried Gouda, salmon marinated in lime and dill, lamb steaks and vegetarian pancakes. ☕
■ *L* 12–3 *D* 7–12
About £19 for two Parking Ample
Closed Bank Hols

Costas Grill

Map 22 A3
14 Hillgate Street W8
01-229 3794
■ Straightforward Greek food, generously served in unpretentious surroundings, keeps the customers faithful, and the prices are most reasonable. Favourites like moussaka, kebabs or garlic sausages are the basis of the menu, with further variety added by charcoal-grilled fish such as sole or red mullet.
■ *L* 12–2.30 *D* 5–10.30
About £18 for two Parking Limited
Closed Sun, Bank Hols & 3 wks Aug–Sept

Cranks

Map 24 B3
8 Marshall Street W1
01-437 9431
Credit Access, Amex, Diners, Visa
■ Good fresh salads accompany daily changing savouries such as vegetable quiche, mushroom flan and splendid spicy lentil balls. There's also a wide variety of biscuits, cakes and desserts. Waitress service after 6.30; candlelit suppers. Staff should cheer up.
■ *Meals* 8am–7pm *Dine & Wine* 6.30–10.30pm
About £14 for two (buffet) or £24 (Dine & Wine)
Parking Difficult
Closed Sun, Bank Hols & few days Xmas

Criterion Brasserie

Map 24 B3
222 Piccadilly W1
01-839 7133
Credit Access, Amex, Diners, Visa
■ A smart, marble-walled brasserie at Piccadilly Circus, next to the Criterion Theatre. The menu offers a good choice of enjoyable dishes, from chicken liver salad and aubergines provençal to bourride, gigot d'agneau, choucroute and omelette savoyarde. Ice creams, gâteaux and flans for dessert. ⊖
■ *L* 12–3, Sun from 12.30 *D* 6–11, Sun 7–10
About £30 for two *Parking* Difficult
Closed 25 Dec

Daquise

Map 23 C4
20 Thurloe Street SW7
01-589 6117
■ Polish and Continental specialities are the stock in trade of this modest but very durable restaurant right by South Kensington station. Vegetable soup, stuffed cabbage, minced veal escalopes and shashlik show the range, and good pâtisserie provides a final boost of calories.
■ *L* 12–3 *D* 6–11.30
About £20 for two *Parking* Difficult
Closed 2 days Xmas

Dining Room ♀

Map 26 C3
Winchester Walk, London Bridge SE1
01-407 0337
■ The vegetarian menu at this stylish basement restaurant is short but interesting and everything tastes very good and fresh. Organic produce features in dishes like aubergine and date mousse, green bean and poached pear with carrot sauce. ⊖
■ *L* 12.30–2.30 *D* 7–10, Sat by arrang.
About £25 for two *Parking* Difficult
Closed L Sat, all Sun, Mon, Bank Hols, 5 days Xmas & 2 wks Aug

Diwana Bhel-Poori House

Map 20 C3
121 Drummond Street NW1
01-387 5556
Credit Access, Diners
■ They don't take bookings, so you might wait for a table at this simple Indian vegetarian restaurant. Be patient, and enjoy the dosas and samosas, the rice cakes and the delicious mango kulfi. Drink refreshing yoghurt lassi, or take along something stronger.
■ *Meals* noon–midnight
About £15 for two *Parking* Limited
Closed 25 Dec

Diwana Bhel-Poori House

Map 22 A1
50 Westbourne Grove W2
01-229 7689
■ A modest and simple restaurant serving some quite delicious Indian vegetarian cooking at bargain prices. Try the light samosas, poori and chat from Bombay, black pea fritters and Gujarati set meals; all are excellent. Leave room for shrickhand made with yoghurt, spices and sugar. Unlicensed.
■ *L* 12–2.45 *D* 6–10.45, Sat & Sun from 12–10.45
About £15 for two *Parking* Limited
Closed Mon & Bank Hols

Ebury Wine Bar

Map 23 D4
139 Ebury Street SW1
01-730 5447
Credit Access, Amex, Diners, Visa
■ A long-established home of good food and well-chosen wines. Rabbit terrine and cauliflower cheese with prawn butter sauce are typical starters, with plats du jour supplementing the favourite main-course grills and cold buffet. Traditional Sunday lunch. ⊖
■ *L* 12–2.45, Sun till 2.30 *D* 6–10.30, Sun till 10
About £27 for two *Parking* Difficult
Closed 25 & 26 Dec

Efes Kebab House ♀

Map 24 B2
80 Great Titchfield Street W1
01-636 1953
Credit Access, Amex, Visa
■ Watch the owner-chefs at work by the entrance of this popular Turkish restaurant. Good-quality lamb and chicken are very well prepared, and you can start with your choice from the extensive hors d'oeuvre list. Sweet sweets from the trolley, Cona or Turkish coffee.
■ *Meals* noon–11.30pm
About £20 for two *Parking* Difficult
Closed Sun, 1 Jan

Faulkners   ☙

Map 20 D3
424 Kingsland Road E8
01-254 6152
■ Fish and chips are a real treat when they're as good as those served in this bright, cheerful restaurant. The fish – many varieties available – is fresh as can be, the batter would be hard to better, and the chips are chunky.
■ L 12–2   D 5–10, Sat meals 11.30–10
About £25 for two   Parking Ample
Closed Sun, Mon & few days Xmas

La Fin de la Chasse

Map 20 D2
176 Stoke Newington Church Street N16
01-254 5975
Credit Access, Amex, Diners, Visa
■ A friendly, informal restaurant with a patio for summer eating. It's very popular, so book, or risk missing pleasures such as Roquefort quenelles with pear purée or chicken with pine kernels, leaf spinach and gratin dauphinoise. A traditional roast adds to the Sunday lunchtime choice. ☙
■ L Sun only 12.30–2   D 7–11
About £30 for two   Parking Difficult
Closed D Sun, 2 wks Easter, 2 wks Aug, Sept & 1 wk Xmas

Flavio

Map 23 B6
1a Langton Street SW10
01-352 7414
Credit Access, Amex, Diners, Visa
■ A very pleasant neighbourhood Italian restaurant just beyond the Worlds End pub. Staff are very welcoming, and the menu covers a familiar span of nicely cooked fare, including eggs florentine, pasta, liver with sage and various ways with veal and chicken. Daily specials add variety.
■ L 12–3   D 6–12
About £30 for two   Parking Limited
Closed Sun & Bank Hols

Foxtrot Oscar

Map 23 C6
79 Royal Hospital Road SW3
01-352 7179
Credit Access, Visa
■ Chelsea chic at very reasonable prices. The day's bill of fare is chalked up on a blackboard and regular favourites include smoked trout, hamburgers and more substantial offerings like steak and kidney pie. Excellent salads, fresh bread, strong coffee, well-chosen house wines. ☙
■ L 12.30–2.30   D 7.30–11.30, Sun till 10.30
About £25 for two   Parking Limited
Closed Bank Hols

Gachon's   ☙

Map 7 B5
269 Creek Road, Greenwich SE10
01-853 4461
Credit Access, Diners, Visa
■ Round the corner from the Cutty Sark, Gachon's offers sound cooking and plenty of choice. Rich onion soup and stuffed mushrooms are popular starters, with vegetable pancakes, boudin blanc and boeuf bourguignon among the main courses. Tea and pastries are served Sat and Sun afternoons. ☙
■ L 12–2.30   D 6.30–10.30
About £15 for two   Parking Limited
Closed D Sun & Tues, all Mon, Bank Hols & 3 wks Jan

Gavins

Map 21 A6
5 Lacy Road, Putney SW15
01-785 9151
Credit Access, Amex, Visa
■ A bright and cheerful Italian restaurant with modern cream and green decor. Homemade pasta comes with a variety of sauces (rigatoni with chicken, peppers and a mild curry sauce is very unusual), and there are salads, soups, dips and lots of sweets.
■ L 12.30–3.30   D 6.30–11
About £16 for two   Parking Difficult

Geale's

Map 22 A2
2 Farmer Street W8
01-727 7969
Credit Access
■ One of the real survivors, an old-fashioned fish and chip restaurant making good use of daily deliveries of haddock, plaice, cod, rock fish and sole. The portions are very ample, and you can push the boat out with a bottle of the house champagne.
■ L 12–3   D 6–11
About £18 for two   Parking Limited
Closed Sun, Mon, also Tues after Bank Hol Mons, last 3 wks Aug, 2 wks Xmas & 1 Jan

Green Cottage

Map 20 B3
9 New College Parade, Finchley Road NW3
01-722 5305
■ Cantonese cooking in a neat, unassuming restaurant where friendly staff are ready with advice. Chicken, duck and seafood make up the bulk of the choice, but roasted lean pork (char siu) is very good, as is beef with chilli and black bean sauce.
■ *Meals* noon–11.30pm
About £20 for two   Parking Difficult
Closed 24, 25 & 26 Dec

The choice is yours.

At home you choose Flora for all the right reasons. You enjoy its light, delicate taste and you know it's made with pure sunflower oil, which is high in essential polyunsaturates, low in saturates, low in cholesterol.

Today you can also choose Flora when eating out because it's now available in portion packs at all the best restaurants in town.

Grill St Quentin

Map 23 C4
136 Brompton Road SW3
01-581 8377
Credit Access, Amex, Diners, Visa
■ A busy basement restaurant almost opposite Harrods, with good food, on-the-ball service and a certain amount of style. The charcoal grill provides the staples – steak, lamb, veal chop, duck, salmon, sole and halibut. Steak tartare and confit are other main courses, plus stuffed tomatoes for vegetarians. ⊟
■ *Meals* noon–midnight, Sun till 11.30
About £26 for two   Parking Difficult

Gurkhas Tandoori

Map 24 B1
23 Warren Street W1
01-388 1640
Credit Access, Amex, Diners, Visa
■ Good eating and excellent value for money make this little Nepalese restaurant very popular, so booking's a good idea, especially at weekends. Lamb, mutton and chicken appear in tandooris, biryanis and a long list of curries, and there's an unusually wide choice of vegetable dishes.
■ *L* 12–2.45 *D* 6–11.45
About £16 for two   Parking Difficult
Closed 25 & 26 Dec

Harry Morgan's

Map 20 B3
31 St John's Wood High Street NW8
01-722 1869
■ The salt beef's among the best in town, but there are many more delights on the menu of one of London's favourite Jewish restaurants: chicken noodle soup, gefilte fish, chopped liver, veal escalopes, roast chicken, meat balls and the very splendid vermicelli-based lokshen pudding.
■ *L* 12–3 *D* 6–10
About £20 for two   Parking Limited
Closed D Fri

Hung Toa

Map 22 B2
54 Queensway W2
01-727 6017
■ A busy Chinese restaurant almost opposite Bayswater station. It's open long hours for straightforward Cantonese food, including really good roast duck and pork. One-plate rice and noodle dishes are cheap and satisfying, and other recommendations include ginger prawns, sea bass and black bean chicken.
■ *Meals* noon–11pm
About £22 for two   Parking Difficult
Closed 25 & 26 Dec

Il Barbino

Map 22 A3
32 Kensington Church Street W8
01-937 8752
Credit Access, Amex, Diners, Visa
■ Il Barbino is a popular little Italian restaurant with good standards of cooking and service. The menu and daily specials combine to provide a very wide choice, from antipasto and pasta to butterfly sardines and many meat and fish main dishes – even seasonal game. ⊟
■ *L* 12–3 *D* 6.30–11.45
About £30 for two   Parking Difficult
Closed Sun & Bank Hols

Indian Inn

Map 20 B1
71 Ballards Lane N3
01-349 0190
Credit Access, Amex, Diners, Visa
■ Neat bright premises, friendly staff and enjoyable, mainly vegetarian, Indian cooking: spicy lentil doughnuts, bhel poori, cabbage with coconut, mushroom curry with blackeye beans. Also some lamb, chicken and fish, and a super sweet (pradhaman) with cane sugar, pasta, nuts and lentils. ♿
■ *L* 12–2.30 *D* 6–11.30, Sat till midnight, Sun till 11
About £19 for two   Parking Ample
Closed 25 Dec

Joe Allen

Map 24 D3
13 Exeter Street WC2
01-836 0651
■ Booking is always advisable at this bustling basement restaurant, whose menu hovers between Europe and America: rack of lamb, grilled Scotch salmon, hot Italian sausage with lentil salad, blueberry shortcake. Solid, dependable cooking, bright but not brisk service.
■ *Meals* noon–1am, Sun till midnight
About £25 for two   Parking Difficult
Closed 25 & 26 Dec

Khyber Pass

Map 23 B5
21 Bute Street SW7
01-589 7311
Credit Access, Amex, Diners, Visa
■ An enduring favourite of many, the Khyber Pass keeps up very decent standards of cooking and service. The menu sticks to familiar Indian dishes: tandoori specialities, kebabs, biryanis, pulao and curries to suit all heat requirements. Good breads and sundries. Murgh mussalum is the house speciality.
■ *L* 12–2.30 *D* 6–11.30
About £20 for two   Parking Difficult
Closed 25 & 26 Dec

Kitchen Yakitori

Map 24 A3
12 Lancashire Court, New Bond Street W1
01-629 9984
■ Short set lunch menus provide a good introduction to Japanese cuisine, and the combination of excellent cooking and fast, efficient service make this a very popular spot. Try one of the eel dishes – chef's speciality. The evening menu is more elaborate and expensive.
■ *L* 12–2.30   *D* 6–9.30
About £26 for two   Parking Difficult
Closed Sun, Bank Hols & 10 days Xmas

Lantern ⑨

Map 20 B3
23 Malvern Road NW6
01-624 1796
Credit Access, Visa
■ Good cooking, a short, simply-priced menu and informal but very prompt service keeps the crowds coming to Lantern, and booking is essential, especially at weekends. Favourites include tagliatelle (meat or vegetable sauce), chicken and asparagus pancakes and crab-filled choux buns. ℮
■ *L* 12–3   *D* 7–midnight
About £18 for two   Parking Ample
Closed 25 & 26 Dec

Laurent Restaurant ⑨

Map 20 B2
428 Finchley Road NW2
01-794 3603
Credit Access, Visa
■ Informal, unpretentious and very popular little restaurant where the choice is simple: three kinds of couscous, basic vegetable, *complet* with lamb and merguez, and *royal* with lamb, merguez and brochette. Start with brik à l'oeuf – a filo pastry parcel containing a soft-cooked egg. Book.
■ *L* 12–2   *D* 6–11
About £25 for two   Parking Ample
Closed Sun & first 3 wks Aug

Lemonia

Map 20 C3
154 Regent's Park Road NW1
01-586 7454
■ Sound cooking and a friendly, lively atmosphere bring the crowds to this splendid Greek restaurant, so be sure to book well ahead. All the favourite dishes are on the menu, and for two or more there's a super-value set meal at £6.25.
■ *D* only 6–11.30
About £20 for two   Parking Difficult
Closed Sun, Bank Hols, 2 wks end Aug & 25 & 26 Dec

Linda's ⑨

Map 20 B3
4 Fernhead Road W9
01-969 9387
Credit Access, Diners, Visa
■ London's first true Vietnamese restaurant is a modest little place run by Vietnamese Linda Blaney and her English husband Robin. There's plenty to enjoy, from beef with rice stick soup and splendid spring rolls to spicy spare ribs, and a special mixed omelette.
■ *L* 12–2   *D* 7–10.15
About £23 for two   Parking Ample
Closed Sun, Bank Hols, 2 wks summer & 2 wks Xmas

Little Akropolis ⑨

Map 24 B2
10 Charlotte Street W1
01-636 8198
Credit Access, Amex, Diners, Visa
■ Small, old-fashioned restaurant with simple decor, long-serving staff and a menu dominated by familiar Greek dishes. Aubergines and artichokes à la grecque, stuffed vine leaves and calamari could precede stifado, kleftiko, afelia or maybe a pilaf. Book. ⑤
■ *L* 12–2.30   *D* 6–10.30
About £25 for two   Parking Difficult
Closed L Sat, all Sun & Bank Hols

Malabar

Map 22 A2
27 Uxbridge Street W8
01-727 8800
Credit Access, Visa
■ A quite stylish, non-flock Indian restaurant offering good cooking and a short but interesting menu. Chicken and lamb Madras, samosas and tikkas are joined by less familiar items such as vegetable cutlets, devilled chicken livers and Friday evening's fish special. Vegetarian thali. Sunday buffet lunch.
■ *L* 12.30–2.45, Sun from 1.00   *D* 6.30–11.15, Sun 6.30–10.45
About £26 for two   Parking Ample
Closed 4 days Xmas & 1 week end Aug

Manna

Map 20 C3
4 Erskine Road NW3
01-722 8028
■ A long-estabished and well-loved vegetarian restaurant where the cooking is straightforward and the prices very low. Mushrooms aïoli, courgette and celery dijonnaise, risotto alla milanese and mango mousse show the range of the menu and blackboard specials.
■ *D* only 6.30–11.30
About £18 for two   Parking Limited
Closed 4 days Xmas

A LOT FOR LESS

Maxies Wine Bar

Map 7 A4
7 Boston Parade, Hanwell W7
01-567 9708
Credit Access, Amex, Diners, Visa
■ The unusual feature of this lively, busy wine bar is that it has a Chinese menu (and a Chinese chef). The range of dishes is familiar: spare ribs, butterfly prawns, chicken and sweetcorn soup, crispy duck, beef in black bean sauce. Service is swift and cheerful.
■ *L* 11.30–2.30   *D* 5.30–10.45, Sun 7–10.30
About £25 for two   Parking Limited
Closed L Sun, 25–28 Dec

Mélange

Map 27 B1
59 Endell Street WC2
01-240 8077
Credit Access, Amex, Diners, Visa
■ Friendly and informal, with crayons provided for doodling over dinner. The menu is modern, and chef Raymond Blanchard shows a light touch in dishes like fish with red pepper sauce, noisettes of pork with grapes and vegetable casserole in a filo pastry nest. ☻
■ *Meals* noon–11.30, Sat D only 6–11.30
About £30 for two   Parking Difficult
Closed L Sat, all Sun, Bank Hols & 10 days Xmas

Le Mercury

Map 20 D3
140a Upper Street N1
01-354 4088
Credit Access, Visa
■ Two floors of closely-packed tables set with candles and fresh flowers. The menu follows the popular formula of Peter Ilic's other restaurants, with dishes such as crab-filled profiteroles hollandaise, herby veal cutlets and duck in Grand Marnier on the shortish, well-chosen menu. Book. ☻
■ *L* 12.30–3   *D* 6–12, Sun meals noon–11pm
About £25 for two   Parking Limited
Closed 25 & 26 Dec

Mother Huff's ⚁

Map 20 B2
12 Heath Street NW3
01-435 3714
Credit Amex, Visa
■ Good-quality produce is the basis for tasty home-cooking at Mother Huff's, whose daily menu is displayed on a blackboard. The usual choice is soup, three hot dishes (roast, casserole, steak and kidney pie), a flan and lots of salads. Nice sweets; traditional Sunday roast. ☻
■ *L* 12–3   *D* 7–11
About £26 for two   Parking Limited
Closed D Mon, all 25 & 26 Dec

Moti Mahal ⚁

Map 23 B5
3 Glendower Place SW7
01-584 8428
Credit Access, Amex, Diners, Visa
■ A comfortable little Indian restaurant in a busy one-way street near South Ken tube. The menu sticks to familiar fare (lamb, chicken and prawns) served in a wide variety of starters, tandoori dishes, curries, biryanis and dhansaks. Good choice of vegetables, including a main course.
■ *Mon–Thurs L* 12–3   *D* 6–11.30
Fri–Sun Meals noon–11.30
About £25 for two   Parking Difficult

Noor Jahan

Map 23 B5
2a Bina Gardens SW5
01-373 6522
Credit Access, Amex, Diners, Visa
■ Long-established, fairly traditional Indian restaurant off Old Brompton Road. The menu offers a straightforward selection of curries and tandoori dishes based on lamb, chicken and prawns. Decent cooking, pleasant service. The restaurant was refurbished in 1988.
■ *L* 12–2.30   *D* 6–11.45, Sun till 11.30
About £26 for two   Parking Limited
Closed 24–26 Dec

Oasis in the City

Map 21 D 4
144 Clerkenwell Road EC1
01-837 7373
Credit Access, Visa
■ Bright and cheerful in pretty pastel shades, the Oasis opens from 11–7 for the service of imaginative, well-prepared food. Chinese, seafood and farmhouse platters are good choices for two, and other dishes run from pappardelle provençale and ginger prawns to steak and oyster pie. ☻
■ *Meals* 11am–7pm
About £30 for two   Parking Difficult
Closed Sat, Sun & Bank Hols

Oliver's

Map 21 B4
10 Russell Gardens W14
01-603 7645
■ Decent portions of fresh, carefully prepared food served in an atmosphere of relaxed informality. Popular choices include soups, lasagne, calf's liver provençale and osso buco, with poached salmon mayonnaise a fishy favourite. Simple sweets. Good coffee. Roast on Sundays. Bring your own wine.
■ *Meals* noon–11
About £23 for two   Parking Limited
Closed 25 & 26 Dec

Ormes ♀

Map 21 C6
67 Abbeville Road SW4
01-673 2568
Credit Access, Amex, Diners, Visa
■ Booking's a must here, as this informal wine bar is a very popular spot. Staff are particularly friendly and well informed, and the food's good, too: pâtés, deep-fried camembert, monk-fish kebabs, lamb Wellington, something for vegetarians, excellent sweets, proper bread. Carefully chosen wines. ㉒
■ *L* 12–2.30, Sat till 2   *D* 6.30–11, Sun 7–10.30
About £30 for two   Parking Ample
Closed 4 days Xmas

Orso

Map 24 D3
27 Wellington Street WC2
01-240 5269
■ Choose carefully to stay within the budget at this chic, relaxed restaurant. The Italian menu provides plenty of choice, from mari-nated sardines and fried courgette flowers to little pizzas, pasta, meat, fish and a lovely chocolate meringue cake. Book.
■ *Meals* noon–midnight
About £30 for two   Parking Difficult
Closed 24 & 25 Dec

Penang ♀

Map 22 A2
41 Hereford Road W2
01-229 2982
Credit Access, Amex, Diners, Visa
■ Fay Tung's unassuming basement restaur-ant is the setting for some fine Malaysian cooking. 'Lipstick' chicken – marinated with various spices and deep-fried – is a must, but so, too, are satay prawns, squid in tamarind sauce, mixed vegetables in coconut milk gravy, rice pudding made with black rice.
■ *D* 6–11, Sun till 10.30
About £25 for two   Parking Difficult
Closed Good Fri & 24 Dec–2 Jan

La Perla ♀

Map 24 B3
28 Brewer Street W1
01-437 2060
Credit Access, Amex, Diners, Visa
■ Good value for money in a friendly Soho Italian restaurant which has recently extended its opening hours. Favourite dishes include lobster soup, risotto with peas and mushrooms, veal valdostana, tortelloni alla crema and a generous plate of mixed fried seafood. ㉒
■ *Meals* noon–11.15
About £25 for two   Parking Difficult
Closed Sun

Le Petit Prince

Map 20 C2
5 Holmes Road NW5
01-267 0752
■ Smart it is not, but for couscous fans this is a little prince among restaurants. Take the vegetable version, or add chicken, spicy meatballs, merguez, cutlets or brochettes. Baked cheese loaf with mayonnaise is a good starter, chocolate mousse a favourite sweet.
■ *L* 12–2.30   *D* 7–11.30
About £20 for two   Parking Difficult
Closed L Sat, Sun, Mon, all Easter wknd, 24–30 Dec & 2 wks Aug

Le Plat du Jour

Map 20 C3
19 Hampstead Road NW1
01-387 9644
Credit Access, Amex, Diners Visa
■ Separate from the restaurant at the rear, this bistro-style wine bar lists its daily offerings on a blackboard: stinging nettle soup, main courses such as chicken escalope or beef goulash, and plated salads. Nice sweets; French and Italian cheeses; good espresso coffee. ㉒
■ *Meals* 11.30am–8pm
About £30 for two   Parking Ample
Closed Sun, Bank Hols & few days Xmas

La Preferita

Map 21 C6
163 Lavender Hill SW11
01-223 1046
Credit Access, Amex, Diners, Visa
■ The menu at this bright Italian restaurant provides a shortish selection of tried and trusted favourites, including artichokes hot or cold, minestrone, spaghetti al cartoccio, scampi and various ways with chicken, veal and steak. Cooking is OK, and careful choice will keep diners within budget. ㉒
■ *L* 12.30–2.30   *D* 7–11.30
About £30 for two   Parking Limited
Closed 25 & 26 Dec & Sun before Bank Hol Mons

Punters Pie

Map 21 C6
183 Lavender Hill SW11
01-228 2660
Credit Access, Amex, Diners, Visa
■ Everything is home-made here, and the vegetables are organically grown. Pies are the main attraction – steak and kidney, cod and shellfish, pasta, even chocolate mousse – but there are also interesting dips to go with crudités and some yummy sweets. Don't miss the sensational garlic bread! ㉒
■ *L* 12–3   *D* 6–11.30   *About £25 for two*
Parking Ample   **Closed** 25 & 26 Dec

Ravi Shankar

Map 20 C3
135 Drummond Street NW1
01-388 6458
Credit Access, Amex, Diners, Visa
■ Indian vegetarian cooking in a popular restaurant just a short walk from Euston station. Samosas, pooris and bhajias could precede a curry or black lentil pancake, with kulfi or shrikhand to finish. Consistently enjoyable food at very friendly prices.
■ *Meals* noon–10.45
About £16 *for two   Parking* Difficult

Sabras   ♨

Map 20 A3
263 High Road, Willesden Green NW10
01-459 0340
Credit Access, Visa
■ As we went to press this well-liked Indian vegetarian restaurant had just re-opened after a major refit. The cooking remains excellent throughout a range of Bombay, Gujarat and South Indian dishes, and if you're unfamiliar with much of the menu the staff will happily help.
■ *Meals* noon–9.30
About £15 *for two   Parking* Limited
Closed Mon, 2 wks Aug & 2 wks Xmas

Sagarmatha

Map 24 B1
399 Euston Road NW1
01-387 6531
Credit Access, Amex, Diners, Visa
■ The sister restaurant to Gurkhas Tandoori, with the same enjoyable standards of cooking and cheerful, pleasant service. Lamb, mutton and chicken appear in curries to suit all palates, and vegetarians have a particularly good choice. Sagarmatha is the original name of Mount Everest.
■ *L* 12–2.45   *D* 6–11.45
About £24 *for two   Parking* Difficult
Closed 25 & 26 Dec

Seashell

Map 21 B4
49 Lisson Grove NW1
01-723 8703
Credit Access, Visa
■ The Seashell prides itself on the quality of its fish, and the throughput of customers testifies that their pride is justified. Plaice, haddock, skate, cod, salmon and Dover sole are the most popular choices, all very fresh, lightly battered and cooked to a T.
■ *L* 12–2   *D* 5.15–10.30
About £27 *for two   Parking* Difficult
Closed Sun, Mon, 25 & 26 Dec

Sofra

Map 25 A4
18 Shepherd Street W1
01-493 3320
Credit Access, Amex, Visa
■ The very popular Turkish restaurant Aspava has taken a new name and expanded into the next-door premises. The menu's the same – good hot and cold starters (try a selection), casseroles and grills (mainly lamb and chicken), steaks and a couple of seafood dishes.
■ *Meals* noon–11.30
About £24 *for two   Parking* Difficult
Closed 25 Dec

Soho Brasserie

Map 27 A2
23 Old Compton Street W1
01-439 3758
Credit Access, Amex, Diners, Visa
■ A favourite of the pop and media worlds, open long hours for a snack or a meal. Warm salad of wild mushrooms, omelette fines herbes, boudin blanc with apple sauce and lamb steak with aubergines and rosemary are typical choices, and there's always some zingy-fresh fish. ☻
■ *Meals* 10am–11.30pm
About £25 *for two   Parking* Ample
Closed Sun, Bank Hols

Tiger under the Table

Map 20 B2
634 Finchley Road, Golders Green NW11
01-458 9273
Credit Access, Amex, Diners, Visa
■ A cool, stylish restaurant specialising in the colourful and sometimes quite zippy cuisine of Singapore. Seafood comes in splendid variety, and other specialities include superb mee goreng (fried yellow noodles with beef, tomatoes and egg). Sunday buffet lunch.
■ *L* 12–3   *D* 6–11.15
About £26 *for two   Parking* Difficult
Closed few days Xmas

Topkapi

Map 22 D1
25 Marylebone High Street W1
01-486 1872
Credit Access, Amex, Diners, Visa
■ A Turkish restaurant with blue-plush banquettes, gilt chairs and brass plates on the walls. Start with a selection of dips and other hors d'oeuvre and go on to a main-course grill (ten varieties of lamb and one chicken). Vegetarian dishes also available.
■ *Meals* noon–11.30
About £25 *for two   Parking* Difficult
Closed 25 & 26 Dec

Villa Estense ♀

Map 21 B5
642 King's Road sw6
01-731 4247
Credit Access, Amex, Visa
■ Very much a favourite with Fulhamites, Villa Estense buzzes with activity, especially in the evenings. The menu is a long list of popular Italian favourites, from home-made pasta and large pizzas to escalope milanese and various sauced main courses. ⊗ &
■ *L* 12.30–2.30   *D* 7–11.30
About £24 *for two*   *Parking* Difficult
Closed D Sun

Welcome Inn ♀

Map 7 B5
191 Streatham High Road sw16
01-769 1607
Credit Access, Amex, Visa
■ The menu is mainly Cantonese at a family-run restaurant that certainly lives up to its name. Hot and sour soup, chicken with cashew nuts and yellow bean sauce, crispy duck and deep-fried shredded beef are all good, and there's a splendid choice for vegetarians.
■ *D* only 5.30–midnight
About £20 *for two*   *Parking* Difficult
Closed 25 & 26 Dec

Wine & Mousaka

Map 7 A4
33 Haven Green, Ealing w5
01-998 4373
Credit Access, Amex, Diners, Visa
■ Two modest, cheerful establishments the smaller is at No. 30 Haven Green: tel 01-997 0287, serving a decent range of Greek dishes at very agreeable prices. Tahim, taramasalata, wine sausages, charcoal grills are typical items, and half-portions are available for children.
■ *L* noon–2.30   *D* 6–11.30
About £24 *for two*   *Parking* Difficult
Closed Sun & Bank Hols

Wine & Mousaka

Map 7 A5
12 Kew Green, Richmond
01-940 5696
Credit Access, Amex, Diners, Visa
■ A simple, cheerful restaurant on the Green at Kew, with a menu that runs the gamut of familiar Greek dishes: houmus taramasalata, kebabs, dolmades, kleftiko and the usual syrupy puds like paklava. Half-portions available for children. Order the good thick Greek coffee.
■ *L* noon–2.30   *D* 6–11.30
About £24 *for two*   *Parking* Ample
Closed Sun & Bank Hols

Woodlands

Map 22 D1
77 Marylebone Lane w1
01-486 3862
Credit Access, Amex, Diners, Visa
■ Part of a large chain on the Indian sub-continent, and one of three in London – all serving wholesome South Indian vegetarian food. Thalis are a good way of sampling several dishes, or go à la carte (staff are very happy to help with choice).
■ *L* 12–3   *D* 6–11
About £25 *for two*   *Parking* Difficult
Closed 25 & 26 Dec

Woodlands

Map 27 A3
37 Panton Street sw1
01-839 7258
Credit Access, Amex, Diners, Visa
■ The same menu here as at the two other Woodlands – South Indian vegetarian – but maybe not quite as good for cooking or service. Best dish on a recent visit was our shrikhand, a delicious dessert made with yoghurt cheese, saffron, almonds and pistachios.
■ *L* 12–3   *D* 5.30–10.45, Sun from 6
About £22 *for two*   *Parking* Difficult
Closed 25 & 26 Dec

Woodlands

Map 7 A4
402A High Road, Wembley, Middx
01-902 9869
Credit Access, Amex, Diners, Visa
■ South Indian vegetarian cuisine is served by friendly staff to the strains of popular Indian music. Subtle spices enhance quality ingredients in a good range that spans rice cakes, lentil doughnuts, dosas and curries; thalis provide a well-balanced cross-section of dishes, plus a sweet. &
■ *L* 12–2.30   *D* 6–10.30
About £22 *for two*   *Parking* Ample
Closed 2–3 days Xmas

Zazou Brasserie

Map 24 B1
74 Charlotte Street w1
01-637 1285
Credit Access, Amex, Diners, Visa
■ The emphasis at this smart brasserie is on seafood and the brochette of turbot, salmon and monkfish is a real winner. They also serve a couple of meat dishes, crudités, salad, niçoise and some oriental-style items. Breakfast 7.30–11.30, brasserie menu from noon. ⊗
■ *Meals* 7.30am–11pm
About £30 *for two*   *Parking* Difficult
Closed Sun & Bank Hols

A LOT FOR LESS

Zia Teresa ♟

Map 23 C4
6 Hans Road SW3
01-589 7634
■ An ideal place to recharge the batteries before – or after – a trip to Harrods. Zia Teresa offers a very wide day-long choice of tasty Italian dishes, from soups and antipasto to pasta, pizza, seafood, chicken and veal. Cooking is dependable, portions generous. ℮
■ *Meals* noon–11
About £22 for two
Parking Difficult
Closed Sun

Economy evening meals can be had at the following restaurants, which are listed in the main London section of the Guide. (Note that prices in the main section include three courses and a full bottle of wine.)

Arirang Korean Restaurant
Map 24 B2

Bangkok
Map 23 B5

Bitter Lemons Taverna
Map 21 B5

Blooms
Map 20 B1

Blooms
Map 21 D4

Café Flo
Map 20 B2

Cheng-du
Map 20 C3

Chuen Cheng Ku
Map 27 A2

Delhi Brasserie
Map 23 B4

Dynasty of Hampstead
Map 20 B2

Ebury Court Hotel Restaurant
Map 25 A6

Fung-Shing
Map 27 A2

Gonbei
Map 20 D3

Good Friends
Map 7 B4

Ikkyu
Map 24 B2

Kensington Tandoori
Map 23 A4

Kundan
Map 21 C5

Last Days of the Raj
Map 27 B1

Lena's Thai Restaurant
Map 21 C6

Lok-Zen
Map 20 C1

Majlis
Map 23 B4

Mandarin Kitchen
Map 22 B2

Memories of India
Map 23 B4

Ming
Map 27 A2

Mr Kong
Map 27 A2

Nanyang
Map 23 B4

New Diamond
Map 27 A2

New Leaf
Map 7 A4

New Shu Shan
Map 27 A2

Peking Duck
Map 20 B1

Piccadilly Restaurant
Map 24 B3

Poons
Map 27 A2

Shanghai
Map 22 A3

Si Chuen
Map 27 A2

Sinar Matahari
Map 7 A4

Singapore Garden
Map 20 B3

Weng Wah House
Map 20 B2

Yung's
Map 27 A2

Cooking in Italy . . .

consists of serving something exquisitely fresh,

with the least amount of modification

in the process of preparation.

ANONYMOUS
Cited in
THE TUSCAN COOKBOOK (1979)

Many excellent cooks

are spoilt by going into the arts.

PAUL GAUGUIN 1848-1903

In Cournos'
MODERN PLUTARCH

LONDON HOTELS UNDER £60 FOR TWO

This is a category comprising modest hotels with limited facilities and accommodation of a reasonable standard but below our 50% grading. Hotels in the main London section, where prices are comparable to those in this section, are listed separately at the end.

Academy Hotel   £D/E

Map 24 C1
21 Gower Street WC1E 6HG
01-631 4115   Telex 24364
Credit Access, Amex, Diners, Visa
■ A highly recommendable little place – three Georgian houses near the British Museum. Bedrooms feature solid darkwood furniture, bright modern fabrics and neat bathrooms. There's a stylish breakfast room and a small library with patio. No dogs.
Amenities laundry service, porterage, 24-hour lounge service.

Rooms 35	*Direct dial* Yes
en suite bath/shower 30	*Room TV* Yes
Parking Difficult	

Adelphi Hotel   £D

Map 23 B4
127 Cromwell Road SW7 4DT
01-373 7177   Telex 8813164
Credit Access, Amex, Diners, Visa
■ Bedrooms in this Victorian town house are modern and well kept, and about half have trouser presses and hairdryers. There's a roomy reception area, a lounge, bar and bright breakfast room. Friendly staff, some with little English.
Amenities laundry service, in-house movies, secretarial services.

Rooms 57	*Direct dial* Yes
en suite bath/shower 57	*Room TV* Yes
Parking Difficult	

Alison House Hotel   £F

Map 23 D4
82 Ebury Street SW1W 9QD
01-730 9529
■ All is shipshape at Alison House, a Georgian building near the coach and railway stations. Bedrooms are neat and compact, with simple furnishings, TVs and hairdryers. One has its own shower room, the rest share three. No children under 12. No dogs.

Rooms 11	*Room phone* No
en suite bath/shower 1	*Room TV* Yes
Parking Difficult	**Closed** Jan

Apollo Hotel   £E

Map 23 A4
18 Lexham Gardens W8 5JE
01-373 3236   Telex 264189
Credit Access, Amex, Diners, Visa
■ In a terrace just off Cromwell Road, the Apollo and its neighbour the Atlas appeal equally to tourists and business people (Maurice Monina is the excellent manager). Accommodation is neat and functional, and most rooms have their own bathrooms. No dogs.
Amenities laundry service, lift, porterage.

Rooms 59	*Direct dial* Yes
en suite bath/shower 50	*Room TV* Yes
Parking Difficult	

Aster House   £D

Map 23 B5
3 Sumner Place SW7 3EE
01-581 5888
Credit Access, Amex, Diners, Visa
■ A nice comfortable bed-and-breakfast hotel, with a pink-marble foyer, a delightful conservatory breakfast room and a pretty little garden. Bedrooms are furnished in smart, modern style and all have neat bath/shower rooms. Housekeeping is a strong point. No dogs.
Amenities garden.

Rooms 14	*Direct dial* Yes
en suite bath/shower 14	*Room TV* Yes
Parking Difficult	

A
C
T
F
O
R
L
E
S
S

Atlas Hotel   £E

Map 23 A4
24 Lexham Gardens W8 5JE
01-373 7873   Telex 264189
Credit Access, Amex, Diners, Visa
■ Next to the Apollo, with the same practical comforts and the same long-serving manager. Rooms with private facilities are split 40 shower/WC and 10 bath/WC. The Atlas has a small evening bar which Apollonians are welcome to use. No dogs.
Amenities laundry service, lift, porterage.

Rooms 66	*Direct dial* Yes
en suite bath/shower 50	*Room TV* Yes
Parking Difficult	

Avonmore Hotel   £E/F

Map 21 B5
66 Avonmore Road W14 8RS
01-603 4296   Telex 945922
■ Quietly located near Olympia Exhibition Hall, the Avonmore is an owner-managed hotel with a cosy, well-kept feel. Bedrooms (on four floors) offer TVs, radio-alarms and mini-bar fridges, and each pair shares a recently refurbished bathroom. No dogs.
Amenities garden, porterage, fax.

Rooms 9	*Room phone* Yes
en suite bath/shower 0	*Room TV* Yes
Parking Limited	

Bryanston Court   £D

Map 22 C1
56 Great Cumberland Place W1H 7FD
01-262 3141   Telex 267076
Credit Access, Amex, Diners, Visa
■ The Theodore family run a smart hotel thats just above our budget limit. Bedrooms are furnished in contemporary style, and all have little shower rooms with WC. There's a comfortable lounge and bar.
Amenities laundry service, secretarial services, lift, porterage, fax.

Rooms 54	*Direct dial* Yes
en suite bath/shower 54	*Room TV* Yes
Parking Limited	

Chesham House Hotel   £E/F

Map 23 D4
64 Ebury Street SW1W 9QD
01-730 8513   Telex 912881
Credit Amex, Diners, Visa
■ Good basic overnight accommodation near Victoria train and coach stations. Bedrooms offer TVs, trouser presses and tea-makers as standard, with hairdryers available on request; they all have washbasins and share five WCs and five bath/shower rooms. Unlicensed. No children under four. No dogs.

Rooms 24	*Room phone* No
en suite bath/shower 0	*Room TV* No
Parking Difficult	

Collin House   £E/F

Map 23 D4
104 Ebury Street SW1W 9QD
01-730 8031
■ Run in friendly fashion by Dafydd and Beryl Thomas, Collin House is a mid-Victorian town residence near Victoria stations. Bedrooms are in comfortable, unfussy style and eight have their own shower and toilet rooms (the rest shower only). There's a pine-furnished breakfast room. No dogs.

Rooms 13	*Room phone* No
en suite bath/shower 8	*Room TV* No
Parking Difficult	

Columbia Hotel   £E

Map 22 B2
95 Lancaster Gate W2 3NS
01-402 0021   Telex 914117
Credit Access, Amex, Visa
■ Overseas tourists are frequent users of this owner-run hotel across the road from Kensington Gardens. Day rooms are large, though not particularly inviting, bedrooms plain and simple; many are geared for multiple occupation.
Amenities laundry service, 24-hour lounge service, lift, porterage.

Rooms 92	*Direct dial* Yes
en suite bath/shower 92	*Room TV* Yes
Parking Limited	

Concord Hotel   £E

Map 23 A4
155 Cromwell Road SW5 0TQ
01-370 4151
Credit Access, Visa
■ A mid-Victorian terraced town house fronting on to busy Cromwell Road. Functional comfort is the order of the day, both in the bedrooms – most of a reasonable size – and in the TV lounge and airy breakfast room.
Amenities laundry service, 24-hour lounge service, porterage.

Rooms 40	*Direct dial* Yes
en suite bath/shower 15	*Room TV* No
Parking Limited	

Craven Gardens Hotel   £E

Map 22 B2
16 Leinster Terrace W2 3ES
01-262 3167   Telex 8955622
Credit Access, Amex, Diners, Visa
■ Modest comforts in a modernised Victorian house near Queensway. Bedrooms are neat and compact, and most have their own tiled bathrooms. The bar, restaurant and reception area have recently been refurbished. No dogs.
Amenities coffee shop (noon–11pm), lift.

Rooms 45	*Direct dial* Yes
en suite bath/shower 41	*Room TV* Yes
Parking Difficult	

A LOT FOR LESS

Diplomat Hotel   £D

Map 23 D4
2 Chesham Street SW1X 8DT
01-235 1544   Telex 9413498
Credit Access, Amex, Diners, Visa
■ Just above the budget limit, a well-run hotel convenient for many London sights. Smart furnishings and high-quality fabrics grace the bedrooms, and lovely Italian tiles line the bathrooms. Note the handsome marble-floored foyer and spiral staircase. *Amenities* laundry service, lift, porterage, fax.
Rooms 29   *Direct dial* Yes   *Room TV* Yes
en suite bath/shower 29   *Parking* Limited

Eden Plaza Hotel   £D/E

Map 23 B4
68 Queen's Gate SW7 5JT
01-370 6111   Telex 916228
Credit Access, Amex, Diners, Visa
■ A very handy base, with Hyde Park, the museums and good shopping nearby. Refurbishment keeps the place trim; day rooms are bright and modern, while bedrooms offer double-glazing, central heating and shower rooms. No dogs. *Amenities* sauna, solarium, laundry service, 24-hour lounge service, fax.
Rooms 65   *Direct dial* Yes   *Room TV* Yes
en suite bath/shower 65   *Parking* Limited

Elizabeth Hotel   £D/E

Map 21 C5
37 Eccleston Square SW1V 1PB
01-828 6812
■ A friendly, privately-owned hotel. Practical, comfort is the order of the day, and bedrooms vary from very small singles to ampler family rooms; three have private shower/WC, four shower only, the rest share. Main day room is a spacious lounge with TV. No dogs.
Rooms 24   *Room phone* No   *Room TV* Some
en suite bath/shower 3   *Parking* Limited

George Hotel   £E

Map 20 C3
58 Cartwright Gardens WC1H 9EL
01-387 6789
Credit Visa
■ New owners have started an improvement programme at their Georgian-crescent hotel. General decor has received attention, and TVs have been installed in the bedrooms, which range from smallish singles to large family rooms. Guests may use the Gardens' tennis courts. Unlicensed. No dogs. *Amenities* fax.
Rooms 39   *Room phone* No   *Room TV* Yes
en suite bath/shower 5   *Parking* Difficult

Kensington Court Hotel   £D

Map 23 A5
33 Nevern Place SW5 9NP
01-370 5151   Telex 8814451
Credit Access, Amex, Diners, Visa
■ A six-storey modern block in a Victorian terrace. Rooms are of a decent size, and all have colour TVs, radio-alarms, direct-dial phones and tea-makers. There's a bar and basement restaurant. Own car park. *Amenities* laundry service, 24-hour lounge service, lift.
Rooms 35   *Direct dial* Yes   *Room TV* Yes
en suite bath/shower 35   *Parking* Limited

Lancaster Court Hotel   £E

Map 22 B2
202 Sussex Gardens W2 3AU
01-402 8438
Credit Access, Amex, Diners, Visa
■ A four-storey Victorian terraced house between Paddington and Lancaster Gate stations. Bedrooms, reached by quite steep steps, are centrally heated, and most have a double and a single bed. There are plenty of public bathrooms/WCs for rooms without their own.
Rooms 42   *Room phone* No   *Room TV* Yes
en suite bath/shower 15   *Parking* Limited

Hotel Lexham   £E

Map 23 A4
32 Lexham Gardens W8 5JU
01-373 6471
Credit Access, Visa
■ The Wilsons, owners for 35 years, have imbued their hotel with warmth and personality, helped for the last six by manager Mr Chalmers. Bedrooms are spick and span, as are the lounges (one with TV) and dining room. Unlicensed. No dogs. *Amenities* laundry service, lift, porterage.
Rooms 63   *Room phone* Yes   *Room TV* No
en suite bath/shower 32   *Parking* Limited

Hotel Lily   £D/E

Map 23 A6
23 Lillie Road SW6 1UG
01-381 1881   Telex 918922
Credit Access, Amex, Diners, Visa
■ A purpose-built modern hotel near Earl's Court Exhibition Centre. Public areas are quite smart and bedrooms, though on the small side, are reasonably well equipped (direct-dial phone, colour TV, radio, alarm clock, tea-makers). *Amenities* laundry service, in-house movies, lift, porterage.
Rooms 106   *Direct dial* Yes   *Room TV* Yes
en suite bath/shower 106   *Parking* Limited

Lonsdale Hotel   £E

Map 24 C1
9 Bedford Place WC1B 5JA
01-636 1812   Telex 296012
Credit Access, Visa
■ Just south of Russell Square and close to the British Museum, the Lonsdale offers straightforward overnight accommodation in decent-sized bedrooms, all with central heating and washbasins. There's a TV lounge and cheerful breakfast room. Unlicensed. No dogs.

Rooms 34	*Room phone* No
en suite bath/shower 2	*Room TV* No
Parking Limited	

Merryfield House   £F

Map 22 C1
42 York Street W1H 1FN
01-935 8326
■ The Tyler-Smith family have been here for over 20 years, providing quiet courtesy and a very civilised atmosphere in a central location. Bedrooms are compact, neat and tidy, with strong floral wallpapers and matching fabrics. Radios, hairdryers, en suite bathrooms. No dogs.

Rooms 7	*Room phone* No
en suite bath/shower 7	*Room TV* Yes
Parking Difficult	

Number Eight Hotel   £D

Map 23 B4
8 Emperor's Gate SW7 4HH
01-370 7516   Telex 263849
Credit Access, Amex, Diners, Visa
■ Pleasant accommodation just off Cromwell Road. The smallest single is tiny, but other rooms are of a decent size and all are well equipped. Corridors and day rooms are in good order, and buffet breakfast is served in the smart basement room. No dogs.
Amenities fax.

Rooms 14	*Direct dial* Yes
en suite bath/shower 13	*Room TV* Yes
Parking Difficult	

Parkwood Hotel   £E

Map 22 C2
4 Stanhope Place W2 2HB
01-402 2241   Telex 268312
Credit Visa
■ A smart town house just a few steps from Hyde Park and the shops of Oxford Street. The entrance hall and reception lounge are quite stylish, and comfortable bedrooms all offer direct-dial phones, TVs, radios and tea-makers. Unlicensed. No dogs.

Rooms 18	*Direct dial* Yes
en suite bath/shower 12	*Room TV* Yes
Parking Difficult	

President Hotel   £E

Map 24 C1
Russell Square WC1N 1DB
01-837 8844   Telex 21822
Credit Access, Amex, Diners, Visa
■ Plain, practical comforts in a large, well-run hotel next to the Imperial. All the bedrooms have bathrooms with separate toilets, and there's a bright bar and restaurant. No dogs.
Amenities laundry service, coffee shop (10.30am–2am), in-house movies, lift, porterage.

Rooms 447 *Direct dial* Yes *Room TV* Yes	
en suite bath/shower 447 *Parking* Ample	

Prince Hotel   £D/E

Map 23 B5
6 Sumner Place SW7 3AB
01-589 6488   Telex 917133
Credit Access, Amex, Diners, Visa
■ In a quiet part of Kensington, the Prince is a well-kept hotel with decent-sized bedrooms. 12 have bath/WC or shower/WC en suite; the rest have showers but no WC. There is a relaxing lounge and a delightful conservatory.
Amenities garden, laundry service, fax.

Rooms 20 *Direct dial* Yes *Room TV* Yes	
en suite bath/shower 12 *Parking* Difficult	

Sorbonne Hotel   £E

Map 23 B4
39 Cromwell Road SW7 2DH
01-589 6636
Credit Access, Amex, Visa
■ Practical comfort at a reasonable price in an unpretentious hotel opposite the Natural History Museum. Bedrooms vary in size, and those with private facilities also have TVs; the others have washbasins and share two bathrooms. Continental Breakfast only. No children under ten. No dogs. *Amenities* lift.

Rooms 18 *Room phone* Yes *Room TV* Some	
en suite bath/shower 10 *Parking* Difficult	

Terstan Hotel   £E

Map 23 A5
29 Nevern Square SW5 9PE
01-373 5368
Credit Access, Visa
■ Run by the same family for nearly 30 years, the Terstan is housed in a Victorian terrace overlooking a quiet square. Bedrooms are smallish, but quite cheerful and comfortable, and there are several public rooms. No dogs.
Amenities garden, games room, laundry service, lift.

Rooms 50 *Room phone* Yes *Room TV* Yes	
en suite bath/shower 25 *Parking* Difficult	

LCT FOR LESS

A LOT FOR LESS

Hotel Willett   £E

Map 23 D5
32 Sloane Gardens SW1W 8DJ
01-824 8415   Telex 926678
■ Ring the bell for entry to this peaceful hotel,
whose bedrooms have recently been improved
with new carpets, curtains and bedspreads. All
rooms have decent modern furniture and neat,
functional bathrooms. A generous full English
breakfast is available. No dogs.
Amenities laundry service, fax.

Rooms 18	*Direct dial* Yes
en suite bath/shower 15	*Room TV* Yes
Parking Difficult	

Yardley Court   £E

Map 7 B5
18 Court Yard, Eltham SE9 5PZ
01-850 1850
■ A neat, old-fashioned little hotel in a creeper-
clad Victorian house. Bedrooms are kept in
spotless condition and five have their own
shower rooms. Tea-makers and hairdryers are
standard. New owners plan full en-suite
facilities.
Amenities garden.

Rooms 9	*Room phone* No
en suite bath/shower 5	*Room TV* Yes
Parking Ample	

Hotels in the main London section of the Guide
where prices are comparable to those in this
section:

Pembroke Court Hotel
Map 22 A2

Bardon Lodge Hotel
Map 7 B5

Colonnade Hotel
Map 20 B3

Hogarth Hotel
Map 23 A5

Mornington Hotel
Map 22 B2

BED & BREAKFAST
UNDER £38 FOR TWO
(INC VAT & SERVICE)

ENGLAND

Allendale, Northumberland: Bishopfield
Barnard Castle, Co Durham: Jersey Farm
  Hotel
Beaminster, Dorset: Bridge House
Bradford, West Yorkshire: Restaurant
  Nineteen
Campsea Ashe, Suffolk: Old Rectory
Cawston, Norfolk: Grey Gables
Chideock, Dorset: Chideock House Hotel
Clun, Shropshire: Old Post Office
Horndon-on-the-Hill, Essex: Hill House
Lanreath, Cornwall: Punch Bowl Inn
Newark-on-Trent, Nottinghamshire:
  Grange Hotel
Ruckhall, Hereford & Worcester: The
  Ancient Camp Inn
St Austell, Cornwall: White Hart Hotel
St Margaret at Cliffe, Kent: Walletts Court
Slaidburn, Lancashire: Hark to Bounty Inn
Tarrant Monkton, Dorset: Langton Arms
Trebarwith Strand, Cornwall: Old Millfloor
Wooler, Northumberland: Ryecroft Hotel
Wooler, Northumberland: Tankerville Arms
  Hotel
Wootton Common, Isle of Wight: Lugleys

SCOTLAND

Annan, Dumfries & Galloway: Warmanbie
  Hotel
Ardnadam, Strathclyde: Firpark Hotel
Ayr, Strathclyde: Balgarth Hotel
Bridge of Cally, Tayside: Bridge of Cally
  Hotel
Cullen, Grampian: Seafield Arms Hotel
Garve, Highland: Inchbae Lodge Hotel
Kingussie, Highland: The Cross
Kirkmichael, Tayside: Log Cabin Hotel
Lochgair, Strathclyde: Lochgair Hotel
Muir of Ord, Highland: Old Arms Hotel

WALES

Harlech, Gwynedd: The Cemlyn
Llannefydd, Clwyd: Hawk & Buckle Inn
Penmaenpool, Gwynedd: George III Hotel

CHANNEL ISLANDS

Sark, Sark: Aval Du Creux Hotel

NORTHERN IRELAND

Portaferry, Co Down: Portaferry Hotel

REPUBLIC OF
IRELAND

Waterville, Co Derry: Huntsman

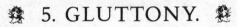

* THE ULTIMATE TEMPTATION

🔖 5. GLUTTONY. 🔖

A LOT FOR LESS

BARGAIN BREAKS

A LOT FOR LESS

BARGAIN BREAKS

All hotels listed are included in the main section of the Guide, where individual entries should be consulted for closures and other relevant details. We have given preference to hotels offering good value compared with their everyday prices.

When are these bargains available?
Dates published are those for which prices could be obtained for bargain breaks operating from November 1988–November 1989. Most hotels do not include Bank Holidays, particularly Easter and Christmas, and many exclude periods of local festivals. Note that many hotels require a week's advance booking.

How many nights are included?
The breaks cover any two consecutive nights, unless we state that they apply to weekends only.

How much does it cost?
Prices quoted are for **one night** for **two people** sharing a double room. We have quoted where possible for a room with private bathroom. Many hotels offer special rates for children. It is important to specify bargain breaks when booking and also to check prices. When we quote 'from £ . . .', the figure is the lowest price available and may not apply at all times.

What do you get?
Bargain-break holidaymakers are entitled to all the hotel's facilities. Meals quoted apply to every day of the stay unless stated otherwise. A full English breakfast is served unless a continental breakfast is indicated.

Hotels are listed by location in alphabetical order within the following sections:

	Page No.
London	188
London Airports	190
England	191
Scotland	225
Wales	230
Channel Islands	233
Isle of Man	233
Northern Ireland	233
Republic of Ireland	234

LONDON

■ **Alexander Hotel**
Weekends Nov, Jan–Mar & Jun–Aug from £70
Breakfast

■ **Athenaeum Hotel**
Weekends from £126
Breakfast

■ **Bardon Lodge Hotel**
Weekends Nov–Mar from £71
Breakfast, dinner

■ **Belgravia-Sheraton**
Weekends Nov–Mar from £97.75
No meals

■ **Bloomsbury Crest Hotel**
Weekends from £64
Breakfast

■ **Bonnington Hotel**
Weekends from £60
Breakfast

■ **Hotel Britannia Inter-Continental**
Weekends Nov–Apr from £99
Continental breakfast

■ **Cannizaro House**
Weekends from £88
Breakfast

■ **Cavendish Hotel**
Weekends (except Xmas, New Year & Easter) from £90
Breakfast

■ **Charing Cross Hotel**
Weekends from £69
Breakfast, £10.95 towards dinner

■ **Charles Bernard Hotel**
Weekends from £45
Breakfast

■ **Chesterfield Hotel**
Weekends from £90
Breakfast

■ **Churchill Hotel**
Weekends May–Dec from £109.25
No meals

■ **The Clive Hotel at Hampstead**
Weekends from £52
Breakfast

■ **Coburg Hotel**
Weekends (except Xmas) from £77
Breakfast, lunch or dinner

■ **Cumberland Hotel**
Weekends (except Xmas, New Year &
Easter) from £86
Breakfast

■ **Drury Lane Moat House Hotel**
Weekends from £100
Breakfast, dinner

■ **Embassy House Hotel**
Weekends from £59
Breakfast

■ **Gore Hotel**
Weekends from £75
Breakfast

■ **Grafton Hotel**
Weekends from £84
Breakfast

■ **Great Northern Hotel**
All year from £61.50
Breakfast

■ **Grosvenor Hotel**
All year from £73
Breakfast

■ **Hendon Hall Hotel**
Weekends from £75
Breakfast

■ **Hilton International Kensington**
Weekends from £60
Breakfast

■ **Hilton International Olympia**
Weekends from £60
Breakfast

■ **Hilton International Regents Park**
Weekends from £60
Breakfast

■ **Hilton Mews at Park Lane**
Weekends from £76
Breakfast

■ **Hogarth Hotel**
Nov–24 Mar & May from £44
Continental breakfast

■ **Holiday Inn (Marble Arch)**
Weekends from £100
Breakfast

■ **Holiday Inn (Mayfair)**
Weekends from £110
Breakfast

■ **Holiday Inn (Swiss Cottage)**
Weekends from £90
Breakfast

■ **Hospitality Inn, Bayswater**
Weekends from £60
Breakfast

■ **Hyatt Carlton Tower**
Weekends from £110
Breakfast

■ **Inn on the Park**
Weekends from £150
Breakfast

■ **Kensington Close Hotel**
Weekends (except Xmas, New Year &
Easter) from £68
Breakfast

■ **Kensington Palace Thistle**
Weekends from £70
Breakfast

■ **Kingsley Hotel**
Weekends from £130
Breakfast, £11 towards dinner

■ **London Embassy Hotel**
Weekends from £60
Breakfast

■ **London Hilton on Park Lane**
Weekends from £105
Breakfast

■ **London Marriott Hotel**
All year from £118
No meals

■ **London Metropole**
All year from £79
Continental breakfast

■ **London Tara**
Weekends all year from £70
Breakfast

■ **Londonderry Hotel**
Weekends from £140
Breakfast

■ **Lowndes Thistle Hotel**
All year from £78
Breakfast

■ **Mandeville Hotel**
Weekends from £60
Breakfast

■ **Marlborough Crest**
Weekends from £84
Breakfast

■ **Le Meridien Piccadilly**
Weekends from £109.25
No meals

■ **The Montcalm**
Weekends from £130
Breakfast

■ **Norfolk Hotel**
All year from £106
Breakfast

■ **Novotel London**
Weekends from £63
Breakfast

■ **Pembridge Court Hotel**
Weekends Nov–Apr from £55
Breakfast

■ **Post House Hotel (Hampstead)**
Weekends (except Xmas, New Year &
Easter) from £58
Breakfast

■ **Ramada Hotel**
Weekends all year from £86
Breakfast

■ **Ramada Inn West London**
Weekends all year from £50
Continental breakfast

■ **Regent Crest Hotel**
Weekends from £78
Breakfast

■ **The Ritz**
Weekends all year from £150
Breakfast

■ **Royal Court Hotel**
All year from £99
Continental breakfast

■ **Royal Garden Hotel**
Weekends from £98
Breakfast

■ **Royal Horseguards Thistle Hotel**
Weekends from £66
Breakfast

■ **Royal Lancaster Hotel**
Weekends from £100
Breakfast

■ **Royal Scot Hotel**
Weekends from £47
Breakfast, £9.25 towards meals

■ **Royal Trafalgar Thistle Hotel**
Weekends from £82
Breakfast

■ **Royal Westminster Thistle Hotel**
All year from £76
Breakfast

■ **Hotel Russell**
Weekends (except Xmas, New Year &
Easter) from £82
Breakfast

■ **St George's Hotel**
Weekends (except Xmas, New Year &
Easter) from £84
Breakfast

■ **The Selfridge**
All year from £78
Breakfast

■ **Sheraton Park Tower**
Weekends from £85
No meals

■ **Stakis St Ermin's Hotel**
Weekends from £72
Breakfast

■ **Strand Palace Hotel**
Weekends (except Xmas, New Year &
Easter) from £68
Breakfast

■ **Swallow International Hotel**
All year from £85
Breakfast, £13 towards 1 meal

■ **Tower Thistle Hotel**
All year from £76
Breakfast

■ **The Waldorf**
Weekends (except Xmas, New Year &
Easter) from £88
Breakfast

■ **Westbury Hotel**
Weekends (except Xmas, New Year &
Easter) from £106
Breakfast

■ **White House**
Weekends from £70
Breakfast

LONDON AIRPORTS

■ **GATWICK**
Copthorne Hotel
Weekends from £77
Breakfast

■ **GATWICK**
Crest Hotel
Weekends from £70
Breakfast, dinner

■ **GATWICK**
Gatwick Hilton International
Weekends from £78
No meals

■ **HEATHROW**
Ariel Hotel
Weekends (except Xmas, New Year &
Easter) from £56
Breakfast

■ **HEATHROW**
Berkeley Arms Hotel
Weekends from £38
Breakfast

■ **HEATHROW**
Excelsior Hotel
Weekends (except Xmas, New Year &
Easter) from £60
Breakfast

■ **HEATHROW**
Heathrow Penta
All year from £66
£12 towards meals

■ **HEATHROW**
Holiday Inn
Weekends from £60
Breakfast

■ **HEATHROW**
Master Robert
Weekends from £34
No meals

■ **HEATHROW**
Post House Hotel
Weekends (except Xmas, New Year &
Easter) from £56
Breakfast

■ **HEATHROW**
Sheraton Heathrow Hotel
Weekends all year from £48.30
No meals

■ **HEATHROW**
Sheraton Skyline
Weekends all year from £75
No meals

■ **HEATHROW**
Skyway Hotel
Weekends (except Xmas, New Year &
Easter) from £48
Breakfast

ENGLAND

■ **ABBERLEY**
Elms Hotel
Weekends only Nov–March from £110
Weekends only Apr–Nov from £120
Breakfast, dinner

■ **ABINGDON**
Upper Reaches Hotel
Weekends (except Xmas, New Year &
Easter) from £80
Breakfast, dinner

■ **ALCESTER**
Arrow Mill
All year from £72
Breakfast, dinner

■ **ALDEBURGH**
Brudenell Hotel
All year (except Xmas, New Year &
Easter) from £70
Breakfast, dinner

■ **ALDEBURGH**
Uplands Hotel
Nov–May from £80
Breakfast, £8 towards dinner

■ **ALDRIDGE**
Fairlawns Hotel
Weekends from £55
Breakfast, dinner

■ **ALLENDALE**
Bishopfield
Nov–Apr from £46
Breakfast, dinner

■ **ALNWICK**
Hotspur Hotel
All year from £55
Breakfast, dinner

■ **ALNWICK**
White Swan Hotel
All year from £65
Breakfast, dinner

■ **ALTON**
Swan Hotel
Weekends (except Xmas, New Year &
Easter) from £68
Breakfast, dinner

■ **ALTRINCHAM**
Bowdon Hotel
Weekends from £56
Breakfast, dinner

■ **ALTRINCHAM**
Cresta Court Hotel
Weekends from £58
Breakfast, dinner

■ **ALTRINCHAM**
George & Dragon Hotel
All year from £40
Breakfast

■ **ALVESTON**
Alveston House Hotel
Weekends from £69
Breakfast, dinner

■ **ALVESTON**
Post House Hotel
Weekends (except Xmas, New Year &
Easter) from £70
Breakfast, dinner

■ **AMBERLEY**
Amberley Inn
1 Nov–30 Mar from £62
31 Mar–31 Aug from £80
Breakfast, dinner

A LOT FOR LESS

■ **AMBLESIDE**
Nanny Brow
Nov–Mar from £63
Breakfast, dinner

■ **AMBLESIDE**
Rothay Manor
1 Nov–23 Mar from £94
Breakfast, dinner

■ **AMBLESIDE**
Wateredge Hotel
1 Nov–mid Dec & mid Jan–12 May from £70
Breakfast, dinner

■ **AMPFIELD**
Potters Heron Hotel
Weekends from £42
Breakfast

■ **ANDOVER**
White Hart Hotel
Weekends (except Xmas, New Year & Easter) from £64
Breakfast, dinner

■ **ARUNDEL**
Norfolk Arms Hotel
All year from £73
Breakfast, dinner

■ **ASCOT**
Berystede Hotel
Weekends (except Xmas, New Year & Easter) from £84
Breakfast, dinner

■ **ASCOT**
Royal Berkshire
Weekends from £120
Breakfast, dinner

■ **ASHFORD**
Eastwell Manor
Sun–Thurs from £125
Breakfast, dinner

■ **ASHINGTON**
Mill House Hotel
Weekends from £60
Breakfast, dinner

■ **AYLESBURY**
Bell Hotel
Weekends (except Xmas, New Year & Easter) from £64
Breakfast, dinner

■ **BAGSHOT**
Pennyhill Park Hotel
Weekends from £155
Breakfast, dinner

■ **BAINBRIDGE**
Rose & Crown
1 Nov–30 Apr from £120
Breakfast, dinner

■ **BAKEWELL**
Hassop Hall Hotel
1 Nov–31 Mar from £45
No meals

■ **BAMBURGH**
Lord Crewe Arms Hotel
Mar–Nov from £62
Breakfast, dinner

■ **BANBURY**
Whateley Hall
Weekends (except Xmas, New Year & Easter) from £74
Breakfast, dinner

■ **BARFORD**
Glebe Hotel
Weekends from £70
Breakfast, £13.50 towards dinner

■ **BARNARD CASTLE**
Jersey Farm Hotel
Weekends from £49
Breakfast, dinner

■ **BARNBY MOOR**
Ye Olde Bell
Weekends (except Xmas, New Year & Easter) from £66
Breakfast, dinner

■ **BARNHAM BROOM**
Barnham Broom Hotel
All year from £75
Breakfast, dinner

■ **BARNSLEY**
Ardsley Moat House
Weekends from £60
Breakfast, dinner

■ **BARNSTAPLE**
Imperial Hotel
All year (except Xmas, New Year & Easter) from £72
Breakfast, dinner

■ **BASILDON**
Crest Hotel
Weekends from £68
Breakfast, dinner

■ **BASINGSTOKE**
Crest Hotel
Weekends from £72
Breakfast, dinner

■ **BASINGSTOKE**
Hilton Lodge
Weekends from £52
Breakfast

■ **BASINGSTOKE**
Hilton National Hotel
Weekends from £52
Breakfast

■ **BASLOW**
Cavendish Hotel
Weekends 1 Nov–31 Mar from £105
No meals

■ **BASSENTHWAITE**
Armathwaite Hotel
Weekends Nov–Apr from £95
Breakfast, dinner

■ **BASSENTHWAITE LAKE**
Pheasant Inn
6 Nov–19 Mar from £70
Breakfast, dinner

■ **BATH**
Apsley House Hotel
Nov–Apr from £75
Breakfast, dinner

■ **BATH**
Bath Hotel
Weekends only £80
Breakfast, dinner

■ **BATH**
Francis Hotel
Weekends (except Xmas, New Year &
Easter) from £84
Breakfast, dinner

■ **BATH**
Hilton National
Weekends from £64
Breakfast

■ **BATH**
Lansdown Grove Hotel
Weekends from £82
Breakfast, dinner

■ **BATH**
Priory Hotel
Nov–Apr from £130
Continental breakfast, dinner

■ **BATH**
Queensbury Hotel
Nov–Mar from £75
Continental Breakfast, 1 dinner

■ **BATH**
Royal Crescent Hotel
Nov–Mar from £165.50
Breakfast, dinner

■ **BATTLE**
Netherfield Place
Oct–Apr from £100
Breakfast, dinner

■ **BEANACRE**
Beechfield House
1 Nov–23 Mar from £97.50
Breakfast, dinner

■ **BEAULIEU**
Montagu Arms Hotel
1 Nov–31 Mar from £80 &
1 Apr–Nov from £110
Breakfast, dinner

■ **BECCLES**
Waveney House Hotel
All year from £58.30
Breakfast, dinner

■ **BEDFORD**
Woodlands Manor Hotel
Weekends from £69.60
Breakfast, dinner

■ **BEESTON**
Wild Boar Hotel
Weekends from £130
Breakfast, dinner

■ **BELFORD**
Blue Bell Hotel
Weekends 26 Feb–30 Nov from £68
Breakfast, dinner

■ **BEMBRIDGE**
Highbury Hotel
Weekends 1 Nov–1 May from £45
Breakfast, dinner

■ **BERWICK-UPON-TWEED**
Kings Arms Hotel
Weekends from £75
Breakfast, dinner

■ **BEVERLEY**
Beverley Arms Hotel
All year (except Xmas, New Year &
Easter) from £64
Breakfast, dinner

■ **BEXINGTON**
Manor Hotel
All year from £32.75
Breakfast, dinner

■ **BIBURY**
Bibury Court Hotel
Nov–Mar (except Cheltenham Gold Cup
week)
from £68
Continental breakfast, dinner

■ **BIBURY**
Swan Hotel
Nov–Easter from £62.50
Breakfast, dinner

■ **BILBOROUGH**
Bilborough Manor Hotel
All year from £99
Breakfast, dinner

■ **BILBROOK**
Dragon House Hotel
Jan & Feb from £60
Breakfast, dinner

A
L
C
T
F
C
R
L
E
S
S

■ BILLINGHAM
Billingham Arms Hotel
Weekends from £38
Breakfast

■ BINGLEY
Bankfield Hotel
Weekends from £59
Breakfast, dinner

■ BIRKENHEAD
Bowler Hat Hotel
Weekends from £64.50
Continental breakfast, dinner

■ BIRMINGHAM
Albany Hotel
Weekends (except Xmas, New Year &
Easter) from £64
Breakfast, dinner

■ BIRMINGHAM
Codben Hotel
Weekends from £45
Breakfast, dinner

■ BIRMINGHAM
Grand Hotel
Weekends from £59
Breakfast, dinner

■ BIRMINGHAM
Norfolk Hotel
Weekends from £50
Breakfast, dinner

■ BIRMINGHAM
Plough & Harrow Hotel
All year from £78
Breakfast

■ BIRMINGHAM
Post House Hotel
Weekends (except Xmas, New Year &
Easter) from £60
Breakfast, dinner

■ BIRMINGHAM
Strathallan Thistle Hotel
Weekends from £52
Breakfast

■ BIRMINGHAM AIRPORT
Excelsior Hotel
Weekends (except Xmas, New Year &
Easter) from £60
Breakfast, dinner

■ BLACKBURN
Blackburn Moat House
Weekends from £68
Breakfast

■ BLACKPOOL
Imperial Hotel
All year from £65
Breakfast, dinner

■ BLACKPOOL
New Clifton Hotel
All year from £58
Breakfast, dinner

■ BLACKPOOL
Pembroke Hotel
All year from £75
Breakfast, dinner

■ BLAKENEY
Manor Hotel
2 Nov–19 May from £78
Breakfast, dinner

■ BLOCKLEY
Lower Brook House
1 Nov–12 Mar from £80
Breakfast, dinner

■ BODYMOOR HEATH
Marston Farm Hotel
Weekends from £80
Breakfast, dinner

■ BOLTON
Crest Hotel
Weekends from £68
Breakfast, dinner

■ BOLTON
Last Drop Village Hotel
Weekends from £64
Breakfast, dinner

■ BOLTON
Pack Horse Hotel
Weekends all year (including weekdays
Jul/Aug) from £52
Breakfast, dinner

■ BOLTON ABBEY
Devonshire Arms
All year from £92
Breakfast, dinner

■ BOREHAM STREET
White Friars Hotel
All year from £70
Breakfast, dinner

■ BOROUGHBRIDGE
Crown Hotel
Weekends (except Xmas & Harrogate
Fairs)
from £60
Breakfast, dinner

■ BOROUGHBRIDGE
Three Arrows Hotel
Nov–Feb from £55
Mar–Apr from £62
Breakfast, dinner

■ BORROWDALE
Borrowdale Hotel
Nov–Mar from £58
Breakfast, dinner

■ **BOSTON**
New England Hotel
Weekends (except Xmas, New Year &
Easter) from £56
Breakfast, dinner

■ **BOURNEMOUTH**
Crest Hotel
All year from £78
Breakfast, dinner

■ **BOURNEMOUTH**
East Cliff Court Hotel
Nov–June from £60
Breakfast, dinner

■ **BOURNEMOUTH**
Highcliff Hotel
All year from £90
Breakfast, dinner

■ **BOURNEMOUTH**
Langtry Manor Hotel
All year from £79
Breakfast, dinner

■ **BOURNEMOUTH**
Norfolk Royale Hotel
All year from £90
Breakfast, dinner

■ **BOURNEMOUTH**
Palace Court Hotel
All year from £70
Breakfast, dinner

■ **BOURNEMOUTH**
Royal Bath Hotel
Weekends from £116
Breakfast, dinner

■ **BOWNESS ON WINDERMERE**
Belsfield Hotel
All year (except Xmas, New Year &
Easter) from £84
Breakfast, dinner

■ **BOWNESS ON WINDERMERE**
Old England Hotel
All year (except Xmas, New Year &
Easter) from £88
Breakfast, dinner

■ **BRACKNELL**
Hilton National
Weekends from £56
Breakfast

■ **BRADFORD**
Victoria Hotel
Weekends (except Xmas, New Year &
Easter) from £50
Breakfast, dinner

■ **BRAINTREE**
White Hart Hotel
Weekends from £52
Breakfast, dinner

■ **BRAITHWAITE**
Ivy House Hotel
Mid Nov–mid Mar (except Xmas & New
Year) from £59
Breakfast, dinner

■ **BRAMHOPE**
Parkway Hotel
Weekends from £62
Breakfast, dinner

■ **BRAMHOPE**
Post House Hotel
Weekends (except Xmas, New Year &
Easter) from £80
Breakfast, dinner

■ **BRAMLEY**
Bramley Grange Hotel
Weekends from £90
Breakfast, dinner

■ **BRAMPTON**
Farlam Hall Hotel
Nov–mid Apr (except Feb & Bank Hols)
from £90
Breakfast, dinner

■ **BRANDON**
Brandon Hall Hotel
Weekends (except Xmas, New Year &
Easter) from £68
Breakfast, dinner

■ **BRANSCOMBE**
Masons Arms
All year from £70
Breakfast, £13 towards dinner

■ **BRENTWOOD**
Brentwood Moat House
Weekends (except Xmas, New Year &
Easter) from £70
Breakfast, dinner

■ **BRIGHTON**
Alexandra Hotel
Weekends only from £54
Breakfast

■ **BRIGHTON**
Bedford Hotel
Weekends Nov–Mar from £71
Breakfast, dinner

■ **BRIGHTON**
Brighton Metropole Hotel
All year (except during conferences,
exhibitions & Bank Hols) from £83
Breakfast, dinner

■ **BRIGHTON**
Courtlands Hotel
All year (except Xmas & Easter) from £65
Breakfast, dinner

A LOT FOR LESS

■ BRIGHTON
Dudley Hotel
Weekends (except Xmas, New Year &
Easter) from £80
Breakfast, dinner

■ BRIGHTON
The Grand
All year from £120
Breakfast, dinner

■ BRIGHTON
Old Ship Hotel
Weekends & any 2 nights Jul & Aug
from £80
Breakfast, dinner

■ BRIGHTON
Ramada Renaissance Hotel
Weekends from £115
Breakfast, dinner

■ BRIGHTON
Sheridan Hotel
Weekends (except Xmas, New Year &
Easter) from £60
Breakfast

■ BRIGHTON
Topps Hotel
Weekends (except Bank Hols) from £58.50
Breakfast, dinner

■ BRISTOL
Crest Hotel
Weekends from £88
Breakfast, dinner

■ BRISTOL
Grand Hotel
Weekends from £65
Breakfast, dinner

■ BRISTOL
Hilton International
Weekends from £56
Breakfast

■ BRISTOL
Holiday Inn
Weekends from £60
Breakfast, £14.50 towards dinner

■ BRISTOL
Redwood Lodge Hotel
Weekends from £75
Breakfast, dinner

■ BRISTOL
Unicorn Hotel
Weekends from £55
Breakfast, dinner

■ BRIXHAM
Quayside Hotel
All year from £66
Breakfast, dinner

■ BROADWAY
Broadway Hotel
1 Nov–Easter (except Xmas, New Year &
Cheltenham Gold Cup) from £52
Breakfast, dinner

■ BROADWAY
Collin House Hotel
All year from £148
Breakfast, dinner

■ BROADWAY
Dormy House
Weekends from £116
Breakfast, dinner

■ BROCKENHURST
Balmer Lawn Hotel
Weekends from £70
Breakfast

■ BROCKENHURST
Careys Manor Hotel
All year from £89.70
Breakfast, dinner

■ BROMLEY
Bromley Court Hotel
Weekends from £89
Breakfast, dinner

■ BROMSGROVE
Grafton Manor
All year from £139
Breakfast, dinner

■ BROMSGROVE
Perry Hall Hotel
Weekends from £59
Breakfast, dinner

■ BROOME
Oaksmere Country House Hotel
Weekends (except Bank Hols, Xmas–New
Year) from £75
Breakfast, dinner

■ BROUGHTON
Broughton Park Hotel
Weekends from £70
Breakfast, dinner

■ BROXTED
Whitehall Hotel
Nov–Mar from £110
Breakfast, dinner

■ BUCKINGHAM
White Hart Hotel
Weekends (except Xmas, New Year &
Easter) from £70
Breakfast, dinner

■ BUCKLOW HILL
Swan
Weekends from £70
Breakfast, dinner

■ **BURBAGE**
Savernake Forest Hotel
All year from £74
Breakfast, dinner

■ **BURFORD**
Bay Tree Hotel
1 Nov–30 Apr from £60
Breakfast, dinner

■ **BURLEY**
Burley Manor Hotel
All year from £73
Breakfast, dinner

■ **BURNLEY**
Keirby Hotel
Weekends from £45
Breakfast, dinner

■ **BURTON UPON TRENT**
Brookhouse Inn
Weekends from £80
Breakfast, dinner

■ **BURTON UPON TRENT**
Riverside Inn
Weekends from £56
Breakfast, dinner

■ **BURY ST EDMUNDS**
Angel Hotel
Weekends from £60
Breakfast, dinner

■ **BURY ST EDMUNDS**
Butterfly Hotel
Weekends from £63
Breakfast, dinner

■ **BURY ST EDMUNDS**
Suffolk Hotel
Weekends (except Xmas, New Year &
Easter) from £64
Breakfast, dinner

■ **CAMBERLEY**
Frimley Hall
Weekends (except Xmas, New Year &
Easter) from £80
Breakfast, dinner

■ **CAMBRIDGE**
Arundel House Hotel
Weekends from £61
Breakfast, dinner

■ **CAMBRIDGE**
Cambridgeshire Moat House
Weekends from £79
Breakfast, dinner

■ **CAMBRIDGE**
Garden House Hotel
Weekends from £94.50
Breakfast, dinner

■ **CAMBRIDGE**
Gonville Hotel
Weekends from £65
Breakfast, dinner

■ **CAMBRIDGE**
Post House Hotel
Weekends (except Xmas, New Year &
Easter) from £92
Breakfast, dinner

■ **CAMBRIDGE**
University Arms Hotel
Weekends & 3 nights mid-week from £61
Breakfast, dinner

■ **CANTERBURY**
Canterbury Hotel
Nov–June from £49
Breakfast, dinner

■ **CANTERBURY**
Chaucer Hotel
Weekends (except Xmas, New Year &
Easter) from £76
Breakfast, dinner

■ **CANTERBURY**
County Hotel
Weekends Nov–Mar (except Xmas & New
Year) from £56
Breakfast

■ **CANTERBURY**
Falstaff Hotel
Weekends (except Xmas & New Year)
from £68
Breakfast, dinner

■ **CANTERBURY**
Howfield Manor
Nov–March from £185
Breakfast, dinner

■ **CANTERBURY**
Slatters Hotel
All year from £74
Breakfast, dinner

■ **CARLISLE**
Crest Hotel
All year from £72
Breakfast, dinner

■ **CARLISLE**
Swallow Hilltop Hotel
All year from £65
Breakfast, 1 lunch, dinner

■ **CARLYON BAY**
Carlyon Bay Hotel
All year (except Xmas, New Year, Easter,
Whitsun & 19 July–10 Sept) from £78.20
Breakfast, dinner

A
L
O
T

F
O
R

L
E
S
S

■ CARLYON BAY
Porth Avallen Hotel
Weekends from £55
Breakfast, dinner

■ CARTMEL
Aynsome Manor Hotel
Oct–May from £54
Breakfast, dinner

■ CARTMEL
Priory Hotel
Mar–Nov (except Bank Hols) from £50
Breakfast, dinner

■ CASTLE CARY
Bond's Hotel
All year from £49
Breakfast, dinner

■ CASTLE COMBE
Manor House Hotel
4 Nov–25 Mar from £125
Breakfast, dinner

■ CHADDESLEY CORBETT
Brockencote Hall
Weekends from £73
Continental breakfast, dinner

■ CHAGFORD
Great Tree Hotel
All year from £74
Breakfast, dinner

■ CHAGFORD
Mill End Hotel
Nov–Mar from £72.50
Breakfast, dinner

■ CHAGFORD
Teignworthy
1 Nov–Xmas & 2 Jan–Easter from £137
Breakfast, dinner

■ CHARINGWORTH
Charingworth Manor Hotel
All year (except Xmas, New Year, Easter
& Cheltenham Gold Cup) from £120
Breakfast, dinner

■ CHARLBURY
Bell at Charlbury
All year from £70
Breakfast, dinner

■ CHARLECOTE
The Charlecote Pheasant
Weekends (including weekday Jul/Aug)
from £70
Breakfast, dinner

■ CHEDINGTON
Chedington Court
All year from £92
Breakfast, dinner

■ CHELMSFORD
Pontlands Park
Weekends from £70
£18.50 towards meals

■ CHELTENHAM
Hotel de la Bere
All year from £175
Continental breakfast, £12.95 towards
dinner

■ CHELTENHAM
Golden Valley Thistle Hotel
Weekends from £54
Breakfast

■ CHELTENHAM
The Greenway
Nov–Apr (except Xmas & The
Cheltenham Hunt Festival) from £150
Breakfast, dinner

■ CHELTENHAM
Queen's Hotel
Weekends (except Xmas, New Year &
Easter) from £88
Breakfast, dinner

■ CHELTENHAM
Wyastone Hotel
Weekends from £45
No meals

■ CHELWOOD
Chelwood House Hotel
Weekends Nov–Mar from £79
Breakfast, dinner

■ CHENIES
Bedford Arms Thistle Hotel
Weekends from £64
Breakfast

■ CHESTER
Abbots Well Hotel
All year from £55
Breakfast, dinner

■ CHESTER
Blossoms Hotel
All year from £75
Breakfast, dinner

■ CHESTER
Chester Grosvenor
Weekends from £135
Breakfast, dinner

■ CHESTER
Crabwall Manor
Weekends from £130
Breakfast, dinner

■ CHESTER
Mollington Banastre Hotel
All year from £45
Breakfast, dinner

A
I
C
T
F
O
R
R
L
E
S
S

■ CHESTER
Post House Hotel
Weekends (except Xmas, New Year &
Easter) from £70
Breakfast, dinner

■ CHESTER
Rowton Hall Hotel
All year from £85
Breakfast, dinner

■ CHESTERFIELD
Chesterfield Hotel
Weekends from £59
Breakfast, dinner

■ CHESTER-LE-STREET
Lumley Castle Hotel
Weekends from £49.75
Breakfast

■ CHICHESTER
Dolphin & Anchor Hotel
Weekends (except Xmas, New Year &
Easter) from £82
Breakfast, dinner

■ CHIDEOCK
Chideock House Hotel
All year from £61
Breakfast, dinner

■ CHIPPING CAMPDEN
Cotswold House Hotel
1 Nov–31 Mar from £88
Breakfast, dinner

■ CHIPPING CAMPDEN
Kings Arms Hotel
All year from £120
Breakfast, dinner

■ CHIPPING CAMPDEN
Noel Arms Hotel
Nov–Apr from £70
Breakfast, dinner

■ CHITTLEHAMHOLT
Highbullen Hotel
Weekends 1 Nov–31 Mar (except Xmas &
New Year) from £67.50
Continental breakfast, dinner

■ CHOLLERFORD
George Hotel
All year from £68
Breakfast, dinner

■ CHURCH STRETTON
Stretton Hall Hotel
1 Nov–31 May from £60
Breakfast, dinner

■ CHURT
Frensham Pond Hotel
Weekends from £80
Breakfast, dinner

■ CIRENCESTER
Fleece Hotel
All year from £67.50
Breakfast, dinner

■ CIRENCESTER
Kings Head Hotel
All year from £62
Breakfast, dinner

■ CIRENCESTER
Stratton House Hotel
All year from £76
Breakfast

■ CLANFIELD
Plough at Clanfield
All year from £85
Breakfast £14.50

■ CLAWTON
Court Barn Country House Hotel
Nov–Jul, Oct–Nov from £64
Breakfast, dinner

■ CLAYTON-LE-WOODS
Pines Hotel
Weekends from £120
Breakfast, dinner

■ CLEARWELL
Clearwell Castle
Weekends Nov–Apr (except Xmas & New
Year) from £85
Breakfast

■ CLEETHORPES
Kingsway Hotel
Weekends from £65
Breakfast, dinner

■ COBHAM
Hilton National
Weekends from £64
Breakfast

■ COLCHESTER
Marks Tey Hotel
Weekends from £100
Breakfast, dinner

■ COLCHESTER
Rose & Crown Hotel
Weekends from £32.50
Breakfast

■ COLEFORD
Speech House
All year (except Xmas, New Year &
Easter) from £72
Breakfast, dinner

■ COLERNE
Lucknam Park
All year from £165
Breakfast, lunch or dinner

■ **CONGLETON**
Great Moreton Hall Hotel
Weekends from £90
Breakfast, dinner

■ **CONISTON**
Coniston Sun Hotel
Nov–Apr (except Jan, Feb, Xmas, Easter &
Bank Hols) from £66
Breakfast, dinner

■ **COODEN**
Cooden Resort Hotel
Weekends from £78
Breakfast, dinner

■ **COODEN BEACH**
Calahonda Hotel
Apr–Oct from £72
Breakfast, dinner

■ **COPDOCK**
Ipswich Moat House
Weekends from £62
Breakfast, dinner

■ **CORFE CASTLE**
Horton's House Hotel
Nov–Feb from £96
Breakfast

■ **CORNHILL-ON-TWEED**
Tillmouth Park Hotel
All year from £100
Breakfast, dinner

■ **CORSE LAWN**
Corse Lawn House Hotel
1 Nov–1 Mar (except Xmas & New Year)
from £90
Breakfast, dinner

■ **CORSHAM**
Rudloe Park Hotel
All year from £60
Breakfast

■ **COVENTRY**
Chase Crest Hotel
Weekends from £66
Breakfast, dinner

■ **COVENTRY**
Crest Hotel
Weekends from £72
Breakfast, dinner

■ **COVENTRY**
De Vere Hotel
Weekends all year (including weekdays
Jul–Aug) from £42
Breakfast

■ **COVENTRY**
Hotel Leofric
All year from £50
Breakfast, dinner

■ **COVENTRY**
Post House Hotel
Weekends (except Xmas, New Year &
Easter) from £56
Breakfast, dinner

■ **CRATHORNE**
Crathorne Hall Hotel
All year (except Xmas) from £70
Breakfast, dinner

■ **CRAWLEY**
George Hotel
Weekends (except Xmas, New Year &
Easter) from £70
Breakfast, dinner

■ **CRICK**
Post House Hotel
Weekends (except Xmas, New Year &
Easter) from £70
Breakfast, dinner

■ **CROOK**
Wild Boar Hotel
All year from £136
Breakfast, dinner

■ **CROOKLANDS**
Crooklands Hotel
All year from £66
Breakfast, dinner

■ **CROSBY-ON-EDEN**
Crosby Lodge Hotel
Nov–Mar from £75
Breakfast, dinner

■ **CROXDALE**
Bridge Hotel
Weekends from £47
Breakfast, dinner

■ **CROYDON**
Holiday Inn
Weekends from £54
Breakfast

■ **CROYDON**
Selsdon Park Hotel
Weekends (except Xmas & New Year)
from £108
Breakfast, dinner

■ **DARLINGTON**
Blackwell Grange Moat House
Weekends from £72
Breakfast, dinner

■ **DARLINGTON**
King's Head Swallow Hotel
Weekends (including weekday Jul/Aug)
from £65
Breakfast, dinner

■ **DARLINGTON**
St George Hotel
Weekends from £50
Breakfast, dinner

■ **DARTMOUTH**
Royal Castle Hotel
All year from £56
Breakfast, dinner

■ **DEDHAM**
Maison Talbooth
All year from £80
Continental breakfast

■ **DERBY**
Crest Hotel
Weekends from £76
Breakfast, dinner

■ **DINNINGTON**
Dinnington Hall
Weekends from £75
Breakfast, dinner

■ **DONCASTER**
Danum Swallow Hotel
Weekends from £62
Breakfast, dinner

■ **DONCASTER**
Doncaster Moat House
Weekends from £60
Breakfast, dinner

■ **DONCASTER**
Earl of Doncaster
Weekends (except Xmas, New Year &
Easter) from £60
Breakfast, dinner

■ **DONCASTER**
Grand St Leger Hotel
Weekends from £65
Breakfast, dinner

■ **DORCHESTER-ON-THAMES**
George Hotel
Weekends from £80
Breakfast, dinner

■ **DORKING**
Burford Bridge Hotel
Weekends (except Xmas, New Year &
Easter) from £88
Breakfast, dinner

■ **DORKING**
White Horse Hotel
Weekends (except Xmas, New Year &
Easter) from £64
Breakfast, dinner

■ **DOVEDALE**
Peveril of the Peak Hotel
All year (except Xmas, New Year &
Easter) from £78
Breakfast, dinner

■ **DOVER**
Crest Hotel
Weekends (except Jul & Aug) from £72
Breakfast, dinner

■ **DOVER**
Dover Moat House
Weekends from £70
Breakfast, dinner

■ **DOVER**
White Cliffs Hotel
Nov–June from £56
Breakfast, dinner

■ **DULVERTON**
Ashwick Country House Hotel
Weekends (except Bank Hols) from £68
Breakfast, dinner

■ **DULVERTON**
Carnarvon Arms Hotel
All year from £58
Breakfast, dinner

■ **DUNCHURCH**
Dun Cow Hotel
Weekends from £79
Breakfast, lunch, dinner

■ **DUNKIRK**
Petty France Hotel
Weekends from £79
Breakfast, dinner

■ **DUNSTABLE**
Old Palace Lodge Hotel
Weekends from £36
No meals

■ **DUNSTER**
Luttrell Arms
All year (except Xmas, New Year &
Easter) from £80
Breakfast, dinner

■ **DURHAM**
Royal County Hotel
Weekends (including weekday Jul/Aug)
from £75
Breakfast, dinner

■ **DUXFORD**
Duxford Lodge Hotel
Weekends from £70
Breakfast, dinner

■ **EAST DEREHAM**
King's Head Hotel
Weekends Nov–May & Oct–Nov from £48
Breakfast, dinner

■ **EAST DEREHAM**
Phoenix Hotel
All year (except Xmas, New Year &
Easter) from £66
Breakfast, dinner

A LOT FOR LESS

■ **EAST GRINSTEAD**
Ye Olde Felbridge Hotel
Weekends from £56
Breakfast

■ **EAST STOKE**
Kemps Country House Hotel
All year from £59
Breakfast, dinner

■ **EASTBOURNE**
Cavendish Hotel
Weekends from £204
Breakfast, dinner

■ **EASTBOURNE**
Grand Hotel
Weekends from £120
Breakfast, dinner

■ **EASTBOURNE**
Queen's Hotel
Weekends Nov–June from £86
Breakfast, dinner

■ **EASTBOURNE**
The Wish Tower
All year (except Xmas, New Year &
Easter) from £66
Breakfast, dinner

■ **EASTLEIGH**
Crest Hotel
Weekends from £56
Breakfast, dinner

■ **EASTON GREY**
Whatley Manor
Weekends from £92
Breakfast, dinner

■ **EGHAM**
Runnymede Hotel
Weekends from £85
Breakfast, dinner

■ **ELY**
Lamb Hotel
All year from £60
Breakfast, dinner

■ **EPPING**
Post House
Weekends (except Xmas, New Year &
Easter) from £60
Breakfast, dinner

■ **ETTINGTON**
Chase Hotel
All year from £90
Breakfast, 1 lunch, dinner

■ **EVERSHOT**
Summer Lodge
All year from £95
Breakfast, dinner

■ **EVESHAM**
Evesham Hotel
Weekends (including weekdays June–Oct)
from £56
Breakfast, lunch, dinner

■ **EXETER**
Buckerell Lodge Crest Hotel
All year from £78
Breakfast, dinner

■ **EXETER**
Rougemont Hotel
Weekends from £60
Breakfast, dinner

■ **EXETER**
White Hart Hotel
Weekends from £30·80
Breakfast

■ **EXMOUTH**
Imperial Hotel
All year (except Xmas, New Year &
Easter) from £84
Breakfast, dinner

■ **FAIRFORD**
Hyperion Hotel
All year from £65
Breakfast, dinner

■ **FAIRY CROSS**
Portledge Hotel
Nov–30 Apr (except Xmas & Bank Hols)
from £64
Breakfast, dinner

■ **FALMOUTH**
Bay Hotel
All year from £76
Breakfast, dinner

■ **FALMOUTH**
Falmouth Hotel
All year (except Xmas & New Year) from
£59·40
Breakfast, dinner

■ **FALMOUTH**
Greenbank Hotel
Weekends from £74
Breakfast, dinner

■ **FAREHAM**
Red Lion Hotel
Weekends from £66
Breakfast, dinner

■ **FARNBOROUGH**
Queen's Hotel
Weekends (except Xmas, New Year &
Easter) from £72
Breakfast, dinner

■ **FARNHAM**
Bishop's Table Hotel
Weekends from £62
Breakfast, dinner

■ **FARNHAM**
Bush Hotel
Weekends (except Xmas, New Year &
Easter) from £72
Breakfast, dinner

■ **FARNHAM**
Trevena House Hotel
All year from £56
Breakfast, dinner

■ **FAWKHAM**
Brandshatch Place
Weekends (except 24 Dec–30 Jan) from
£165
Breakfast, dinner

■ **FELIXSTOWE**
Brook Hotel
Weekends from £46
Breakfast, dinner

■ **FELIXSTOWE**
Orwell Moat House
Weekends from £145
Breakfast, lunch, dinner

■ **FERNDOWN**
Dormy House
Weekends from £115
Breakfast, 1 lunch, dinner

■ **FINDON**
Findon Manor
Weekends from £50
Breakfast, dinner

■ **FRAMLINGHAM**
Crown Hotel
All year (except Xmas, New Year &
Easter) from £78
Breakfast, dinner

■ **FRESHFORD**
Homewood Park
Weekdays only 1 Nov–end Mar from £115
Continental breakfast, dinner

■ **FRESHWATER**
Farringford Hotel
Weekends Nov–Dec, Mar–May & Oct–Nov
from £55
Breakfast, 1 lunch, dinner

■ **FROME**
Mendip Lodge Hotel
All year from £74
Breakfast, dinner

■ **FROME**
Selwood Manor
1 Nov–31 Mar from £160
Breakfast, dinner

■ **GARFORTH**
Hilton National
Weekends from £56
Breakfast

■ **GATESHEAD**
Springfield Hotel
All year from £52
Breakfast, dinner

■ **GATESHEAD**
Swallow Hotel Gateshead
Weekends (including weekday Jul/Aug)
from £65
Breakfast, dinner

■ **GLASTONBURY**
George & Pilgrims Hotel
All year from £70
Breakfast, dinner

■ **GLOUCESTER**
Crest Hotel
Weekends from £86
Breakfast, dinner

■ **GLOUCESTER**
Hatton Court
All year from £46·75
Breakfast, dinner

■ **GOATLAND**
Mallyan Spout Hotel
All year from £70
Breakfast, lunch, dinner

■ **GODALMING**
Inn on the Lake
Weekends from £40
Breakfast, dinner

■ **GOLANT**
Cormorant Hotel
1 Nov–31 May from £52
Breakfast, dinner

■ **GOODWOOD**
Goodwood Park Hotel
Weekends from £75
Breakfast, dinner

■ **GOUDHURST**
Star & Eagle
Nov–Mar from £63
Breakfast, £9.25 towards meals

■ **GRASMERE**
Michael's Nook
3 Nov–22 Mar (except Xmas & New Year)
from £110
Breakfast, dinner

■ **GRASMERE**
Swan Hotel
All year (except Xmas, New Year &
Easter) from £80
Breakfast, dinner

A LOT FOR £55

■ **GRASMERE**
Wordsworth Hotel
1 Nov–31 Mar (except Xmas, New Year &
Easter) from £76 (midweek) & £95
(weekend)
Breakfast, dinner

■ **GREAT AYTON**
Ayton Hall
Weekends from £75
Breakfast, 1 lunch, dinner

■ **GREAT DUNMOW**
Saracen's Head Hotel
Weekends (except Xmas, New Year &
Easter) from £68
Breakfast, dinner

■ **GREAT MILTON**
Le Manoir aux Quat' Saisons
All year (Sun–Thurs) from £180
Continental breakfast, dinner

■ **GREAT SNORING**
Old Rectory
Nov–Mar (except Xmas, New Year &
Easter) from £76
Breakfast, dinner

■ **GREAT YARMOUTH**
Carlton Hotel
All year (except Xmas & New Year) from
£64
Breakfast, dinner & £6.95 towards lunch

■ **GRETA BRIDGE**
Morritt Arms Hotel
All year from £55
Breakfast, dinner

■ **GRIMSBY**
Crest Hotel
All year from £60
Breakfast, dinner

■ **GRIMSBY**
Humber Royal Crest Hotel
All year from £66
Breakfast, dinner

■ **GRIMSTHORPE**
Black Horse Inn
Weekends Nov–1 May from £70
Breakfast, dinner

■ **GRIMSTON**
Congham Hall
Weekends from £220
Breakfast, dinner

■ **GRINDLEFORD**
Maynard Arms Hotel
All year from £64
Breakfast, dinner

■ **GRIZEDALE**
Grizedale Lodge
1 Nov–27 Apr from £52
Breakfast, dinner

■ **GUILDFORD**
Angel Hotel
Weekends (except Xmas, New Year &
Easter) from £68
Breakfast, dinner

■ **GUILDFORD**
University Post House Hotel
Weekends (except Xmas, New Year &
Easter) from £84
Breakfast, dinner

■ **HACKNESS**
Hackness Grange Country Hotel
All year from £75 (weekdays) £85
(weekends)
Breakfast, dinner

■ **HADLEY WOOD**
West Lodge Park
Weekends Nov–end Mar from £60
Breakfast

■ **HALIFAX**
Holdsworth House
Weekends from £85
Breakfast, 1 dinner

■ **HARLOW**
Harlow Moat House
Weekends from £58
Breakfast, dinner

■ **HAROME**
Pheasant Hotel
Nov–20 May (except Jan–Feb) from £60
Breakfast, dinner

■ **HARPENDEN**
Glen Eagle Hotel
Weekends from £33
No meals

■ **HARPENDEN**
Harpenden Moat House Hotel
Weekends from £76
Breakfast, dinner

■ **HARROGATE**
Crown Hotel
Weekends (except Xmas, New Year &
Easter) from £70
Breakfast, dinner

■ **HARROGATE**
Granby Hotel
Weekends from £75
Breakfast, dinner

■ **HARROGATE**
Hospitality Inn
Weekends from £60
Breakfast, dinner

■ HARROGATE
Majestic
Weekends (except Xmas, New Year &
Easter) from £90
Breakfast, dinner

■ HARROGATE
Old Swan Hotel
All year (except Trade Fairs) from £89
Breakfast, dinner

■ HARROGATE
Russell Hotel
All year from £70
Breakfast, dinner

■ HARROGATE
Hotel St George
All year from £76
Breakfast, dinner

■ HARROGATE
Studley Hotel
Weekends (except Xmas & major
conferences & exhibitions) from £69
Breakfast, dinner

■ HARROW WEALD
Mansion House at Grim's Dyke
Weekends from £72
Breakfast, dinner

■ HARTLEPOOL
Grand Hotel
Weekends from £118
Breakfast, dinner

■ HASLEMERE
Lythe Hill Hotel
Weekends from £77
Breakfast, £13.50 towards meals

■ HATCH BEAUCHAMP
Farthings Country House Hotel
Nov–Mar & Oct–Nov from £79
Breakfast, dinner

■ HATFIELD
Comet Hotel
Weekends from £55
Breakfast, dinner

■ HAVANT
Bear Hotel
Weekends from £56
Breakfast, dinner

■ HAVANT
Post House Hotel
All year (except Xmas, New Year &
Easter) from £82
Breakfast, dinner

■ HAWKCHURCH
Fairwater Head Hotel
All year (except Jan–Feb) from £68
Breakfast, dinner

■ HAWKHURST
Tudor Arms Hotel
All year from £71
Breakfast, dinner

■ HAWKSHEAD
Field Head House
7 Nov–19 Mar (except Xmas & New Year)
from £120
Breakfast, dinner

■ HAYDOCK
Post House Hotel
Weekends (except Xmas, New Year &
Easter) from £64
Breakfast, dinner

■ HAYTOR
Bel Alp House Country Hotel
All year from £108
Breakfast, dinner

■ HELLAND BRIDGE
Tredethy Country Hotel
All year (except Xmas, New Year, Bank
Hols, June, Aug & Sept) from £55
Breakfast, dinner

■ HELMSLEY
Black Swan Hotel
All year (except Xmas, New Year &
Easter) from £110
Breakfast, dinner

■ HELMSLEY
Feversham Arms Hotel
All year from £56
Breakfast, dinner

■ HEMEL HEMPSTEAD
Post House Hotel
Weekends (except Xmas, New Year &
Easter) from £58
Breakfast, dinner

■ HENLEY IN ARDEN
Yew Trees Hotel
All year from £72
Breakfast, dinner

■ HEREFORD
Green Dragon Hotel
All year (except Xmas, New Year &
Easter) from £76
Breakfast, dinner

■ HEREFORD
Hereford Moat House
Weekends from £60
Breakfast, dinner

■ HERTINGFORDBURY
The White Horse
Weekends (except Xmas, New Year &
Easter) from £78
Breakfast, dinner

A LOT FOR LESS

■ HETHERSETT
Park Farm Hotel
Weekends (except Bank Hols) from £47
Breakfast

■ HIGH WYCOMBE
Crest Hotel
Weekends from £78
Breakfast, dinner

■ HILLINGDON
Master Brewer Hotel
Weekends from £34
No meals

■ HINTLESHAM
Hintlesham Hall
Nov–end Mar from £250
Breakfast, £30 towards meals

■ HOCKLEY HEATH
Nuthurst Grange
Weekends from £60
Continental breakfast

■ HOLBETON
Alston Hall Hotel
Jan–Mar from £56
Breakfast, dinner

■ HOPE
Poachers Arms Hotel
All year from £60
Breakfast, dinner

■ HOPE COVE
Cottage Hotel
1 Nov–23 Mar from £55
Breakfast, dinner

■ HOPE COVE
Lantern Lodge Hotel
Nov–Mar, June & Oct–Nov from £47
Breakfast, dinner

■ HORTON-CUM-STUDLEY
Studley Priory Hotel
1 Oct–30 Apr from £88
Breakfast, dinner

■ HUDDERSFIELD
George Hotel
Weekends (except Xmas, New Year &
Easter) from £56
Breakfast, dinner

■ HUDDERSFIELD
Pennine Hilton National
Weekends from £56
Breakfast

■ HULL
Crest Hotel (Humber Bridge)
Weekends from £66
Breakfast, dinner

■ HULL
Waterfront Hotel
Weekends from £44
Breakfast, dinner

■ HUNGERFORD
Bear at Hungerford
Weekends from £65
Breakfast, dinner

■ HUNTINGDON
Brampton Hotel
Weekends from £69
Breakfast, dinner

■ HUNTINGDON
George Hotel
Weekends (except Xmas, New Year &
Easter) from £66
Breakfast, dinner

■ HUNTINGDON
Old Bridge Hotel
Weekends from £150
Breakfast, 1 dinner

■ HUNTSHAM
Huntsham Court Hotel
Weekends Feb–Apr from £95
Breakfast, dinner

■ HURSTBOURNE TARRANT
Esseborne Manor
All year from £65
Breakfast, £5 towards dinner

■ HYTHE
Fredericks Hotel
All year from £99
Breakfast, dinner

■ ILKLEY
Craiglands Hotel
All year (except Xmas, New Year &
Easter) from £68
Breakfast, dinner

■ IPSWICH
Post House Hotel
Weekends (except Xmas, New Year &
Easter) from £56
Breakfast, dinner

■ KENDAL
Woolpack Hotel
Weekends from £68
Breakfast, dinner

■ KENILWORTH
Clarendon House Hotel
Weekends from £60
Breakfast, dinner

■ KENILWORTH
De Montfort Hotel
Weekends (including weekdays Jul/Aug)
from £53
Breakfast, dinner

■ **KESWICK**
The Keswick
All year (except Xmas, New Year &
Easter) from £70
Breakfast, dinner

■ **KIDDERMINSTER**
Stone Manor Hotel
Weekends from £80.50
Breakfast, dinner

■ **KILDWICK**
Kildwick Hall
All year from £87.90
Breakfast, £13.95 towards meals

■ **KILVE**
Meadow House
All year from £169
Breakfast, dinner

■ **KINGHAM**
Mill House Hotel
All year from £92
Breakfast, dinner

■ **KINGSBRIDGE**
Buckland-Tout-Saints Hotel
All year (except Jan) from £93
Breakfast, dinner

■ **KINGS LYNN**
Butterfly Hotel
Weekends from £63
Breakfast, dinner

■ **KINGS LYNN**
Duke's Head
Weekends (except Xmas, New Year &
Easter) from £70
Breakfast, dinner

■ **KINTBURY**
Dundas Arms
All year from £72.90
Breakfast, dinner

■ **KIRBY FLEETHAM**
Kirby Fleetham Hall
All year from £112
Breakfast, dinner

■ **KNARESBOROUGH**
Dower House
Weekends from £75
Breakfast, dinner

■ **KNUTSFORD**
The Cottons Hotel
Weekends from £70
Breakfast, dinner

■ **LACOCK**
Sign of the Angel
Weekends from £90
Breakfast, dinner

■ **LANCASTER**
Post House Hotel
Weekends (except Xmas, New Year &
Easter) from £72
Breakfast, dinner

■ **LANGHO**
Northcote Manor
Weekends from £31
Breakfast

■ **LANGLEY-ON-TYNE**
Langley Castle
All year from £75
Breakfast, dinner

■ **LAVENHAM**
Swan Hotel
All year (except Xmas, New Year &
Easter) from £94
Breakfast, dinner

■ **LEAMINGTON SPA**
Regent Hotel
All year from £57
Breakfast, dinner

■ **LEDBURY**
Hope End Country House Hotel
Nov–Mar from £100

■ **LEEDS**
Crest Hotel
Weekends from £64
Breakfast, dinner

■ **LEEDS**
Hilton International
Weekends from £56
Breakfast

■ **LEEDS**
Merrion Hotel
Weekends from £67
Breakfast, dinner

■ **LEEDS**
Metropole
Weekends (except Xmas, New Year &
Easter) from £56
Breakfast, dinner

■ **LEEDS**
Queen's Hotel
Weekends (except Xmas, New Year &
Easter) from £64
Breakfast, dinner

■ **LEICESTER**
Belmont Hotel
Weekends from £60
Breakfast, dinner

■ **LEICESTER**
Grand Hotel
Weekends from £59
Breakfast, dinner

■ **LEICESTER**
Post House Hotel
Weekends (except Xmas, New Year &
Easter) from £56
Breakfast, dinner

■ **LEICESTER**
Hotel St James
All year from £39.50
Breakfast

■ **LEIGH**
Greyhound Hotel
All year from £50
Breakfast, dinner

■ **LEIGHTON BUZZARD**
Swan Hotel
Weekends (except Xmas night & New
Year's night) from £65
Breakfast, dinner

■ **LENHAM**
Chilston Park
All year from £130
Breakfast, dinner

■ **LETCHWORTH**
Broadway Hotel
Weekends from £58
Breakfast

■ **LEWDON**
Fox' Earth Lewtrenchard Manor
All year (except Bank Hols) from £110
Breakfast, dinner

■ **LEWES**
Shelleys Hotel
Weekends Nov–Apr from £83
Breakfast, dinner

■ **LICHFIELD**
George Hotel
Weekends (Nov –Mar) from £54
Breakfast, dinner

■ **LIFTON**
Arundell Arms
Nov–May from £70
Breakfast, dinner

■ **LINCOLN**
Eastgate Post House
Weekends (except Xmas, New Year &
Easter) from £70
Breakfast, dinner

■ **LINCOLN**
Moor Lodge Hotel
All year from £62
Breakfast, dinner

■ **LINCOLN**
White Hart Hotel
Weekends (except Xmas, New Year &
Easter) from £86
Breakfast, dinner

■ **LINTON**
Woodhall Hotel
Weekends from £104
Breakfast, dinner

■ **LISKEARD**
The Well House
Nov–Mar (except Sat) from £87.50
Continental breakfast, dinner

■ **LITTLE WYMONDLEY**
Redcoats Farmhouse Hotel
Weekends from £69
Breakfast, dinner

■ **LIVERPOOL**
Atlantic Tower Hotel
Weekends from £44
Breakfast

■ **LIVERPOOL**
Britannia Adelphi Hotel
Weekends from £59
Breakfast, dinner

■ **LIVERPOOL**
Crest Hotel, Liverpool-City
All year from £64
Breakfast, dinner

■ **LIVERPOOL**
Liverpool Moat House
Weekends (except 7–8 Apr) from £68
Breakfast, 1 dinner

■ **LIVERPOOL**
St George's Hotel
Weekends (except Xmas, New Year &
Easter) from £54
Breakfast, dinner

■ **LOFTUS**
Grinkle Park Hotel
Weekends from £84
Breakfast, dinner

■ **LONG MELFORD**
Black Lion Hotel
All year (Sun, Mon only) from £45
Breakfast, dinner

■ **LONG MELFORD**
Bull Hotel
All year (except Xmas, New Year &
Easter) from £80
Breakfast, dinner

■ **LONGHAM**
The Bridge House
Weekends from £50
Continental breakfast

■ **LONGHORSLEY**
Linden Hall Hotel
Weekdays Nov–Mar & weekends Apr–Oct
from £79
Breakfast, dinner

■ **LOOE**
Talland Bay Hotel
Feb–May & Oct–Nov from £65
Breakfast, dinner

■ **LOSTWITHIEL**
Carotel Motel
All year from £48
Breakfast, dinner

■ **LOUGHBOROUGH**
King's Head Hotel
Weekends from £50
Breakfast, dinner

■ **LOWER SLAUGHTER**
Lower Slaughter Manor
All year from £115
Continental breakfast, dinner

■ **LOWER SWELL**
Old Farmhouse Hotel
1 Nov–18 Dec, 26 Jan–31 Oct (except
Bank Hols & Cheltenham Gold Cup Week)
from £50
Breakfast, dinner

■ **LUDLOW**
Feathers Hotel
All year from £85
Breakfast, dinner

■ **LUTON**
Chiltern Hotel
Weekends from £74
Breakfast, dinner

■ **LUTON**
Crest Hotel
Weekends from £70
Breakfast, dinner

■ **LUTON**
Leaside Hotel
Weekends (except Bank Hols) from £74
Breakfast, dinner

■ **LUTON**
Strathmore Thistle Hotel
Weekends from £78
Breakfast, dinner

■ **LUTTERWORTH**
Denbigh Arms Hotel
Weekends from £75
Breakfast, dinner

■ **LYDDINGTON**
Marquess of Exeter
Weekends from £60
Breakfast, £10 towards dinner

■ **LYME REGIS**
Alexandra Hotel
20 Oct–18 Dec & 3 Feb–13 May from £66
Breakfast, dinner

■ **LYMINGTON**
Passford House Hotel
Nov–May from £85
Breakfast, dinner

■ **LYMINGTON**
Stanwell House Hotel
Weekends from £88
Breakfast, dinner

■ **LYMPSHAM**
Batch Farm Country Hotel
All year from £55
Breakfast, dinner

■ **LYNDHURST**
Crown Hotel
All year from £37
Breakfast, dinner

■ **LYNDHURST**
Lyndhurst Park Hotel
All year from £73
Breakfast, dinner

■ **LYNMOUTH**
Tors Hotel
Mar–May & end Sept–Nov from £55
Breakfast, dinner

■ **LYNTON**
Hewitts Hotel
All year from £67.50
Breakfast, dinner

■ **LYNTON**
Lynton Cottage Hotel
Nov–May from £70.50
Breakfast, dinner

■ **LYTHAM ST ANNE'S**
Clifton Arms Hotel
Weekends from £70
Breakfast, dinner

■ **MACCLESFIELD**
Sutton Hall
All year from £87.90
Breakfast, dinner

■ **MAIDEN NEWTON**
Maiden Newton House
Nov–Dec & Feb–Apr (Sun–Thur only)
from £75
Breakfast, dinner

■ **MAIDENCOMBE**
Orestone Manor
1 Nov–20 Dec, 1 Mar–25 May & 1 Oct–26
Nov from £66
Breakfast, dinner

■ **MAIDENHEAD**
Crest Hotel
Weekends from £92
Breakfast, dinner

■ **MAIDSTONE**
Larkfield Hotel
Weekends (except Xmas, New Year &
Easter) from £70
Breakfast, dinner

■ **MALDON**
Blue Boar Hotel
Weekends (except Xmas, New Year &
Easter) from £35
Breakfast, dinner

■ **MALMESBURY**
Old Bell Hotel
All year from £88
Breakfast, dinner

■ **MALVERN**
Abbey Hotel
Weekends from £58
Breakfast, dinner

■ **MALVERN**
Colwall Park Hotel
All year from £70
Breakfast, dinner

■ **MALVERN**
Cottage in the Wood Hotel
All year from £56
Breakfast, dinner

■ **MALVERN**
Foley Arms Hotel
All year from £66
Breakfast, £11 towards dinner

■ **MANCHESTER**
Britannia Hotel
Weekends from £52
Breakfast, dinner

■ **MANCHESTER**
Copthorne Hotel
Weekends from £57
Breakfast, dinner

■ **MANCHESTER**
Grand Hotel
Weekends (except Xmas, New Year &
Easter) from £48
Breakfast, dinner

■ **MANCHESTER**
Holiday Inn, Crowne Plaza
Weekends from £54
Breakfast

■ **MANCHESTER**
Novotel Manchester West
Weekends from £55
Breakfast, dinner

■ **MANCHESTER**
Hotel Piccadilly
Weekends from £79
Breakfast, dinner

■ **MANCHESTER**
Portland Thistle Hotel
Weekends from £56
Breakfast

■ **MANCHESTER**
Post House Hotel
Weekends (except Xmas, New Year &
Easter) from £66
Breakfast, dinner

■ **MANCHESTER**
Willow Bank Hotel
Weekends from £52
No meals

■ **MANCHESTER AIRPORT**
Excelsior Hotel
Weekends (except Xmas, New Year &
Easter) from £76
Breakfast, 1 dinner

■ **MANCHESTER AIRPORT**
Hilton International
Weekends from £64
Breakfast

■ **MARKET HARBOROUGH**
Three Swans Hotel
Weekends from £39
Breakfast

■ **MARKINGTON**
Hob Green Hotel
Weekends from £90
Breakfast, dinner

■ **MARLBOROUGH**
Ivy House
Weekends from £90
Breakfast, £15.75 towards dinner

■ **MATLOCK**
Riber Hall
21 Oct–30 Apr from £96
Breakfast, 1 lunch, dinner

■ **MATLOCK BATH**
New Bath Hotel
All year (except Xmas, New Year &
Easter) from £78
Breakfast, dinner

■ **MAWNAN SMITH**
Budock Vean Hotel
All year from £72
Breakfast, dinner

■ **MELKSHAM**
King's Arms Hotel
All year from £53
Breakfast, dinner

■ **MELLOR**
Millstone Hotel
Weekends from £50
Breakfast

■ **MELTON MOWBRAY**
George Hotel
Weekends from £70
Breakfast, dinner

■ **MELTON MOWBRAY**
Harboro' Hotel
Weekends (except Xmas, New Year &
Easter) from £60
Breakfast, dinner

■ **MIDDLECOMBE**
Periton Park
All year from £83
Breakfast, dinner

■ **MERE**
Old Ship Hotel
All year from £58
Breakfast

■ **MERIDEN**
Manor hotel
Weekends (except weekdays Jul–Aug)
from £54
Breakfast, dinner

■ **MICKLETON**
Three Ways Hotel
Weekends from £68
Breakfast, dinner

■ **MIDDLE WALLOP**
Fifehead Manor
1 Nov–Good Fri from £80
Breakfast, dinner

■ **MIDDLESBOROUGH**
Hospitality Inn
Weekends from £61
Breakfast, dinner

■ **MIDDLETON IN TEESDALE**
Teeside Hotel
10 Oct–1 May from £58
Breakfast, weekdays

■ **MIDDLETON STONEY**
Jersey Arms
All year from £150
Breakfast, dinner

■ **MIDHURST**
Spread Eagle Hotel
All year from £80
Breakfast, dinner

■ **MILFORD-ON-SEA**
South Lawn Hotel
Nov–May (except Xmas & Easter) from
£69
Breakfast, dinner

■ **MILTON DAMEREL**
Woodford Bridge Hotel
June–Sept from £79
Breakfast, dinner

■ **MINSTER LOVELL**
Old Swan Hotel
All year from £150
Breakfast, dinner

■ **MONTACUTE**
King's Arms Inn
All year from £104
Breakfast

■ **MONK FRYSTON**
Monk Fryston Hall
Weekends (except Xmas & New Year)
from £68
Breakfast, dinner

■ **MORETON-IN-MARSH**
Manor House Hotel
Nov–Apr from £79.50
Breakfast, dinner

■ **MORETON-IN-MARSH**
Redesdale Arms Hotel
All year from £67
Breakfast, dinner

■ **MORETONHAMPSTEAD**
Manor House Hotel
Weekends from £86.50
Breakfast, dinner

■ **MORETONHAMPSTEAD**
White Hart Hotel
All year from £60
Breakfast, dinner

■ **MOTTRAM ST ANDREW**
Mottram Hall Hotel
Weekends from £64
Breakfast, dinner

■ **MUCH BIRCH**
Pilgrim Hotel
Weekends (including weekdays Oct–Mar)
from £58
Breakfast, dinner

■ **MUDEFORD**
Avonmouth Hotel
All year (except Xmas, New Year &
Easter) from £72
Breakfast, dinner

■ **MULLION**
Polurrian Hotel
1 Mar–25 May & Sept–10 Dec from £69
Breakfast, dinner

■ **NEASHAM**
Newbus Arms Hotel
All year (except Xmas) from £68
breakfast, dinner

■ **NEWBURY**
Chequers Hotel
Weekends (except Xmas, New Year &
Easter) from £68
Breakfast, dinner

■ **NEWBURY**
Elcot Park Hotel
Weekends from £75
Breakfast, dinner

■ **NEWBY BRIDGE**
Swan Hotel
Weekends 4 Nov–16 Dec from £64
13 Jan–22 Mar from £70
Breakfast, dinner

■ **NEWCASTLE UNDER LYME**
Clayton Lodge Hotel
All year from £58
Breakfast, dinner

■ **NEWCASTLE UNDER LYME**
Post House Hotel
Weekends (except Xmas, New Year &
Easter) from £56
Breakfast, dinner

■ **NEWCASTLE UPON TYNE**
County Thistle Hotel
Weekends from £32
Breakfast, dinner

■ **NEWCASTLE UPON TYNE**
Crest Hotel
Weekends from £68
Breakfast, dinner

■ **NEWCASTLE UPON TYNE**
Gosforth Park Thistle Hotel
Weekends from £70
Breakfast

■ **NEWCASTLE UPON TYNE**
Holiday Inn
Weekends Nov–Apr from £55
Breakfast

■ **NEWCASTLE UPON TYNE**
Newcastle Moat House
Weekends all year, weekdays July–Aug
from £132
Breakfast, £9.50 towards meals

■ **NEWCASTLE UPON TYNE**
Stakis Airport Hotel
All year from £62
Breakfast, dinner

■ **NEWCASTLE UPON TYNE**
Swallow Hotel
Weekends (including weekday Jul/Aug)
from £60
Breakfast, 1 lunch, dinner

■ **NEWINGTON**
Newington Manor Hotel
Weekends from £50
Breakfast, £9.50 towards meals

■ **NEWLYN**
Higher Faugan Hotel
Nov–May from £64
Breakfast, dinner

■ **NEWMARKET**
Newmarket Moat House
Weekends from £58
Breakfast, dinner

■ **NEW MILTON**
Chewton Glen Hotel
Nov–31 Mar (only available Saturday
night if staying 3 nights) from £153
Continental breakfast, dinner

■ **NEWPORT PAGNELL**
Welcome Lodge
Weekends (except Xmas, New Year &
Easter) from £37
Breakfast, dinner

■ **NEWQUAY**
Atlantic Hotel
Mar–14 Nov from £71.30
Breakfast, dinner

■ **NEWQUAY**
Hotel Bristol
Weekends Nov–20 May from £65
Breakfast, dinner

■ **NEWQUAY**
Hotel Riviera
Weekends Nov–May, Oct–Nov (except
Bank Hols) from £55
Breakfast, dinner

■ **NEWTON SOLWAY**
Newton Park Hotel
All year from £54
Breakfast, dinner

■ **NORTH HUISH**
Brookdale House
Nov–Easter from £80
Breakfast, dinner

■ **NORTH PETHERTON**
Walnut Tree Inn
Weekends from £62
Breakfast

■ **NORTH STIFFORD**
Stifford Moat House
Weekends from £60
Breakfast, dinner

■ **NORTH STOKE**
Springs Hotel
Weekends from £115.50
Breakfast, dinner

■ **NORTHAMPTON**
Northampton Moat House
Weekends from £64
Breakfast, dinner

■ **NORTHAMPTON**
Swallow Hotel
Weekends from £76
Breakfast, dinner & 1 lunch

■ **NORTHAMPTON**
Westone Moat House
Weekends from £42
Breakfast

■ **NORWICH**
Maid's Head Hotel
Weekends from £70
breakfast, dinner

■ **NORWICH**
Hotel Nelson
All year from £72
Breakfast, dinner

■ **NORWICH**
Hotel Norwich
Nov–Mar from £58, Apr–Nov from £65
Breakfast, dinner

■ **NORWICH**
Post House Hotel
Weekends (except Xmas, New Year &
Easter) from £76
Breakfast, dinner

■ **NOTTINGHAM**
Albany Hotel
Weekends from £58
Breakfast, dinner

■ **NOTTINGHAM**
Royal Moat House International
Weekends from £80
Breakfast, dinner

■ **NOTTINGHAM**
Savoy Hotel
Weekends from £48
Breakfast

■ **NOTTINGHAM**
Stakis Victoria Hotel
Weekends from £68
Breakfast, dinner

■ **OAKHAM**
Hambleton Hall
Nov–Apr (ex Sats) from £50
Continental breakfast

■ **OLD HARLOW**
Green Man Hotel
Weekends from £70
Breakfast, dinner

■ **ORMESBY ST MARGARET**
Ormesby Lodge Hotel
Weekends from £56
Breakfast, £11.75 towards dinner & 1
lunch

■ **OSWESTRY**
Wynnstay Hotel
All year from £66
Breakfast, dinner

■ **OTLEY**
Chevin Lodge
Weekends from £65
Breakfast, dinner

■ **OTTERBURN**
Percy Arms Hotel
All year from £60
Breakfast, dinner

■ **OUNDLE**
Talbot Hotel
Weekends from £72
Breakfast, dinner

■ **OXFORD**
Linton Lodge Hotel
Weekends from £56
Breakfast

■ **OXFORD**
Oxford Moat House
Weekends from £79
Breakfast, dinner

■ **OXFORD**
Randolph Hotel
Weekends from £84
Breakfast, dinner

■ **OXFORD**
Welcome Lodge
Weekends from £39
Breakfast

■ **PAIGNTON**
Palace Hotel
All year from £64
Breakfast, dinner

■ **PAIGNTON**
Redcliffe Hotel
Nov–May from £60
Breakfast, dinner

■ **PAINSWICK**
Painswick Hotel
Weekends (except Xmas & National Hunt
Week) from £65
Breakfast, £12.50 towards dinner

■ **PANGBOURNE**
The Copper Inn
Weekends from £62.50
Breakfast, £15.95 towards dinner

■ **PARKGATE**
Ship Hotel Inn
Weekends from £58
Breakfast, dinner

■ **PARKHAM**
Penhaven Country House
Nov–May from £65
Breakfast, dinner

■ **PENRITH**
North Lakes Gateway Hotel
All year from £90
Breakfast, dinner

■ **PENZANCE**
Abbey Hotel
Nov–Apr from £65
Breakfast, dinner

■ **PETERBOROUGH**
Crest Hotel
Weekends from £64
Breakfast, dinner

■ **PETERBOROUGH**
Peterborough Moat House
Weekends from £62
Breakfast, dinner

■ **PETERSFIELD**
Langrish House
Weekends from £58
Breakfast, dinner

■ **PLYMOUTH**
Astor Hotel
Weekends from £58
Breakfast, dinner

■ **PLYMOUTH**
Copthorne Hotel
Weekends from £57
Breakfast

■ **PLYMOUTH**
Duke of Cornwall Hotel
Weekends from £55
Breakfast, dinner

■ **PLYMOUTH**
Holiday Inn
All year from £60
Breakfast

■ **PLYMOUTH**
Mayflower Post House Hotel
Weekends from £72
Breakfast, dinner

■ **PLYMOUTH**
Novotel
Weekends from £50
Breakfast, dinner

■ **POCKLINGTON**
Feathers Hotel
Weekends Nov–31 Mar from £110
Breakfast, dinner & 1 lunch

■ **POOLE**
Hospitality Inn, The Quay
Weekends from £65
Breakfast, dinner

■ **POOLE**
Mansion House
Weekends from £98
Breakfast, dinner

■ **PORLOCK**
Oaks Hotel
Weekends Nov–Mar (except Xmas, Easter) from £55
Breakfast, dinner

■ **PORTLOE**
Lugger Hotel
Mid Mar–mid Nov from £76
Breakfast, £8 towards dinner

■ **PORTREE**
Rosedale Hotel
May–Sept from £70
Breakfast, dinner

■ **PORTSMOUTH**
Crest Hotel
Weekends from £80
Breakfast, dinner

■ **PORTSMOUTH**
Holiday Inn
Weekends from £60
Breakfast

■ **PORTSMOUTH**
Hospitality Inn
All year from £63
Breakfast, dinner

■ **PORTSMOUTH**
Pendragon Hotel
Weekends from £64
Breakfast, dinner

■ **POWBURN**
Breamish House Hotel
Nov–30 Dec, Feb–Apr from £72
Breakfast, dinner

■ **PRESTBURY**
Bridge Hotel
Weekends from £65
Breakfast

■ **PRESTON**
Crest House Hotel
Weekends from £68
Breakfast, dinner

■ **PRESTON**
Novotel
Weekends from £46
Breakfast, £9.50 towards meals

■ **PRESTON**
Tickled Trout Hotel
Weekends from £62
Breakfast

■ **PULBOROUGH**
Chequers Hotel
Nov–Mar from £54, Apr–Nov from £58
Breakfast, dinner

■ **QUORN**
Quorn Country Hotel
Weekends from £68
Breakfast, dinner

■ **RAVENSTONEDALE**
Black Swan
Weekends Nov–May from £32
Breakfast, £13 towards dinner

■ **READING**
Caversham Hotel
Weekends from £60
Breakfast

■ **READING**
Post House Hotel
Weekends from £70
Breakfast, dinner

■ **READING**
Ramada Hotel
Weekends from £72
Breakfast, dinner

■ **REIGATE**
Bridge House Hotel
Weekends from £47.50
Continental breakfast

■ **RENISHAW**
Sitwell Arms Hotel
Weekends from £29
Breakfast

■ **RICHMOND**
Petersham Hotel
Weekends from £90
Breakfast, dinner

■ **RIPON**
Ripon Spa Hotel
All year from £84
Breakfast, dinner

■ **ROCHESTER**
Crest Hotel
Weekends from £72
Breakfast, dinner

■ **ROMSEY**
White Horse Hotel
Weekends from £76
Breakfast, dinner

■ **ROSEDALE ABBEY**
Milburn Arms Hotel
All year from £54
Breakfast, dinner

■ **ROSS-ON-WYE**
Chase Hotel
All year from £90
Breakfast, dinner

■ **ROSS-ON-WYE**
Pengethley Manor Hotel
All year (except Bank Hols) from £100
Breakfast, dinner

■ **ROTHERHAM**
Rotherham Moat House
Weekends from £57
Breakfast, dinner

■ **ROTHERWICK**
Tylney Hall
Weekends from £105
Breakfast, dinner

■ **ROWSLEY**
Peacock Hotel
Weekends from £66
Breakfast, dinner

■ **RUGBY**
Three Horse Shoes Hotel
Weekends from £55
Breakfast, dinner

■ **RUNCORN**
Crest Hotel
Weekends from £76
Breakfast, dinner

■ **RUSPER**
Ghyll Manor
Weekends from £75
Breakfast, dinner

■ **RYDE (I of W)**
Hotel Ryde Castle
All year from £69.90
Breakfast, lunch or dinner

■ **RYE**
George Hotel
All year from £78
Breakfast, dinner

■ **RYE**
Mermaid Inn
All year from £82
Breakfast, dinner

■ **SAFFRON WALDEN**
Saffron Hotel
Weekends from £36.75
Continental Breakfast

■ **ST ALBANS**
Noke Thistle Hotel
All year from £54
Breakfast

■ ST ALBANS
Sopwell House Hotel
Weekends from £64
Breakfast, dinner

■ ST AUSTELL
White Hart Hotel
Nov–May weekends from £70
Breakfast, dinner

■ ST IVES
Boskerris Hotel
Easter–July, Sept–Oct from £50
Breakfast, dinner

■ ST IVES
Garrack Hotel
Nov–May (except Easter & Bank Hols)
from £58
Breakfast, dinner

■ ST IVES
Slepe Hall Hotel
Weekends from £62.50
Breakfast, dinner

■ ST IVES
Tregenna Castle Hotel
All year from £70
Breakfast, dinner

■ ST MAWES
Rising Sun Inn
Nov–Apr from £35
Breakfast

■ ST MAWES
Hotel Tresanton
Mar–June, Oct–Nov from £83
Breakfast, dinner

■ SALCOMBE
Marine Hotel
Nov–31 Mar from £94
Breakfast, dinner

■ SALCOMBE
Soar Mill Cove Hotel
All year from £80
Breakfast, dinner

■ SALCOMBE
South Sands Hotel
Nov–May from £75
Breakfast, dinner

■ SALCOMBE
Tides Reach Hotel
Mar–May & Oct from £94
Breakfast, dinner

■ SALISBURY
Rose & Crown Hotel
Weekends from £83
Breakfast, dinner

■ SAMLESBURY
Tickled Trout Hotel
Weekends from £62
Breakfast

■ SANDBACH
Chimney House Hotel
Weekends (except Xmas) from £32
Breakfast, dinner

■ SANDOWN
Melville Hall Hotel
Nov–27 May from £40
Breakfast

■ SAUNTON
Saunton Sands Hotel
Nov–Jun, Sept & Oct (except Xmas, Easter
& Whitsun) from £70
Breakfast, dinner

■ SCARBOROUGH
Crown Hotel
All year from £75
Breakfast, dinner

■ SCARBOROUGH
Holbeck Hall Hotel
Nov–Apr from £66
Breakfast, dinner

■ SCARBOROUGH
Palm Court Hotel
All year from £56
Breakfast, dinner

■ SCARBOROUGH
Royal Hotel
All year from £78
Breakfast, dinner & 1 lunch

■ SEAHOUSES
Olde Ship Hotel
Easter–Nov from £40
Breakfast

■ SEALE
Hog's Back Hotel
All year from £66
Breakfast, dinner

■ SEAVIEW
Seaview Hotel
All year from £60
Breakfast, dinner

■ SEDLESCOMBE
Brickwall Hotel
All year from £59
Breakfast, dinner

■ SENNEN
Tregiffian Hotel
Mar–May, Sept & Oct from £96
Breakfast, dinner

■ **SHAFTESBURY**
Grosvenor Hotel
All year from £60
Breakfast, dinner

■ **SHAFTESBURY**
Royal Chase Hotel
All year from £74
Breakfast, dinner

■ **SHALDON**
Ness House Hotel
All year from £42.34
Breakfast

■ **SHEDFIELD**
Meon Valley Hotel
All year from £80
Breakfast, dinner

■ **SHEFFIELD**
Grosvenor House Hotel
Weekends from £56
Breakfast, dinner

■ **SHEFFIELD**
Hallam Tower Post House Hotel
Weekends from £70
Breakfast, dinner

■ **SHEFFIELD**
St George Swallow Hotel
Weekends from £75
Breakfast, 1 lunch, dinner

■ **SHEPPERTON**
Shepperton Moat House
Weekends from £31
Breakfast, dinner

■ **SHEPPERTON**
Warren Lodge Hotel
Weekends from £45
Breakfast

■ **SHERBORNE**
Eastbury Hotel
Weekends from £88
Breakfast, dinner

■ **SHERBORNE**
Post House Hotel
All year from £68
Breakfast, dinner

■ **SHIFNAL**
Park House Hotel
Weekends from £72
Breakfast, dinner

■ **SHIPTON-UNDER-WYCHWOOD**
Lamb Inn
All year from £32.50
Breakfast

■ **SHREWSBURY**
Albrighton Hall Hotel
Weekends from £62
Breakfast, £15 towards dinner

■ **SHREWSBURY**
Lion Hotel
All year from £72
Breakfast, dinner

■ **SHREWSBURY**
Prince Rupert Hotel
Weekends from £64
Breakfast, dinner

■ **SIDMOUTH**
Belmont Hotel
Nov–July, Sept & Oct (except Xmas,
Easter, Whitsun) from £58
Breakfast, dinner

■ **SIDMOUTH**
Fortfield Hotel
Nov–12 May from £58
Breakfast, dinner

■ **SIDMOUTH**
Hotel Riviera
Weekends 28 Oct–1 May from £70.15
Breakfast, dinner, Sun lunch

■ **SIDMOUTH**
Victoria Hotel
Nov–May & Oct (except Xmas, Easter,
Whitsun) from £76
Breakfast, dinner

■ **SILCHESTER**
Romans Hotel
Weekends from £80
Breakfast, dinner

■ **SIMONSBATH**
Simonsbath House Hotel
End Jan–Nov from £50
Breakfast

■ **SIX MILE BOTTOM**
Swynford Paddocks Hotel
Weekends from £90
Breakfast, dinner

■ **SLAIDBURN**
Hark to Bounty Inn
All year from £75
Breakfast, dinner

■ **SLOUGH**
Holiday Inn
Weekends from £70
Breakfast

■ **SOLIHULL**
George Hotel
Weekends from £58
Breakfast, dinner

■ SOLIHULL
St John's Swallow Hotel
Weekends (including weekday in Aug)
from £70
Breakfast, dinner

■ SOMERTON
The Lynch Country House Hotel
All year from £70
Breakfast, dinner

■ SOMERTON
Red Lion Hotel
All year from £44
Breakfast, lunch or dinner

■ SONNING ON THAMES
White Hart Hotel
Weekends (except Xmas) from £170
Breakfast, dinner

■ SOUTH MARSTON
South Marston Hotel
Weekends from £60
Breakfast, £13 towards dinner

■ SOUTH MILFORD
Selby Fork Hotel
All year from £70
Breakfast, dinner

■ SOUTH MIMMS
Crest Hotel
Weekends from £82
Breakfast, dinner

■ SOUTH MOLTON
Whitechapel Manor
Nov–Apr (except Xmas & New Year) from
£121.50
Breakfast

■ SOUTH NORMANTON
Swallow Hotel
Weekends (including weekday in Aug)
from £78
Breakfast, 1 lunch, dinner

■ SOUTHAMPTON
Dolphin Hotel
Weekends from £60
Breakfast, dinner

■ SOUTHAMPTON
Polygon Hotel
Weekends from £64
Breakfast, dinner

■ SOUTHAMPTON
Post House Hotel
Weekends from £64
Breakfast, dinner

■ SOUTHAMPTON
Southampton Park Hotel
Weekends from £40
Breakfast

■ SOUTHWELL
Saracen's Head Hotel
Weekends from £68
Breakfast, dinner

■ STAFFORD
Tillington Hall Hotel
Any 2 days Jul, Aug from £105
Breakfast, 1 lunch, dinner

■ STAMFORD
Crown Hotel
Weekends Nov–Apr from £100
Breakfast, £10 towards dinner

■ STAMFORD
George of Stamford
All year from £80
Breakfast, 1 dinner

■ STANSTEAD ABBOTTS
Briggens House Hotel
All year (except Xmas, New Year &
Easter) from £90
Breakfast, dinner

■ STANTON HARCOURT
Harcourt Arms
All year from £66
Breakfast, £10 towards dinner

■ STEVENAGE
Roebuck Inn
Weekends from £52
Breakfast, dinner

■ STOCKBRIDGE
Grosvenor Hotel
Weekends from £70
Breakfast, dinner

■ STOCKPORT
Alma Lodge Hotel
All year from £48
Breakfast, dinner

■ STOCKTON-ON-TEES
Swallow Hotel
Weekends from £68
Breakfast, 1 lunch, dinner

■ STOKE FLEMING
Stoke Lodge Hotel
Nov–May & Oct from £52
Breakfast, dinner

■ STOKE MANDEVILLE
Belmore Hotel
Weekends (except Xmas) from £38
Continental breakfast

■ STOKE-ON-TRENT
North Stafford Hotel
Weekends from £64
Breakfast, dinner

■ **STON EASTON**
Ston Easton Park
Nov–Mar from £140
Breakfast, dinner

■ **STONEHOUSE**
Stonehouse Court Hotel
Weekends from £88
Breakfast, dinner

■ **STORRINGTON**
Abingworth Hall
All year (except Xmas) from £102
Breakfast, dinner

■ **STOURBRIDGE**
Talbot Hotel
Weekends from £52
Breakfast, dinner

■ **STOW-ON-THE-WOLD**
Fosse Manor Hotel
Nov–Apr, May–Aug from £55
Breakfast, dinner

■ **STOW-ON-THE-WOLD**
Grapevine Hotel
All year from £54
Breakfast, dinner

■ **STOW-ON-THE-WOLD**
Unicorn Crest Hotel
All year from £78
Breakfast, dinner

■ **STRATFIELD TURGIS**
Wellington Arms
Weekends from £40
Breakfast

■ **STRATFORD-UPON-AVON**
Alveston Manor
Weekends from £84
Breakfast, dinner

■ **STRATFORD-UPON-AVON**
Billesley Manor
All year from £110
Breakfast, dinner

■ **STRATFORD-UPON-AVON**
Dukes Hotel
Weekends Nov–Mar from £68
Breakfast, dinner

■ **STRATFORD-UPON-AVON**
Ettington Park Hotel
Any 2 nights Jun–Aug from £130
Breakfast, dinner

■ **STRATFORD-UPON-AVON**
Falcon Hotel
All year from £75
Breakfast, dinner

■ **STRATFORD-UPON-AVON**
Grosvenor House Hotel
All year (except Cheltenham Races, Royal
Show, NEC events & Xmas) from £59
Breakfast, dinner

■ **STRATFORD-UPON-AVON**
Moat House International
Weekends all year (except 25–26 Dec & 1
Jan) from £83
Breakfast, lunch or dinner

■ **STRATFORD-UPON-AVON**
Shakespeare Hotel
Weekends from £92
Breakfast, dinner

■ **STRATFORD-UPON-AVON**
Stratford House Hotel
Nov–Mar (except Sat) from £70 May–Oct
(except Fri & Sat, Easter, Royal Show &
Cheltenham week) from £92
Breakfast, £15 towards meals

■ **STRATFORD-UPON-AVON**
Swans Nest
Weekends from £68
Breakfast, dinner

■ **STRATFORD-UPON-AVON**
Welcombe Hotel
Weekends from £110
Breakfast, dinner

■ **STRATFORD-UPON-AVON**
White Swan
Weekends from £74
Breakfast, dinner

■ **STREATLEY-ON-THAMES**
Swan at Streatley
Weekends from £90
Breakfast, dinner

■ **STREET**
Bear Hotel
All year from £62
Breakfast, dinner

■ **STREET**
Wessex Hotel
All year from £57
Breakfast, 1 dinner

■ **STROUD**
Bear of Rodborough
All year from £74
Breakfast, dinner

■ **SUDBURY**
Mill
All year from £72
Breakfast, £11.75 towards dinner

■ **SUNDERLAND**
Seaburn Hotel
Weekends (including weekdays Jul/Aug)
from £65
Breakfast, 1 lunch, dinner

■ **SUTTON COLDFIELD**
Moor Hall Hotel
Weekends from £56
Breakfast, dinner

■ **SUTTON COLDFIELD**
New Hall Hotel
All year from £128
Breakfast, dinner

■ **SUTTON COLDFIELD**
Penns Hall Hotel
Weekends from £65
Breakfast, dinner

■ **SWINDON**
Blusdon House Hotel
Weekends from £90
Breakfast, dinner

■ **SWINDON**
Crest Hotel
Weekends from £72
Breakfast, dinner

■ **SWINDON**
Pear Tree at Purton
Weekends from £90
Breakfast, dinner

■ **SWINDON**
Post House Hotel
Weekends from £66
Breakfast, dinner

■ **TARRANT MONKTON**
Langton Arms
1 Nov–30 Mar from £30
Breakfast

■ **TAUNTON**
Castle Hotel
All year from £110
Breakfast, dinner

■ **TAUNTON**
County Hotel
Weekends from £64
Breakfast, dinner

■ **TAUNTON**
Deane Gate Hotel
Weekends from £85
Breakfast, dinner

■ **TEBAY**
Tebay Mountain Lodge Hotel
All year (except Xmas) from £40
Breakfast, dinner

■ **TELFORD**
Telford Hotel Golf & Country Club
Weekends from £70
Breakfast, dinner

■ **TELFORD**
Telford Moat House
Weekends (except 26–30 Dec) from £62
Breakfast, dinner

■ **TETBURY**
Calcot Manor
Nov–mid Mar from £128
Breakfast, dinner

■ **TETBURY**
Close at Tetbury
All year (except Cheltenham week &
Badminton trials) from £120
Breakfast, dinner

■ **TETBURY**
Snooty Fox Hotel
All year from £85
Breakfast, dinner

■ **TEWKESBURY**
Bell Hotel
All year from £84
Breakfast, dinner

■ **TEWKESBURY**
Bredon Manor
All year from £84
Breakfast, dinner

■ **TEWKESBURY**
Royal Hop Pole Hotel
All year from £84
Breakfast, £8 toward lunch, dinner

■ **TEWKESBURY**
Tewkesbury Park Hotel
Weekends from £75
Breakfast, dinner

■ **THEBERTON**
Theberton Grange
Nov–24 Dec & Feb–20 Mar from £66
Breakfast, £10 towards dinner

■ **THETFORD**
Bell
Weekends from £70
Breakfast, dinner

■ **THORNABY-ON-TEES**
Post House Hotel
Weekends from £56
Breakfast, dinner

■ **THORNBURY**
Thornbury Castle Hotel
Nov–18 Mar from £122
Continental breakfast, dinner

■ **THORNTON-LE-FYLDE**
River House
Weekends from £80
Breakfast, dinner

■ **THURLESTONE**
Thurlestone Hotel
Nov–16 Mar from £82
Breakfast, dinner

■ **TICKTON**
Tickton Grange Hotel
Weekends from £35
Breakfast

■ **TONBRIDGE**
Rose & Crown Hotel
Weekends from £68
Breakfast, dinner

■ **TORQUAY**
Grand Hotel
All year from £78
Breakfast, dinner

■ **TORQUAY**
Homers Hotel
All year from £62
Breakfast, dinner

■ **TORQUAY**
Imperial Hotel
All year from £146
Breakfast, dinner

■ **TORQUAY**
Kistor Hotel
Nov–26 May from £53
Breakfast, 1 lunch, dinner

■ **TORQUAY**
Livermead Cliff Hotel
All year from £62
Breakfast, 1 dinner & 1 lunch or dinner

■ **TORQUAY**
Livermead House Hotel
All year from £62
Breakfast, 1 dinner & 1 lunch or dinner

■ **TORQUAY**
Osborne Hotel
All year from £100
Breakfast, dinner

■ **TORQUAY**
Palace Hotel
All year (except Easter & Xmas) from £74
Breakfast, lunch or dinner

■ **TRURO**
Alverton Manor
Weekends from £95
Breakfast, dinner

■ **TUNBRIDGE WELLS**
Royal Wells Inn
Weekends from £80
Breakfast, £17.50 towards dinner

■ **TUNBRIDGE WELLS**
Spa Hotel
Weekends from £50
Breakfast, dinner & 1 lunch or dinner

■ **TURNERS HILL**
Alexander House
Weekends from £187
Continental breakfast, lunch, dinner

■ **TUTBURY**
Ye Olde Dog & Partridge
Weekends from £50
Breakfast

■ **ULLSWATER**
Leeming House Hotel
All year from £110
Breakfast, dinner

■ **ULLSWATER**
Rampsbeck Hotel
All year (except mid-week only Apr–June
& Sept–Oct) from £70
Breakfast, dinner

■ **ULLSWATER**
Sharrow Bay Hotel
Weekdays Nov–23 Mar from £167
Breakfast, dinner

■ **UNDERBARROW**
Greenriggs Country House
Weekends Nov, Dec & Mar from £62
Breakfast, dinner

■ **UPPER SLAUGHTER**
Lords of the Manor Hotel
Nov–Mar (except Xmas, New Year &
Cheltenham Gold Cup) from £105
Breakfast, dinner

■ **UPPINGHAM**
Falcon Hotel
Weekends from £54
Breakfast, dinner

■ **UTTOXETER**
White Hart Hotel
Weekends from £25
Breakfast

■ **VENTNOR**
Royal Hotel
All year from £60
Breakfast, dinner

■ **VERYAN**
Nare Hotel
Oct–May from £35.50
Breakfast, dinner

■ **WADHURST**
Spindlewood Hotel
Nov–Mar & Oct from £70
Breakfast, dinner

■ **WAKEFIELD**
Cedar Court Hotel
Weekends from £66
Breakfast, dinner

■ **WAKEFIELD**
Post House Hotel
Weekends from £56
Breakfast, dinner

■ **WAKEFIELD**
Swallow Hotel
All year from £60
Breakfast, 1 lunch, dinner

■ **WALBERTON**
Avisford Park Hotel
Weekends Nov–26 Feb from £85, 3 Mar–
20 Aug from £95
Breakfast, dinner

■ **WALLINGFORD**
George Hotel
Weekends from £138
Breakfast, dinner

■ **WALLINGFORD**
Shillingford Bridge Hotel
Oct–Apr from £75
Breakfast, dinner

■ **WALLS**
Barrastow House Hotel
Nov–Apr (except 19 Dec–5 Jan) from £68
Breakfast, lunch, dinner

■ **WALSALL**
Barons Court Hotel
All year from £69
Breakfast, dinner

■ **WALSALL**
Crest Hotel
Weekends from £66
Breakfast, dinner

■ **WANSFORD-IN-ENGLAND**
Haycock Hotel
Weekends from £70
Breakfast, 1 dinner

■ **WANTAGE**
Bear Hotel
Weekends (except Xmas) from £59
Breakfast, dinner

■ **WARMINSTER**
Bishopstrow House
Nov–22 Mar from £120
Continental Breakfast, dinner

■ **WARRINGTON**
Lord Daresbury Hotel
Weekends & daily Jul–Aug from £190
Breakfast, dinner

■ **WARWICK**
Hilton National
Weekends from £64
Breakfast

■ **WASHINGTON**
George Washington Hotel
Weekends from £74
Breakfast, dinner

■ **WASHINGTON**
Post House Hotel
Weekends from £64
Breakfast, dinner

■ **WATERINGBURY**
Wateringbury Hotel
Weekends from £64
Breakfast, dinner

■ **WATFORD**
Hilton National
Weekends from £52
Breakfast

■ **WEEDON**
Crossroads Hotel
Weekends from £64
Breakfast, £13.50 towards meals

■ **WELWYN GARDEN CITY**
Crest Hotel
Weekends from £66
Breakfast, dinner

■ **WEMBLEY**
Hilton National
Weekends from £52
Breakfast

■ **WEST BROMWICH**
West Bromwich Moat House
Weekends from £55
Breakfast, dinner

■ **WEST CHILTINGTON**
Roundabout Hotel
All year from £73
Breakfast, lunch or dinner

■ **WEST RUNTON**
Links Country Park Hotel
All year from £70
Breakfast, £12.25 towards dinner

■ **WESTON-SUPER-MARE**
Grand Atlantic Hotel
All year from £66
Breakfast, dinner

■ **WESTONBIRT**
Hare & Hounds Hotel
All year from £68
Breakfast, dinner

■ **WETHERAL**
Crown Hotel
Weekends from £84
Breakfast, £14 towards dinner

■ **WETHERBY**
Penguin Hotel
Weekends from £56
Breakfast

■ **WEYBRIDGE**
Oaklands Park Hotel
Weekends from £39
Breakfast

■ **WEYBRIDGE**
Ship Thistle Hotel
Weekends (including weekdays in summer) from £74
Breakfast, dinner

■ **WHIMPLE**
Woodhays
Nov–Easter from £98
Breakfast, dinner

■ **WHITWELL-ON-THE-HILL**
Whitwell Hall Country House Hotel
Nov–Apr from £70
Breakfast, dinner

■ **WILLERBY**
Grange Park Hotel
All year (except Xmas, New Year) from £75.40
Breakfast, dinner

■ **WILLERBY**
Willberby Manor Hotel
Weekends from £30
No meals

■ **WILMSLOW**
Stanneylands Hotel
Weekends from £105
Breakfast, lunch, £19 towards dinner

■ **WILMSLOW**
Valley Lodge Hotel
Weekends from £115
Breakfast, dinner

■ **WIMBORNE MINSTER**
The Kings Head
All year (except Xmas) from £80
Breakfast, dinner

■ **WINCANTON**
Holbrook House Hotel
All year from £57
Breakfast, dinner

■ **WINCHESTER**
Lainston House
Weekends from £80
Breakfast, dinner

■ **WINCHESTER**
Royal Hotel
All year from £71
Breakfast, dinner

■ **WINCHESTER**
The Wessex
Weekends from £80
Breakfast, dinner

■ **WINDERMERE**
Langdale Chase Hotel
Nov–Apr from £72
Breakfast, dinner

■ **WINDERMERE**
Miller Howe Hotel
Weekends Nov, Mar & Apr from £150
Breakfast, dinner

■ **WINDSOR**
Castle Hotel
Weekends from £92
Breakfast, dinner

■ **WINDSOR**
Oakley Court Hotel
Weekends from £72
Breakfast

■ **WINKTON**
Fisherman's Haunt Hotel
Nov–20 Mar from £45
Breakfast, £6 towards meals

■ **WINSFORD**
Royal Oak Inn
Weekdays from £90
Breakfast, dinner

■ **WINTERBOURNE**
Grange Hotel at Northwoods
Weekends from £74
Breakfast, dinner

■ **WISHAW**
Belfry Hotel
Weekends from £105
Breakfast, dinner

■ **WITHERSLACK**
Old Vicarage
All year from £89
Breakfast, dinner

■ **WIVELISCOMBE**
Langley House Hotel
All year from £84
Breakfast, dinner

■ **WOBURN**
Bedford Arms Hotel
All year (except Xmas & Easter) from £84
Breakfast, dinner

■ **WOLVERHAMPTON**
Gold Thorn Hotel
Weekends from £52
Breakfast

■ **WOLVERHAMPTON**
Mount Hotel
All year from £59
Breakfast, dinner

■ **WOODBRIDGE**
Seckford Hall Hotel
All year from £90
Breakfast, £15.50 towards dinner

■ **WOODFORD BRIDGE**
Prince Regent Hotel
All year from £58
Breakfast

■ **WOODSTOCK**
Bear Hotel
All year (except Xmas, New Year &
Easter) from £107
Breakfast, dinner

■ **WOODSTOCK**
Feathers Hotel
Nov–Mar from £85
Breakfast, dinner

■ **WOODY BAY**
Woody Bay Hotel
All year from £56
Breakfast, dinner

■ **WOOLACOMBE**
Woolacombe Bay Hotel
Nov–20 Dec, Feb–15 Jul & Sep–Oct from
£71
Breakfast, 1 dinner

■ **WOOLER**
Ryecroft Hotel
All year from £60
Breakfast, dinner

■ **WOOLER**
Tankerville Arms Hotel
All year from £49.50
Breakfast, dinner

■ **WORCESTER**
Giffard Hotel
Weekends from £72
Breakfast, dinner

■ **WORFIELD**
Old Vicarage Hotel
All year (except 24 Dec–1 Jan) from
£67.50
Breakfast, dinner

■ **WORTHING**
Beach Hotel
Nov–Apr from £58.50
Breakfast, lunch or dinner

■ **WROTHAM HEATH**
Post House Hotel
Weekends from £88
Breakfast, dinner

■ **YATTENDON**
Royal Oak Hotel
Weekends (except Xmas & Easter) from
£80
Breakfast, £10 towards dinner

■ **YELVERTON**
Moorland Links Hotel
Weekends from £73
Breakfast, dinner

■ **YEOVIL**
Manor Crest Hotel
All year from £74
Breakfast, dinner

■ **YORK**
Abbey Park Hotel
Weekends from £60
Breakfast

■ **YORK**
Abbots Mews Hotel
Nov–May from £66
Breakfast, dinner

■ **YORK**
Hill Hotel
All year (except 15 Dec–20 Jan) from £56
Breakfast, dinner

■ **YORK**
Judges Lodgings
Nov–Easter (except Xmas, New Year &
Easter) from £47.50
Breakfast, dinner

■ **YORK**
Middlethorpe Hall
Nov–Mar from £130
Breakfast, dinner

■ **YORK**
Mount Royale Hotel
All year from £90
Breakfast, dinner

■ **YORK**
Post House Hotel
Weekends from £70
Breakfast, dinner

■ **YORK**
Royal York Hotel
All year from £100
Breakfast, dinner

■ YORK
Swallow Chase Hotel
All year from £82
Breakfast, 1 lunch, dinner

■ YORK
Viking Hotel
All year from £42
Breakfast, dinner

■ YORK
York Crest Hotel
All year from £72
Breakfast

■ YOXFORD
Satis House
Weekends from £59.50
Breakfast, £9.50 towards meals

SCOTLAND

■ ABERDEEN
Bucksburn Moat House
Weekends from £69
Breakfast, dinner

■ ABERDEEN
Caledonian Thistle Hotel
Weekends from £44
Breakfast

■ ABERDEEN
Copthorne Hotel
Weekends from £55
Breakfast

■ ABERDEEN
Holiday Inn
Weekends from £55
Breakfast

■ ABERDEEN AIRPORT
Skean Dhu Hotel Aberdeen Airport
Weekends from £54
Breakfast, dinner

■ ABERDEEN AIRPORT
Skean Dhu Dyce Hotel
Weekends from £52
Breakfast, dinner

■ ABERDEEN
Stakis Tree Tops Hotel
All year from £72
Breakfast, dinner

■ ABERDEEN
Swallow Imperial Hotel
All year £55
Breakfast, dinner

■ AIRTH
Airth Castle Hotel
Weekends Nov–Apr from £137
Breakfast, dinner

■ ALTNAHARRA
Altnaharra Hotel
Mar–Apr & mid Sept–Nov from £70
Breakfast, dinner

■ ALYTH
Lands of Loyal Hotel
All year from £56
Breakfast, dinner

■ ANNAN
Warmanbie Hotel
Weekends 16 Nov–23 Sept from £59
Breakfast, dinner

■ ANSTRUTHER
Craw's Nest Hotel
Weekends (including any 2 nights m/wk)
from £55
Breakfast

■ ARDENTINNY
Ardentinny Hotel
Mid Mar–May & Oct from £59
Breakfast, dinner

■ ARDUAINE
Loch Melfort Hotel
28 Mar–5 May from £35
Breakfast, dinner

■ AUCHTERARDER
The Gleneagles Hotel
All year from £145
Breakfast, dinner

■ AUCHTERHOUSE
Old Mansion House Hotel
Weekends from £50
Breakfast

■ AVIEMORE
Post House Hotel
All year from £72
Breakfast, dinner

■ AVIEMORE
Stakis Badenoch Hotel
All year from £50
Breakfast, dinner

■ AVIEMORE
Stakis Coylumbridge Resort Hotel
All year (except Easter, Xmas & New
Year) from £88
Breakfast, dinner

■ AVIEMORE
Stakis Four Seasons Hotel
All year from £144
Breakfast, dinner

■ AYR
Balgarth Hotel
Nov–Mar from £49
Breakfast, dinner

■ **AYR**
Caledonian Hotel
All year from £55
Breakfast, dinner

■ **AYR**
Pickwick Hotel
Weekends Oct–Mar from £75
Breakfast

■ **BALLACHULISH**
Ballachulish Hotel
All year from £50
Breakfast, dinner

■ **BALLATER**
Tullich Lodge
All year from £130
Breakfast, dinner

■ **BANCHORY**
Invery House
Nov–Mar from £130
Breakfast, dinner

■ **BANCHORY**
Raemoir House Hotel
Weekends from £75
Breakfast, dinner

■ **BARRHILL**
Kildonan Hotel
All year from £88
Breakfast, dinner

■ **BONNYRIGG**
Dalhousie Castle Hotel
Weekends Nov–May from £62
Breakfast, dinner

■ **BRIDGE OF CALLY**
Bridge of Cally Hotel
Jan–Apr from £30
Breakfast

■ **CALLANDER**
Roman Camp Hotel
Mid Mar–mid May & mid Oct–mid Nov
from £92
Breakfast, dinner

■ **CLEISH**
Nivingston House
Weekends all year (including weekdays
Nov–Mar) from £75
Breakfast, dinner

■ **CRAIGNURE**
Isle of Mull Hotel
Mid Apr–mid Oct from £136
Breakfast, dinner

■ **DULNAIN BRIDGE**
Muckrach Lodge Hotel
Nov–22 Dec & 5 Jan–Mar from £66
Breakfast, dinner

■ **DIRLETON**
Open Arms Hotel
Nov–8 May from £154
Breakfast, dinner

■ **DRYBURGH**
Dryburgh Abbey Hotel
All year (except Easter, Whitsun & Aug
Bank Hol) from £45
Breakfast, dinner

■ **DUNBLANE**
Cromlix House
Nov–Mar from £175
Breakfast, dinner

■ **DUNFERMLINE**
King Malcolm Thistle Hotel
Weekends from £44
Breakfast

■ **DUNKELD**
Hillhead of Dunkeld
Nov–15 Mar (except Bank Hols) from
£60.35
Breakfast

■ **EAST KILBRIDE**
Bruce Hotel
Weekends from £55
Breakfast, dinner

■ **EAST KILBRIDE**
Stuart Hotel
Weekends from £38.40
Breakfast

■ **EDINBURGH**
Albany Hotel
Nov–Apr from £60
Breakfast, dinner

■ **EDINBURGH**
Barnton Thistle Hotel
Aug–Sep from £55
Breakfast

■ **EDINBURGH**
Braid Hills Hotel
All year from £60
Breakfast, lunch & dinner

■ **EDINBURGH**
Bruntsfield Hotel
All year from £58
Breakfast, dinner

■ **EDINBURGH**
Caledonian Hotel
All year from £85
Breakfast, dinner

■ **EDINBURGH**
Carlton Highland Hotel
Weekends Nov–July & Oct from £70
Breakfast, dinner

■ EDINBURGH
Crest Hotel
Weekends from £70
Breakfast

■ EDINBURGH
Edinburgh Sheraton
Weekends from £65
Breakfast

■ EDINBURGH
Ellersley House Hotel
All year from £59
Breakfast, dinner

■ EDINBURGH
George Hotel
Weekends from £70
Continental breakfast

■ EDINBURGH
Hilton National
Weekends from £64
Breakfast

■ EDINBURGH
Howard Hotel
Weekends Nov–Mar
Breakfast, dinner

■ EDINBURGH
King James Thistle Hotel
All year from £52
Breakfast

■ EDINBURGH
Post House Hotel
Weekends from £64
Breakfast, dinner

■ EDINBURGH
Royal Scot Hotel
Weekends from £70
Breakfast, 1 lunch, dinner

■ EDINBURGH
Stakis Grosvenor Hotel
All year from £66
Breakfast, dinner

■ ELGIN
Mansion House Hotel
Weekends from £60
Breakfast, dinner

■ ELLON
Mercury Motor Inn
All year from £66
Breakfast, dinner

■ ERSKINE
Crest Hotel
Weekends from £74
Breakfast, dinner

■ ETTRICKBRIDGE
Ettrickshaws Hotel
Mar–Nov from £68
Breakfast, dinner

■ FORFAR
Royal Hotel
Weekends from £57
Breakfast, dinner

■ GARVE
Inchbae Lodge Hotel
All year from £60
Breakfast, dinner

■ GATEHOUSE OF FLEET
Cally Palace Hotel
Weekends Nov & Dec, Mar–May & Oct–Nov from £70
Breakfast, dinner

■ GATEHOUSE OF FLEET
Murray Arms
All year from £74
Breakfast, dinner

■ GLASGOW
Albany Hotel
Weekends from £60
Breakfast, dinner

■ GLASGOW
Central Hotel
Weekends from £45
Breakfast, dinner

■ GLASGOW
Copthorne Hotel
Weekends from £57
Breakfast

■ GLASGOW
Crest Hotel Glasgow City
Weekends from £80
Breakfast, dinner

■ GLASGOW
Hospitality Inn
Weekends (except Xmas & New Year)
from £36
No meals

■ GLASGOW
Kelvin Park Lorns Hotel
All year from £29.50
Breakfast, dinner

■ GLASGOW
Stakis Grosvenor Hotel
All year from £80
Breakfast, dinner

■ GLASGOW
Swallow Hotel
Weekends (including weekday Jul/Aug)
from £65
Breakfast, 1 lunch, dinner

■ GLASGOW
Tinto Firs Thistle Hotel
Weekends from £70
Breakfast, dinner

■ GLASGOW
White House
Weekends from £48.50
No meals

■ GLASGOW AIRPORT
Excelsior Hotel
Weekends from £62
Breakfast, dinner

■ GLASGOW AIRPORT
Stakis Normandie Hotel
All year from £54
Breakfast, dinner

■ GLENLIVET
Blairfindy Lodge Hotel
Nov–Mar (except Xmas & New Year) from £44
Breakfast

■ GLENROTHES
Balgeddie House Hotel
Weekends from £49.50
Breakfast, dinner

■ HAWICK
Kirklands Hotel
Weekends from £50
Breakfast, dinner

■ HUMBIE
Johnstounburn House Hotel
Nov–16 Apr from £95
Breakfast, dinner

■ INGLISTON
Norton House Hotel
Weekends from £40
Breakfast, dinner

■ INVERNESS
Bunchrew House Hotel
All year from £85
Breakfast, dinner

■ INVERNESS
Caledonian Hotel
All year from £73
Breakfast, dinner

■ INVERNESS
Dunain Park Hotel
Nov–Apr from £94.50
Breakfast, dinner

■ INVERNESS
Kingsmills Hotel
Weekends from £70
Breakfast, 1 lunch, dinner

■ INVERNESS
Mercury Hotel
Weekends (except Xmas & New Year) from £48
Breakfast

■ INVERNESS
Station Hotel
All year from £66
Breakfast, dinner

■ IRVINE
Hospitality Inn
Weekends from £69
Breakfast, dinner

■ ISLE OF RASSAY
Isle of Rassay Hotel
Apr–Sept from £60
Breakfast, dinner

■ KELSO
Sunlaws House Hotel
All year from £192
Breakfast, dinner

■ KENMORE
Kenmore Hotel
Nov–Mar from £65
Breakfast, dinner

■ KILCHRENAN
Ardanaiseig
Apr–Oct from £130
Breakfast, dinner

■ KILDRUMMY
Kildrummy Castle Hotel
Nov–May from £144
Breakfast, dinner

■ KILWINNING
Montgreenan Mansions House
Weekends from £135
Breakfast, dinner

■ KINCLAVEN BY STANLEY
Ballathie House
Nov–18 Dec, 7 Jan–Feb & 5 Mar–June from £88
Breakfast, dinner

■ KINLOCHBERVIE
Kinlochbervie Hotel
All year from £80
Breakfast, dinner

■ KINLOCH RANNOCH
Loch Rannoch Hotel
All year from £71
Breakfast, dinner

■ KINROSS
Windlestrae Hotel
Weekends Nov–15 Dec, 5 Jan–10 June & 10 Sept–Oct from £45
Breakfast

■ **KYLE OF LOCHALSH**
Lochalsh Hotel
All year from £65
Breakfast, dinner

■ **LANGBANK**
Gleddoch House Hotel
Weekends from £90
Breakfast, dinner

■ **LERWICK**
Shetland Hotel
Weekends from £66
Breakfast, dinner

■ **LETHAM**
Fernie Castle Hotel
All year from £80
Breakfast, dinner

■ **LOCHGAIR**
Lochgair Hotel
Nov–Apr from £35
Breakfast, dinner

■ **LUNDIN LINKS**
Old Manor Hotel
Weekends Nov–Apr & Oct from £66.75
Breakfast, dinner

■ **MILNGAVIE**
Black Bull Thistle Hotel
Weekends from £46
Breakfast, £11 towards dinner

■ **MOFFAT**
Mercury Hotel
All year from £70
Breakfast, dinner

■ **MUIR OF ORD**
Ord Arms Hotel
All year from £30
Breakfast, £5 towards lunch, £10 towards dinner

■ **NAIRN**
Golf View Hotel
All year from £68
Breakfast, dinner

■ **NEWBURGH**
Udny Arms Hotel
Weekends from £60
Breakfast, dinner

■ **NEWTON STEWART**
Bruce Hotel
All year from £126
Breakfast, dinner

■ **NEWTON STEWART**
Creebridge House
All year from £68
Breakfast, dinner

■ **NEWTON STEWART**
Kirroughtree Hotel
All year from £102
Breakfast, dinner

■ **NORTH BERWICK**
Marine Hotel
All year from £76
Breakfast, dinner

■ **OBAN**
Columbia Hotel
Nov–June (except Xmas & New Year, Easter & Whitsun) from £49
Breakfast, dinner

■ **OLD MELDRUM**
Meldrum House Hotel
Weekends Mar–Nov from £177
Breakfast, dinner

■ **ONICH**
Onich Hotel
Nov–19 May (except Xmas & New Year) from £58
Breakfast, dinner

■ **PEEBLES**
Cringletie House Hotel
Nov–21 Dec & 11 Mar–12 May from £70
Breakfast, dinner

■ **PEEBLES**
Park Hotel
All year (except Xmas & New Year) from £76
Breakfast, lunch & dinner

■ **PEEBLES**
Peebles Hotel Hydro
Weekdays Nov–Mar from £120
Breakfast, dinner

■ **PEEBLES**
Tontine Hotel
All year from £64
Breakfast, dinner

■ **PERTH**
Royal George Hotel
All year from £64
Breakfast, dinner

■ **PERTH**
Stakis City Mills Hotel
All year from £62
Breakfast, dinner

■ **PERTH**
Station Hotel
Weekends from £45
Breakfast, dinner

■ **PITCAPLE**
Pittodrie House Hotel
Nov–Apr from £80
Breakfast, dinner

A LOT FOR LESS

■ **PITLOCHRY**
Atholl Palace Hotel
All year from £72
Breakfast, dinner

■ **PITLOCHRY**
Green Park Hotel
26 Mar–9 May from £70
Breakfast, dinner

■ **PITLOCHRY**
Pitlochry Hydro Hotel
Mar–Nov from £80
Breakfast, dinner

■ **ROTHES**
Rothes Glen Hotel
Nov–Apr, weekends from £44
Breakfast

■ **ST ANDREWS**
Old Course Golf & Country Club
All year from £99.50
Breakfast, 1 dinner

■ **ST ANDREWS**
Rufflets Hotel
Nov–Apr from £37
Breakfast, dinner

■ **ST ANDREWS**
Rusacks Hotel
All year from £80
Breakfast, dinner

■ **SCOURIE**
Eddrachilles Hotel
Mar–Oct from £57.50
Breakfast, dinner

■ **SCOURIE**
Scourie Hotel
Mid Mar–mid May & Oct from £38.33
Breakfast, dinner

■ **SELKIRK**
Phillipburn House Hotel
All year from £70
Breakfast, dinner

■ **SKEAPOST BRIDGE**
Skeapost House Hotel
Apr–Oct (except Whitsun week) from £76
Breakfast, dinner

■ **SOUTH QUEENSFERRY**
Forth Bridges Moat House
All year from £70
Breakfast, dinner

■ **STEWARTON**
Chapeltoun House
Nov–Apr from £100
Breakfast, dinner

■ **STONEHAVEN**
Stonehaven Commodore Hotel
All year from £62
Breakfast, dinner

■ **STORNAWAY**
Caberfeidh Hotel
All year from £45
Breakfast, dinner

■ **STRANRAER**
North West Castle Hotel
Weekends from £69.50
Breakfast, lunch & dinner

■ **TARBERT**
Stonefield Castle Hotel
Nov–Mar from £58
Breakfast, dinner

■ **TIRORAN**
Tiroran House
Late May–early Oct from £110
Breakfast, dinner

■ **TROON**
Marine Highland Hotel
Nov–Mar (except Xmas & New Year) from £70
Breakfast, dinner

■ **TROON**
Piersland House Hotel
Weekends Nov–Apr (except Xmas & New Year) from £49.50
Breakfast, dinner

■ **TROON**
Sun Court Hotel
All year from £70
Breakfast, dinner

■ **ULLAPOOL**
Ceilidh Place
Nov–Mar from £40
Breakfast

■ **WICK**
Mercury Hotel
All year £66
Breakfast, dinner

WALES

■ **ABERGWESYN**
Llwynderw Hotel
Nov–Dec, Mar–Oct from £130
Breakfast, dinner

■ **ABERSOCH**
Port Tocyn Hotel
25 Mar–19 May, 25 Sept–6 Nov from £68
Breakfast, dinner

■ **ABERSOCH**
Riverside Hotel
Mar–Nov from £70
Breakfast, dinner

■ **BARRY**
Mount Sorrel Hotel
Weekends from £60
Breakfast, dinner

■ **BEAUMARIS**
Bulkeley Arms Hotel
Nov–Apr from £60
Breakfast, dinner

■ **BEDDGELERT**
Royal Goat Hotel
Oct–Apr from £66
Breakfast, dinner

■ **BETWS-Y-COED**
Royal Oak Hotel
All year from £53
Breakfast, dinner

■ **BRECHFA**
Ty Mawr Country House Hotel
All year from £60
Breakfast, dinner

■ **CAERNARFON**
Stables Hotel
Weekends (except Xmas, Easter, July &
Aug) from £60
Breakfast, dinner

■ **CARDIFF**
Angel Hotel
Weekends from £63
Breakfast, £9 towards lunch, £15 towards
dinner

■ **CARDIFF**
Crest Hotel
Weekends from £68
Breakfast, dinner

■ **CARDIFF**
Park Hotel
Weekends from £59
Breakfast, dinner

■ **CARDIFF**
Post House Hotel
Weekends from £66
Breakfast, dinner

■ **CARDIFF**
Royal Hotel
Weekends from £55
Breakfast, dinner

■ **CARMARTHEN**
Ivy Bush Royal Hotel
Weekends from £56
Breakfast, dinner

■ **CHEPSTOW**
Castle View Hotel
All year from £112
Breakfast, dinner

■ **CHEPSTOW**
St Pierre Hotel
All year from £94
Breakfast, dinner

■ **COLWYN BAY**
Hotel Seventy Degrees
All year from £62
Breakfast, dinner

■ **CONWY**
Sychant Pass Hotel
All year from £59
Breakfast, dinner

■ **COYCHURCH**
Coed-y-Mwstwr Hotel
All year (except Xmas) from £80
Continental breakfast, dinner

■ **CRICKHOWELL**
Gliffaes Country House Hotel
Mid Mar–Nov from £76
Breakfast, dinner

■ **FISHGUARD**
Fishguard Bay Hotel
All year from £55
Breakfast, dinner

■ **GLYN CEIRIOG**
Golden Pheasant Hotel
All year from £70.90
Breakfast, dinner

■ **GWBERT-ON-SEA**
Cliff Hotel
All year from £72
Breakfast, dinner

■ **LAKE VYRNWY**
Lake Vyrnwy Hotel
All year (except Bank Hols) from £59.50
Breakfast, packed lunch, dinner

■ **LAMPHEY**
Court Hotel
All year from £59
Breakfast, dinner

■ **LLANARMON DYFFRYN CEIRIOG**
Hand Hotel
Nov–Mar from £75 Apr–Nov from £82
Breakfast, 1 dinner

■ **LLANDDERFEL**
Pale Hotel
Nov–Mar from £105
Breakfast, dinner

■ **LLANDUDNO**
Bodysgallen Hall
Nov–Apr from £116
Breakfast, dinner

■ **LLANDUDNO**
Empire Hotel
All year from £66
Breakfast, 1 lunch, dinner

■ **LLANDUDNO**
St Tudno Hotel
All year (except Xmas & New Year) from £62
Breakfast, dinner

■ **LLANELLI**
Stradey Park Hotel
Weekends from £48
Breakfast, dinner

■ **LLANGOLLEN**
Royal Hotel
All year from £68
Breakfast, dinner

■ **LLANGYBI**
Cwrt Bleddyn Hotel
Weekends from £84
Breakfast, dinner

■ **LLANNEFYDD**
Hawk & Buckie Inn
All year from £50
Breakfast, dinner

■ **LLANRHAEADR**
Llanrhaeadr Hall
All year from £80
Breakfast, dinner

■ **LLANRWST**
Meadowsweet Hotel
All year from £68
Breakfast, dinner

■ **MACHYNLLETH**
Wynnstay Arms
All year from £64
Breakfast, dinner

■ **MISKIN**
Miskin Manor
All year (except 24 Dec–3 Jan) from £90
Breakfast, dinner

■ **MONMOUTH**
King's Head Hotel
All year from £75
Breakfast, dinner

■ **MUMBLES**
Langland Court Hotel
All year from £140
Breakfast, dinner

■ **NEWPORT**
Hilton National
Weekends from £60
Breakfast

■ **NEWPORT**
Kings Hotel
Weekends from £56
Breakfast, dinner

■ **NORTHOP**
Soughton Hall
Weekends from £125
Breakfast, dinner

■ **PENMAENPOOL**
George III Hotel
Nov–Apr (except Bank Hols) from £136.40
Breakfast, dinner

■ **PRESTEIGNE**
Radnorshire Arms Hotel
All year from £66
Breakfast, dinner

■ **ROSSETT**
Llyndir Hall Hotel
Weekends from £80
Breakfast, dinner

■ **RUTHIN**
Castle Hotel & Myddleton Arms
All year from £56
Breakfast, packed lunch, dinner

■ **RUTHIN**
Ruthin Castle
All year from £65
Breakfast, dinner

■ **ST DAVIDS**
Warpool Court Hotel
Nov–21 Dec, 3 Jan–12 May, 25 Sept–Oct from £60
Breakfast, dinner

■ **SWANSEA**
Dragon Hotel
Weekends from £64
Breakfast, dinner

■ **THREE COCKS**
Three Cocks Hotel
Nov, Feb–Nov (except Bank Hols & Royal Welsh week) from £68
Breakfast, dinner

■ **TINTERN ABBEY**
Beaufort Hotel
All year from £57
Breakfast, dinner

■ **TINTERN ABBEY**
Royal George Hotel
Weekends from £39
Breakfast

■ **WOLF'S CASTLE**
Wolf's Castle Country Hotel
Nov–Jul from £95
Breakfast, £9 towards meals

CHANNEL ISLANDS

■ **ALDERNEY, ST ANNE**
Inchalla Hotel
Nov–17 Dec, 1 Jan–25 June, 17 Sept–Nov
from £260 (incl. flight)
Breakfast, dinner

■ **GUERNSEY, ST MARTINS**
La Trelade Hotel
Nov–Apr from £30
Breakfast, £4 towards meals

■ **GUERNSEY, ST PETER PORT**
Flying Dutchman Hotel
Nov–Jan, Mar–15 May, Oct–Nov from £30
Breakfast, £6.50 towards meals

■ **GUERNSEY, ST PETER PORT**
St Pierre Park Hotel
Weekdays 3 nights Nov–31 Mar from
£199 (incl. flight)
Breakfast

■ **JERSEY, GOREY**
Moorings Hotel
Nov–Apr from £49
Breakfast

■ **JERSEY, HAVRE DES PAS**
Hotel de la Plage
Apr–Nov from £31
Breakfast, dinner

■ **JERSEY, HAVRE DES PAS**
Ommaroo Hotel
Nov–May from £54
Breakfast, dinner

■ **JERSEY, ST BRELADE'S BAY**
Hotel L'Horizon
Weekdays Nov–Mar (except Xmas & New
Year) from £60
Breakfast

■ **JERSEY, ST HELIER**
Apollo Hotel
Weekends Nov–Sept from £52
Breakfast, dinner

■ **JERSEY, ST HELIER**
Beaufort Hotel
Weekends Nov–Mar from £57
Breakfast, dinner

■ **JERSEY, ST HELIER**
Pomme D'or Hotel
Nov–Apr from £64
Breakfast, dinner

■ **JERSEY, ST PETER**
Mermaid Hotel
Nov–Mar weekends from £50
Breakfast, dinner

■ **JERSEY, ST SAVIOUR**
Longueville Manor Hotel
Nov–18 Mar weekends from £85
Breakfast, dinner

ISLE OF MAN

■ **DOUGLAS**
Sefton Hotel
Weekends Nov–Apr (except Xmas, New
Year & Easter) from £96
Breakfast, dinner

■ **RAMSEY**
Grand Island Hotel
Nov–31 Mar weekends from £76
Breakfast, dinner

NORTHERN IRELAND

■ **BELFAST**
Europa Hotel
Weekends from £45
Breakfast

■ **BELFAST**
Wellington Park Hotel
Weekends from £52.90
Breakfast, dinner

■ **DUNMURRY**
Conway Hotel
Weekends from £45
Breakfast, dinner

■ **HOLYWOOD**
Culloden Hotel
Weekends from £80
Breakfast

■ **LARNE**
Magheramorne House Hotel
Weekends all year (except Xmas) from
£146
Breakfast, dinner

■ **LONDONDERRY**
Everglades Hotel
Weekends from £46
Breakfast, dinner

■ **NEWTOWNARDS**
Strangford Arms Hotel
Weekends from £30
No meals

■ **PORTBALLINTRAE**
Bayview Hotel
All year from £50
Breakfast, 1 lunch, high tea

A
L
O
T

F
O
R

L
E
S
S

REPUBLIC OF IRELAND

■ **BALLINA**
Downhill Hotel
Weekends from £130
Breakfast, 1 dinner

■ **BALLYLICKEY**
Sea View House Hotel
Apr–Oct (except Bank Hol weekends)
from £77
Breakfast, dinner

■ **BALLYNAHINCH**
Ballynahinch Castle
Nov–Mar & Oct (except Xmas & New
Year & Oct Bank Hol weekend) from £110
Breakfast, dinner

■ **BUNRATTY**
**Fitzpatrick's Shannon Shamrock
Hotel**
Weekends from £70
Breakfast, dinner

■ **CARRICKMACROSS**
Nuremore Hotel
All year from £40
Breakfast, 1 lunch, 1 dinner

■ **CASHEL**
Cashel House Hotel
Nov, Mar–May from £78.75
Breakfast

■ **CASHEL**
Cashel Palace Hotel
Nov–Mar from £144
Breakfast, dinner

■ **CLIFDEN**
Hotel Ardagh
Apr–June & Sept–Oct from £65
Breakfast, dinner

■ **CLIFDEN**
Rock Glen Hotel
Mid Mar–May, mid Sept–mid Oct from £44
Breakfast & £16 towards dinner

■ **CLONMEL**
Arbutus Lodge Hotel
Weekends from £180
Breakfast, dinner

■ **CLONMEL**
Clonmel Arms Hotel
Weekends from £50
Breakfast, dinner

■ **CORK**
Jurys Hotel
Weekends Nov–May from £49.50
Breakfast

■ **DUBLIN**
Berkeley Court
Weekends (except 20/21 Jan & 17/18 Feb)
from £75
Breakfast

■ **DUBLIN**
Blooms Hotel
Weekends from £115
Breakfast, £12 towards dinner

■ **DUBLIN**
Gresham Hotel
Weekends (except International Rugby
weekends) from £49
Breakfast, £14 towards meals

■ **DUBLIN**
Jurys Hotel
Weekends Nov–May from £49.50
Breakfast

■ **DUBLIN**
Royal Dublin Hotel
Nov–May from £50
Breakfast, £13 towards dinner

■ **DUBLIN**
Westbury Hotel
Weekends (except International weekends)
from £150
Breakfast

■ **DUNADRY**
Dunadry Inn
Weekends from £47.50
Breakfast, 1 dinner

■ **GALWAY**
Ardilaun House Hotel
Weekends from £75
Breakfast, 1 dinner

■ **GALWAY**
Galway Ryan Hotel
Weekends from £55
Breakfast, 1 dinner

■ **GLEN OF AHERLOW**
Aherlow House Hotel
Weekends from £38
Breakfast

■ **GOREY**
Marlfield House
Weekends Nov–May from £130
Breakfast, dinner

■ **KENMARE**
Park Hotel Kenmare
Nov–Apr from £125
Breakfast, 1 dinner

■ **KILLARNEY**
Killarney Great Southern Hotel
All year (except Jan & Feb) from £54
Breakfast

■ **KILLINEY**
Court Hotel
Weekends from £47
Breakfast

■ **KILLINEY**
Fitzpatrick's Castle Hotel
Weekends (except Xmas, Rugby
International weekends) from £70
Breakfast, 1 dinner

■ **KINSALE**
Actons Hotel
All year from £63
Breakfast, dinner

■ **KNOCKLOFTY**
Knocklofty House Hotel
All year from £150
Breakfast, dinner

■ **LIMERICK**
Jurys Hotel
Weekends Nov–May from £49.50
Breakfast

■ **LIMERICK**
Limerick Inn Hotel
Weekends from £78
Breakfast, 1 dinner

■ **LIMERICK**
New Greenhills Hotel
Weekends Dec–Apr, Oct–Nov from £50
Breakfast

■ **MAYNOOTH**
Moyglare Manor
Sun–Thur Nov, Jan–Feb from £70
Breakfast, £10 towards lunch, £15 towards
dinner

■ **OUGHTERARD**
Connemara Gateway Hotel
All year from £45
Breakfast, 1 dinner

■ **PROSPEROUS**
Curryhills House Hotel
Weekends from £54
Breakfast, dinner

■ **RATHNEW**
Tinakilly House
Nov–20 Dec, 1 Feb–30 June, 1 Sept–Nov
from £90
Breakfast, dinner

■ **SCOTSHOUSE**
Hilton Park
Weekends Apr–Sept from £92
Breakfast, dinner

■ **SLIGO**
Sligo Park Hotel
All year from £45
Breakfast, dinner

■ **SPIDDAL**
Bridge House Hotel
All year from £42
Breakfast

■ **WATERFORD**
Ardree Hotel
Weekends Nov–Mar from £37
Breakfast

■ **WATERVILLE**
Waterville Lake Hotel
Apr–Sept from £108
Breakfast, dinner

■ **WEXFORD**
White's Hotel
All year (except 21 Oct–7 Nov) from
£75.50
Breakfast, dinner

■ **WICKLOW**
Old Rectory
24 Mar–29 Oct from £86
Breakfast, dinner

Thought depends
absolutely on the stomach, but in spite of that,
those who have the best stomachs
are not the best thinkers.

VOLTAIRE 1694-1778
Letter To D'Alembert,
20 August 1770

I know about details,
and if I have introduced or perfected a hundred
details in my time, I shall be content.
After all, no chef has even invented a hundred dishes.

CHARLES RITZ
Cited by Stephen Watts in
THE RITZ (1963)

HOTELS RESTAURANTS AND INNS

LONDON
239

LONDON AIRPORTS
327

ENGLAND
333

SCOTLAND
721

WALES
799

CHANNEL ISLANDS
827

ISLE OF MAN
838

NORTHERN IRELAND
841

REPUBLIC OF IRELAND
849

A recipe

is not meant to be followed exactly -

it is a canvas on which you can embroider.

Improvise and invent. Add the zest of this,

a drop of that, a tiny pinch of the other...

ROGER VERGE
CUISINE OF THE SUN
Trans. Caroline Conran (1979)

According to the Spanish proverb,

four persons are wanted to make a good salad (dressing):

a spendthrift for oil, a miser for vinegar,

a counsellor for salt and a madman to stir it all up.

ABRAHAM HAYWARD 1801-84
THE ART OF DINING

HOTELS
RESTAURANTS
AND INNS

LONDON

W2 — Abbey Court Hotel — NEW ENTRY — £B/C

PH **Map 22 A2**
20 Pembridge Gardens
W2 4DU
01–221 7518
Telex 262167

Credit Access, Amex, Diners, Visa

An up-market bed and breakfast hotel near Notting Hill Gate. Best bedrooms are of a decent size, but most are quite compact; decor and furnishings are attractive, and there are three four-poster rooms. Hairdryers, trouser presses, remote-control TVs and various thoughtful extras are provided, and all rooms except one have whirlpool baths. A smart reception lobby is the only public room, breakfast being served in the bedrooms. **Amenities** patio, fax, laundry service.

| Rooms 22 | Direct dial Yes | Confirm by arrang. | Parking Difficult |
| Ensuite bath/shower 22 | Room TV Yes | | Room service 24 hours |

WC2 — Ajimura

R **Map 27 B1**
51 Shelton Street WC2
01-240 0178

Japanese cooking
Set L £5.50 **Set D** from £9.90
About £38 *for two*
Seats 60 *Parties* 25
Parking Difficult
Credit Access, Amex, Diners, Visa

Simple, unfussy decor and mainly Western staff in a Japanese restaurant that is popular before and after the theatre. The menu contains the classics of Japanese cuisine, including sashimi and sushi (raw fish dishes, the former served with greens and soy sauce, the latter on vinegared rice). Tempura and teriyaki are listed among the specialities, and there are various set meals (cook-it-yourself sukiyaki sounds fun).

Lunch 12–3 *Dinner* 6–11, Sun 6–10.30
Closed L Sat & Sun & all Bank Hols

W8 — Al Gallo d'Oro

R **Map 21 B5**
353 Kensington High Street
W8
01-603 6951

Italian cooking
About £48 *for two*
Seats 60 *Parties* 25
Parking Difficult
Credit Access, Amex, Diners, Visa

A bustling modern Italian restaurant whose decor includes framed prints from Cassells Poultry Book of 1870. Cooking is robust and reliable, with plenty of good, strong flavours. A selection from the trolley is a popular starter, the pasta's very decent, and there are ample fish and meat dishes, made yet ampler by weekly specials such as osso bucco and saltimbocca. Straightforward sweets; good strong espresso. ✆.

Lunch 12.15–2.45, Sun 12.15–2.15   *Dinner* 6.45–11.45
Closed L Sat & all Bank Hols

W1 — Al Hamra — NEW ENTRY

R **Map 25 A4**
31 Shepherd Market W1
01-493 1954

Lebanese cooking
About £40 *for two*
Seats 60 *Parties* 40
Parking Difficult
Credit Access, Amex, Diners, Visa

One of the very best Lebanese restaurants in London, and therefore frequently packed to overflowing. The chief appeal of the menu is the enormous selection of starters both hot and cold, including houmus, stuffed vine leaves, liver, spicy little sausages and chicken winglets. These, in quantity, will make a very splendid meal, but main courses – usually grilled meats – are available, along with excellent homemade sweetmeats. Service is very civilised and good-humoured.

Closed 25 Dec & 1 Jan

W1 — Alastair Little — ✄

R **Map 27 A2**
49 Frith Street W1
01-734 5183

About £50 *for two*
Seats 34
Parking Difficult

A small modern restaurant in Soho is the setting for high-profile chef Alastair Little's imaginative, up-to-date cuisine. His shortish menu changes constantly, tempting with such dishes as smoked haddock on a bed of brown lentils, mullet with minty pesto and succulent sauté of lamb served with whole cloves of garlic. The wine list is also short and select: note Gewürztraminer Bollenberg '85 (Cattin), Pinot Noir '83 (Mondavi). No credit cards. ✆

Lunch 12.30–2.30   *Dinner* 7.30–11.15
Closed Sat, Sun, Bank Hols & 3 wks Aug

We welcome bona fide complaints and recommendations
on the tear-out pages at the back of the book for readers' comment.
They are followed up by our professional team.

SW7   Alexander Hotel   67%   £B/C

H Map 23 B5
9 Sumner Place SW7 3EE
01-581 1591
Telex 917133

Credit Access, Amex, Diners, Visa

The owners of this gracious Victorian hotel have not stinted on its refurbishment. Having restored the public rooms to quiet elegance, they turned their attention to bedrooms. Over the past few years all the generously proportioned bedrooms have been totally redecorated, with attractive furnishings, good-quality fabrics and ample seating. Bathrooms, with showers, are tiled and have plenty of mirrors. No dogs. *Amenities* garden, in-house movies, fax, laundry service.

Rooms 40	*Direct dial* Yes	*Confirm by* arrang.	*Parking* Difficult
Ensuite bath/shower 40	*Room TV* Yes	*Last dinner* 8	*Room service* 24 hours

**We publish annually,
so make sure you use the current edition.
It's worth it!**

N1   Anna's Place

R Map 20 D2
90 Mildmay Park N1
01-249 9379

Swedish cooking

About £33 for two
Seats 44
Parties 10
Parking Limited

Anna Hegarty runs her friendly, informal restaurant with a nice personal touch. The menu is almost entirely Swedish and begins – of course – with gravad lax and pickled herrings. Meatballs are a popular main dish, while more sophisticated offerings include diced fillet of beef marinated in mustard, and turbot with brown butter and horseradish. To finish, there are desserts like Swedish applecake. In summer you can eat in a little courtyard at the back.

Lunch 12.15–2.15   *Dinner* 7.15–11
Closed Sun, Mon, Bank Hols, 2 wks Easter, 2 wks Xmas & all Aug

W1   Arirang Korean Restaurant

R Map 24 B2
31 Poland Street W1
01-437 6633

Korean cooking
Set L from £10 **Set D** from £11
About £30 for two
Seats 90 *Parties* 45
Parking Limited
Credit Access, Amex, Diners, Visa

Owner Tony Wee is the best guide to the long menu at his excellent Korean restaurant. Fiery flavours make themselves felt in such dishes as a hearty soup of meat balls and soy bean cake, and delicious garlicky bracken stalks, while the pickled cabbage is strictly for fire-eaters. Barbecued spare ribs are a speciality, but our favourite dish remains bulgogi, thin strips of spicy marinated beef. Wine generally does not stand up to this cooking, so drink beer or tea.

Lunch 12–3   *Dinner* 6–11
Closed Sun, some Bank Hols & 25 Dec

SW1   Arirang House

R Map 22 C3
3 Park Close SW1
01-581 1820

Korean cooking
Set L *from* £6.50
Set D *from* £15
Seats 40 *Parties* 10
Parking Difficult
Credit Access, Amex, Diners, Visa

Booking is essential at this friendly little Korean restaurant near Knightsbridge Barracks. There's no set pattern to a Korean meal and it's up to you to choose the serving order – though Mrs Bae and her assistants are happy to assist in your selection. Typically fiery offerings are cabbage pickle and spiced radish, while a house speciality is yuk hue – sweet tender strips of raw beef with pears.

Lunch 12–2.30   *Dinner* 6–10.30   *About £42 for two*
Closed Sun, some Bank Hols, 25 & 26 Dec, 1–3 Jan

**We welcome bona fide complaints and recommendations
on the tear-out pages at the back of the book for readers' comment.
They are followed up by our professional team.**

SW8 · L'Arlequin ★★ · ♛ ♟

R Map 21 C6
123 Queenstown Road SW8
01-622 0555

French cooking

Lunch 12.30–2
Dinner 7.30–10.30
Set L £14.50
About £80 *for two*
Seats 45
Parties 12
Parking Ample

Credit Access, Amex, Diners, Visa
Closed Sat, Sun, Bank Hols, 1
wk Xmas & 3 wks Aug

Christian Delteil is not only one of our finest chefs but also one of the most charmingly modest, and it's greatly to the diner's advantage that he rarely leaves his kitchen. Flavours in his dishes are always subtle but well defined, presentation a joy to the eye, and on a recent visit everything worked perfectly: breast of pigeon with a simple, superb jus, succulent grouse, delicate lamb's brains served on blinis, pear pancakes with the subtlest of orange sauces. Service is professional yet sunny, and there's an orthodox list of classic wines.
Specialities petit chou farci à l'ancienne, filet de loup à la coriandre, gigot de lapereau farci pâtes fraîches, chaudfroid de framboises.
♟ Well-chosen ⊖ ♿

NW1 · Asuka *NEW ENTRY*

R Map 21 C4
209a Baker Street NW1
01-486 5026

Japanese cooking
Set L £7.50 **Set D** from £23
About £60 *for two*
Seats 45 *Parties* 16
Parking Difficult
Credit Access, Amex, Diners, Visa

Tucked away at the northern end of Baker Street is an elegant Japanese restaurant, plushly decorated, with strikingly modern high-back chairs in glossy black wood. The menus are fairly standard, but the food is distinguished by great freshness and notably clear flavours. The various set menus (including one for vegetarians) are a very good way of getting to know Japanese cuisine, though the charming waitresses will gladly assist with choosing à la carte.

Lunch 12–3   *Dinner* 6–10.30
Closed L Sat, all Sun & Bank Hols

W1 · Athenaeum Hotel   80% · £A

HR Map 25 A4
116 Piccadilly W1V 0BJ
01-499 3464
Telex 261589

Rooms 112
Ensuite bath/shower 112
Direct dial Yes
Room TV Yes
Confirm by 6
Last dinner 10.30
Parking Limited
Room service 24 hours

Credit Access, Amex, Diners, Visa

A quiet, restrained professional-ism is notable among the staff at this splendid modern hotel, whose situation overlooking Green Park is ideal for all that Central London has to offer. The day rooms are intimate and in-viting, particularly the mahog-any-panelled bar, which features an impressive range of malt whiskies. All bedrooms are dou-ble-glazed and air-conditioned: there are 22 suites, mainly open-

plan, furnished and equipped to the highest standards. Other rooms, recently refurbished, retain their handsome, solid furniture, and all rooms have splendidly luxurious bathrooms with marble tiling, good lighting and an excellent stock of toiletries. No dogs.
Amenities hairdressing, in-house movies, secretarial services, fax, valeting, laundry service.

Restaurant · ♛

Set L from £15.50
Set D £25
About £60 *for two*
Seats 45
Parties 48

Comfortable surroundings, polished service and a very good kitchen under Derek Fuller. His varied à la carte menu covers dishes both classical and more adventurous, from a brilliant mousseline of sole with lobster sauce to veal chop with rosemary, salmon wrapped in lettuce and succulent lamb with a delicate garlic sauce. Very good sweets, super coffee, sound wines. Business lunch and pre-theatre menus available. ♟ Well-chosen ⊖

Lunch 12.30–3, Sun 12.30–2.30   *Dinner* 6–10.30, Sun 7–10

W1	**Au Jardin des Gourmets**	♕

R Map 27 A1
5 Greek Street W1
01-437 1816

French cooking
Set L & D from £13.95
About £50 for two
Seats 95 *Parties* 45
Parking Difficult
Credit Access, Amex, Diners, Visa

Elegant surroundings, competent cooking and one of the best wine lists in the country combine to good effect at this comfortable Soho restaurant. Starters are not wildly exciting but main courses feature more imaginative offerings like monkfish and lobster in butter sauce as well as nicely executed classic dishes such as entrecôte marchand de vin. Wine bargains include Ch. Larcis-Ducasse '82 and Ch. Lafite '76. ⊏ Outstanding ♀ Well-chosen ⊜ ᵶ

Lunch 12.30–2.30 *Dinner* 6.30–11.30
Closed L Bank Hols, all Sun & 4 days Easter

NW8	**L'Aventure**	

R Map 20 B3
3 Blenheim Terrace NW8
01-624 6232

French cooking
Set L & D Sun only £10.50
About £50 for two
Seats 38
Parking Limited
Credit Amex, Visa

Catherine Parisot's restaurant is a pretty little place with a warm and friendly ambience. She and her chef Christian Bretèche decide on the menus – short but interesting selections of highly enjoyable dishes such as mussels with spinach in puff pastry, chicken with morels or fillet of beef with a creamy Roquefort sauce. Sweets might include a marvellous sablé à la truffe au chocolat. Book. ♀ Well-chosen ⊜

Lunch 12.30–2.30 *Dinner* 7–11, Sun 7.30–10
Closed L Sat, Bank Hols & 1 wk Xmas

Our inspectors *never* book in the name of Egon Ronay's Guides.
They disclose their identity only if they are considering an establishment
for inclusion in the next edition of the Guide.

W1	**Bahn Thai**	

R Map 27 A2
21a Frith Street W1
01-437 8504

Thai cooking
About £43 for two
Seats 100
Parties 60
Parking Difficult
Credit Access, Amex, Visa

A ground and first-floor Soho restaurant that's a firm favourite with connoisseurs of authentic Thai cooking. Fragrant herbs and aromatic roots, sweet nuts and fiery chilli are used to sensational effect in dishes like spicy fish cakes with sweet-sour peanut sauce, chicken soup flavoured with coconut cream, lemon and galangal, and beef or beancurd in a jungle curry with fresh Thai herbs and beans. Carefully selected wines. ♀ Well-chosen ᵶ

Lunch 12–2.45, Sun 12.30–2.30 *Dinner* 6–11.15, Sun 6.30–10.30
Closed 4 days Easter & Xmas

SW7	**Bangkok**	♖

R Map 23 B5
9 Bute Street SW7
01-584 8529

Thai cooking

About £35 for two
Seats 60
Parties 20
Parking Limited

Mr Tootbunnag and his family have been providing consistently enjoyable eating and swift, willing service for 20 years at their unpretentious Thai restaurant. You can see the chefs at work preparing long-standing favourites such as satays with peanut sauce, soup with little pasta balls, pork with chillis and first-rate Thai rice noodles. The house wine is a good crisp Sauvignon Blanc that suits the delicate cooking to a T. ♀ Well-chosen

Lunch 12.15–2.15 *Dinner* 6.30–11
Closed Sun, Bank Hols & 2 wks late Aug

SE3	**Bardon Lodge Hotel** 59%	£D/E

H Map 7 B5
15 Stratheden Road SE3 7TH
01-853 4051

Credit Access, Visa

Donald and Barbara Nott run a very friendly hotel that was originally two Victorian houses. The day rooms comprise a delightful lounge and a smart cocktail bar with leather chesterfields and plush banquettes. Bedrooms vary in size but are all clean and bright as a new pin. Furnishings are neat – often in pine – and the usual modern accessories are to be found. Most rooms have their own private showers. *Amenities* garden, fax.

Rooms 37	*Direct dial* Yes	*Confirm by* arrang.	*Parking* Limited
Ensuite bath/shower 28	*Room TV* Yes	*Last dinner* 9.30	*Room service* Limited

SW13   Barnaby's   ♁

R Map 21 A6
39b High Street, Barnes SW13
01-878 4750

French cooking

About £40 for two
Seats 24
Parking Limited

Claude Harry's cooking goes from strength to strength at this pretty restaurant near the river. Wife Jenny is a charming hostess and there's something of the atmosphere of a restaurant du quartier, though the food is infinitely superior. Changing twice yearly, the menu features delights like colourful vegetable terrine with leek sauce, brochette of monkfish with shallot butter sauce, and delicious chocolate bavarois. Reservations are essential. ☺

Lunch 12.30–1.30   *Dinner* 7–10.15
Closed L Mon & Sat, all Sun, Bank Hols & 3 wks Sept

**Changes in data sometimes occur in establishments
after the Guide goes to press.
Prices should be taken as indications rather than firm quotes.**

SW3   Basil Street Hotel   70%   £B

HR Map 22 C3
Basil Street SW3 1AH
01-581 3311
Telex 28379

Rooms 90
Ensuite bath/shower 70
Direct dial Yes
Room TV Yes
Confirm by arrang.
Last dinner 9.45
Parking Ample
Room service 24 hours

Credit Access, Amex, Diners, Visa

Built in 1910, the Basil Street Hotel still exudes much period charm, and it's a great favourite with discerning American and European visitors. The ambience is comparable with that of a country house, and the lounge is a very attractive mix of chintz, antiques and Oriental rugs. A major refurbishment programme has brought more chic to the bedrooms, which are maintained to the highest standards and are generally spacious; in the bathrooms – also impeccably kept – are bathrobes and large snowy towels. Courtly, old-world staff match the traditional appeal of the surroundings, the porters being particularly helpful and obliging.
Amenities secretarial services, fax, valeting, laundry service.

The Dining Room   ♕

Set L £11
About £48 for two
Seats 90
Parties 50

A splendidly traditional dining room in terms of both atmosphere and service. The menu is in keeping and makes good use of fresh produce. The beef consommé is as good as ever, and other choices run from Roquefort-filled mushrooms and rabbit pâté to seafood symphony, braised guinea fowl and the perennial favourite roast beef with Yorkshire pudding. Carefully chosen wines, with good Beaujolais Crus from Pierre Ferraud. Evening pianist. ♙ Well-chosen ☺

Lunch 12.30–2.15   *Dinner* 6.30–9.45, Sun 7–9.30
Closed L Sat

SW3   Beaufort   £B

PH Map 23 C4
33 Beaufort Gardens
SW3 1PP
01-584 5252
Telex 929200

Credit Access, Amex, Diners, Visa
Closed 10 days Xmas

Two adjoining terraced houses make up this delightful hotel, located in a leafy Victorian square close to Harrods and Beauchamp Place. Comfort and style are the key words here, as evidenced in the elegant lounge with deep sofas, original watercolours, glossy magazines and help-yourself 'honour' bar. Variously sized bedrooms, individually furnished in the utmost good taste, have very comfortable beds and every modern convenience from hairdryers to cassette players with tapes. Chocolates, fresh flowers, and fold-out maps are typically thoughtful touches. An excellent continental breakfast is served in the rooms (no other meals available).
Amenities secretarial services, fax, valeting, laundry service.

| *Rooms* 29 | *Direct dial* Yes | *Confirm by* arrang. | *Parking* Difficult |
| *Ensuite bath/shower* 29 | *Room TV* Yes | *Last dinner* None | *Room service* All day |

SW1   Belgravia-Sheraton   79%   £A

H Map 23 D4
20 Chesham Place SW1X 8HQ
01-235 6040
Telex 919020

Rooms 89
Ensuite bath/shower 89
Direct dial Yes
Room TV Yes
Confirm by 4
Last dinner 10.30
Parking Difficult
Room service 24 hours

Credit Access, Amex, Diners, Visa

Just a short walk from the shops of Sloane Street and Knightsbridge, this modern Belgravia hotel is run in very professional style by general manager Doreen Boulding and her young, eager-to-please staff. A warm welcome and a cool glass of pink champagne await in the lobby-lounge, while in the little library bar guests can dip into the current best-selling hardbacks. Impeccably kept bedrooms, mainly of a good size, have generously proportioned beds, personally controlled air conditioning, mini-bars and remote-control TVs, plus thoughtfully appointed bathrooms. No dogs.
Amenities in-house movies, secretarial services, fax, valeting, laundry service.

NW3   Benihana

R Map 20 B3
100 Avenue Road NW3
01-586 9508

Japanese cooking
Set D from £11.95
About £60 for two
Seats 112 *Parties* 112
Parking Limited
Credit Access, Amex, Diners, Visa

A smart, ultra-modern and spacious restaurant where diners sit eight to a table. The short menu offers chicken, steak and seafood as a main dish, with an appetiser, soup, salad, vegetables, rice and green tea all included in the price. Watching the accomplished chef twirling his utensils at the teppan-yaki bar is all part of the fun. A children's menu is available on Sundays. Booking is essential.

Lunch 12–3, Sat & Sun 1–3   *Dinner* 6.30–12
Closed Mon & 25 Dec

W1   Bentley's

R Map 24 B3
11 Swallow Street W1
01-734 4756

Seafood
About £55 for two
Seats 140
Parking Difficult

Credit Access, Amex, Diners, Visa

Just off Piccadilly, this charming, old-fashioned restaurant draws the crowds with some first-class seafood. Simple choices are best so that the freshness of the fish may speak for itself. Oysters, whitebait or salmon fishcake start the meal well, while main courses run the gamut from dressed crab and seafood platter to grilled sole and supreme of halibut with asparagus. Simple sweets. Drink the excellent Muscadet Domaine des Dorices.   🍷 Well-chosen   ⊖

Lunch 12–3   *Dinner* 6–10.30
Closed Sun, Bank Hols & 24–26 Dec

SW1   The Berkeley   90%   £A

HR Map 22 D3
Wilton Place SW1X 7RL
01-235 6000
Telex 919252

Rooms 160
Ensuite bath/shower 160
Direct dial Yes
Room TV Yes
Confirm by arrang.
Last dinner 10.15
Parking Ample
Room service 24 hours

Credit Access, Amex, Diners, Visa

Even when this sumptuous hotel is full, the ratio of staff to guests (three to two) makes for superlative service. Cars are parked, luggage is whisked to the large, beautifully furnished bedrooms and guests are welcomed in the spacious brown and grey marble foyer. Lutyens panelling from the old Berkeley is a feature of one of the lounges. There are two bars, one overlooking a pool whose roof rolls back in summer to let the sunshine in. Most bedrooms are luxurious, with generous seating areas and well-equipped bathrooms with lovely big baths. No dogs. *Amenities* indoor swimming pool, sauna, solarium, gymnasium, beauty salon, hairdressing, teletext, secretarial services, fax, cinema, valeting, laundry service, kiosk.   *see over*

The Berkeley Restaurant ♛♛

Set L £15
About £70 for two
Seats 60
Parties 10

The well-heeled dine in style at this elegant establishment. French in flavour, English in interpretation, the menu includes such dishes as melon with Parma ham, onion soup, sole meunière and steak Diane. Game birds frequently feature. Cooking is sound and reliable. The well-laden sweet trolley includes a good apple pie. Pipes may not be smoked. Good classic wines: for an excellent keenly-priced Italian white, try the Venegazzu Pinot Grigio. ♟ Well-chosen ℮

Lunch 12.30–2.30, Sun 12.45–2.15 *Dinner* 6.30–10.45, Sun 7–10.15
Closed Sat

W1 | The Berkshire Hotel 76% *NEW ENTRY* **£A**

HR Map 24 A3
350 Oxford Street W1N 0BY
01-629 7474
Telex 22270

Rooms 147
Ensuite bath/shower 147
Direct dial Yes
Room TV Yes
Confirm by 6
Last dinner 11
Parking Ample
Room service 24 hours

Credit Access, Amex, Diners, Visa

Formerly the Stratford Court, this is a luxurious hotel with a civilised, intimate atmosphere. Furniture and fittings are of a high quality throughout, with some Oriental touches among the essentially English decor. The drawing room has panelled walls, rich, chintzy drapes and a variety of inviting settees and easy chairs; a harpist plays soothingly in the afternoon. Air-conditioned bedrooms range from compact
singles to quite roomy doubles and twins; all have stylish floral fabrics and walnut-veneered furniture. The usual accessories are provided, and all rooms have sumptuously appointed bathrooms. Smartly dressed staff offer service of a high standard. *Amenities* laundry service, valeting, in-house movies, teletext, secretarial services, fax.

Ascot Restaurant *NEW ENTRY* ♛

Set L from £13.50
About £68 for two

The panelled restaurant, with pictures and prints of Ascot races on the walls, is an elegant, comfortable setting for a nicely varied menu prepared by Stephan Levs. Dishes for vegetarians and the weight-conscious are available along with such choices as veal consommé with chicken dumplings, braised roulade of salmon, lamb in a fine Madeira sauce and medallions of New Forest venison. Traditional specials (roast beef on Tuesday, shepherd's pie on Saturday) provide extra lunchtime variety.

Lunch 12.30–2.30 *Dinner* 6–11

**We welcome bona fide complaints and recommendations
on the tear-out pages at the back of the book for readers' comment.
They are followed up by our professional team.**

SW3 | Bibendum *NEW ENTRY*

R Map 23 C5
Michelin House,
81 Fulham Road SW3
01-581 5817

Set L £17.50
About £68 for two
Seats 72
Parking Difficult

The renovated Michelin building is magnificent, and stained glass is a marvellous feature of this roomy, lively and trendy first-floor restaurant. Simon Hopkinson, ex-Hilaire, provides something for everyone, from firm, piquant endives au gratin, wrapped in ham and served with a bubbling cheese sauce, to sole meunière, sweetbreads with black butter, mustard-sauced rabbit and entrecôte steak marchand de vin. Boiled bacon with split peas and carrots strikes a traditional English note. Fresh-baked apple tart is a very good way to finish an excellent meal. Note de Bortoli Late Harvest Botrytis Semillon from Australia on a short, selective wine list. ℮

Lunch 12.30–2.30 *Dinner* 7–11
Closed D Sat, all Sun & Bank Hols

EC2 — Bill Bentley's

R Map 26 D1
Swedeland Court
202 Bishopsgate, EC2
01-283 1763

Seafood
About £55 for two
Seats 90 *Parties* 90
Parking Difficult
Credit Access, Diners, Visa

One of the City's best known lunchtime meeting places, and for many years a stronghold of fresh fish and seafood. Native and rock oysters, mussels marinière, smoked fish mousse and grilled herrings with mustard sauce are popular starters, while main courses run from crab salad to poached turbot hollandaise. There are also plenty of meat dishes and a few daily specials – ask the head waiter for his recommendations. 🍷 Well-chosen ℗

Lunch only 11.30–3
Closed Sat, Sun & Bank Hols

NW1 — Le Bistroquet

R Map 20 C3
273 Camden High Street NW1
01-485 9607

Set L from £7.50
Set D from £9.50
About £47 for two
Seats 100 *Parties* 35
Parking Difficult
Credit Access, Amex, Visa

Tables here are set between large plants or in intimate alcoves and corners. It's a lively, trendy place, and Paul Whitaker's cooking more than fulfils the promise of a varied and imaginative menu. Fresh pasta is a favourite, and other temptations could include gravlax of monkfish, coulibiac, confit d'oie and braised ox tongue with Madeira sauce. Also good salads and sweets. Book. 🍷 Well-chosen ℗

Lunch 12–3, Sun 12–4   *Dinner* 7–11.30, Sun 7–11
Closed 3 days Xmas & 1 Jan

SW6 — Bitter Lemons Taverna

R Map 21 B5
98 Lillie Road SW6
01-381 1069

Greek cooking
Set L & D £8.50 (2 or more)
About £33 for two
Seats 80 *Parties* 80
Parking Limited
Credit Access, Visa

A new rear seating area has made Bitter Lemons a more roomy and comfortable place for enjoying familiar Greek fare. Specialities include moussaka, kioftedes, stuffed vine leaves and afelia. Also on the menu are tasty dips, spicy and winy sausages, charcoal grills and Continental dishes. Parties of two or more should go for the mezedes (£8.50 a head), a good selection of traditional Greek dishes. Live music Friday and Saturday evenings.

Lunch 12–3
Dinner 6–12

SW7 — Blakes Hotel   76%   £A

HR Map 23 B5
33 Roland Gardens SW7 3PF
01-370 6701
Telex 8813500

Rooms 55
Ensuite bath/shower 55
Direct dial Yes
Room TV Yes
Confirm by arrang.
Last dinner 11.30
Parking Difficult
Room service 24 hours

Credit Access, Amex, Diners, Visa

A highly imaginative hotel created from a row of Victorian town houses. In the striking foyer, black walls are set off by natural leather and bamboo furniture and beautiful arrangements of dried flowers. Oriental colours catch the eye in the intimate bar and lounge, while the bedrooms are breathtaking – for example, the room draped in black and red silk and equipped with black antique furniture and matching marble bathroom. Up a floor, the tone lightens to pale grey furnishings and decor, lighter but just as stunning as the other rooms. All have mini-bars, safe boxes, dimmer switches and stereo radio/cassettes. No dogs.
Amenities fax, laundry service.

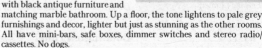

Restaurant   ♔

About £100 for two
Seats 36

A black and white restaurant where colour is provided by Eastern exotica in the form of costumes and cushions. The imaginative menu draws its inspiration worldwide and the dishes are competently cooked, if sometimes a little over-elaborate. Start perhaps with salad of foie gras and black truffles, while main course might be baked turbot with dill and lemon or roast guinea fowl filled with pecans and prunes,. Excellent desserts. ℗ 🍴

Lunch 12.30–2.30   *Dinner* 7.30–11.30
Closed 25 & 26 Dec

NW11 & E1 — Bloom's

R **Map 20 B1**
130 Golders Green Road NW11
01-455 1338

Map 21 D4
90 Whitechapel High Street E1
01-247 6001

Jewish cooking
About £28 for two
Parking Ample
Golders Green   Seats 80
Whitechapel High St
Seats 150   *Parties* 150
Credit Access, Visa

Restaurants come and go, but Bloom's are an apparently permanent fixture on the London scene, serving hefty portions of robust fare prepared to strict kosher standards under the supervision of the Beth Din. Salt beef keeps its place as the favourite dish, but there are plenty of other perennial fancies, including Viennas, stuffed poultry necks and roast turkey. Chomp chopped liver and herring as you work your way through a hillock of rye bread to start, eat latkes with the beef and if you're not by then about to go pop order some lockshen pudding. The waiters have a good line in dry humour, but there's nothing at all amusing about the Israeli wines – try lemon tea.

Golders Green – Meals noon–9.30
Whitechapel High St – Meals 11.30–10, Sun 11.30–3pm (2pm in winter)
Closed Fri (Golders Green), Sat, 25 Dec & Jewish hols

WC1 — Bloomsbury Crest Hotel   62%   £B/C

H **Map 24 C1**
Coram Street,
Russell Square WC1N 1HT
01-837 1200
Telex 22113

Credit Access, Amex, Diners, Visa

Major moves are afoot at this modern hotel just off Russell Square. The lobby and a bar are being remodelled, and older bedrooms are being brought up to the standard of the best – fresh and bright, with attractive, coordinated fabrics and good accessories. Executive rooms get various extra little touches, and there are a couple of rooms with spa baths.   *Amenities* in-house movies, secretarial services, fax, laundry service, coffee shop (7am–10.45pm).

Rooms 239	*Direct dial* Yes	*Confirm by* 6	*Parking* Ample
Ensuite bath/shower 239	*Room TV* Yes	*Last dinner* 10.45	*Room service* All day

SW12 — Bombay Bicycle Club

R **Map 21 C6**
95 Nightingale Lane SW12
01-673 6217

Indian cooking
About £45 for two
Seats 65
Parties 75
Parking Ample
Credit Access, Visa

The beautiful people of Wandsworth eat regularly and often at this modern Indian restaurant specialising in the authentic cuisine of the British Raj. Interesting menus are well laid out, results on the plate enjoyable if erratic. Our starters of chicken tikka and cod in a lightly spiced batter were good and sweet nan bread was delicious; but knuckle of lamb was overcooked and the sauce lacked individuality. Choose fresh mango as a refreshing finale. Good Indian lager.

Lunch 12–3   *Dinner* 7–11.30
Closed L Mon–Fri, D Sun & Xmas

SW7 — Bombay Brasserie   ♛

R **Map 23 B4**
Courtfield Close,
Courtfield Rd SW7
01-370 4040

Indian cooking
Set L £8.95
Seats 180 *Parties* 100
Parking Limited
Credit Access, Amex, Diners, Visa

One of London's best Indian restaurants, with decor from colonial days and a menu that visits all parts of India. Here you will find favourite snacks from Bombay, tandoori delights from the North-West Frontier, traditional Parsi fare, fiery Kashmiri-style lamb and Goan dishes rich in coconut. Fine food, but dishes are often served lukewarm. The lunchtime buffet is popular, especially on Sunday, and booking is essential in the evenings.

Lunch 12.30–2.30   *Dinner* 7.30–midnight   *About £44 for two*
Closed 25–27 Dec

WC1 — Bonnington Hotel   59%   £C/D

H **Map 24 C1**
92 Southampton Row
WC1B 4BH
01-242 2828
Telex 261591

Credit Access, Amex, Diners, Visa

Continuing refurbishment is improving the accommodation at this Bloomsbury Hotel, where pleasant, friendly staff provide good personal service. All but a few rooms have private bathrooms, and hairdryers and trouser presses have been installed. Public areas include a bright, cheerful bar and a barrel-vaulted lounge overlooked by a quiet little gallery with some writing desks.
Amenities in-house movies, secretarial services, fax, laundry service.

Rooms 222	*Direct dial* Yes	*Confirm by* 6	*Parking* Ample
Ensuite bath/shower 200	*Room TV* Yes	*Last dinner* 9.30	*Room service* 24 hours

Any person using our name to obtain free hospitality is a fraud.
Proprietors, please inform the police and us.

W14   Boucha's *NEW ENTRY*

Ⓡ **Map 21 B5**
3 North End Parade,
North End Road W14
01-603 0613

About £45 for two
Seats 24
Parties 24
Parking Ample
Credit Access, Amex, Visa

Splendid window boxes adorn the outside, while inside all is flamboyant lemon yellow. Vincent Guy's menu combines traditional and modern elements, with dishes such as bubble and squeak with egg and bacon, mushroom and herb pancakes, chicken breast filled with salmon mousse (served on a delicious red pepper purée) and a splendid bread and butter pudding. Very enjoyable food, carefully prepared and neatly presented. Marco Wizla is your friendly, chatty host. ℮

Dinner only 7–11, Sun 7–10.30
Closed Bank Hols

SW10   La Bouillabaisse

Ⓡ **Map 23 B6**
116 Finborough Road SW10
01-370 4183

Seafood
Set D £16
About £65 for two
Seats 52
Parking Difficult
Credit Access, Amex, Diners, Visa

Formerly L'Olivier, this pleasantly light basement restaurant has joined the fishy mainstream of the Pierre Martin group and has for specialities bouillabaisse and bourride. Besides these splendid Mediterranean soups there are abundant shellfish, fish and meat dishes, salads, pasta, lovely feuilletés and a set menu that offers hors d'oeuvre and cochonailles, raviolis, soupe au pistou, a meat or fish main course, cheese or dessert and coffee – all for a remarkable £16. ♀ Well-chosen ℮

Dinner only 7.30–11.30   **Closed** Sun, 2 wks Xmas & 4 wks July/Aug

WC2   Boulestin   ♛♛

Ⓡ **Map 27 B2**
1a Henrietta Street WC2
01-836 7061

Set L £15
About £90 for two
Seats 75
Parking Difficult

Credit Access, Amex, Diners, Visa

An elegant basement restaurant styled with flair to give an English look. Kevin Kennedy's printed menu and daily specials provide a well-balanced choice of dishes, and generally they work very well. High point of a recent meal was succulent, pinkly tender fillet of lamb served with a well-reduced sauce, stuffed aubergines and lovely baby turnips. Lobster-sauced quenelles of turbot was another excellent choice (though the portion was small and the plate so hot that the sauce was cooking on it). Brûlée de miel au gingembre was a delicious dessert. There's a splendid cellar with a fine showing of burgundies: Marsannay Blanc (Fougeray de Beauclair) '86, Clos de Cortons (Faiveley) '78. ➢ Outstanding ♀ Well-chosen ℮

Lunch 12.30–2.30   *Dinner* 7.30–11.15
Closed L Sat, all Sun, Bank Hols, last 3 wks Aug & 10 days Xmas

---

We welcome bona fide complaints and recommendations
on the tear-out pages at the back of the book for readers' comment.
They are followed up by our professional team.

W1   Hotel Britannia Inter-Continental   80%   £A

Ⓗ **Map 22 D2**
Grosvenor Square W1A 3AN
01-629 9400
Telex 23941

Rooms 354
Ensuite bath/shower 354
Direct dial Yes
Room TV Yes
Confirm by 6
Last dinner 11.30
Parking Limited
Room service 24 hours

Credit Access, Amex, Diners, Visa

Behind the discreet, elegant facade overlooking the square are modern, well-equipped bedrooms and stylish public areas. The luxurious, chandeliered lobby has plenty of chairs and sofas and further comfortable seating is to be found in the dark blue, pine-panelled cocktail lounge and the clubby Pine Bar. The air-conditioned bedrooms have good-quality furniture and plenty of extras, while bath-

rooms offer bathrobes, hairdryers, telephone extensions and showers. Studio rooms offer more space and there are 13 suites, including two penthouses with videos and whirlpool baths. *Amenities* hairdressing, in-house movies, teletext, secretarial services, fax, laundry service, coffee shop (7am–11pm), kiosk, shopping arcade.

W1   Brown's Hotel   77%   £A

H Map 25 B4
Albemarle & Dover Streets
W1A 4SW
01-493 6020
Telex 28686

Rooms 133
Ensuite bath/shower 133
Direct dial Yes
Room TV Yes
Confirm by arrang.
Last dinner 10
Parking Difficult
Room service 24 hours

Credit Access, Amex, Diners, Visa

Opened in 1837, Mr James Brown's fashionable hotel, which gradually expanded to take in 14 elegant town houses, is today a solid symbol of old-fashioned English values. Mellow wood panelling, chintz sofas and fresh flowers give public areas like the lounge the charm of a country house, while leather seating and coal fires create a cosy club atmosphere in the bar. Bedrooms range from splendid suites furnished with fine antiques to spacious single rooms in a pleasant modern style and studio suites with attractive sitting rooms. All have mini-bars and well-equipped bathrooms.
Amenities men's hairdressing, valeting, laundry service.

EC1   Bubb's

R Map 26 A1
329 Central Markets,
Smithfield EC1
01-236 2435

French cooking
About £60 for two
Seats 80
Parties 40
Parking Difficult

Its popularity with business people makes booking essential at this lively French restaurant bubbling with Gallic charm. Given its location on the edge of Smithfield market, dishes such as lamb en croûte and boeuf bordelaise feature excellent meat, and there are fish dishes including delicious grilled bream with crisply cooked vegetables. Sweets such as crème brûlée and vacherin glacé are most enjoyable. Madame Bubb supervises friendly staff. 🍷 Well-chosen 🕑

Lunch 12–2   *Dinner* 6.30–9.30
Closed Sat, Sun, Bank Hols, 2 wks Aug & 10 days Xmas

SW15   Buzkash

R Map 21 A6
4 Chelverton Road SW15
01-788 0599

Afghan cooking
About £40 for two
Seats 44
Parking Limited

Credit Access, Amex, Diners, Visa

Service is exceptionally friendly and helpful at this Afghan restaurant adorned with lovely rugs and wooden carvings. You'll be served a sauced potato cake to nibble on as you read the tempting menu, which includes a wide range of excellent, fresh vegetable dishes. Try kohi – roast lamb with blackcurrant, cinnamon and onion – as a main course and delicious spicy carrot kulfi or coconut halva to finish.

Lunch 12–2.30   *Dinner* 6–11, Fri & Sat till 11.30, Sun till 10.30
Closed L Sun & 3 days Xmas

SW1   Cadogan Thistle Hotel   71%   £A

H Map 23 D4
75 Sloane Street SW1X 9SG
01-235 7141
Telex 267893

Rooms 72
Ensuite bath/shower 72
Direct dial Yes
Room TV Yes
Confirm by 6
Last dinner 10
Parking Difficult
Room service 24 hours

Credit Access, Amex, Diners, Visa

Up-to-date comfort and yesterday's charm in a handsome turreted hotel associated with Wilde, Whistler and Lillie Langtry. A sedate, stylish tone is set in the oak-panelled foyer, where there's a splendid old cage lift protected by a preservation order. The Edwardian bar features an interesting collection of photographs. Bedrooms vary from really spacious to fairly small, and some of the singles and rear-facing rooms can be noisy. Remote-control TVs, mini-bars, trouser presses and hairdryers are modern conveniences, while some of the older bathrooms keep their original hand-painted tiles as a link with the past. Breakfast is nothing special. No dogs. *Amenities* garden, tennis, in-house movies, secretarial services, fax, valeting.

★ For a *discount* on next year's guide, see **An Offer for Answers**. ★

NW3 — Café Flo

R **Map 20 B2**
205 Haverstock Hill NW3
01-435 6744

Set L from £5.45
Set D from £7.25
About £36 for two
Seats 40
Parking Difficult
Credit Access, Visa

Cheerful and colourful decor, polished wooden tables and a friendly, informal atmosphere create a splendid modern brasserie. The short, quarterly changing menu offers an interesting selection of dishes which are extremely well prepared. Start with perhaps a fresh beetroot and mâche salad followed by smoked French sausages with flageolet beans or chicken with coriander and chilli. Dessert might be a delicious tarte tatin or chocolate mousse. Sunday brunch.

Lunch Noon–2.45, Sat & Sun 10–3.45   *Dinner* 6–11.30, Sat 6.30–11.30, Sun 6.30–11

W1 — Café Royal Grill Room ♛ ♛ ♛

R **Map 24 B3**
68 Regent Street W1
01-439 6320

French cooking
Set L & D £17
About £70 for two
Seats 65
Parking Ample
Credit Access, Amex, Diners, Visa

The decor is famously rococo, with gilt galore, elaborate mouldings, mirrored walls and painted ceiling panels. The French menu runs from foie gras to gratin of scallops and scampi, veal Orloff, châteaubriand and seasonal game, and though the cooking plays second fiddle to the surroundings it is certainly acceptable. Service is nothing special, but there's a good classic wine list: La Lagune '70, Corton Charlemagne Bonneau du Martray '83. ☙

Lunch 12.30–3   *Dinner* 6–11
Closed L Sat & all Sun

SW19 — Cannizaro House   79%   *NEW ENTRY*   £B

H **Map 7 B5**
West Side, Wimbledon
Common SW19 4UF
01-879 1464
Telex 9413837

Rooms 54
Ensuite bath/shower 54
Direct dial Yes
Room TV Yes
Confirm by 6
Last dinner 10.30
Parking Ample
Room service 24 hours

Credit Access, Amex, Diners, Visa

A small fortune has been spent on turning this imposing country house overlooking the Common into a supremely comfortable, luxurious hotel. Public rooms like the splendid pale green drawing room have been lavishly furnished with paintings, antiques, sumptuous armchairs and sofas, gilt mirrors and handsome drapes, and the result is indeed impressive. Bedrooms too are superbly appointed, with the  prettiest fabrics and top-quality reproduction furniture; those in the new wing are smaller, with lesser views. Sparkling marble bathrooms have every extra, from radio speakers and phones to cosseting bathrobes. Excellent porterage makes a good first impression.
Amenities garden, secretarial services, fax, laundry service.

🍷 indicates a **well-chosen** house wine

SW3 — The Capital   80%   £A

HR **Map 23 C4**
22 Basil Street SW3 1AT
01-589 5171
Telex 919042

Rooms 52
Ensuite bath/shower 52
Direct dial Yes
Room TV Yes
Confirm by arrang.
Last dinner 10.30
Parking Limited
Room service 24 hours

Credit Access, Amex, Diners, Visa

Tucked away in a quiet street behind Harrods, this luxury hotel is a haven of tranquillity amid the bustle of Knightsbridge. Turn-of-the-century decor and fine antiques give a warm and cosy feel to public areas like the elegant foyer and stylish lounge. Half the bedrooms are now redesigned in strikingly masculine mood, with maroon and brown tones complementing the antique furniture.  Tapestries and sporting pictures complete the gentlemanly effect, while lovely marbled bathrooms offer every luxury. Work is now under way on the remaining rooms and these will have a lighter, more feminine decor. Polite, friendly service just occasionally falls short of perfection.
Amenities secretarial services, fax, laundry service.   *see over*

The Capital Restaurant ♛

French cooking

Set L £16.50
Set D from £27.50
About £83 for two
Seats 40
Parties 22

Dine here and you dine in style, surrounded by extravagant drapes and ruffled blinds, crystal chandeliers and specially commissioned Limoges porcelain. The uncompromisingly French menu – no translation – is equally impressive. John Elliott's thoughtfully devised, skilfully executed dishes range from a cassoulet of crisp young vegetables in pastry with port wine sauce to a trio of lamb, veal and beef sauced with Meaux mustard. Wines include superb white burgundies. ▭ Outstanding ♟ Well-chosen ℮

Lunch 12.30–2.15, Sun 12.30–2   *Dinner* 6.30–10.30, Sun 7–9.45

SW1   Le Caprice

R Map 25 B4
Arlington House,
17 Arlington Street SW1
01-629 2239

About £50 for two
Seats 75
Parking Limited

Credit Access, Amex, Diners, Visa

Arty black and white decor sets the tone of this sophisticated brasserie. Menus are full of interest, simple things being transformed by imaginative treatment: salmon fishcakes are teamed with sorrel sauce, grilled monkfish with wild rice risotto. Even the humble bangers and mash go up-market, featuring veal sausages. Charles Fontaine's own sweet creations are superb, and there's a splendid Sunday brunch.
♟ Well-chosen ℮

Lunch 12–3   *Dinner* 6–12
Closed 25 Dec–2 Jan

We publish annually,
so make sure you use the current edition.
It's worth it!

W1   Caravan Serai

R Map 22 D1
50 Paddington Street W1
01-935 1208

Afghan cooking
Set L £7.50
About £40 for two
Seats 50 *Parties* 50
Parking Difficult
Credit Access, Amex, Diners, Visa

An offshoot of the Buzkash in Putney, this comfortable restaurant offers the same menu of Afghan dishes. The cooking is consistently enjoyable, with lamb and chicken prepared in various ways being the main feature. Start perhaps with pasta served with minced lamb and a dash of yoghurt and, to follow, try the clay oven specialities such as chopan kebab – lamb barbecued then pan-fried with vegetables. Ice cream to finish.

Lunch 12–3 *Dinner* 6–11, Sat 6–11.30, Sun 6–10.30
Closed 25 & 26 Dec

SE6   Casa Cominetti

R Map 7 B5
129 Rushey Green, Catford
SE6
01-697 2314

Italian cooking
About £45 for two
Seats 50 *Parties* 30
Parking Ample
Credit Access, Amex, Diners, Visa

The Lipparelli family have been running this delightfully old-fashioned restaurant for two years. Luigi Lipparelli sometimes cooks, but this is largely the province of the long-established Raphael Innaccone. The food is very good – Italian favourites incorporating capably prepared fresh ingredients. A typical meal might start with tagliatelle with salmon, advance to calf's liver with onion and brandy sauce, and conclude with cassata.

Lunch 12–2.15 *Dinner* 7–10.30
Closed Sun, Mon, Bank Hols & 5 days Xmas

SW8   Cavaliers' *NEW ENTRY*   ⚜

R Map 21 C6
129 Queenstown Road,
Battersea SW8
01-720 6960

Set L from £15.50 **Set D** £23.50
About £55 for two
Seats 45 *Parties* 45
Parking Limited
Credit Access, Amex, Diners, Visa

Ambitious David Cavalier has reopened the old Chez Nico premises as a stage for his considerable talents. Typical of his modern-style cooking are dishes such as a mosaic of vegetables bound in cream cheese with an avocado mayonnaise surrounded by cucumber and courgette, well-presented roast lobster in puff pastry, and beef in a superb red wine and rosemary sauce. Excellent British cheeses. Interesting wines from Loire include Vouvray back to 1921. ℮

Lunch 12–2 *Dinner* 7.15–10.30, Sat till 11
Closed all Sun & Mon

SW1   Cavendish Hotel   69%   £A/B

H Map 25 B4
Jermyn Street SW1Y 6JF
01-930 2111
Telex 263187

Credit Access, Amex, Diners, Visa

A comfortable, well-run hotel rebuilt in 1966 on the prime central site of the original Cavendish. The foyer, with its marble floor and mahogany panelling, makes a fine impression on arrival; beyond this is an intimate, club-style cocktail bar, while up on the first floor there's another bar and the Gallery, open long hours for snacks. There are also various meeting and reception rooms. Bedrooms are of a decent size, with fitted furniture and light, contemporary decor. Mini-bars, remote-control TVs and hairdryers are standard. The odd sign of wear and tear is showing. No dogs.
Amenities satellite TV, in-house movies, secretarial services, fax, valeting, laundry service, coffee shop (7am–11pm).

Rooms 254	Direct dial Yes	Confirm by 6	Parking Ample
Ensuite bath/shower 254	Room TV Yes	Last dinner 11	Room service 24 hours

Our inspectors *never* book in the name of Egon Ronay's Guides.
They disclose their identity only if they are considering an establishment
for inclusion in the next edition of the Guide.

W1   Chaopraya Restaurant   ♛

R Map 22 D1
22 St Christopher's Place W1
01-486 0777

Thai cooking
Set L £15 Set D £20
About £40 for two
Seats 85 Parties 85
Parking Limited
Credit Access, Amex, Diners, Visa

A smart basement restaurant where you can find authentic Thai cooking and friendly, charming service. The lengthy menu draws its inspiration from many areas and the cooking is careful and precise, using notably fresh herbs and spices. Starters include barbecued beef or pork, or steamed noodle roll with pork and soy sauce, with sukiyaki beef or chicken, or fried sliced chicken with basil to follow. Sweets are cool and refreshing.

Lunch noon–3   *Dinner* 6.30–11
Closed L Sat, all Sun & Bank Hols

WC2   Charing Cross Hotel   58%   £B/C

H Map 27 B3
Strand WC2N 5HX
01-839 7282
Telex 261101

Credit Access, Amex, Diners, Visa

The welcome is friendly at this deceptively large hotel, whose public rooms retain a certain lofty grandeur. Bedrooms, mainly twins, are of a good size, with freestanding furniture and fairly unprepossessing decor. It's worth asking for one of the few 'Premium Premium' rooms, which are better equipped and generally more pleasant. *Amenities* sauna, solarium, keep-fit equipment, beauty salon, hairdressing, laundry service, 24-hour lounge service. &

Rooms 218	Direct dial Yes	Confirm by 6	Parking Difficult
Ensuite bath/shower 218	Room TV Yes	Last dinner 10.30	Room service None

NW3   Charles Bernard Hotel   57%   £D

H Map 20 B2
5 Frognal NW3 6AL
01-794 0101
Telex 23560

Credit Access, Amex, Diners, Visa

Bedrooms have been redecorated in restful '80s style at this purpose-built hotel in a quiet residential street. Neat lightwood units provide good writing surfaces, and all the bathrooms have been prettily retiled. Day rooms are as before – quite roomy and comfortable, but with the fairly stark look of the '70s. Many of the staff stayed with the new owners, so service remains courteous, friendly and efficient.
Amenities fax, laundry service.

Rooms 57	Direct dial Yes	Confirm by arrang.	Parking Limited
Ensuite bath/shower 57	Room TV Yes	Last dinner 9.15	Room service Limited

Changes in data sometimes occur in establishments
after the Guide goes to press.
Prices should be taken as indications rather than firm quotes.

SW1   Chelsea Hotel   72%   £A

H Map 23 D4
Sloane Street SW1X 9NU
01-235 4377
Telex 919111

Rooms 225
Ensuite bath/shower 225
Direct dial Yes
Room TV Yes
Confirm by 6
Last dinner 11
Parking Difficult
Room service 24 hours

Credit Access, Amex, Diners, Visa

Handy for Harrods and other Knightsbridge landmarks, the Chelsea has just undergone a major facelift in its public areas. There's a '30s flavour in the day rooms, with chrome, patterned mirrors and walnut much in evidence. From the stylish lobby-lounge a staircase leads up to the bar and restaurant and, on the top floor, the boardrooms and conference suites. The whole of this area is topped by a very splendid glass roof. Attention has now turned to improving the decor in the corridors and in the bedrooms, where in some cases the generous beds and other furnishings leave little floor space. No dogs.
Amenities hairdressing, in-house movies, fax, laundry service, kiosk.

NW1   Cheng-du   *NEW ENTRY*

R Map 20 C3 London
9 Parkway NW1
01-485 8058

Chinese cooking
Set L and D £12.80
About £30 for two
Seats 70
Parking Limited
Credit Access, Amex, Diners, Visa

A chic, modern Chinese restaurant just a couple of minutes from Camden Town underground. Warning flames are scattered liberally over the menu, signifying hot, spicy Szechuan dishes such as bang-bang chicken, pork shreds with Szechuan pickle soup, sea spice prawns and braised duck in a sweet-sour plum sauce (a speciality). Beef slices in oyster sauce and tangerine peel chicken exemplify the milder fare. Friendly service. 🍷 Well-chosen

Lunch 12–2.30   *Dinner* 6.30–11.30
Closed Sun before Bank Hols

W1   Chesterfield Hotel   72%   £A

H Map 25 A4
35 Charles Street W1X 8LX
01-491 2622
Telex 269394

Rooms 113
Ensuite bath/shower 113
Direct dial Yes
Room TV Yes
Confirm by arrang.
Last dinner 10.30
Parking Difficult
Room service 24 hours

Credit Access, Amex, Diners, Visa

A civilised Mayfair hotel that was once the home of the fourth Earl of Chesterfield. The tone of the public rooms is set by the elegant foyer with its black-and-white marble-tiled floor, fluted columns, panelling and Venetian chandelier. There's also a library-lounge, and a clubby bar where a pianist plays nightly. Bed-rooms, all with space for a coffee table and couple of easy chairs, are provided with various thoughtful extras, including a note pad and pencil by the phone and a bottle of mineral water. Porters and reception staff are notably smart, friendly and helpful. No dogs.
Amenities in-house movies, fax, laundry service.

W11   Chez Moi   ♕   ♧

R Map 21 A4
1 Addison Avenue,
Holland Park W11
01-603 8267

French cooking
Set D £12.50
About £60 for two
Seats 45 *Parking* Ample
Credit Access, Amex, Diners, Visa

A deep red decor makes this two-roomed restaurant warm and inviting and well-spaced tables create a feeling of unhurried relaxation. There's a fairly traditional à la carte menu, coupled with a more adventurous monthly-changing menu which takes advantage of seasonal produce. Lamb is the restaurant's speciality and you should certainly include one of the variations on this theme in your meal. 🍷 Well-chosen 🍷

Lunch 12.30–2   *Dinner* 7–11
Closed Sun, Bank Hols, 2 wks Aug & 2 wks Xmas

If we recommend **meals** in a Hotel or Inn,

a separate entry is made for its restaurant.

W14   Chinon   ⑨

R Map 21 A4
  25 Richmond Way W14
01-602 5968

Set L from £7.50
About £55 for two
Seats 24
Parties 30
Parking Difficult
Credit Access, Amex, Visa

Barbara Deane and Jonathan Hayes are chef-partners at this pleasant
little pink-decorated restaurant. Their short menus have a modern
ring, and though the odd lapse occurs, cooking shows flair and artistry.
Typical dishes: scallops and shitaki mushrooms with chervil butter
sauce, guinea fowl with thyme and Calvados, passion fruit mousse
with a tuille of fresh berries. Some fine Touraine wines – Vouvray
from Huet, Chinon from Raffault. ⚑ Well-chosen ☺ ⟁

Lunch 12–2 *Dinner* 7–10.30, Fri & Sat 7–11
Closed L Sat, all Sun, Bank Hols & Aug/Sept, 1 wk Xmas

W4   Christian's   ⑨

R Map 21 A5
  Station Parade, Burlington
Lane, Chiswick W4
01-995 0382

About £45 for two
Seats 35
Parking Ample

In a small parade of shops close to Chiswick Park tube station,
Christian's is a small and charming neighbourhood restaurant with a
friendly and relaxed atmosphere. Christian Gustin prepares a short,
monthly-changing menu of interesting, fresh-flavoured dishes such as
cucumber and mint soup, vegetable mille-feuille with a tomato coulis,
breast of chicken with herb sauce, poached haddock with orange and
hot chocolate and rum soufflé.

Dinner only 7.30–10.15
Closed Sun & Mon, 3 days Xmas & 2 wks in winter

W1   Chuen Cheng Ku

R Map 27 A2
  17 Wardour Street W1
01-734 3281

Chinese cooking
Set D from £13
About £32 for two
Seats 400 *Parties* 250
Parking Difficult
Credit Access, Amex, Diners, Visa

A vast restaurant with a menu to match, Chuen Cheng Ku seats 400
and is always busy. Dodge the trolleys laden with dim sum, find a seat
and enjoy familiar favourites or more unusual offerings like duck's
feet with fish lips, shredded jelly fish, fried shark's fin with scrambled
eggs or belly pork with yams. Ice creams, sorbets or perhaps lychees
for dessert.

Meals 11am–11.45pm
Closed 24 & 25 Dec

W1   Churchill Hotel   80%   £A

HR Map 22 D1
   30 Portman Square
W1A 4ZX
01-486 5800
Telex 264831

Rooms 485
Ensuite bath/shower 485
Direct dial Yes
Room TV Yes
Confirm by 6
Last dinner 11
Parking Limited
Room service 24 hours

Credit Access, Amex, Diners, Visa

Exemplary housekeeping, good
maintenance and cheerful, willing staff make for high standards
at this impressive building overlooking Portman Square. The
magnificent marble foyer, with
its glittering chandeliers, fresh
flowers and smart yellow and
grey decor (a recurrent theme)
leads to a spacious sunken lounge
and there's a striking red and
gold bar with murals by Ishi-
kawa. By contrast the decor in

the restaurant is theatrical. Bedrooms are luxuriously appointed, with
attractive fabrics and quality furniture including writing desks.
Bathrooms are modern and well fitted. No dogs. **Amenities** garden,
hairdressing, satellite TV, in-house movies, teletext, secretarial
services, fax, valeting, laundry service, shopping arcade.

The Arboury

Set L £16.50
Set D £25
About £60 for two
Seats 72

The unique decor of this restaurant is reminiscent of a futuristic film
set but the food remains traditional, with a buffet lunch (roast plus a
hot dish) or a menu that includes grilled sole, pan-fried liver and
chargrilled lamb cutlets. A spa selection caters for the health conscious.
The dinner menu is more ambitious. Good wines from fine growers:
Jordan Cabernet Sauvignon '79, Nuits St. Georges Faiveley '82. ☺
⟁

Lunch 12–2.30
Dinner 7–11

SW1   Ciboure   ♀

R Map 23 D4
21 Eccleston Street SW1
01-730 2505

French cooking
Set L £13
About £55 for two
Seats 36
Parking Ample
Credit Access, Amex, Diners, Visa

A stylish and well-run Belgravia restaurant where chef Richard Price (now a partner in the business) blends classical cooking skills with a thoroughly modern feel for artistic presentation. Daily-changing menus range from light lunch dishes like rabbit terrine with walnut and figs or calf's liver on braised endives to more ambitious and often novel evening fare such as brill with vanilla sauce.
♀ Well-chosen ☺

Lunch 12–2.30   *Dinner* 7–11
Closed L Sat, all Sun, Bank Hols & 1 wk end Aug

EC3   City Brasserie

R Map 26 D2
Plantation House,
Mincing Lane EC3
01-220 7094

French cooking
About £46 for two
Seats 200 *Parties* 220
Parking Difficult
Credit Access, Amex, Diners, Visa

Booking is advisable at Peter Langan's City venture in the basement of Plantation House. An imaginative menu of stylishly presented dishes, based on quality ingredients, ranges from a delicious spinach and walnut soup and a superb scallop mousse to a simple sole with lobster sauce or succulent breast of guinea fowl. Finish with a tempting dessert or the magnificent selection of French cheeses. ♀ Well-chosen ☺

Lunch only 11.30–3
Closed Sat, Sun & Bank Hols

EC4   City Miyama   ♀

R Map 26 B2
17 Godliman Street EC4
01-489 1937

Japanese cooking
Set L from £9
About £60 for two
Seats 80 *Parties* 20
Parking Difficult
Credit Access, Amex, Diners, Visa

Enter this sophisticated restaurant via a striking hall of highly polished black and white marble. On the ground floor are the teppan-yaki bar and sushi counter, where the chef's dexterity is a delight to observe. Downstairs is the restaurant proper, offering a full menu of tempting appetizers followed by soup and a wide choice of fish and meat dishes, accompanied by salads and plain boiled rice.

Lunch 12–3   *Dinner* 6–10
Closed Sat, Sun & Bank Hols

We welcome bona fide complaints and recommendations
on the tear-out pages at the back of the book for readers' comment.
They are followed up by our professional team.

W1   Claridge's   90%   £A

HR Map 24 A3
Brook Street W1A 2JQ
01-629 8860
Telex 21872

Rooms 191
Ensuite bath/shower 191
Direct dial Yes
Room TV Yes
Confirm by arrang.
Last dinner 11.30
Parking Difficult
Room service 24 hours

Credit Access, Amex, Diners, Visa

Attentive liveried staff are much in evidence at this renowned hotel whose very name conjures up an image of discreet luxury and elegance. A sweeping staircase dominates the foyer where a fire blazes in cold weather; drinks are served not in a bar, but in the gracious lounge, and you can take afternoon tea in the relaxing reading room next door. Bedrooms, many currently being refurbished, fall into two categories – those in a splendid Art Deco style or in a more classical tradition. All have specially made extra large mattresses, soft pastel shades, sumptuous fabrics and magnificently solid, old-fashioned bathrooms. No dogs. *Amenities* hairdressing, secretarial services, fax, valeting, laundry service. ♿

Restaurant ♕

French cooking

About £90 for two
Seats 110
Parties 12

Delightfully thoughtful, old-fashioned service adds to the pleasure of dining at this elegantly pink and peach restaurant. Dishes like chiffonnade de légumes et crustacés au parfum de truffe – an enjoyable crab and vegetable mousse – or fresh salmon with a leek sauce are very capably prepared and served with excellent vegetables. Simple grills, too, and delicious sweets and petits fours to finish. Good classic wine list strong in Bordeaux. ♟ Well-chosen ⊖

Lunch 12.30–3 *Dinner* 7–11.30
Closed 26 & 27 Dec & 2 Jan

The Causerie ♕

Set L from £11
Seats 40
Parties 10

A tempting buffet display (smörgåsbord at lunchtime) is the central feature of this charming little restaurant with curved couches for two at pink-clothed tables. Superb raw materials are used on a varied carte and there's also a wide selection of grills. Cooking is sound and service impeccable. Good classic wine list strong in Bordeaux. Ideal for pre- or post-theatre dinner. ♟ Well-chosen ⊖ ๒

Lunch 12–3 *Dinner* 5.30–11, Sun 7–11
Closed Sat & some Bank Hols

| W8 | Clarke's ★ | ⌘ |

R Map 22 A3
124 Kensington Church Street
W8
01-221 9225

Lunch 12.30–2
Dinner 7.30–10
Set L from £14
Set D £25
About £60 for two
Seats 90
Parking Difficult

Credit Access, Visa
Closed Sat, Sun, Bank Hols, 1 wk Easter, 2 wks Aug & 10 days Xmas

A bright, modern restaurant where, with enthusiasm, skill and dedication, Sally Clarke produces dishes of marvellous subtlety, flavour and eye appeal. Her daily-changing menus provide a short but varied selection at lunchtime and a no-choice but perfectly balanced feast every evening. Moist, smooth duck, veal and pistachio terrine, for example, might be followed by saddle of rabbit marinated in

thyme and lemon zest. To finish, superb Stilton and home-baked biscuits, plus wonderful coffee ice cream. Skilfully chosen wines. *Specialities* veal liver and prosciutto ham salad tossed with balsamic vinegar and shallot olive oil, chargrilled red snapper with papaya relish, fruit fool made with yoghurt and cream. ♟ Well-chosen ⊖

⊳ is our symbol for an **outstanding** wine list

| W1 | The Clifton-Ford 71% | £B |

H Map 22 D1
47 Welbeck Street W1M 8DN
01-486 6600
Telex 22569

Rooms 245
Ensuite bath/shower 245
Direct dial Yes
Room TV Yes
Confirm by 6
Last dinner 11
Parking Ample
Room service 24 hours

Credit Access, Amex, Diners, Visa

Major attractions at the Clifton-Ford are its location just north of Oxford Street – fairly quiet, but ideal for shopping; exemplary standards of maintenance and housekeeping; and excellent, friendly service that makes you feel like a guest who really matters. That good feeling starts at reception and continues into the elegant, relaxing lounge and handsome panelled bar. Modern comfort is the order of the day in

the bedrooms, all of a good size, with built-in units and neat, tiled bathrooms. New this year are 25 bedrooms (built on the roof) and a business centre.
Amenities in-house movies, secretarial services, fax, valeting, laundry service.

| NW3 | Clive Hotel at Hampstead 63% | £B/C |

H **Map 20 C3**
Primrose Hill Road,
Hampstead NW3 3NA
01-586 2233
Telex 22759
Credit Access, Amex, Diners, Visa

Business travellers and tourists are big business at this modern hotel north of Regent's Park. Accommodation ranges from practical singles with showers to twins (the majority) and top-floor Plaza Rooms, the last affording many extra touches of luxury. Foyer, lounge and bar are open-plan, and there are extensive conference and function facilities. Housekeeping and maintenance could be better.
Amenities in-house movies, secretarial services, laundry service.

Rooms 96	*Direct dial* Yes	*Confirm by* 6	*Parking* Limited
Ensuite bath/shower 96	*Room TV* Yes	*Last dinner* 10	*Room service* 24 hours

| W2 | Coburg Hotel 61% | £C/D |

H **Map 22 B2**
129 Bayswater Road W2 4RJ
01-229 3654
Telex 268235
Credit Access, Amex, Diners, Visa

A major refurbishment is planned by the new owner of this distinctive Edwardian hotel above Queensway tube station. Bedrooms so far upgraded have colourful furnishings and smart built-in units, and are equipped with hairdryers, trouser presses, remote-control TVs and tea-makers. Bright compact bathrooms all have showers. Public areas include a stylish foyer and spacious lounge bar. *Amenities* in-house movies, secretarial services, fax, laundry service.

Rooms 125	*Direct dial* Yes	*Confirm by* 6	*Parking* Difficult
Ensuite bath/shower 83	*Room TV* Most	*Last dinner* 9.30	*Room service* All day

| W9 | Colonnade Hotel 58% | £D/E |

H **Map 20 B3**
2 Warrington Crescent
W9 1ER
01-286 1052
Telex 298930
Credit Access, Amex, Diners, Visa

A rambling Georgian building in a residential area of Maida Vale. Bedrooms come in a variety of sizes and styles, the best being the brightly decorated suites with whirlpool baths and in-house movies. One little room for children is modelled on the captain's quarters aboard ship. Recent improvements include the enlargement of the bar and restaurant and the provision of a little garden.
Amenities garden, laundry service.

Rooms 53	*Room phone* Yes	*Confirm by* arrang.	*Parking* Limited
Ensuite bath/shower 40	*Room TV* Yes	*Last dinner* 10	*Room service* All day

**We publish annually,
so make sure you use the current edition.
It's worth it!**

| W1 | The Connaught 91% | £A |

HR **Map 22 D2**
Carlos Place W1Y 6AL
01-499 7070

Rooms 90
Ensuite bath/shower 90
Direct dial Yes
Room TV Yes
Confirm by arrang.
Last dinner 10.30
Parking Difficult
Room service 24 hours

Credit Access

Smallest and most discreet of London's grand hotels, the Connaught jealously guards the privacy of its guests: there's no brochure and even the telex and fax numbers are ex-directory. Such an impenetrable front can be frustrating to those who never seem able to make a booking, but for the fortunate elite who do get to stay, it's worth every penny. Public rooms offer superb traditional comforts reminiscent of a more gracious age, while impeccably turned out staff – most in morning dress – also recall a bygone era. Bedrooms retain an aura of understated luxury, with antique furniture, fresh flowers and high-quality carpets and curtains. Superb bathrooms. No dogs.
Amenities valeting, laundry service.

Restaurant ★   ⚜ ⚜ ⚜

Lunch 12.30–2.30
Dinner 6.30–10.15
Set L & D from £33.80
About £68 for two
Seats 80
Parties 10

Sadly, standards continue to slip at this once outstanding restaurant. The beautifully panelled dining room remains as magnificent as ever but service from impeccably attired waiters is haughty and intimidating. An uneven performance from the kitchen too, with a lovely starter like sole quenelles double-sauced with champagne and lobster leading on to tough, dry beef medallions accompanied by mediocre vegetables and, finally, wild strawberry tart on a pastry base that's best forgotten. Conventional but unexciting list of classic wines.
Specialities pâté de turbot froid au homard, sauce pudeur; rendez-vous du pêcheur, sauce légère au parfum d'Armorique; salmi de canard strasbourgeoise en surprise. ♥ Well-chosen ⊖ &

★ For a *discount* on next year's guide, see **An Offer for Answers.** ★

EC2   Corney & Barrow   ⚜

Ⓡ **Map 26 C1**
109 Old Broad Street EC2
01-638 9308

Set L £31
About £110 for two
Seats 30
Parking Difficult

Credit Access, Amex, Diners, Visa

From the service to the decor everything is highly polished at this elegant, exclusive City restaurant. Quality is the keynote of carefully prepared and beautifully presented dishes such as medallions of Scottish sirloin, marinated fillet of hare and rabbit in an orange sauce, and fresh scallops with smoked bacon. The admirably concise wine list features some splendid clarets and burgundies. ♥ Well-chosen ⊖

Lunch only 12–2.30
Closed Sat, Sun & Bank Hols

SW10   La Croisette

Ⓡ **Map 23 A6**
168 Ifield Road SW10
01-373 3694

Seafood
Set L & D £20
About £56 for two
Seats 55 *Parties* 10
Parking Difficult
Credit Access, Amex, Diners, Visa

The price of a meal in this colourful basement restaurant gets you kir, nibbles, two fish courses, cheese, salad, sweet and coffee. Fine fresh produce is prepared fairly simply: oysters, scallops, the famous plâteau de fruits de mer, feuilletés, daily specials like skate beurre noisette or John Dory with Noilly. A few meat dishes also available. The waiters much prefer to speak their native French.

Lunch 12.30–2.30   *Dinner* 7–11.30
Closed L Tues, all Mon & 2 wks Xmas

SW14   Crowthers   ⌕

Ⓡ **Map 21 A6**
481 Upper Richmond Road
West, East Sheen SW14
01-876 6372

Set L £15 **Set D** £25
About £64 for two
Seats 28
Parking Ample
Credit Access

You can be sure of a good meal at this pretty little restaurant where Philip Crowther and Andrew Eastwick do most of the cooking while their partners Shirley and Nicola run front of house. The fixed-price menu, supplemented by several dishes of the day, is full of interest and the cooking is accomplished – try the beautifully roasted lamb with garlic and thyme sauce. Desserts are a high point. ♣

Lunch 12–2   *Dinner* 7–10.45
Closed L Sat & 4 days Xmas

W1   Cumberland Hotel   69%   £B

ⒽⓇ **Map 22 D2**
Marble Arch W1A 4RF
01-262 1234
Telex 22215

Credit Access, Amex, Diners, Visa

Improvements to this large and busy hotel at Marble Arch include the redesign of the public rooms, creating a foyer-lounge, a new bar and the quarry-tiled Mall, comprising a Japanese restaurant, an oak-panelled bar, shops and a snack bar. Comfortable bedrooms have mini-bars and good bathrooms; guests in the Executive rooms have their own check-in and lounge. ***Amenities*** sauna, secretarial services, fax, laundry service, coffee shop (6.30am–midnight).

Rooms 907	*Direct dial* Yes	*Confirm by* 6	*Parking* Ample
Ensuite bath/shower 907	*Room TV* Yes	*Last dinner* 10.30	*Room service* 24 hours

see over

Austen's Restaurant   ♕

Set L from £13.50
About £72 for two
Seats 72
Parties 30

Austen's Restaurant, which replaces the Wyvern, is in Art Deco style, with a smart marble-countered bar, recessed spotlighting and cartoon prints. Mike Preston remains at the culinary helm, producing enjoyable dishes that range from game pâté and a salad of poached quail's eggs with asparagus to grilled sole with bananas and chutney, braised oxtail and a nice light sultana sponge pudding with lemon sauce. Willing, attentive service.

Lunch 12–2.30   *Dinner* 6.30–10.30

SW3   Dan's

R **Map 23 C5**
119 Sydney Street sw3
01-352 2718

Set D £15
About £42 for two
Seats 50
Parties 34
Parking Difficult
Credit Amex, Diners, Visa

Dan's is a bright, pretty restaurant that really comes into its own in summer, when garden tables are in great demand. All year round there's an enjoyable eating to be had from a simple choice that runs from seafood terrine with tomato coulis to calf's liver and bacon, lamb noisettes and fruit-filled hazelnut meringue. Evening set menu, lunchtime à la carte. 🍷 Well-chosen ℮

Lunch 12.30–2.30   *Dinner* 7.30–11
Closed L Sat, all Sun, Bank Hols & 10 days Xmas

SW3   Daphne's

R **Map 23 C5**
112 Draycott Avenue sw3
01-589 4257

French cooking
About £48 for two
Seats 85
Parties 30
Parking Limited
Credit Access, Amex, Diners, Visa

Screening and plants give an air of privacy to this spacious restaurant prettily decorated in dark red and pink. The menu of reliable French dishes such as noisettes d'agneau and sole véronique is supplemented by more imaginative plats du jour like loup de mer with fennel, medallions of venison, and roast pheasant. Soufflés are a house speciality – our airy confection flavoured with Grand Marnier was delicious. 🍷 Well-chosen ℮ ♿

Lunch 12.30–2.30   *Dinner* 7.30–12
Closed Sun, Bank Hols & 4 days Xmas

W1   Defune

R **Map 22 D1**
61 Blandford Street w1
01-935 8311

Japanese cooking

About £65 for two
Seats 30
Parking Difficult

Credit Amex, Diners

A tiny, simple restaurant popular with Japanese diners, a testimony to the standard of cooking. The dishes are clearly described on the menu and the sushi (the house speciality) is depicted in an illustrated menu in the entrance, making things nice and easy for the novice. On offer are Japanese kebabs, delicately flavoured soups, appetising stews and excellent teriyakis. A good selection of fresh fruit to finish. Book.

Lunch 12–2.30   *Dinner* 6–10.30
Closed Sun, Bank Hols & 1 wk Xmas

★ For a *discount* on next year's guide, see **An Offer for Answers**. ★

SW7 & W1   Delhi Brasserie

R **Map 23 B4**
134 Cromwell Road sw7
01-370 7617

Map 27 A2
44 Frith Street w1
01-437 8261

Set meals £12.50
About £34 for two

Cromwell Road
Seats 34 Parties 45

Frith Street
Seats 56 Parties 25
Parking Limited

Crisp service and talented cooking make for enjoyable meals at these modern Indian restaurants, one on busy Cromwell Road, the other a younger, very similar sister establishment in Soho – new to the Guide this year. Accomplished use of herbs and spices produces a variety of interesting flavours. The menu includes many familiar favourites based on lamb, chicken and prawns, as well as more unusual items such as quails marinated in yoghurt or chargrilled trout. We enjoyed a tender lamb Madras in a rich but not too fiery sauce; the vegetable biryani is a popular choice for those who don't want meat and there are good value thalis and complete set meals.

Cromwell Road, Lunch 12–2.30   *Dinner* 6–11.30
Frith Street, Lunch 12–2.30   *Dinner* 5.30–midnight

NW8 — Don Pepe 🍴

R Map 20 B3
99 Frampton Street NW8
01-262 3834

Spanish cooking
About £42 for two
Seats 70
Parties 30
Parking Limited
Credit Access, Amex, Diners, Visa

The Garcia family come from Galicia in north-western Spain and there's an interesting regional slant to their menu. Try classic Galician dishes like tripe and chick peas with hot red pimento or hake and potatoes in green pepper sauce. It's all good hearty fare served in a lively atmosphere (plenty of Spanish families at weekends). There's a tapas bar too. Wine list includes over 20 Riojas. 🍷 Well-chosen

Lunch 12–2.45   *Dinner* 7–12.15, Sun 7–10
Closed 24, 25 & 26 Dec

W1 — The Dorchester

H Map 22 D3
Park Lane W1A 2HJ
01-629 8888
Telex 887704

The Dorchester, one of the world's most renowned luxury hotels, closes its doors on the 23rd December 1988 for a comprehensive refurbishment programme that has been costed at over £70 million. Bedrooms and bathrooms will be raised even higher in quality, and new features include an Oriental restaurant, a night club, a health club and a business centre. Reopening is scheduled for the spring season of 1990.

W4 — La Dordogne   *NEW ENTRY*

R Map 21 A5
5 Devonshire Road,
Chiswick W4
01-747 1836

French cooking
About £40 for two
Seats 60 *Parties* 25
Parking Difficult
Credit Access, Amex, Diners, Visa

Just off Chiswick High Road, La Dordogne is a French owned and staffed restaurant decorated with prints, drawings and Victorian photographs. The menu offers quite a reasonable choice, from salade gourmande (with foie gras, cured duck and a fried quail's egg) to escalope of Dover sole with chervil butter sauce, lamb cooked with honey and mint and fillet of beef with a Roquefort sauce. Generally decent cooking; service short on English. ℮

Lunch noon–2.30   *Dinner* 7–11
Closed L Sat, all Sun, Bank Hols, 1 wk Xmas & 4 days Easter

NW1 — Dorset Square Hotel   76%   £B

H Map 21 C4
39 Dorset Square NW1 6QN
01-723 7874
Telex 263964

Rooms 48
Ensuite bath/shower 48
Direct dial Yes
Room TV Yes
Confirm by 6
Last dinner 10
Parking Difficult
Room service 24 hours

Credit Access, Amex, Visa

More suites of superb style and comfort in a house across the square have increased the scope of this delightful civilised town-house hotel that makes the most of its charming Regency character while adding a thoughtful range of modern comforts. Bedrooms in the main hotel are splendidly tasteful, with quality furnishings and nice antique pieces. Extras include remote-control TVs, mini-bars, dressing gowns, and impressive bathrooms with scales and pampering toiletries. Small public rooms include an elegant foyer lounge and a basement bar due to be enlarged. No children under ten. No dogs.

Amenities secretarial services, fax, restaurant (7am–10pm).

SW3 — Drakes

R Map 23 C5
2a Pond Place SW3
01-584 4555

English cooking
Set L & D Sun £17.25
About £65 for two
Seats 85
Parking Difficult
Credit Access, Amex, Diners, Visa

You can expect an enjoyable meal at this smart but informal split-level restaurant. There's a good choice of dishes on the à la carte menu, backed up by a short list of weekly specials. Start with asparagus with puff pastry filled with chervil hollandaise or warm salad of smoked duck; move on to spit roast wild boar or corn-fed chicken poached in Madeira. 🍷 Well-chosen ℮

Lunch Sun only 12.30–3   *Dinner* 6.30–11, Sun 7–10.30
Closed L Mon–Sat exc. for private hire, Bank Hols

WC2   Drury Lane Moat House Hotel   68%   £A/B

H **Map 27 B1**
10 Drury Lane WC2B 5RE
01-836 6666
Telex 8811395

Credit Access, Amex, Diners, Visa

Public rooms at this modern theatreland hotel include Maudie's Bar, a popular meeting place with sophisticated dark blue decor and Osbert Lancaster cartoons. Bedrooms, all with remote-control TVs and individual air conditioning, feature smart bamboo-style furnishings, a theme picked up in the picture and mirror frames. New and refurbished rooms are pleasantly done out with soft pastel fabrics. *Amenities* in-house movies, secretarial services, fax, laundry service.

Rooms 153	*Direct dial* Yes	*Confirm by* 6	*Parking* Difficult
Ensuite bath/shower 153	*Room TV* Yes	*Last dinner* 11	*Room service* 24 hours

SW1   Dukes Hotel   81%   £A

HR **Map 25 B4**
35 St James's Place
SW1A 1NY
01-491 4840
Telex 28283

Rooms 60
Ensuite bath/shower 60
Direct dial Yes
Room TV Yes
Confirm by 6
Last dinner 10
Parking Difficult
Room service 24 hours

Credit Access, Amex, Diners, Visa

A beautifully preserved Edwardian hotel in a quiet courtyard yet only minutes from the West End. A sense of elegance and peace, coupled with outstanding service, are notable features. Fine period furniture, plenty of fresh flowers and burgundy decor give a warm, clubby feel to the foyer, while comfortable chairs and sofas, an open fire and plenty of paintings make for a delightful sitting room. Bedrooms offer a high degree of comfort and cleanliness; they have fine antiques, top-quality fabrics and wallcoverings and cosy settees and armchairs. Excellent, fully tiled bathrooms are equipped with bathrobes and good toiletries. No under sevens. No dogs.
Amenities secretarial services, fax, laundry service.

Restaurant   ♛

Set L from £17
About £75 for two
Seats 35
Parties 12

Andrew Marshall's cooking, which mixes traditional English fare with more inventive French dishes, is highly accomplished and he uses excellent quality fresh produce on which to exercise his talents – saucing is especially good. Start with a chicken salad with pine kernels and move on to fillet of lamb with fresh basil and white port sauce. Sweets off the trolley include a superb bread and butter pudding. ♟ Well-chosen ⊖

Lunch 12.30–2.30   *Dinner* 6–10, Sun 7–10

W1   Durrants Hotel   65%   £B/C

H **Map 22 D1**
George Street W1H 6BJ
01-935 8131
Telex 894919

Credit Access, Amex, Visa

Keynotes at this privately owned hotel are the club-like charm of the public rooms and old-fashioned standards of personal service from courteous staff. A handsome staircase dominates the foyer, and there is a cosy bar and comfortable panelled lounge. Smartly refurbished bedrooms are basically in two styles, one with military touches, the other more chic and feminine. There are three very attractive suites. No dogs. *Amenities* secretarial services, fax, laundry service.

Rooms 95	*Direct dial* Yes	*Confirm by* 6	*Parking* Ample
Ensuite bath/shower 86	*Room TV* Yes	*Last dinner* 6	*Room service* All day

NW3   Dynasty of Hampstead

R **Map 20 B2**
291 Finchley Road NW3
01-794 5920

Chinese cooking
Set L and D from £10.95
About £35 for two
Seats 70 *Parties* 40
Parking Ample
Credit Access, Amex, Diners, Visa

A very friendly Chinese restaurant run by the charming Mr Frank Wu. Szechuan specialities, such as bang-bang chicken and fiery hot chilli beef, are a feature but Peking dishes are available too – the flavoursome crispy duck served with pancakes and hoysin sauce is to be recommended. Excellent seafood and impeccably cooked rice can't fail to please. Simple desserts such as lychees, ice cream and fruit to finish. ♿

Lunch 12–12.30 Fri & Sat   *Dinner* 6–11.15 Mon–Fri, Sat 6–11.30
Meals Sun 1–11pm   **Closed** L Mon–Thurs & 1 wk Xmas

SW1   Eatons   ⑨

R **Map 23 D5**
49 Elizabeth Street SW1
01-730 0074

About £40 for two
Seats 40
Parking Limited

Credit Access, Amex, Diners, Visa

The consistently enjoyable cooking at this small but comfortable restaurant has attracted a large number of regulars who add to the warm and friendly atmosphere. There's a good choice of dishes on the à la carte menu and a supplementary list takes advantage of fresh seasonal ingredients. Starter might be blinis with smoked salmon and sour cream with pork in Calvados sauce to follow. Finish with an airy lemon cheesecake.

Lunch 12–2   *Dinner* 7–11.15
Closed Sat, Sun & Bank Hols

SW1   Ebury Court Hotel   57%   £C/D

HR **Map 25 A6**
26 Ebury Street SW1W 0LU
01-730 8147

Credit Access, Visa

The charming Tophams continue to run their Victorian terrace hotel with every consideration of their guests' requirements. The pleasing public areas include a writing room-cum-lounge and a club bar (where guests can become temporary members) with a small patio. Bedrooms come in varying shapes and sizes but all have plenty of old-fashioned appeal, as do both the public and private bathrooms.
Amenities laundry service.

Rooms 39	*Direct dial* Yes	*Confirm by* arrang.	*Parking* Difficult
Ensuite bath/shower 12	*Room TV* No	*Last dinner* 9	*Room service* 24 hours

Restaurant

Set L £7.20
About £36 for two
Seats 35

Chef Patrick O'Connor has reigned over this intimate little restaurant for a quarter of a century, providing straightforward, unpretentious meals. The cooking is excellent and the materials universally fresh. Start with the day's hors d'oeuvre, home-made taramasalata or smoked chicken and celery soup; move on to a super grilled Dover sole with lobster butter, served with delicious vegetables. Simple desserts include zabaglione and baked egg custard with apricots. ℮

Lunch 12–2   *Dinner* 7–9

SW7   Embassy House Hotel   58%   £C/D

H **Map 23 B4**
31 Queen's Gate SW7 5JA
01-584 7222
Telex 8813387

Credit Access, Amex, Diners, Visa

The hotel is a conversion of four private houses built around 1860, and original features like mirrored doors and elaborate ceiling work survive. Some parts were looking a little weary on our last visit, particularly the bar-lounge and restaurant. Redecoration will no doubt freshen up the bedrooms, which have comfortable beds and well-kept bathrooms. Friendly staff and generally good housekeeping.
Amenities laundry service, 24-hour lounge service.

Rooms 68	*Direct dial* Yes	*Confirm by* 6	*Parking* Limited
Ensuite bath/shower 68	*Room TV* Yes	*Last dinner* 9.45	*Room service* Limited

---

Our inspectors *never* book in the name of Egon Ronay's Guides.
They disclose their identity only if they are considering an establishment
for inclusion in the next edition of the Guide.

SW3   English Garden

R **Map 23 C5**
10 Lincoln Street SW3
01-584 7272

Set L £12.50
About £50 for two
Seats 65
Parties 30
Parking Difficult
Credit Access, Amex, Diners, Visa

The rear section is a leafy conservatory, the front part more intimate. The menu is essentially English and both cooking and service are excellent. Try potted meats or a chequerboard of freshwater fish to start, then maybe salmon fish cakes or collops of beef with plum brandy. Sweets include a delicious ginger fruit pudding. Note excellent Ch. Trotanoy '79 and Pinot Noir from Mondavi on a good wine list. ℮

Lunch 12.30–2.30, Sun 12.30–2   *Dinner* 7.30–11.30, Sun 7.30–10
Closed Good Fri, 25 & 26 Dec

SW3 · English House

R Map 23 C4
3 Milner Street SW3
01-584 3002
English cooking

Set L from £10.50
About £65 for two
Seats 65 *Parties* 65
Parking Limited
Credit Access, Amex, Diners, Visa

All is delightful at this intimate little Victorian-style restaurant, from the charming floral decor to recipes culled from Tudor, 18th-century and Victorian cooks. First-class ingredients shine in dishes such as a double fresh crab mousse, turbot and scallop creams, and beautifully tender steak with a superb malt whisky sauce. Sweets are a must, especially the rich gingerbread and butter pudding with Devonshire cream. 🍷 Well-chosen ⊖

Lunch 12–2.30, Sun 12.30–2   *Dinner* 7.30–11.30, Sun 7.30–10
Closed Good Fri & 25 & 26 Dec

EC2 · Equities *NEW ENTRY*

R Map 26 C1
1 Finsbury Avenue EC2
01-247 1051

Set L from £14.50
Set D £12.50
About £55 for two
Seats 90
Parking Difficult
Credit Access, Amex, Diners, Visa

A smart split-level restaurant overlooking a new piazza and waterfall. Cooking and presentation both shine, and flavours throughout are excellent. Main dishes are either grills or slightly more elaborate choices like sautéed strips of fillet steak in a rich, sweet chilli sauce. Peach poached in champagne with strawberry sorbet makes a splendid finale. Well-kept English and Continental cheeses. Shorter brunch menu (11am–1pm) and sound, concise wine list. Booking advisable.

Lunch 11–3   *Dinner* 6.30–9.30
Closed Sat, Sun & Bank Hols

W1 · L'Escargot

R Map 27 A2
48 Greek Street W1
01-437 2679

About £52 for two
Seats 100
Parties 50
Parking Difficult
Credit Access, Amex, Diners, Visa

Busy first-floor restaurant (booking essential) and equally busy ground-floor brasserie (no bookings taken). The regular menu and the daily specials provide a tempting choice, and Martin Lam generally does justice to his ingredients. A typical autumn selection could include hot terrine of smoked haddock with a chive beurre blanc, maize-fed chicken on a bed of wild mushrooms and compote of quinces with clotted cream. Vegetables are excellent. 🍷 Well-chosen ⊖

Lunch 12.30–2.30   *Dinner* 6.30–11.15
Closed L Sat, all Sun & Bank Hols

W1 · L'Etoile *NEW ENTRY*

R Map 24 B2
30 Charlotte Street W1
01-636 7189

French cooking

About £64 for two
Seats 70
Parties 30
Parking Difficult

Credit Access, Amex, Diners, Visa

The restaurant's decor has changed little since 1902, but the affable Greek owner has modernised the kitchens and established an excellent team of young French chefs. The menu has a very traditional ring, epitomised in our superb roast grouse with all the proper trimmings. Turbot à la monégasque, with prawns, onions and a splendid aïoli, is a house speciality, and other popular items include fish soup, poached or grilled salmon, sautéed kidneys, roast duck and steak béarnaise. Lovely gâteaux on the sweet trolley. To accompany the fine food are sound classic wines, including some good half-bottles. Service runs smoothly and amiably. 🍷 Well-chosen ⊖ ♿

Lunch 12.30–2.30   *Dinner* 7–10
Closed Sat, Sun, Bank Hols, Aug & 1 wk Xmas

Any person using our name to obtain free hospitality is a fraud.
Proprietors, please inform the police and us.

SW10 · La Famiglia

R Map 23 B6
7 Langton Street SW10
01-351 0761

Italian cooking
About £38 for two
Seats 170
Parties 40
Parking Limited
Credit Access, Amex, Diners, Visa

There's been an addition to La Famiglia. The purchase of an adjacent restaurant has doubled the capacity and added a garden capable of seating 90. Quinto Cecchetti continues to cook with great style such favourites as grilled monkfish with lemon and garlic, charcoal-grilled lamb and delicious home-made pasta. Simple sweets include tira mi su. Sound Italian wine list with some memorable bottles such as Sassicaia and Bricco dell'Uccellone (Barbera). ⊖

Lunch 12–3   *Dinner* 7–12
Closed Bank Hols

SW1 — La Fantaisie Brasserie

R **Map 22 C3**
14 Knightsbridge Green SW1
01-589 0509

French cooking
Set L from £9.50
About £45 for two
Seats 65 *Parties* 50
Parking Limited
Credit Access, Amex, Diners, Visa

French customers contribute to the very Gallic atmosphere at an authentic provincial brasserie nearly opposite Harrods. There are few frills but some finesse about the cooking, and seasonal salads and fruits are a feature. Typical choices include crab bisque with aïoli, toasted goat's cheese with hazelnuts and winter leaves, mussel-sauced halibut and sliced breast of duck served with a pickled garlic sauce. French provincial cheeses, cold desserts. ☺

Lunch 12–3   *Dinner* 7–10.30
Closed Sun, Bank Hols & 10 days Xmas

SW3 — The Fenja   £B

P H **Map 23 D5**
69 Cadogan Gardens
SW3 2RB
01-589 7333
Telex 934272

Rooms 13
Ensuite bath/shower 13
Direct dial Yes
Room TV Yes
Confirm by 6
Last dinner 9
Parking Difficult
Room service 24 hours

Credit Access, Amex, Diners, Visa

High-class bed and breakfast accommodation in a Victorian town house close to Sloane Square. Bedrooms are individually appointed, and quality fabrics, fine bed linen and antique furniture all contribute to a feeling of style and luxury. Bathrooms are particularly well equipped, with fluffy towels, bathrobes and superior toiletries; there's even a phone by the loo! The only public place to meet is a smart but very small drawing room, where drinks may be ordered. Breakfast and other meals are taken in the bedrooms, fine in the larger rooms with a table and chairs but not so handy in the smaller ones. No dogs.
Amenities fax, laundry service.

SW3 — Fifty-One Fifty-One   *NEW ENTRY*

R **Map 23 C5**
Chelsea Cloisters,
Sloane Avenue SW3
01-730 5151

American cooking
Set Brunch £17.95, children
£8.95
Seats 160 *Parking* Ample
Credit Access, Amex, Diners, Visa

New Orleans has come to Chelsea in this bright new restaurant with valet parking. Cajun music sets the scene for exciting Southern-States cooking: sample the rich trio of gumbo, turtle and mussel soups, shrimps Creole with dirty (yes!) rice, and authentic Louisiana jambalaya. 'Blackened' dishes intrigue: try swordfish seared in this special Cajun way. Finish with Mardi Gras cheesecake or key lime pie. Interesting, exclusively North American wines.

Lunch 12–3, Sun Brunch 11.30–4   *Dinner* 6.30–11.30, Sun 6.30–10.30   *About £60 for two*

W1 — Fortyseven Park Street   *NEW ENTRY*   £A

P H **Map 22 D2**
47 Park Street,
Mayfair W1Y 4EB
01-491 7282
Telex 22116

Credit Access, Amex, Diners, Visa

Standard, superior and de luxe suites provide superb accommodation in the heart of Mayfair. All suites have a kitchen, bedroom, living room and bathroom; furniture is of the finest quality, tastefully chosen and coordinated, and beds boast the very best linen. Champagne is laid on soon after check-in, and room service includes a splendid breakfast and a menu from Le Gavroche (this is a Roux Brothers enterprise). No dogs. *Amenities* secretarial services, fax, laundry service.

| *Rooms* 52 | *Direct dial* Yes | *Confirm by* arrang. | *Parking* Difficult |
| *Ensuite bath/shower* 52 | *Room TV* Yes | | *Room service* All day |

SW7 — Forum Hotel   60%   £B

H **Map 23 B4**
97 Cromwell Road SW7 4DN
01-370 5757
Telex 919663

Credit Access, Amex, Diners, Visa

On the busy road to Heathrow and routes west, the Forum tower block has 24 floors of rooms grouped round the central lift shaft. The throughput of visitors is enormous, and the emphasis is on practicality rather than charm. Bedrooms provide a reasonable night's rest, but room service is restricted to Executive/Superior rooms.
Amenities in-house movies, secretarial services, fax, laundry service, coffee shop (6.30am–1am).

| *Rooms* 907 | *Direct dial* Yes | *Confirm by* 6 | *Parking* Ample |
| *Ensuite bath/shower* 907 | *Room TV* Yes | *Last dinner* 10.30 | *Room service* All day |

WC2	**Frère Jacques**

R Map 27 B2
38 Long Acre wc2
01-836 7823

Set L £13.95
Set D £15.95
About £45 for two
Seats 64 *Parties* 14
Parking Difficult
Credit Access, Amex, Diners, Visa

The decor is cool and crisp, the atmosphere relaxing, the staff smart and helpful, the menu mainly from the sea. Mediterranean-style fish soup, shellfish platter, trout normande and sole with vermouth and chive butter sauce are typical dishes, all well prepared from very fresh ingredients. Warm goat's cheese salad is a nice starter, and there are some meat and vegetarian main courses and good pâtisserie. The restaurant is above a brasserie and wine bar. ℮

Lunch 12–2.45 *Dinner* 6–11.30, Sun 7–10.30
Closed 24–26 Dec

W1	**Frith's** ♣

R Map 27 A2
14 Frith Street w1
01-439 3370

About £52 for two
Seats 60
Parties 45
Parking Difficult

Credit Access, Visa

Carla Tomasi now owns the popular little Soho restaurant where she has worked as chef for four years. Monthly-changing menus in the modern British mode are admirably health-conscious: there is always fish, some kind of poached meat dish and a vegetarian offering. Results can be most enjoyable, as in raw scallops with soy and olive oil, breast of pigeon with Seville oranges and glazed turnips, and blueberry meringue. Book. ℮

Lunch 12.30–2.30 *Dinner* 7.30–11.15
Closed L Sat, all Sun, Bank Hols & 10 days Xmas

Changes in data sometimes occur in establishments
after the Guide goes to press.
Prices should be taken as indications rather than firm quotes.

W1	**Fuji**

R Map 24 B3
36 Brewer Street w1
01-734 0957

Japanese cooking
Set D from £25
About £55 for two
Seats 54 *Parties* 15
Parking Difficult
Credit Access, Amex, Diners, Visa

Decor may be simple and unpretentious but food is of the highest standard at this Soho Japanese restaurant. There's a good choice of set dinners (best bet for the uninitiated) or you can venture into the à la carte menu, which offers some excellent traditional dishes. Seafood is the main interest, with a few meat offerings. Helpful waitresses will gladly assist in your selection.

Lunch 12.30–2.30 *Dinner* 6–10.45
Closed L Sat & Sun, L Bank Hols, 2 wks Xmas

SW6	**Fulham Diner** *NEW ENTRY*

R Map 21 B5
616 Fulham Road sw6
01-736 9171

Chinese cooking
Set L £5.95 Set D £12.50
About £40 for two
Seats 65 *Parties* 65
Parking Limited
Credit Access, Diners, Visa

Behind the unassuming facade, this friendly Chinese restaurant offers pleasant modern decor and a fairly conservative range of decently prepared dishes. Go for classic favourites like wun tun soup and chicken in yellow bean sauce, or try something a little more adventurous like beautifully fresh and plump steamed scallops in garlicky sauce. Peking duck is available in single portions, and for three or more fish-lovers there's a special seafood feast. ♥ Well-chosen

Lunch 12–2.30 *Dinner* 6–11.30
Closed 25 Dec

WC2	**Fung-Shing**

R Map 27 A2
15 Lisle Street wc2
01-437 1539

Chinese cooking
Set meals from £8
About £34 for two
Seats 90 *Parties* 30
Parking Limited
Credit Access, Amex, Diners, Visa

Refurbished decor makes for a pleasant, relaxing atmosphere in which to enjoy attractive, well-prepared Chinese food. The long menu of familiar favourites includes some popular specialities such as crispy spicy eel; venison with spring onion and ginger; sizzling spicy prawns, beef or veal, and lovely crispy quail with a barbecue sauce. Complimentary sliced oranges provide a refreshing finale.

Meals noon–11.30
Closed 25 & 26 Dec

EC4 — Le Gamin

R Map 26 B1
31 Old Bailey EC4
01-236 7931

French cooking
Set L £21
About £50 for two
Seats 120 *Parties* 160
Parking Difficult
Credit Access, Amex, Diners, Visa

For many years a City favourite, Le Gamin is a basement French restaurant with a fixed-price lunch menu that includes kír, three courses, wine and coffee. Black pudding with creamed apple sauce, smoked salmon quiche, sole with saffron, crispy leg of duck and sirloin steak with shallot sauce show the range. Good French cheeses, well-made sweets. Cooking is excellent, service geared up to today's quickish City lunch. ☺

Lunch only 12–2.30
Closed Sat, Sun & Bank Hols

W1 — Le Gavroche ★★ ♕♕ ♟

R Map 22 D2
43 Upper Brook Street W1
01-408 0881

French cooking

Lunch 12–2
Dinner 7–10.30
Set L £19.50
Set D £42.50
About £100 for two
Seats 70
Parties 22
Parking Difficult

Credit Access, Amex, Diners, Visa
Closed Sat, Sun, Bank Hols & 2 wks Xmas

There is no better service anywhere than in Albert Roux's marvellous restaurant, and while Silvano is in charge so it should remain. Nowhere could you improve upon such dishes as ballotine de foie gras à l'ancienne, gâteau aux deux mousses de légumes, or poulet fermier sauté en cocotte aux lentilles et thym and we can still taste our sablé aux framboises which was simply divine. A particularly fine classic cellar with a wonderful collection of clarets (Château Petrus 1979, 1976, 1971); for an excellent Margaux at a keen price, try Château La Gurgue 1983. *Specialities* soufflé suissesse, mousseline de homard au champagne, assiette du boucher, sablé aux fraises.
⊃ Outstanding ☺

SW1 — Gavvers

R Map 23 D5
61 Lower Sloane Street SW1
01-730 5983

Set L £15.50
Set D £23
About £39 for two
Seats 62
Parking Difficult
Credit Access, Amex, Diners, Visa

Now open for lunch as well as dinner, Gavvers is part of the Roux Brothers empire. Set menus (the evening one includes half a bottle of house wine) provide a small choice of capably prepared dishes such as leek soup with chervil, fish terrine beurre rouge, chicken breast à la normande and braised tongue with port. Service is fairly rapid, so this isn't really a place for lingering. ♀ Well-chosen ☺

Lunch 12–2.30   *Dinner* 7–11
Closed L Sat & all Sun

**We welcome bona fide complaints and recommendations
on the tear-out pages at the back of the book for readers' comment.
They are followed up by our professional team.**

W1 — Gay Hussar

R Map 27 A1
2 Greek Street W1
01-437 0973

Hungarian cooking
Set L £10.50
About £48 for two
Seats 35
Parties 10
Parking Difficult

There have been many changes of personnel at this famous Hungarian restaurant since the departure of Victor Sassie but chef Laslo Holecz is still producing the excellent meals which have been pleasing diners here for ten years. Particularly recommendable dishes from the long menu are the fish salad, csirke paprikash galuskával – succulent chicken in creamy sauce served with thimble dumplings – and rote grütze, a delicious soft fruit pudding.

Lunch 12.30–2   *Dinner* 5.30–11
Closed Sun, Bank Hols

EC4 — Ginnan

R Map 26 B1
5 Cathedral Place EC4
01-236 4120

Japanese cooking
Set L from £5.70
Set D from £18.50
About £45 for two
Seats 45 *Parking* Difficult
Credit Access, Amex, Diners, Visa

Japanese businessmen flock to this agreeable little restaurant at midday, making booking essential. Located in a modern shopping precinct by St Paul's, it offers an excellent-value set lunch plus a short à la carte selection that includes favourites like sukiyaki and shabu shabu. Besides sashimi there are interesting starters like steamed egg pudding, tofu steak with ginger sauce, and soya bean soup. Evenings are quieter.

Lunch 12–2.30   *Dinner* 6–10
Closed D Sat, all Sun & Bank Hols

WC2 — Giovanni's

R Map 27 B2
10 Goodwin's Court,
55 St Martin's Lane WC2
01-240 2877

Italian cooking
About £50 for two
Seats 40 *Parties* 12
Parking Ample
Credit Access, Amex, Diners, Visa

Owner Giovanni Colla provides the welcome while chef Ramon Pareden creates the Italian dishes that find favour with business-people and theatregoers alike. Typical main courses include fried squid, sole fillets with prawns and capers, veal with marsala and rice, entrecôte with red wine and black olives and chicken with asparagus. Cassata and zabaglione make fitting finales.

Lunch 12.30–2.30   *Dinner* 6.30–11
Closed L Sat, all Sun, Bank Hols

SW7 — The Gloucester   78%   £A

H Map 23 B5
4 Harrington Gardens
SW7 4LH
01-373 6030
Telex 917505

Rooms 531
Ensuite bath/shower 531
Direct dial Yes
Room TV Yes
Confirm by 6
Last dinner 10.15
Parking Ample
Room service 24 hours

Credit Access, Amex, Diners, Visa

Behind a fairly unremarkable facade there's a good deal of style and luxury about this busy modern hotel near Cromwell Road. The galleried, marble-floored reception area is impressive, and there are bars to suit all moods and tastes. Large, well-designed bedrooms with smart walnut veneer offer useful work areas and little dressing rooms with hairdryers and trouser presses. Air-conditioning keeps things comfortable, and bedside consoles control TV, video, radio and lights. Well-kept, well-equipped bathrooms. Butler service and a pleasant private lounge for top-floor rooms. *Amenities* sauna, solarium, whirlpool bath, beauty salon, hairdressing, in-house movies, secretarial services, fax, laundry service, coffee shop (6.30am–1am).

We publish annually,
so make sure you use the current edition.
It's worth it!

WC1 — Gonbei

R Map 20 D3
151 King's Cross Road WC1
01-278 0619

Japanese cooking

About £30 for two
Seats 24
Parties 20
Parking Limited

Booking is essential at this homely little restaurant serving authentic, modestly-priced Japanese food. Friendly staff will guide you through a familiar menu of tasty meat and raw fish dishes, including beautifully presented sushi and excellent beef teriyaki with a nicely dressed salad. There are no sweets or fruit for afters, but connoisseurs make do with green tea.

Dinner only 6–10.30, Sat till 10
Closed Sun, Bank Hols, 2 wks Xmas & 1 wk Aug

NW7 & SW3 — Good Earth

R Map 7 B4
143 The Broadway, Mill Hill
NW7
01-959 7011
Map 23 C4
223 Brompton Road SW3
01-584 3658
Map 23 C5
91 Kings Road SW3
01-352 9231
Chinese cooking
Set L & D £11.25
About £45 for two
Credit Access, Amex, Diners, Visa

Consistently good food and friendly, efficient service ensure the lasting popularity of these three smart, modern Chinese restaurants (there's an equally good fourth one in the family – see under Esher). Familiar favourites from all the regions appear on the varied menus, as well as a few not quite so usual, like sliced lamb and cucumber soup, braised yellow flower fish, lettuce-wrapped meats, duck with pickled ginger and sizzling mixed vegetables.

The Broadway – Lunch 12–2.15, Sun 12.30–2.45   *Dinner* 6–11.15, Sun till 1045   *Seats* 100 *Parties* 30 *Parking* Limited
Brompton Road – Meals 12–11.15, Sun till 10.45   *Seats* 100 *Parties* 40 *Parking* Difficult
Kings Road – Meals 12.30–11.45, Sun till 11   *Seats* 70 *Parking* Difficult   **Closed** 4 days Xmas

E14 — Good Friends ♧

R Map 7 B4
139 Salmon Lane
Limehouse, E14
01-987 5541

Chinese cooking
Set meals from £10
Seats 144 *Parties* 60
Parking Limited
Credit Access, Amex, Diners, Visa

The two Mr Cheungs have been satisfying hungry diners in their pleasant restaurant for a quarter of a century, providing a wide range of reliably cooked dishes using good fresh ingredients. You might start with abalone and Chinese mushroom soup, sesame prawns on toast or prawn crackers, then move on to a special sweet and sour fish with spicy sauce or chicken with bitter melon.

Meals noon–11.30   *About £30 for two*
Closed 24, 25 & 26 Dec

**We publish annually,
so make sure you use the current edition.
It's worth it!**

SW7 — Gore Hotel   65%   £B/C

H Map 22 B3
189 Queen's Gate SW7 5EX
01-584 6601
Telex 296244

Credit Access, Amex, Diners, Visa

High standards of comfort and decor characterize this former town house. Public rooms are smart and relaxing, while bedrooms are attractively decorated and furnished in individual style with good accessories. Large rooms are luxurious indeed, and romantics should head for the Tudor Suite, complete with rug-strewn wooden floor, four-poster and leaded windows. No dogs. *Amenities* satellite TV, teletext, fax, laundry service, coffee shop (8am–3pm, 6–9pm).

Rooms 54	Direct dial Yes	Confirm by 4	Parking Difficult
Ensuite bath/shower 54	Room TV Yes	Last dinner 9	Room service 24 hours

SW1 — The Goring   77%   £A

H Map 25 A6
Beeston Place, Grosvenor
Gardens SW1W 0JW
01-834 8211
Telex 919166

Rooms 90
Ensuite bath/shower 90
Direct dial Yes
Room TV Yes
Confirm by arrang.
Last dinner 10
Parking Limited
Room service 24 hours

Credit Access, Amex, Diners, Visa

Small, supremely comfortable and very well run: that sums up The Goring, a family-managed hotel between Victoria station and Buckingham Palace. Sink into one of the comfortable leather armchairs in the lounge and discreet staff are instantly on hand should you require a drink from the adjoining bar. The black and white foyer has recently been painted Wedgwood pink as part of a continuous cycle

of refurbishment. A third of the bedrooms are totally redecorated every year. Each is individually furnished in pastels, with furniture of the highest quality and lots of thoughtful extras. En suite bathrooms are extremely smart. No dogs.
Amenities secretarial services, fax, valeting, laundry service

SW4   The Grafton

R **Map 21 C6**
45 Old Town, Clapham SW4
01-627 1048

French cooking
Set L £12.50 **Set D** £22
About £57 for two
Seats 70 *Parties* 60
Parking Ample
Credit Access, Amex, Diners, Visa

A comfortable, elegant French restaurant in a 17th-century building, reputedly the oldest in Clapham. Starters include delicious home-prepared salmon, vegetable terrine on a spicy tomato coulis and wild pigeon served with fig vinegar sauce. Follow with sea bass with anise sauce or breast of duck with traditional French tartlet; finish with home-made sorbet or perhaps lemon mousse with kiwi fruit and vodka sauce. Three-course Sunday brunch.

Lunch 12.30–2.30, Sun 12–3   *Dinner* 7–11.30
Closed L Sat, D Sun, all Mon & last 3 wks Aug

W1   Grafton Hotel   61%   £B

H **Map 24 B1**
130 Tottenham Court
Road W1P 9HP
01-388 4131
Telex 297234

Credit Access, Amex, Diners, Visa

The Grafton's location at the northern end of Tottenham Court Road makes it a convenient base for visiting the British Museum, Regent's Park or West End shops. A splendid drawing room with bar provides a relaxing ambience which contrasts with the lively cellar wine bar. Bedrooms (some of executive status) are modern with lightwood furniture. All have en-suite facilities.
Amenities in-house movies, secretarial services, fax, laundry service.

Rooms 236	*Direct dial* Yes	*Confirm by* 6	*Parking* Difficult
Ensuite bath/shower 236	*Room TV* Yes	*Last dinner* 10	*Room service* 24 hours

SW1   Gran Paradiso

R **Map 25 B6**
52 Wilton Road SW1
01-828 5818

Italian cooking
About £40 for two
Seats 50
Parties 25
Parking Ample
Credit Access, Amex, Diners, Visa

Good ingredients and careful cooking produce enjoyable meals at this long-established Italian restaurant close to Victoria. Minestrone is home-made and full of flavour, pasta comes al dente and tastily sauced, calf's liver Veneziana is tender and delicious. Vegetables are excellent (properly cooked sauté potatoes). Simple sweets, good coffee, courteous service. Drink the excellent Chianti Classico Rocca delle Macie. Rooftop garden for alfresco eating. 🅿 &

Lunch 12–2.30   *Dinner* 6–11.15
Closed L Sat, all Sun, Bank Hols & 2 wks Aug

Our inspectors *never* book in the name of Egon Ronay's Guides.
They disclose their identity only if they are considering an establishment
for inclusion in the next edition of the Guide.

EC2   Great Eastern Hotel   55%   £C

H **Map 26 D1**
Liverpool Street EC2M 7QN
01-283 4363 Telex 886812

Credit Access, Amex, Diners, Visa
Closed 8 days Xmas

The grandeur of yesteryear can still be glimpsed in some corners of this somewhat battered railway hotel caught up in the redevelopment of Liverpool Street station. Attractions include a pleasant wine bar and spacious refurbished bedrooms, but bathrooms and corridors are much in need of a new look.
Amenities solarium, hairdressing, in-house movies, secretarial services, fax, laundry service, 24-hour lounge service.

Rooms 164	*Direct dial* Yes	*Confirm by* 6	*Parking* Difficult
Ensuite bath/shower 134	*Room TV* Yes	*Last dinner* 10	*Room service* None

N1   Great Northern Hotel   63%   £C/D

H **Map 20 C3**
King's Cross N1 9AN
01-837 5454
Telex 299041

Credit Access, Amex, Diners, Visa
Closed 3 days Xmas

Opened in 1854, London's oldest railway hotel stands just behind King's Cross and St Pancras stations. Though no longer the grand old lady of its Victorian heyday, it offers perfectly adequate accommodation for travellers. Nicely modernised bedrooms, most with spacious en suite bathrooms, have pine furniture, trouser presses and mini-bars. Public areas include a comfortable cane-furnished lounge and pine-clad bar. *Amenities* in-house movies, fax, laundry service. &

Rooms 89	*Direct dial* Yes	*Confirm by* 6	*Parking* Ample
Ensuite bath/shower 78	*Room TV* Yes	*Last dinner* 10	*Room service* 24 hours

W1   Greenhouse   ♕

R **Map 25 A4**
27a Hay's Mews W1
01-499 3331

About £54 for two
Seats 85
Parties 10
Parking Difficult

Credit Access, Amex, Diners, Visa

A bright, roomy restaurant in the heart of Mayfair. Keith Saxby is the new chef who cooks in sound, unspectacular style through a pleasing variety of dishes ranging from spring vegetable soup and chicken satay to stuffed trout, paillard of veal and charcoal grills that include a trio of fillets with mint hollandaise. Nice simple sweets, and a short, select wine list: Ch. Langoa Barton St Julien '78. Friendly waitress service. ♟ Well-chosen ℗

Lunch 12–2.30 *Dinner* 7–11, Sat from 7.30
Closed L Sat & all Sun, Bank Hols (inc. Easter Sat) & 24 Dec–4 Jan

W1   Green Park Hotel   70%   *NEW ENTRY*   £B

H **Map 25 A4**
Half Moon Street W1Y 8BP
01-629 7522
Telex 28856

Rooms 160
Ensuite bath/shower 160
Direct dial Yes
Room TV Yes
Confirm by 6
Last dinner 10.45
Parking Difficult
Room service 24 hours

Credit Access, Amex, Diners, Visa

Converted from a row of period houses in a narrow street just off Piccadilly, this stylish hotel could hardly be more centrally situated. It's an attractive, comfortable place, with a marble-floored foyer and twin lounges filled with plants, fresh flowers and plenty of inviting seats. The adjoining bar is equally appealing, with contemporary decor but a warm, traditional feel. Bedrooms, whether singles, twins, doubles

or triples, are of a decent size and up-to-date in their appointments; trouser presses, hairdryers and remote-control TVs are standard (no double-glazing). Neat tiled bathrooms throughout, with whirlpool baths for de luxe rooms and suites. No dogs. *Amenities* secretarial services, fax, laundry service, coffee shop (7am–10.30pm). ⅍

SW1   Green's Restaurant   ♕

R **Map 25 B4**
36 Duke Street SW1
01-930 4566

English cooking
About £50 for two
Seats 60
Parties 30
Parking Difficult
Credit Access, Amex, Diners, Visa

Mahogany panelling and green decor lend an atmosphere of a typical English club and the cooking is in keeping, with an emphasis on superbly fresh seafood, competently cooked. Traditional hot specials at lunchtime include liver and bacon, fish cakes and steamed syrup sponge, while evenings may bring slightly more exotic fare. Top flight white burgundies: Chablis from Domaine Laroche, Chassagne Montrachet from Morey and Olivier Leflaive. ♟ Well-chosen ℗ ⅍

Lunch 12.30–2.45 *Dinner* 6.30–10.45
Closed D Sun & Bank Hols

WC2   Grimes

R **Map 27 B2**
6 Garrick Street WC2
01-836 7008

Seafood
About £45 for two
Seats 50
Parties 40
Parking Difficult
Credit Access, Amex, Diners, Visa

Seafood is the speciality of this unpretentious little restaurant that also serves a few meat dishes. Simple choices tend to be the best, from seasonal oysters and appetising platters of smoked fish to excellent fish cakes, poached salmon, and panfried Dover sole. Sauces can disappoint. The Italian-inspired tiromini was the pick of some rather unadventurous sweets. ℗

Lunch 12–3 *Dinner* 5.30–11.30
Closed L Sat, all Sun & Bank Hols

SW1   Grosvenor Hotel   61%   £B/C

H **Map 25 A6**
101 Buckingham Palace
Road SW1W 0SJ
01-834 9494
Telex 916006

Credit Access, Amex, Visa

This handsome hotel is characterised by a grand lobby with galleried landing and sweeping staircase. Bedrooms have attractively inlaid wooden furniture, stylish fabrics, good desk space and lighting and comfortable easy chairs; bathrooms boast marble effect vanity units, smart tiling, good toiletries and telephone extensions.
Amenities hairdressing, in-house movies, fax, laundry service, laundry room, 24-hour lounge service, kiosk.

| *Rooms* 360 | *Direct dial* Yes | *Confirm by* 6 | *Parking* Difficult |
| *Ensuite bath/shower* 360 | *Room TV* Yes | *Last dinner* 10 | *Room service* All day |

| W1 | **Grosvenor House   84%** | **£A** |

H Map 22 D2
Park Lane W1A 3AA
01-499 6363
Telex 24871

Rooms 466
Ensuite bath/shower 466
Direct dial Yes
Room TV Yes
Confirm by arrang.
Last dinner 11
Parking Limited
Room service 24 hours

Credit Access, Amex, Diners, Visa

Excellent service remains an outstanding feature of this Lutyens-designed hotel overlooking Hyde Park. From the top-hatted doorman and spruce page boys to reception staff and tail-coated management, everyone does a fine job, and bedrooms are properly serviced in the evening. All rooms have lobbies to eliminate corridor noise, though the public area air-conditioning intrudes in a few. There are 66 antique-furnished suites all with superbly fitted bathrooms. Day rooms include a smart, sophisticated bar. No dogs. *Amenities* indoor swimming pool, sauna, solarium, whirlpool bath, gymnasium, beauty salon, hairdressing, in-house movies, secretarial services, fax, valeting, laundry service, coffee shop (7am–10pm). &

| W1 | **The Guinea** | |

R Map 24 A3
30 Bruton Place W1
01-499 1210

Set L £12.95
About £80 *for two*
Seats 60
Parties 25
Parking Difficult
Credit Access, Amex, Diners, Visa

An intimate, busy and well-run restaurant entered through the lounge of a traditional English pub. The Aberdeen Angus beef is what most people come for – entrecôte, rump and fillet cooked to perfection by Antonio Albuquerque, who's had 17 years of practice here. Also asparagus, oysters, salmon and lobster, plus a few simple sweets. Excellent coffee rounds off a well-prepared, professionally served meal. ℗

Lunch 12.30–2.30   *Dinner* 6.30–11
Closed L Sat, all Sun, Bank Hols, 4 days Easter & 4 days Xmas

| W1 | **Guinea Grill** | |

R Map 24 A3
26 Bruton Place W1
01-629 5613

About £80 *for two*
Seats 60
Parking Difficult

Credit Access, Amex, Diners, Visa

You choose your food from a counter display just inside the entrance to this long, narrow restaurant. The choice is basically high-quality grills, including chicken, lamb and succulent prime steaks. In support are some simple starters and sweets, asparagus, smoked salmon and trout, artichoke hearts, crème caramel, fresh berry fruits. A classic wine list, still with some Haut-Brion '61 and Lafite '62.
🍷 Well-chosen ℗

Lunch 12.30–2.30   *Dinner* 6.30–11
Closed L Sat, all Sun, 25 & 26 Dec, 1 Jan

**If we recommend meals in a Hotel or Inn,
a separate entry is made for its restaurant.**

| W11 | **The Halcyon   80%** | **£A** |

HR Map 21 B4
81 Holland Park W11 3RZ
01-727 7288
Telex 266721

Rooms 44
Ensuite bath/shower 44
Direct dial Yes
Room TV Yes
Confirm by 6
Last dinner 11.30
Parking Limited
Room service 24 hours

Credit Access, Amex, Diners, Visa

Two Victorian town houses are the foundation of one of London's most luxurious and exclusive small hotels. The Belle Epoque style has been faithfully and lavishly reproduced, and the quality of design and decor is evident at every turn, with handsome period furnishings completing the authentic ensemble. If the day rooms are impressive, the bedrooms are even more so, and the suites are quite stunning. Luxury abounds, from the deep carpets and inviting armchairs to the silent air conditioning, the satellite TVs, the cosseting extras and the marvellous Italian marble bathrooms, which offer a host of pampering personal touches. No dogs. *Amenities* in-house movies, teletext, secretarial services, fax, laundry service.

Kingfisher Restaurant ♛

01-221 5411
Set L £19.25
About £60 for two
Seats 56

A fashionable and attractive restaurant beneath the hotel, with chic decor of pinks and greens, designer-smart tiled floor and a little patio for summer eating. There's an Italian feel to the surroundings, the service (under Luciano Paris) and many of James Robins's dishes, such as crab, coriander and ricotta ravioli and carpaccio with flaked parmesan. Other delights include medallions of beef with foie gras and baby turnips and some really super sweets. Wines are good, but pricey. ♀ Well-chosen ☯

Lunch 12.30–2.30   *Dinner* 7.30–11.30

Our inspectors *never* book in the name of Egon Ronay's Guides.
They disclose their identity only if they are considering an establishment
for inclusion in the next edition of the Guide.

W2 — Halepi

R **Map 22 B2**
18 Leinster Terrace W2
01-723 4097

Greek cooking
About £40 for two
Seats 70
Parking Difficult
Credit Access, Amex, Diners, Visa

Robust Greek food served in an atmosphere of bustling, often noisy, informality. You can see the chefs at work behind the illuminated food counter, preparing tasty dishes that include kebabs, grills and casseroles. Charcoal-grilled sea bass was an excellent choice on a recent visit. Start with a selection of dips and salads served with hot pitta bread, and round things off with gooey Greek sweets or fresh fruit.

Meals noon–midnight
Closed 25 & 26 Dec

EC4 — Hana-Guruma

R **Map 26 B2**
49 Bow Lane EC4
01-236 6451

Japanese cooking
Set L £25 **Set D** from £18
About £56 for two
Seats 200 *Parties* 50
Parking Difficult
Credit Access, Amex, Diners, Visa

A choice of venue greets the customer at this two-storey Japanese restaurant where the seating is divided into several different areas. Upstairs, the feel is of a traditional restaurant while downstairs informality prevails. The lunchtime menu features a choice of set dishes, following the traditional Japanese order – ideal for the novice, who is gently steered towards a well-balanced selection of dishes. Lunchtimes are busy, so booking is essential. ♿

Lunch 12–2.30   *Dinner* 6–10
Closed Sat, Sun, Bank Hols & 25 Dec–5 Jan

Changes in data sometimes occur in establishments
after the Guide goes to press.
Prices should be taken as indications rather than firm quotes.

NW1 — Harewood Hotel   58%   £C

H **Map 21 C4**
Harewood Row NW1 6SE
01-262 2707
Telex 297225

Credit Access, Amex, Diners, Visa

A six-storey purpose-built hotel next to Marylebone railway station. Public areas have been newly refurbished. Bedrooms, though mainly compact in size, feel fresh and bright, with white walls, simple functional units and pleasant fabrics. All have remote-control TVs, hairdryers and tea/coffee-makers; many have trouser presses too. Pleasing bathrooms have marble-effect tiling. No dogs.
Amenities satellite TV, in-house movies, laundry service.

Rooms 93	*Direct dial* Yes	*Confirm by* 6	*Parking* Difficult
Ensuite bath/shower 93	*Room TV* Yes	*Last dinner* 9.30	*Room service* All day

SW17   Harveys ★★   ♛ ⑨

R **Map 21 B6**
2 Bellevue Road,
Wandsworth Common SW17
01-672 0114

Lunch 12.30–2.30
Dinner 7.30–11
Set L £13.50
Set D £24
About £74 *for two*
Seats 44
Parking Ample

Credit Access, Visa
Closed L Sat, all Sun, Bank Hols
& 2 wks Xmas

Marco-Pierre White is a much talked about chef whose reputation is
amply confirmed by a visit to his charming restaurant. A deceptive
impression of freedom and spontaneity characterises his style, but
much care and thought goes into dishes like the superb caviar-beaded
poached oysters served on soft tagliatelle, or raviolis of langoustines
in basil sauce, or the tarragon-flavoured noisettes of lamb en crépinette.
Desserts, too, are marvellous. Selective list of excellent wines from
first-rate growers. ***Specialities*** tagliatelle of oysters beurre champagne, panaché of hot foie gras and sea scallops, roast pigeon from
Bresse with ravioli of wild mushrooms, biscuit glacé with hazelnut
praline and raspberry sauce. ♟ Well-chosen ⊖ ♣

NW4   Hendon Hall Hotel   65%   £C

H **Map 20 A1**
Ashley Lane NW4 1HE
01-203 3341
Telex 8956088

Credit Access, Amex, Diners, Visa

The handsome Georgian frontage stands in marked contrast to the
rather anonymous suburban setting. Inside, this is essentially a modern
hotel with elegant, relaxing day rooms and comfortable, if slightly
dated, bedrooms. Six rooms have been totally refurbished, and these
are models for the rest. The hotel has a self-contained, purpose-built
conference and banqueting suite. Helpful, smiling service. ***Amenities***
garden, in-house movies, secretarial services, laundry service.

Rooms 52	*Direct dial* Yes	*Confirm by* 6	*Parking* Ample
Ensuite bath/shower 51	*Room TV* Yes	*Last dinner* 10.30	*Room service* 24 hours

 indicates a **well-chosen** house wine

SW6   Hiders

R **Map 21 B5**
755 Fulham Road SW6
01-736 2331

Set L & D from £14.50
About £40 *for two*
Seats 65
Parties 35
Parking Ample
Credit Access, Amex, Visa

Fresh clean flavours and beautifully unfussy presentation add up to
some real treats in this quietly opulent restaurant. Simple yet elegant
dishes might include pigeon terrine served with sliced pigeon breast
and onion marmalade, and roast monkfish marinated in olive oil,
garlic and herbs. Desserts range from a tempting trio of white, milk
and bitter chocolate mousse to a steaming-hot spiced jam sponge with
crème anglaise. ♟ Well-chosen ⊖

Lunch 12.30–2.30   *Dinner* 7.30–11.30
Closed L Sat, all Sun, Bank Hols & 1 wk Xmas

SW7   Hilaire

R **Map 23 B5**
68 Old Brompton Road SW7
01-584 8993

Set L £14.50
Set D £22
About £60 *for two*
Seats 42
Parking Difficult

Credit Access, Amex, Diners, Visa

Set menus – longer and more ambitious in the evening – offer a select
choice of dishes skilfully prepared by Bryan Webb. Starters like cream
of celeriac soup, chunky game terrine with onion chutney or ravioli
of langoustines could come before calf's liver presented on a super
orange and green peppercorn sauce, or maybe pheasant with wild rice
and leeks. To finish, perhaps St. Emilion au chocolat or a tangy fruit
sorbet. The beautifully judged wine list is as strong in California and
Australia as in fine burgundy from the best growers. Excellent half-
bottles. Service flows pleasantly under charming manager Dominic
Ford. ⊃ Outstanding ♟ Well-chosen ⊖

Lunch 12.30–2.30   *Dinner* 7.30–11
Closed L Sat, all Sun & Bank Hols

W11   Hilton International Kensington   69%   £B

H Map 21 A4
179 Holland Park Avenue,
W11 4UL
01-603 3355
Telex 919763

Credit Access, Amex, Diners, Visa

High-speed lifts serve seven floors of bedrooms at this 1970s hotel, and rooms are kept secure by a computerised key system. All rooms have dispense bars, individual air conditioning and well-equipped bathrooms. Day rooms include a spacious, airy foyer-lounge. The self-service breakfast is not recommended. *Amenities* beauty salon, hairdressing, satellite TV, in-house movies, secretarial services, fax, laundry service, 24-hour lounge service, shopping arcade.

| *Rooms* 606 | *Direct dial* Yes | *Confirm by* 6 | *Parking* Ample |
| *Ensuite bath/shower* 606 | *Room TV* Yes | *Last dinner* 11 | *Room service* None |

W14   Hilton International Olympia   66%   *NEW ENTRY*   £B

H Map 21 B5
Kensington High Street
W14 8NL
01-603 3333
Telex 22229

Credit Access, Amex, Diners, Visa

Complete refurbishment has put everything in good order, from the roomy marble-floored foyer to the split-level bar-coffee shop and the bedrooms. These range from 72 singles to Plaza rooms with a separate lounge and check-in. All have the expected accessories of mini-bar, trouser press and hairdryer.
Amenities in-house movies, secretarial services, fax, laundry service, coffee shop (11am–10.30pm), kiosk.

| *Rooms* 406 | *Direct dial* Yes | *Confirm by* arrang. | *Parking* Difficult |
| *Ensuite bath/shower* 406 | *Room TV* Yes | *Last dinner* 10.30 | *Room service* 24 hours |

NW8   Hilton International Regent's Park   73%   £B

H Map 20 B3
Lodge Road, St John's Wood
NW8 7JT
01-722 7722
Telex 23101

Rooms 377
Ensuite bath/shower 377
Direct dial Yes
Room TV Yes
Confirm by 6
Last dinner 10.30
Parking Ample
Room service 24 hours

Credit Access, Amex, Diners, Visa

Formerly the Ladbroke Westmoreland, this well-run modern hotel overlooking Lord's cricket ground continues its programme of refurbishment and upgrading. There are now a greater number of de luxe 'Plaza' bedrooms (occupants enjoy guaranteed parking and express check-in) with super-comfortable beds and extras from fresh fruit to towelling robes. Standard bedrooms are being continuously upgraded,

and a majority sport chic colour schemes and smart, fitted furniture; excellent bathrooms with high-pressure showers. Public areas include a sleek modern foyer, a comfortable lounge bar and a bright new restaurant modelled on a New York deli. *Amenities* in-house movies, secretarial services, fax, laundry service, coffee shop (9.30am–11.30pm).

W1   Hilton Mews at Park Lane   71%   £A/B

H Map 22 D3
2 Stanhope Row, Park Lane
W1Y 7HE
01-493 7222
Telex 24665

Rooms 71
Ensuite bath/shower 71
Direct dial Yes
Room TV Yes
Confirm by 6
Parking Limited
Room service 24 hours

Credit Access, Amex, Diners, Visa

Yet another change of name for the Ladbroke at Park Lane, formerly the Ladbroke Curzon. This discreet modern hotel tucked away just off Park Lane underwent a £2 million face-lift some two years ago and now offers comfort and style in generous measure. A marble-floored foyer leads down to the open-plan lounge and dining area, where bleached wood furniture, chintzy fabrics and indoor plants create a pleasantly traditional effect. Air-conditioned bedrooms are compact but well designed with luxurious fabrics and equally stylish furniture. Small, marble-effect bath or shower rooms provide complimentary toiletries. There's no restaurant, but room service includes meals. No dogs. *Amenities* secretarial services, fax, laundry service.

| W11 | Hiroko of Kensington Hilton |

R Map 21 A4
Kensington Hilton Hotel,
179 Holland Park Avenue W11
01-603 5003

Japanese cooking
Set L from £8.50 Set D from £20
Seats 74 Parties 40
Parking Ample
Credit Access, Amex, Diners, Visa

A pleasantly relaxed, high-standard Japanese restaurant reached either from the street or via the Kensington Hilton Hotel. Take advice from friendly, attractive staff or plan your own meal from the sushi, sashimi and yakitori along with less familiar delights such as unajyu (grilled eel served on rice with clear soup), kaki fry (deep-fried Japanese oysters) or tonkatsu (pork cutlet). Beautifully presented fresh fruit to finish. &

Lunch 12–2.30   *Dinner* 6–10.30   **Closed** L Mon, some Bank Hols, 25 & 26 Dec & 1–4 Jan   *About £48 for two*

| SW5 | Hogarth Hotel   59% | £D |

H Map 23 A5
Hogarth Road SW5 0QQ
01-370 6831
Telex 8951994

Credit Access, Amex, Diners, Visa
Closed 3 days Xmas

A welcoming hotel with a personal feel close to the Earl's Court Exhibition Centre. The newly refurbished foyer is smart and bright, setting the cheery tone throughout. The neat bedrooms are fitted with modern units and attractive coordinating furnishings; bathrooms are compact, functional and clean. Those in single rooms have showers only. All rooms have tea/coffee-makers and hairdryers. Enthusiastic, helpful staff. **Amenities** secretarial services, fax, laundry service.

| *Rooms* 86 | *Direct dial* Yes | *Confirm by* 4 | *Parking* Limited |
| *Ensuite bath/shower* 86 | *Room TV* Yes | *Last dinner* 9 | *Room service* 24 hours |

| W1 | Hokkai |

R Map 24 B3
59 Brewer Street W1
01-734 5826

Japanese cooking
Set L from £8 Set D from £16
About £40 for two
Seats 42 Parties 16
Parking Difficult
Credit Access, Amex, Diners, Visa

Bamboo screens and paper panels form the simple, typically Japanese decor of this pleasant restaurant. The relatively short menu has been chosen to appeal to both Western and Japanese diners, the set meals offering good value. These centre round the main dish, which may be tempura, beef teriyaki or hokkai habe (a fish and vegetable stew). The rice is good and refreshing green tea is on offer.

Lunch 12.30–2.30   *Dinner* 5.30–10, Sun 6–10
Closed L Sun & 25 & 26 Dec

Changes in data sometimes occur in establishments
after the Guide goes to press.
Prices should be taken as indications rather than firm quotes.

| W1 | Holiday Inn (Marble Arch)   71% | £A |

H Map 22 C1
134 George Street W1H 6DN
01-723 1277
Telex 27983

Rooms 241
Ensuite bath/shower 241
Direct dial Yes
Room TV Yes
Confirm by 6
Last dinner midnight
Parking Ample
Room service 24 hours

Credit Access, Amex, Diners, Visa

Good news for arrivals in that there's free residents' parking in the basement of this 16-year-old hotel just north of Marble Arch. Also down below is the leisure centre, and at ground level an airy lobby lounge and cane-furnished bar. Bedrooms are appointed in smartly contemporary style, and accessories include trouser presses, hairdryers and individual temperature controls; in the bathrooms,

ample toiletries and towels. There are two floors of non-smoking rooms, and the 12th floor, comprising Club Europe rooms, has its own check-in. **Amenities** indoor swimming pool, sauna, solarium, whirlpool bath, gymnasium, beauty salon, in-house movies, secretarial services, fax, laundry service, coffee shop (7am–11.30pm). &

W1   Holiday Inn (Mayfair)   73%   £A

H Map 25 B4
3 Berkeley Street W1X 6NE
01-493 8282
Telex 24561

Rooms 186
Ensuite bath/shower 186
Direct dial Yes
Room TV Yes
Confirm by 6
Last dinner 10.30
Parking Difficult
Room service 24 hours

Credit Access, Amex, Diners, Visa

A central position just off Piccadilly is one of the strengths of the Mayfair Holiday Inn, which was converted some time ago from an office block. The reception area is bright and modern, with a welcoming feel that is not always echoed by reception staff. There's a little recessed lounge area with clusters of chairs, settees and tables, and a split-level bar-lounge. Bedrooms, the subject of a decorative update in 1988, have the usual modern conveniences of hairdryers, trouser presses, mini-bars and remote-control TVs. Compact bathrooms have functional suites and plenty of mirror surfaces.
Amenities in-house movies, secretarial services, fax, laundry service.

NW3   Holiday Inn (Swiss Cottage)   79%   £A

H Map 20 B3
128 King Henry's Road
NW3 3ST
01-722 7711
Telex 267396

Rooms 305
Ensuite bath/shower 305
Direct dial Yes
Room TV Yes
Confirm by 6
Last dinner 10.30
Parking Ample
Room service 24 hours

Credit Access, Amex, Diners, Visa

Refurbishment continues at this multi-storey hotel a short walk from Regent's Park. Polished marble now adorns the new reception, which opens into a split-level bar-lounge furnished with inviting cream leather settees and richly patterned armchairs. Spacious bedrooms – three floors are still to be redecorated – feature generous-size beds and modern units, and are equipped with mini-bars, remote-control TVs and good bathrooms with hairdryers.. High-flying executives get special treatment in luxurious top-floor suites, with lots of helpful extras. *Amenities* garden, indoor swimming pool, sauna, solarium, gymnasium, beauty salon, hairdressing, pool table, satellite TV, in-house movies, secretarial services, fax, laundry service, kiosk. &

**We welcome bona fide complaints and recommendations
on the tear-out pages at the back of the book for readers' comment.
They are followed up by our professional team.**

W2   Hospitality Inn, Bayswater   62%   £C

H Map 22 B2
104 Bayswater Road W2 3HL
01-262 4461
Telex 22667

Credit Access, Amex, Diners, Visa

A modern hotel overlooking Kensington Gardens yet conveniently located for the West End. Chandeliers and huge plants add a touch of luxury to the foyer and lounge bar, where pretty pastel furnishings create a relaxing ambience. Standard bedrooms are simply appointed and have individual air conditioning and mini-bars; de luxe rooms are more stylish and offer tiled bathrooms.
Amenities in-house movies, secretarial services, laundry service.

Rooms 175	*Direct dial* Yes	*Confirm by* 6	*Parking* Ample
Ensuite bath/shower 175	*Room TV* Yes	*Last dinner* 10.15	*Room service* 24 hours

| **W1** | **Hospitality Inn   67%   *NEW ENTRY*** | **£B** |
| | **Piccadilly** | |

H Map 27 A3
39 Coventry Street W1V 8EZ
01-930 4033
Telex 8950058

Credit Access, Amex, Diners, Visa

If Piccadilly Circus is the hub of the universe, then the Hospitality Inn must be the world's most centrally located hotel. London's day and night life unfold outside the very portals, and guests are just moments away from theatreland and countless restaurants. Double glazing ensures a good night's sleep in the decent-sized and very comfortable bedrooms, one floor of which is for non-smokers. The lobby-lounge and bar are small but stylish, with marble-tiled floors and attractive pillars. There are six conference rooms. Breakfast is no great shakes, but staff are really charming and helpful. No dogs.
Amenities in-house movies, laundry service.

Rooms 92	*Direct dial* Yes	*Confirm by* 6	*Parking* Limited
Ensuite bath/shower 92	*Room TV* Yes	*Last dinner* 11.30	*Room service* 24 hours

**We welcome bona fide complaints and recommendations
on the tear-out pages at the back of the book for readers' comment.
They are followed up by our professional team.**

| **SW3** | **L'Hotel** | **£B/C** |

PH Map 23 C4
28 Basil Street SW3 1AT
01-589 6286
Telex 919042

Credit Amex, Visa

Press the buzzer for entry to a smart little hotel near Harrods and Hyde Park. Decor is mainly in attractive country style, though the café/wine bar, where Continental breakfast is served, has a Parisian feel. Bedrooms, all twin-bedded, feature pleasant contemporary fabrics and pine furniture that is modern but in old-fashioned style. Smart, bright bathrooms are supplied with nice big towels.
Amenities laundry service, wine bar (7.30am–11pm Mon–Fri).

Rooms 12	*Direct dial* Yes	*Confirm by* arrang.	*Parking* Difficult
Ensuite bath/shower 12	*Room TV* Yes		*Room service* None

| **WC2** | **Howard Hotel   84%** | **£A** |

HR Map 24 D3
Temple Place,
Strand WC2 2PR
01-836 3555
Telex 268047

Rooms 136
Ensuite bath/shower 136
Direct dial Yes
Room TV Yes
Confirm by 6
Last dinner 11
Parking Ample
Room service 24 hours

Credit Access, Amex, Diners, Visa

Overlooking the Embankment, between Waterloo and Blackfriars bridges, this is a thoroughly modern hotel – though you might think otherwise on entering the lofty foyer-lounge with its Ionic, marble-clad columns and Adam-style friezes. Polite, efficient management is a strong point, and a friendly doorman parks your car while you check in at reception. Bedrooms feature French-style reproduction furniture, mini-bars, air conditioning with individual heating control, opulent marbled bathrooms – and three telephones. Seventh-floor suites enjoy stunning river views. Japanese businessmen love the place and are rewarded with Japanese breakfast. No dogs. *Amenities* satellite TV, in-house movies, secretarial services, fax, valeting, laundry service.

| | **Quai D'or Restaurant** | ♕ |

About £89 for two
Seats 65
Parties 200

Typically of the Howard, decorative pastiche overlays the modern fabric: here, a domed and elaborately moulded ceiling looks down on to simple picture windows. But there's nothing hybrid about Gerhard Reisepatt's long classic menu which begins with stalwarts like French onion soup and lobster bisque (soups are a speciality) and continues with sauced entrées, grills and roasts, all admirably prepared and presented. Fine wines include first-rate burgundies. ☺ ᕗ

Lunch 12.30–3, Sun 12.30–2.30
Dinner 6.30–11

SW1 — Hyatt Carlton Tower — 89% — £A

HR **Map 23 D4**
2 Cadogan Place SW1X 9PY
01-235 5411
Telex 21944

Rooms 224
Ensuite bath/shower 224
Direct dial Yes
Room TV Yes
Confirm by 6
Last dinner 11.15
Parking Ample
Room service 24 hours

Credit Access, Amex, Diners, Visa

A major improvement programme is finally completed at this luxury hotel. The Chinoiserie Lounge is splendidly opulent, with its lacquered tables and oriental objets d'art, while the new ninth-floor leisure centre enjoys spectacular panoramic views over London. Tastefully appointed bedrooms feature mini-bars, room safes and individually controlled air conditioning. Sizes vary from adequate through larger de luxes to suites, culminating in the high-security Presidential Suite. Marble-clad bathrooms offer every comfort. No dogs.
Amenities garden, sauna, solarium, steam bath, gymnasium, beauty salon, hairdressing, tennis, satellite TV, in-house movies, teletext, secretarial services, fax, valeting, laundry service, kiosk.

Chelsea Room ★ 👑👑

Lunch 12.30–2.45
Dinner 7–10.45, Sun till 10.30
Set L £19.50
Set D £32
About £95 *for two*
Seats 60
Parties 30

Recently reopened with a splendid conservatory extension and smart new pastel decor, the Chelsea Room maintains its relaxed and elegant ambience under Jean Quéro's experienced direction. Chef Bernard Gaume's well devised, imaginative menu offers treats like baked oysters sauced with green peppercorns and sorrel; red mullet bouillabaisse; and beautifully tender lamb fillet served with a flan of spinach, tomato and mushroom. Standards of cooking are occasionally uneven and sweets in particular can be disappointing. Exceptional cellar with fine clarets and burgundies. *Specialities* foie gras chaud aux baies de cassis, fricassée du turbot et homard aux champignons sauvages, fruits frais au gratin. ➪ Outstanding ♟ Well-chosen ⊜ ♿

Rib Room 👑👑

Set L £21.50
About £60 *for two*
Seats 86
Parties 14
Parking Ample

Subtle lighting, gleaming darkwood panelling and a sunken central dining area add up to a sophisticated setting for some simple but excellent eating. Superb roast rib of Aberdeen Angus beef is the main attraction, with tempting alternatives like fillet steak or mixed grill, poached salmon or scampi brochette. There's also a lavish cold seafood platter and some rather ordinary trolley sweets. Concise but interesting wine list. ♟ Well-chosen ⊜

Lunch 12.30–2.45, Sun till 2.30
Dinner 7–11.15, Sun till 10.30

We publish annually,
so make sure you use the current edition.
It's worth it!

SW1   Hyde Park Hotel   85%   £A

H Map 22 C3
66 Knightsbridge SW1Y 7LA
01-235 2000
Telex 262057

Rooms 186
Ensuite bath/shower 186
Direct dial Yes
Room TV Yes
Confirm by 6
Last dinner 11
Parking Difficult
Room service 24 hours

Credit Access, Amex, Diners, Visa

Impressive proportions and a certain Edwardian grandeur have survived at this imposing hotel which has cultivated its own special brand of luxury and elegance. The foyer with its multi-coloured marble, ornate columns, gilt mirrors and chandeliers is particularly impressive, and the day rooms have a similar tasteful opulence. Many of the bedrooms are on a grand scale, and furnished in traditional style, often with appropriate Edwardian pieces. All the suites overlook Hyde Park, and the Park Room with its panoramic view of Rotten Row is a delightful place for breakfast. *Amenities* hairdressing, satellite TV, in-house movies, secretarial services, fax, valeting, laundry service, coffee shop (7am–midnight).

We publish annually,
so make sure you use the current edition.
It's worth it!

W1   Ikeda   ♀

R Map 24 A3
30 Brook Street W1
01-629 2730

Japanese cooking
Set L from £9.50
Set D from £23
Seats 32 *Parties* 8
Parking Difficult
Credit Access, Amex, Diners, Visa

Such is the reputation of this tiny restaurant that you'll need to book well ahead just for counter space, and at least a week in advance for a table. Whether you go for sushi or sashimi or a full-scale meal, you'll enjoy wonderfully fresh, beautifully prepared food. Staff will help you select from the very traditional menu but expect a few language difficulties.

Lunch 12–2.30   *Dinner* 6.30–10.30   *About £68 for two*
Closed Sat, Sun, Bank Hols & 25 Dec–3 Jan

W1   Ikkyu

R Map 24 B2
67 Tottenham Court Road W1
01-636 9280

Japanese cooking
About £35 for two
Seats 70
Parties 40
Parking Difficult
Credit Access, Amex, Diners, Visa

It's essential to book at this busy, informal good-value basement restaurant. Friendly Japanese waitresses, with varying command of English, serve gigantic helpings; lovely raw fish salad and assorted sushi both come in two-person portions. Other more delicately-sized delights include fried tofu in ginger sauce, chicken and spring onion yakitori, and salted cuttlefish. Wash them all down with Japanese brown tea.

Lunch 12–2.30   *Dinner* 6–10.20, Sun 7–10
Closed L Sun, all Sat & 10 days Xmas

SW1   L'Incontro   *NEW ENTRY*   ♕

R Map 23 D5
87 Pimlico Road SW1
01-730 3663

Italian cooking
Set L £12.50
About £70 for two
Seats 70
Parking Limited
Credit Access, Amex, Diners Visa

A designer-chic Italian restaurant, the new venture of Gino Santini. Cool tiles set the scene, and the cliché-free menu focuses on Venetian specialities. Pasta is home-made and first rate. Fish is a favourite medium; try the fresh cuttle fish with squid ink. Freshness of ingredients, a subtle use of herbs and pure-flavoured sauces are the keynotes. Chicken is maize-fed and roast quails are served with polenta. Some fine Italian reds from the Veneto. ♟ Well-chosen ☺
&

Lunch 12.30–2.30, Sat & Sun till 3.30   *Dinner* 7–11.30, Sun till 10.30
Closed Bank Hols

WC2 — Inigo Jones ★ ♕ ⌀

R Map 27 B2
14 Garrick Street WC2
01-836 6456

Lunch 12.30–2.30
Dinner 5.30–11.30
Set L £18.25
Set D £18.25
About £105 for two
Seats 85
Parties 30
Parking Difficult

Credit Access, Amex, Diners, Visa
Closed L Sat, all Sun & Bank
Hols & 12 days Xmas

A comfortable and stylish restaurant where Paul Gayler cooks delicious dishes from the finest quality produce and presents them with care. The lunchtime menu also thoughtfully doubles for pre-theatre, from 5.30–7pm, taking account of the restaurant's position in the heart of the West End. While the menus are still interesting, they have perhaps lost a little of their excitement. Wonderful wine list: Bourgueil (Lamé) '76, Volnay Taillepieds (de Montille) '71. *Specialities* jalousie of asparagus and leeks with walnut butter; cappucino of oysters and chervil; marinaded salmon in beetroot juice with saffron-infused scallops; white chocolate and poppyseed parfait with baked figs. ⊃ Outstanding ♀ Well-chosen ⊘

W1 — Inn on the Park   89% £A

HR Map 22 D3
Hamilton Place,
Park Lane W1A 1AZ
01-499 0888
Telex 22771

Rooms 228
Ensuite bath/shower 228
Direct dial Yes
Room TV Yes
Confirm by 4
Last dinner 11.45
Parking Ample
Room service 24 hours

Credit Access, Amex, Diners, Visa

One of London's outstanding hotels, geared to today's international jet-setting business traveller. Service is superb not only in terms of quality but also in the friendliness of the well-drilled staff. Improvements are happening all the time, the latest being the addition of conservatories to the magnificent second-floor suites. All the bedrooms are models of stylish design and decor, and the bathrooms offer luxurious toiletries, huge fluffy towels and bathrobes snug enough to hibernate in. Day rooms like the panelled lounge and civilised bars provide all that could be asked in space and comfort. *Amenities* garden, satellite TV, in-house movies, secretarial services, fax, valeting, laundry service, coffee shop (noon–2am), shopping arcade. &

Four Seasons Restaurant ♕♕

Set L £18, Sun £21
Set D £25
About £85 for two
Seats 62

Good cooking and superb drinking in civilised, stylish surroundings. Game terrine with beetroot and walnut salad, feuilleté of scallops with vermouth sauce and splendid roast duck with kumquats, spices and a purée of dates and figs typify the tempting choice, and there's an 'alternative cuisine' menu with a complete luncheon counting fewer than 600 calories. The great, uncompromisingly classic cellar is strongest in Bordeaux and still has some Cheval Blanc '47. ⊃ Outstanding ⊘ 🍷 &

Lunch 12–3   *Dinner* 7–11

Lanes ♕

Set L from £19.75
Set D from £20
About £60 for two
Seats 75

Fixed-price buffet luncheons, including service, VAT and wine throughout the meal, remain a popular choice here, with a selection from the ample hors d'oeuvre table as either starter or main course. Hot dishes include grills, prime roast beef, steamed salmon and sautéed lamb. Similar evening choice, plus vegetarian, reduced-calorie and after-theatre menus. Vegetables are very good, and there's a fair selection of sweets on the trolley. ⊃ Outstanding ⊘ &

Lunch 12–3   *Dinner* 6–11.45, Sun till 11.30

| W1 | Inter-Continental Hotel   86% | £A |

HR Map 22 D3
1 Hamilton Place W1V 0QY
01-409 3131
Telex 25853

Rooms 496
Ensuite bath/shower 496
Direct dial Yes
Room TV Yes
Confirm by 6
Last dinner 11.30
Parking Ample
Room service 24 hours

Credit Access, Amex, Diners, Visa

All guests' wants are skilfully anticipated at this sophisticated modern hotel in a superb position on Hyde Park Corner. The vast, elegant foyer leads to a smart and luxurious lounge with supremely comfortable seating. Equally relaxing is the stylish Soufflé Bar where pre-dinner drinks come with a piano accompaniment, and the refurbished coffee shop with its striking Rotten Row mural. Bedrooms are most attractive, with seating areas, air-conditioning, double glazing and mini-bars. No dogs. **Amenities** sauna, solarium, whirlpool bath, steam bath, gymnasium, beauty salon, hairdressing, satellite TV, in-house movies, fax, valeting, laundry service, coffee shop (7am–midnight), shopping arcade, courtesy car. &

| Le Soufflé   ★★ | ♛♛ |

French cooking

Lunch 12.30–3, Sun 12–4
Dinner 7–11.30, Sun 7–11
Set L £21.50
Set D £34.50
About £90 *for two*
Seats 76

Closed L Sat, Good Fri, 26 Dec &
1 Jan

The decor may have changed, but Peter Kromberg's imaginative menu of splendid French dishes remains as stunning as ever. Choice is difficult, though with the set menu of beautifully contrasting dishes itself a masterpiece. Soufflés of course are superb, either as starters or sweets – ours, served with Grand Marnier cream, was exquisite. Other delights range from a delicious concoction of asparagus and smoked salmon to the tenderest duck with a rich confit. **Specialities** La grande assiette de saumon; la sole soufflé homardine aux deux caviars; le canard Gressingham, gratin de moelle de légumes; le soufflé banane aux raisins et rhum. One of London's best cellars, still with some Latour '45 and '61 and the now delicious '84 Chablis Blanchots from Laroche. ⊃ Outstanding ♀ Well-chosen ℮ &

Our inspectors *never* book in the name of Egon Ronay's Guides.
They disclose their identity only if they are considering an establishment
for inclusion in the next edition of the Guide.

| WC2 | Interlude |

R Map 27 B2
7 Bow Street WC2
01-379 6473

French cooking
Set L £19.50 **Set D** £24.50
About £80 *for two*
Seats 45 *Parties* 24
Parking Difficult
Credit Access, Amex, Diners, Visa

Handy for opera-goers, this elegant little restaurant by the Royal Opera House offers pre-performance dinners as well as fixed-price and à la carte menus. Enjoyable, beautifully presented dishes range from sweetbreads with raspberry vinegar sauce and lobster salad with broccoli confit to the tenderest pink lamb in a superb pastry case. Delicious petits fours accompany excellent coffee. Selection of fine Amagnacs going back to 1912. ♀ Well-chosen ℮

Lunch 12–2   *Dinner* 6–11.30
Closed L Sat, all Sun, Bank Hols & 3 wks Aug

N4   Jacques   ⚶

R **Map 20 D2**
130 Blackstock Road N4
01-359 3410

Set L Sun £12.60
Set D from £17
About £45 for two
Seats 44
Parking Ample
Credit Access

Jacques Herbert has invested time, money and his considerable personality in his restaurant and has reaped a just reward; his loyal following is now so large that booking is essential. His short menu offers carefully prepared dishes such as terrines with onion marmalade, herby rack of lamb and breast of duck with a rich cream and peppercorn sauce. Excellent wines at fair prices. Sunday brunch. ♀ Well-chosen ⊖

Lunch Sat 12–3, Sun till 2   *Dinner* 7–10.45
Closed L Mon–Fri, all Bank Hols, last 2 wks Aug & 10 days Xmas

W1   Jams

R **Map 25 B4**
42 Albemarle Street W1
01-493 3600

About £60 for two
Seats 95
Parties 55
Parking Difficult

Credit Access, Amex, Visa

Californian cuisine draws the in crowd to this modern restaurant just up from Piccadilly. Tip-top produce, unfussy preparation and eye-catching plating highlight interesting dishes like red pepper pancakes with salmon roe and baby sweetcorn sauce, maize-fed chicken with super French fries or grilled veal chops with wild mushrooms and a brandy cream. Pecan pie makes a splendid finale. California and France share a sound wine list. Set pre-theatre dinner available.

Lunch 12–2.30   *Dinner* 7–11
Closed L Sat, Sun & Bank Hols

SW3   Joe's Café

R **Map 23 C4**
126 Draycott Avenue SW3
01-225 2217

About £40 for two
Seats 95
Parties 20
Parking Limited

Credit Access, Amex, Diners, Visa

Fashion man Joseph Ettedgui's restaurant oozes modern chic, and the menu is an up-to-date, up-market reworking of brasserie fare. Boned quail and endive salad, baked goat's cheese en croûte, black and white tagliatelle with pine nuts and herbs, entrecôte with rock salt butter – these are typical dishes, ably prepared from the best produce. Lighter lunchtime choices include salade niçoise and salmon fish cakes. Sunday brunch. Good-quality, well-chosen wines. ♀ Well-chosen

Lunch 12–3.30   *Dinner* 7.30–11.30
Closed D Sun & 1 wk Xmas

⟹ is our symbol for an **outstanding** wine list

W1   Kaya

R **Map 27 A2**
22 Dean Street W1
01-437 6630

Korean cooking
Set L from £7 **Set D** £22
About £45 for two
Seats 70 *Parties* 45
Parking Difficult
Credit Access, Amex, Diners, Visa

Popular with the local Oriental community, Kaya is a Korean restaurant well known for its good food and friendly ambience. The menu offers a comprehensive range of starters, from bean curd fried with seaweed to spicily dressed pig's trotters and the famous preserved pickles. Many of the main courses are prepared at the table, including marinated meats and splendid pot dishes like mussels with fish, vegetables and noodles.

Lunch 12–3   *Dinner* 6–11
Closed L Sun & all 25 Dec & 1 Jan

SW1   Ken Lo's Memories of China

R **Map 25 A6**
67 Ebury Street SW1
01-730 7734

Chinese cooking

Set L from £15.50
Set D from £20.50
About £60 for two
Seats 80
Parties 20
Parking Limited

Credit Access, Amex, Diners, Visa

Coolly sophisticated decor, courteous service and a high standard of cooking are combined in one of the capital's best Chinese restaurants. A well laid-out menu combines the familiar – crispy spring rolls, hot and sour soup, Peking duck, beef in oyster sauce – with more unusual dishes such as crab meat in cabbage rolls, three-spiced salt and pepper pork choplettes and splendid quick-fried scallops, prawns and chicken in hot black bean sauce. Noodle and bean-curd dishes feature in a section of old family favourites and specialities. Sweets include glazed apples and bananas, sorbets, ice creams and lovely crispy red bean paste pancakes. ♀ Well-chosen

Lunch 12–2.30   *Dinner* 7–10.45
Closed All Sun & Bank Hols

SW10   Ken Lo's Memories of China Chelsea   *NEW ENTRY*

R **Map 21 B5** Harbour Yard,
Chelsea Harbour sw10
01-352 4953

Chinese cooking
Set meals from £25
About £60 for two
Seats 164 *Parties* 50
Parking Ample
Credit Access, Amex, Diners, Visa

Chef Tang set foot outside China for the first time to catch the opening
of Ken Lo's smart new restaurant in the glitzy Chelsea Harbour
development. His talents were immediately evident, and with two
other chefs he should help the second Memories to emulate the first.
The dishes we tried were from the temporary introductory menu –
salt and pepper pork choplettes, Cantonese lobster with ginger and
spring onion, Mongolian barbecued lamb; all really delicious! &

Lunch 12–2.30   *Dinner* 7–10.45
Closed D Sun & all Mon

Changes in data sometimes occur in establishments
after the Guide goes to press.
Prices should be taken as indications rather than firm quotes.

WC1   Kenilworth Hotel   63%   £B

H **Map 24 C2**
97 Great Russell Street
WC1B 3LB
01-637 3477
Telex 25842

Credit Access, Amex, Diners, Visa

A red-brick hotel convenient for theatres, shops and the city, and
almost next to the British Museum. It's a smart, well-run place whose
pleasant day rooms include an elegant foyer-lounge with watered silk
wall coverings, stylish curtains and a carpeted marble floor. Bedrooms,
furnished with neat, lightwood units, have good modern bathrooms
(shower rooms in singles).
Amenities in-house movies, secretarial services, fax, laundry service.

| Rooms 182 | Direct dial Yes | Confirm by 6 | Parking Ample |
| Ensuite bath/shower 182 | Room TV Yes | Last dinner 10.30 | Room service 24 hours |

NW1   Kennedy Hotel   64%   £C

H **Map 20 C3**
Cardington Street NW1 2LP
01-387 4400
Telex 28250

Credit Access, Amex, Diners, Visa

A new wing of 36 bedrooms is being built at this late-'60s hotel near
Euston Station. Existing accommodation is compact, with neat
modern decor, functional fitted units and tiled bathrooms. Tea-makers,
hairdryers and trouser presses are standard, and some rooms have
mini-bars. Plans are afoot to restyle part of the foyer and the adjoining
bar-lounge. *Amenities* patio, in-house movies, secretarial services,
laundry service.

| Rooms 361 | Direct dial Yes | Confirm by 6 | Parking Limited |
| Ensuite bath/shower 361 | Room TV Yes | Last dinner 10.30 | Room service Limited |

W8   Kensington Close Hotel   64%   £C

H **Map 23 A4**
Wright's Lane W8 5SP
01-937 8170
Telex 23914

Credit Access, Amex, Diners, Visa

Quietly tucked away behind Kensington High Street, this large red-
brick hotel features a stylishly modern open-plan restaurant-cum-
coffee-shop, and a leafy patio garden with ornamental pond and ducks.
Best bedrooms have darkwood furniture and quilted bedcovers; all
are equipped with tea-makers and radios.
Amenities garden, indoor swimming pool, sauna, solarium, gymnasium, squash, fax, laundry service, coffee shop (11am–11pm), kiosk.

| Rooms 522 | Direct dial Yes | Confirm by 6 | Parking Limited |
| Ensuite bath/shower 522 | Room TV Yes | Last dinner 10.30 | Room service None |

W8   Kensington Palace Thistle   69%   £B/C

H **Map 22 B3**
De Vere Gardens W8 5AF
01-937 8121
Telex 262422

Credit Access, Amex, Diners, Visa

Major refurbishment is nearing completion at this well-placed, stylish
hotel. Best bedrooms have pleasing views of Kensington Gardens, and
are spacious and equipped with bed settees, mini-bars, safes, hairdryers,
trouser presses and remote-control TVs. Compact bathrooms are also
well-equipped. Residents have their own intimate bar, as well as the
elegant Victorian-style Tavern. No dogs. *Amenities* in-house
movies, fax, laundry service, coffee shop (7am–11.45pm), kiosk.

| Rooms 299 | Direct dial Yes | Confirm by 6 | Parking Difficult |
| Ensuite bath/shower 299 | Room TV Yes | Last dinner 10.15 | Room service 24 hours |

W8   Kensington Place   *NEW ENTRY*

R **Map 22 A2**
201 Kensington Church
Street w8
01-727 3184

About £40 for two
Seats 90
Parties 90
Parking Limited
Credit Access, Visa

Light, modern, design-conscious and an instant success, Kensington Place is open long hours for a good choice of superior brasserie-style food. Fish soup is a blend of ancient and modern – a good rich base, a fillet of whiting, threads of vegetables, traditional trimmings – and other choices include bangers and mâche (for weightwatching pundits?), and baked tamarillo. Service is young and relaxed, cooking more than capable.   ✆

Meals 12–11.45, Sun till 10.30
Closed 3 days end Aug & 3 days Xmas

W8   Kensington Tandoori

R **Map 23 A4**
1 Abingdon Road w8
01-937 6182

Indian cooking
Set meals from £6.95
About £32 for two
Seats 76 *Parties* 30
Parking Limited
Credit Access, Amex, Diners, Visa

An imaginatively decorated Indian restaurant with tables separated by etched glass screens and planters of greenery affording some degree of privacy. A wide and familiar variety of tikkas, curries, kormas and biryanis is on offer. The thalis (meat or vegetarian) are a good choice, reflecting the general careful cooking of this establishment. Good quality Indian desserts, including an excellent gulab jam. Staff are courteous and helpful.

Meals noon–midnight
Closed 25 Dec

We welcome bona fide complaints and recommendations
on the tear-out pages at the back of the book for readers' comment.
They are followed up by our professional team.

WC1   Kingsley Hotel   63%   £B/C

H **Map 24 C2**
Bloomsbury Way wc1a 2sd
01-242 5881
Telex 21157

Credit Access, Amex, Diners, Visa

The turreted, red-brick Kingsley dates from Victorian times, and there's an agreeably traditional feel to the public rooms. Bedrooms come in two types, easily preferable being Executive rooms (the majority) with decent lightwood fitted units, pretty fabrics, hairdryers, trouser presses and bedside controls; they also get their beds turned down at night. Standard rooms and their bathrooms are considerably more basic. No dogs. *Amenities* in-house movies, laundry service.

Rooms 145	*Direct dial* Yes	*Confirm by* 6	*Parking* Difficult
Ensuite bath/shower 145	*Room TV* Yes	*Last dinner* 10	*Room service* 24 hours

SW1   Knightsbridge Green Hotel   *NEW ENTRY*   £C

PH **Map 22 3C**
159 Knightsbridge
sw1x 7pd
01-584 6274

Credit Access, Amex, Visa
Closed 5 days Xmas

A quiet, well-kept hotel, family-owned and with friendly staff. Refurbishment has smartened the reception area, the corridors and the nicely furnished bedrooms, 16 of which are suites with double room, reception room and bathroom. A Continental or full English breakfast is served in the rooms. On the first floor there's a pleasant club room with facilities for making tea or coffee. No dogs. *Amenities* fax, laundry service.

Rooms 22	*Direct dial* Yes	*Confirm by* arrang.	*Parking* Difficult
Ensuite bath/shower 22	*Room TV* Yes		*Room service* None

NW1   Koto

R **Map 20 C3**
75 Parkway nw1
01-482 2036

Japanese cooking
Set L from £6
Set D from £14
Seats 50 *Parties* 20
Parking Ample
Credit Access, Amex, Diners, Visa

The pleasures of this unpretentious Japanese restaurant range from friendly staff and good value for money to an inviting sushi bar with a helpful photographic menu. Set meals of sushi and tempura may tempt the newcomer, while the main menu offers such delights as succulent fried mackerel and deliciously fresh salmon. Deep fried beancurd makes a tasty starter, and there's a superb display of fresh fruit for afters.

Lunch 12.30–2.30   *Dinner* 6–10.30   *About £38 for two*
Closed L Sun & Bank Hols

SW1   Kundan

Map 21 C5
3 Horseferry Road SW1
01-834 3434

Indian cooking

Set L & D £10
About £35 *for two*
Seats 135
Parties 150
Parking Ample

Credit Access, Amex, Diners, Visa

Close to the Embankment and Houses of Parliament, this comfortable basement restaurant is home to some very impressive North Indian and Pakistani cooking by Aziz Khan. His menu is a fairly straightforward one, but his culinary prowess raises the restaurant way above the ordinary. Fine ingredients and sagacious use of spices are evident throughout, and dishes not to miss include the charcoal grills and the splendid Karahi Kabab Sarhadi – subtly spiced diced chicken with onions and peppers served sizzling on a cast-iron skillet. Excellent vegetables, outstanding rice and breads, milky-rich sweets. Staff are unfailingly friendly, courteous and attentive.

Lunch 12–3 *Dinner* 7–11.30
Closed Sun & Bank Hols

See INSPECTOR FOR A DAY

W1   Lal Qila   ♀

Map 24 B1
117 Tottenham Court Road
W1 01-387 5332

Indian cooking
Set L & D from £7.95
About £40 *for two*
Seats 65 *Parties* 65
Parking Limited
Credit Access, Amex, Diners, Visa

A leading light among the new generation of Indian restaurants, Lal Qila is an oasis of peace and calm amid the bustle of Tottenham Court Road. Chef Ayub Ali's aromatic, carefully spiced cooking maintains consistently high standards – whether in meat or vegetarian thalis or in specialities like tandoori trout, quail korma and lamb's brain masala. On Sundays there's a popular help-yourself buffet.

Lunch 12–3 *Dinner* 6–11.30
Closed 25 & 26 Dec

W1   Langan's Bistro

Map 24 A1
26 Devonshire Street W1
01-935 4531

French cooking
About £40 *for two*
Seats 38
Parking Difficult

Credit Access, Amex, Diners, Visa

Booking is advisable at this popular, atmospheric bistro where the unfussy menu offers a sensible number of interesting dishes. Onion marmalade does wonders for the chicken and veal terrine, which we followed with a nicely poached salmon trout served with a tasty dill sauce. Other choices include roast guinea fowl and pork with a ginger and honey sauce. Puddings are simple but good. ☻

Lunch 12.30–2.30 *Dinner* 7–11.30
Closed L Sat, all Sun & Bank Hols

W1   Langan's Brasserie   ♀

Map 25 A4
Stratton Street W1
01-491 8822

About £55 *for two*
Seats 200
Parking Limited

Credit Access, Amex, Diners, Visa

Modern art lines the walls of this informal, bustling, fashionable restaurant where you can enjoy a competently cooked meal in a lively atmosphere. There's a good variety of English and French classic dishes on the menu – starter might be artichaut farci paloise or soufflé aux épinards, with pigeon and hare pie or crevettes à la niçoise to follow. There's an imaginative list of desserts with which to finish. ☻

Lunch 12.30–2.45 *Dinner* 7–11.45, Sat 8–12.45
Closed L Sat, all Sun & Bank Hols

W1   Last Days of the Empire

Map 27 A2
42 Dean Street W1
01-439 0972

Indian cooking
About £40 *for two*
Seats 80
Parties 80
Parking Limited
Credit Access, Amex, Diners, Visa

Previously called Last Days of the Raj, this is a stylish Indian restaurant with pleasant, helpful staff and a high standard of cooking. Familiar dishes include chats and kebabs, charcoal-grilled tandoori specialities and curries based on lamb, chicken and seafood. Vegetables and breads are good, too, and for sweet you might try rasmali (curd cheese with cream and pistachios).

Lunch 12–3 *Dinner* 6–11.30
Closed 25 & 26 Dec

WC2 | Last Days of the Raj *NEW ENTRY*

R **Map 27 B1**
22 Drury Lane WC2
01-836 1628

Indian cooking
About £35 for two
Seats 50
Parties 60
Parking Limited
Credit Access, Amex, Diners, Visa

The style here is one of thoughtful authenticity, and careful cooking makes up for a slight shortage of charm. Chicken, lamb and seafood appear in a good variety of starters, tandoori dishes and curries, and specials include meat and vegetarian thalis and murgh musallam (whole baby chicken in a mild, creamy sauce). Khir – scented rice with date sugar, milk and coconut – is a delicious sweet.

Lunch 12–2.30   *Dinner* 5.30–11.30, Sun 6–11.30
Closed L Sun, L Bank Hols, 24–26 Dec

SW10 | Left Bank *NEW ENTRY*

R **Map 23 B6**
88 Ifield Road SW10
01-352 0970

Set L £8.50
Set D £12.50
About £40 for two
Seats 95 *Parties* 40
Parking Difficult
Credit Access, Amex, Diners, Visa

Owner Fernando Peire and his youthful, enthusiastic staff create a relaxed, informal atmosphere at this elegantly unfussy restaurant. Carefully cooked, imaginative dishes range from an artichoke heart with leek and almonds in puff pastry, to calf's liver in a subtle citrus fruit sauce, with excellent vegetables. Tempting sweets. Note the Clos de la Curé St Emilion '82 among good clarets. ♀ Well-chosen ℮

Lunch 12–2.30   *Dinner* 7–11
Closed L Sat & D Sun

W2 | Leinster Towers Hotel   55%   £D

H **Map 22 B2**
Leinster Gardens W2 3AU
01-262 4591
Telex 291634

Credit Access, Amex, Diners, Visa

Popular with tour operators, the Leinster Towers offers reasonable comfort at realistic prices. Housekeeping is adequate, staff are friendly and the location is both convenient and fairly quiet. 40% of the bedrooms are rather basic singles, with little shower rooms, the rest twins and doubles. There is a small bar and an airy lounge that opens onto a patio. English breakfast not for gourmets. No dogs.
Amenities in-house movies, laundry service.

| *Rooms* 163 | *Room phone* Yes | *Confirm by* 6 | *Parking* Difficult |
| *Ensuite bath/shower* 163 | *Room TV* Yes | *Last dinner* 9.30 | *Room service* None |

We publish annually,
so make sure you use the current edition.
It's worth it!

W11 | Leith's   ♔

R **Map 21 B4**
92 Kensington Park Road
W11
01-229 4481

Set D from £23.50
About £80 for two
Seats 90 *Parties* 35
Parking Limited
Credit Access, Amex, Diners, Visa

Vegetarians and meat-eaters have their own separate menus at Prue Leith's highly sophisticated restaurant. All other starters are totally eclipsed by the superb and irresistible hors d'oeuvre trolley, while main courses such as scallop and salmon sausage with asparagus, and lamb with sautéed sweet peppers and roasted garlic are imaginative and colourful. Sweets include profiteroles with the most superb chocolate sauce. Excellent coffee and petits fours to finish. ♀ Well-chosen ℮

Dinner only 7.30–11.30
Closed 2 days during Notting Hill Carnival (Aug) & 4 days Xmas

SW11 | Lena's Thai Restaurant   ♟

R **Map 21 C6**
196 Lavender Hill SW11
01-228 3735

Thai cooking
Set L from £8.50
About £30 for two
Seats 50 *Parties* 50
Parking Limited
Credit Access, Amex, Diners, Visa

A pleasant Thai restaurant which is popular in the evenings. Dishes to try include prawns and sweetcorn in a delicious potato basket; king prawns stuffed with crab meat; tom yum soup with prawns, mushrooms and lemon grass; green beef curry with coconut milk and round white baby aubergines. The house special is a mixed seafood hotpot with a gently spiced sauce. Order plenty, as portions are not large.

Lunch 12–2.45   *Dinner* 6.30–11.30, Sun 7–11.30
Closed L Sun & Mon & 3 days Xmas

W1 — Lindsay House

R **Map 27 A2**
21 Romilly Street W1
01-439 0450

English cooking
Set L £12.50
About £60 for two
Seats 35 Parties 20
Parking Difficult
Credit Access, Amex, Diners, Visa

Ring the doorbell for admission to this pleasant little restaurant where Paul Hodgson, once at Carrier's, holds sway in the kitchen. Owner Malcolm Livingston has recreated the private house style of his other restaurants, English House and English Garden, and the quintessentially British dishes include Cornish fish pie, ginger and rum junket and 'Scarlet Windsor Salad' – seasonal red fruits and vegetables topped with red Windsor cheese. ♀ Well-chosen

Lunch 12.30–2   *Dinner* 6–12, Sun 7–10
Closed 25 Dec & Good Fri

N10 — Lok-Zen

R **Map 20 C1**
138 Fortis Green Road N10
01-883 4202

Chinese cooking

About £28 for two
Seats 42
Parking Ample

Credit Access, Amex, Diners, Visa

An attractive restaurant with pretty table settings, two enormous Chinese fans and plenty of hanging greenery. Peking and Cantonese dishes feature on the menu, and the food is well-prepared from good-quality ingredients. Recommendable dishes include a delicious bang-bang chicken and cucumber, chicken satay, excellent crispy aromatic duck and drunken fish in rice wine sauce. Finish with a crisp sesame toffee banana. Book. ♀ Well-chosen

Lunch 12–2.30
Dinner 6–11.30, Sun till 11

Our inspectors *never* book in the name of Egon Ronay's Guides.
They disclose their identity only if they are considering an establishment
for inclusion in the next edition of the Guide.

W2 — London Embassy Hotel   68%   £C

H **Map 22 A2**
150 Bayswater Road W2 4RT
01-229 1212
Telex 27727

Credit Access, Amex, Diners, Visa

Good levels of accommodation and general service exist at this modern hotel, a popular choice with both business and tourist markets. On the lower floors are the standard bedrooms, above them the more stylish Executive rooms. Recent additions include a three-channel movie service and a security card key system. The bar and lounge are quite small for the hotel's capacity.
Amenities in-house movies, laundry service.

Rooms 193	Direct dial Yes	Confirm by 6	Parking Ample
Ensuite bath/shower 193	Room TV Yes	Last dinner 10.15	Room service 24 hours

W1 — London Hilton on Park Lane   84%   £A

H **Map 22 D3**
Park Lane W1A 2HH
01-493 8000
Telex 24873

Rooms 446
Ensuite bath/shower 446
Direct dial Yes
Room TV Yes
Confirm by 6
Last dinner 1am
Parking Ample
Room service 24 hours

Credit Access, Amex, Diners, Visa

A major landmark on fashionable Park Lane, this luxury high-rise hotel boasts some of London's finest views. Public rooms include a gracious, spacious lobby-lounge/coffee shop, a night club, a Victorian pub and the stylish top-floor cocktail bar. There is a brightly lit shopping arcade and, in the basement, Trader Vic's, a popular spot in Polynesian style. Tastefully appointed bedrooms have Geor-

gian-style furnishings, chintzy fabrics and up-to-the-minute accessories for maximum comfort. Marble bathrooms are also sumptuously fitted. Executive rooms (24th to 27th floors) have even more facilities, plus a separate check-in. **Amenities** sauna, solarium, hairdressing, in-house movies, secretarial services, laundry service, coffee shop (7am–2am). ㅁ

Sir Christopher Wren

Said, 'I am going to dine with some men.

If anybody calls

Say I'm designing St Pauls'.

E.C. BENTLEY 1875-1956
BIOGRAPHY FOR BEGINNERS

In carving a partridge

I splashed (Miss Markham) with gravy from head to foot;

and though I saw three distinct brown rills of animal juice

trickling down her cheek, she had the complaisance

to swear that not a drop had reached her.

Such circumstances are the triumph of civilised life.

SYDNEY SMITH 1771-1845

Cited by Pullar in
CONSUMING PASSIONS

A master cook!

why he's the man of men

For a professor; he designs, he draws,

He paints, he carves, he builds, he fortifies,

Makes citadels of curious fowl and fish.

Some he dry-ditches, some moats around with broths,

Mounts marrow bones, cuts fifty-angled custards,

Rears bulwark pies; and for his outer works,

He raiseth ramparts of immortal crust,

And teacheth all the tactics at one dinner -

What ranks, what files to put his dishes in,

The whole art military! Then he knows

The influence of the stars upon his meats,

And all their seasons, tempers and qualities;

And so to fit his relishes and sauces,

He has nature in a pot, 'bove all the chemists

Or airy brethren of the rosy cross.

He is an architect, an engineer,

A soldier, a physician, a philosopher,

A general mathematician.

BEN JONSON 1572-1637

Cited in
THE GENTLE ART OF COOKERY

W1   London Marriott Hotel   80%   £A

H **Map 22 D2**
Grosvenor Square W1A 4AW
01-493 1232
Telex 268101

Rooms 228
Ensuite bath/shower 228
Direct dial Yes
Room TV Yes
Confirm by 6
Last dinner 10.30
Parking Ample
Room service 24 hours

Credit Access, Amex, Diners, Visa

Proximity to Grosvenor Square and the American Embassy is one reason for this Georgian-style hotel's popularity with the many American business people who throng its narrow reception foyer and mezzanine public areas. There are extensive function and meeting facilities, plus a business centre. Bedrooms are all of similar style with plenty of wardrobe space, but comfort and decor somewhat disappoint in so prestigious an hotel. Suites have impressive lounges but very compact bedrooms and bathrooms. The helpfulness of the doorman is unhappily not always a reflection of the attitude of reception staff. No dogs. *Amenities* in-house movies, secretarial services, fax, valeting, laundry service, coffee shop (7.30am–2am). &

W2   London Metropole   63%   £B

H **Map 22 C1**
Edgware Road W2 1JU
01-402 4141
Telex 23711

Credit Access, Amex, Diners, Visa

Refurbished bedrooms are much to be preferred at this tower block hotel with some spectacular views from the upper floors. Newer rooms are very pleasant, with attractive colour schemes and smart units. Extras include air conditioning and direct-dial telephones. There is plenty of comfortable seating in the bar. No dogs. *Amenities* hairdressing, in-house movies, secretarial services, fax, laundry service, coffee shop (7am–11pm), kiosk.

Rooms 586	*Direct dial* Yes	*Confirm by* 6	*Parking* Ample
Ensuite bath/shower 586	*Room TV* Yes	*Last dinner* 11	*Room service* 24 hours

W8   London Tara Hotel   69%   £B/C

H **Map 23 A4**
Scarsdale Place,
Wrights Lane, Kensington W8 5SR
01-937 7211
Telex 918834

Credit Access, Amex, Diners, Visa

There's plenty of choice for guests at this vast modern hotel, from relaxing lounges to the Tingles Promenade, a colourful complex of interconnecting bars and discos. In contrast to the huge public areas, bedrooms are on the small side, but light, airy and well equipped with compact tiled bathrooms. No dogs. *Amenities* in-house movies, secretarial services, fax, laundry service, brasserie (7am–11pm). &

Rooms 831	*Direct dial* Yes	*Confirm by* 6	*Parking* Ample
Ensuite bath/shower 831	*Room TV* Yes	*Last dinner* 12.30am	*Room service* 24 hours

W1   Londonderry Hotel   84%   £A

H **Map 22 D3**
19 Old Park Lane W1Y 8AP
01-493 7292
Telex 263292

Rooms 150
Ensuite bath/shower 150
Direct dial Yes
Room TV Yes
Confirm by 6
Last dinner 11
Parking Limited
Room service 24 hours

Credit Access, Amex, Diners, Visa

The most notable point about this nine-storey hotel (rather dwarfed by its taller neighbour the Hilton) is its superb classical decor throughout. Bronze statues stand aloofly in the gracious foyer, with its highly polished marble floor and mahogany and gilt period chairs. Gilt-framed oil paintings adorn the rich burgundy brocade walls of the bar, which has the appearance of a very elegant library. Bedrooms are beautifully fitted with Italianate furniture in cream and apricot and coordinating floral fabrics; some have balconies overlooking Hyde Park. All have luxurious bathrooms with marble walls and floors, bidets and shower facilities. No dogs. *Amenities* satellite TV, in-house movies, secretarial services, fax, valeting.

**Our inspectors are our full-time employees;
they are professionally trained by us.**

SW5   Lou Pescadou   ♉

Map 23 A5
241 Old Brompton Road sw5
01-370 1057

About £35 for two
Seats 60
Parking Limited
Credit Access, Amex, Diners, Visa

There's no booking at this busy bistro-style restaurant, so arrive early or expect to be parked in the small basement bar. The menu leans firmly towards seafood, with mussels, oysters, squid and the market choice of white fish. Pizzas, omelettes and salads also appear, and everything is capably prepared and generously served. Overall, a lively, fun place with friendly French staff and decent fresh food. ☺

Lunch 12–3   *Dinner* 7–12
Closed 10 days Xmas & all Aug

SW1   The Lowndes 79%   £A

Map 23 D4
Lowndes Street sw1x 9es
01-235 6020
Telex 919065

Rooms 79
Ensuite bath/shower 79
Direct dial Yes
Room TV Yes
Confirm by 6
Last dinner 10.45
Parking Limited
Room service 24 hours

Credit Access, Amex, Diners, Visa

Standards of service are exemplary and a peaceful atmosphere prevails at this fine modern Belgravia hotel. Lofty ceilings and neoclassical decoration give a dignified feel to the marble-floored foyer and elegant lounge, while the Chinese Chippendale-style bar decorated in soft reds and golds is a delightful place to sample the Lowndes' cocktails. Personalised security cards ensure maximum safety and privacy in the immaculately appointed bedrooms, which feature luxurious furnishings and extras like mini-bars, trouser presses and fresh fruit and flowers. Bathrooms are truly sumptuous, with marble walls, deep-pile carpets, bath robes and telephone extensions. No dogs. **Amenities** in-house movies, fax, valeting, laundry service.

SE19   Luigi's

Map 7 B5
129 Gypsy Hill, Dulwich se19
01-670 1843

Italian cooking
Set L £12.50
About £45 for two
Seats 65 *Parties* 25
Parking Ample
Credit Access, Amex, Diners, Visa

A reliable Italian restaurant, cool and quite chic in black and white set off by some greenery. The menu is fairly straightforward: grilled sardines, excellent rigatoni Sicilian-style, veal with lemon and capers, a simple but delicious fritto misto of seafood. Other favourites include calf's liver (with sage or alla veneziana) and Scotch sirloin prepared as you please. The waiters, in typical Italian fashion, are more than a little extrovert.

Lunch 12–2.30   *Dinner* 6.30–11.15
Closed L Sat, all Sun, Bank Hols & Aug

SW7   Majlis

Map 23 B4
32 Gloucester Road sw7
01-584 3476

Indian cooking
Set L & D £11
About £32 for two
Seats 32 *Parties* 32
Parking Limited
Credit Access, Amex, Diners, Visa

A conventional range of Indian dishes based on lamb, chicken and prawns is well prepared and served in this small restaurant, which has the same connections as its near neighbour Memories of India. Specialities include lamb pasanda and its mild nawabi variant, chicken jhal frazi and king prawn massala. There are two different set meals available for lone diners – a thoughtful and fairly rare option. Kingfisher beer is a good accompaniment.

Lunch 12–2.30   *Dinner* 5.30–11.30
Closed 25 & 26 Dec

W8   Mandarin

Map 23 A4
197c Kensington High Street
w8   01-937 1551

Chinese cooking
Set L £10 *Set D* £15
About £39 for two
Seats 60 *Parties* 50
Parking Limited
Credit Access, Amex, Diners, Visa

Peking, Szechuan and Malaysian dishes feature on the menu of this smart basement restaurant (entrance in Allen Street). Succulent barbecued spare ribs are a reliable choice, and the chicken with cashew nuts and yellow bean sauce is equally popular. Szechuan specialities include sea-spice vegetables in a subtle tangy sauce, and there's a limited choice of sweets – toffee-glazed apples, bananas and lychees, or sorbets. Service is friendly and courteous.

Meals noon–11.30
Closed 24–26 Dec

W2   Mandarin Kitchen

R Map 22 B2
14 Queensway W2
01-727 9012

Chinese cooking
Set meals £7.50
About £35 for two
Seats 100 *Parties* 100
Parking Ample
Credit Access, Amex, Diners, Visa

Seafood is something of a speciality at this smart Chinese restaurant at the park end of Queensway. Steamed sea bass, carp with ginger and spring onions, sizzling hot king prawns in mandarin sauce are just a few of the tempting possibilities, and the hot and sour soup made with lobster meat is equally hard to resist. Cooking is sound and unpretentious, and there's plenty of choice for meat-eaters too.

Meals noon–11.30
Closed 25 & 26 Dec

W1   Mandeville Hotel   65%   £B

H Map 22 D1
Mandeville Place W1M 6BE
01-935 5599
Telex 269487

Credit Access, Amex, Diners, Visa

Conveniently situated for the West End, this modern hotel welcomes its guests into a spacious, attractive reception lounge with walls covered by modern artwork. The two bars on offer include one in a traditional pub style. Featuring cane furniture, the bedrooms – which are about to undergo refurbishment – are of uniform size and decor and incorporate modern, compact bathrooms. *Amenities* in-house movies, laundry service, coffee shop (7am–11am, noon–10.30pm).

Rooms 165	*Direct dial* Yes	*Confirm by* 6	*Parking* Difficult
Ensuite bath/shower 165	*Room TV* Yes	*Last dinner* 11	*Room service* 24 hours

WC2   Manzi's

R Map 27 A2
1 Leicester Street WC2
01-734 0224

Seafood
About £40 for two
Seats 80
Parking Difficult
Credit Access, Amex, Diners, Visa

London's oldest seafood restaurant is still a popular spot and its ground floor room is permanently bustling with voluble, extrovert waiters and with diners enjoying the atmosphere as well as the superbly fresh fish. The best dishes to choose are the simple classics such as potted shrimps, Dover sole and crab salad, but there are some steaks on the menu for meat-eaters. Finish with the fresh fruit salad. 🍷

Lunch 12–2.30   *Dinner* 5.30–11.30, Sun 6–11
Closed L Sun

WC1   Marlborough Crest   70%   £A

H Map 24 C2
Bloomsbury Street WC1B 3QD
01-636 5601
Telex 298274

Rooms 169
Ensuite bath/shower 169
Direct dial Yes
Room TV Yes
Confirm by 6
Last dinner 11.30
Parking Difficult
Room service 24 hours

Credit Access, Amex, Diners, Visa

Ideally placed close to the West End and theatreland, this elegant hotel has a very welcoming feel. Warm colours, beautiful flower arrangements and a classical theme make for a pleasing foyer where you can relax in olive green leather armchairs and settees, and there's also a quiet, intimate little residents' lounge. Lively souls can head for the brasserie, where a pianist tickles the ivories six nights a week, or the popular Duke's Head bar with its turn-of-the-century atmosphere. Bedrooms have well-coordinated decor, plenty of extras and neat bathrooms with shower facilities; superior rooms are larger. No dogs. *Amenities* in-house movies, fax, laundry service, brasserie (7am–11.30pm). ♿

EC2   Le Marmiton

R Map 26 C1
11 Blomfield Street EC2
01-588 4643

French cooking
About £45 for two
Seats 95
Parties 60
Parking Difficult

Authentic French dishes are speedily served by equally authentic French waitresses at this bustling city bistro. Choose from a short but appetising selection that includes starters like duck galantine, seafood crêpe and stuffed mushrooms, and main dishes ranging from pork medallion with Roquefort to lamb steak with garlic butter. Finish with excellent cheeses (choice of three chèvres) or a simple, familiar dessert like pear Belle Hélène. Wines include delicious '86 white burgundies. 🍷

Lunch only 12–2.45 **Closed** Sat, Sun, Easter Fri–Mon & 25 Dec–2 Jan

NW1   Martin's

R **Map 20 C3**
239 Baker Street NW1
01-935 3130

Set L from £12.50
About £55 for two
Seats 60
Parties 20
Parking Difficult
Credit Access, Amex, Diners, Visa

You'll need to book at Martin Coldicott's pretty restaurant, whose walls, menus and wine list feature the work of a talented modern artist. At work in the kitchen is Robert Hendry, who also has an artist's eye for presentation. His short, imaginative menu, boosted by a few market specials, is typified by our timbale of chicken and crab, grilled venison with sweet garlic and a very good gratin of fruit. Some fine wines, notably burgundies. 🍷 Well-chosen 🍴

Lunch 12–3, Sun 12–2   *Dinner* 6–11, Sun 6.30–10.30
Closed L Sat & Bank Hols

W1   Masako   ♕

R **Map 22 D1**
6 St Christopher's Place W1
01-935 1579

Japanese cooking
Set L £15 **Set D** £23
About £60 for two
Seats 44 *Parties* 30
Parking Difficult
Credit Access, Amex, Diners, Visa

A simple yet elegant restaurant where kimono'd waitresses serve at polished black tables and paper lanterns and screens add a delicate touch. The menu offers such dishes as sashimi, deep-fried marinated chicken, seafood and vegetable soup and beef teriyaki, with excellent o-cha tea and a good selection of fresh fruit to finish. Downstairs is a cosy sushi bar with an uncomplicated menu offering superbly fresh fish. Book at lunchtimes.

Lunch 12–2   *Dinner* 6–10
Closed Sun & Bank Hols

W1   May Fair Inter-Continental Hotel   84%   £A

HR **Map 25 A4**
Stratton Street W1A 2AN
01-629 7777
Telex 262526

Rooms 307
Ensuite bath/shower 307
Direct dial Yes
Room TV Yes
Confirm by 6
Last dinner 10.30
Parking Difficult
Room service 24 hours

Credit Access, Amex, Diners, Visa

Efficient porters and courteous staff in the elegant reception set the tone for this lovely hotel. Leather seating and antique pieces grace the small lounge area and there's an intimate, atmospheric cocktail bar. De luxe bedrooms are French style – in pale greens and beiges – or English, in dark green, rust and wine colours. Silk wallpaper, excellent fitted units hiding TVs and mini-bars, writing desks and armchairs give a feeling of luxury which is continued in the tiled bathrooms equipped with thick towels and good toiletries. No dogs.
Amenities satellite TV, in-house movies, secretarial services, fax, laundry service, coffee shop (7.30am–11pm). ♿

Le Château   ♕

Set L Sun £15.50
Set D £26
About £65 for two
Seats 65
Parties 25

The discreetly elegant restaurant is a delightful setting for Michael Coaker's skilful cooking. There's a gourmet menu and an à la carte offering a thoughtful selection of dishes from which to choose; good fresh ingredients are handled with flair to produce such delights as turbot steak sprinkled with peppercorns in a light ginger sauce and fillets of sea bass in hot spices. Good classic wine list. 🍷 Well-chosen
🍴 ♿

Lunch 12.30–2.30, Sun 12–2.30   *Dinner* 6.30–10.30
Closed L Sat

Changes in data sometimes occur in establishments
after the Guide goes to press.
Prices should be taken as indications rather than firm quotes.

SW1	Le Mazarin ★	👑 ⑂

R Map 21 C5
30 Winchester Street SW1
01-828 3366

French cooking

Dinner only 7–11.30
Set D from £19.50
About £53 for two
Seats 50
Parties 50
Parking Limited

Credit Access, Amex, Diners, Visa
Closed Sun, Bank Hols & 1 wk
Xmas

Delicate pink walls and soft, discreet lighting create a pleasantly intimate atmosphere for enjoying the refined talents of chef René Bajard. His French menus (three-course table d'hôte or five-course gastronomique) offer a succession of delights, from foie gras with Perigord truffles right through to a ramekin of strawberries in red wine. Service is very polished and professional. There are some good French wines, but the reds are sometimes absurdly young (Hermitage La Chapelle '86!).
Specialities éventail de magret fumé de canard au vinaigre de framboises; médaillons de homard sauce Nantua et ses petits primeurs; tranchettes d'onglet poêlé aux échalotes; délice aux deux chocolats et sa crème anglaise à la menthe fraîche. 🍷 Well-chosen ꝏ

SW7	Memories of India

R Map 23 B4
18 Gloucester Road SW7
01-589 6450
Indian cooking
Set L & D £11
About £32 for two
Seats 50 *Parties* 50
Parking Limited
Credit Access, Amex, Diners, Visa

Behind the dark glass window is a cosy, dimly-lit interior, opening on to a little patio at the back. Enjoyably prepared dishes range through the chicken, lamb and seafood repertoires, including a splendidly fiery chicken vindaloo and specialities like lamb pasanda and charcoal-grilled king prawns. Good vegetable dishes, too, such as fresh greens cooked in butter and spices; and classic desserts like kulfi and guleb jamon. Note the useful set meal for one.

Lunch noon–2.30   *Dinner* 5.30–11.30
Closed 25 & 26 Dec

★ For a *discount* on next year's guide, see **An Offer for Answers.** ★

SW3	Ménage à Trois

R Map 23 C4
15 Beauchamp Place SW3
01-589 4252

About £55 for two
Seats 72
Parties 35
Parking Difficult

Credit Access, Amex, Diners, Visa

Befores and afters are the stock in trade of this fashionable basement restaurant offering modern, inventive cooking. Many of the dishes have a trio theme: cheesy pastry parcels, shellfish soups, salads of raw beef, duck foie gras, magret and crackling, chocolate terrine, truffle and ice cream. Pasta, lobster and caviar are other favourites. A superb wine list includes wonderful Cabernets from California (Ridge, Heitz, Mondavi, Phelps). ➥ Outstanding 🍷 Well-chosen ꝏ

Lunch 12–3   *Dinner* 7–12.15, Sun 7–11
Closed L Sat & Sun, all Good Fri, 25 & 26 Dec

W1	Le Meridien Piccadilly 84%	£A

HR Map 25 B4
Piccadilly W1V 0BH
01-734 8000
Telex 25795

Rooms 284
Ensuite bath/shower 284
Direct dial Yes
Room TV Yes
Confirm by 6
Last dinner 11.20
Parking Valet
Room service 24 hours

Credit Access, Amex, Diners, Visa

Superb public areas make the greatest impression at this lavishly refurbished old hotel only a stone's throw from Piccadilly Circus. The marble entrance hall leads to a glass domed and galleried reception, and there is an ornately panelled lounge and a clubby dark green cocktail bar. The luxurious leisure complex in the basement also houses a splendid drawing room cum library. Pleasant bedrooms have quality

furnishings, many extras, and smart, well-stocked, marble-clad bathrooms. *Amenities* indoor swimming pool, sauna, solarium, whirlpool bath, gymnasium, beauty salon, hairdressing, squash, billiards, snooker, satellite TV, in-house movies, fax, valeting, laundry service, coffee shop (7am–11.30pm), kiosk. ♿   *see over*

Oak Room ★ ♛♛♛

French cooking

Lunch 12–2.30
Dinner 7–10
Set L £17.50
Set D from £26
About £85 *for two*
Seats 50
Parties 10

Closed L Sat, all Sun & Bank Hols

An elaborate ceiling, Venetian chandeliers, and limed oak panelling make this one of the most spectacular dining rooms in London. David Chambers' high-class French menus – created in association with a top French chef – are equally impressive, with skilled saucing giving a touch of distinction to such dishes as the excellent rosette de boeuf, and aiguillettes de canard. Sophisticated desserts come with a par-

ticularly enjoyable sauce anglaise. The wine list, though sporting some good bottles, could be improved and expanded.
Specialities le gaspacho de langoustine à la crème de courgettes, cassolette de homard aux asperges vertes, galette de jeune pigeon et pois gourmands. ♟ Well-chosen ⊖ 🐾 ♿

EC1   **Le Mesurier**   *NEW ENTRY*   ♨

R Map 20 D3
113 Old Street EC1
01-251 8117

About £45 *for two*
Seats 25
Parties 25
Parking Difficult

Credit Access, Visa

Gillian Enthoven only opens her tiny Clerkenwell restaurant Monday to Friday lunchtimes, and it's very advisable to book. Her menu is short but imaginative, her cooking very skilled, with marvellous flavours and delightful presentation. A typical meal could comprise delicate chicken quenelles with a lobster flavoured sauce, medallions of veal with lemon and a light-as-a-feather hazelnut meringue with strawberries. ⊖

Lunch Mon–Fri only 12–3
Closed Sat, Sun, Bank Hols, 3 wks Aug & 1 wk Xmas

Our inspectors *never* book in the name of Egon Ronay's Guides.
They disclose their identity only if they are considering an establishment
for inclusion in the next edition of the Guide.

SW1   **Mijanou**   ♨

R Map 23 D5
143 Ebury Street SW1
01-730 4099

French cooking
Set L £12.50 **Set D** from £21.50
About £55 *for two*
Seats 30 *Parties* 24
Parking Difficult
Credit Access, Amex, Diners, Visa

Two little rooms, one strictly for non-smokers, make a pleasantly intimate setting for enjoying Sonia Blech's very accomplished cooking. Flavours are fresh and pure, sauces superb in dishes such as lobster terrine with lemon grass and cognac, duck foie gras in puff pastry with red and white grapes, or tournedos with wild mushrooms. Neville Blech is a most civilised host, and the fine food is accompanied by superb wines. ⊂ Outstanding ♟ Well-chosen ⊖

Lunch 12.30–2   *Dinner* 7.30–11
Closed Sat, Sun, Bank Hols, 1 wk Easter, 3 wks Aug & 2 wks Xmas

---

W1   **Ming**   *NEW ENTRY*

R Map 27 A2
35 Greek Street W1
01-734 2721

Chinese cooking
Set L & D from £7.50
About £35 *for two*
Seats 70
Parties 24
Parking Difficult

Credit Access, Amex, Diners, Visa

The cuisine at this stylish corner restaurant is mainly from Peking and Canton, with a little Szechuan to spice things up. One of the most popular orders is Mongolian lamb, crisply cooked and wrapped in lettuce leaves. The choice includes familiar dishes like sweet and sour pork or beef in oyster sauce and also more arcane chef's specials such as duck's web with fish lips, fried chicken with jellyfish, and banana-flavoured crispy seafood rolls. Joint-owner Mr Ha, formerly with Ken Lo at Memories of China, is a very capable chef, and his serving staff are particularly friendly and helpful.

Meals noon–11.45, Fri & Sat noon–midnight
Closed 25 & 26 Dec

W1   Mr Kai

R **Map 22 D2**
65 South Audley Street,
Mayfair W1
01-493 8988

Chinese cooking
About £50 for two
Seats 120 *Parties* 70
Parking Limited
Credit Access, Amex, Diners, Visa

Flamboyant dish descriptions add to the fun at this stylish Chinese restaurant with a mainly Pekinese menu. Cooking is reliable throughout the range, from the 'Bones of the Mayfair Dragon' (barbecued spare ribs) to drunken fish, prawns with green peppers, deep-fried aromatic duck (a speciality) and shredded beef with oyster sauce. Finish perhaps with 'Mr Kai's Fruit Mountain' or red bean paste pancakes.

Lunch 12–2.30   *Dinner* 7–11.30
Closed Bank Hols.

WC2   Mr Kong   *NEW ENTRY*   ♀

R **Map 27 A2**
21 Lisle Street WC2
01-437 7341

Chinese cooking
Set D from £6.80
About £30 for two
Seats 110
Parking Limited
Credit Access, Amex, Diners, Visa

Mr Kong and his partner Mr Lo share the cooking at this bright, attractive and friendly Chinese restaurant, whose extensive, largely Cantonese menu is extended still further by daily specials. The latter could include interesting treatments of eel and venison or – a dish we enjoyed enormously – tender nuggets of chicken and beef, quick-fried and served with a splendid sauce and fresh mango. Orange quarters for a refreshing finish. First-class cooking. ♀ Well-chosen &

Meals noon–1.45am
Closed 4 days Xmas

W1   Miyama

R **Map 25 A4**
38 Clarges Street W1
01-499 2443

Japanese cooking
Set L from £6.80
Set D £23
Seats 65 *Parties* 10
Parking Difficult
Credit Access, Amex, Diners, Visa

Booking is very advisable at this popular Japanese resturant, whose plain white decor has a cool, modern elegance. Set meals are a good idea for the uninitiated, while those who feel confident with the à la carte can choose from a varied selection that includes sashimi, tempura, teriyaki and some specialities which are prepared at the table. Quite expensive, but the food is good and the service exemplary.

Lunch 12.30–2.30   *Dinner* 6.30–10.30   *About £70 for two*
Closed L Sat, all Sun & Bank Hols

Any person using our name to obtain free hospitality is a fraud.
Proprietors, please inform the police and us.

SW3   Monkeys   *NEW ENTRY*   ♀

R **Map 23 C5**
1 Cale Street, Chelsea Green
SW3
01-352 4711

Set L £13.50
Set D £17.50
About £50 for two
Seats 35 *Parties* 12
Parking Difficult

A splendid little restaurant with well-spaced tables, pine panelling and a veritable colony of monkey prints and paintings. Monkeys' business includes game birds, cooked to perfection and served with the traditional trimmings. Besides grouse, pheasant and partridge you could find more unusual winged things such as ptarmigan, teal, widgeon and woodcock. Ungamy main courses run from steamed scallops with ginger to grilled contrefilet, with roasts on Sunday. Salad of spinach, straw potatoes and pigeon breast makes a lovely starter, and hot treacle tart, served with cream, ice cream or *real* custard, is a prince among puddings. There are some excellent wines, including fine old Rhônes and clarets. ♀ Well-chosen ⊕

Lunch 12.30–2.30   *Dinner* 7.30–11.30
Closed Sat, Sun, 25 & 26 Dec, 23 Mar–10 Apr & 3 wks Aug

W11   Monsieur Thompsons

R **Map 21 B4**
29 Kensington Park Road
W11   01-727 9957

French cooking
Set L £13.50 **Set D** £14.50
About £50 for two
Seats 55 *Parties* 35
Parking Difficult
Credit Access, Amex, Diners, Visa

Modern French cooking in cheerful, informal surroundings. The menu is short but quite varied, typical choices running from snails with a puff-pastry case and a crunchy mini-ratatouille to brill with cauliflower and beetroot sauce, beef bordelaise and duck breast with lychees and ginger. Sorbets and ice creams; cheese from Androuet. The food is well prepared and attractively plated, but service is sometimes rather casual and inattentive.

Lunch 12.30–2.30   *Dinner* 7.30–10.30
Closed Bank Hols & 10 days Xmas

W1   The Montcalm   77%   £A

H **Map 22 D1**
Great Cumberland Place
W1A 2LF
01-402 4288
Telex 28710

Rooms 114
Ensuite bath/shower 114
Direct dial Yes
Room TV Yes
Confirm by 6
Last dinner 10
Parking Ample
Room service 24 hours

Credit Access, Amex, Diners, Visa

Impeccable service keeps this discreetly luxurious hotel in the premier class, for staff under general manager Jonathan Orr Ewing's expert direction are unfailingly courteous, helpful and efficient. Another great plus is the location, in an attractive and surprisingly quiet Georgian crescent only two minutes' walk from Marble Arch. Decor throughout is smartly contemporary (lots of dark leather armchairs and glass-topped tables) though this is supplemented in the open-plan lounge and bar areas by some elegant French-style pieces. Prettily coordinated bedrooms range from well-equipped standard through more luxurious studios to sumptuous split-level suites.
Amenities in-house movies, secretarial services, fax, laundry service.

W2   Mornington Hotel   63%   £D

H **Map 22 B2**
12 Lancaster Gate W2 3LG
01-262 7361
Telex 24281

Credit Access, Amex, Diners, Visa
Closed 10 days Xmas

Friendly, efficient service is the hallmark of this Swedish-run hotel near Kensington Gardens. A real feeling of homeliness is created by its small-scale public areas which feature a mahogany-panelled foyer-lounge and a genuinely attractive library-style bar. Most bedrooms have been refurbished in clean pastel shades and incorporate well-designed furniture and modern bathrooms. Scandinavian-style breakfast. *Amenities* sauna, laundry service.

| *Rooms* 70 | *Direct dial* Yes | *Confirm by* arrang. | *Parking* Limited |
| *Ensuite bath/shower* 70 | *Room TV* Yes | *Last dinner* None | *Room service* None |

W1   Mostyn Hotel   65%   £B/C

H **Map 22 D2**
Bryanston Street W1H 0DE
01-935 2361
Telex 27656

Credit Access, Amex, Diners, Visa

Redecoration is keeping the Mostyn in good order, and further improvements have taken place during 1988. Staff are smart and welcoming, and general standards of comfort and housekeeping are good. Bedrooms and bathrooms vary considerably in size; room service is efficient, and care has been taken to provide good towels and toiletries. The marble foyer impresses among the day rooms.
Amenities in-house movies, secretarial services, laundry service.

| *Rooms* 123 | *Direct dial* Yes | *Confirm by* 6 | *Parking* Ample |
| *Ensuite bath/shower* 123 | *Room TV* Yes | *Last dinner* 9.30 | *Room service* 24 hours |

SW1   Motcombs

R **Map 23 D4**
26 Motcomb Street SW1
01-235 6382

About £50 for two
Seats 70
Parties 16
Parking Limited

Credit Access, Amex, Diners, Visa

Smooth, professional service is combined with warm-hearted Italian friendliness at this smart, clubby restaurant where prime meat, fresh fish and carefully chosen vegetables are competently handled. The simplest dishes, such as grilled sea bass, smoked chicken and châteaubriand, are the most successful and the grilled calf's liver with bacon is particularly good. Vegetables are full of flavour and sweets and coffee are delicious. ♥ Well-chosen ⊕

Lunch 12–3   *Dinner* 7–11
Closed All Sun, Bank Hols, D 24 Dec & all 25 & 26 Dec

W1   Mount Royal Hotel   58%   £C

H **Map 22 D2**
Marble Arch W1A 4UR
01-629 8040
Telex 23355

Credit Access, Amex, Diners, Visa

1988 saw the start of an overall refurbishment programme at this large hotel on a prime site among the West End shops. Public areas can be extremely busy, and it is a relief to reach the bedrooms, where there is room to sit in comfort or write at a desk. Large bathrooms have tubs and showers. No dogs.
Amenities hairdressing, laundry service, coffee shop (7am–11.30pm), kiosk.

| *Rooms* 700 | *Direct dial* Yes | *Confirm by* 6 | *Parking* Ample |
| *Ensuite bath/shower* 700 | *Room TV* Yes | *Last dinner* 9.30 | *Room service* Limited |

WC2   Mountbatten Hotel   74%   £A

H **Map 27 B2**
Seven Dials,
Covent Garden WC2H 9HD
01-836 4300
Telex 298087

Rooms 127
Ensuite bath/shower 127
Direct dial Yes
Room TV Yes
Confirm by 6
Last dinner 10.30
Parking Difficult
Room service 24 hours

Credit Access, Amex, Diners, Visa
Closed 2 days Xmas

A stylish hotel in the heart of Covent Garden that's dedicated to the memory of the late Lord Mountbatten. There's an impressive foyer, resplendent with Italian marble, and a luxurious drawing room boasting chandeliers, deep sofas and framed reproductions of paintings from the Mountbatten family home. A pianist adds a soothing touch to the polo-themed cocktail bar, while the restaurant takes its inspiration from His Lordship's days in Burma. Double-glazed bedrooms have pretty soft furnishings and are thoughtfully equipped, though singles are rather small. Super marble-clad bathrooms, with whirlpool baths in suites. One floor is non-smoking.
Amenities satellite TV, in-house movies, fax, laundry service.

W1   Le Muscadet

R **Map 22 D1**
25 Paddington Street W1
01-935 2883

French cooking
About £42 for two
Seats 30
Parking Difficult
Credit Access, Visa

An exceptionally friendly little restaurant just off Baker Street. Cooking is robust French provincial, portions (with the exception of vegetables) are generous and daily specials in particular are full of interest. Start perhaps with a well-seasoned asparagus soup, then move on to creamy chicken vol-au-vent or hearty cassoulet, leaving room for the excellent cheeseboard. Our puddings came from a local pâtisserie. ⊖

Lunch 12.15–2.30   *Dinner* 7.15–11, Sat 7.15–10
Closed L Sat, all Sun, Bank Hols, 3 wks Aug & 10 days Xmas

W1   Nakamura   *NEW ENTRY*

R **Map 22 D1**
31 Marylebone Lane W1
01-935 2931

Japanese cooking
Set L from £6.50
About £60 for two
Seats 58 *Parties* 30
Parking Difficult
Credit Access, Amex, Diners, Visa

Screens, tables and chairs in pale wood are set against white walls in this simply but quietly stylish Japanese restaurant. Sit at the sushi bar and watch sushi and sashimi being prepared or descend the narrow spiral staircase to sample set lunches or select from the comprehensive à la carte menu. The tempura is notable for its crisp, light batter and we also enjoyed the sukiyaki.

Lunch 12–2.30   *Dinner* 6–10.30, Sun till 10
Closed L Sun, all Sat & Bank Hols

SW7   Nanyang

R **Map 23 B4**
112 Cromwell Road SW7
01-370 0803

Chinese cooking
Set L £4.95 *Set D* £11.50
About £34 for two
Seats 80 *Parties* 50
Parking Difficult
Credit Access, Amex, Diners, Visa

A comfortable, modern Chinese restaurant with unfussy decor and some pleasing greenery. The long menu draws on Szechuan and Singapore cuisine, with spicy hot dishes thoughtfully marked with a warning flame. Fresh flavours and light sauces are much in evidence, and the meals are very enjoyable. Familiar dishes include bang-bang chicken, pork dumplings, prawns with ginger and spring onions and above-average crispy aromatic duck. Good vegetables.

Lunch 12.30–2.30
Dinner 6–11.45

WC2   Neal Street Restaurant

R **Map 27 B2**
26 Neal Street WC2
01-836 8368

About £65 for two
Seats 70
Parties 65
Parking Difficult

Credit Access, Amex, Diners, Visa

The menu is full of interest at Antonio Carluccio's chic modern restaurant, ranging from good simple things like scrambled eggs with smoked eel to mushroom specialities such as game ravioloni (*sic*) with wild mushroom sauce, baccalà with porcini and polenta, and borlotti beans with cèpes. Ingredients are tiptop, cooking sound, and presentation most attractive. Excellent house wines from Sicily and a powerful showing of fine Italian reds. Book. ⬛ Well-chosen ⊖ 🍷 ⅙

Lunch 12.30–2.30   *Dinner* 7.30–11
Closed Sat, Sun, Bank Hols & 1 wk Xmas

WC2　　　　　　　New Diamond　*NEW ENTRY*

R Map 27 A2
23 Lisle Street WC2
01-437 2517

Chinese cooking
Set D from £14 for two
About £25 for two
Seats 100
Parking Difficult
Credit Access, Diners, Visa

A Chinatown restaurant popular not only for its good food but also for service that works well and stays polite even at the busiest times. Steamed scallops, spicy salted squid and sizzling eel in black bean sauce are part of a good seafood choice, while meat-eaters will find plenty of fairly similar variations on duck, chicken, beef and pork. Lamb appears in one of the excellent hot pot dishes.

Meals 3–3
Closed 25, 26 & 27 Dec

W5　　　　　　　New Leaf　　　　　　　　　　　　　　　♀

R Map 7 A4
35 Bond Street, Ealing W5
01-567 2343

Chinese cooking
Set meals from £8
About £30 for two
Seats 90 *Parties* 40
Parking Ample
Credit Access, Amex, Visa

This popular Chinese restaurant is now in the very capable hands of front-of-house manager Henry Soon and his chef-partner Mr Chan. Although the decor has been refurbished, there are no plans to change the menu of largely Cantonese dishes, which includes such firm favourites as perfectly steamed plump scallops and superb fried shredded beef.

Lunch 12–2.15　*Dinner* 6–11.30
Closed L Sun & all 25 & 26 Dec

WC2　　　　　　　New Shu Shan

R Map 27 A2
36 Cranbourn Street, WC2
01-836 7501

Chinese cooking
Set meals from £7
About £32 for two
Seats 70
Parking Limited
Credit Access, Amex, Diners, Visa

A friendly, family-run Chinese restaurant with simple decor and a menu mainly of Cantonese and Szechuan dishes (the latter printed in warning red). Dishes come to the table freshly prepared and full of good flavours; hot and sour soup is packed with all the proper ingredients, and the lemon chicken is exceptionally good; red bean pancakes are a must for dessert. The tea is also excellent.

Meals noon–midnight
Closed 25 & 26 Dec

Our inspectors are our full-time employees;
they are professionally trained by us.

W1　　　　　　　Ninety Park Lane　　　　　　　♛♛

R Map 22 D2
90 Park Lane W1
01-409 1290

French cooking
Set D from £33
About £102 for two
Seats 80
Parking Ample
Credit Access, Amex, Diners, Visa

Luxury is the keynote for both the sumptuous surroundings and the food. Stephen Goodlad applies modern touches to classic skills on a menu that tempts with escalope of foie gras with lentils, peas and Calvados, baby sole soufflé perfumed with tarragon and lamb with Lyon sausage and lemon balm. Service is of a high order – smart, attentive and very professional. Note Hermitage La Chapelle '61, Latour '59 and Lafite '45 on a fine wine list. ⌔ Outstanding 🅔 🍴

Lunch 12–2.30　*Dinner* 7.30–10.45
Closed L Sat, all Sun & Bank Hols

SW7　　　　　　Norfolk Hotel　69%　　　　　　£A

H Map 23 B4
Harrington Road SW7 3ER
01-589 8191
Telex 268852

Credit Access, Amex, Diners, Visa

A smart, friendly doorman sets the pleasant, welcoming tone that runs through this well-managed South Kensington hotel. A cosy little lounge is tucked under the sweep of the cantilevered staircase in the foyer, and there are various other areas to unwind, including a quiet cocktail bar, a panelled pub bar and a basement coffee shop/wine bar. Bedrooms, all with attractive lightwood reproductive furnishings, range from singles with showers only to suites and studios. The usual accessories are to hand, and all but the singles boast whirlpool baths. Duvets are standard, but sheets and blankets are available on request. No dogs. *Amenities* sauna, solarium, gymnasium, in-house movies, secretarial services, fax, laundry service, coffee shop (10am–11pm).

Rooms 97	Direct dial Yes	Confirm by 6	Parking Limited
Ensuite bath/shower 97	Room TV Yes	Last dinner 10.30	Room service 24 hours

W6 — Novotel London 65% — £C/D

H **Map 21 A5**
1 Shortlands, Hammersmith
W6 8DR
01-741 1555
Telex 934539

Credit Access, Amex, Diners, Visa

A large modern hotel beside Hammersmith flyover. The carpeted foyer is a lively concourse leading to service shops and an in-house business centre. There's also a lounge area and pub-style bar. Air-conditioned and double-glazed bedrooms with rather austere furnishings offer practical fitted units, neat bathrooms and mini-bars. *Amenities* hairdressing, in-house movies, secretarial services, laundry service, laundry room, coffee shop (6.30am–midnight), kiosk. &

Rooms 633	*Direct dial* Yes	*Confirm by* 7	*Parking* Ample
Ensuite bath/shower 633	*Room TV* Yes	*Last dinner* 12	*Room service* All day

SW7 — Number Sixteen — £B/C

PH **Map 23 B5**
16 Sumner Place SW7 3EG
01-589 5232
Telex 266638

Credit Access, Amex, Diners, Visa

Four town houses have been turned into a delightful hotel offering comfort and personal service. The restful lounge features antiques, fine fabrics and tasteful colour schemes, and there's a small bar. Hairdryers, fridges, sewing kits and fresh flowers are found in the bedrooms, some of which have little terraces leading to the garden and conservatory. Continental breakfast is served in the rooms. No children under 12. *Amenities* garden, fax, laundry service.

Rooms 32	*Direct dial* Yes	*Confirm by* arrang.	*Parking* Difficult
Ensuite bath/shower 32	*Room TV* Yes		*Room service* All day

NW1 — Odette's

R **Map 20 C3**
130 Regent's Park Road NW1
01-586 5486

About £50 for two
Seats 55
Parties 25
Parking Limited
Credit Access, Amex, Diners, Visa

Chef John Armstrong continues in fine and confident form at this elegant and richly appointed restaurant. Drawing on the cooking traditions of various countries, he has developed a boldly individual style. Regularly changing menus feature flavoursome delights like rabbit and pheasant terrine with bitter orange sauce and hot brioche, followed by fillet of beef with bone marrow and its own rich sauce. Excellent desserts include iced chocolate pudding. ☯

Lunch 12.30–2.30   *Dinner* 7.30–11
Closed L Sat, all Sun, Bank Hols, 2 wks Aug & 10 days Xmas

W1 — Odins ★ ♕

R **Map 24 A1**
27 Devonshire Street W1
01-935 7296

Lunch 12.30–2.30
Dinner 7–11.30
About £70 for two
Seats 60
Parties 8
Parking Difficult

Credit Access, Amex, Diners, Visa
Closed L Sat, all Sun & Bank Hols

A remarkable collection of paintings and prints is the outstanding decorative element of this elegant, softly lit restaurant. Chef Chris German continues in splendid form, his innovative, well conceived menus combining plenty of imagination with a pleasing simplicity. Starters might include beautifully fresh poached monkfish with butter sauce followed by sweet, tender young roast lamb with a delicate

spinach mousse. Vegetables, too, are impeccable, and sweets are a particular strength. A well balanced wine list features some excellent burgundies and Rhônes. *Specialities* guinea-fowl terrine with onion marmalade; medallion of venison with port and juniper sauce; poached pear with amaretto sauce. ☕ Well-chosen ☯

W1 — One Two Three

R **Map 24 A3**
27 Davies Street W1
01-409 0750

Japanese cooking
Set L from £8.50
Set D from £23
Seats 50 *Parties* 50
Parking Limited
Credit Access, Amex, Diners, Visa

A simple but stylish Mayfair restaurant where the tables are separated by delicate screens to give privacy and the Japanese food is expertly cooked. Presentation is beautiful and the service is charming and attentive. Try the tempura – excellent deep-fried courgettes, carrot and white fish – and sashimi, featuring raw salmon, turbot and cuttlefish with delicious dips and sauces. A popular belly pork long-simmered in sake is particularly good.

Lunch 12–2.30   *Dinner* 6.30–10.30   *About £50 for two*
Closed Sat, Sun, Bank Hols & 24 Dec–5 Jan

W11 192 *NEW ENTRY*

R Map 21 B4
192 Kensington Park Road
W11
01-229 0482

About £40 for two

Credit Access, Amex, Diners, Visa

Angela Dwyer in the kitchen and Androna Calles front of house are proving an excellent partnership at this popular, stylish place. The menu changes with every meal, providing plenty of interest with dishes as diverse as tataki of tuna with Japanese garnishes, brawn with sauce ravigote and pot-roasted leg of lamb with aromatic vegetables. Nice sweets, too, and sound wines with many available by the glass. ♥ Well-chosen ©

Lunch 12.30–3.30, Sun 1–3.30 *Dinner* 7.30–11.30
Closed D Sun, Bank Hols & 1 wk Xmas

EC4 Oscar's

R Map 26 A2
5 Temple Avenue,
Temple Chambers EC4
01-353 6272

French cooking
About £48 for two
Seats 40 *Parties* 35
Parking Limited
Credit Access, Amex, Diners, Visa

A popular, family-run restaurant where booking is advisable at lunchtimes. Grace Skelton dispenses charm and efficiency front of house while Jose Antonio brings a confident touch to both ambitious and simple dishes in the kitchen. Raw materials are of the highest quality and fresh fish plays a large part on the menu – ask for the daily specials. Precisely cooked vegetables and well-judged sauces contribute to an excellent meal. ©

Lunch 12–3 *Dinner* 6.30–9.30
Closed Sat, Sun, Bank Hols, 10 days Xmas & 3 wks Aug

SW6 Otters *NEW ENTRY*

R Map 21 B6
271 New Kings Road SW6
01-371 0434

Set L £6.95, Sun £12.95
About £42 for two
Seats 54
Parking Limited

Credit Access, Amex, Diners, Visa

A serious and smart new addition to the Fulham restaurant scene. Adventurous ideas and combinations such as rack of lamb with Dijon mustard, golden syrup and ground hazelnuts, or noisette of monkfish with green peppercorns and black grape sauce typify the style. Not all the dishes are equally successful but it's fun to delve into the menu and join the adventure. Short good wine list: Morgon Domaine La Chanaise '85; Ch. Léoville Poyferré '78.

Lunch 12–3, Sun till 2.30 *Dinner* 7–11
Closed D Sun

W1 Park Lane Hotel 80% £A

HR Map 25 A4
Piccadilly W1Y 8BX
01-499 6321
Telex 21533

Rooms 323
Ensuite bath/shower 323
Direct dial Yes
Room TV Yes
Confirm by 6
Last dinner 11.30
Parking Ample
Room service 24 hours

Credit Access, Amex, Diners, Visa

Although the Piccadilly approach is grander, the main entrance to this splendid 1920s hotel is at the rear, in Brick Street. The newly revamped, marble-clad foyer is bright and elegant, while the airy, glass-roofed Palm Court lounge with its inviting seating arrangements remains as delightfully traditional as ever. There's also a smartly contemporary cane-furnished bar. Refurbishment of the

bedrooms continues and those that are now completed sport period furniture. All have excellent, well-equipped bathrooms and there are 54 suites (eight with whirlpool baths). *Amenities* solarium, keep-fit equipment, beauty salon, hairdressing, teletext, secretarial services, fax, valeting, laundry service, coffee shop (12am–11.30pm), kiosk.

Bracewells Restaurant ♨♨

Set L £15
Set D £22
About £85 for two
Seats 60
Parties 12

New chef David Ryan has got off to a flying start at this sophisticated, softly-lit restaurant, concentrating on quality of ingredients, careful saucing and striking presentation. Classically-inspired dishes with modern touches range from mille-feuille of lovely fresh lobster with a dedicate herb butter sauce to deliciously tender venison noisettes sauced with muscat grapes and Chablis. Superb desserts, all smoothly served under Oscar Bassam's expert direction. ♥ Well-chosen ©

Lunch 12–2.30 *Dinner* 7–10.30, Sat 7–11.30
Closed L Sat, all Sun & Bank Hols

WC2   Pastoria Hotel   63%   £B/C

H Map 27 A3
St Martins Street WC2H 7HL
01-930 8641
Telex 25538

Credit Access, Amex, Diners, Visa
Closed 24–27 Dec

The Pastoria is located just off Leicester Square and within easy walking distance of the National Gallery. Public areas comprise a stylish marble-floored foyer and a sleek coffee-shop. Uniformly equipped bedrooms (hairdryers, remote-control TVs) have attractive pastel colour schemes and neat bathrooms. Housekeeping is commendable though staff could be warmer. *Amenities* fax, laundry service, coffee shop (Mon–Sat 7am–10pm), 24-hour lounge service.

Rooms 58	*Direct dial* Yes	*Confirm by* 6	*Parking* Difficult
Ensuite bath/shower 58	*Room TV* Yes	*Last dinner* 10	*Room service* Limited

**If we recommend meals in a Hotel or Inn,
a separate entry is made for its restaurant.**

EC2   Pavilion

R Map 26 C1
Finsbury Circus Gardens EC2
01-628 8224

French cooking
About £50 for two
Seats 28 *Parties* 24
Parking Limited

Credit Access, Amex, Diners, Visa

The Pavilion is a small, simple and charming lunchtime restaurant serving enjoyable French food and marvellous wines. Duck liver pâté with Armagnac, turbot sauce nantaise and fillet of beef with Roquefort butter are typical choices. The cheeseboard is a winner, and a faultlessly chosen wine list includes the exquisite Riesling Clos Haüserer (Zind-Humbrecht) '85 and Ch. Cadet Piola St. Emilion '66. Friendly service and a very civilised atmosphere. Booking essential.
Outstanding   🍷 Well-chosen

Lunch only 12–2.30   **Closed** Sat, Sun & Bank Hols

NW11   Peking Duck

R Map 20 B1
30 Temple Fortune
Parade NW11
01-458 3558

Chinese cooking
Set L & D from £10
About £34 for two
Seats 40 *Parking* Limited
Credit Access, Amex, Diners, Visa

The name says it all – this is a simple Chinese restaurant where owner Mr Wong skilfully cooks a variety of Peking dishes including diced chicken with cashew nuts and whole crispy duck. There are Cantonese specialities too. Try the Teppan dishes such as chicken shreds in yellow bean sauce or lamb with spring onions. Seafood fans will find plenty of choice.

Lunch 12–2.30   *Dinner* 6–11.30, Sat 6–12
Closed Tues & 25 & 26 Dec

W2   Pembridge Court Hotel   64%   £D/E

H Map 22 A2
34 Pembridge Gardens
W2 4DX
01-229 9977
Telex 298363

Credit Access, Amex, Diners, Visa

Close to both Notting Hill Gate and the popular Portobello Road antiques market, this former Victorian house has been much improved. Bedrooms have been redecorated and refurbished to a high standard; many of the bathrooms sport chic Italian tiling. The three top-floor rooms are the largest and most stylish; all rooms are equipped with trouser presses and hairdryers. Public areas include a neat little lobby with exposed brickwork, a feature that is duplicated in the downstairs bar. There's also a charming little alcoved lounge. Staff are notably warm and friendly, giving the whole place a happy, human face.
Amenities secretarial services, fax, laundry service.

Rooms 26	*Direct dial* Yes	*Confirm by* 6	*Parking* Limited
Ensuite bath/shower 26	*Room TV* Yes	*Last dinner* 11.30	*Room service* 24 hours

NW6   Peter's

R Map 20 B3
65 Fairfax Road NW6
01-624 5804

Set L from £11
Set D £14.50
About £40 for two
Seats 55 *Parties* 60
Parking Limited
Credit Access, Amex, Diners, Visa

A cheerful and unpretentious restaurant serving classical French cooking. The menu has a fixed price for each course and there's a good choice. Starters might be garlicky squid or a puff pastry parcel of avocado, salmon and spinach; move on to sirloin with green peppercorns in cream and brandy sauce. Enticing sweets. Traditional Sunday lunch. Good French wines: Gewürztraminer (Zind Humbrecht) '85, Corton Bressandes (Tollot Beaut) '80. 🍷 Well-chosen

Lunch 12–2.30, Sun 12.30–3   *Dinner* 6.30–11.30
Closed L Sat, D Sun, all Bank Hols & D Xmas Day & all Boxing Day

W8   Phoenicia

R Map 23 A4
11 Abingdon Road w8
01-937 0120

Lebanese cooking
Set L & D from £10.55
About £44 *for two*
Seats 90 *Parties* 90
Parking Limited
Credit Access, Amex, Diners, Visa

This very civilised Lebanese restaurant maintains high standards in terms of cooking, comfort and service. The last is friendly but not rapid, so this is a place to linger and relax. The mezze are a must – a host of delights both hot and cold, from sautéed chicken livers and goats' cheese with thyme to meat-stuffed pitta, falafel, kebbeh, tabouleh and puréed aubergines. Charcoal grill main courses. Great-value buffet lunch at £6.

Meals noon–11.45
Closed 25 & 26 Dec

W1   Piccadilly Restaurant

R Map 24 B3
31 Great Windmill Street w1
01-734 4956

Italian cooking
About £33 *for two*
Seats 40 *Parties* 12
Parking Difficult

Credit Access, Amex, Visa

A haven of homely charm, also known as the Little Cottage, where honest, enjoyable Italian food is served at very reasonable prices, with decent wines to match. It's immensely popular, with regulars returning again and again for the splendid prosciutto San Daniele, the excellent pasta, the nicely sauced meat dishes, the plain grills, the simple but delicious sweets. Always lots of daily specials.

Lunch 12–2.30   *Dinner* 6–11
Closed Sun, Bank Hols & 3/4 days Xmas

SW11   Pollyanna's

R Map 21 C6
2 Battersea Rise sw11
01-228 0316

About £45 *for two*
Seats 80
Parties 30
Parking Ample

Credit Access, Amex, Visa

A marvellous cellar is the perfect partner for Eamonn Connolly's accomplished cooking at this upmarket bistro. Norman Price, the urbane owner, generates a lively atmosphere and explains the extensive daily blackboard specials, which include hot vegetarian dishes and interesting salads. Among many delicious dishes are aubergine and artichoke mousse with tomato coulis, fillets of monkfish and red mullet on pink peppercorn sauce, and grilled calf's liver on lemon compote. Sweets are splendid – try the dark and white chocolate mousse. The all-French wine list will satisfy the most demanding enthusiast. It includes Bourgneuf Pomerol '78, Chateau d'Yquem '76 and the gorgeous Nuits St. Georges Les Roncières (Avery bottling) '69.
  ▷ Outstanding   ♀ Well-chosen   ⊘

Lunch Sun only 1–3   *Dinner* 7–12
Closed D Sun, L Mon–Sat, 1 Jan & 4 days Xmas

SW1   Pomegranates

R Map 21 C5
94 Grosvenor Road sw1
01-828 6560

Set L from £13
Set D from £14.50
About £60 *for two*
Seats 40 *Parties* 12
Parking Difficult
Credit Access, Amex, Visa

The lengthy menu at this delightful restaurant is as cosmopolitan as the clientele. Faithfully-executed dishes range from Mexican baked crab to Filipino oxtail with peanuts. Flavours are superb. We enjoyed the oyster-filled pastry parcels with lime, and a fiery West Indian goat curry. Interesting wines reflect a catholic taste: Beaujolais Crus from Pierre Ferraud; the sumptuous Semillon Late Harvest (De Bortoli) from Australia. ♀ Well-chosen   ⊘

Lunch 12.30–2.15   *Dinner* 7.30–11.15
Closed L Sat, all Sun, Easter & Xmas

WC2   Poons

R Map 27 A2
4 Leicester Street wc2
01-437 1528

Chinese cooking
Set L £9.50
About £25 *for two*
Seats 90
Parties 50
Parking Difficult

Decor is ordinary, service sometimes brusque, but the food's good, as the crowds testify. Most of the menu is fairly familiar Cantonese, but two sections are of particular interest: excellent wind-dried duck, pork, bacon and liver sausages are a speciality, as are the original hot pots, which include the wind-dried items plus chicken, beef, salted fish and braised eel. Dumpling soup is a good starter, fresh oranges the best of the simple sweets.

Meals noon–11.30
Closed Sun & 3 days Xmas

WC2 — Poons of Covent Garden ♀

R **Map 27 B2**
41 King Street WC2
01-240 1743

Chinese cooking
Set D from £16.50
About £50 for two
Seats 120 *Parties* 120
Parking Difficult
Credit Amex, Diners, Visa

There's atmosphere aplenty at Bill Poon's bustling restaurant, with customers sharing in the excitement of some dramatic high-flame cooking in the open-view kitchen. Making just a few concessions to Western tastes, the menu offers a wide and interesting choice of Cantonese dishes, from steamed fish in black bean sauce to deep-fried duck with yam paste. Wind-dried bacon, stir-fried with bamboo shoots and water chestnuts, is a speciality.

Meals noon–11.30
Closed Sun & 4 days Xmas

W1 — Portman Inter-Continental Hotel   79%   £A

H **Map 22 D1**
22 Portman Square W1H 9FL
01-486 5844
Telex 261526

Rooms 275
Ensuite bath/shower 275
Direct dial Yes
Room TV Yes
Confirm by 6
Last dinner 11
Parking Ample
Room service 24 hours

Credit Access, Amex, Diners, Visa

Major refurbishment has given a facelift to this popular modern hotel conveniently situated near Marble Arch and Park Lane. Groups of inviting armchairs and settees and lovely flower arrangements create a welcoming impression in the elegant panelled foyer. Other public areas include a smart coffee shop, an attractive split-level bar where a pianist plays nightly, and numerous function suites. Good-size

bedrooms – some with balconies – are furnished in a variety of styles, with newer rooms having bamboo furniture and pastel colour schemes. Staff are pleasant and cheerful, but breakfasts only average.
Amenities tennis, satellite TV, in-house movies, secretarial services, fax, laundry service, coffee shop (11am–midnight), kiosk. &

W11 — Portobello Hotel   62%   £B/C

H **Map 21 B4**
22 Stanley Gardens W11 2NG
01-727 2777
Telex 268349

Credit Access, Amex, Diners, Visa
Closed 7 days Xmas

Part of a quiet Victorian terrace, this highly individual town house hotel has a pleasant darkwood reception area, stylish lounge and bright basement bar. Bedrooms range in size from cabins to suites. All have handsome military-style furnishings augmented by TVs, mini-bars and tea-makers; some superior rooms offer sitting areas and garden views.
Amenities garden, laundry service, 24-hour restaurant.

| *Rooms* 25 | *Direct dial* Yes | *Confirm by* arrang. | *Parking* Difficult |
| *Ensuite bath/shower* 25 | *Room TV* Yes | *Last dinner* Any time | *Room service* All day |

SW3 — Ports   *NEW ENTRY*

R **Map 22 C4**
11 Beauchamp Place SW3
01-581 3837

Portuguese cooking
Set L £8.75
About £48 for two
Seats 45 *Parties* 30
Parking Difficult
Credit Access, Amex, Diners, Visa

A prettily tiled basement restaurant with a pleasantly relaxed ambience. The Portuguese menu changes every few weeks, and fish features strongly: we enjoyed skewered monkfish served with tomato sauce, and the speciality bacalhau (dried salt cod) accompanied by onions, black olives, olive oil and garlic. Cooking is reasonable, and if the waiters occasionally get muddled it's all part of the fun. ℮

Lunch 12.30–2.30   *Dinner* 7–11.30
Closed all Sun, Bank Hols & 5 days Xmas

NW3 — Post House Hotel (Hampstead)   65%   £C

H **Map 20 B2**
215 Haverstock Hill NW3 4RB
01-794 8121
Telex 262494

Credit Access, Amex, Diners, Visa

This modern hotel has a welcoming air with its relaxing foyer-lounge and cheerful cocktail bar. Constant updating keeps bedrooms fresh and in good repair: executive rooms boast handsome darkwood units and prettily coordinated colour schemes, and restyling of remaining accommodation is under way. Mini-bars and well-equipped bathrooms throughout. No dogs. ***Amenities*** secretarial services, fax, laundry service, 24-hour lounge service.

| *Rooms* 140 | *Room phone* Yes | *Confirm by* 6 | *Parking* Ample |
| *Ensuite bath/shower* 140 | *Room TV* Yes | *Last dinner* 10.30 | *Room service* All day |

EC2 | Le Poulbot ★

R Map 26 B2
45 Cheapside EC2
01-236 4379

French cooking

Lunch only 12–3
Set L £24.50
About £70 for two
Seats 50
Parking Difficult

Credit Access, Amex, Diners, Visa
Closed Sat, Sun, Bank Hols &
1 wk Xmas

An intimate basement restaurant that runs smoothly and efficiently under charming manager
Jean Cottard. Book, and look
forward to enjoying the talents
of new chef Philippe Vandewalle,
who cooks with a nice light touch
and a true artist's eye. Some
dishes are simple, others more
elaborate, but all are prepared
with consistent confidence and
panache. There's a short, very
good wine list: Côte de Beaune
Blanc from M. Joliette is quite delicious.

Specialities sous-presse de volaille fermière et foie gras au fenouil
fondant; envelope de saumon d'Ecosse aux truffes et jeunes poireaux;
rognonnade de foie de veau au vinaigre de vin vieux; tartelette de
fraises des bois gratinée. ♟ Well-chosen ℰ

W1 | Princess Garden *NEW ENTRY*

R Map 22 D2
8 North Audley Street W1
01-493 3223

Chinese cooking
About £50 for two
Seats 200
Parties 150
Parking Difficult
Credit Access, Amex, Diners, Visa

A Mayfair Chinese restaurant, more elegant and attractive than most
of those in nearby Soho, and with higher prices. The food is good, and
the menu tempts with the likes of succulent fried scallops, chicken
and prawns in a potato basket and spicy-hot pork with onions and
green peppers. Also shark's fins, bean curd dishes, excellent vegetables
and a good choice of sweets, including pancakes, almond jelly and
Peking profiteroles.

Lunch 12–2.30   *Dinner* 6.30–11.30
Closed Easter Day, 25 & 26 Dec

SW7 | Pun ♟

R Map 23 B5
53 Old Brompton Road SW7
01-225 1609

Chinese cooking
Set D from £9.80
About £45 for two
Seats 60 *Parties* 30
Parking Difficult
Credit Access, Amex, Diners, Visa

Cantonese, Peking and Szechuan dishes share a varied menu in a
smart, unpretentious Chinese restaurant near South Kensington
station. King prawns, served sizzling and fuming with the powerful
aroma of chilli, make a splendid centrepiece, and other dishes to try
include hot and sour soup, Szechuan double-cooked pork with green
peppers, and Kung-Po chicken with water chestnuts. Friendly staff.

Lunch 12–3   *Dinner* 6–11.30, Sat 12–11.30, Sun 12–11
Closed 25 &.26 Dec

W8 | Le Quai St Pierre

R Map 23 A4
7 Stratford Road W8
01-937 6388

Seafood

About £60 for two
Seats 50
Parking Difficult

Credit Access, Amex, Diners, Visa

A cheerful, relaxed and very French seafood restaurant, where you
can find a varied selection of fish dishes cooked with great care and
attention to detail. Salads, feuilletés and the plateau de fruits de mer
are the popular choices here, and there are also six daily specials
according to what fish is available that day. Meat eaters are offered a
limited selection of dishes, and sweets are simple.

Lunch 12.30–2.30   *Dinner* 7–11.30
Closed L Mon & all Sun

NW2 | Quincy's 84 ♟

R Map 20 B2
675 Finchley Road NW2
01-794 8499

Set L £14.50
Set D £17.50
About £40 for two
Seats 30 *Parties* 30
Parking Ample
Credit Access, Visa

Scrubbed pine tables, bare wood floors and green decor create an
attractive setting at this popular little restaurant. Sandy Anderson's
modern, imaginative style of cooking is enhanced by his attractive
presentation. Expertly prepared dishes range from fresh salmon
marinated in lime to best end of lamb with celeriac timbale.
Scrumptious sweets, super cheeses and good wines at reasonable
prices. Be sure to book. ♟ Well-chosen ℰ

Lunch Sun only 12–2   *Dinner* 7.30–10.30, Sun 7–9.30
Closed 26 Dec & 1 Jan

W1   Ramada Hotel   71%   £A/B

H **Map 24 B2**
10 Berners Street W1A 3BE
01-636 1629
Telex 25759

Rooms 232
Ensuite bath/shower 232
Direct dial Yes
Room TV Yes
Confirm by 6
Last dinner 10
Parking Difficult
Room service 24 hours

Credit Access, Amex, Diners, Visa

Much of the Edwardian splendour of the original building survives in this imposing hotel just north of Oxford Street. The spacious lobby-lounge with its marble floors and columns, spectacularly high moulded ceiling, wrought-iron balcony and huge chandelier has plenty of comfortable chairs and sofas, and the bar area is equally impressive. Good-sized bedrooms have standard decor of quilted floral bedcovers,

with padded headboards, easy chairs and curtains all in toning pink, plus decent polished wood furniture and brass light fittings. All are equipped with radios, trouser presses, hairdryers and individual temperature controls. Tiled bathrooms have shower facilities. No dogs.
Amenities in-house movies, fax, laundry service, kiosk. &

SW6   Ramada Inn West London   61%   £C

H **Map 23 A6**
47 Lillie Road SW6 1UQ
01-385 1255
Telex 917728

Credit Access, Amex, Diners, Visa

A large modern hotel near Earls Court Exhibition Centre. Practical comfort is the order of the day, and three floors of bedrooms have been smartly restyled, making them preferable to the rather utilitarian unimproved rooms. There's a large, well-planned foyer and a jolly bar. The hotel is popular with tourists, so personal service is not a strong point. No dogs. *Amenities* in-house movies, secretarial services, fax, laundry service, coffee shop (11am–11pm).

Rooms 500	*Direct dial* Yes	*Confirm by* 6	*Parking* Ample
Ensuite bath/shower 500	*Room TV* Yes	*Last dinner* 10.30	*Room service* None

SW5   Read's   ♕

R **Map 23 B5**
152 Old Brompton Road SW5
01-373 2445

Set L £11.50, Sun £14.50
Set D £21.50
About £68 *for two*
Seats 70 *Parties* 20
Parking Difficult
Credit Access, Amex, Diners, Visa

Owner Keith Read continues to oversee the kitchen of his summery little restaurant, minimising any problems caused by another change of chef. The short, weekly-changing menu makes imaginative use of fresh produce such as a mixed lettuce salad topped with goujons of brill, spring lamb served rare with ratatouille, and beautifully poached sole with a delicious apple and cider sauce. Sweets include a superb marzipan in flaky pastry. ♀ Well-chosen ❷

Lunch 12.30–2.30, Sun till 3   *Dinner* 7.30–11
Closed D Sun, Bank Hol Mons & 10 days Xmas

W1   Red Fort   ♕

R **Map 27 A2**
77 Dean Street W1V
01-437 2525

Indian cooking
About £40 *for two*
Seats 160 *Parties* 100
Parking Difficult
Credit Access, Amex, Diners, Visa

One of the West End's favourite Indian restaurants, with enjoyable Moghul cooking and stylish, comfortable surroundings. Besides the usual tandoori dishes and mild curries based on lamb, chicken and prawns there are a few less familiar items such as masha (scooped-out onions filled with beans), deep-fried cottage cheese, tandoori duck and Goan-style fish. Meat and vegetarian thalis provide a good cross-section of dishes, and on Sunday there's a help-yourself lunchtime buffet. &

Lunch 12–3   *Dinner* 6–11.30   **Closed** 25 & 26 Dec

W1   Regent Crest Hotel   62%   £B

H **Map 24 A1**
Carburton Street W1P 8EE
01-388 2300
Telex 22453

Credit Access, Amex, Diners, Visa

The second floor of this West End hotel has been converted to New Executive rooms with bright, bold prints, dark-stained fitted units and numerous accessories. There are also Lady Crest rooms and rooms for non-smokers. Most day rooms are on the first floor. Sound insulation in our bedroom was inadequate, and housekeeping needs brushing up. No dogs. *Amenities* in-house movies, secretarial services, fax, laundry service, coffee shop (11am–12.30am), kiosk. &

Rooms 320	*Direct dial* Yes	*Confirm by* 6	*Parking* Ample
Ensuite bath/shower 320	*Room TV* Yes	*Last dinner* 10.30	*Room service* 24 hours

SW7   Rembrandt Hotel   67%   £B

H Map 23 C4
11 Thurloe Place SW7 2RS
01-589 8100
Telex 295828

Credit Access, Amex, Diners, Visa

Good conference facilities plus a luxurious health club are popular attractions at this large hotel. Marble steps lead from an elegant foyer to the bar-lounge and there's also a leafy conservatory. Bedrooms are well equipped, with radios, TVs and hairdryers. Most have trouser presses. Bathrooms include shower facilities. *Amenities* indoor swimming pool, sauna, solarium, whirlpool bath, steam bath, gymnasium, beauty salon, in-house movies, fax, laundry service.

Rooms 200	*Direct dial* Yes	*Confirm by* 6	*Parking* Difficult
Ensuite bath/shower 200	*Room TV* Yes	*Last dinner* 10	*Room service* 24 hours

W1   The Ritz   87%   £A

HR Map 25 B4
Piccadilly W1V 9DG
01-493 8181
Telex 267200

Rooms 130
Ensuite bath/shower 130
Direct dial Yes
Room TV Yes
Confirm by 6
Last dinner 11
Parking Difficult
Room service 24 hours

Credit Access, Amex, Diners, Visa

No expense is being spared in restoring this fabulous hotel to its original glory. Bedrooms have lost the bland look they acquired in the seventies and now mirror César Ritz's original design: crisp white walls with a hint of colour picking out the gilded French directoire moulding. Some rooms retain the original brass bedsteads; all have marble fireplaces from French châteaux. Bathrooms are compact and well equipped, with gold taps hinting at past opulence. Public rooms still show signs of wear. Staff are immaculately groomed but service is not always of a standard merited by this famous hotel. No dogs.
Amenities garden, hairdressing, in-house movies, secretarial services, fax, valeting, laundry service, kiosk.

Restaurant   *NEW ENTRY*   ♕♕♕

Set L £22, Sun £26
Set D £42.50
About £100 *for two*
Seats 120
Parties 10
Parking Limited

Credit Access, Amex, Diners, Visa

The decor, perhaps the most grand and elegant in London, still outshines the cooking and service, but chef Keith Stanley certainly knows what he's doing. Dishes enjoyed on a recent visit included vegetable tortellini in a herby, aromatic broth; terrine in aspic; rolled loin of pork with apricot stuffing; and summer pudding. The rolls were good, but coffee disappointed. Classic wines on a very pricy list.
⊳ Outstanding   ♥ Well-chosen   ☺   ₫

Lunch 12.30–2.30, Sun till 2   *Dinner* 6.30–11, Sun 7–10.30

SW1   Royal Court Hotel   70%   £A

H Map 23 D5
Sloane Square SW1W 8EG
01-730 9191
Telex 296818

Rooms 99
Ensuite bath/shower 99
Direct dial Yes
Room TV Yes
Confirm by 6
Last dinner 10.30
Parking Limited
Room service 24 hours

Credit Access, Amex, Diners, Visa

A comfortable and convenient place to stay, small enough to benefit from a personal style of management and with a welcoming atmosphere behind its period facade. The chandeliered reception area doubles as a lounge, and the basement café-bar is an alternative to the adjoining tavern. 1988 saw big improvements in the bedrooms, where trouser presses, hairdryers, tea-makers and mini-bars were added as

stylish refurbishment took place. The newly decorated corridors feature framed theatre programmes and memorabilia. Staff are well turned-out, friendly and efficient, clearly motivated by a very competent manager. No dogs. *Amenities* in-house movies, secretarial services, fax, laundry service, coffee shop (10.30am–11.30pm).

W8   Royal Garden Hotel   81%   £A

HR Map 22 A3
Kensington High Street
W8 4PT
01-937 8000
Telex 263151

Rooms 390
Ensuite bath/shower 390
Direct dial Yes
Room TV Yes
Confirm by 6
Last dinner 11.30
Parking Ample
Room service 24 hours

Credit Access, Amex, Diners, Visa

A marble-floored foyer-lounge with plants, chandeliers and deep sofas gives visitors a stylish first impression at this tall modern hotel overlooking Kensington Gardens. The split-level gallery bar is a good place to relax with a drink, and there's an equally appealing lounge bar and coffee shop. Bedrooms are kept very comfortable by individually controlled central heating, and all are equipped with mini-bars,

hairdryers, security chains and spyholes; suites also have safes. Luxurious bathrooms offer a good range of toiletries, and most have bidets. No dogs. *Amenities* beauty salon, hairdressing, in-house movies, secretarial services, fax, valeting, laundry service, coffee shop (7am–11pm), kiosk.

Royal Roof Restaurant   ♛

Set L from £18.50
About £70 for two

Modern French cooking is enjoyed in an elegant setting with a marvellous vista right at the top of the hotel. The views are matched by skilfully prepared food: ballotine of duck with a redcurrant sauce, lobster any way you want, veal with watercress sauce garnished with aubergine fritters and spinach, traditional grills. Service is very professional, and the wine list includes some fine clarets and interesting Californians: Essencia Orange Muscat (Andrew Quady) '85. &

Lunch 12–2.30   *Dinner* 7–11.30
Closed L Sat, all Sun & Bank Hols

We welcome bona fide complaints and recommendations
on the tear-out pages at the back of the book for readers' comment.
They are followed up by our professional team.

SW1   Royal Horseguards Thistle Hotel   72%   £A/B

H Map 25 C4
Whitehall Court SW1A 2EJ
01-839 3400
Telex 917096

Rooms 262
Ensuite bath/shower 262
Direct dial Yes
Room TV Yes
Confirm by 6
Last dinner 10.30
Parking Limited
Room service 24 hours

Credit Access, Amex, Diners, Visa

Built in the style of a Gothic French château, this is a very comfortable hotel close to the Thames Embankment. Panelling and a marble floor grace the hall, and there's a discreetly luxurious lounge and a coffee shop that's open from very early to very late. Bedrooms of various sizes (the biggest have river views) are generally smart, and all are provided with tea-makers, hairdryers and trouser presses. 118

new bedrooms were due to come on stream at the end of 1988, while more distant proposals include a leisure centre. No dogs.
Amenities terrace, in-house movies, secretarial services, fax, laundry service, coffee shop (7.30am–1am).

★ For a *discount* on next year's guide, see **An Offer for Answers**. ★

W2 · Royal Lancaster Hotel · 80% · £A

H **Map 22 B2**
Lancaster Terrace W2 2TY
01-262 6737
Telex 24822

Rooms 418
Ensuite bath/shower 418
Direct dial Yes
Room TV Yes
Confirm by 6
Last dinner 11.15
Parking Limited
Room service 24 hours

Credit Access, Amex, Diners, Visa

Impressive views of Kensington Gardens and Hyde Park are to be had from this tall modern hotel. On the ground floor are the spacious reception area and a lively brasserie-style café, while at first floor level there's a peaceful and sophisticated lounge with deep-cushioned sofas, period furniture and a grand piano, and a characterful bar. The bedrooms, many of which are rather compact, have been attractively refurbished with smart modern lightwood furniture and a pastel decor with coordinating fabrics. The twelve studio rooms and reserve club rooms are superbly appointed. No dogs. *Amenities* beauty salon, hairdressing, in-house movies, secretarial services, fax, laundry service, valeting, coffee shop (7am–12 midnight), kiosk.

WC1 · Royal Scot Hotel · 57% · £C

H **Map 20 D3**
100 King's Cross Road
WC1 X 9DT
01-278 2434 Telex 27657

Credit Access, Amex, Diners, Visa

White marble has smartened up the busy lobby-lounge, while the cosy, convivial bar has a sort of Gold Rush theme plus some stained glass. Bedrooms and bathrooms – all with showers over the tubs – have a generally functional feel, and from our experience the 'do not disturb' notice is needed to deter the early morning chambermaid. *Amenities* in-house movies, laundry service, coffee shop (10.30am–10.30pm)

| *Rooms* 350 | *Direct dial* Yes | *Confirm by* 6 | *Parking* Limited |
| *Ensuite bath/shower* 350 | *Room TV* Yes | *Last dinner* 10 | *Room service* None |

 indicates a **well-chosen** house wine

WC2 · Royal Trafalgar Thistle Hotel · 66% · £B

H **Map 27 A3**
Whitcomb Street,
Trafalgar Square WC2 7HG
01-930 4477 Telex 298564

Credit Access, Amex, Diners, Visa
Closed 3/4 days Xmas

The National Gallery is just a few steps from this modern hotel, whose central location is a boon to both business visitors and holidaymakers. Bedrooms, though by no means large, are comfortable and well equipped, with practical (if not universally pristine) fitted units and bright, tiled bathrooms. There's a smart lounge and two bars. *Amenities* patio, in-house movies, secretarial services, fax, laundry service, coffee shop (7.30am–11.30pm).

| *Rooms* 108 | *Direct dial* Yes | *Confirm by* 6 | *Parking* Difficult |
| *Ensuite bath/shower* 108 | *Room TV* Yes | *Last dinner* 11.30 | *Room service* 24 hours |

SW1 · Royal Westminster Thistle Hotel · 72% · £A

H **Map 25 A6**
Buckingham Palace Road
SW1W 0QT
01-834 1821
Telex 916821

Rooms 135
Ensuite bath/shower 135
Direct dial Yes
Room TV Yes
Confirm by 6
Last dinner 11.30
Parking Difficult
Room service 24 hours

Credit Access, Amex, Diners, Visa

Just a short walk from Victoria Station and major tourist attractions, this is a fine modern hotel offering all the creative comforts. Oriental vases take the eye in the marble-floored foyer, and there is a striking Chinese carpet in the splendid lounge. The mood changes to Parisian in the long-hours Café Saint Germain. Double-glazed, air-conditioned bedrooms are generally of a good size, with neat pickled pine furniture and a wide range of accessories, including trouser presses, mini-bars and wall safes. Larger rooms have the additional facility of a sofa bed. Well-equipped tiled bathrooms throughout. *Amenities* in-house movies, fax, laundry service, coffee shop (7am–11pm).

SE1   RSJ

R **Map 26 A3**
13a Coin Street SE1
01-928 4554

Set L £12.75
Set D £12.75
About £52 for two
Seats 60
Parties 25
Parking Limited

Credit Access, Amex, Visa

The main dining room, in pretty pastel shades, is upstairs, and it's essential to book at this very popular spot near the South Bank complex. Ian Stabler's cooking is reliable and highly accomplished, as he demonstrates in an appealing selection of dishes that are equally pleasing to eye and palate: pastry parcels of seafood with a delicious shellfish sauce, suprême of pheasant with a chestnut mousse, traditional chocolate pot topped with praline cream. The cellar is remarkable for its unrivalled collection of over 50 wines from the Loire Valley including superb Bourgueils (Lamy), Chinons (Couly Dutheil) and the ambrosial Coteaux du Layon (Morgat) 1959. ⮞ Outstanding 🍷 Well-chosen 🅮

Lunch 12–2   *Dinner* 6–11
Closed L Sat, all Sun, Bank Hols & 4 days Xmas

Changes in data sometimes occur in establishments
after the Guide goes to press.
Prices should be taken as indications rather than firm quotes.

SW1   Rubens Hotel   65%   £B

H **Map 25 A6**
Buckingham Palace Road
SW1W 0PS
01-834 6600
Telex 916577

Credit Access, Amex, Diners, Visa

The Rubens provides neat, practical accommodation just a stroll from Buckingham Palace. Identically decorated bedrooms, though not large, are comfortable and well equipped, with trouser presses, hairdryers and bathroom telephone extensions. The library lounge is just the place for a quiet browse, and besides the redesigned bar area there will be a new coffee lounge. No dogs. *Amenities* in-house movies, teletext, secretarial serices, fax, laundry service.

Rooms 191	*Direct dial* Yes	*Confirm by* 6	*Parking* Difficult
Ensuite bath/shower 191	*Room TV* Yes	*Last dinner* 10	*Room service* 24 hours

W1   Rue St Jacques   ★   ♛

R **Map 24 B2**
5 Charlotte Street W1
01-637 0222

Lunch 12.30–2.30
Dinner 7.30–11.15
Set L £17.50
Set D £35
About £90 for two
Seats 60
Parties 18
Parking Difficult

Credit Access, Amex, Diners, Visa
Closed L Sat, all Sun & Bank Hols

Intimate, luxurious surroundings for the marvellous team of chef Gunther Schlender and manager Vincent Calcerano. Gunther's French menu is well balanced, with dishes to suit most tastes (including always a vegetarian main course) and recent happy memories include ravioli of fish and shellfish with a light fish soup, and a splendid parfait of nougat and apricots. Presentation is attractive without being elaborate, service skilled and friendly, and the wine list exceptional, with especially fine burgundies: Vougeot (Bertagna) '76, Pommard Pezerolles (de Montille) '71. *Specialities* terrine de foie gras et ris de veau, pigeonneau de Bordeaux au foie gras et au jus de truffes, pyramide de chocolat amer. ⮞ Outstanding 🍷 Well-chosen 🅮

WC1   Hotel Russell   68%   £A/B

H **Map 24 C1**
Russell Square WC1B 5BE
01-837 6470
Telex 24615

Credit Access, Amex, Diners, Visa

A splendid example of turn-of-the-century architecture, this handsome hotel boasts impressive marble columns and archways and an imposing stairway in the foyer. Nicest public room is King's Bar, strongly reminiscent of a gentleman's club. Bedrooms range from compact to large and have pastel colour schemes, ruched curtains and functional furniture; bathrooms are basic and modern. *Amenities* fax, valeting, laundry service, coffee shop (10am–midnight).

Rooms 320	*Direct dial* Yes	*Confirm by* 6	*Parking* Difficult
Ensuite bath/shower 320	*Room TV* Yes	*Last dinner* 10.30	*Room service* 24 hours

Saga

olton Street W1

Japanese cooking
Set L from £7.20
Set D from £23
Seats 90 *Parties* 12
Parking Difficult
Credit Access, Amex, Diners, Visa

On the ground floor of this small, formally decorated Japanese restaurant is a Teppan Yaki (griddle) counter at which diners can also have any other item from the menu. Downstairs is the main restaurant and a sushi counter where the food is carefully prepared and beautifully presented. Soups include an excellent misoshiru, while the main course might be tempura. Finish with fresh fruit or sorbet. Booking is essential.

Lunch 12–2.30   *Dinner* 6.30–10.30   *About £67 for two*
Closed Sun, Bank Hols, 1 wk Xmas & 1 wk Aug

W1   ### St George's Hotel   65%   **£A/B**

H Map 24 A2
Langham Place W1N 8QS
01-580 0111
Telex 27274

Credit Access, Amex, Diners, Visa

Occupying the ground and 9th to 15th floors of a tower block belonging to the BBC, this conveniently situated modern hotel attracts media stars and events. The street-level lift whisks guests to the open-plan rooftop bar-lounge and restaurant, which enjoy panoramic views. These are shared by the spacious bedrooms, which have fitted units, mini-bars, remote-control TVs, and good bathrooms.
Amenities fax, laundry service.

Rooms 86	*Direct dial* Yes	*Confirm by* 6	*Parking* Limited
Ensuite bath/shower 86	*Room TV* Yes	*Last dinner* 10	*Room service* 24 hours

---

SW1   ### St James Court Hotel   75%   **£A**

HR Map 25 B5
Buckingham Gate
SW1E 6AF
01-834 6655
Telex 938075

Rooms 400
Ensuite bath/shower 400
Direct dial Yes
Room TV Yes
Confirm by 6
Last dinner 11.30
Parking Ample
Room service 24 hours

Credit Access, Amex, Diners, Visa

A grand-scale Edwardian apartment block, converted into a luxury hotel in 1985. Striking features include a fine courtyard with ornamental trees and flowers around a period fountain, the world's longest terracotta frieze (depicting scenes from Shakespeare's plays) and an impressive marble-floored foyer-lounge. Bedrooms are equipped to a high standard with smart reproduction furniture, satellite TVs and  mini-bars; de-luxe rooms have air-conditioning. Bathrooms are sumptuous. The self-contained business centre offers an extensive range of facilities. Staff are efficient but somewhat lacking in warmth. No dogs. *Amenities* sauna, solarium, whirlpool bath, gymnasium, secretarial services, fax, laundry service, coffee shop (7am–midnight).

Auberge de Provence

01–821 1899
French cooking
Set L £17.50
About £52 for two
Seats 90

Yves Gravelier is the new chef at this Provence-style restaurant where Mediterranean dishes are competently cooked. A tasty starter is finely minced lamb and purée of aubergine with a red pepper sauce; John Dory is poached in crab stock with black olives, and there's a good authentic navarin of lamb. Enjoyable puddings, fine cheeseboard, efficient Gallic service. A decent wine list features some good burgundies and Rhônes.   ♀ Well-chosen   ☺

Lunch 12–2.30   *Dinner* 7.30–11
Closed L Sat & all Sun

Inn of Happiness   ♛

01-821 1931
Chinese cooking
Set L £14.50
About £48 for two
Seats 110
Parties 60

A large, light and dramatically stylish Chinese restaurant with hand-painted clouds on the ceiling and an open-air section for summer eating. The menu covers Szechuan, Peking and Cantonese cuisines, and the specialities are whole fresh pomfret, Szechuan tea-smoked duck and sliced sole in a Chinese wine sauce with wood-ear mushrooms. There are numerous vegetarian main courses, and red bean pancakes make a delicious sweet. Very attentive service.

Lunch 12.30–2.30   *Dinner* 7.30–11.30
Closed 25 Dec

SW1   Salloos   ♔

R **Map 22 D3**
  62 Kinnerton Street sw1
01-235 4444

Pakistani cooking

About £50 for two
Seats 65
Parking Limited

Credit Access, Amex, Diners, Visa

In a quiet Knightsbridge street, a sophisticated Pakistani restaurant
with excellent service. The cooking is subtle, distinctive and different:
both yakhni consommé and mulligatawny soup are excellent; tandoori
lamb chops are the best in London; chicken jalfrezi shows a deft use
of capsicum and ginger; bataire quails are mildly spiced, then cooked
in the tandoor; kulfi ice cream is delicious. Good breads and rice.
Above average wine list.

Lunch 12–2.30   *Dinner* 7–11.15
Closed Sun & Bank Hols

**We welcome bona fide complaints and recommendations
on the tear-out pages at the back of the book for readers' comment.
They are followed up by our professional team.**

SW3   San Frediano

R **Map 23 C5**
  62 Fulham Road sw3
01-584 8375

Italian cooking

About £44 for two
Seats 96
Parking Difficult

Credit Access, Diners, Visa

Families are made particularly welcome at durable San Fred's, where
the waiters play their part in the happy, lively ambience. Sound
Italian cooking packs in the regulars, who come for old favourites like
minestrone, noodles with fresh tomato, pesto and cream or calf's liver
with sage, or daily specials such as prawn soup, marinated vegetables
or roast poussin stuffed with chestnuts. Fresh fruit salad makes a good
finale. Booking advised.   ℰ

Lunch 12.30–2.30   *Dinner* 7.15–11.15
Closed Sun & Bank Hols

SW3   San Lorenzo

R **Map 23 C4**
  22 Beauchamp Place sw3
01-584 1074

Italian cooking

About £48 for two
Seats 120
Parking Difficult

Lorenzo and Mara Berni have completed 24 years at their perennially
popular restaurant, chef Gino Borella nearly 20. Consistency is a
keynote throughout a menu that runs from excellent pasta and first-
rate prosciutto to calf's liver, sea bass, zampone and a bollito misto for
the winter. Service is friendly and relaxed, and there's a very good
Italian wine list. A nice place for diner à deux. Book   ℰ 占

Lunch 12.30–3, Sat 12.30–3.30   *Dinner* 7.30–11.30
Closed Sun & Bank Hols

SW19   San Lorenzo Fuoriporta

R **Map 7 B5**
  38 Worple Road Mews
Wimbledon sw19
01-946 8463

Italian cooking

About £45 for two
Seats 100 *Parties* 40
Parking Limited
Credit Access, Amex, Diners, Visa

One of the most popular and enduring of Italian restaurants, with
good food, friendly staff and alfresco summer eating. Start perhaps
with fresh asparagus and go on to pasta, grilled prawns with rice,
peppercorn-sauced lamb or veal with aubergine, mozzarella and
tomatoes. Good vegetables, crisp salads and, for dessert, the San
Lorenzo special – a cold pancake filled with whipped cream and
sprinkled with crushed almond biscuits, whisky and Tia Maria.   ℰ

Lunch 12.30–3   *Dinner* 7–11, Sun till 10
Closed Bank Hols

SW3   San Martino

R **Map 23 C4**
  103 Walton Street sw3
01-589 3833

Italian cooking

About £50 for two
Seats 48
Parking Limited

Credit Access, Amex, Diners, Visa

The regular items on the Italian menu run a fairly familiar gamut,
and it's the daily specials that attract attention: good bresaola and
carpaccio, stuffed calamari with wild mushroom sauce, grilled sea
bass with fresh herbs, succulent roast baby goat Roman style. Wine is
also taken seriously: note the excellent Tuscan and Piedmontese (two
fine Dolcettos) and some first-rate grappas. Extrovert owner Constanzo
Martinucci and his staff create a warm, genial atmosphere.   占

Lunch 12–2.45   *Dinner* 7–11.30
Closed 25 & 26 Dec, Easter Sun & Mon

314   LONDON

SW1   Santini   ♛ ♊

R Map 25 A6
29 Ebury Street SW1
01-730 4094

Italian cooking
Set L £12.50
About £70 for two
Seats 65
Parking Limited
Credit Access, Amex, Diners, Visa

A chic and cool Italian restaurant, handy for Victoria Station. The menu avoids the clichés of Italian cooking and features some less common Venetian specialities which are carefully prepared. Pasta is made on the premises as in delicious tagliolini with a creamy shellfish sauce. Authentic osso buco is properly made, and try the hot carpaccio with matchstick courgettes or ruccola in season. Enjoyable sweets and excellent coffee. Good wines include a fine Pinot Nero. Book.
🍷 Well-chosen 🄔 &

Lunch 12.30–2.30   *Dinner* 7–11.30
Closed L Sat & Sun & all Bank Hols

WC2   The Savoy   91%   £A

HR Map 24 D3
Strand WC2R 0EU
01-836 4343
Telex 24234

Rooms 202
Ensuite bath/shower 202
Direct dial Yes
Room TV Yes
Confirm by arrang.
Last dinner 11.30
Parking Ample
Room service 24 hours

Credit Access, Amex, Diners, Visa

Currently celebrating its first glorious century, this beautifully run hotel is the very epitome of style and elegance. From the splendid, bustling entrance hall, where immaculately uniformed staff provide faultless service, to the renowned American Bar, striking pillared lounge and the new Upstairs Bar, the atmosphere is always special, unmistakably individual. The river-facing suites with their wonderfully ornate plasterwork, period furnishings and original bathrooms are magnificent. Other rooms are delightfully Art Deco, and all offer flowers, fruit, superb bed linen – plus the very latest in hi-tech cable TV. No dogs. *Amenities* hairdressing, in-house movies, secretarial services, fax, valeting, laundry service, coffee shop (12am–12pm).

Restaurant ★   ♛♛

Lunch 12.30–2.30, Sun 12.30–2
Dinner 7.30–11.30, Sun 7–10.30
Set L from £19.50
Set D £24.25
About £70 for two
Seats 140
Parties 80

Consistency and complexity of cooking characterizes Anton Edelmann's interesting and daily-changing menus at this most luxurious restaurant. Classical dishes presented in the modern manner provide a perfect marriage of old and new, with choices such as a simple but stunning salad of langoustines and Chinese artichokes, and richly sauced pigeon breast stuffed with a delicate fruit purée.
Service runs with effortless precision under the direction of Luigi Zambon. *Specialities* foie gras en gelée aux vieux porto, délice de turbot aux légumes beurre safran, suprême de canard en chemise aux raisins, pêche en tulipe à la Nellie Melba. 🍷 Well-chosen 🄔 🍴 &

Grill Room ♛

Set D from £17.50
About £75 for two
Seats 85
Parties 12

Traditionalists everywhere praise the superb roasts, grills and wonderful daily specialities like pot roast chicken or jugged hare offered at this handsome, yew-panelled restaurant. Even more elaborate offerings such as seafood and smoked salmon soup or magret duckling with lentils and port wine sauce have a simplicity and lightness of touch, while favourite among sweets remains the incomparable bread and butter pudding. 🍷 Well-chosen 🄔 &

Lunch 12.30–2.30   *Dinner* 6–11.15
Closed L Sat, all Sun, Bank Hols & Aug

W1   Scotts   ♛ ♛

R Map 22 D2
20 Mount Street W1
01-629 5248

About £90 for two
Seats 125
Parties 12
Parking Difficult

Credit Access, Amex, Diners, Visa

A most elegant restaurant in which to enjoy sound cooking at daunting prices. Seafood dishes, both standard and adventurous, feature largely and famously on the menu and the quality of the produce is top-notch. Meat eaters are also well catered for. Great wines at very high prices: clarets back to Domaine de Chevalier '45, several Rhônes from the '60s, Cabernet Sauvignon Jordan '80.
⊃ Outstanding   🍷 Well-chosen   🄯

Lunch 12.30–2.45   *Dinner* 6–10.45, Sun 7–10
Closed L Sun & Bank Hols

W1   The Selfridge   80%   £A

H Map 22 D1
Orchard Street W1H 0JS
01-408 2080
Telex 22361

Rooms 298
Ensuite bath/shower 298
Direct dial Yes
Room TV Yes
Confirm by 6
Last dinner 10.30
Parking Ample
Room service 24 hours

Credit Access, Amex, Diners, Visa

Just a stone's throw from the Oxford Street shops, the Selfridge is a luxury hotel where the sense of ease and comfort is in splendid contrast to the bustle outside. Public rooms are handsome and discreetly sumptuous: the foyer with its chandeliers and Italian marble, the elegantly furnished, cedar-panelled lounge, the summery Orchard Terrace, Stoves Bar with its antiques and country feel. Bedrooms offer a very high

standard of air-conditioned, soundproofed comfort, with smart darkwood furniture and thoughtfully equipped tiled bathrooms. Staff are very efficient but sometimes a bit short of charm. No dogs.
Amenities in-house movies, secretarial services, fax, valeting, laundry service, coffee shop (9am–11pm).

W8   Shanghai

R Map 22 A3
38c Kensington Church
Street W8 01-938 2501

Chinese cooking
Set L £7.50 **Set D** £12.50
About £35 for two
Seats 80 *Parties* 80
Parking Difficult
Credit Access, Amex, Diners, Visa

You'll find flavoursome fare at this smart modern restaurant on two floors. The food tends to be aromatic rather than fiery and highly recommendable dishes include Shanghai special feast – spare ribs, spring rolls, scallops, deep-fried eel, duck and pancakes – Tung-po pork in spicy/sweet sauce, garlicky Tibetan lamb and fish slices in gingery sauce. Finish with red bean paste pancakes, toffee apple, toffee banana or exotic fruits.

Lunch 12—2.15   *Dinner* 6.30–11.15
Closed Bank Hols & 4 days Xmas

**We publish annually,
so make sure you use the current edition.
It's worth it!**

EC3   Shares

R Map 26 C2
12 Lime Street EC3
01-623 1843

Set L £20.50
About £58 for two
Seats 78
Parties 20
Parking Difficult
Credit Access, Amex, Diners, Visa

Expect the talk to be of stocks and shares at this popular City restaurant catering for business lunches. The short, fixed-price menu of three or four courses offers reliably-prepared, interesting dishes, from a tasty crêpe Arnold Bennett to chicken breast in a cream sauce spiked with brandy and salmon en papillote. Tempting sweets include strawberries tossed in hot caramel with green peppercorns. 🄯

Lunch only 11.30–3
Closed Sat & Sun, Bank Hols

SW1   Sheraton Park Tower   83%   £A

H Map 22 D3
101 Knightsbridge SW1X 7RN
01-235 8050
Telex 917222

Rooms 295
Ensuite bath/shower 295
Direct dial Yes
Room TV Yes
Confirm by 4
Last dinner 11.30
Parking Limited
Room service 24 hours

Credit Access, Amex, Diners, Visa

With its stark grey outline softened at ground level by a leafy pavement garden, this sturdy cylindrical tower has become something of a Knightsbridge landmark. Inside, all is unashamed luxury, from the discreetly-lit open-plan foyer with its marble floor and splendid central flower arrangement to the strikingly elegant Rotunda Lounge and the sumptuous Champagne Bar, styled along the

lines of a Parisian brasserie. Good-sized bedrooms, many with panoramic views over London, boast attractive contemporary decor and well-equipped modern bathrooms. Suites, though luxuriously appointed, are more '70s in style. No dogs. *Amenities* terrace, hairdressing, satellite TV, in-house movies, secretarial services, fax, valeting, laundry service, coffee shop (7am–11.30pm). ♿

W1   Sherlock Holmes Hotel   63%   *NEW ENTRY*   £B

H Map 22 D1
108 Baker Street W1M 1LB
01-486 6161
Telex 8954837

Credit Access, Amex, Diners, Visa

Signs of the great detective abound in this recently refurbished hotel, from the lookalike porter to numerous paintings and drawings depicting scenes from the books. The hotel comprises three separate houses, with the main entrance in Baker Street. There's some seating in the foyer, and also a quiet lounge and a pleasant bar with bamboo chairs and low, comfortable sofas. In the restaurant next to the bar an indifferent buffet breakfast is served. Bedrooms are of a reasonable size, with well-lit desk space, a couple of armchairs, trouser presses and hairdryers. Bathrooms are compact and functional.
Amenities in-house movies, secretarial services, fax, laundry service.

Rooms 126	*Direct dial* Yes	*Confirm by* 6	*Parking* Difficult
Ensuite bath/shower 126	*Room TV* Yes	*Last dinner* 10	*Room service* 24 hours

We publish annually,
so make sure you use the current edition.
It's worth it!

W1   Shogun

R Map 22 D2
Adams Row W1
01-493 1877

Japanese cooking
Set D from £20
About £62 for two
Seats 65 *Parties* 100
Parking Limited
Credit Access, Amex, Diners, Visa

Vaulted cellar premises make a characterful setting, enhanced by a handsome model of a Samurai warrior. The main menu is very traditional, with teriyaki, tempura, sashimi and sushi for main courses, plus deep-fried vegetables, chicken, pork and oysters. Dainty starters, soups and a variety of set dinner menus, plus one written in Japanese for the more learned or adventurous. Good cooking and helpful service.

Dinner only 6–11
Closed Mon, Bank Hols & 1 wk Xmas

W1   Si Cheun   *NEW ENTRY*   ⚏

R Map 27 A2
56 Old Compton Street W1
01-437 2069

Chinese cooking
Set L & D from £7.80
About £25 for two
Seats 65 *Parties* 36
Parking Difficult
Credit Amex, Diners, Visa

Polite service and much above average cooking at a Chinese restaurant in bustling Soho. Szechuan and Pekingese dishes predominate on a fairly conventional menu, and good memories of recent visits include outstanding hot and sour soup, succulent steamed scallops with soy and ginger, fried shredded beef and super red bean paste pancakes. Tea-smoked and crispy aromatic duck are other favourites, along with dumplings and various noodle dishes.

Lunch 12–2.30   *Dinner* 5.30–11.30
Closed Sun, 25 & 26 Dec

SW1   Simply Nico ★★   ♔ ♗

R Map 25 B6
48a Rochester Row SW1
01-630 8061

French cooking

Lunch 12.30–2
Dinner 7.30–11
About £88 *for two*
Seats 34
Parties 6
Parking Ample

Credit Access, Amex, Diners, Visa
Closed Sat, Sun, Bank Hols, 2 wks
Aug & 8–10 days Xmas

Simply brilliant cooking in a stylishly appointed little restaurant that's one of the most talked about in the whole country. Nico Ladenis is the exciting, excitable and occasionally daunting chef, and every dish he creates carries his hallmark of excellence – a blend of flawless technique and unfussily artistic presentation. Examples of his mastery (each dish could be a speciality) include ballotine of foie gras with a lovely light Sauternes jelly, escalope of turbot served on a bed of spinach with a frothy champagne sauce and tournedos of beef with wild mushrooms. There's a fine selection of French cheeses and sweets that are hard to resist. Wines, especially burgundies, are chosen with great care.   ♀ Well-chosen   ☺   🍷

W13   Sinar Matahari

R Map 7 A4
146 The Broadway,
West Ealing W13
01-840 4450

Indonesian cooking
Set meals from £9
Seats 65 *Parties* 50
Parking Limited
Credit Access, Amex, Visa

Strong local support makes it imperative to book at weekends for this popular Indonesian restaurant. Cooking standards are thorough and highlights of dishes that mingle robust and fruity flavours include excellent chicken saté and soto kambing, a tasty lamb soup. Willing service will guide you through the menu. Sweets can be a disappointment.

Lunch 12–2   *Dinner* 6–10.30, Sat 6–11   *About* £30 *for two*
Closed L Sat, all Mon & 25 & 26 Dec

NW6   Singapore Garden   ♗

R Map 20 B3
83 Fairfax Road NW6
01-328 5314

South-East Asian cooking
About £30 *for two*
Seats 88
Parties 100
Parking Ample
Credit Access, Amex, Diners, Visa

A bright Chinese restaurant done out in white and green, with plants and smart prints adding chic. The menu is varied, with Singapore and Malaysian specialities complementing more familiar fare like crispy aromatic duck, Pacific prawns (with ginger, chilli, black bean, oyster or tomato sauce), barbecued pork and Szechuan beef. Portions are generous, cooking very capable, service courteous and helpful. Tables are set on the pavement in fine weather.

Lunch 12–2.30   *Dinner* 6–10.30, Sat till 11
Closed 1 wk Xmas

SW1   Stafford Hotel & Restaurant

See page 325

SW1   Stakis St Ermin's Hotel   73%   £B

H Map 25 B5
Caxton Street SW1H 0QW
01-222 7888
Telex 917731

Rooms 291
Ensuite bath/shower 291
Direct dial Yes
Room TV Yes
Confirm by 6
Last dinner 10.15
Parking Limited
Room service 24 hours

Credit Access, Amex, Diners, Visa

Queen Victoria still reigned when this centrally located hotel first opened its doors, and today's visitors sense the splendour of a bygone age in the public areas. Marble and ornate plasterwork are much in evidence, and there are plenty of inviting armchairs and sofas. The cocktail bar has a delightful club-like atmosphere, and there's a grand ballroom. Bedrooms on five floors around the entrance courtyard are gen-

erally quite compact, with pleasant modern decor and furnishings.
Amenities patio, satellite TV, in-house movies, laundry service.

WC2   Strand Palace Hotel   62%   £C

H Map 24 D3
Strand WC2R 0JJ
01-836 8080
Telex 24208

Credit Access, Amex, Diners, Visa

Polite staff are kept very busy at this favourite hotel with an ideally
central location, where tourists and business visitors throng the stylish
foyer-lounge and two smart bars. Simple bedrooms have coordinated
furnishings and fitted units, some now showing signs of wear. Smartest
rooms - on the seventh floor - have been refurbished.
Amenities secretarial services, fax, laundry service, coffee shop
(6.30am–12.30am), kiosk. &

| Rooms 771 | Direct dial Yes | Confirm by 6 | Parking Difficult |
| Ensuite bath/shower 771 | Room TV Yes | Last dinner 10 | Room service None |

SW1   Suntory   ♕

R Map 25 B4
72 St James's Street SW1
01-409 0201

Japanese cooking
Set L £12   Set D £23
About £80 for two
Seats 120 Parties 50
Parking Difficult
Credit Access, Amex, Diners, Visa

This is the place to learn about the art of Japanese cuisine, with
friendly staff being very willing to explain the mysteries of the
tappan-yaki bar, where guests sit round individual iron griddles set
in each table, and the comprehensive menu served in the comfortable
ground-floor restaurant. Beautifully-prepared and presented dishes
include dobin-mushi, a delicious soup with chicken and prawns,
excellent yakitori, and superb chiraski sushi.

Lunch 12–2   *Dinner* 7–10
Closed Sun, Bank Hols, 25–28 Dec & 31 Dec–3 Jan

SW3   Le Suquet

R Map 23 C5
104 Draycott Avenue SW3
01-581 1785

Seafood
About £58 for two
Seats 58
Parties 16
Parking Difficult
Credit Access, Amex, Diners, Visa

Straightforward preparations of good fresh seafood bring the crowds
to this fashionable French restaurant, which comprises a ground-floor
room, places for about eight at the bar and an upstairs overspill room.
Oysters, scallops, fish soup, lobster, feuilletés and salads are excellent,
and the substantial seafood platter is a great favourite. Daily specials
often include sea bass grilled and served with a simple beurre blanc.
Service seems warmer than of old. ♀ Well-chosen ☯

Lunch 12.30–3   *Dinner* 7–11.30

W1   Sutherlands   ★ NEW ENTRY   ♕ ⌇

R Map 24 B3
45 Lexington Street W1
01-434 3401

Lunch 12.15–2.15
Dinner 6.15–11.15
Set L from £16.80
About £60 for two
Seats 45
Parties 20
Parking Difficult

Credit Access, Amex, Visa
Closed L Sat, all Sun & Bank
Hols

Behind the discreet clouded-glass
windows all is understated chic
– from the stylish mirrored decor
to the jet-black designer chairs.
Chef and co-owner Garry Holli-
head is more than a match for
this sophisticated setting; his
short, tempting menus display
their own kind of artistry in
dishes like pithivier of oysters
and seaweed with a light ginger
jacqueline, and saddle of wild
boar with blackcurrants. Por-
tions are fashionably small. Concise yet wide-ranging wine list.
Specialities crayfish and baby lobster with morels in a Château
Chalon sauce, baby brioche filled with warm Brie on a salad of nettle
and soft herbs, nage of spring fruit in a spun sugar cage.
♀ Well-chosen ❦

SW5   Swallow International Hotel   65%   £C

H Map 23 A4
147c Cromwell Road SW5 0TH
01-370 4200
Telex 27260

Credit Access, Amex, Diners, Visa

A large modern hotel that's especially geared to tour groups. Bustling
public areas include a marble-clad foyer and a spacious bar-lounge.
Recently updated bedrooms are compact but neat, with good storage
and writing space, and cheerful modern decor. Executive rooms offer
more accessories and smarter bathrooms. Service is a little casual at
times. *Amenities* in-house movies, secretarial services, fax, laundry
service, coffee shop (7am–midnight).

| Rooms 417 | Direct dial Yes | Confirm by 6 | Parking Limited |
| Ensuite bath/shower 417 | Room TV Yes | Last dinner 11 | Room service 24 hours |

W1 — Swiss Centre, The Chesa

R **Map 27 A3**
2 New Coventry Street W1
01-734 1291

Set L £15.50 **Set D** £19.50
About £50 for two
Seats 55
Parties 80
Parking Limited
Credit Access, Amex, Diners, Visa

The smooth running of this reliable restaurant continues under a new manager and chef. On the menu are a good variety of dishes, mainly basically French style but, of course, Swiss delicacies such as air-cured beef and ham from the Engadine, melted Swiss raclette cheese and rösti potatoes also feature. There's also a fixed-price 'Menu Gourmet Suisse'. Expect sound cooking of good ingredients. Selection of mostly Swiss wines. ☺

Meals noon–midnight
Closed 1 Jan & 25 & 26 Dec

NW3 — Swiss Cottage Hotel   64%   £C/D

H **Map 20 B3**
4 Adamson Road,
Swiss Cottage NW3 3HP
01-722 2281
Telex 297232

Credit Access, Amex, Diners, Visa

Part of a terrace of handsome Victorian houses makes up this peacefully situated hotel. Founded by an art and antiques collector, it's full of lovely old things. A gilded desk catches your eye in the reception hall and there are more antiques in the elegant high-ceilinged lounge. Bedrooms vary in size but are all pleasantly furnished, many with fine old wardrobes and writing desks. No dogs.
Amenities patio garden, laundry service.

Rooms 65	*Direct dial* Yes	*Confirm by* 6	*Parking* Ample
Ensuite bath/shower 65	*Room TV* Yes	*Last dinner* 9	*Room service* 24 hours

Our inspectors *never* book in the name of Egon Ronay's Guides.
They disclose their identity only if they are considering an establishment
for inclusion in the next edition of the Guide.

SW10 — T'ang   ⊈

R **Map 23 B6**
294 Fulham Road SW10
01-351 2599

South East Asian cooking
About £50 for two
Seats 70
Parties 30
Parking Limited
Credit Access, Amex, Diners, Visa

The decor is cool, the menu a concise and imaginative selection of South-East Asian cuisine. Partner Tony Pat comes up with some really delicious dishes, including crispy duck in a crunchy pancake basket, and succulent prawns with lemon and lime leaves. The pork dumplings are good, too, and tofu rolls make a nice change from the spring variety. Service on our last visit was far from enthusiastic, and the food's pricey.

Lunch 12–2.30   *Dinner* 7–11.30
Closed L Sat, all Sun, Bank Hols & 3 wks end Dec–Jan

SW3 — La Tante Claire   ★★★   ⊈

R **Map 23 C6**
68 Royal Hospital Road SW3
01-352 6045

French cooking

Lunch 12.30–2
Dinner 7–11.15
Set L £18.50
About £110 for two
Seats 45
Parking Limited

Credit Access, Amex, Diners, Visa
Closed Sat, Sun, Bank Hols, 10 days Xmas, 10 days Easter & 3 wks Aug/Sept

Superlatives are in order for Pierre Koffmann's coolly elegant restaurant where nothing is left to chance. The short menu of supremely conceived dishes, beautifully put together, changes twice a year, and everything is so superb that choice is difficult. Our highlights included a rich tourte feuilletée de canard with wonderful pastry and a soufflé chaud exquisitely flavoured with pistachio. The aristocratic wine list has plenty of half-bottles at approachable prices. ***Specialities*** galette de foie gras au sauternes et échalottes rôties, pied de cochon aux champignons des bois, filet de chevreuil au chocolat amer et vinaigre de framboises, croustade de pommes. ☞ Outstanding
♙ Well-chosen ☺ 🍷

WC2   Thomas de Quincey's   *NEW ENTRY*   ♛

Map 24 D3
36 Tavistock Street WC2
01-240 3773

Set L £16.75
About £70 for two
Seats 50
Parties 50
Parking Difficult

Credit Access, Amex, Diners, Visa

An extremely well-run restaurant with a collection of prints and paintings that include a splendid portrait of de Quincey himself. The seasonal menu offers an imaginative and tempting interpretation of classical dishes: terrine of duck à l'orange with a salad of berries and leaves; Dover sole with a sauce of wine, cream and wild mushrooms and a feuilleté of asparagus; lamb fillets in an Oriental-inspired sauce. Vegetables excel, and the sweet trolley is a real pleasure, with such items as soufflé à la neige, pear bavarois and white chocolate gâteau. Outstanding cheeses, too. Note the fine collection of 30 vintage Armagnacs including a 1912 from Francis Darroze.   ♟ Well-chosen ℮

Lunch 12–2.30   *Dinner* 6–11.15, Sat 7–11.30
Closed L Sat, all Sun, Bank Hols & 10 days Xmas

SW5   Tiger Lee   ★   ♛

Map 23 A5
251 Old Brompton Road SW5
01-370 2323

Chinese cooking

Set D from £20
About £55 for two
Seats 56
Parties 20
Parking Limited

Credit Access, Amex, Diners, Visa
Closed 24 & 25 Dec

Top-quality seafood plays a star-ring role at this small chic Chinese restaurant, and there's no point in counting the cost: you need to go for the specials to appreciate the true genius of the cooking. Try for example pin yee soup – a delicious blend of crab and langoustines with white fish, herbs and shredded Chinese cabbage – or crispy stuffed grouper fish – freshly flown in from the Indian Ocean and delicately spiced with

ginger. For meat-eaters there are treats like hand-reared guinea fowl. *Specialities* stir-fried baby lobster, stuffed king prawns, yam baskets with diced scallops and roast pine kernels, crispy roast pigeon squabs. ♟ Well-chosen   ⅋

E1   Tower Thistle Hotel   73%   £B

Map 26 D3
St Katherine's Way E1 9LD
01-481 2575
Telex 885934

Rooms 826
Ensuite bath/shower 826
Direct dial Yes
Room TV Yes
Confirm by 6
Last dinner 10
Parking Ample
Room service 24 hours

Credit Access, Amex, Diners, Visa

The site for this modern hotel is one of the capital's most spectac-ular – on the Thames next to Tower Bridge and the Tower of London. The marbled lobby is bright with greenery, and there are plenty of armchairs and sofas; the Thames Bar has a nautical theme highlighted by a handsome model of a sailing ship. Double-glazed, air-conditioned bedrooms with river views are equipped with trouser presses and hairdryers, with many extras (and a separate check-out) for Executive rooms. Service failed to impress on our last visit, and breakfast was not a towering success. No dogs.
Amenities in-house movies, secretarial services, fax, laundry service, coffee shop (7.30am–midnight).

SE10   Treasure of China   *NEW ENTRY*

Map 7 B5 10 Nelson Road,
Greenwich SE10
01-858 9884

Chinese cooking
Set L from £16
Set D from £11
About £42 for two
Seats 78 *Parties* 42
Credit Access, Amex, Diners, Visa

Stylish modern Chinese restaurant with a well-composed menu of dishes from many regions. Cooking is sound in all departments, from starters such as grilled dumplings and aromatic crispy lamb to Cantonese drunken fish, chilli beef and braised duck with mushrooms and bamboo shoots. There are plenty of vegetable dishes, and an interesting speciality is baked coconut-flavoured seafood rice served in a coconut shell.

Lunch 12.00–2.30, Sun till 3   *Dinner* 6–11.30, Fri & Sat till 12, Sun 6.30–11.30   *Parking* Limited   **Closed** 2 days Xmas

SW3   Les Trois Plats   *NEW ENTRY*

R **Map 23 C5**
4 Sydney Street, Chelsea SW3
01-352 3433

French cooking
Set D £23
About £46 for two
Seats 48 *Parties* 48
Parking Difficult
Credit Access, Amex, Diners, Visa

The all-in price at the Roux brothers' sub-basement restaurant gets you kir, canapés, three courses, coffee, petits fours and half a bottle of house wine, with VAT and service included. Cooking is very acceptable throughout a short menu, where typical items run from duck rillettes and feuilleté of mussels to goujonnettes of sole, baby chicken with morels (very few) and a duo of coffee and orange bavarois. ⊖

Dinner only 7–11
Closed Sun, Bank Hols

SW7   Tui

R **Map 23 C4**
19 Exhibition Road SW7
01-584 8359

Thai cooking
About £46 for two
Seats 60
Parking Difficult

Credit Access, Amex, Diners, Visa

Subtle flavours and artistic presentation are features of Thai cooking at this popular restaurant near the museums. Favourites include tom yum (soup flavoured with lemon grass and chillis), chicken with ginger and Chinese mushrooms, and crisp-fried noodles with a tamarind sauce, prawns and pork. Staff are gentle and courteous, and the good food is matched by thoughtfully chosen wines including a delicious Saumur as the house white. Quick lunch menu. ♀ Well-chosen

Lunch 12–2.30, Sun till 3   *Dinner* 6.30–11, Sun 7–10.30
Closed Bank Hols & 2–3 days Xmas

SW3   Turner's

R **Map 23 C4**
87 Walton Street SW3
01-584 6711

Set L from £14.75
Set D from £19.75
About £70 for two
Seats 54
Parties 20
Parking Difficult

Credit Access, Amex, Diners, Visa

Brian Turner, a friendly Yorkshireman, greets and looks after guests at his fashionable and sophisticated restaurant. He's a true professional, which is not always the case with some of his front-of-house team. Chef Mark Clayton shows sound technique and a fine instinct for combinations. His ever-changing menus feature such dishes as consommé of young rabbit with herbs, artichoke heart with a mousse of duck's hearts, and fillet of veal in a cream of sweetcorn and wild mushroom sauce. Shrewdly chosen wines, notably Bordeaux châteaux on the rise: Dassault St. Emilion 1982, Siran Margaux 1981. Booking is advisable in the evening. ♀ Well-chosen

Lunch 12.30–2.45, Sun 12.30–2.45   *Dinner* 7.30–11, Sun 7.30–11
Closed L Sat, Bank Hols & 1 wk Xmas

W1   The Veeraswamy   ♕

R **Map 24 B3**
99 Regent Street W1
01-734 1401

Indian cooking

Set L £9.50
About £47 for two
Seats 129
Parties 60
Parking Ample

Credit Access, Amex, Diners, Visa

London's longest-established Indian restaurant is a bright and stylish second-floor dining room overlooking the lower sweep of Regent Street. Here you can sample the pick of the various regional cuisines – there's a specialist chef for each one – and appreciate the thought and care put into the choice and preparation of ingredients. Starters range from lentil dumplings and shrimp masala to sole fritters with fresh coriander chutney. To follow, choose trout or other delights from the tandoor; or perhaps a creamy lamb pasanda or fiery coconut-flavoured chicken Goa. There are thalis for vegetarians, good breads and rice, and lovely sweets. Lunch is an excellent self-service hot buffet.

Lunch 12–2.30   *Dinner* 6–11.30, Sun 7–10.30
Closed 25 & 26 Dec

NW3   Wakaba   ♧

R **Map 20 B3**
122A Finchley Road NW3
01-586 7960

Japanese cooking
Set L from £6.90
Set D from £17.80
About £50 for two
Seats 55 *Parking* Difficult
Credit Access, Amex, Diners, Visa

Wakaba has moved from College Crescent into roomier, more attractive and quite stylish premises on Finchley Road. Traditional Japanese dishes like sushi, sashimi and tempura is what they specialise in, and the cooking is under the expert care of Mr. Yoshihara (his wife attends to front of house with typical Japanese charm). Set meals are a good way for beginners to get to know the cuisine.

Lunch 12–2.30   *Dinner* 6.30–11
Closed Sun, 1 wk Aug & 4 days Xmas

WC2 — The Waldorf 77% — £A

H Map 24 D3
Aldwych WC2B 4DD
01-836 2400
Telex 24574

Rooms 310
Ensuite bath/shower 310
Direct dial Yes
Room TV Yes
Confirm by 6
Last dinner 11
Parking Difficult
Room service 24 hours

Credit Access, Amex, Diners, Visa

Eighty years old, the Waldorf still cuts a stylish figure in the gentle curve of Aldwych. Its classical facade is picked up inside in a discreet marble and darkwood foyer of pleasing proportions and in the elegant and spacious Palm Court (where tea dances are back in fashion). There are two bars, one with a clubby atmosphere; the other, the Footlights, has its own street entrance. Bedrooms are smart and stylish, and the 18 suites have antique furnishings. All rooms are equipped with mini-bars, hairdryers and satellite TV, and there are thick, fluffy towels and good toiletries in the bathrooms.
Amenities hairdressing, fax, valeting, brasserie (10am–midnight), kiosk.

SW3 — Waltons — ♨

R Map 23 C4
121 Walton Street SW3
01-584 0204

Set L £13
Set D £19.50 after 10pm
About £95 *for two*
Seats 70
Parties 65
Parking Limited

Credit Access, Amex, Diners, Visa

The strong yellow and grey decor and the heavy, billowing fabrics set a rich, reassuring tone at Walton Street's most famous restaurant. The menus combine conservative luxury (smoked salmon with salmon mousse, game pâté, lobster, terrine of truffled foie gras) with a hint of the adventurous: warm pheasant and chestnut salad, roast lamb with crab and a red pepper sauce, ragoût of calf's kidneys and sweetbreads in honey vinegar sauce. Good fresh ingredients are respectfully treated to retain their fine natural flavours. Sunday lunch centres around traditional roasts or a fish dish. The wine list includes some excellent clarets (Ch. Figeac 1978) and red burgundies (Chambertin 1982 from A. Rousseau). Discreet, courteous service. ♟ Well-chosen ☙

Lunch 12.30–2.30, Sun 12.30–2 *Dinner* 7.30–11.30, Sun 7.30–10.30
Closed 4 days Easter & 25 & 26 Dec

NW3 — Weng Wah House

R Map 20 B2
240 Haverstock Hill NW3
01-794 5123

Chinese cooking
Set D from £9.50
About £30 *for two*
Seats 80 *Parties* 120
Parking Ample
Credit Access, Amex, Diners, Visa

Spicy dishes from Singapore are among the offerings at this smart restaurant on Haverstock Hill. Set meals cater for those unsure of what to order; the knowledgeable may plump for moist and beautifully flavoured aromatic duck or sizzling lamb with ginger and spring onions. Vegetarians are well served with tofu dishes, vegetable stir-fries and curries.

Lunch Mon–Sat noon–2.45 *Dinner* Mon–Fri 6–11.30, Sat 6–midnight
Meals Sun noon–11.30 **Closed** 25 & 26 Dec

W1 — The Westbury 79% — £A

HR Map 24 A3
Conduit Street W1A 4UH
01-629 7755
Telex 24378

Rooms 243
Ensuite bath/shower 243
Direct dial Yes
Room TV Yes
Confirm by 6
Last dinner 11.30
Parking Limited
Room service 24 hours

Credit Access, Amex, Diners, Visa

Excellent standards of service and a continuing programme of improvements and refurbishment help to keep this splendid Mayfair hotel a civilised haven. The marble-floored foyer with its plush seating and roaring fire sets the elegant, welcoming tone that continues throughout tastefully appointed day rooms like the handsome, pine-panelled Tennyson Room (a perfect setting for afternoon tea) and the intimate, polo-themed cocktail bar. Bedrooms, too, are of the same high standard, with their darkwood furniture and lovely floral fabrics; there are also a number of suites in the same style. Compact private bathrooms offer excellent toiletries and hairdryers. *Amenities* in-house movies, secretarial services, fax, valeting, laundry service.

The Polo Restaurant *NEW ENTRY*

Set L from £16.50
Set D £26.95
About £75 for two

Comfortable surroundings and professional service back up Philip Corrick's enjoyable cooking. Deft touches are evident in splendid dishes like smoked salmon sausage with a silky-smooth sea-urchin sauce, magret of duck with cider vinegar or a hot Kirsch soufflé served with pistachio ice cream. There's an excellent selection of fine French and British cheeses. Decent wine list strong on Bordeaux.

Lunch 12–2.45   *Dinner* 7–10

★ For a *discount* on next year's guide, see **An Offer for Answers.** ★

NW1   White House   73%   £B

H **Map 24 A1**
Albany Street NW1 3VP
01-387 1200
Telex 24111

Rooms 580
Ensuite bath/shower 580
Direct dial Yes
Room TV Yes
Confirm by 6
Last dinner 11
Parking Difficult
Room service 24 hours

Credit Access, Amex, Diners, Visa

Originally built as a block of flats in the 1930s, this pleasant hotel stands just north of the busy Marylebone/Euston Road not far from Regent's Park. The spacious pillared foyer leads to a stylish bar and a smart coffee shop. Double-glazed bedrooms with quality lightwood furniture and tasteful colour schemes are equipped with mini-bars and have tiled bathrooms with radio-speakers, hairdryers and useful

toiletries. Top-floor rooms are extra luxurious, with their own check-in and residents' lounge. Efficient staff lack personality and breakfast is only average. No dogs.
Amenities in-house movies, secretarial services, fax, laundry service, coffee shop (7am–11pm), kiosk. &

W1   White Tower

R **Map 24 B2**
1 Percy Street W1
01-636 8141

Greek cooking
About £50 for two
Seats 70
Parties 16
Parking Limited
Credit Access, Amex, Diners, Visa

Crossing the threshold of this excellent and elegant Greek restaurant is to enter a time warp of the 1960s. Certain dishes are outstanding. The fish salad is uniquely fresh because it is made twice a day in very small quantities; and the specially reared ducklings with bulghur wheat stuffing are superbly crisp. Other good dishes range from dolmades and moussaka to braised capama of lamb. Solicitous service of the old school. Good wines at highish prices.

Lunch 12.30–2.30   *Dinner* 6.30–10.30
Closed Sat, Sun, Bank Hols & 1 wk Xmas

W2   Whites Hotel   80%   £A

H **Map 22 B2**
Lancaster Gate W2 3NR
01-262 2711
Telex 24771

Rooms 54
Ensuite bath/shower 54
Direct dial Yes
Room TV Yes
Confirm by 6.30
Last dinner 10.30
Parking Limited
Room service 24 hours

Credit Access, Amex, Diners, Visa

Long-serving manager Michael Wills leads by example here, and service and housekeeping are both outstanding. The feeling of luxury starts in the foyer, resplendent with rug-covered marble floors, chandeliers and inviting armchairs. The panelled reading room is a haven of dignified calm, and a pianist provides soothing entertainment in the cocktail bar. Bedrooms continue the theme with hand-

some furnishings and extras ranging from individually controlled air conditioning to teletext TVs, mini-bars and safes. Bathrooms are no less opulent, offering thick towels, bathrobes and bountiful supplies of toiletries, plus telephone extensions and radio/TV speakers. No dogs.
Amenities in-house movies, secretarial services, fax, laundry service.

SW1   Wilbraham Hotel   57%   £D

H Map 23 D4
Wilbraham Place,
Sloane Street SW1X 9AE
01-730 8296

There's precious little Daniel Mullane doesn't know about running a hotel, and the Wilbraham attracts many regulars with his fine management and courteous personal service. Day rooms are modest, quiet and peaceful, and bedrooms are cosy and appealing in an old-fashioned way. Rooms vary considerably in size, but all are well kept, and most have their own bath/shower rooms. Note that credit cards are not accepted. No dogs. *Amenities* valeting, laundry service.

Rooms 52	Direct dial Yes	Confirm by arrang.	Parking Limited
Ensuite bath/shower 40	Room TV Some	Last dinner 9.45	Room service 24 hours

SW1   Wiltons   ♕

R Map 25 B4
55 Jermyn Street SW1
01-629 9955

English cooking
About £75 for two
Seats 90
Parties 16
Parking Difficult
Credit Access, Amex, Diners, Visa

A club-like restaurant of the old school with formal service and staunchly traditional food, soundly cooked. Oysters are a famous starter here, or try the succulent langoustine cocktail. Follow with one of the lobster dishes, a grill or superbly fresh poached salmon with a light hollandaise sauce. Finish with a good quality English cheese or a traditional pudding. 🍷 Well-chosen ℮

Lunch 12.30–2.30   *Dinner* 6.30–10.30
Closed L Sat, all Sun, Bank Hols, last wk July & 2 wks Aug

Our inspectors *never* book in the name of Egon Ronay's Guides.
They disclose their identity only if they are considering an establishment
for inclusion in the next edition of the Guide.

SW12   Yours Faithfully   *NEW ENTRY*   ♕

R Map 21 C6
4 Nightingale Lane SW12
01-675 5771

Set Sun L £13
Set D from £16.50
About £50 for two
Seats 55 Parties 55
Parking Limited
Credit Amex

The expertise of the interior designer owner has turned an old greengrocer's shop into a stylish and fashionable restaurant with roomy, well-spaced tables and a pleasant bar area. The food is good, fresh ingredients being treated with respect on an interesting, up-to-date menu: tartlet of vineyard snails with wild mushrooms and chives; poached breast of poulet noir with salmon mousse and mango sauce; dark chocolate and Tia Maria terrine. ℮ ♿

Lunch Sun 1–3, Mon–Sat by arrang.   *Dinner* 7.30–10.30
Closed D Sun

W1   Yumi

R Map 22 D1
110 George Street W1
01-935 8320

Japanese cooking
Set L from £6.90
Set D from £22.50
Seats 78 Parties 16
Parking Difficult
Credit Access, Amex, Diners, Visa

Yumi Fujii, the charming owner, is always on hand to greet guests at this delightful Japanese restaurant, and her staff are paragons of politeness. You can eat sushi in the ground-floor bar or go downstairs and enjoy a selection of carefully prepared, fairly familiar dishes. The set dinner is a good choice for those not well versed in Japanese cuisine. Private dining rooms are available.

Lunch 12–2.30   *Dinner* 6–10.45   About £53 for two
Closed L Sat, all Sun, Bank Hols, 1 wk Aug & 10 days Xmas

Changes in data sometimes occur in establishments
after the Guide goes to press.
Prices should be taken as indications rather than firm quotes.

W1 — Yung's

R Map 27 A2
23 Wardour Street W1
01-437 4986

Chinese cooking
Set meals from £6.50
About £20 for two
Seats 100 Parties 20
Parking Difficult
Credit Access, Amex, Diners, Visa

Two tiny floors provide close-packed seats for 100 in a perennially popular Chinese restaurant in the heart of Soho. The menu is essentially Cantonese, with seafood a major feature, from sweetcorn and crab soup to steamed sea bass, quick-fried scallops, and baked lobster. Meat dishes, too, and everything deftly cooked and full of flavour. The only sweet is refreshing quarters of orange.

Meals 4pm–5am
Closed 24 & 25 Dec

W1 — Zazou

W1   **Zazou**   *NEW ENTRY*

R Map 24 B1
74 Charlotte Street W1
01-436 5133

About £60 for two
Seats 45
Parking Difficult

Credit Access, Amex, Diners, Visa

Situated below a lively bar/brasserie, Zazou is chic, stylish and successful. The menu leans towards the sea, with Billingsgate and Boulogne the chief sources for oysters, lobsters, langoustines, and white fish served either grilled, with olive oil and lemon, or steamed with ginger, spring onions and soy sauce. Meaty alternatives include crispy duck with pancakes, calf's liver and roast lamb. Superb British cheese selection; simple sweets. ♀ Well-chosen ⊖

Lunch 12–2.30   Dinner 7–11.30
Closed L Sat, all Sun & Bank Hols

SW3 — Ziani

SW3   **Ziani**

R Map 23 C5
45 Radnor Walk SW3
01-351 5297

Italian cooking
About £45 for two
Seats 50
Parties 25
Parking Ample
Credit Access, Amex, Diners, Visa

A bright and fashionable little restaurant with a tiled floor and a small bar area. Northern Italy is the main inspiration for the excellent cooking, and among the best dishes are pasta, quail with polenta, carpaccio (try it dressed with prime olive oil and shavings of Parmesan) and a very superior fritto misto di pesce that includes whitebait, squid, prawns and salmon. Friendly, obliging staff enhance the pleasures of the table. ♀ Well-chosen ⊖

Lunch 12.30–2.45   Dinner 7–11.30
Closed Bank Hols

SW1 — Stafford Hotel

SW1   **Stafford Hotel**   77%   £A

HR Map 25 B4
St James's Place SW1A 1NJ
01-493 0111
Telex 28602

Rooms 62
Ensuite bath/shower 62
Direct dial Yes
Room TV Yes
Confirm by 6
Last dinner 10.30
Parking Limited
Room service 24 hours

Credit Access, Amex, Diners, Visa

A fine hotel in the heart of the West End, with the calm relaxed atmosphere of an exclusive private club. Porters and reception staff provide a genuinely warm welcome in the stylish foyer, where pictures line the walls and leather chesterfields offer instant ease. Beyond the foyer is a most attractive lounge with antiques and abundant fresh flowers, and a cosily inviting bar with access to a little garden. Individually

appointed bedrooms contain a variety of high-quality fabrics and furnishings, with everything in complete harmony; bathrooms, too, are individual and very pretty.
Amenities garden, terrace, laundry service, in-house movies, satellite TV, secretarial services, fax.

Restaurant   ♛

Set L £18.25
Set D £23
About £77 for two
Seats 60
Parties 12

After 25 years at the helm, Armando Rodriguez still delights diners with his culinary skills. His menu is French, of the traditional school, and among his specialities are lobster (bisque, Thermidor, Cardinal), veal chops with rosemary, duck with green peppercorns and cherries Jubilee. Complementing the menu is a good, classic wine list: note Ch. Branaire Ducru '78 and Vosne Romanée "Clos de Réas" (Gros) '80. ⊖ &

Lunch 12.30–2.30
Dinner 6–10.30, Sun from 6.30

All human history attests

That happiness for man - the hungry sinner,

Since Eve ate apples, much depends on dinner!

LORD BYRON 1788-1824

DON JUAN

I know

a little restaurant

Behind a brownstone stoop

Where *pottage du jour* is French

For a can of onion soup.

OGDEN NASH 1902-71

TRY IT SUNS. AND HOLS:
IT'S CLOSED THEN

HOTELS
RESTAURANTS
AND INNS

LONDON
AIRPORTS

GATWICK

Chequers Thistle Hotel   66%   £C

H **Map 7 B5** Surrey
Brighton Road,
Horley RH6 8PH
Crawley (0293) 786992
Telex 877550

Credit Access, Amex, Diners, Visa

A former Tudor coaching inn, now much enlarged, to the north of the airport on the A23. Carved wood panelling and bookshelves make for a cosy foyer, and there's also an attractive bar-lounge and a pubby saloon bar. Bedrooms are cheerfully decorated in pastel shades and have compact bathrooms. Courtesy bus to the airport. *Amenities* garden, outdoor swimming pool, in-house movies, secretarial services, fax, laundry service, coffee shop (10am–10pm).

Rooms 78	*Direct dial* Yes	*Confirm by* 6	*Parking* Ample
Ensuite bath/shower 78	*Room TV* Yes	*Last dinner* 10	*Room service* 24 hours

Copthorne Hotel   69%   £C

H **Map 7 B5** West Sussex
Copthorne, Nr Crawley
RH10 3PG
Copthorne (0342) 714971
Telex 95500

Credit Access, Amex, Diners, Visa

Just off junction 10 of the M23, the Copthorne is fronted by a 16th-century farmhouse. Old beams preserve period feel in some of the day rooms, while others have a more contemporary appeal. Bedrooms, many down distant, dingy corridors, are in neat, practical style, with light pine furnishings and bold floral fabrics; hairdryers and trouser presses are standard, and there are bedside controls for TV and radio. Some aspects of service and housekeeping disappointed on a recent visit, and the buffet breakfast was awful. Airport coach. *Amenities* garden, sauna, solarium, keep-fit equipment, hairdressing, squash, putting, croquet, in-house movies, secretarial services, laundry service, coffee shop (5.30am–10.45pm), kiosk, children's playground   ᕦ

Rooms 223	*Direct dial* Yes	*Confirm by* 6	*Parking* Ample
Ensuite bath/shower 223	*Room TV* Yes	*Last dinner* 11	*Room service* 24 hours

Crest Hotel, Gatwick   58%   £C

H **Map 7 B5** West Sussex
Langley Drive,
Crawley RH11 7SX
Crawley (0293) 29991
Telex 877311

Credit Access, Amex, Diners, Visa

Four miles south of Gatwick on the outskirts of Crawley, this is a purpose-built hotel geared to the air traveller. There's a bright, cheerful foyer, and open-plan public areas (including two contemporary bars and a coffee shop) are furnished to a high standard. Compact bedrooms – some reserved for non-smokers, others for women – are well equipped. *Amenities* garden, games room, in-house movies, secretarial services, fax, laundry service.

Rooms 231	*Direct dial* Yes	*Confirm by* 6	*Parking* Ample
Ensuite bath/shower 231	*Room TV* Yes	*Last dinner* 10	*Room service* Limited

**We welcome bona fide complaints and recommendations
on the tear-out pages at the back of the book for readers' comment.
They are followed up by our professional team.**

Gatwick Concorde Hotel   56%   £C/D

H **Map 7 B5** West Sussex
Church Road,
Lowfield Heath RH11 0PQ
Crawley (0293) 33441
Telex 87287

Credit Access, Amex, Diners, Visa

If you like planes, book a room overlooking one of the main runways to watch the comings and goings. Bedrooms in the smart new wing have attractive lightwood furniture, teletext, hairdryers, tea/coffee-makers and good, albeit compact, bathrooms. Best of the public rooms is the bar, which has dark oak furniture and a pubby atmosphere. *Amenities* in-house movies, secretarial services, fax, laundry service, 24-hour lounge service.

Rooms 121	*Direct dial* Yes	*Confirm by* 6	*Parking* Ample
Ensuite bath/shower 121	*Room TV* Yes	*Last dinner* 10.15	*Room service* None

Gatwick Hilton International 76% £B

H **Map 7 B5** West Sussex
RH6 0LL
Gatwick (0293) 518080
Telex 877021

Rooms 552
Ensuite bath/shower 552
Direct dial Yes
Room TV Yes
Confirm by arrang.
Last dinner 11
Parking Ample
Room service 24 hours

Credit Access, Amex, Diners, Visa

A modern hotel just four minutes' walk from the airport terminals. A plant-filled atrium with a facsimile of a Gypsy Moth aeroplane hanging from the ceiling forms the central core of the hotel, with bedrooms looking inwards to give a galleried effect. A smart split-level coffee shop with white marble tables and a traditional panelled bar provide pleasant spots to relax in. Bedrooms have cool, restful decor, smart light-wood units and two easy chairs; modern conveniences include electronic door locks and TVs displaying flight information.
Amenities garden, indoor swimming pool, sauna, solarium, whirlpool bath, gymnasium, hairdressing, satellite TV, secretarial services, fax, valeting, laundry service, coffee shop (24 hours). &

Gatwick Moat House 62% £C

H **Map 7 B5** Surrey
Longbridge Roundabout,
Horley RH6 0AB
Horley (0293) 785599
Telex 877138

Credit Access, Amex, Diners, Visa

The functional exterior of this modern hotel on the A23 hides a warm, attractive interior. Light wood and greenery grace the foyer-lounge and on the first floor a smart lounge bar has nice dark cane furnishings. Bedrooms boast pretty coordinating fabrics, good writing surfaces and storage space and air conditioning. Courtesy coach to the airport. *Amenities* in-house movies, secretarial services, fax, laundry service, coffee shop (2.30pm–11pm). &

Rooms 120	*Direct dial* Yes	*Confirm by* 6	*Parking* Ample
Ensuite bath/shower 120	*Room TV* Yes	*Last dinner* 10.15	*Room service* Limited

Gatwick Penta Hotel 71% £B/C

H **Map 7 B5** Surrey
Povey Cross Road RH6 0BE
Crawley (0293) 820169
Telex 87440

Rooms 260
Ensuite bath/shower 260
Direct dial Yes
Room TV Yes
Confirm by 6
Last dinner 11
Parking Ample
Room service All day

Credit Access, Amex, Diners, Visa

A modern, purpose built hotel, with a large car park. Leather sofas, brass table lamps and plentiful greenery grace the attractive foyer-lounge, while the bar is in the style of an old Brighton Belle Pullman car. A comprehensive conference centre has been newly refurbished. The spacious, functionally modern bedrooms are air-conditioned and soundproofed, and all have tea/coffee-makers; singles have mini-bars and trouser presses. The neat, fully-tiled bathrooms all have shower units. Transport to the airport is provided. *Amenities* garden, indoor swimming pool, sauna, solarium, whirlpool bath, keep-fit equipment, squash, in-house movies, laundry service, coffee shop (11am–6pm), 24-hour lounge service, kiosk. &

★ For a *discount* on next year's guide, see **An Offer for Answers.** ★

Post House Hotel 63% £B/C

H **Map 7 B5** Surrey
Povey Cross Road, Horley
RH6 0BA
Horley (0293) 771621
Telex 877351

Credit Access, Amex, Diners, Visa

This purpose-built hotel has good functional accommodation, constantly upgraded and well maintained. Public areas include a lobby, modern lounge and small cocktail bar. Bedrooms have darkwood units and modern soft furnishings. All have compact shower bathrooms, double glazing and good facilities. Some have individual air-conditioning. Courtesy coach. *Amenities* patio, outdoor swimming pool, in-house movies, fax, laundry service, coffee shop (10.45am–10.45pm), kiosk. &

Rooms 216	*Direct dial* Yes	*Confirm by* 6	*Parking* Ample
Ensuite bath/shower 216	*Room TV* Yes	*Last dinner* 10.30	*Room service* 24 hours

HEATHROW

Ariel   65%   £C

H **Map 5 E2** Middlesex
Bath Road, Hayes UB3 5AJ
01-759 2552
Telex 21777

Credit Access, Amex, Diners, Visa

The circular design of this modern hotel creates an appealingly intimate air and in the centre is an attractively flower-filled patio. An ornamental fountain graces the open-plan lounge and there's a stylish cocktail bar. Bedrooms mainly have smart Italian darkwood furniture, pastel colour schemes, brass light fittings and up-to-date, well-equipped bathrooms. Courtesy coach to airport. *Amenities* garden, in-house movies, secretarial services, laundry service.

Rooms 177	*Direct dial* Yes	*Confirm by* 6	*Parking* Ample
Ensuite bath/shower 177	*Room TV* Yes	*Last dinner* 11	*Room service* 24 hours

Berkeley Arms Hotel   65%   £C/D

H **Map 5 E2** Middlesex
Bath Road, Cranford TW5 9QE
01-897 2121
Telex 935728

Credit Access, Amex, Diners, Visa

A stylish hotel on the A4 just two miles from Heathrow, with a courtesy coach laid on for travellers. The elegantly up-to-date public areas are decorated in cool pastel colours and large potted plants and flower arrangements abound. Colourful wool bedcovers create a striking note in the attractive bedrooms, which are equipped with white laminate built-in units, two armchairs and decent bathrooms. *Amenities* garden, fax, laundry service.

Rooms 40	*Direct dial* Yes	*Confirm by* 6	*Parking* Ample
Ensuite bath/shower 40	*Room TV* Yes	*Last dinner* 10	*Room service* 24 hours

Excelsior Hotel   72%   £B

H **Map 5 E2** Middlesex
Bath Road, West Drayton
UB7 0DU
01-759 6611
Telex 24525

Rooms 600
Ensuite bath/shower 600
Direct dial Yes
Room TV Yes
Confirm by 6
Last dinner 11
Parking Ample
Room service 24 hours

Credit Access, Amex, Diners, Visa

A convenient location close to the airport terminals, together with a well-equipped leisure complex, makes this hotel a favourite choice with air crews and business people alike. Public areas have an elegant traditional feel and include a marble-floored foyer and panelled bar. Bedrooms have attractive modern furniture, plus remote-control TVs, tea-makers and fully-tiled, well-stocked bathrooms. There are additional accessories like mini-bars, trouser presses and bath robes in the executive rooms, and suites. No dogs. *Amenities* garden, indoor swimming pool, sauna, solarium, whirlpool bath, gymnasium, massage parlour, hairdressing, in-house movies, secretarial services, fax, laundry service, coffee shop (10am–midnight), kiosk. ở.

Our inspectors are our full-time employees;
they are professionally trained by us.

Heathrow Park Hotel   57%   £C

H **Map 5 E2** Middlesex
Bath Road, Longford,
West Drayton UB7 0EQ
01-759 2400
Telex 934093

Credit Access, Amex, Diners, Visa

Major refurbishment is nearing completion at this low-rise hotel overlooking one of the airport's main runways. Public areas include a comfortable foyer and two stylish bars. Attractively decorated bedrooms offer air conditioning, triple glazing and carpeted bathrooms. Superior rooms in a separate wing feature sofa beds and kitchenettes. No dogs. *Amenities* hairdressing, games room, in-house movies, secretarial services, coffee shop (10.30am–11.30pm), kiosk.

Rooms 305	*Direct dial* Yes	*Confirm by* 6	*Parking* Ample
Ensuite bath/shower 305	*Room TV* Yes	*Last dinner* 10	*Room service* Limited

Heathrow Penta Hotel   69%   £B

Map 5 E2 Middlesex
Bath Road,
Hounslow TW6 2AQ
01-897 6363
Telex 934660

Credit Access, Amex, Diners, Visa

A low-rise, modern hotel within the airport boundary, affording splendid runway views from the good-sized, double-glazed bedrooms. These offer drink dispensing machines, plenty of writing space and modern, tiled bathrooms. Downstairs, there's a vast foyer, two bars and well-equipped conference facilities. Courtesy coach.
Amenities garden, indoor swimming pool, sauna, hairdressing, in-house movies, secretarial services, fax, laundry service.

Rooms 645	*Direct dial* Yes	*Confirm by* 6	*Parking* Ample
Ensuite bath/shower 645	*Room TV* Yes	*Last dinner* 10.30	*Room service* 24 hours

**Changes in data sometimes occur in establishments
after the Guide goes to press.
Prices should be taken as indications rather than firm quotes.**

Holiday Inn   73%   £B/C

Map 5 E2 Middlesex
Stockley Road,
West Drayton UB7 9NA
West Drayton (0895) 445555
Telex 934518

Rooms 394
Ensuite bath/shower 394
Direct dial Yes
Room TV Yes
Confirm by 6
Last dinner 11
Parking Ample
Room service 24 hours

Credit Access, Amex, Diners, Visa

Located north of junction 4 of the M4, this modern hotel makes a favourable first impression with its spacious and elegantly designed foyer: there's plenty of comfortable seating here but if you prefer more intimate surroundings, try the mock-Tudor bar with its bare brick walls and old beams. Good-sized bedrooms feature darkwood modern units, ample writing space, easy chairs and accessories like hairdryers,

radios, mini-bars and trouser presses. Bathrooms, too, are very well equipped. *Amenities* garden, indoor swimming pool, sauna, solarium, keep-fit equipment, tennis, 9-hole golf course, in-house movies, secretarial services, fax, laundry service, coffee shop (6.30am–11.30pm), kiosk, airport coach. ₻

Master Robert Hotel   57%   £C/D

Map 5 E2 Middlesex
366 Great West Road
TW5 0BD
01-570 6261
Telex 9413782

Credit Access, Amex, Diners, Visa

Some three miles from Heathrow this pleasant hotel offers some motel-style accommodation. There's an attractive bar-lounge with lightwood panelling and comfortable sofas and a little-used residents' lounge. Some bedrooms have patios and carports; the remainder, in a purpose-built block, have parking spaces. All have simple fitted units, two easy chairs and fully tiled bathrooms. No dogs. *Amenities* garden, in-house movies, laundry service, coffee shop (10am–6pm). ₻

Rooms 96	*Direct dial* Yes	*Confirm by* 6	*Parking* Ample
Ensuite bath/shower 96	*Room TV* Yes	*Last dinner* 10.45	*Room service* Limited

Post House Hotel   68%   £C

Map 5 E2 Middlesex
Sipson Road, West Drayton
UB7 0JU
01-759 2323
Telex 934280

Credit Access, Amex, Diners, Visa

This 10-storey hotel is located alongside the M4. The busy public areas include an open-plan foyer with pine-panelled walls, plus three bars, including one for residents. Standard bedrooms (some for non-smokers) have tea-makers, trouser presses, hairdryers and TVs. Executive club room guests have leisure facilities and limited room service. Courtesy coach. *Amenities* garden, in-house movies, secretarial services, fax, laundry service, coffee shop (6am–1.30am), kiosk.

Rooms 600	*Direct dial* Yes	*Confirm by* 6	*Parking* Ample
Ensuite bath/shower 600	*Room TV* Yes	*Last dinner* 10.30	*Room service* None

Sheraton-Heathrow Hotel   70%   £C

H **Map 5 E2** Middlesex
Bath Road,
West Drayton UB7 0HJ
01-759 2424
Telex 934331

Rooms 440
Ensuite bath/shower 440
Direct dial Yes
Room TV Yes
Confirm by arrang.
Last dinner 11.30
Parking Limited
Room service 24 hours

Credit Access, Amex, Diners, Visa

Located alongside the A4 west of
Heathrow, this modern low-rise
hotel combines comfort with convenience. The elegant foyer, with
its black marble floor, leads on to
a spacious lounge area with comfortable seating beside gleaming
brass urns filled with fresh flowers. A second lounge area doubles
as a cocktail bar. There are two
more bars: one dark and intimate; the other plush and pubby.
Sound-proofed bedrooms have
simple built-in units with tan leather-look chairs. Trouser presses, TVs
and hairdryers are standard. Modern bathrooms are well equipped.
Courtesy coach to the airport. *Amenities* garden, indoor swimming
pool, sauna, solarium, keep-fit equipment, snooker, in-house movies,
fax, laundry service, coffee shop (6.30am–11.30pm).

Sheraton Skyline   77%   £A/B

HR **Map 5 E2** Middlesex
Bath Road, Hayes UB3 5BP
01-759 2535
Telex 934254

Rooms 355
Ensuite bath/shower 355
Direct dial Yes
Room TV Yes
Confirm by 4
Last dinner 11
Parking Ample
Room service 24 hours

Credit Access, Amex, Diners, Visa

A tropical patio with palm trees,
swimming pool, lounge bar and
steel band forms a popular
centrepiece to this modern hotel.
Further entertainment is available six nights a week at Diamond
Lil's bar, while those who prefer
a quiet drink can opt for the
dimly lit Edwardian bar. Extensive conference facilities add to
the attractions. Bedrooms are
spacious and decorated to a high
standard, with smart fabric wall-
coverings, coordinating fabrics and good-quality furniture. Decent-
sized bedrooms are smartly appointed; eight have shower only.
Courtesy coach to airport. *Amenities* garden, indoor swimming
pool, sauna, solarium, beauty salon, hairdressing, in-house movies,
laundry service, coffee shop (6am–1am), shopping arcade.

Colony Room   ♕

French cooking

Set L £16.95, Sun brunch £13.50
About £64 for two
Seats 155
Parties 60

Traditional standards of service and sound, classical French cooking
are on offer at this grand, formal restaurant. The bi-annually changing
menus have monthly supplements to take advantage of seasonal
produce and good fresh ingredients are used. Starters range from
exotic soups to flavoursome terrines, while the main course might be
turbot stuffed with wild rice and coriander. Finish with the vast
selection of French cheeses and the laden sweet trolley. ⊖ ♿

Lunch 12.30–2.30   *Dinner* 7–11, Fri & Sat till 11.30
Closed L Sat & Sun & every lunchtime in Aug

Skyway Hotel   63%   £C

H **Map 5 E2** Middlesex
Bath Road, Hayes UB3 5AW
01-759 6311
Telex 23935

Credit Access, Amex, Diners, Visa

A purpose-built hotel offering pleasant accommodation. The open-
plan lounge is smartly contemporary, while the decor in the bar
changes weekly. The practical, modern bedrooms have fitted units;
superior rooms boast air conditioning, trouser presses and hairdryers.
Courtesy coach. *Amenities* outdoor swimming pool, whirlpool
bath, hairdressing, games room, snooker, in-house movies, secretarial
services, valeting, laundry service, coffee shop (10am–midnight).

Rooms 437	*Direct dial* Yes	*Confirm by* 6	*Parking* Ample
Ensuite bath/shower 437	*Room TV* Yes	*Last dinner* 10.30	*Room service* Limited

HOTELS
RESTAURANTS
AND INNS

ENGLAND

ABBERLEY — Elms Hotel   74%   £C

Map 10 B4
Hereford & Worcester
Nr Worcester WR6 6AT
Great Witley (0299) 896666
Telex 337105

Rooms 25
Ensuite bath/shower 25
Direct dial Yes
Room TV Yes
Confirm by arrang.
Last dinner 9
Parking Ample
Room service 24 hours

Credit Access, Amex, Diners, Visa

An imposing Queen Anne mansion commanding fine views over formal gardens and parkland. Public rooms with a smattering of antiques include an attractive half-panelled library-bar with an elaborately carved mantelpiece. Main-house bedrooms again feature antiques and solid, traditional comforts while coach-house rooms are slightly lighter and brighter in style though equally well appointed.

All provide lots of thoughtful extras, from hairdryers and fresh flowers to sherry and reading matter. Top-floor main-house rooms and some bathrooms will benefit from an extensive refurbishment programme that is already well under way. No dogs. *Amenities* garden, tennis, putting, croquet, secretarial services, fax, laundry service.

ABINGDON — Upper Reaches Hotel   64%   £C

Map 5 D2 Oxfordshire
Thames Street OX14 3JA
Abingdon (0235) 22311

Credit Access, Amex, Diners, Visa

A friendly welcome awaits at this converted mill house beside the Thames, and you can hear the mill stream rush by as you relax with a drink in the comfortable bar-lounge. Bright and cheerful main-house bedrooms are equipped with tea-makers, hairdryers and remote-control TVs. Six rooms in a riverside annexe have slightly superior decor and more space. Modern bathrooms offer complimentary toiletries. *Amenities* garden, mooring.

Rooms 26	*Room phone* Yes	*Confirm by* 6	*Parking* Ample
Ensuite bath/shower 26	*Room TV* Yes	*Last dinner* 9.30	*Room service* All day

ALCESTER — Arrow Mill   £D/E

Map 4 C1 Warwickshire
Arrow B49 5NL
Alcester (0789) 762419
Telex 312522

Credit Access, Amex, Diners, Visa

The Woodhams family have turned a flour mill with a nine-hundred-year history into a charming and cheerful inn. The mill stream still turns the water wheel, which stands on display in a bar, along with a collection of sporting guns. Immaculately kept bedrooms are individually decorated and furnished, mainly with handsome pine pieces. Excellent bathrooms. *Amenities* garden, shooting, clay-pigeon shooting, coarse and game fishing, laundry service.

Rooms 15	*Direct dial* Yes	*Confirm by* arrang.	*Parking* Ample
Ensuite bath/shower 11	*Room TV* Yes	*Last dinner* 9.30	*Room service* All day

ALDBOROUGH — Old Red Lion Restaurant   ♀

Map 6 C1 Norfolk
Norwich
Cromer (0263) 761451

Set L £8.85
Set D £9.95
About £35 for two
Seats 40 *Parties* 40
Parking Ample
Credit Access, Visa

A traditional country restaurant with a standard range of international dishes on the menu. Bruno Diluzio's meals, however, are well above average and have necessitated a new extension to accommodate the diners who return again and again for the friendly atmosphere and assured cooking. We enjoyed a tasty minestrone soup, with tender, perfectly cooked calf's liver to follow. Home-made sweets from the trolley or ice cream to finish. ⊖

Lunch 12.30–2.30   *Dinner* 7–10.30
Closed D Sun & all Mon

ALDEBURGH — Brudenell Hotel   60%   £C/D

Map 6 D3 Suffolk
The Parade IP15 5BU
Aldeburgh (072 885) 2071

Credit Access, Amex, Diners, Visa

Aldeburgh's old-fashioned charms are well reflected in this traditional seaside hotel. The airy picture-windowed lounge enjoys spectacular views of the North Sea, as do half the bedrooms; remaining accommodation overlooks the Snape marshes. Decor ranges from solidly traditional to starkly '60s to smartly up-to-date, and there's double glazing throughout. *Amenities* sea fishing, hotel boat, games room, laundry service, children's play area.

Rooms 47	*Room phone* Yes	*Confirm by* arrang.	*Parking* Ample
Ensuite bath/shower 47	*Room TV* Yes	*Last dinner* 9	*Room service* 24 hours

ALDEBURGH Uplands Hotel 60% £E

H Map 6 D3 Suffolk
Victoria Road IP15 5DX
Aldeburgh (072 885) 2420

Credit Access, Amex, Diners, Visa

A small, comfortable, family-run hotel with a well-deserved name for hospitality. It's right opposite the parish church, just a short stroll from the sea, and the day rooms offer the varied charms of inviting sofas, open fires and garden views. Centrally heated bedrooms have individual appeal, whether in the main house or in chalets in the well-kept grounds. Neat, modern bathrooms.
Amenities garden.

Rooms 20	Direct dial Yes	Confirm by arrang.	Parking Ample
Ensuite bath/shower 17	Room TV Yes	Last dinner 8.30	Room service All day

ALDEBURGH Wentworth Hotel 65% £D/E

H Map 6 D3 Suffolk
Wentworth Road IP15 5BD
Aldeburgh (072 885) 2312

Credit Amex, Diners, Visa
Closed 27 Dec–16 Jan

For over 60 years this traditional seafront hotel has been run by the Pritt family and their friendly, efficient service ensures return visits from many guests. An open fire is a feature of both the snug bar and one of the lounges; the second more spacious lounge is furnished in smart cane. Bedrooms have been further upgraded, the majority now having en suite bathrooms.
Amenities garden, secretarial services, laundry service.

Rooms 31	Direct dial Yes	Confirm by arrang.	Parking Ample
Ensuite bath/shower 28	Room TV Yes	Last dinner 8.45	Room service All day

**If we recommend meals in a Hotel or Inn,
a separate entry is made for its restaurant.**

ALDRIDGE Fairlawns Hotel 60% £D/E

H Map 10 C4 West Midlands
Little Aston Road,
Walsall WS9 0NU
Walsall (0922) 55122
Telex 339873

Credit Access, Amex, Diners, Visa

Six new suites have been added since our last visit to this modern hotel on the A454. The lobby has had a facelift too, as have the masculine bar and adjacent conservatory. Standards of housekeeping remain high and staff are friendly and unobtrusive.
Amenities garden, patio, games room, snooker, secretarial services, laundry service, 24-hour lounge service.

Rooms 36	Direct dial Yes	Confirm by 6	Parking Ample
Ensuite bath/shower 36	Room TV Yes	Last dinner 10	Room service Limited

ALFRISTON Moonrakers Restaurant ♫

R Map 7 B6 East Sussex
High Street, Nr Polegate
Alfriston (0323) 870472

Set D £14.90
About £40 for two
Seats 32
Parties 32
Parking Ample

A consistently popular restaurant in a 16th-century building which takes its name from the village's smuggling history. Elaine Wilkinson cooks prime ingredients in a skilful and pleasingly straightforward manner, displaying a natural flair for saucing. You might start with sautéed mushrooms with cream and pine kernels, then beef Wellington or roast duck with red wine and kumquat sauce. Sweets include home-made delights such as hot frangipan flan and banana meringue with butterscotch sauce. Excellent tea and coffee and home-made truffles to round off the meal. Beautiful, selective wine list – Aligoté from de Villaine, Côte Rôtie (Guigal) '80, Lieserer Beerenauslese (Dr Thanisch) '76. ⌂ Outstanding ♀ Well-chosen ℗

Lunch by arrang. only *Dinner* 7–9.15, Sat 6.45–9.45 **Closed** L Sat, all Sun & Mon, Bank Hols (exc. Good Fri) & mid Jan–mid Feb

ALLENDALE Bishopfield 61% £F

H Map 15 B4 Northumberland
Nr Hexham NE47 9EJ
Allendale (043 483) 248

Credit Access, Diners
Closed 4 wks from Xmas

More than five thousand acres of shooting are a big attraction at this hotel adjoining a working farm. Located in converted cattle byres around a cobbled courtyard, it's run with unaffected friendliness by the Fairless family. Simple bedrooms have plain white walls and dark-stained units, while day rooms include a pleasant beamed lounge.
Amenities garden, riding, shooting, clay-pigeon shooting, coarse & game fishing, bicycles, snooker, secretarial services. ♿

Rooms 11	Direct dial Yes	Confirm by arrang.	Parking Ample
Ensuite bath/shower 11	Room TV Yes	Last dinner 7.30	Room service All day

ALNWICK   Hotspur Hotel   54%   £E

H **Map 14 B3** Northumberland
Bondgate Without NE66 1PR
Alnwick (0665) 602924

Credit Access, Visa
Closed 25 Dec & 1 Jan

A friendly atmosphere makes up for any lack of frills at this stone-built hotel outside the town walls. There are two jolly bars (one decorated with armour) and also a comfy TV room and sunny lounge. Bedrooms are neatly furnished with fitted units and tea-makers. Bathrooms are tidy and well-kept. Rooms at the rear have garden access.
Amenities garden.

Rooms 28	*Direct dial* Yes	*Confirm by* arrang.	*Parking* Ample
Ensuite bath/shower 18	*Room TV* Yes	*Last dinner* 9	*Room service* None

ALNWICK   White Swan Hotel   58%   £D/E

H **Map 14 B3** Northumberland
Bondgate Within NE66 1TD
Alnwick (0665) 602109

Credit Access, Amex, Diners, Visa

A grand function room with panelling salvaged from the Titanic's sister ship is at the heart of this old coaching inn in the town centre. Beyond the cheery hall is an interesting bar decorated with fly fishing rods. Recently refurbished bedrooms (some in a wing at the rear) have simple furnishings. Three executive rooms can be converted to meeting rooms.
Amenities garden, secretarial services, laundry service.

Rooms 41	*Direct dial* Yes	*Confirm by* 6	*Parking* Ample
Ensuite bath/shower 40	*Room TV* Yes	*Last dinner* 9	*Room service* 24 hours

**We publish annually,
so make sure you use the current edition.
It's worth it!**

ALSAGER   Manor House Hotel   60%   £E

H **Map 10 B3** Cheshire
Audley Road ST7 2QQ
Alsager (0270) 878013

Credit Access, Amex, Diners, Visa

An old farmhouse and barn, sympathetically extended, make up this friendly hotel not far from the M6. There's a heavily beamed bar, bedecked with horse brasses, and a comfortable, modern lounge. Plenty of old timbers give character to the eight older bedrooms; newer rooms are more spacious. Some have bath, some shower only. All are neat and well kept. No dogs.
Amenities garden, laundry service.

Rooms 28	*Direct dial* Yes	*Confirm by* arrang.	*Parking* Ample
Ensuite bath/shower 28	*Room TV* Yes	*Last dinner* 9.30	*Room service* All day

ALTON   Grange Hotel   60%   £E

H **Map 5 D3** Hampshire
17 London Road,
Holybourne GU34 4EG
Alton (0420) 86565

Credit Access, Amex, Diners, Visa
Closed 25 Dec

Enthusiastic owners David and Andrea Levene are busy improving this converted family house on the outskirts of Alton, using strikingly vibrant colour schemes in the refurbishment of the bedrooms. Older-style rooms are more basic but there are modern half-tiled bathrooms throughout. Public areas include a plushly furnished lounge (shame about the beer mats) and a cosy, simply decorated bar.   *Amenities* garden, putting, croquet, laundry service, children's play area.

Rooms 15	*Direct dial* Yes	*Confirm by* arrang.	*Parking* Ample
Ensuite bath/shower 15	*Room TV* Yes	*Last dinner* 9	*Room service* All day

ALTON   Swan Hotel   57%   £D

H **Map 5 D3** Hampshire
High Street GU34 1AT
Alton (0420) 83777

Credit Access, Amex, Diners, Visa

Traces of period charm survive at this updated old inn with a delightful foyer-lounge and two contrasting bars, one the preserve of the locals. Bedrooms vary in size and decor, the nicest ones having pretty green and blue fabrics. All have tea-makers, TVs and direct-dial telephones. Creaking floorboards are part of the charm.
Amenities laundry service.

Rooms 38	*Direct dial* Yes	*Confirm by* 6	*Parking* Ample
Ensuite bath/shower 38	*Room TV* Yes	*Last dinner* 9.30	*Room service* Limited

ALTRINCHAM — Bowdon Hotel — £D/E

H Map 10 B2
Greater Manchester
Langham Road, Bowdon WA142HT
061-928 7121
Telex 668208

Credit Access, Amex, Diners, Visa

1988 saw many changes and improvements at the Bowdon Hotel, which comprises a Victorian main building and modern extensions for accommodation. 40 new bedrooms have washed pine furniture, pastel colour schemes and designer fabrics, and existing bedrooms have been upgraded. All the public areas have been redecorated and a roomy new public bar created. The hotel was graded at 57% in our 1988 Guide. *Amenities* laundry service.

Rooms 80	*Direct dial* Yes	*Confirm by* 6	*Parking* Ample
Ensuite bath/shower 80	*Room TV* Yes	*Last dinner* 10	*Room service* 24 hours

ALTRINCHAM — Cresta Court Hotel 59% — £E

H Map 10 B2
Greater Manchester
Church Street WA14 4DP
061-927 7272
Telex 667242

Credit Access, Amex, Diners, Visa

An early '70s red-brick hotel with extensive public areas that include a spacious foyer-lounge and choice of three bars. Modestly furnished bedrooms have fitted units and are equipped with remote-control TVs, tea-makers, trouser presses and hairdryers. De luxe rooms offer freestanding furniture, attractive colour schemes, mini-bars and toiletries. Good conference facilities. *Amenities* in-house movies, secretarial services, laundry service, coffee shop (10am–6pm).

Rooms 139	*Direct dial* Yes	*Confirm by* 6	*Parking* Ample
Ensuite bath/shower 139	*Room TV* Yes	*Last dinner* 11	*Room service* 24 hours

ALTRINCHAM — George & Dragon Hotel 59% — £D/E

H Map 10 B2
Greater Manchester
Manchester Road WA14 4PH
061-928 9933
Telex 665051

Credit Access, Amex, Diners, Visa

A white pebbledash building on the A56, with excellent motorway connections. There's no lounge as such but the main bar provides plenty of comfortable seating. Most of the bedrooms are in a new wing and these – though not large – have attractive pastel colour schemes and decent freestanding furniture. Half the main-house rooms are similarly appointed; others are more basic. *Amenities* secretarial services, laundry service, 24-hour lounge service.

Rooms 47	*Direct dial* Yes	*Confirm by* arrang.	*Parking* Ample
Ensuite bath/shower 47	*Room TV* Yes	*Last dinner* 9.45	*Room service* All day

**Our inspectors *never* book in the name of Egon Ronay's Guides.
They disclose their identity only if they are considering an establishment
for inclusion in the next edition of the Guide.**

ALVESTON — Alveston House Hotel 64% — £D

H Map 4 B2 Avon
Nr Bristol BS12 2LJ
Thornbury (0454) 415050
Telex 449212

Credit Access, Amex, Diners, Visa

Easy to spot with its yellow paintwork, this extended period house stands on the A38 just five minutes from the M4/M5 link. Bedrooms, mostly singles, have writing space and decent lighting; gradual upgrading is taking place, with more attractive fabrics and smarter furnishings. The foyer-lounge has plenty of modern chesterfields and easy chairs, and there is a summer conservatory-style bar. *Amenities* garden, secretarial services, laundry service.

Rooms 30	*Direct dial* Yes	*Confirm by* arrang.	*Parking* Ample
Ensuite bath/shower 30	*Room TV* Yes	*Last dinner* 9.30	*Room service* All day

ALVESTON — Post House Hotel 62% — £C/D

H Map 4 B2 Avon
Thornbury Road,
Nr Bristol B12 2LL
Thornbury (0454) 412521
Telex 444753

Credit Access, Amex, Diners, Visa

This particular Post House is an extended Tudor inn standing by the A38. Day rooms have a lot of period charm, especially the beamed and flagstoned bar. Spacious, well-furnished bedrooms are in the modern part; some have balconies and views of the cricket green where W G Grace played. Five rooms are equipped for disabled guests. *Amenities* garden, outdoor swimming pool, golf driving range, putting, pool table, fax, laundry service, children's play area. &

Rooms 75	*Direct dial* Yes	*Confirm by* 6	*Parking* Ample
Ensuite bath/shower 75	*Room TV* Yes	*Last dinner* 10	*Room service* None

AMBERLEY   Amberley Inn   57%   £E

H **Map 4 B2** Gloucestershire
Nr Stroud GL5 5AF
Amberley (045 387) 2565

Credit Access, Amex, Visa

A solid Cotswold stone inn standing high up on Minchinhampton
Common with splendid valley views. Characterful public rooms
include a delightful lounge bar with panelling and fine mullioned
windows. Above the restaurant extension there is a handsome,
spacious new bedroom with a pretty tiled bathroom. Other rooms are
homely and appealing, including four in the Garden House. Cheerful
staff. *Amenities* garden.

Rooms 14	*Room phone* Yes	*Confirm by* 6	*Parking* Ample
Ensuite bath/shower 13	*Room TV* Yes	*Last dinner* 9.30	*Room service* Limited

AMBLESIDE   Kirkstone Foot Hotel   65%   £E

HR **Map 13 D5** Cumbria
Kirkstone Pass Road
LA22 9EH
Ambleside (05394) 32232

Credit Access, Amex, Diners, Visa
Closed 3 Dec–beg. Feb

A neat white-painted hotel that's run with great pride and professionalism by Jane and Simon Bateman. Set in attractive gardens running
down to a tumbling mountain stream, it offers traditional comforts in
its cheerfully-appointed bar area and relaxing lounge. Decently-
furnished bedrooms vary in size but all have remote-control TVs,
radio-alarms, tea-makers and well-kept tiled bathrooms. No dogs.
Amenities garden, croquet, laundry service.

Rooms 16	*Direct dial* Yes	*Confirm by* arrang.	*Parking* Ample
Ensuite bath/shower 16	*Room TV* Yes	*Last dinner* 8	*Room service* None

Restaurant

English cooking

Set D £13.50
About £35 *for two*
Seats 60
Parties 12

Dinner here runs along well-regulated lines, starting at 8 o'clock sharp
and proceeding at the same pace at each table. The no-choice five-
course meal begins with fish (perhaps salmon with hollandaise),
continues with a good home-made soup and almost always goes on to
a roast accompanied by nice fresh vegetables. Highlight of the meal is
the scrumptious sweet trolley (plenty of choice here) and there's a
well-kept cheeseboard. No smoking. ☺ &

Dinner 7.30 for 8
Closed 3 Dec–beg. Feb

AMBLESIDE   Nanny Brow   62%   £E

H **Map 13 D5** Cumbria
Clappersgate LA22 9NF
Ambleside (05394) 32036

Credit Access, Amex, Visa

Take the Coniston Road out of Ambleside to reach this charming
Edwardian house in superb gardens perched on a hillside overlooking
the Brathay valley. Guests are made to feel immediately at home in
the relaxing lounge with its welcoming log fire and lovely fell views.
There's also a pleasant bar that doubles as a billiards room. Main-
house bedrooms are comfortably traditional, with pretty chintz
furnishings. Garden-wing suites have their own sitting rooms and
some also have kitchen/dining areas. Ground-floor rooms open on to
the garden terrace, while first-floor rooms have balconies.
Amenities garden, solarium, whirlpool bath, coarse fishing, snooker,
laundry service.

Rooms 19	*Direct dial* Yes	*Confirm by* arrang.	*Parking* Ample
Ensuite bath/shower 19	*Room TV* Yes	*Last dinner* 7.45	*Room service* All day

AMBLESIDE   Rothay Manor   71%   £C/D

HR **Map 13 D5** Cumbria
Rothay Bridge LA22 0EH
Ambleside (053 94) 33605

Rooms 18
Ensuite bath/shower 18
Direct dial Yes
Room TV Yes
Confirm by arrang.
Last dinner 9
Parking Ample
Room service All day

Credit Access, Amex, Diners, Visa

A Regency house which was once
the home of a wealthy Liverpool
merchant and still retains some
of its fine original features, including the cast iron railings on
the verandah and a glasshouse.
Inside, three charming lounges,
bedecked with floral displays,
have good antique furniture and
artwork by local artists on the
walls. The bedrooms, seven of
which have private balconies,
are individually furnished and

continued ...

Closed early Jan–early Feb

well equipped with radio alarms, iced water, fruit, magazines, electric blankets and hairdryers. The modern, carpeted bathrooms have shower cubicles or over-the-tub fitments and generous towels. Two lodges house suites, one suitable for disabled guests. No dogs.
Amenities garden, croquet, laundry service. &

Restaurant   ♛

Set L Sun £10.50
Set D £19
About £50 for two
Seats 65
Parties 50

Mahogany tables, crystal glassware and silver candelabra make a luxurious setting in which to enjoy Jane Binns' daily-changing five-course menus. Top quality produce is competently handled, the local char, poached in a white wine court bouillon, being particularly good. Starter might be asparagus tartlets with local ham or home-made terrine; finish with the sweet trolley or cheese. Buffet lunches only except Sunday, when there's a traditional roast. &

Lunch 12.30–2, Sun 12.45–1.30   *Dinner* 8–9
Closed early Jan–early Feb

AMBLESIDE   Wateredge Hotel   63%   £D/E

HR **Map 13 D5** Cumbria
Borrans Road LA22 0EP
Ambleside (053 94) 32332

Credit Access, Amex, Visa
Closed mid Dec–mid Feb

Steady improvements have taken place here, and what were two 17th-century fishermen's cottages have been extended and transformed into a hotel of considerable charm and comfort, at little cost in period appeal. The lounges are a great delight – pretty rooms with beams, assorted inviting chairs, fresh flowers and picture windows that look on the head of Lake Windermere. Bedrooms in the original part have a beamed, cottagy charm, with some nice old pieces of furniture. Modern rooms, furnished in pine, tend to be larger, and there are five roomy suites with patios and balconies in an annexe. No children under seven.
Amenities garden, coarse fishing, boating, laundry service.

Rooms 23	*Direct dial* Yes	*Confirm by* 5	*Parking* Ample
Ensuite bath/shower 23	*Room TV* Yes	*Last dinner* 8.30	*Room service* Limited

Restaurant   *NEW ENTRY*

Set D £15.90
About £45 for two
Seats 45
Parties 25

The set menu proposes a couple of starters, soup, sorbet, a choice of two main courses, sweets, cheese, then coffee in the lounge. Cooking is acceptable throughout, from cheese-topped prawns or smoked breast of chicken with hazelnut vinaigrette to spinach and sorrel soup, salmon with a simple but good butter sauce and banana toffee flan. Staff tend to dash about, and kitchen noises are liable to intrude. ⊖

Dinner 7–8.30
Closed mid Dec–mid Feb

We publish annually,
so make sure you use the current edition.
It's worth it !

AMPFIELD   Potters Heron Hotel   60%   £D

H **Map 5 D3** Hampshire
Nr Romsey SO51 9ZF
Chandler's Ford (0703) 266611
Telex 47459

Credit Access, Amex, Diners, Visa

Low thatch gives this charming white-painted hotel a delightful beetle-browed appearance. Inside, the day rooms continue the rustic theme. Most bedrooms have beamed ceilings, simple laminate units and rather drab fabrics; newer rooms have more appealing decor and furnishings. All have plentiful modern comforts and good tiled bathrooms. *Amenities* garden, sauna, keep-fit equipment, snooker, in-house movies, laundry service, 24-hour lounge service. &

Rooms 60	*Direct dial* Yes	*Confirm by* 6	*Parking* Ample
Ensuite bath/shower 60	*Room TV* Yes	*Last dinner* 10	*Room service* Limited

---

ANDOVER   White Hart Hotel   £D/E

I Map 4 C3 Hampshire
Bridge Street SP10 1BH
Andover (0264) 52266

Credit Access, Amex, Diners, Visa

In the centre of town, the White Hart was once a popular stopover on the coaching route between London and the West Country. The day rooms are linked one with another, with beams and decent country furniture preserving a little of the inn's period character. Bedrooms of various sizes and styles provide very acceptable overnight accommodation; ten have recently been smartly refurbished and their bathrooms improved. A pleasant, friendly atmosphere prevails.

| Rooms 21 | Room phone Yes | Confirm by 6 | Parking Limited |
| Ensuite bath/shower 21 | Room TV Yes | Last dinner 9.30 | Room service Limited |

ARUNDEL   Norfolk Arms Hotel   61%   £D/E

H Map 5 E4 West Sussex
22 High Street BN18 9AD
Arundel (0903) 882101
Telex 878436

Credit Access, Amex, Diners, Visa

Built by the tenth Duke of Norfolk beneath the battlements of his castle, this red-brick Georgian coaching inn offers traditional comforts in its main-house bedrooms and smartly refurbished lounge. There's a choice of two bars. Bedrooms, in a courtyard block, are modern and compact but comfortable and well equipped: hairdryers, trouser presses, tea-makers and carpeted bathrooms throughout.
Amenities games room, in-house movies, laundry service. &

| Rooms 34 | Direct dial Yes | Confirm by 6 | Parking Ample |
| Ensuite bath/shower 34 | Room TV Yes | Last dinner 10 | Room service All day |

Changes in data sometimes occur in establishments
after the Guide goes to press.
Prices should be taken as indications rather than firm quotes.

ASCOT   Berystede Hotel   68%   £B

H Map 5 E2 Berkshire
Bagshot Road,
Sunninghill SL5 9JH
Ascot (0990) 23311
Telex 847707

Credit Access, Amex, Diners, Visa

Nine acres of formal gardens and natural woodland is the setting for this turreted Victorian hotel, with modern additions, only five minutes from the M3. The elegant foyer-lounge has a fine oak staircase and an elaborate gilt chandelier, and there are lovely garden views from the relaxing cocktail bar. Bedrooms, of varying sizes, include four luxurious suites in the turrets of the old house. All rooms are stylishly furnished and well-equipped; Executive rooms offer mini-bars and other extras. Good modern bathrooms.
Amenities garden, outdoor swimming pool, golf practice net, putting, croquet, games room, pool table, in-house movies, fax, laundry service.

| Rooms 91 | Direct dial Yes | Confirm by 6 | Parking Ample |
| Ensuite bath/shower 91 | Room TV Yes | Last dinner 9.45 | Room service 24 hours |

ASCOT   Royal Berkshire   77%   £B

HR Map 5 E2 Berkshire
London Rd, Sunninghill
SL5 0PP
Ascot (0990) 23322
Telex 847280

Rooms 82
Ensuite bath/shower 82
Direct dial Yes
Room TV Yes
Confirm by 6
Last dinner 9.30
Parking Ample
Room service 24 hours

Credit Access, Amex, Diners, Visa

A mellow red-brick Queen Anne house which was for over 100 years the home of the Churchill family. The decor throughout is in pastel shades of blue, grey and pink, applied with fashionable techniques such as rag rolling and stippling. The public rooms have fine garden views and include a lounge and bar with pleasing reproduction furniture, comfortable sofas and pretty drapes. Bedrooms are quietly

luxurious, with attractive bedcovers to match the elaborate curtaining, good furniture and plenty of extras. Smartly tiled bathrooms have phone extensions and good towels and toiletries. *Amenities* garden, indoor swimming pool, sauna, whirlpool bath, tennis, squash, putting, croquet, secretarial services, fax, laundry service, helipad.

Restaurant ♛

Set L £15.50
Set D £22.50
About £87 *for two*
Seats 46
Parties 24

Views across extensive lawns are a feature of this smart restaurant. The daily-changing fixed-price and seasonal à la carte menus offer combinations such as fillet of English lamb seasoned with lavender and grilled foie gras with raspberries and ginger sauce, and top quality ingredients are competently handled. Comprehensive wine list with exhaustive commentary includes Marques de Grinon Cabernet Sauvignon '82, Tualatin Pinot Noir '83. ♀ Well-chosen ℮

Lunch 12–2, Sun 12.15–2.30   *Dinner* 7.30–9.30
Parking Ample

**We welcome bona fide complaints and recommendations
on the tear-out pages at the back of the book for readers' comment.
They are followed up by our professional team.**

ASHBOURNE   Callow Hall ♧

RR **Map 10 C3** Derbyshire
Mappleton Road DE6 2AA
Ashbourne (0335) 43403

Set Sun L £8.75
Set D £16.50
About £44 *for two*
Seats 80 *Parties* 50
Parking Ample
Credit Access, Amex, Diners, Visa

The Spencer family have been the local bakers in Ashbourne for five generations and it was in the bakery that chef patron David Spencer served his apprenticeship. In his mansion restaurant it is therefore not surprising to find excellent desserts and baked goods, and David's enthusiasm is evident in starters like fresh asparagus in puff pastry, and succulent guinea fowl with pineapple or loin of veal with wild mushrooms.

Lunch Sun 12.30–1.30, Mon–Sat by arrang. only   *Dinner* 7.30–9.30, Sun by arrang.

BEDROOMS 11   £C
With bath/shower 11

Major renovation has increased the number of charming bedrooms. All have antique furniture, en suite bathrooms and extras like remote TVs, hairdryers and trouser presses.

ASHFORD   Eastwell Manor   82% £B

HR **Map 7 C5** Kent
Eastwell Park, Boughton
Aluph TN25 4HR
Ashford (0233) 35751
Telex 966281

Rooms 24
Ensuite bath/shower 24
Direct dial Yes
Room TV Yes
Confirm by arrang.
Last dinner 9.30
Parking Ample
Room service 24 hours

Credit Access, Amex, Diners, Visa

Surrounded by farmland and formal gardens, this splendid mock-Jacobean mansion was virtually rebuilt in the 1920s using stonework from much older buildings. The main entrance via a flagstoned courtyard leads to nobly proportioned day rooms featuring carved oak panelling, fine moulded ceilings and huge open hearths where welcoming fires crackle. Elegant, very spacious bedrooms – each 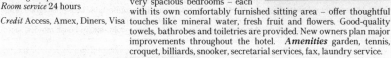 with its own comfortably furnished sitting area – offer thoughtful touches like mineral water, fresh fruit and flowers. Good-quality towels, bathrobes and toiletries are provided. New owners plan major improvements throughout the hotel.   **Amenities** garden, tennis, croquet, billiards, snooker, secretarial services, fax, laundry service.

Restaurant ♛

Set L £13.50, Sun £14.50
Set D £20
About £80 *for two*
Seats 65
Parties 35

The arrival of youthful chef David Richards has brought a new enthusiasm to this splendid dining room with a lofty timbered ceiling. Thoughtfully composed menus offer a short, tempting selection of dishes, attractively presented but occasionally marred by inconsistent cooking. Recent successes included a colourful warm salad of scallops with asparagus and crispy bacon, nicely roasted lamb fillet with a basil mousse and light Madeira sauce, and a delicious lemon tart served with sharp passion fruit cream. ♀ Well-chosen ℮

Lunch 12.30–2, Sun 12–2   *Dinner* 7–9.30, Fri & Sat till 10

ASHFORD-IN-THE-WATER — Riverside Country House Hotel 65% £D

H **Map 10 C2** Derbyshire
Fennell Street DE4 1QF
Bakewell (062 981) 4275

Credit Access, Amex, Visa

In a delightful village setting by the river Wye, the Taylors' elegant little hotel is a very friendly, relaxing place. The oak-panelled hall also serves as a bar, and there's a cosy lounge overlooking the garden and river. Each of the seven bedrooms is individually decorated and furnished, with antiques a feature throughout. Bedrooms are very smartly kept. ***Amenities*** garden, laundry service.

Rooms 7	*Direct dial* Yes	*Confirm by* arrang.	*Parking* Ample
Ensuite bath/shower 7	*Room TV* Yes	*Last dinner* 9.30	*Room service* Limited

ASHINGTON — Mill House Hotel £E

I **Map 5 E3** West Sussex
Mill Lane RH20 3BZ
Ashington (0903) 892426

Credit Access, Amex, Diners, Visa
Closed 25 & 26 Dec

CHANGED HANDS

Hospitality and comfort are the watchwords of the hard-working Falconer Wrights, who run their attractive inn with care. Public rooms include a small but welcoming cocktail bar overlooking the pretty garden and a relaxing split-level lounge with magazine-strewn tables and an open fire. The cottagy bedrooms are compact but homely, with traditional furnishings, and bath/shower rooms are well-equipped. ***Amenities*** garden, laundry service.

Rooms 11	*Direct dial* Yes	*Confirm by* arrang.	*Parking* Ample
Ensuite bath/shower 9	*Room TV* Yes	*Last dinner* 10	*Room service* Limited

ASKHAM — Queen's Head Inn £E/F

I **Map 13 D5** Cumbria
Nr Penrith CA10 2PF
Hackthorpe (093 12) 225

Modest but delightful accommodation in a friendly old village inn. A coal fire warms the bar, where horse brasses and copper kettles shine from the beams. The residents' lounge is no less delightful, with comfortable sofas and a large collection of pottery figures. These two rooms are kept absolutely spotless, as are the cottagy bedrooms, which share two carpeted bathrooms. In the garden is the inn's star attraction, a very splendid model railway. No dogs.

Rooms 6	*Room phone* No	*Confirm by* arrang.	*Parking* Ample
Ensuite bath/shower 0	*Room TV* No	*Last dinner* 7.30	*Room service* All day

ASPLEY GUISE — Moore Place *NEW ENTRY* 72% £D

HR **Map 5 E1** Bedfordshire
The Square, Nr Woburn
MK17 8DN
Milton Keynes (0908) 282000

Rooms 54
Ensuite bath/shower 54
Direct dial Yes
Room TV Yes
Confirm by arrang.
Last dinner 10
Parking Ample
Room service 24 hours

Credit Access, Amex, Diners, Visa
Closed 4 days Xmas

Named after its original owner Francis Moore, this imposing Georgian mansion stands in the heart of a peaceful village just minutes from junction 13 of the M1. Thoughtfully renovated and extended, its attractive day rooms – including an airy, glass-roofed reception and relaxing bar-lounge – are decorated and furnished in handsome period style. Light, pretty bedrooms in the main house and two annexes are all of a generous size and have comfortable beds plus a good range of modern accessories. Neatly kept private bathrooms. ***Amenities*** garden, games room, pool table, in-house movies, secretarial services, fax, laundry service.

Restaurant *NEW ENTRY*

Set L £9.50
Set D £12.50
About £50 for two
Seats 58
Parties 30
Parking Ample

Accomplished cooking in the modern mode is the formula at this pleasant, picture-windowed restaurant. Typical offerings range from moist, flavoursome veal sweetbreads with a rich red wine sauce and casserole of wild mushrooms to poached salmon with a pike soufflé and chive sauce, or chicken breast filled with tomato and basil and sauced with dill butter. Enjoyable sweets like marvellously zesty lemon torte to finish. Service could be improved. ⊜ ♿

Lunch 12.30–2.15 *Dinner* 7.30–10
Closed L Sat & 4 days Xmas exc. L 25 Dec

ASTON CLINTON   Bell Inn   74%   £C

HR Map 5 E2
Buckinghamshire
London Road HP22 5HP
Aylesbury (0296) 630252
Telex 83252

Rooms 21
Ensuite bath/shower 21
Direct dial Yes
Room TV Yes
Confirm by arrang.
Last dinner 9.45
Parking Ample
Room service All day

Credit Access, Visa

A superb early 17th-century inn which, although much extended and modernised, has retained its simple frontage and old world charm. Pine panelling graces the entrance hall and elegant drawing room, while the delightful Smoking Room has a character all of its own with its old fireplace, flagstone floor and polished brass tables. Bedrooms in the courtyard have direct access to the gardens, some even having their own terrace: several rooms have Bavarian handpainted furniture, including two four posters. All are decorated to a high standard and have fine antique pieces and lots of extras. The bathrooms boast bidets, shower facilities and good toiletries.
Amenities garden, laundry service. &

Restaurant ★   ♛

Lunch 12.30–1.45
Dinner 7.30–9.45
Set L £15.50, Sun £18.50
About £66 for two
Seats 100
Parties 20

Frescoes of a pastoral idyll surround diners at this elegant restaurant where Kevin Cape weaves his culinary magic. His well-thought-out menus are classically based and there is a separate menu exceptionnel which is served at 8pm and has to be ordered by 11am on the day. His meals are wonderful, both in taste and appearance, and saucing is superb. One of the great cellars: many gems from Bordeaux, the Rhône and Germany; lovely things from the New World, too (Moss Wood Cabernet Sauvignon, Margaret River).
Specialities chausson de truffe en surprise, civet de homard bourguignonne, gâteau de gibier, soufflé au chocolat. ▭ Outstanding
♟ Well-chosen ⊘

♟ indicates a **well-chosen** house wine

AVENING   Gibbons   *NEW ENTRY*   ⚐

R Map 4 B2 Gloucestershire
Nr Tetbury GL8 8NF
Nailsworth (045 383) 3070

Set L £11.50
Set D from £15.80
About £45 for two
Seats 24 Parties 28
Parking Ample
Credit Access, Amex, Diners, Visa

Philip Gibbons cooks with steady assurance at this rustic-style restaurant on the B4014. There's a Gallic influence in his regularly-changing fixed-price menus, with starters like mouclade (mussels in a creamy spiced broth) and main courses such as filet d'agneau au beurre (roast lamb with butter sauce). Fish is a speciality – we enjoyed the brill with spinach and fromage blanc. Flavours are well defined and presentation is pleasant. Booking advised.

Lunch 12.30–2.00   Dinner 7.30–9.30, Sat till 10
Closed L Sat & Mon, all Sun & Bank Hols

AXBRIDGE   Oak House   £E

I Map 4 A3 Somerset
The Square BS26 2AP
Axbridge (0934) 732444

Credit Access, Amex, Diners, Visa
Closed 10 days Xmas

Next to the church on Axbridge's medieval market square, the Oak House is an attractive old inn where guests will find comfort and hospitality. Most of the bedrooms are of a decent size, with practical freestanding furniture, cottage fabrics and tidy carpeted bathrooms (seven en suite, the other two share). Central heating keeps out the cold. Staff are friendly, if a shade casual. No dogs.
Amenities laundry service.

| Rooms 9 | Direct dial Yes | Confirm by arrang. | Parking Ample |
| Ensuite bath/shower 7 | Room TV Yes | Last dinner 9.30 | Room service All day |

AYLESBURY   Bell Hotel   57%   £D

H **Map 5 D2** Buckinghamshire
Market Square HP20 1TX
Aylesbury (0296) 89835

Credit Access, Amex, Diners, Visa

Pleasant overnight accommodation in a friendly little hotel on the
market square. Bedrooms are modestly but quite comfortably
appointed, with polished wooden furniture and bold floral curtains.
All have tea-making facilities and private bathrooms. A log fire keeps
the lounge bar cosy in winter, and the Market Bar is a favourite with
locals. Breakfast is served in a small, homely restaurant.
Amenities secretarial services, laundry service.

Rooms 17	*Direct dial* Yes	*Confirm by* 6	*Parking* Difficult
Ensuite bath/shower 17	*Room TV* Yes	*Last dinner* 9.30	*Room service* All day

AYLESBURY   Pebbles   ۹

R **Map 5 D2** Buckinghamshire
Pebble Lane
Aylesbury (0296) 86622

Set L from £10.50
Set D from £18
About £66 for two
Credit Access, Amex, Diners, Visa
Seats 36 *Parties* 42
Parking Limited

Jeremy Blake O'Connor is the enthusiastic new chef-patron at Pebbles,
a cosy two-roomed restaurant in the centre of town. His menu is
nicely varied and he draws inspiration from the great chefs in dishes
such as galette de foie gras de canard or roast milk-fed squab with
young vegetables and a Madeira-enriched jus. Not all dishes succeed
completely, but our meal ended in fine style with the lightest of oeufs
à la neige. ℮

Lunch 12–2.15, Sun till 3   *Dinner* 7–11
Closed D Sun, all Mon, Bank Hols & 1 wk Jan

BAGSHOT   Pennyhill Park Hotel   78%   £C

HR **Map 5 E3** Surrey
College Ride GU19 5ET
Bagshot (0276) 71774
Telex 858841

Rooms 47
Ensuite bath/shower 47
Direct dial Yes
Room TV Yes
Confirm by arrang.
Last dinner 10.30
Parking Ample
Room service 24 hours

Credit Access, Amex, Diners, Visa

Half a mile off the A30, Pennyhill
Park is a fine 19th century house
set in 112 acres of immaculate
gardens and parkland complete
with a trout lake. Chief day rooms
are a long, handsome entrance
hall, a Tudor-style bar and an
elegant lounge. Bedrooms in the
main house are splendidly spacious, with great style and character and some eye-catching
antiques; the majority are modern rooms in two annexes which

are less charming but equally roomy and comfortable. All rooms have
superb bathrooms with de luxe toiletries and second TVs.
Amenities garden, outdoor swimming pool, sauna, solarium, keep-
fit equipment, tennis, 9-hole golf course, putting, riding, stabling, game
fishing, clay-pigeon shooting, fax, laundry service, helipad.

Latymer Restaurant   ♔

Set L from £13.50
Set D £24.50
Seats 50

Seasonal produce gets expert handling from Paul Bingham in this
intimate, comfortable restaurant. Fine pure flavours take centre stage
in delicious dishes like beef and brown lentil broth with herbs and
root vegetables, or roast partridge cooked to the minute, its juices
seeping succulently into a potato galette. Sweets maintain the high
standard, and there are English farmhouse cheeses. Good wines, too:
Soave Classico (Zenato), Ch. Potensac 1981, Ch. Ausone 1976. ℮ &

Lunch 12.30–2.30   *Dinner* 7.30–10.30
About £60 for two

BAINBRIDGE   Rose & Crown Hotel   £E

I **Map 15 B6** North Yorkshire
Nr Leyburn DL8 3EE
Wensleydale (0969) 50225

Credit Access, Visa

A sturdy inn which has dominated the village since the 15th century.
The cosy lounge bar has panelling, pretty upholstery and a fine stone
fireplace and there is a homely residents' lounge with traditional
armchairs. Bedrooms are individually and tastefully decorated in
Laura Ashley style; three have four-posters and the remaining
furniture is freestanding and attractively modern. Bathrooms are of
an equally high standard. *Amenities* pool table.

Rooms 13	*Room phone* No	*Confirm by* 6	*Parking* Ample
Ensuite bath/shower 11	*Room TV* Yes	*Last dinner* 9.15	*Room service* None

BAKEWELL — Fischer's

See under BASLOW

BAKEWELL — Hassop Hall Hotel 77% £C/D

H Map 10 C2 Derbyshire
Hassop DE4 1NS
Great Longstone (062 987) 488
Telex 378485

Rooms 12
Ensuite bath/shower 12
Direct dial Yes
Room TV Yes
Confirm by arrang.
Last dinner 9.30
Parking Ample
Room service All day

Credit Access, Amex, Diners, Visa
Closed 3 days Xmas

A handsome building with a long and colourful history that's documented as far back as the Domesday Book. The house has been associated with only five families since that time, and current owners the Chapmans continue to restore and maintain it with great care and enthusiasm. Antiques, oil paintings and open log fires set the tone of the spacious public rooms, which now include a non-smoking sitting room adjacent to the recently refurbished oak-panelled bar. Breakfast is served in the bedrooms, which are large and luxurious, with beautifully embroidered bed linen and equally sumptuous bathrooms. No dogs. *Amenities* garden, tennis, secretarial services, laundry service, 24-hour lounge service.

BAMBURGH — Lord Crewe Arms Hotel 57% £E

H Map 14 B2 Northumberland
Front Street NE69 7BL
Bamburgh (066 84) 243

Credit Access, Visa
Closed end Oct–week before Easter

Thanks to hospitable owners, this former farmhouse in the shadow of Bamburgh Castle makes a very pleasant and appealing hotel. The characterful beamed bar is very cosy, and so are the two homely lounges (one for non-smokers). Some of the simple, neat bedrooms are being refurbished and given private bathrooms. No children under five.
Amenities coffee shop (10am–10pm summer).

Rooms 25	*Room phone* No	*Confirm by* arrang.	*Parking* Ample
Ensuite bath/shower 20	*Room TV* Yes	*Last dinner* 9	*Room service* Limited

BAMPTON — Huntsham Court

See under HUNTSHAM

BANBURY — Banbury Moat House 59% £D/E

H Map 5 D1 Oxfordshire
27 Oxford Road OX16 9AH
Banbury (0295) 59361
Telex 838967

Credit Access, Amex, Diners, Visa

Behind the elegant Georgian facade of this impressive hotel is a smart, period-style interior. Ornate moulded ceilings, chandeliers and leather chesterfields give character to the foyer-lounge, while the bar, though spacious, is cosy and intimate. Bedrooms have pleasing built-in furniture, tasteful decor and bright, modern bathrooms with shower facilities. Tea/coffee-makers and remote-control TVs are standard.
Amenities clay-pigeon shooting, fax, laundry service.

Rooms 52	*Direct dial* Yes	*Confirm by* 6	*Parking* Ample
Ensuite bath/shower 52	*Room TV* Yes	*Last dinner* 9.45	*Room service* 24 hours

BANBURY — Whately Hall 66% £C

H Map 5 D1 Oxfordshire
Banbury Cross OX16 0AN
Banbury (0295) 3451
Telex 837149

Credit Access, Amex, Diners, Visa

Period appeal and modern comfort in a long-established hotel by Banbury Cross. The character of the mullioned exterior continues in the panelled lobby, which together with an adjacent lounge provides plenty of space to relax. There's also a bar and coffee shop. 30 spacious bedrooms are in the original building, the rest – smaller and more functional – in a wing. *Amenities* garden, croquet, snooker, pool table, fax, laundry service, coffee shop (10am–5.30pm). ⅃

Rooms 74	*Direct dial* Yes	*Confirm by* 6	*Parking* Ample
Ensuite bath/shower 74	*Room TV* Yes	*Last dinner* 9.45	*Room service* 24 hours

If we recommend **meals** in a Hotel or Inn,
a separate entry is made for its restaurant.

BARFORD   The Glebe at Barford   61%   £D/E

H Map 10 C4 Warwickshire
Church Street CV35 8BS
Warwick (0926) 624218
Telex 312440

Credit Access, Amex, Diners, Visa

You can find pleasant accommodation at this very handsome Georgian house by the village church. Public rooms include a comfortable bar, a small and peaceful residents' lounge and a smartly refurbished restaurant with a stylish conservatory. The well-proportioned bedrooms are furnished with solid, traditional pieces and have adequate en suite bathrooms. Housekeeping is good and the staff are friendly and cheerful. No dogs. *Amenities* garden, laundry service.

Rooms 15	*Direct dial* Yes	*Confirm by* arrang.	*Parking* Ample
Ensuite bath/shower 14	*Room TV* Yes	*Last dinner* 9.30	*Room service* All day

BARNARD CASTLE   Jersey Farm Hotel   59%   £F

H Map 15 B5 Co. Durham
West Town Pastures Farm,
Darlington Rd DL12 8TA
Teesdale (0833) 38223

The hotel side continues to grow, while the working farm, with its herds of pedigree Highland and Jersey cattle, is becoming more of a hobby. The whole place is neat, bright, and comfortable, with a smart new reception area, a lounge in place of the disco and a bar with plenty of red plush. Spotlessly kept bedrooms have modern furnishings, pretty floral fabrics and carpeted bathrooms (a few singles have shower/WC only). Four full suites, with nine more due by end of 1988, are in stone cottages across the yard. A leisure centre is also planned. This is a friendly, popular place with most obliging staff. *Amenities* garden, laundry service.

Rooms 15	*Direct dial* Yes	*Confirm by* arrang.	*Parking* Ample
Ensuite bath/shower 15	*Room TV* Yes	*Last dinner* 9	*Room service* Limited

BARNBY MOOR   Ye Olde Bell   61%   £D

H Map 11 D2 Nottinghamshire
Nr Retford DN22 8QS
Retford (0777) 705121

Credit Access, Amex, Diners, Visa

With its name clearly emblazoned on the side, this former coaching inn is easy to spot on the A638, close to Sherwood Forest. The reception lounge has a comfortable, traditional look, with wing chairs around a log fire. There's a large bar, too. Refurbishment has improved bedrooms: superior ones have hairdryers, trouser presses, sofas and modern tiled bathrooms. Standard rooms are more compact but practical. *Amenities* garden, laundry service.

Rooms 55	*Direct dial* Yes	*Confirm by* 6	*Parking* Ample
Ensuite bath/shower 55	*Room TV* Yes	*Last dinner* 9.45	*Room service* Limited

BARNHAM BROOM   Barnham Broom Hotel   62%   £D/E

H Map 6 C1 Norfolk
Honingham Road NR9 4DD
Barnham Broom (060 545) 393
Telex 975711

Credit Access, Amex, Diners, Visa

Excellent sports facilities make this pleasantly informal hotel a popular spot. Public areas include two lively bars, one with a patio overlooking the golf course. The practical bedrooms are equipped with direct-dial phones and tea/coffee makers. *Amenities* patio, indoor & outdoor swimming pools, sauna, solarium, keep-fit equipment, beauty salon, hairdressing, tennis, squash, golf course, snooker, secretarial services, laundry service, coffee shop (9am–11pm). &

Rooms 52	*Direct dial* Yes	*Confirm by* arrang.	*Parking* Ample
Ensuite bath/shower 52	*Room TV* Yes	*Last dinner* 9.30	*Room service* Limited

▷ is our symbol for an **outstanding** wine list

BARNSDALE BAR   TraveLodge   54%   £E

H Map 11 D1
West Yorkshire
A1 Trunk Road, Nr Pontefract
WF8 3JB
Pontefract (0977) 620711
Telex 557457
Credit Access, Amex, Diners, Visa

This well-kept modern hotel in a service area on the southbound A1 provides simple overnight accommodation. There's a small lounge area in the foyer providing limited seating. All bedrooms are twins or doubles, and are equipped with tea-makers, complimentary drinks trays and remote-control TVs. Refurbished rooms have brighter decor and deep carpets. Compact bathrooms, all with showers, are spotless. *Amenities* garden, coffee shop (7am–10pm).

Rooms 65	*Direct dial* Yes	*Confirm by* 6	*Parking* Ample
Ensuite bath/shower 65	*Room TV* Yes	*Last dinner* 10.15	*Room service* None

BARNSLEY — Ardsley Moat House — 66% — £D

H **Map 10 C2** South Yorkshire
Doncaster Road,
Ardsley S71 5EH
Barnsley (0226) 289401
Telex 547762

Credit Access, Amex, Diners, Visa

Much extended since the 18th century, this well-run hotel set back from the A635 appeals to both business and leisure visitors. A warm welcome awaits beyond the stone-floored foyer, and there's a choice of bars. The 18 bedrooms in the main house are generally larger and more traditional than the equally comfortable majority in the wing. Trouser presses, tea-makers and bedside controls are standard. *Amenities* garden, games room, secretarial services, laundry service.

Rooms 62	Direct dial Yes	Confirm by 6	Parking Ample
Ensuite bath/shower 62	Room TV Yes	Last dinner 10.30	Room service 24 hours

BARNSTAPLE — Imperial Hotel — 60% — £D

H **Map 3 D2** Devon
Taw Vale Parade EX32 8NB
Barnstaple (0271) 45861

Credit Access, Amex, Diners, Visa

A sturdy Edwardian building standing near the river Taw. The story of Tarka the Otter is set in these parts, and in the lounge are specially commissioned paintings of episodes from the book. This lounge is sometimes used for meetings, but there are also two bars and a comfortably furnished foyer. Bedrooms are generally modest in decor and fittings, though a number have been smartly updated. *Amenities* garden, laundry service.

Rooms 56	Direct dial Yes	Confirm by 6	Parking Ample
Ensuite bath/shower 56	Room TV Yes	·Last dinner 9	Room service 24 hours

BARNSTAPLE — Lynwood House — ♀

RR **Map 3 D2** Devon
Bishop's Tawton Road
Barnstaple (0271) 43695

Seats 60
Parties 80
Parking Ample

Credit Access, Visa

An informal downstairs room offers a simple menu while a more elegant upstairs restaurant has a strong emphasis on fish dishes. Both rooms are attractive in presentation and the food is competently prepared and served by the Roberts family. Good, fresh ingredients are used throughout and a splendid fish soup is particularly noteworthy. Excellent home-made meringues with clotted cream make for a luscious dessert. 🍷 Well-chosen

Lunch 12–2 *Dinner* 7–10
About £40 (upstairs) *for two* *About* £32 (downstairs)

BEDROOMS 3 £D
With bath/shower 3

Three bedrooms are equipped with en suite shower rooms, TVs, radios, direct dial telephones, trouser presses, hairdryers and tea/coffee makers. No children or dogs.

★ For a *discount* on next year's guide, see **An Offer for Answers**. ★

BASILDON — Crest Hotel — 59% — £C/D

H **Map 7 B4** Essex
Cranes Farm Road SS14 3DG
Basildon (0268) 3955
Telex 995141

Credit Access, Amex, Diners, Visa

Just off the A127 and about two miles from the town centre, this early-70s hotel overlooks a little fishing lake. Day rooms are pleasantly relaxing, bedrooms practical and well equipped, with remote-control TV/radios, trouser presses and tea-makers. Executive, Lady Crest and the new Study rooms have various additional features. *Amenities* garden, putting, games room, in-house movies, secretarial services, fax, laundry service.

Rooms 116	Direct dial Yes	Confirm by 6	Parking Ample
Ensuite bath/shower 116	Room TV Yes	Last dinner 9.45	Room service 24 hours

BASINGSTOKE — Crest Hotel — 65% — £C

H **Map 5 D3** Hampshire
Grove Road RG21 3EE
Basingstoke (0256) 468181
Telex 858501

Credit Access, Amex, Diners, Visa

By a roundabout south of the centre, Basingstoke's Crest offers a good standard of modern comfort and decor. Bedrooms are neat and well designed, and apart from standard rooms there are better-equipped Executive and Lady Crest rooms. Among the day rooms are two bars, one with a cheerful conservatory area, and a cane-furnished lobby-lounge. Housekeeping is up to the mark throughout. *Amenities* garden, snooker, pool table, in-house movies, secretarial services, fax.

Rooms 85	Direct dial Yes	Confirm by 6	Parking Ample
Ensuite bath/shower 85	Room TV Yes	Last dinner 9.45	Room service 24 hours

BASINGSTOKE	Hilton Lodge 63%	£B/C

H   **Map 5 D3** Hampshire
Old Common Road,
Black Dam RG21 3PR
Basingstoke (0256) 460460
Telex 859038
Credit Access, Amex, Diners, Visa

A modern purpose-built hotel (formerly the Ladbroke Lodge) close to junction 6 of the M3. It's a popular business choice, and the facilities for meetings and conferences are extensive. Public areas are in bright, contemporary style, like the practically appointed bedrooms and 24 new Gold Star rooms. Neat, compact bathrooms. *Amenities* garden, indoor swimming pool, sauna, keep-fit equipment, pool table, in-house movies, secretarial services, fax, laundry service.   &

Rooms 144	*Direct dial* Yes	*Confirm by* 6	*Parking* Ample
Ensuite bath/shower 144	*Room TV* Yes	*Last dinner* 10	*Room service* 24 hours

BASINGSTOKE	Hilton National 65%	£C

H   **Map 5 D3** Hampshire
Aldermaston Roundabout,
Ringway North RG24 9NV
Basingstoke (0256) 20212
Telex 858223

Credit Access, Amex, Diners, Visa

This sprawling hotel (formerly the Ladbroke) is purpose-built for the business visitor. Day rooms include a cane-furnished reception area and large, split-level cocktail lounge. Best bedrooms are the 30 new ones with pleasant modern decor, floral soft furnishings and good accessories like trouser presses and hairdryers. Compact older rooms are due to be refurbished. *Amenities* indoor swimming pool, keep-fit equipment, snooker, in-house movies, fax, laundry service.

Rooms 138	*Direct dial* Yes	*Confirm by* 6	*Parking* Ample
Ensuite bath/shower 138	*Room TV* Yes	*Last dinner* 11	*Room service* Limited

We welcome bona fide complaints and recommendations
on the tear-out pages at the back of the book for readers' comment.
They are followed up by our professional team.

BASLOW	Cavendish Hotel 74%	£C/D

H   **Map 10 C2** Derbyshire
DE4 1SP
Baslow (024 688) 2311
Telex 547150

Rooms 24
Ensuite bath/shower 24
Direct dial Yes
Room TV Yes
Confirm by arrang.
Last dinner 10
Parking Ample
Room service 24 hours

Credit Access, Amex, Diners, Visa

All the bedrooms enjoy superb views over the hills and woods of the Chatsworth Estate, and many of the hotel's fine furnishings came from Chatsworth itself. The ample entrance hall, with its paintings, prints and red-brick floor, sets the tone for the public rooms, which include an intimate bar and a most inviting lounge made cosy in winter by an open fire. Bedrooms are of a good size and beautifully furnished with locally crafted pieces. Two deep armchairs, a side table, books and a mini-bar are among the many comforts, and all rooms have very well-equipped bathrooms. No dogs.
Amenities garden, golf practice net, putting, game fishing, laundry service.

BASLOW	Fischer's at Baslow Hall *NEW ENTRY*	⑨

RR   **Map 10 C2** Derbyshire
Calver Road
Baslow (024 688) 3259

Set L £12.50, Sun £10.50
About £58 *for two*
Seats 50
Parties 12
Parking Ample
Credit Access, Amex, Diners, Visa

October 13th saw the start of a splendid new venture for Max Fischer and his wife Susan, formerly at Fischer's in Bakewell. Their restaurant with rooms is an Elizabethan-style building set back off the road in five acres of grounds with towering chestnuts. Standards of cooking will no doubt remain the same, with starred delights like fish and game terrines, salmon and turbot with chervil sauce and the best of the season's game.   ⊘ &

Lunch 12–1.30   *Dinner* 7–9.30
Closed D Sun & all Mon

BASSENTHWAITE   Armathwaite Hall   65%   £D

H **Map 13 C5** Cumbria
Nr Keswick CA12 4RE
Bassenthwaite Lake
(059 681) 551
Telex 64319

Credit Access, Amex, Diners, Visa

Deer and sheep roam the parkland surrounding this imposing mansion overlooking the lake. Inside, a baronial atmosphere is engendered by the dark oak panelling, hunting trophies and oil paintings, while the cocktail bar is dominated by a massive carved mantelpiece dating from 1562. The spacious bedrooms in the main house have boldly patterned fabrics and contemporary furniture; those in the coach house have mahogany freestanding pieces. Bathrooms range from functional to luxurious in the suites. *Amenities* garden, indoor swimming pool, sauna, solarium, whirlpool bath, gymnasium, tennis, squash, pitch & putt, croquet, coarse fishing, games room, snooker, pool table, in-house movies, fax, valeting, laundry service

Rooms 42	*Direct dial* Yes	*Confirm by* 4	*Parking* Ample
Ensuite bath/shower 42	*Room TV* Yes	*Last dinner* 9.30	*Room service* 24 hours

BASSENTHWAITE LAKE   Pheasant Inn   65%   £D/E

H **Map 13 C5** Cumbria
Cockermouth CA13 9YE
Bassenthwaite Lake (059 681) 234

Closed 25 Dec

There's a lovely timeless quality about this old-fashioned inn near the A66. Main rooms are full of character and have nice homely touches like open fires, decorative brasses and bowls of fresh flowers. The rustic, wood-panelled bar is especially authentic, with its country chairs, copper-topped tables and hunting prints. Bedrooms are attractively furnished to a high standard and housekeeping throughout is excellent. *Amenities* garden.

Rooms 20	*Room phone* No	*Confirm by* 4	*Parking* Ample
Ensuite bath/shower 20	*Room TV* No	*Last dinner* 8.15	*Room service* All day

We publish annually,
so make sure you use the current edition.
It's worth it!

BATH   Apsley House Hotel   76%   £C/D

H **Town plan A3** Avon
141 Newbridge Hill BA1 3PT
Bath (0225) 336966
Telex 449212

Rooms 7
Ensuite bath/shower 7
Direct dial Yes
Room TV Yes
Confirm by 6
Last dinner 9
Parking Ample
Room service 24 hours

Credit Access, Amex, Diners, Visa

Just over a mile to the west of the city, on the A431, this very civilised and comfortable hotel is run by the Davidsons to the most exacting standards. Constant improvements and careful maintenance keep their gracious William IV mansion in fine fettle, and housekeeping is immaculate. Good-sized bedrooms are tastefully furnished in period style, with brass beds and prettily coordinated fabrics; attic rooms

have the best views. Radio-alarms are standard and spotless modern bathrooms have bidets and shower attachments. The elegant restaurant overlooks the garden and hills beyond, and there's also a comfortable lounge and agreeable bar. No children under 14 years. No dogs. *Amenities* garden, fax, laundry service.

BATH   Bath Hotel   66%   £D

H **Town plan C5** Avon
Widcombe Basin BA2 4JP
Bath (0225) 338855
Telex 445876

Credit Access, Amex, Diners, Visa

This smart modern hotel enjoys an attractive setting where the river Avon meets the canal. Picture windows make the most of the view in the bar-lounge, where cane furniture and large plants add to the summery feel. Bedrooms are decorated in pastel shades and furnished with lightwood pieces. Tea-makers and mini-bars are standard. Capable, friendly staff.
Amenities garden, coarse fishing, fax, laundry service, kiosk. &

Rooms 94	*Direct dial* Yes	*Confirm by* 6	*Parking* Ample
Ensuite bath/shower 94	*Room TV* Yes	*Last dinner* 9.30	*Room service* 24 hours

BATH

Map 4 B3
Town plan opposite

Population 84,000

The Romans settled in Bath because of the waters and built baths used for therapy and recreation. In the 18th century spa treatment reached the peak of fashion and Bath was greatly enlarged at this time. Being wholly built within the space of a century, all its buildings are of the same classic, elegant style. Its Georgian character and charm remained unchanged until very recently. Yet Bath has become the centre of much environmental controversy: should the face of Bath be gradually eroded to develop it as a 20th-century commercial city, or should it be enshrined for ever as a masterpiece of urban architecture?

Annual Events
Bath Festival (music and drama)
May–June
Royal Bath and West Show

Sights Outside City
Cheddar Gorge, Wooky Hole Caves, Wells Cathedral, Glastonbury Abbey, Longleat House and Safari Park, Castle Combe Village, Lacock Abbey and Village, Stourhead House and gardens, Avebury Circles, Corsham Court

Tourist Information Centre
Abbey Church Yard
Telephone Enquiries Bath 462831

Fiat Dealer
Motor Services (Bath) Ltd
Locksbrook Road
Bath
Avon BA1 2PW
Tel. Bath 428000

1 Abbey *15th c* B4
2 American Museum at Claverton Manor *2½ miles, life in the New World from 17th c to 1860* C3
3 Artsite B4
4 Assembly Rooms *finely restored Georgian Suite, also houses world-famous Museum of Costume* A2
5 Bath Industrial Heritage Centre A2
6 Bath Spa Station B5
7 Botanical Gardens in Victoria Park A2
8 The Circus, Royal Crescent and Lansdown Crescent *superb examples of Georgian town-planning* A1 & A2
9 Guildhall Banqueting Room *fine Adam-style room* B3
10 Herschel House A3
11 Holburne of Menstrie Museum *paintings, silver, objects d'art* C2
12 Huntingdon Centre B2
13 Lansdown Race-course A1
14 Museum of Bookbinding B4
15 National Museum of Photography B3
16 Postal Museum B3
17 Pulteney Bridge *Adam bridge lined with shops* B3
18 Pump Room and Roman Baths *the heart of Bath, includes Britain's finest Roman remains* B4
19 Sally Lunn's House *oldest House in Bath* B4
20 Sham Castle *18th-c folly and viewpoint* C2
21 Theatre Royal A3
22 Tourist Information Centre B4
23 University C3
24 Victoria Art Gallery *works by mainly West Country Artists; glass; Delft; horology* B3

Bath F/I/A/T

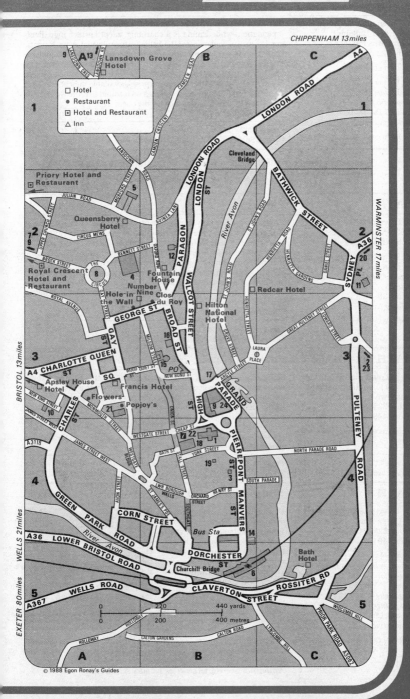

CHIPPENHAM 13 miles

- □ Hotel
- • Restaurant
- ⊡ Hotel and Restaurant
- △ Inn

© 1988 Egon Ronay's Guides

BATH — Clos Du Roy 🍷

R **Town plan B3** Avon
7 Edgar Buildings,
George Street BA1 2EE
Bath (0225) 64356

French cooking

Set L *from* £9.50
Set D *from* 18.95
About £56 for two
Seats 27 *Parties* 14
Parking Limited

Credit Access, Amex, Diners, Visa

The Roys run this friendly restaurant; Philippe is a chef of skill and imagination, while Emma is a charming, adept hostess. Ingredients are top quality, and many of the dishes feature unusual, even dramatic combinations – cream of courgette and aubergine soup with a julienne of squid; paupiette of guinea fowl and lobster with vanilla sauce; an iced terrine of almond and mixed fruit with an almond and amaretti sauce. A la carte and 'menu surprise' available lunchtimes and evenings. Note the fine dessert wines on a sound list: Ch. Guiteronde '83, Anjou Moulin Touchais '62, Ch. d'Yquem '76.
🍷 Well-chosen ⊕

Lunch 12–2   *Dinner* 7–10.15
Closed Sun, Mon, Bank Hols, 2 wks Jan–Feb & 1 wk Aug

Any person using our name to obtain free hospitality is a fraud.
Proprietors, please inform the police and us.

BATH — Flowers 🍷

R **Town plan A3** Avon
27 Monmouth Street
Bath (0225) 313774

Set L £8.50
Set D from £15
About £40 for two
Seats 26
Parties 30
Parking Ample

Credit Access, Amex, Diners, Visa

Enjoyable food at very reasonable prices is served at this attractive and unpretentious restaurant. The three-course lunch menu offers a short choice of tasty dishes such as duck pâté, loin of pork or poached hake with cucumber, lemon and burnt butter. Typical dishes on the wider-ranging dinner menu (main course determines the meal price) are fish soup with mussels and prawns, roast duck with plum sauce and rack of lamb with a breadcrumb, parsley and garlic crust. Cheese or a lovely sweet – perhaps chocolate mousse or bread and butter pudding – to round things off. Service is friendly, helpful and pleasantly unhurried. ⊕

Lunch 12–2   *Dinner* 7–10.30
Closed Sun, Mon, Bank Hols (exc. Good Fri) & 2 wks Xmas

BATH — Fountain House   *NEW ENTRY*   £C/D

PH **Town plan B2** Avon
9 Fountain Buildings,
Lansdown Road BA1 5DV
Bath (0225) 338622
Telex 444905

Credit Access, Amex, Diners, Visa

Many original features have been retained at this Georgian town house with a marble-floored entrance hall. Its strength is the luxurious, all-suite accommodation, each suite having a smartly furnished lounge, excellent bathroom, some really nice prints and pictures, ironing facilities and a table for breakfast, to which guests serve themselves from a fully equipped kitchen, having had fresh rolls, croissants, milk, and the morning newspaper delivered to the door.
Amenities laundry room, secretarial services.

| Rooms 14 | Direct dial Yes | Confirm by arrang. | Parking Limited |
| Ensuite bath/shower 14 | Room TV Yes | | Room service None |

BATH — Francis Hotel   70%   £B/C

H **Town plan A3** Avon
Queen Square BA1 2HH
Bath (0225) 24257
Telex 449162

Rooms 94
Ensuite bath/shower 94
Direct dial Yes
Room TV Yes
Confirm by 6
Last dinner 10
Parking Limited
Room service 24 hours

Credit Access, Amex, Diners, Visa

Originally six private houses dating from 1723, the handsome Francis Hotel stands on the south side of Queen Square, close to many of Bath's tourist spots. The reception area sets a tone of gracious period charm that continues in the club-like bar and the beautifully appointed lounge – a haven of deep-cushioned comfort. Bedrooms in the main building are in keeping with good-quality fabrics and some fine pieces of furniture. The remaining rooms, equally bright and spacious, are in a newer wing. All rooms have recently been or are being refurbished. Excellent management and staff.
Amenities secretarial services, laundry service, fax.

BATH — Hilton National — 66% — £B/C

H Town plan B3 Avon
Walcot Street BA1 5BJ
Bath (0225) 63411
Telex 449519

Credit Access, Amex, Diners, Visa

A centrally-located modern hotel by the river Avon. The marble-floored foyer leads on to a bar, lounge and brasserie, all in restful, contemporary style. Lightwood furnishings and floral fabrics are used in most of the bedrooms, which have practical bathrooms and good accessories. Staff could smile and care a little more.
Amenities in-house movies, secretarial services, laundry service, coffee shop (10am–11pm).

Rooms 122	Direct dial Yes	Confirm by 6	Parking Difficult
Ensuite bath/shower 122	Room TV Yes	Last dinner 10	Room service 24 hours

BATH — Hole in the Wall

R Town plan A3 Avon
16 George Street BA1 2EN
Bath (0225) 25242

Set L from £18.50
Set D from £22
About £60 for two
Seats 55 Parties 16
Parking Difficult
Credit Access, Amex, Diners, Visa

An elegant restaurant where attentive service is offered by waiters in traditional garb. Chef Martin Barrett provides a range of interesting, acceptably cooked dishes. Start with salad of avocado, Cornish crab and pink grapefruit or three different cheese-filled filo parcels with tomato and basil sauce; main course might be fillet of beef, lamb and veal with sauces of marrow, fresh mint and tarragon respectively.
♀ Well-chosen ℮

Lunch 12.30–2 Dinner 7–10
Closed L Sun & L Bank Hols

Our inspectors are our full-time employees;
they are professionally trained by us.

BATH — Landsdown Grove Hotel — 66% — £C/D

H Town plan A1 Avon
Landsdown Road BA1 5EH
Bath (0225) 315891
Telex 444850

Credit Access, Amex, Diners, Visa

Constant updating keeps the Jackmans' rambling stone-built hotel in excellent shape. This year it was the turn of the function rooms and nearly a third of the accommodation to be smartly refurbished. Bedrooms are all individually styled and well equipped, and some have spectacular views over the city. Public areas include an attractive reception, cane-furnished bar and elegant drawing room.
Amenities garden, secretarial services, fax, laundry service.

Rooms 41	Direct dial Yes	Confirm by 6	Parking Ample
Ensuite bath/shower 41	Room TV Yes	Last dinner 9.30, Sun 9	Room service 24 hours

BATH — Number Nine — 57% — NEW ENTRY — £D/E

H Town plan A3 Avon
Miles Buildings BA1 2QS
Bath (0225) 25462
Telex 449212

Credit Access, Amex, Diners, Visa

A Georgian gem in one of Bath's most delightful walkways a stone's throw from the Assembly Rooms. An elegant first-floor lounge offers antiques and traditional Georgian furniture. Bedrooms, three of which are in an annexe 50 yards away, are cosily but stylishly furnished, many with canopied beds, and there are pleasing touches such as magazines and potpourri. No children under 14. No dogs.
Amenities garden, laundry service.

Rooms 9	Direct dial Yes	Confirm by 6	Parking Limited
Ensuite bath/shower 9	Room TV Yes	Last dinner 9.00	Room service All day

BATH — Popjoy's — ♔

R Town plan A3 Avon
Beau Nash's House, Sawclose
Bath (0225) 460494

Set D £17.50
About £48 for two
Seats 32
Parties 30
Parking Limited

Credit Access, Visa

Beau Nash and Juliana Popjoy once shared this fine Georgian house, now an elegant, comfortable setting for an enjoyable, intimate meal. The menu changes regularly, with about half a dozen choices for each course. Typical dishes: duck liver parfait in port wine jelly; sea bass with an excellent butter sauce; medallions of veal served on a ragout of celery, walnuts and apple; a good rich chocolate and orange truffle cake. A two-course pre-theatre menu is served at 6pm. There's an attractively presented wine list with top white burgundies from Ampeau and Leflaive and the superb Californian Cabernet from Stag's Leap. ♀ Well-chosen ℮

Lunch 12–2, Sun 12–2.30 Dinner 6–10, Sat 6–10.30, Sun 7–9.30
Closed Sat, all Sun & 2 wks Xmas

BATH　　　　Priory Hotel　82%　　　　£B

HR **Town plan A2** Avon
Weston Road BA1 2XT
Bath (0225) 331922
Telex 44612

Rooms 21
Ensuite bath/shower 21
Direct dial Yes
Room TV Yes
Confirm by arrang.
Last dinner 9.30
Parking Ample
Room service 24 hours

Credit Access, Amex, Diners, Visa

An air of peace and tranquillity is apparent as you enter the attractive foyer of this elegant Georgian hotel. Antiques and comfortable sofas abound in the flower-filled lounge areas, which are also supplied with books and magazines. French windows lead from the drawing room into the delightful garden for a stroll on mellow evenings. Bedrooms are individually decorated in fine taste using top-quality fabrics,

period furniture and harmonious, restful colour schemes; bathrooms are carpeted and tiled and have thermostatically controlled showers. Housekeeping is immaculate and service is professional but relaxed. No children under ten. No dogs. *Amenities* garden, outdoor swimming pool, croquet, secretarial services, laundry service.

Restaurant　　　　♛

Set L from £12, Sun from £15
Set D from £20
About £70 for two
Seats 64
Parties 40

The elegant dining room with immaculately appointed tables provides a suitable setting for Michael Collom's refined cooking. The menus offer a good choice of dishes with the emphasis on seafood for starters – choose perhaps gravad lax or poached scallops with garlic. Main course might be succulent rosettes of lamb. Cheeses are outstanding and service is attentive and knowledgeable. Very fine classic wine list.
▷ Outstanding　♟ Well-chosen　🍷

Lunch 12.30–2
Dinner 7.15–9.30

BATH　　　　The Queensberry Hotel　*NEW ENTRY*　£C/D

PH **Town Plan A2** Avon
Russel Street BA1 2QT
Bath (0225) 447928
Telex 445628

Credit Access, Amex, Diners, Visa
Closed 2 wks Xmas/New Year

A haven of peace in the throng of the city, the Queensberry is a magnificently restored Georgian building with a lovely patio garden. Bedrooms feature stylish contemporary decor and antique furniture, and several boast 18th-century stucco ceilings and cornices. Continental breakfast is served in the rooms, where light meals and bar drinks are also available. Staff are charming and efficient. No dogs. *Amenities* patio, fax, laundry service.

Rooms 25	*Direct dial* Yes	*Confirm by* arrang.	*Parking* Limited
Ensuite bath/shower 25	*Room TV* Yes		*Room service* 24 hours

We publish annually,
so make sure you use the current edition.
It's worth it!

BATH　　　　Redcar Hotel　59%　　　　£D

H **Town plan B2** Avon
Henrietta Street BA2 6LR
Bath (0225) 69151
Telex 444842

Credit Access, Amex, Diners, Visa

Practical accommodation in a cosy hotel converted from three Georgian houses. Bedrooms are appointed in straightforward style, and the majority have their own tiled bathrooms. The main day room is a bar-lounge with chandeliers and a baby grand. Things are beginning to look a little dated here and there, and some of the staff could be smarter. *Amenities* in-house movies, secretarial services, laundry service, 24-hour lounge service.

Rooms 31	*Direct dial* Yes	*Confirm by* arrang.	*Parking* Limited
Ensuite bath/shower 23	*Room TV* Yes	*Last dinner* 10.30	*Room service* All day

BATH Royal Crescent Hotel 87% £B

HR Town plan A2 Avon
16 Royal Crescent BA1 2LS
Bath (0225) 319090
Telex 444251

Rooms 45
Ensuite bath/shower 43
Direct dial Yes
Room TV Yes
Confirm by arrang.
Last dinner 9.30
Parking Limited
Room service 24 hours

Credit Access, Amex, Diners, Visa

Comprising the central two houses of Bath's famous Royal Crescent, this outstanding hotel lives up to its awesome environs in every way. Public rooms are gracious, elegant, supremely comfortable, with fine paintings from the hotel group's private collection, antique furnishings and a lovely 16th-century Brussels tapestry. Bedrooms – some in the Dower House – are equally luxurious. All are individually decorated with excellent period furniture, high-quality soft furnishings, original oils and ornaments. Four-posters and half-testers are much in evidence, as are thoughtful extras. Bathrooms (some a little small) are well equipped. Top marks for cleanliness, maintenance and service. No dogs. *Amenities* garden, plunge pool, whirlpool bath, croquet, secretarial services, fax, valeting, laundry service.

Restaurant ★ ♛♛

Lunch 12.30–2
Dinner 7–9.30
Set L £15
Set D £29.50
About £75 for two
Seats 65
Parties 42

The Dower house is an elegant setting for Michael Croft's refined cooking. His interesting and imaginative menus make decisions difficult. Start, perhaps, with a trout timbale filled with ragout of seafood on shellfish sauce, graduate to saddle of venison on pepper sauce with summer berries and conclude (if you can) with soufflé lemon tart. Accomplished service does justice to the excellent cooking and presenta-

tion. Still a good classic wine list with especially fine claret (Ducru-Beaucaillou '61) but no longer outstanding as some of the burgundy and Alsace producers listed have better reputations than their wines merit. *Specialities* gâteau of rabbit with creamed morels and leeks, wild pigeon Pithivier, hot dessert soufflés. ♀ Well-chosen ☺ ♿

If we recommend **meals** in a Hotel or Inn,
a separate entry is made for its restaurant.

BATTLE Netherfield Place 77% £D/E

HR Map 7 B6 East Sussex
Netherfield TN33 9PP
Battle (042 46) 4455
Telex 95284

Rooms 12
Ensuite bath/shower 12
Direct dial Yes
Room TV Yes
Confirm by arrang.
Last dinner 9.30
Parking Ample
Room service All day

Credit Access, Amex, Diners, Visa

The thoughtful Colliers are continually making improvements to their stylish 1920s country house set in beautifully kept grounds. Relaxation is the keynote of the public rooms, which include two peaceful lounges, one with an adjoining cocktail bar. Bedrooms range from charming attic rooms with sloping ceilings and dormer windows to handsomely furnished rooms with draped beds. Fruit, chocolates,

dressing gowns and luxurious towels are just some of the extras, and bathrooms are lavishly equipped. No dogs.
Amenities garden, teletext, secretarial services, laundry service.

see over

Netherfield Place Restaurant   ♛ ♪

Set L from £9.50
Set D £15
Seats 36
Parties 80

Guests in this elegant dining room benefit from the lovely fresh produce grown in chef-patron Michael Collier's prize garden. It is treated with respect in his thoughtfully prepared dishes, which include veal in a Calvados and pistachio sauce, venison with a pear and cranberry sauce, and a nut roast for vegetarians. The rambling wine list has some fine old clarets and burgundies. ⊝

Lunch 12.30–2   *Dinner* 7–9.30
About £50 *for two*

Our inspectors *never* book in the name of Egon Ronay's Guides.
They disclose their identity only if they are considering an establishment
for inclusion in the next edition of the Guide.

BAWTRY   Crown Hotel   65%   £D/E

H **Map 11 D2** South Yorkshire
High Street DN10 6JW
Doncaster (0302) 710341
Telex 547089

Credit Access, Amex, Diners, Visa

Once an important staging post for London-Edinburgh mail coaches, the Crown retains the atmosphere of bygone days, notably in the bar with its prints and fine old furnishings. Other areas are more modern, including 40 bedrooms in an adjoining wing. All bedrooms offer tea-makers and teletext TV, with more extras in the six Club rooms. Helpful, motivated manager.
Amenities garden, secretarial services, laundry service.

Rooms 57	*Direct dial* Yes	*Confirm by* 6	*Parking* Ample
Ensuite bath/shower 57	*Room TV* Yes	*Last dinner* 9.45	*Room service* 24 hours

---

BEACONSFIELD   Bellhouse Hotel   67%   £C

H **Map 5 E2** Buckinghamshire
Oxford Road HP9 2XE
Gerrards Cross (0753) 887211
Telex 848719

Credit Access, Amex, Diners, Visa

A comprehensive improvement programme is under way at this well-run hotel, with a leisure complex and additional accommodation heading the list. All the bedrooms are spacious and well equipped, with writing desks, smart mirrored wardrobes and gleaming bathrooms. The vast, airy foyer-lounge features a pretty little tropical garden. The hotel stands by the A40, 12 miles from Heathrow.
Amenities garden, in-house movies, laundry service.

Rooms 118	*Direct dial* Yes	*Confirm by* 6	*Parking* Ample
Ensuite bath/shower 118	*Room TV* Yes	*Last dinner* 9.45	*Room service* 24 hours

---

BEAMINSTER   Bridge House   *NEW ENTRY*   ♪

RR **Map 4 A4** Dorset
Beaminster DT8 3AY
Beaminster (0308) 862200

Set D £12.50
About £35 *for two*
Seats 38
Parking Ample

Credit Access, Visa

Real home cooking and a good family atmosphere are keynotes. The building dates back to the 16th century, and the dining rooms have beams, log-fired stoves and a plain, unfussy decor that matches the style of cooking. Paula Blake relies on quality produce and a true instinct for flavour, and typical dishes run from hearty fish soup and lamb-stuffed tomatoes to monkfish and scallop kebab, duckling with game sauce and slow-cooked steak casserole. Good fresh vegetables, home-made ices, fine English cheeses. ⊝

Lunch Sun 12.30–2.30   *Dinner* 7.15–9.30   **Closed** D Sun

BEDROOMS 3   £F
With bath/shower 1

One of the antique-furnished bedrooms has a bathroom en suite, while the others, a pretty single and a very large double, share one. No children. No dogs.

★ For a *discount* on next year's guide, see **An Offer for Answers**. ★

BEANACRE

Beechfield House   77%   **£C**

HR Map 4 B2 Wiltshire
Nr Melksham SN12 7PU
Melksham (0225) 703700
Telex 444969

Rooms 24
Ensuite bath/shower 24
Direct dial Yes
Room TV Yes
Confirm by arrang.
Last dinner 9.15
Parking Ample
Room service All day

Credit Access, Amex, Diners, Visa

There have been lots of recent changes at this Victorian country house. Eight bedrooms have been added, as has a new restaurant. (The two rooms where guests dined have been converted to a drawing room and private dining room.) Unchanged and as welcoming as ever is the cosy bar area, where drinks are dispensed from a mahogany dresser. Generously proportioned bedrooms, including some in an adjacent

coachhouse, are tastefully furnished with period furniture and quality fabrics. Among many thoughtful extras in bedrooms and bathrooms are magazines, fresh fruit and flowers, hairdryers, trouser presses, sewing kits and toiletries. No dogs. *Amenities* garden, outdoor swimming pool, tennis, secretarial services, laundry service.

Restaurant   ♕

Set L & D £12
About £58 *for two*
Seats 45
Parties 20

A brand new restaurant in an extension overlooking the fountains is the home for Jeremy Shutter's interesting and imaginative menus. Dishes like the beautifully moist pigeon breast on seasonal leaves with tangy vinaigrette and flavoursome poached turbot with sorrel sauce amply illustrate both correct cooking and first-class presentation. The cellar remains excellent: Juliénas (Gobet) '85; Pinot Noir (Clos du Val) '83; Brauneberger Juffer Sonnenuhr Beerenauslese (Von Schorlemmer) '76. ☞ Outstanding ♈ Well-chosen ℗

Lunch 12.30–1.45   *Dinner* 7–9.15, Fri & Sat 7–9.30

BEARSTED

Suefflé

R Map 7 C5 Kent
The Green, Nr Maidstone
Maidstone (0622) 37065

Set L from £9.95
Set D £17.95
About £55 *for two*
Seats 40 *Parties* 44
Parking Ample
Credit Access, Amex, Diners, Visa

A new chef and a new cocktail bar have been installed at this charming little restaurant overlooking the village green. The concise but imaginative à la carte dinner menu changes every month or so, while lunchtimes bring a simpler blackboard menu. Start with pigeon and duck terrine before moving on to lamb en croûte with a rich rosemary sauce. Finish with strawberry timbale. ♈ Well-chosen ℗

Lunch 12–2   *Dinner* 7–10
Closed L Sat, all Sun & 3 days Xmas

BEAULIEU

Montagu Arms Hotel   65%   **£D/E**

H Map 4 C4 Hampshire
Palace Lane SO42 7ZL
Beaulieu (0590) 612324
Telex 47276

Credit Access, Amex, Diners, Visa

Wisteria tumbles over the walls of this former coaching inn, now a popular venue for visitors to the New Forest. Traditional lounges offer period furniture and deep armchairs, while the bar features beams and an open fireplace. Some of the bedrooms have recently been individually decorated and furnished with antique pieces; six have four-posters and three boast Victorian brass beds. Good bathrooms. *Amenities* garden, secretarial services, laundry service.

Rooms 26	*Direct dial* Yes	*Confirm by* 6	*Parking* Ample
Ensuite bath/shower 26	*Room TV* Yes	*Last dinner* 9.30	*Room service* 24 hours

BECCLES

Waveney House Hotel   60%   **£E**

H Map 6 D2 Suffolk
Puddingmoor NR34 9PL
Beccles (0502) 712270

Credit Access, Amex, Diners, Visa

Check directions when booking at this riverside hotel, as a one-way system tends to tangle travellers. The pretty stone building dates from 1592. Public rooms are pleasant and bedrooms, some with beams, are neatly furnished with reproduction darkwood furniture. Carpeted bathrooms are well maintained. Staff are very efficient and local Lowestoft kippers make breakfasts memorable. *Amenities* garden, coarse fishing, secretarial services, laundry service.

Rooms 13	*Direct dial* Yes	*Confirm by* 6	*Parking* Ample
Ensuite bath/shower 11	*Room TV* Yes	*Last dinner* 9.30	*Room service* All day

BEDFORD — Bedford Moat House   65%   £D/E

H **Map 5 E1** Bedfordshire
2 St Mary's Street MK42 0AR
Bedford (0234) 55131
Telex 825243

Credit Access, Amex, Diners, Visa

A tall modern hotel on the banks of the Great Ouse. Recent improvements include marble in the foyer, glass frontage to the bar-lounge and new carpets in the corridors. Bedrooms, all with attractive lightwood furnishings and contemporary fabrics, are equipped with remote-control TVs, hairdryers and trouser presses. *Amenities* sauna, whirlpool bath, keep-fit equipment, in-house movies, secretarial services, laundry service, coffee shop (10.30am–10.30pm).

Rooms 100	*Direct dial* Yes	*Confirm by* 6	*Parking* Ample
Ensuite bath/shower 100	*Room TV* Yes	*Last dinner* 9.45	*Room service* 24 hours

BEDFORD — Woodlands Manor Hotel   72%   £D

H **Map 5 E1** Bedfordshire
Green Lane, Clapham
MK41 6EP
Bedford (0234) 63281
Telex 825007

Rooms 21
Ensuite bath/shower 21
Direct dial Yes
Room TV Yes
Confirm by 6
Last dinner 9.45
Parking Ample
Room service 24 hours

Credit Access, Amex, Visa

Set in wooded grounds just off the A6 north of Bedford, this late-Victorian mansion provides peace, abundant comfort and high standards of service. Entry is into a spacious and warmly welcoming foyer with polished wood panelling, a fine carved fireplace and inviting leather chesterfields; leading from this is an equally pleasant lounge where a drink may be enjoyed (there's no bar). Bedrooms are, with few exceptions, of a very decent size and smartly traditional, with freestanding furniture and lots of personal touches; three rooms are on their own in a separate cottage. Well-equipped bathrooms. No children under seven. No dogs.
Amenities garden, secretarial services, laundry service.

BEESTON — Wild Boar Inn   £D/E

H **Map 10 B2** Cheshire
Nr Tarporley CW6 9NN
Bunbury (0829) 260309
Telex 61222

Credit Access, Amex, Diners, Visa

Extensive improvements were nearing completion at the time of our visit to this striking black-and-white half-timbered hotel on the A49. Day rooms are stylishly elegant, while the reception area boasts a huge raftered ceiling and imposing carved fireplace. Attractively decorated bedrooms in a separate building next door have quality wooden furnishings and up-to-date accessories. Smart private bathrooms. Graded at 60% in the 1987 Guide. *Amenities* garden.

Rooms 37	*Direct dial* Yes	*Confirm by* 6	*Parking* Ample
Ensuite bath/shower 37	*Room TV* Yes	*Last dinner* 10	*Room service* 24 hours

BELFORD — Blue Bell Hotel   £D/E

I **Map 14 B2** Northumberland
Market Square NE70 7NE
Belford (066 83) 543

Credit Access, Amex, Diners, Visa

The market square of an unspoilt country town is the setting for this sturdy 17th-century inn. The public areas include a mellow, main bar and a comfortable lounge. Good-sized bedrooms are mostly furnished with solid, traditional pieces (one has a four-poster) and the nicest rooms look over a fine garden and open fields. The bathrooms are well heated and well kept.
Amenities garden, putting.

Rooms 15	*Direct dial* Yes	*Confirm by* 6	*Parking* Ample
Ensuite bath/shower 15	*Room TV* Yes	*Last dinner* 9	*Room service* Limited

BEMBRIDGE — Highbury Hotel   60%   £E/F

H **Map 5 D4** Isle of Wight
Lane End PO35 5SU
Isle of Wight (0983) 872838

Credit Access, Amex, Diners, Visa
Closed 3 wks Oct & 24–27 Dec

The friendly Cobb family have been running their extended Edwardian house as a hotel for over 25 years. Homely public rooms with period furniture and amusing bric-a-brac include two lounges and a snug little bar. Spick-and-span bedrooms have all sorts of thoughtful extras, from biscuits and hairdryers to sewing kits and soap flakes. *Amenities* garden, outdoor swimming pool, sauna, solarium, croquet, laundry service.

Rooms 9	*Room phone* Yes	*Confirm by* arrang.	*Parking* Ample
Ensuite bath/shower 8	*Room TV* Yes	*Last dinner* 10	*Room service* All day

BERKHAMSTED — Swan Hotel — £E/F

I Map 5 E2 Hertfordshire
139 High Street HP4 3HJ
Berkhamsted (044 27) 71451
Telex 82257

Credit Access, Visa

Thanks to a cheerful red facade, this Tudor inn is easy to find on Berkhamsted's main thoroughfare. A sense of history is fostered by well-trodden floors. Dark oak furniture gives a homely feel to the back bar and there are two lounges with velour three-piece suites. Charming bedrooms have candlewick covers and simple units. Bathrooms, private and public, are well kept.
Amenities laundry service.

Rooms 19	*Direct dial* Yes	*Confirm by* arrang.	*Parking* Limited
Ensuite bath/shower 13	*Room TV* Yes	*Last dinner* 10	*Room service* Limited

BERWICK-UPON-TWEED — Kings Arms Hotel — 59% — £D/E

H Map 14 B2 Northumberland
Hide Hill TD15 1EJ
Berwick-upon-Tweed
(0289) 307454

Credit Access, Amex, Diners, Visa

A pleasant hotel which has been redecorated throughout. Smart, comfortable armchairs offer relaxation in the attractive lounge and there's a newly furnished cocktail bar. Bedrooms have marble-effect wallpaper in pastel colours with matching drapes, solid darkwood furniture and tiled, carpeted bathrooms. All have hairdryers, trouser presses and radios; 11 have four-poster beds. *Amenities* garden, snooker, laundry service, coffee shop (11am–7pm summer).

Rooms 36	*Room phone* Yes	*Confirm by* arrang.	*Parking* Difficult
Ensuite bath/shower 36	*Room TV* Yes	*Last dinner* 10	*Room service* 24 hours

Our inspectors *never* book in the name of Egon Ronay's Guides. They disclose their identity only if they are considering an establishment for inclusion in the next edition of the Guide.

BEVERLEY — The Anvil — ♧

R Map 11 E1 Humberside
3 Market Place
Hull (0482) 862860

About £30 for two
Seats 40
Parties 30
Parking Ample

Credit Access, Amex, Visa

There's a cottage feel to this first-floor restaurant, with its floral fabrics and antique pine tables. The care given to the decor is echoed in the menu, which offers popular dishes as well as more unusual ones, and in the standard of cooking and choice of raw materials. Tasty dishes include spicy beetroot and cabbage soup and pork fillet with orange and stem ginger sauce. ♉ Well-chosen

Dinner only 7–10, Sat till 10.30
Closed Sun, Mon & 25 Dec

BEVERLEY — Beverley Arms Hotel — 60% — £C/D

H Map 11 E1 Humberside
North Bar Within HU17 8DD
Hull (0482) 869241
Telex 597568

Credit Access, Amex, Diners, Visa

A 300-year-old inn with a handsome Georgian frontage. A friendly welcome awaits guests, and there's a pleasant atmosphere throughout the day rooms, which include two bars, one overlooking the courtyard. Bedrooms, some in a modern extension, have nearly all been upgraded; they are generally of a good size, with well-kept bath/shower rooms. *Amenities* laundry service, coffee shop (9.30am–7.30pm, Sat & Sun 10.30am–5pm), secretarial services.

Rooms 61	*Direct dial* Yes	*Confirm by* 6	*Parking* Ample
Ensuite bath/shower 61	*Room TV* Yes	*Last dinner* 9.45	*Room service* 24 hours

BIBURY — Bibury Court Hotel — 56% — £D/E

H Map 4 C2 Gloucestershire
Nr Cirencester GL7 5NT
Bibury (028 574) 337

Credit Access, Amex, Diners, Visa
Closed 2 weeks Xmas

Next to the church on a most attractive bend of the river Coln, this imposing mansion goes back nearly 400 years. Best of the public rooms is the oak-panelled lounge, where there are plenty of large, lived-in armchairs. Bedrooms lack facilities (no TVs or radios) and many show shortcomings in maintenance and housekeeping. Owners and staff need to get their act together swiftly.
Amenities garden, croquet, game fishing.

Rooms 16	*Direct dial* Yes	*Confirm by* arrang.	*Parking* Ample
Ensuite bath/shower 9	*Room TV* No	*Last dinner* 8.45	*Room service* All day

BIBURY   Swan Hotel   60%   £D/E

H **Map 4 C2** Gloucestershire
Nr Cirencester GL7 5NW
Bibury (028 574) 204
Telex 437360

Credit Access, Visa

The creeper-covered Swan Hotel stands across the road from its well-kept garden with sparkling trout stream that joins the river Coln. An air of provincial calm prevails, and log fires keep things cosy in the traditional day rooms. Bedrooms, including a couple of family rooms, are prettily decorated with matching floral fabrics. Bathrooms are compact, clean and bright.
Amenities garden, game fishing.

Rooms 25	*Direct dial* Yes	*Confirm by* 6	*Parking* Ample
Ensuite bath/shower 23	*Room TV* Yes	*Last dinner* 8.30	*Room service* All day

BIDEFORD   Yeoldon House   60%   £D/E

H **Map 2 C2** Devon
Durrant Lane, Northam
EX39 2RL
Bideford (023 72) 74400

Credit Access, Amex, Diners, Visa

A lane leads off the A386 to this sturdily built Victorian house overlooking the river Torridge. It's a very relaxing place, and the day rooms have the warm and welcoming feel of a private house. Neat bedrooms, most with fine views, are furnished in modern or traditional style, the star of the show being the honeymoon suite with its mahogany four-poster.
Amenities garden, putting, sea fishing, laundry service.

Rooms 10	*Direct dial* Yes	*Confirm by* arrang.	*Parking* Ample
Ensuite bath/shower 10	*Room TV* Yes	*Last dinner* 8.30	*Room service* All day

**We welcome bona fide complaints and recommendations
on the tear-out pages at the back of the book for readers' comment.
They are followed up by our professional team.**

BIGBURY ON SEA   Burgh Island   62%   £E

H **Map 3 D3** Devon
TQ7 4AU
Bigbury on Sea (0548) 810514

Credit Access, Amex, Visa
Closed Jan–mid Feb

Phone from the car park at Bigbury and a Land Rover or sea tractor will take you to this unique Art Deco hotel on its own island. The place is looking its old self again, thanks to a huge investment in 1930s furniture and the dedication of Beatrice and Tony Porter. The showpiece is the Palm Court with its lovely peacock dome and mirrored cocktail bar, but the Ganges room, part of which is the captain's cabin from the old HMS Ganges, runs it close. A number of bedrooms have balconies, and seven of the bathrooms are now the real thing from the '30s. Half-board terms only. No dogs.
Amenities garden, keep-fit equipment, tennis, snooker, sea fishing, laundry service.

Rooms 13	*Direct dial* Yes	*Confirm by* arrang.	*Parking* Ample
Ensuite bath/shower 13	*Room TV* Yes	*Last dinner* 9	*Room service* Limited

BILBROOK   Dragon House Hotel   63%   £E

H **Map 3 E1** Somerset
Nr Minehead TA24 6HQ
Washford (0984) 40215

Credit Access, Amex, Diners, Visa

A smugglers' drinking den in the 17th century, now a quiet, relaxing retreat on the right side of the law. The owners are friendly and enthusiastic, and the lounge and bar are particularly cosy. Bedrooms, all now with bath/shower en suite, have the cottage charm of beams, creaking floors and sloping ceilings and the modern facility of remote-control TVs. Roadside rooms can be noisy.
Amenities garden, croquet, laundry service.

Rooms 10	*Direct dial* Yes	*Confirm by* arrang.	*Parking* Ample
Ensuite bath/shower 10	*Room TV* Yes	*Last dinner* 9.30	*Room service* Limited

BILBROUGH — Bilbrough Manor Hotel 77% £C

HR Map 11 D1 North Yorkshire
Nr York YO2 3PH
Tadcaster (0937) 834002

Rooms 12
Ensuite bath/shower 12
Direct dial Yes
Room TV Yes
Confirm by arrang.
Last dinner 9.30
Parking Ample
Room service 24 hours

Credit Access, Amex, Diners, Visa

The splendid view over the Yorkshire countryside may be the reason why there has been a building on this site for over 700 years. The atmospheric entrance foyer has stone floors and arches, antique furniture and a fine fireplace. Next door, the bar area has comfortable armchairs and couches, while the exquisite panelled drawing room has further deep-cushioned seating. The spacious bedrooms are individually designed and decorated, with top-quality fabrics framing the mullioned windows and period-style furniture; easy chairs and attractive table lamps give a homely feel. Bathrooms are carpeted and prettily tiled and all have showers and brass fittings. No children under 12. No dogs.
Amenities garden, croquet, secretarial services, laundry service.

Restaurant ♛

Set L from £10, Sun £9.75
Set D from £17.50
About £60 for two
Seats 56
Parties 44

A splendid panelled dining room provides a suitable setting for Idris Caldora's elegant and delicious meals. His menus are mainly modern French cooking with many classical dishes also included, and top quality fresh ingredients are expertly handled. You might start with chicken mousse on a bed of celeriac then move on to sautéed fillet of veal in blackcurrant liqueur and ginger sauce, with a citrus fruit terrine to finish. ⊖ &

Lunch 12–2 *Dinner* 7–9.30

BILLINGHAM — Billingham Arms Hotel 58% £E

H Map 15 C5 Cleveland
The Causeway TS23 2HD
Stockton-on-Tees (0642) 553661
Telex 587746

Credit Access, Amex, Diners, Visa

Best bedrooms at this town-centre hotel are the 40-odd Club rooms with good working space, a tub chair, modern accessories and private bathrooms. There are some small singles with shower/WC and some quite good standard rooms without en suite facilities. Several bars include one featuring carved panelling built for but never fitted in the QE2. **Amenities** solarium, games room, pool table, in-house movies, secretarial services, laundry service.

Rooms 63	*Direct dial* Yes	*Confirm by* arrang.	*Parking* Ample
Ensuite bath/shower 55	*Room TV* Yes	*Last dinner* 11	*Room service* 24 hours

BINGLEY — Bankfield Hotel 66% £C

H Map 10 C1 West Yorkshire
Bradford Road BD16 1TV
Bradford (0274) 567123

Credit Access, Amex, Diners, Visa

Sandblasting has brightened up the dour Gothic exterior of this essentially Victorian hotel. Inside, public areas are now smartly refurbished – though retaining fine original features like the wood panelling in the entrance hall. Fair-sized bedrooms, located mainly in modern extensions, offer contemporary-style furnishings, tea-makers, hairdryers and tiled bathrooms. Executive rooms are larger and provide more extras. **Amenities** garden, pool table, laundry service.

Rooms 99	*Direct dial* Yes	*Confirm by* arrang.	*Parking* Ample
Ensuite bath/shower 99	*Room TV* Yes	*Last dinner* 9.30	*Room service* 24 hours

BIRDLIP — Kingshead House *NEW ENTRY* ᛐ

R Map 4 B2 Gloucestershire
Nr Gloucester GL4 8JH
Gloucester (0452) 862299

Set L from £8, Sun £9.25
Set D £13.50
About £38 for two
Seats 30 *Parties* 36
Parking Ample
Credit Access, Amex, Diners, Visa

Judy and Warren Knock run this pleasant, traditional village restaurant. Judy's a good, imaginative cook and evenings bring the widest choice with delights that run from creamy onion soup and salmon mousse with samphire to lamb bordelaise and baked fillet of pork with spinach, Stilton and walnuts. Good cheeses, tempting sweets, strong cafetière coffee. Carefully selected list of interesting wines and excellent sherries. ♀ Well-chosen ⊖ &

Lunch 12.15–2.15, Sun noon–2.15 *Dinner* 7.15–10
Closed L Sat, D Sun & all Mon

BIRMINGHAM

Map 10 C4
Town plan opposite

Population 1,007,600

Birmingham is the centre of one of Britain's most dynamic regions. It achieved industrial fame as a result of a fine tradition of craftsmanship. Today the city is noted for its production of motor cars, electrical equipment, machine tools and plastics. It has a splendid tradition in metal ware, including gold and silver work. Birmingham sponsored the £20m plus National Exhibition Centre at Bickenhill, just nine miles south-east of the city. This exhibition centre is Britain's first ever purpose-designed centre and ranks among the most modern in the world.

Sights Outside City
Airport, Coughton Court, Black Country Museum, Ragley Hall, Packwood House, Warwick Castle, West Midland Safari Park, Arbury Hall, Charlecote Park, Stratford-upon-Avon

Information Office
Birmingham Convention & Visitor Bureau, Ticket Shop & Tourist Information Centre, City Arcade, Birmingham B2 4TX
Telephone 021–643 2514

1 Alexandra Theatre C3
2 Aston Hall *Jacobean masterpiece open to public* D1
3 Baskerville House B2
4 Botanical Gardens A3
5 Bull Ring Shopping Centre *rotunda, multi-level shopping centre and market* C/D3
6 Cannon Hill Park C3
7 Central Libraries B2
8 Council House B2
9 Hall of Memory B2
10 Hippodrome Theatre C3
11 Lickey Hills *500 beautiful acres with views from Beacon Hill of ten counties* C3
12 Midland Red Bus Station C3
13 Museum and Art Gallery *from Veronese to Picasso via Hogarth and Constable* B2
14 Museum of Science and Industry *a link with the Industrial Revolution* B1
15 Repertory Theatre A/B2
16 New Street Station C3
17 Post Office Tower B1
18 St Chad's Cathedral *first English Roman Catholic Cathedral since Reformation* C1
19 St Philip's Cathedral *18th-c Palladian with later Burne-Jones windows* C2
20 Tourist Information Centre C2
21 Town Hall *meeting place and home of Symphony Orchestra* B2
22 University of Aston D1
23 University of Birmingham C3

Birmingham

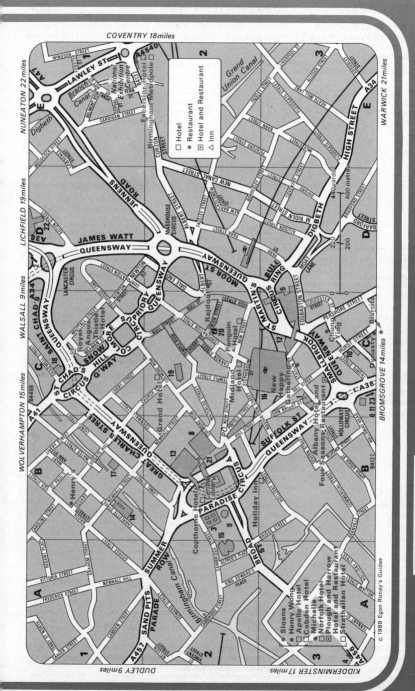

BIRKENHEAD   Bowler Hat Hotel   66%   £C/D

H Map 10 A2 Merseyside
2 Talbot Road, Oxton L43 2HH
051-652 4931
Telex 628761

Credit Access, Amex, Diners, Visa

Hats off to this tile-hung Victorian hotel for friendly staff, a warm atmosphere and very comfortable bedrooms, some with traditional furnishings, others modern. Trouser presses, mini-bars, complimentary sherry and fresh fruit are provided, and all rooms have sitting areas and bathroom telephone extensions. Spaniard Antonio Dominguez is the courteous and conscientious manager.
Amenities garden, in-house movies, laundry service.

Rooms 30	*Direct dial* Yes	*Confirm by* arrang.	*Parking* Ample
Ensuite bath/shower 30	*Room TV* Yes	*Last dinner* 9.45	*Room service* All day

We publish annually,
so make sure you use the current edition.
It's worth it!

BIRMINGHAM   Albany Hotel   72%   £C/D

HR Town plan C3
West Midlands
Smallbrook, Queensway B5 4EW
021-643 8171
Telex 337031

Rooms 254
Ensuite bath/shower 254
Direct dial Yes
Room TV Yes
Confirm by 6
Last dinner 11
Parking Limited
Room service 24 hours

Credit Access, Amex, Diners, Visa

Just a brief walk from New Street railway station is this impressive modern hotel where handsome accommodation is on offer. Stylish grey sofas give the foyer an elegant air and up on the mezzanine floor you'll find an open-plan lounge and a chic black and grey cocktail bar. Other public areas include a fine leisure centre and extensive conference facilities. The high-standard bedrooms boast pretty coordinated colour

schemes, smart Italian furniture, trouser presses, hairdryers, mini-bars, individually controlled air-conditioning and excellent tiled bathrooms. 20 per cent of the rooms, classed as Executive, are similar but larger. *Amenities* indoor swimming pool, solarium, squash, snooker, secretarial services, laundry service..

Four Seasons Restaurant   ♕

Set L £11.50
Set D £15
About £48 *for two*
Seats 70

A smart restaurant with a history of 22 years' high quality cooking by Peter Inger. His well thought-out menus offer a fine choice of interesting and imaginative dishes such as stir-fried lobster, crab claws, vegetables and beanshoots, fillet of brill baked with tomato and chervil and a trio of fillets (beef, lamb and veal) with three sauces. Saucing is a particularly strong point and vegetables come crisp and hot. ♟ Well-chosen ⊖ ♿

Lunch 12.30–2.30   *Dinner* 7.30–11
Closed L Sat, all Sun & Bank Hols

BIRMINGHAM   Apollo Hotel   64%   £D

H Town plan A3
West Midlands
243 Hagley Road, Edgbaston
B16 9RA
021-455 0271
Telex 336759
Credit Access, Amex, Diners, Visa

A modern red-brick hotel standing in the suburbs on the A456, the Apollo is geared chiefly to business people and the conference trade. The main public area for guests not attending a conference is a comfortable combined lounge and bar (plans include a new foyer and lounge). Double-glazed bedrooms are kept in good repair, and all have hairdryers, trouser presses and practical, up-to-date bathrooms. *Amenities* laundry service.

Rooms 118	*Direct dial* Yes	*Confirm by* 6	*Parking* Ample
Ensuite bath/shower 118	*Room TV* Yes	*Last dinner* 10.30	*Room service* 24 hours

BIRMINGHAM — Biarritz

R Town plan C3
West Midlands
148 Bromsgrove Street
021-622 1989

French cooking

Set L £7.50
Set D £19
About £44 for two
Seats 40
Parking Ample

Credit Access, Amex, Diners, Visa

Chef Carl Timms makes daily trips to the local markets to select the best and freshest produce for his kitchen. Seafood dominates the seasonally changing menus and it's enhanced by excellent sauces. The set-price six-course dinner is full of interest, beginning perhaps with Mediterranean fish soup and going on to goat's cheese in a flaky pastry case, followed by a refreshing water ice. Next might come salmon trout with sorrel sauce, accompanied by nice crisp vegetables, followed by French and English cheeses, and a tea parfait sauced with mango. Some meat dishes too, and fine classic wines (Ch. Léoville-Poyferré '78, Ch. Latour '49). 🍷 Well-chosen ℗

Lunch 12–2   Dinner 7–10.30
Closed L Sat, all Sun, Bank Hols & 1 wk Xmas

BIRMINGHAM — Birmingham Metropole 81% £C/D

H Town plan E1
West Midlands
National Exhibition Centre
B40 1PP
021-780 4242
Telex 336129

Rooms 700
Ensuite bath/shower 700
Direct dial Yes
Room TV Yes
Confirm by arrang.
Last dinner 10.30
Parking Ample
Room service 24 hours

Credit Access, Amex, Diners, Visa
Closed 24 Dec–2 Jan

Superb conference facilities and a position in the grounds of the National Exhibition Centre make this large, efficiently run hotel ideal for business people. The impressive public areas include a well-designed foyer-reception with marble floors and a central seating area, an elegant lounge and the Cotswold Arms pub. Bedrooms in the main Metropole building have spacious twin and double beds; singles are in the adjacent Warwick building. All are of Executive standard, with restful colour schemes, practical writing desks and well-equipped, up-to-date bathrooms. There are also numerous suites. Courtesy coach.
Amenities sauna, solarium, hairdressing, squash, in-house movies, secretarial services, fax, laundry service, kiosk.

BIRMINGHAM — Chung Ying

R Town plan C3
West Midlands
16 Wrottesley Street
021-622 5669

Chinese cooking
Set meals from £6.70
Seats 240 Parties 240
Parking Limited
Credit Access, Amex, Diners, Visa

Quantity in no way impairs quality at this smart Chinese restaurant near the wholesale market. Mr Wong's lengthy menu (over 300 items) offers an excellent selection of carefully prepared Cantonese dishes. From tangy hot and sour soup to succulent fried king prawns and scallops in bird's nest, flavours and textures are nicely judged. Forty varieties of dim sum include several tasty buns. Friendly and efficient service. &

Meals noon–11.30   About £25 for two
Closed Xmas Day

Changes in data sometimes occur in establishments
after the Guide goes to press.
Prices should be taken as indications rather than firm quotes.

BIRMINGHAM — Cobden Hotel 59% £E

H Town plan A3
West Midlands
166 Hagley Road
Edgbaston B16 9NZ
021-454 6621 Telex 339715

Credit Access, Amex, Diners, Visa

A brand-new leisure centre is the latest addition to this steadily-improving suburban hotel. Sitting in the smart bar overlooking the garden it's hard to believe that this was a temperance establishment. Executive bedrooms offer neat units, mini-bars and well-equipped bathrooms. Remaining accommodation is fairly basic. *Amenities* garden, indoor swimming pool, sauna, solarium, whirlpool bath, gymnasium, croquet, secretarial services, fax, laundry service.

Rooms 265	Direct dial Yes	Confirm by 6	Parking Ample
Ensuite bath/shower 200	Room TV Yes	Last dinner 9.45	Room service 24 hours

BIRMINGHAM   Copthorne Hotel   74%   £C

H **Town plan B2**
West Midlands
Paradise Circus B3 2HJ
021-200 2727
Telex 339026

Rooms 215
Ensuite bath/shower 215
Direct dial Yes
Room TV Yes
Confirm by 6
Last dinner 10.30
Parking Ample
Room service 24 hours

Credit Access, Amex, Diners, Visa

Its striking black glass exterior makes this ultra-modern hotel a landmark on the city's inner ring road. Smart, open-plan public areas include a marble-floored foyer and the sophisticated, midnight-blue Bullion bar. Executives will appreciate the excellent business and health facilities. Good-size bedrooms, with pale grey and deep pink decor, are extremely comfortable and well equipped, with admirable bathrooms. Staff are friendly and obliging, but serve-yourself breakfasts can prove disappointing.
Amenities indoor swimming pool, sauna, solarium, whirlpool bath, steam room, gymnasium, in-house movies, secretarial services, fax, laundry service, coffee shop (7am–11.30pm). ⅓

BIRMINGHAM   Dynasty

R **Town plan C3**
West Midlands
93 Hurst Street
021-622 1410

Chinese cooking
Set L £5.90 **Set D** from £7.50
Seats 120 *Parties* 70
Parking Ample
Credit Access, Amex, Diners, Visa

In the rapidly changing city centre, a bright Chinese restaurant on two floors. It's a popular place, thanks to generally reliable cooking, excellent presentation and charming service overseen by smiling owner Raymond Cheung. The menu treads a fairly familiar path through Cantonese and Peking cuisine, including dim sum, spicy spare ribs, traditional crispy duck and numerous sizzling dishes (fillet steak, beef, lamb, chicken, squid and oysters). ⅓

Meals noon–11.30, Sat noon–midnight   *About* £38 *for two*
Closed Bank Hols & 3 days Xmas

BIRMINGHAM   Grand Hotel   61%   £D

H **Town plan C2**
West Midlands
Colmore Row B3 2DA
021-236 7951 Telex 338174

Credit Access, Amex, Diners, Visa
Closed 4 days Xmas

Modern improvements have failed to quash the Victorian grandeur of this city-centre hotel, seen at its most magnificent in the impressive Grosvenor Suite function room. The Penny Black, with its philatelic prints, is the liveliest of the three bars. Spacious bedrooms with pink and green decor have military-style furniture and good bathrooms.
Amenities in-house movies, fax, laundry service.

Rooms 167	*Direct dial* Yes	*Confirm by* 6	*Parking* Difficult
Ensuite bath/shower 167	*Room TV* Yes	*Last dinner* 9.45	*Room service* 24 hours

BIRMINGHAM   Henry's   *NEW ENTRY*   ⅋

R **Town plan B1**
West Midlands
27 St Paul's Square
021-200 1136

Chinese cooking
Set L from £8.50
About £25 *for two*
Seats 90 *Parking* Difficult
Credit Access, Amex, Diners, Visa

Splendid service and light, subtle cooking make this Cantonese restaurant stand out from the crowd. Familiar favourites such as stuffed crab's claws, hot and sour soup, barbecued pork and succulent chicken with tangy lemon sauce are based on the freshest of ingredients and resulting flavours are wonderfully clear and true. Lovely crisp vegetables accompany, and sweets include delicious red bean paste pancakes.

Lunch 12–2   *Dinner* 6–11, Sat 11.30
Closed Sun, Bank Hols & last wk Aug

BIRMINGHAM   Henry Wong

R **Town plan A3**
West Midlands
283 High Street, Harborne
021-427 9799

Chinese cooking
Set L from £8
About £28 *for two*
Seats 130 *Parties* 20
Credit Access, Amex, Diners, Visa

A wide-ranging selection of mainly Cantonese dishes based on good-quality ingredients is carefully prepared at this comfortable Chinese restaurant in a suburban street. Enjoyable starters like excellent sesame king prawn toasts and very fresh scallops with cashews and water chestnuts can be followed by, say, first-rate fillet steak with ginger and black bean sauce or Ho Dong spare ribs. Friendly service.

Lunch 12–2   *Dinner* 6–11, Sat till 11.30
Closed Sun, L Bank Hols, 25 Dec & 1 wk Aug

BIRMINGHAM — Holiday Inn 72% £C

H Town plan B3
West Midlands
Central Square,
Holliday Street B1 1HH
021-631 2000
Telex 337272

Rooms 295
Ensuite bath/shower 295
Direct dial Yes
Room TV Yes
Confirm by 6
Last dinner 11
Parking Ample
Room service 24 hours

Credit Access, Amex, Diners, Visa

Making a solid statement on the Birmingham skyline is this modern high-rise hotel. Automatic doors lead to the plush foyer and in the adjoining lounge, chesterfields provide comfortable seating. The lounge bar, with its subtle lighting and warm colour scheme, is inviting, while the verdant poolside bar adds a tropical touch. There are five categories of accommodation, from standard rooms to junior suites, and one floor is for non-smokers. All rooms have tea-makers, hairdryers, trouser presses, mini-bars and teletext TVs. Non-slip floors are a feature of the neat bathrooms. *Amenities* patio, indoor swimming pool, sauna, solarium, keep-fit equipment, in-house movies, fax, laundry service, coffee shop (10.30am–11pm), kiosk. &

BIRMINGHAM — Ladbroke International Hotel

See PENGUIN HOTEL

BIRMINGHAM — Metropole and Warwick Hotel, Birmingham

See BIRMINGHAM METROPOLE HOTEL

BIRMINGHAM — Michelle

R Town plan A3
West Midlands
182 High Street Harborne
021-426 4133

Set L from £4.20
Set D from £7.50
Seats 44 *Parties* 60
Parking Limited
Credit Access, Visa

A bustling, suburban bistro where Christian Bishop cooks in robust, dependable style. Soup has a real taste of the stock pot and garlic often pops up – garlic bread, garlic butter in breast of chicken, garlic mayonnaise with plump prawns. Steaks, plain or sauced, are a popular choice, and boeuf stroganoff is a speciality of the house. There's a short, sound wine list with excellent Touraine Rouge and Blanc as house wines. ♟ Well-chosen ⊜

Lunch 12–2 *Dinner* 7–10, Fri & Sat 7–10.30 *About* £32 *for two*
Closed L Bank Hols & all Sun

BIRMINGHAM — Midland Hotel 65% £C/D

H Town plan C2
West Midlands
New Street B2 4JT
021-643 2601 Telex 338419

Credit Access, Amex, Diners, Visa

The elegance of this privately owned city-centre hotel is slowly being restored, and Georgian marble creates an air of classical splendour in the foyer. The lounge is equally grand, and there are no less than five bars. Good-sized bedrooms have smart freestanding furniture, tea-makers, trouser presses and hairdryers. Staff are friendly, if sometimes a touch flamboyant. *Amenities* satellite TV, secretarial services, fax, laundry service, coffee shop (10.30am–6pm).

Rooms 107	*Direct dial* Yes	*Confirm by* 6	*Parking* Limited
Ensuite bath/shower 107	*Room TV* Yes	*Last dinner* 10	*Room service* 24 hours

BIRMINGHAM — New Happy Gathering

R Town plan C3
West Midlands
43 Station Street
021-643 5247

Chinese cooking
Set meals from £8
Seats 120 *Parties* 120
Parking Ample
Credit Access, Amex, Diners, Visa

Enjoyable Cantonese cooking is the order of the day at the Chan family's roomy first-floor restaurant. Tasty appetisers range from toasted king prawns with sesame seeds to shredded chicken and shark's fin soup; the wide selection of skilfully prepared main dishes features tempting options such as baked crab in ginger and spring onion, steamed duck with plum sauce, and tender fried beef with cashew nuts. Sweet endings include banana fritters.

Meals noon–midnight *About* £20 *for two*
Closed 3 days Xmas

 indicates a **well-chosen** house wine

BIRMINGHAM | Norfolk Hotel 55% | £E

H Town plan A3
West Midlands
257 Hagley Road B16 9NH
021-454 8071 Telex 339715

Credit Access, Amex, Diners, Visa
Closed 25 Dec–2 Jan

A substantial red-brick hotel two miles from Birmingham on the A456. In the public areas, potted plants, deep-pile carpets and attractive decor make a pleasing impression, while the good leisure and function facilities are popular and full of life. Bedrooms are good-sized and comfortable, offering radio alarms and tea/coffee-makers. *Amenities* garden, keep-fit equipment, pitch & putt, in-house movies, fax, laundry service.

Rooms 183	*Direct dial* Yes	*Confirm by* 6	*Parking* Ample
Ensuite bath/shower 88	*Room TV* Most	*Last dinner* 9.30	*Room service* 24 hours

---

BIRMINGHAM | Penguin Hotel 60% | £C

H Town plan C2
West Midlands
New Street B2 4RX
021-631 3331
Telex 338331

Credit Access, Amex, Diners, Visa

A former department store in the city centre. Guests can relax in Harvey's café/bar, or take a lift and enjoy the view from the top-floor cocktail bar. Bedrooms, some quite small, are equipped with tea-makers and trouser presses; Gold Star rooms have many extras. Some corridors and bedrooms are far from pristine, and refurbishment plans are welcome. *Amenities* in-house movies, secretarial services, laundry service, coffee shop (9am–5.30pm Mon–Sat).

Rooms 192	*Direct dial* Yes	*Confirm by* arrang.	*Parking* Difficult
Ensuite bath/shower 192	*Room TV* Yes	*Last dinner* 10.30	*Room service* 24 hours

---

BIRMINGHAM | Plough & Harrow Hotel 79% | £B

HR Town Plan A3
West Midlands
135 Hagley Road, Edgbaston
B16 8LS
021-454 4111
Telex 338074

Rooms 44
Ensuite bath/shower 44
Direct dial Yes
Room TV Yes
Confirm by arrang.
Last dinner 10.30
Parking Ample
Room service 24 hours

Credit Access, Amex, Diners, Visa

An oasis of tradition amidst the surrounding modern office blocks, this splendid red-brick Victorian hotel is justly re-nowned for its excellent service from staff who embody old-world courtesy. Fresh flower dis-plays grace the welcoming en-trance hall and there is ample plushly comfortable seating in the solidly handsome lounge bar. The majority of bedrooms are housed in a modern extension  and, although some redecoration would be beneficial, they remain attractive rooms where period-style furnishings are complemented by up-to-date accessories like teletext TVs, trouser presses and hairdryers. Carpeted bathrooms are luxuriously equipped. *Amenities* garden, sauna, in-house movies, secretarial services, fax, laundry service.

Restaurant ♛

Set L £19.50
Set D £27.50
About £80 *for two*
Seats 70

A comfortable, formal restaurant, with polished and efficient service, where the choice of menus ranges from a set-price English luncheon to a gourmet's dinner and seasonally-changing carte of imaginative modern dishes. Typical delights include warm duck breast salad with raspberry dressing, admirably fresh steamed wild salmon with a pike mousse, and roast venison flavoured with crushed coffee beans and woodland berry sauce. ♥ Well-chosen ⊖

Lunch 12.30–2.30 *Dinner* 7.15–10.30, Sun 7–9.30

BIRMINGHAM | Post House Hotel 60% | £C/D

H Map 10 C4 West Midlands
Chapel Lane,
Great Barr B43 7BG
021-357 7444
Telex 338497

Credit Access, Amex, Diners, Visa

This smart, purpose-built hotel not far from junction 7 of the M6 is popular with business visitors. Day rooms include a bar-lounge well stocked with comfortable settees, and the colonial-style Raffles bar. Best bedrooms have colourful furnishings and useful extras, while Executive rooms have bed settees as well as double beds. *Amenities* garden, outdoor swimming pool, secretarial services, fax, laundry service, coffee shop (7am–10pm), children's playground.

Rooms 204	*Direct dial* Yes	*Confirm by* 6	*Parking* Ample
Ensuite bath/shower 204	*Room TV* Yes	*Last dinner* 10.30	*Room service* 24 hours

BIRMINGHAM — Rajdoot

R Town plan C2
West Midlands
12 Albert Street 021-643 8805

Indian cooking
Set L from £6
Set D from £10.50
Seats 74 *Parties* 30
Parking Ample
Credit Access, Amex, Diners, Visa

A bright, smart and justly popular restaurant in the heart of the city and an enduring fixture on the Birmingham eating scene. The cooking is North Indian and very enjoyable, with tandoori dishes a speciality. Curries span a good range, including kidneys, fish, lobster and quail as well as lamb and chicken. The waiters are dressed in smart green tunics and handsome headdress. &

Lunch 12–2.30 *Dinner* 6.30–11.30 *About* £40 *for two*
Closed L Sun, Bank Hols & all 25 & 26 Dec

BIRMINGHAM — Royal Angus Thistle Hotel 65% £C/D

H Town plan C1
West Midlands
St Chaps, Queensway B4 6HY
021-236 4211
Telex 336889

Credit Access, Amex, Diners, Visa

Day rooms have a light and airy feel at this modern city-centre hotel. White-painted brickwork and greenery create a summery effect in the comfortable lounge, the theme continuing in the bar with cane chairs, conservatory extension and many plants. Good-sized bedrooms are smartly decorated and well-equipped, with fully-tiled bathrooms; executive rooms offer teletext and mini-bars.
Amenities in-house movies, fax, laundry service.

Rooms 135	Direct dial Yes	Confirm by 6	Parking Ample
Ensuite bath/shower 135	Room TV Yes	Last dinner 10.15	Room service 24 hours

BIRMINGHAM — Sloans

R Town plan A3
West Midlands
27 Chad Square,
Hawthorne Road, Edgbaston
021-455 6697

Set L £11.50, Sun £12
Seats 60 *Parties* 32
Parking Ample
Credit Access, Amex, Diners, Visa

Cooking at this modern suburban restaurant is extremely competent, although it does not quite match the panache of the Narbett family's earlier establishment, the Bell at Belborough. An imaginative menu includes dishes like prawns, monkfish and sole poached in a salmon mousse or veal cutlets with girolle mushrooms and rosemary. Crème brûlée is among the enjoyable sweets. Excellent wine list strong in domaine-bottled burgundy. ♥ Well-chosen ⊜ &

Lunch 12–2.30 *Dinner* 7–10 *About* £58 *for two*
Closed L Sat, Sun, Bank Hols & 1 wk after Xmas

BIRMINGHAM — Strathallan Thistle Hotel 66% £C/D

H Town plan A3
West Midlands
225 Hagley Road
Edgbaston B16 9RY
021-455 9777
Telex 336680
Credit Access, Amex, Diners, Visa

A distinctive polygonal tower identifies this smart modern hotel not far from Edgbaston cricket ground. Soft lighting and stylishly traditional furnishings create a mood of quiet elegance in the foyer-lounge and there's a choice of two bars – one discreetly luxurious, the other cheerfully American in theme. Bedrooms are mostly small, but attractively furnished and well equipped.
Amenities in-house movies, fax, laundry service.

Rooms 167	Direct dial Yes	Confirm by 6	Parking Ample
Ensuite bath/shower 167	Room TV Yes	Last dinner 10	Room service 24 hours

⇨ is our symbol for an **outstanding** wine list

BIRMINGHAM AIRPORT — Excelsior Hotel 60% £C/D

H Town plan E2
West Midlands
Coventry Road B26 3QW
021-782 8141
Telex 338005

Credit Access, Amex, Diners, Visa

The now redundant light tower is a striking feature of this '30s hotel alongside the A45 and next to the airport cargo terminal. Old aircraft prints adorn the Buccaneer Bar, which like the lounge is furnished in simple, modern style. Bedrooms, quite pretty in pastels, have practical built-in furniture, hairdryers, trouser presses (not all) and neatly fitted bathrooms.
Amenities garden, snooker, secretarial services, fax, laundry service.

Rooms 141	Direct dial Yes	Confirm by 6	Parking Ample
Ensuite bath/shower 141	Room TV Yes	Last dinner 10.15	Room service 24 hours

If we recommend **meals** in a Hotel or Inn,
a separate entry is made for its restaurant.

BLACKBURN — Blackburn Moat House — 56% — £E

H Map 10 B1 Lancashire
Preston New Road BB2 7BE
Blackburn (0254) 64441
Telex 63271

Credit Access, Amex, Diners, Visa

You can recognise this early 1970s hotel on the A677 between Blackburn and the M6 by its distinctive gabled roof. Public areas comprise a spacious reception/lounge with leather chesterfields, a pleasant bar and good conference facilities. Bedrooms have recently been completely refurbished and are equipped with decent bathrooms, trouser presses, tea/coffee-makers and hairdryers. *Amenities* garden, snooker, in-house movies, secretarial services, fax, laundry service.

Rooms 98	Direct dial Yes	Confirm by 6	Parking Ample
Ensuite bath/shower 98	Room TV Yes	Last dinner 10	Room service 24 hours

BLACKHEATH — Bardon Lodge Hotel

See under LONDON

BLACKPOOL — Imperial Hotel — 68% — £C

H Map 10 A1 Lancashire
North Promenade FY1 2HB
Blackpool (0253) 23971
Telex 677376

Credit Access, Amex, Diners, Visa

General Manager John Herdman has outlasted many owners at this famous hotel overlooking the sea. Recent improvements include a floor of smart new bedrooms with excellent bathrooms; other rooms are also due for refurbishment. The main bar has a splendid Edwardian atmosphere, and there's a night club in the basement. *Amenities* indoor swimming pool, sauna, solarium, hairdressing, in-house movies, secretarial services, fax, laundry service, kiosk.

Rooms 174	Direct dial Yes	Confirm by 6	Parking Ample
Ensuite bath/shower 174	Room TV Yes	Last dinner 10.30	Room service 24 hours

BLACKPOOL — New Clifton Hotel — 60% — £D/E

H Map 10 A1 Lancashire
Talbot Square FY1 1ND
Blackpool (0253) 21481
Telex 67570

Credit Access, Amex, Diners, Visa

The New Clifton stands right on the seafront opposite the North Pier. Extensive day rooms include a Victorian-style foyer, several bars and a night club. Bedrooms range from good-sized sea-facing rooms, some with decent modern furniture, to more compact and often dated looking inner rooms. A new central heating system has been installed, and other improvements will be welcome. *Amenities* snooker, in-house movies, laundry service.

Rooms 83	Direct dial Yes	Confirm by 6	Parking Difficult
Ensuite bath/shower 83	Room TV Yes	Last dinner 10	Room service 24 hours

BLACKPOOL — Pembroke Hotel — 68% — £C

H Map 10 A1 Lancashire
North Promenade FY1 2JQ
Blackpool (0253) 23434
Telex 677469

Credit Access, Amex, Diners, Visa

A high-rise hotel where clever design has resulted in nearly all rooms having sea views. A spacious reception leads to the popular conference facilities, a nightclub/leisure centre and an upstairs lounge bar. Bedrooms have plenty of writing/storage space; half of them are newly refurbished. *Amenities* garden, indoor swimming pool, sauna, solarium, keep-fit equipment, games room, pool table, in-house movies, secretarial services, fax, laundry service, children's play area.

Rooms 206	Direct dial Yes	Confirm by 6	Parking Ample
Ensuite bath/shower 206	Room TV Yes	Last dinner 10.30	Room service 24 hours

Our inspectors are our full-time employees; they are professionally trained by us.

BLACKWATER — Blackbird Cottage — *NEW ENTRY*

R Map 2 B3 Cornwall
Nr Redruth TR4 8EY
St Day (0209) 820347

About £40 for two
Seats 18
Parties 18
Parking Ample

Credit Access, Amex, Visa

A charming cottage restaurant by the A30, with prints and pictures on the walls and fresh flowers on the tables. Sue and Peter Oswald produce their own charcuterie, and a plateful served with home-made pickles starts a meal in fine style. Other offerings could include Cantonese-style sea bass, fillet of beef with a red wine and mushroom sauce and spicy apple and raisin crumble. ℮

Lunch 12.30–2 *Dinner* 7–9.30
Closed L Mon, all Sun & 25 & 26 Dec

BLAKENEY — Blakeney Hotel 60% *NEW ENTRY* £C/D

H **Map 6 C1** Norfolk
Nr Holt NR25 7NE
Cley (0263) 740797

Credit Access, Amex, Diners, Visa

The quayside setting is a valuable asset of this owner-run red-brick hotel dating from the 1920s. A first-floor sun lounge takes full advantage of the views, and other spots to relax include a choice of bars. Bedrooms vary in size, decor, furnishings and accessories, and therefore in price; some annexe rooms have their own patios. *Amenities* garden, indoor swimming pool, sauna, solarium, bicycles, games room, secretarial services, laundry service. &

Rooms 51	*Direct dial* Yes	*Confirm by* 6	*Parking* Ample
Ensuite bath/shower 51	*Room TV* Yes	*Last dinner* 9.30	*Room service* 24 hours

BLAKENEY — Manor Hotel 57% £D/E

H **Map 6 C1** Norfolk
Nr Holt NR25 7ND
Cley (0263) 740376

Closed 3 wks Dec

Birdwatchers and yachtsmen take refuge from the elements in this 16th-century farmhouse overlooking the saltings. The accent is on comfort in the traditional bar and two-level lounge leading on to a charming walled garden. Bedrooms are bright and cheerful, with practical bathrooms. Most are in a single-storey block adjoining the main house. *Amenities* garden, bowling green, laundry service.

Rooms 31	*Room phone* No	*Confirm by* arrang.	*Parking* Ample
Ensuite bath/shower 31	*Room TV* Yes	*Last dinner* 8.45	*Room service* All day

★ For a *discount* on next year's guide, see **An Offer for Answers.** ★

BLANCHLAND — Lord Crewe Arms Hotel 64% £D/E

H **Map 15 B4** Northumberland
Nr Consett, Co. Durham
DH8 9SP
Blanchland (043 475) 251

Credit Access, Amex, Diners, Visa

With its roots in the 13th century, the Lord Crewe Arms has many fascinating features, including an ancient barrel-vaulted crypt (now the bar) and a huge stone fireplace with priest hole. Prettily decorated bedrooms come in all shapes and sizes, and about half are in cottages across the cobbled square. Nice touches like books, magazines and sherry accompany modern accessories and spick-and-span bathrooms (three with whirlpool baths). *Amenities* garden, laundry service.

Rooms 15	*Direct dial* Yes	*Confirm by* arrang.	*Parking* Ample
Ensuite bath/shower 15	*Room TV* Yes	*Last dinner* 9.15	*Room service* All day

BLANDFORD FORUM — La Belle Alliance ♕ ⌕

RR **Map 4 B4** Dorset
Whitecliffe Mill Street
DT11 7BN
Blandford (0258) 52842

Set D £16.95
About £42 *for two*
Seats 26 *Parties* 34
Parking Ample
Credit Access, Amex, Diners, Visa

BEDROOMS 5 **£E**
With bath/shower 5

Drinks in the comfortable lounge precede the excellent set price dinner at this spacious Victorian house where Lauren Davison is a charming hostess. Perfectly cooked turbot in beurre blanc might follow a delicious tartelette of wild mushroom and there are tempting sweets and good English cheeses to finish. The menu changes monthly, and there are also special gourmet dinners on Sundays preceding Bank Holidays (book for these). ℮

Lunch Private parties only   *Dinner* 7–9.30, sat till 10
Closed Sun excl those preceding Bank Hols & 1st 3 wks Jan

Individually decorated bedrooms have TVs, hairdryers, phones and tea/coffee-making equipment. A morning newspaper accompanies a hearty breakfast. Children and dogs by arrangement.

BLOCKLEY — Lower Brook House 60% £D/E

H **Map 4 C1** Gloucestershire
Moreton-in-Marsh GL56 9DS
Blockley (0386) 700286

Credit Access, Diners
Closed Jan

Named after the brook that runs through the garden, this delightful 17th-century house offers traditional comforts and service in a quiet village setting. Settees sit invitingly in the cosy beamed lounge, whose rustic charms are shared by the adjacent little bar. Bedrooms make up in character what they lack in size; many have sloping ceilings, and all boast their own neat bath or shower rooms. *Amenities* garden, laundry service.

Rooms 8	*Room phone* No	*Confirm by* arrang.	*Parking* Ample
Ensuite bath/shower 8	*Room TV* Yes	*Last dinner* 9	*Room service* Limited

BODYMOOR HEATH Marston Farm Hotel 63%   £E

H Map 10 C4 Warwickshire
Dog Lane, Nr Sutton
Coldfield B76 9JD
Tamworth (0827) 872133

Credit Access, Amex, Diners, Visa

A pleasant converted farmhouse in a rural setting, but just 100 yards from the M42. New owners Michael and Catherine Walsh are a friendly, unassuming couple, and the hotel has a good feel from smiling staff. Two peaceful little lounges and a traditional one are just right for relaxing, and the bedrooms manage to be both roomy and cosy. No dogs. *Amenities* garden, outdoor swimming pool, tennis, coarse fishing, laundry service.

| Rooms 17 | Direct dial Yes | Confirm by arrang. | Parking Ample |
| Ensuite bath/shower 17 | Room TV Yes | Last dinner 9.45 | Room service 24 hours |

BOGNOR REGIS Royal Norfolk Hotel   £D/E

H Map 5 E4 West Sussex
The Esplanade PO21 2LH
Bognor Regis (0243) 826222
Telex 477575

Credit Access, Amex, Diners, Visa

Extensive improvements are under way to restore this hotel to its former Regency splendour. Public areas include several function rooms, lounges and a relaxing bar. The spacious bedrooms, some with sea views, have been completely refurbished with new fitted furniture, carpets and chairs; all now have en suite bathrooms. Graded at 63% in 1988 Guide. *Amenities* garden, outdoor swimming pools, tennis, putting, croquet, secretarial services, fax, laundry service.

| Rooms 51 | Direct dial Yes | Confirm by arrang. | Parking Ample |
| Ensuite bath/shower 51 | Room TV Yes | Last dinner 9.30 | Room service 24 hours |

**Any person using our name to obtain free hospitality is a fraud.
Proprietors, please inform the police and us.**

BOLTON Crest Hotel 58%   £C/D

H Map 10 B1
Greater Manchester
Beaumont Road BL3 4TA
Bolton (0204) 651511
Telex 635527

Credit Access, Amex, Diners, Visa

Peaceful surroundings and comfortable accommodation are to be found at this red-brick hotel a short drive off the M61 at Junction 5. There's cosy seating in the lounge and the cocktail bar adjoins the patio for al fresco drinking. Standard bedrooms have pine units and compact modern bathrooms; Executive and Lady Crest rooms boast many extras. *Amenities* garden, games room, pool table, in-house movies, secretarial services, fax, laundry service.

| Rooms 100 | Direct dial Yes | Confirm by 6 | Parking Ample |
| Ensuite bath/shower 100 | Room TV Yes | Last dinner 9.45 | Room service 24 hours |

BOLTON Last Drop Village Hotel 68%   £D

H Map 10 B1
Greater Manchester
Hospital Road, Bromley Cross
BL7 9PZ
Bolton (0204) 591131
Telex 635322

Credit Access, Amex, Diners, Visa

A carefully restored collection of old farm buildings makes up the Last Drop Village and at its centre is this characterful hotel (ask for directions when booking.) The recently extended leisure club is a great attraction, and the spacious split-level cocktail bar features a mass of fascinating artefacts – not least, an old carriage housing the telephone! Good-sized bedrooms, mostly furnished in pine, are comfortable and well equipped. Executive rooms (three new ones in a small cottage) have posher bathrooms and extras like bathrobes and wine. *Amenities* garden, indoor swimming pool, sauna, solarium, whirlpool bath, gymnasium, hairdressing, squash, satellite TV, fax, laundry service, coffee shop (10am–5.30pm), 24-hour lounge service.

| Rooms 83 | Direct dial Yes | Confirm by 6 | Parking Ample |
| Ensuite bath/shower 83 | Room TV Yes | Last dinner 10 | Room service Limited |

BOLTON Pack Horse Hotel 58%   £E

H Map 10 B1
Greater Manchester
Bradshawgate BL1 1DP
Bolton (0204) 27261
Telex 635168

Credit Access, Amex, Diners, Visa

A red-brick hotel overlooking a pretty garden square in the town centre. Public areas include two pleasing bars, one Regency style with leaded window panes and a mahogany fireplace. Bedrooms are bright and cheerful, most having lightwood units, pastel colour schemes and stylish fabrics. Refurbishment of some bedrooms with oak furniture. There are also three suites. Bathrooms are neat and clean. *Amenities* in-house movies, secretarial services, fax, laundry service.

| Rooms 75 | Direct dial Yes | Confirm by arrang. | Parking Ample |
| Ensuite bath/shower 72 | Room TV Yes | Last dinner 10 | Room service 24 hours |

BOLTON ABBEY Devonshire Arms 75% £D

H **Map 15 B6**
North Yorkshire
Nr Skipton BD23 6AJ
Bolton Abbey (075 671) 441
Telex 51218

Rooms 40
Ensuite bath/shower 40
Direct dial Yes
Room TV Yes
Confirm by 6
Last dinner 10
Parking Ample
Room service 24 hours

Credit Access, Amex, Diners, Visa

The original coaching inn dates from about 1750, but the hotel is much extended and the majority of the bedrooms are in a modern block. These have recently been refurbished, but the best rooms are still those in the old part – spacious and individually decorated, with splendidly solid furnishings, brass or four-poster beds, paintings and smart modern bathrooms. There's a welcoming log fire in the entrance hall, beyond which are two elegant lounges and a traditionally appointed bar. The whole place is well cared for, and the setting in the Yorkshire Dales National Park is most attractive.
Amenities garden, croquet, game fishing, secretarial services, fax, laundry service. &

BONCHURCH Winterbourne Hotel 68% £C/D

H **Map 5 D4** Isle of Wight
Nr Ventnor PO38 1RQ
Isle of Wight (0983) 852535

Credit Access, Amex, Diners, Visa
Closed mid Dec–mid Feb

Enthusiastic owners have made a hospitable hostelry of this stone house in beautiful gardens overlooking the sea. Public rooms include an elegant first-floor lounge with doors opening on to the terrace and lawns. Bedrooms (five in an adjacent converted coach house) are furnished to a high standard and most have sea or garden views.
Amenities garden, outdoor swimming pool, putting, in-house movies, secretarial services, laundry service.

Rooms 19	*Direct dial* Yes	*Confirm by* arrang.	*Parking* Ample
Ensuite bath/shower 17	*Room TV* Yes	*Last dinner* 10	*Room service* All day

BOREHAM STREET Smugglers Wheel *NEW ENTRY* ♝

R **Map 7 B6** East Sussex
Nr Herstmonceux, Hailsham
Herstmonceux (0323) 832293

Set L £8.50, Sun £8.75
Set D £9.75
About £38 *for two*
Seats 60 *Parties* 30
Parking Ample
Credit Access, Amex, Diners, Visa

A charming restaurant with exposed beams and chintzy fabrics; outside, magnificent views of the Sussex Downs are to be had from the lovely garden. The Scamardella brothers have achieved a successful blend of the good points of both English and Italian family restaurants and both cuisines are reflected in the menus. Good fresh ingredients are competently cooked and the magnificent sweet table draws the eye throughout the meal. ☺ &

Lunch 12–2 *Dinner* 7–9.30
Closed D Sun, all Mon & Bank Hols

BOREHAM STREET White Friars Hotel 63% £D/E

H **Map 7 B6** East Sussex
Nr Herstmonceux BN27 4SE
Herstmonceux (0323) 832355

Credit Access, Amex, Diners, Visa

Just a few miles from various South Coast resorts, this friendly, traditional hotel is set in five acres of well-kept gardens and grounds by the A271. Bedrooms, all with modern digital alarms and tea-makers, are divided between the main house and an adjacent cottage; two rooms in the latter have sun terraces. There are two bars and a nice little lounge.
Amenities garden, putting, laundry service.

Rooms 19	*Direct dial* Yes	*Confirm by* arrang.	*Parking* Ample
Ensuite bath/shower 19	*Room TV* Yes	*Last dinner* 9	*Room service* All day

BOROUGHBRIDGE Crown Hotel 65% £E

H **Map 15 C6** North Yorkshire
Horsefair YO5 9LB
Harrogate (0423) 322328
Telex 57906

Credit Access, Amex, Diners, Visa

Visitors who stay at this former coaching inn in the centre of town clearly put business before pleasure, so the sauna and solarium have been converted to a conference room. Relaxation is achieved in the convivial bar and popular wine bar. Bedrooms are practical, with fitted furniture in the standard rooms; dark free-standing pieces in executive rooms. *Amenities* patio, in-house movies, laundry service, coffee shop (10am–10pm). &

Rooms 43	*Direct dial* Yes	*Confirm by* arrang.	*Parking* Ample
Ensuite bath/shower 43	*Room TV* Yes	*Last dinner* 9.45	*Room service* 24 hours

BOROUGHBRIDGE — Three Arrows Hotel 61% — £D/E

H Map 15 C6 North Yorkshire
Horsefair YO5 9LL
Boroughbridge (0423) 322245

Credit Access, Amex, Diners, Visa
Closed 28–30 Dec

A sturdy Victorian house set in 26 pleasant acres a mile from the A1. The lounge is a room of quiet dignity, with nice garden views, and there's an elegant bar. Bedrooms come in a variety of styles, but all have hairdryers, tea-makers and well-lit writing space. Some rooms are large enough for sofas, and one sports a brass half-tester bed and a little dressing area.
Amenities garden, laundry service.

| Rooms 17 | Room phone Yes | Confirm by arrang. | Parking Ample |
| Ensuite bath/shower 17 | Room TV Yes | Last dinner 9 | Room service All day |

BORROWDALE — Borrowdale Hotel 60% — £C/D

H Map 13 C5 Cumbria
Keswick on Derwentwater
CA12 5UY
Borrowdale (076 87) 84224

Credit Access, Visa

There's a friendly air to this roadside hotel just a stone's throw from Derwentwater. Chintzy armchairs, magazines and standard lamps make the lounge areas cosy and welcoming and the bar looks on to a delightful garden. Superior bedrooms have four-poster beds and plenty of luxurious extras; all rooms have remote control TVs, radio alarms, plenty of wardrobe and drawer space and neat carpeted bathrooms. Half board terms only. *Amenities* garden, laundry service.

| Rooms 34 | Direct dial Yes | Confirm by 4 | Parking Ample |
| Ensuite bath/shower 34 | Room TV Yes | Last dinner 9.15 | Room service Limited |

BORROWDALE — Stakis Lodore Swiss Hotel 73% — £C/D

H Map 13 C5 Cumbria
Nr Keswick CA12 5UX
Borrowdale (059 684) 285
Telex 64305

Rooms 72
Ensuite bath/shower 72
Direct dial Yes
Room TV Yes
Confirm by arrang.
Last dinner 9.30
Parking Ample
Room service 24 hours

Credit Access, Amex, Diners, Visa
Closed Jan & Feb

If a peaceful setting is what you want, the Stakis Lodore Swiss comes up trumps. It stands by Derwentwater, with nothing but hills and streams around, in an area of great natural beauty. There are splendid views from the lounge (a vast and rather soulless room) and from front-facing bedrooms. All bedrooms are double-glazed, heating is good, and extras run from fruit and biscuits to mini-bars and

hairdryers. Young staff provide cheerful, willing service. Fine leisure facilities. No dogs. *Amenities* garden, indoor & outdoor swimming pools, sauna, solarium, keep-fit equipment, beauty salon, hairdressing, tennis, squash, games room, in-house movies, secretarial services, laundry service, kiosk, nanny, children's playground.

BOSHAM — Millstream Hotel 65% — £D

H Map 5 D4 West Sussex
Bosham Lane, Nr Chichester
PO18 8HL
Bosham (0243) 573234

Credit Access, Amex, Diners, Visa

Mixed parentage (a 16th-century malthouse linked to 18th-century cottages and a small manor house) has resulted in a hotel that has a timeless charm. Public rooms range from the cheerful cane-furnished bar to the elegant lounge, with its deep armchairs and grand piano. Individually decorated bedrooms are very well equipped, with TVs, wall safes, trouser presses and hairdryers.
Amenities garden, laundry service. &

| Rooms 29 | Direct dial Yes | Confirm by 6 | Parking Ample |
| Ensuite bath/shower 29 | Room TV Yes | Last dinner 9.30 | Room service Limited |

BOSTON — New England Hotel 57% — £D/E

H Map 11 F3 Lincolnshire
9 Wide Bargate PE21 6SH
Boston (0205) 65255

Credit Access, Amex, Diners, Visa

This modest town-centre hotel has a large reception area that includes the lounge and bar. This has an attractive ribbed plaster ceiling and wood-panelled walls, but the effect is marred by plastic wing armchairs and a coal-effect electric fire. Bedrooms are clean and well kept but somewhat dated, with oldish fitted units. All rooms have remote control TVs, tea-makers and radio alarms. Staff are friendly.
Amenities laundry service.

| Rooms 25 | Room phone Yes | Confirm by 6 | Parking Ample |
| Ensuite bath/shower 25 | Room TV Yes | Last dinner 10 | Room service Limited |

BOTLEY   Cobbett's   ♀

R **Map 5 D4** Hampshire
13 The Square
Botley (048 92) 2068

French cooking
Set L from £8 **Set D** £15
About £50 for two
Seats 40 *Parties* 14
Parking Ample
Credit Access, Amex, Visa

The cooking here is very good, very French, very well presented. Lucie Skipworth, who comes from St Emilion, is in charge of the kitchen, while her affable husband, Charles, runs front of house. Both à la carte and fixed-price menus are offered. A typical meal might begin with brioche filled with liver and kidneys and served with mustard sauce, followed by roast pork with garlic sabayon. Try the délice de cassis if available. ℮

Lunch 12–2.30, Sat by arrang.   *Dinner* 7.30–10, Sat 7–10
Closed L Mon, all Sun, Bank Hols & 2 wks summer

BOUGHTON MONCHELSEA   Tanyard Hotel   63%   £E

HR **Map 7 C5** Kent
Wierton Hill,
Nr Maidstone ME17 4JT
Maidstone (0622) 44705

Credit Access, Amex, Diners, Visa
Closed 24 Dec & Feb

Jan Davies has succeeded in creating an informal house party atmosphere at her delightful medieval yeoman's house overlooking the Weald (check directions). Low, beamed ceilings, sloping floors, leaded windows and inglenooks abound in the cosy day rooms, while the equally characterful bedrooms with modern furniture have many comforting extras and well-equipped bathrooms. No children under six. No dogs. *Amenities* garden.

Rooms 5	*Direct dial* Yes	*Confirm by* arrang.	*Parking* Ample
Ensuite bath/shower 5	*Room TV* Yes	*Last dinner* 8	*Room service* All day

Restaurant   ♀

Set D £16.10
About £39 for two
Seats 14

Guests enjoy a pre-dinner drink in the drawing room while perusing the no-choice set menu served in a superb beamed dining room with a bread oven, and inglenook fire place. Jan Davies' set menu reflects her capable, straightforward style; first-class local produce gets careful treatment, and a typical meal might include flambéed scampi in sherry and chive sauce followed by fillet of beef in a peppercorn sauce, Amaretto soufflé and excellent cheeses. Residents only. ℮

Dinner only at 8
Closed 24 Dec–1 Mar

BOURNEMOUTH   Carlton Hotel   78%   £B

H **Town plan E2** Dorset
East Overcliff BH1 3DN
Bournemouth (0202) 22011
Telex 41244

Rooms 65
Ensuite bath/shower 65
Direct dial Yes
Room TV Yes
Confirm by 6
Last dinner 9.45
Parking Ample
Room service 24 hours

Credit Access, Amex, Diners, Visa

In the same ownership as Fredrick's Hotel at Maidenhead, this fine clifftop hotel reaps the benefit of highly professional management and efficient, smartly dressed staff. Always a comfortable, well-appointed place, it's better still after an ambitious programme that has seen the remodelling of the day rooms to include an elegant new library, boutique and cocktail bar. Craftsmanship and good taste are evident throughout. The spacious, well-furnished bedrooms, many with private balconies and sea views are now being refurbished. Bathrooms are first class. No dogs. *Amenities* garden, outdoor swimming pool, sauna, solarium, whirlpool bath, gymnasium, beauty salon, hairdressing, snooker, in-house movies, secretarial services, fax, laundry service.

BOURNEMOUTH   Crest Hotel   60%   £C

H **Town plan E1** Dorset
The Lansdowne BH1 2PR
Bournemouth (0202) 23262
Telex 41232

Credit Access, Amex, Diners, Visa

Convenient for both seafront and town centre, this distinctive circular hotel also offers conference facilities, making it popular with business visitors during the week. Bedroom decor has improved following refurbishment. Features now include double glazing, soft furnishings in light pastels and new wood furniture. Bathrooms too have been upgraded and incorporate new showers.
Amenities games room, snooker, secretarial services, fax.

Rooms 102	*Direct dial* Yes	*Confirm by* 6	*Parking* Ample
Ensuite bath/shower 102	*Room TV* Yes	*Last dinner* 9.45	*Room service* Limited

BOURNEMOUTH

Map 4 C4
Town plan opposite

Population 149,700

The founding of Bournemouth can be dated to 1810 when a Dorset squire built a summer residence and let it to friends. It has developed from this beginning into a seaside resort receiving nearly 2 million visitors a year. The town is mainly Victorian but contains interesting additions, particularly from the 1930s. It is noted for its parks and gardens as well as its entertainment facilities.

Annual Events
Daffodil Vintage Car Rally *April*
Festival of Nostalgia *May*
Esso Bristol to Bournemouth Vintage Vehicle Run *June*
Health Week Flower Festival *June*
Summer Pops *June/July*
Dance Festival *July*
Folk Festival, Regatta and Carnival *July/August*
Clowns Festival *August*
Kite Festival *August*
World Powerboat Championships *September*

Sights Outside City
Hengistbury Head, Christchurch Priory, Christchurch Tricycle Museum, Corfe Castle, Compton Acre Gardens, Brownsea Island, Kingston Lacy House and Park, Merley Tropical Bird Gardens, Wimbourne Minster.

Information Centre
Westover Road
BH1 2BLL
Telephone Bournemouth 291715

1 Big Four Railway Museum and Model Exhibiton **C1**
2 Boscombe Pier **E2**
3 Bournemouth Natural Science Society Museum **E1**
4 Bournemouth Pier and Leisure Centre *including a theatre, discothèque, shops and amusements* **D3**
5 Bournemouth Transport Museum **E1**
6 Casa Magni Shelley Museum **E2**
7 Ice Skating Rink **D2**
8 International Centre *including concert halls, swimming pool and fitness centre* **C3**
9 King's Park with Miniature Railway **E1**
10 Meyrick Park **A1/B1**
11 Pavilion Theatre **D2**
12 Prehistoric World **C1**
13 Queen's Park **E1**
14 R. L. Stevenson Memorial Gardens **A3**
15 Russell Cotes Art Gallery and Museum **D2**
16 Shell House **E2**
17 Winter Gardens Theatre **B3**

Fiat Dealer
Caffyns PLC
674–680 Wimbourne Road, Winton
Bournemouth
BH9 2EF
Tel. Bournemouth 512121

Bournemouth

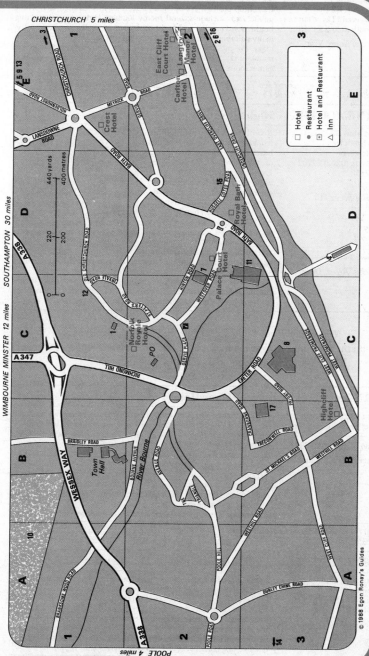

CHRISTCHURCH 5 miles

SOUTHAMPTON 30 miles

WIMBOURNE MINSTER 12 miles

POOLE 4 miles

□	Hotel
●	Restaurant
▣	Hotel and Restaurant
△	Inn

East Cliff Court Hotel

Langtry Manor Hotel

Carlton Hotel

Crest Hotel

Royal Bath Hotel

Palace Court Hotel

Norfolk Royale Hotel

PO

Town Hall

Highcliff Hotel

River Bourne

CHRISTCHURCH ROAD

HOLDENHURST ROAD

LANSDOWNE ROAD

METRICK ROAD

BATH ROAD

OLD CHRISTCHURCH ROAD

RUSSELL COTES ROAD

BATH ROAD

EXETER ROAD

RICHMOND HILL

HINTON ROAD

WESTOVER ROAD

BOURNE AVENUE

AVENUE ROAD

BRADLEY ROAD

WESSEX WAY

BRANKSOME WOOD ROAD

POOLE HILL

POOLE ROAD

DURLEY CHINE ROAD

WEST HILL ROAD

ST. MICHAEL'S ROAD

WEST HILL ROAD

WESTHILL ROAD

TREGONWELL ROAD

PRIORY ROAD

BEACON ROAD

EAST OVERCLIFF DRIVE

BOURNEMOUTH FALL CLIFF DRIVE

A338

A347

A338

440 yards

400 metres

© 1988 Egon Ronay's Guides

BOURNEMOUTH   East Cliff Court Hotel   58%   £E

H Town plan E2 Dorset
East Overcliff Drive BH1 3AN
Bournemouth (0202) 24545

Credit Access, Amex, Visa

Its clifftop position is a splendid feature of this seaside hotel, whose public areas include several roomy lounges. Bedrooms, all sporting bright new curtains and bedspreads, are generally large and lofty, many suitable for families and the best having private balconies to make the most of the views. Bathrooms are fully tiled and well maintained. *Amenities* outdoor swimming pool, sauna, solarium, games room, laundry service.

Rooms 70	*Direct dial* Yes	*Confirm by* 6	*Parking* Ample
Ensuite bath/shower 70	*Room TV* Yes	*Last dinner* 8.45	*Room service* 24 hours

BOURNEMOUTH   Highcliff Hotel   72%   £B/C

H Town plan B3 Dorset
St Michael's Road,
West Cliff BH2 5DU
Bournemouth (0202) 27702
Telex 417153

Rooms 110
Ensuite bath/shower 110
Direct dial Yes
Room TV Yes
Confirm by 6
Last dinner 9
Parking Limited
Room service 24 hours

Credit Access, Amex, Diners, Visa

Recent improvements at this handsome hotel high above the beach include the reconstruction of two floors of bedrooms to Executive standard. All rooms are of a very good size, with easy chairs, breakfast tables and writing desks, plus mini-bars and other accessories. There are several luxurious suites in coastguard cottages standing in the grounds. A sunny conservatory terrace and cocktail bar afford delightful prospects, and the hotel has its own pub and a disco night spot. Staff are very friendly and smart. No dogs.
Amenities garden, outdoor swimming pool, sauna, solarium, tennis, putting, snooker, pool table, in-house movies, secretarial services, fax, laundry service, nanny (summer), children's play area.

**We welcome bona fide complaints and recommendations
on the tear-out pages at the back of the book for readers' comment.
They are followed up by our professional team.**

BOURNEMOUTH   Langtry Manor Hotel   62%   *NEW ENTRY*   £D/E

H Town plan E1 Dorset
26 Derby Road, East Cliff
BH1 3QB
Bournemouth (0202) 23887

Credit Access, Amex, Diners, Visa

In the favoured East Cliff area of Bournemouth, the manor was built by Edward VII (then the Prince of Wales) as a home for Lillie Langtry. The period atmosphere is carefully preserved by owner Pamela Hamilton Howard and her son, and Edwardian dinners are a feature on Saturdays. Public rooms like the lounge and bar are staunchly old-fashioned, and bedrooms ranging from singles to the very fine Edward VII suite are appointed in an individual style that combines character, comfort and pleasant personal touches. Some of the rooms are in a lodge across the road. Staff are friendly and relaxed, and a good breakfast starts the day.
Amenities garden, secretarial services, laundry service.

Rooms 30	*Direct dial* Yes	*Confirm by* arrang.	*Parking* Ample
Ensuite bath/shower 30	*Room TV* Yes	*Last dinner* 8.30	*Room service* All day

BOURNEMOUTH   Norfolk Royale Hotel   68%   *NEW ENTRY*   £B/C

H Town plan C2 Dorset
Richmond Hill
Bournemouth (0202) 21521
Telex 418474

Credit Access, Amex, Diners, Visa

Reopened after expensive refurbishment, this striking Edwardian hotel enjoys a prime town-centre location. Public areas like the foyer-lounge and club-like bar are comfortably stylish, while well-equipped bedrooms contrast modern chintzy fabrics with attractive pine furnishings. Excellent bathrooms. Standards of service fail to match the fine surroundings. No dogs. *Amenities* garden, indoor swimming pool, sauna, whirlpool bath, steam bath, satellite TV, in-house movies, teletext, fax, laundry service, coffee shop (7.30am–10pm).

Rooms 95	*Direct dial* Yes	*Confirm by* 6	*Parking* Ample
Ensuite bath/shower 95	*Room TV* Yes	*Last dinner* 10.30	*Room service* 24 hours

BOURNEMOUTH — Palace Court Hotel 66% £D/E

H Town plan D2 Dorset
Westover Road BH1 2BR
Bournemouth (0202) 27681
Telex 418451

Credit Access, Amex, Diners, Visa

Sea views and a central location ensure the continuing popularity of this 1930s hotel. Spacious public rooms include a split-level foyer with brown leather chesterfields and a comfortable lounge and bar with striking blue upholstery and black, marble-effect decor. Bright, simply furnished bedrooms, many with balconies, offer tea-makers and neat bathrooms. *Amenities* sauna, solarium, keep-fit equipment, games room, snooker, laundry service.

Rooms 107	Direct dial Yes	Confirm by arrang.	Parking Ample
Ensuite bath/shower 107	Room TV Yes	Last dinner 9	Room service 24 hours

BOURNEMOUTH — Royal Bath Hotel 78% £B/C

H Town plan D2 Dorset
Bath Road BH1 2EW
Bournemouth (0202) 25555
Telex 41375

Rooms 133
Ensuite bath/shower 133
Direct dial Yes
Room TV Yes
Confirm by arrang.
Last dinner 9.30
Parking Ample
Room service 24 hours

Credit Access, Amex, Diners, Visa

A really elegant hotel overlooking the bay. The new leisure pavilion is a major attraction, and other improvements include new carpeting throughout the public area. Bold colours and luxurious fabrics are a feature both here and in the bedrooms, many of which have been refurbished to 'superior' status. Bathrooms are well stocked with high-quality toiletries and thick towels. Smart staff do their jobs in a  courteous, professional way, and the whole place is in fine form for its 150th birthday. *Amenities* garden, indoor swimming pool, sauna, solarium, whirlpool bath, steam room, gymnasium, beauty salon, hairdressing, putting, snooker, in-house movies, secretarial services, fax, valeting, laundry service, nanny (in summer), helipad. &

We publish annually,
so make sure you use the current edition.
It's worth it!

BOWNESS ON WINDERMERE — Belsfield Hotel 63% £C/D

H Map 13 D5 Cumbria
Kendal Road LA23 3EL
Windermere (096 62) 2448
Telex 65238

Credit Access, Amex, Diners, Visa

Lovely views of the lake can be enjoyed from the elegant public rooms of this spacious Victorian mansion. For real peace, try the quiet little library. Most of the good-sized bedrooms have been smartly refurbished with quality furniture and fabrics; some have superb views. Friendly, efficient staff.
Amenities garden, indoor swimming pool, sauna, solarium, tennis, putting, games room, snooker, pool table, children's playground.

Rooms 66	Direct dial Yes	Confirm by 6	Parking Ample
Ensuite bath/shower 66	Room TV Yes	Last dinner 9.30	Room service 24 hours

BOWNESS ON WINDERMERE — Gilpin Lodge 64% NEW ENTRY £B

HR Map 13 D5 Cumbria
Crook Road LA23 3NE
Windermere (096 62) 2295

Credit Access, Amex, Diners, Visa
Closed 2 wks Jan

John and Christine Cunliffe have left their partner running the Hole in the Wall at Bath to run a country hotel that was once John's grandparents' family home. The setting, two miles from Bowness on the B5284, is 20 acres of woodlands and extensive formal gardens, and the accent is on personal service and home comforts, both in the public areas and in the splendidly adapted bedrooms. The latter are furnished with pine and wicker, and all have sofas and easy chairs, books, plants and excellent carpeted bathrooms with corner baths, fluffy towels and good supplies of toiletries. No dogs.
Amenities garden, laundry service.

Rooms 6	Direct dial Yes	Confirm by arrang.	Parking Ample
Ensuite bath/shower 6	Room TV Yes	Last dinner 9	Room service All day
			see over

Gilpin Lodge Restaurant   *NEW ENTRY*   ⑨

Set D £17
About £44 for two
Seats 32
Parties 25

Christine Cunliffe cooks in homely, unpretentious style at her pretty country restaurant, and her daily-changing menu makes fine use of good fresh produce. A typical five-course dinner could start with asparagus hollandaise or smoked trout mousse, then a soup or sorbet, with roast duck, sirloin steak or salmon with tarragon cream sauce as the centrepiece. Nice sweets and a plate of good English cheeses round off a very pleasant meal. ⊖ &

Dinner only 7–9
Closed 2 wks Jan

BOWNESS ON WINDERMERE   Jackson's Bistro   ⑨

R Map 13 D5 Cumbria
Windermere (096 62) 6264

About £28 for two
Seats 45
Parking Limited

Credit Access, Amex, Visa

Victorian decor and an old kitchen range in the cosy basement room provide a pleasant setting in which to enjoy unpretentious and familiar dishes, which always include a choice for vegetarians. You might start with mushrooms and smoked bacon with red wine and garlic or spiced meatballs in tomato, herb and garlic sauce before moving on to a trio of beef, lamb and pork fillets in Madeira sauce. Simple sweets.

Dinner only 6.30–10, Sat 6.30–10.30
Closed Sun Oct–April, 25 & 26 Dec & 3 wks Jan

BOWNESS ON WINDERMERE   Old England Hotel   65%   £C

H Map 13 D5 Cumbria
  Church Street LA23 3DF
Windermere (096 62) 2444
Telex 65194

Credit Access, Amex, Diners, Visa

The gardens of this Lakeland stone hotel run right down to the water and the bedrooms to go for are those at the front with the pretty views. Public areas include a drinks terrace on the roof of the picture-windowed dining room and two bars.
Amenities garden, outdoor swimming pool, solarium, beauty salon, hairdressing, golf practice net, snooker, fax, laundry service, children's play area.

Rooms 82	Direct dial Yes	Confirm by 6	Parking Difficult
Ensuite bath/shower 82	Room TV Yes	Last dinner 9.15	Room service 24 hours

**Our inspectors are our full-time employees;
they are professionally trained by us.**

BRACKNELL   Hilton National   67%   £B/C

H Map 5 E2 Berkshire
  Bagshot Road RG12 3QJ
Bracknell (0344) 424801
Telex 848058

Credit Access, Amex, Diners, Visa

Decor and general repair are very good at the former Ladbroke Hotel, where recent developments include more bedrooms and conference facilities. Bedrooms are kitted out with a good range of up-to-date accessories, and there are a number of superior Gold Star rooms and suites; no-smoking rooms are also available. *Amenities* garden, plunge pool, sauna, whirlpool bath, keep-fit equipment, games room, pool table, in-house movies, fax, laundry service.

Rooms 170	Direct dial Yes	Confirm by arrang.	Parking Ample
Ensuite bath/shower 170	Room TV Yes	Last dinner 10	Room service 24 hours

**Our inspectors *never* book in the name of Egon Ronay's Guides.
They disclose their identity only if they are considering an establishment
for inclusion in the next edition of the Guide.**

BRADFORD | Baron Hotel 59% | £D/E

H Map 10 C1 West Yorkshire
Highfield Road, Idle BD10 8QH
Bradford (0274) 611111
Telex 517229

Credit Access, Amex, Diners, Visa
Closed 1 wk Xmas

A modern hotel by the ring road, north of the city centre. Day rooms are open-plan, and the bar features collections of water jugs and rare Mouton Rothschild wines. Best bedrooms are 12 attractive suites with antique pine furniture and large circular baths. The owner is friendly and helpful, his staff less so. *Amenities* indoor swimming pool, sauna, solarium, whirlpool bath, keep-fit equipment, in-house movies, laundry service, 24-hour lounge service.

Rooms 45	*Direct dial* Yes	*Confirm by* arrang.	*Parking* Ample
Ensuite bath/shower 45	*Room TV* Yes	*Last dinner* 9	*Room service* Limited

BRADFORD | Restaurant Nineteen ★ ♛ ◿

RR Map 10 C1
West Yorkshire
19 North Park Road,
Heaton BD9 4NT
Bradford (0274) 492559

Dinner only 7–9.30, Sat till 10
Set D from £19
About £50 for two
Seats 40
Parties 8
Parking Ample

Credit Amex, Diners, Visa
Closed Sun, Mon, 1 wk June, 2 wks Sept & 1 wk Xmas

A prettily decorated dining room with well-spaced, candlelit tables makes an elegant formal setting for the excellent dishes produced by the talented and dedicated Stephen Smith. His four-course menus, changing almost daily, present mostly English style fare in imaginatively modern and beautifully presented guise. Creations like his meltingly tender three medallions of Scots roe deer, each topped with a different

purée and served with a marvellous selection of vegetables, amply demonstrate this chef's sense of perfectionism. Well-balanced wine list. *Specialities* mousse of scallop roe with sautéed scallops and langoustine sauce; roast saddle of venison with broccoli mousse and rowanberry jelly; English duckling, the leg casseroled in red wine and orange, the breast stuffed with prunes, herbs and the liver and roasted. 🍷 Well-chosen ㊉

BEDROOMS 7 £F
With shower 3

Simple, homely bedrooms have freestanding furniture and candle-wick bedspreads. Three have their own shower cubicles. Black-and-white TVs. No dogs.

Changes in data sometimes occur in establishments
after the Guide goes to press.
Prices should be taken as indications rather than firm quotes.

BRADFORD | Novotel 60% | £D/E

H Map 10 C1 West Yorkshire
Merrydale Road BD4 6SA
Bradford (0274) 683683
Telex 517312

Credit Access, Amex, Diners, Visa

A location on the edge of a trading estate off the M606 three miles south of the city centre, makes this modern hotel ideal for business visitors. Spacious public rooms have plenty of relaxing seating, and bedrooms are bright and well lit, with generous writing space. Good maintenance is particularly obvious in bathrooms and their separate WCs.
Amenities garden, outdoor swimming pool, in-house movies, laundry service. ♿

Rooms 136	*Direct dial* Yes	*Confirm by* 7	*Parking* Ample
Ensuite bath/shower 136	*Room TV* Yes	*Last dinner* Midnight	*Room service* All day

BRADFORD | Stakis Norfolk Gardens Hotel 64% | £C

H Map 10 C1 West Yorkshire
Hall Ings BD1 5SH
Bradford (0274) 734734
Telex 517573

Credit Access, Amex, Diners, Visa

Six floors of double-glazed bedrooms provide smart, comfortable accommodation in the centre of the city. Floral fabrics complement handsome reproduction furniture, and all rooms offer trouser presses and hairdryers, plus nice little touches like bowls of fruit. Well-kept tiled bathrooms. Public areas, including extensive conference facilities, have been refurbished. Helpful management and staff.
Amenities in-house movies, secretarial services, fax, laundry service.

Rooms 126	*Direct dial* Yes	*Confirm by* 6	*Parking* Ample
Ensuite bath/shower 126	*Room TV* Yes	*Last dinner* 10	*Room service* 24 hours

BRADFORD   Victoria Hotel   61%   £C/D

H **Map 10 C1** West Yorkshire
Bridge Street BD1 1JX
Bradford (0274) 728706
Telex 517456

Credit Access, Amex, Diners, Visa

This imposing Victorian hotel is in the city centre situated opposite
the Transport Exchange. Boldly patterned sofas and heavy drapes
emphasise the elegance of the lofty pillared foyer, and the bar has a
fine tented ceiling and striking pink and royal blue decor. Spacious
bedrooms, in smart, traditional style, have modern accessories, some
with hairdryers and trouser presses.
Amenities laundry service.

| Rooms 59 | Direct dial Yes | Confirm by 6 | Parking Limited |
| Ensuite bath/shower 59 | Room TV Yes | Last dinner 10 | Room service 24 hours |

**We welcome bona fide complaints and recommendations
on the tear-out pages at the back of the book for readers' comment.
They are followed up by our professional team.**

BRAINTREE   White Hart Hotel   *NEW ENTRY*   £E

I **Map 6 C3** Essex
Bocking End CM7 6AB
Braintree (0376) 21401
Telex 98835

Credit Access, Amex, Diners, Visa

Old-world charm and up-to-date comfort in a town-centre coaching
inn. The beamy bars have a friendly 'local' atmosphere, and up on the
first floor there is a little residents' lounge/meeting room. Radio-
alarms, tea-makers, trouser presses and hairdryers are among the
ample accessories in the bedrooms, largest of which are in the rear
extension. Bathrooms, too, are well equipped. No dogs.
Amenities in-house movies, secretarial services.

| Rooms 34 | Direct dial Yes | Confirm by 6 | Parking Ample |
| Ensuite bath/shower 34 | Room TV Yes | Last dinner 10.30 | Room service Limited |

BRAITHWAITE   Ivy House Hotel   61%   £E

H **Map 13 C5** Cumbria
Nr Keswick CA12 5SY
Braithwaite (059 682) 338

Credit Access, Visa

The new bar-lounge is a welcome addition to this small, family-run
hotel. Its 17th-century origins are reflected in the main lounge – a cosy
room with heavy beams, open log fire and chintzy wing chairs.
Individually decorated bedrooms have mostly traditional furniture
(including two four-posters) plus tea-makers, hairdryers and electric
blankets. Two have showers only (one remote en suite). No children. No
dogs.

| Rooms 10 | Room phone No | Confirm by arrang. | Parking Ample |
| Ensuite bath/shower 9 | Room TV Yes | Last dinner 7.30 | Room service Limited |

BRAMHALL   Bramhall Moat House   £D/E

H **Map 10 B2** Cheshire
Bramhall Lane South SK7 2 EB
061-439 8116 Telex 668464

Credit Access, Amex, Diners, Visa
Closed 1 week Xmas

Graded at 55% in our 1988 Guide, the Moat House will no doubt rate
quite a lot higher on the completion of a major improvement
programme due to be finished after we went to press. This work
included the total refurbishment of existing bedrooms and the building
of 25 more – all with private bathrooms. The lounge bar will be
completely rebuilt, and a new formal restaurant was also under
construction when we looked in. No dogs.
Amenities fax, laundry service. &

| Rooms 65 | Direct dial Yes | Confirm by 6 | Parking Ample |
| Ensuite bath/shower 65 | Room TV Yes | Last dinner 9.45 | Room service 24 hours |

BRAMHOPE   Parkway Hotel   63%   £C/D

H **Map 10 C1** West Yorkshire
Otley Road, Bramhope,
Nr Leeds LS16 8AG
Leeds (0532) 672551
Telex 556614

Credit Access, Amex, Diners, Visa

Substantial gardens make an attractive setting for this large mock-
Tudor hotel on the A660 six miles from Leeds. Bedrooms, including
two equipped for the disabled, have remote-control TVs, hairdryers,
trouser presses and tea-makers. Newer ones have balconies. Vinyl-
floored bathrooms with showers have modern suites and plenty of
extras. Public rooms include a spacious foyer and traditional bar-
lounge. *Amenities* garden, laundry service. &

| Rooms 103 | Direct dial Yes | Confirm by 6 | Parking Ample |
| Ensuite bath/shower 103 | Room TV Yes | Last dinner 10 | Room service 24 hours |

BRAMHOPE — Post House Hotel 66% £C

H Map 10 C1 West Yorkshire
Bramhope, Nr Leeds LS16 9JJ
Leeds (0532) 842911
Telex 556367

Credit Access, Amex, Diners, Visa.

Standing in ample grounds on the A660, this modern, purpose-built hotel is a useful stopover. Bedrooms offer space and comfort in plenty, and all have remote-control TVs, mini-bars and trouser presses. Public areas include a sunken bar-lounge and a health club.
Amenities garden, indoor swimming pool, sauna, solarium, whirlpool bath, keep-fit equipment, secretarial services, fax, laundry service, 24-hour lounge service, coffee shop (10.30am–10.30pm).

Rooms 129	*Direct dial* Yes	*Confirm by* 6	*Parking* Ample
Ensuite bath/shower 129	*Room TV* Yes	*Last dinner* 10.30	*Room service* None

BRAMLEY — Bramley Grange Hotel 65% £C/D

H Map 5 E3 Surrey
Horsham Road,
Nr Guildford GU5 0BL
Guildford (0483) 893434
Telex 859948

Credit Access, Amex, Visa

A mock-Tudor building standing in seven acres of grounds in the village centre. The facade hides a smart modern interior, and much of the public area is given over to conference and function rooms. Bedrooms are airy, spacious and well kept; half have been refurbished in chic pastels and now sport very fetching Italian-tiled bathrooms.
Amenities garden, tennis, putting, croquet, secretarial services, laundry service.

Rooms 28	*Direct dial* Yes	*Confirm by* arrang.	*Parking* Ample
Ensuite bath/shower 28	*Room TV* Yes	*Last dinner* 10	*Room service* 24 hours

Our inspectors *never* book in the name of Egon Ronay's Guides.
They disclose their identity only if they are considering an establishment
for inclusion in the next edition of the Guide.

BRAMPTON — Farlam Hall Hotel 73% £B

HR Map 13 D4 Cumbria
Hallbankgate CA8 2NG
Hallbankgate (069 76) 234

Rooms 13
Ensuite bath/shower 13
Direct dial Yes
Room TV Yes
Confirm by arrang.
Last dinner 8.30
Parking Ample
Room service All day

Credit Access, Amex, Visa
Closed 1 wk Xmas & all Feb

A typically solid 17th-century Border farmhouse, much extended in Victorian times, on the A689 two miles from Brampton. Immediately in front of it is a charming ornamental lake, busy with wildfowl and guarded by mature trees. Inside, the charming Quinion and Stevenson families have made it very much their home, stocking it with delightful antiques and contributing thoughtful touches to their 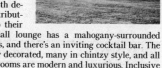 guests' enjoyment. A small lounge has a mahogany-surrounded fireplace and garden views, and there's an inviting cocktail bar. The bedrooms are individually decorated, many in chintzy style, and all have myriad extras; bathrooms are modern and luxurious. Inclusive terms only. No children under five. *Amenities* garden, croquet.

Restaurant ♨ ♖

Set D £18
About £45 *for two*
Seats 40
Parties 40

The spacious, sumptuously decorated dining room with fine quality table settings provides a delightful venue in which to sample Barry Quinion's professional, unfussy cooking. Top quality produce, much of it local, features in the set price, limited choice menu, which changes daily. Starter might be home-made soup or a light avocado mousse; for the main course, perhaps roast local guinea fowl in kumquat and black grape sauce. Excellent sweets. ☺ ⌚

Dinner only 8 for 8.30
Closed 1 wk Xmas & all Feb

BRAMPTON · Tarn End · ♀

RR **Map 13 D4** Cumbria
Talkin Tarn CA8 1LS
Brampton (069 77) 2340

French cooking
About £42 for two
Seats 30
Parties 40
Parking Ample
Credit Access, Amex, Diners, Visa

At Domenico Tellatin's solid old stone restaurant you can enjoy mainly French dishes cooked with a sure touch. There's a weekly-changing list of special supplements and vegetarians are well-catered for with some imaginative dishes. Start with a puff pastry case filled with asparagus in hollandaise sauce; move on to maize-fed chicken breast, served with mustard seed sauce. Bar snacks only are available at lunchtimes. ⊖ &

Lunch By arrang. only   *Dinner* 7.30–9
Closed All Feb & D Sun 1st Nov–end Feb to non-residents

BEDROOMS 6   £E
With bath/shower 4

The simple bedrooms have darkwood fitted furniture, TVs and tea-making facilities. A cosy lounge on the ground floor caters for both residents and diners. No dogs.

BRANDON · Brandon Hall Hotel   69% · £C/D

H **Map 11 D4** Warwickshire
Brandon, Nr Coventry
CV8 3FW
Coventry (0203) 542571
Telex 31472

Credit Access, Amex, Diners, Visa

Brandon Hall is a pleasant country house standing in extensive grounds on the edge of the village. It has real warmth and personality, thanks to the charming general manager, his likeable staff and the very elegant and inviting day rooms. Bedrooms generally offer a high standard of style and comfort, with smart Italianate darkwood furniture and chic pastel shades. *Amenities* garden, squash, pitch and putt, games room, secretarial services, fax, laundry service.

Rooms 60	*Direct dial* Yes	*Confirm by* arrang.	*Parking* Ample
Ensuite bath/shower 60	*Room TV* Yes	*Last dinner* 9.30	*Room service* 24 hours

BRANSCOMBE · Masons Arms   64% · £E

H **Map 3 E2** Devon
Nr Seaton EX12 3DJ
Branscombe (029 780) 300

Credit Access, Visa

In an unspoilt village near the sea, the Masons Arms is a delightful Devonshire inn dating from the 14th century. Most of the bedrooms are in cottages grouped round the main building; pretty fabrics and some choice pieces of antique or period furniture give character, and many rooms have exposed beams. The bar, in the oldest part, is rich in rustic charm, and there's a quiet upstairs lounge.
Amenities garden.

Rooms 22	*Direct dial* Yes	*Confirm by* arrang.	*Parking* Ample
Ensuite bath/shower 19	*Room TV* Yes	*Last dinner* 9	*Room service* All day

**Changes in data sometimes occur in establishments
after the Guide goes to press.
Prices should be taken as indications rather than firm quotes.**

BRAUNTON · Otters Restaurant   *NEW ENTRY* · ♀

R **Map 2 C1** Devon
30 Caen Street
Barnstaple (0271) 813633

Set D £10.50
About £32 for two
Seats 38
Parties 40
Parking Ample

Credit Access, Visa

Open for dinner only, Monday to Saturday, this smart, well-run restaurant stands in a little row of shops on the road to Saunton. Carol Cowie has built up a regular clientele with her more than capable cooking. Her menus, which change every seven or eight weeks according to the season, offer abundant choice, from traditional prawn cocktail and Mediterranean savoury clafoutis to salmon fillet with spinach marbling (served in a pancake with dill sauce), roast veal kidneys, and marinated venison in puff pastry parcels with a delicious plum and orange sauce. Tempting sweets, too, and sound wines – Ch. Latour St Bonnet '82, good burgundies (Chanson, Faiveley). Efficient service is led by George Cowie. ♀ Well-chosen ⊖

Dinner only 7–10.30   **Closed** Sun, Mon (winter), 25 & 26 Dec, 1 Jan, 2 wks Feb & 2 wks Oct

BRAY-ON-THAMES Waterside Inn ★★ ♛ ⌐

R **Map 5 E2** Berkshire
Ferry Road
Maidenhead (0628) 20691

French cooking

Lunch 12–2
Dinner 7–10
Set L Wed–Fri £19.50, Sat & Sun
£23.50
Set D £40.50
About £105 for two
Seats 75
Parties 80
Parking Ample

Credit Access, Amex, Diners, Visa
Closed L Tues, D Sun Oct–
Easter, all Mon & Bank Hols &
25 Dec–mid Feb (excl. L 25 Dec)

The riverside location and luxurious modern decor provide a fitting background for the by now legendary skills of Michel Roux. Despite occasional over-adherence to the stated aim that dishes should not be served too hot, it is impossible to withhold admiration for his masterly handling of outstanding raw materials. Our saucisson de lapereau was followed by fillet steak with truffle sauce and a delicious gratin savoyard, an impressive cheeseboard and a memorable mille-feuille with chocolate mousse, cream and raspberries. Very fine cellar at high prices with wonderful clarets (Ch. Figeac '61, Cheval Blanc '47). *Specialities* tronçonnettes de homard poêlées minute au porto blanc, caneton challendais Juliette, pêche gourmand selon 'Michel'. ⌐ Outstanding 🏆 Well-chosen ℮

We publish annually,
so make sure you use the current edition.
It's worth it!

BRENTWOOD Brentwood Moat House 67% £C

H **Map 7 B4** Essex
London Road CM14 4NR
Brentwood (0277) 225252
Telex 995182

Credit Access, Amex, Diners, Visa

In spite of modern extensions, this busy 16th-century hunting lodge still retains its Tudor splendour. Original open fireplaces, oak beams and panels are the order of the day here. Bedrooms range in style from the traditional elegance of the three main-house suites to the up-to-date comforts of the motel-style rooms in the garden wing. Modern bathrooms throughout.
Amenities garden, fax, laundry service. ৬

Rooms 39	*Direct dial* Yes	*Confirm by* Noon	*Parking* Ample
Ensuite bath/shower 39	*Room TV* Yes	*Last dinner* 10.30	*Room service* 24 hours

BRENTWOOD Post House Hotel 62% £C

H **Map 7 B4** Essex
Brook Street CM14 5NF
Brentwood (0277) 260260

Credit Access, Amex, Diners, Visa

A mid-70s red-brick hotel close to the M25/A12 interchange. Bedrooms are generally of a good size, with double-glazing, remote-control TVs and mini-bars as standard and various extras in Executive rooms. Cheerful day rooms include a well-furnished lobby, two bars and a coffee shop. A health and fitness club is due to open in 1989.
Amenities garden, outdoor swimming pool, coffee shop (7am–10.30pm).

Rooms 120	*Direct dial* Yes	*Confirm by* 6	*Parking* Ample
Ensuite bath/shower 120	*Room TV* Yes	*Last dinner* 10	*Room service* Limited

BRIDLINGTON Expanse Hotel 60% £E

H **Map 15 D6** Humberside
North Marine Drive YO15 2LS
Bridlington (0262) 675347

Credit Access, Amex, Diners, Visa

An old-style, family-run seaside hotel. Mr and Mrs Seymour are coming up for 40 years at the helm, and their enthusiasm and friendliness are not diminished. Day rooms are cosy and relaxing, and the public bar is popular with both locals and holiday-makers. Bright, comfortable bedrooms are being upgraded and modernised; direct-dial phones are now standard, and all rooms except three have private facilities en suite. No dogs. *Amenities* laundry service.

Rooms 49	*Direct dial* Yes	*Confirm by* arrang.	*Parking* Ample
Ensuite bath/shower 46	*Room TV* Yes	*Last dinner* 8.30	*Room service* 24 hours

BRIGHTON

Map 7 B6
Town plan opposite

Population 153,700

Brighton is Regency squares and terraces, the maze of art and junk shops called the Lanes, the beach and piers, the conferences and entertainments, the milling crowds in Brighton, and the quiet lawns of Hove, a day out for Londoners, a holiday and retirement centre, a commuter's town and a university town. The person most responsible for all this was George IV, who made it the vogue and commissioned his unique palace, the Royal Pavilion.

Annual Events
Brighton Festival *May*
Glyndebourne *May–Aug*
London to Brighton veteran car run *Nov*

Sights Outside Town
Arundel Castle, Petworth House, Bluebell Railway

Information Centres
Marlborough House, Old Steine and Sea-front opp. West Street
Telephone Brighton 23755

Fiat Dealers
Tilleys (Sussex) Ltd
100 Lewes Road
Brighton BN2 3QA
Tel. Brighton 603244
Map reference D1

Tilleys (Sussex) Ltd
2 Church Road
Hove BN3 2FL
Tel. Brighton 738949
Map reference A2

1 Aquarium and Dolphinarium **D3**
2 Booth Bird Museum *British birds in natural surroundings* **B1**
3 Brighton & Hove Albion F.C. **A1**
4 Brighton Conference & Exhibition Centre **C3**
5 Churchill Square **C3**
6 County Cricket Ground **A2**
7 Devil's Dyke *4 miles, Sussex beauty spot* **B1**
8 Information Centres **C3**
9 The Lanes *network of old fisherman's cottages, now world centre for antiques* **C3**
10 Marina **E3**
11 Museum & Art Gallery **C/D3**
12 Palace Pier **D3**
13 Preston Park and Preston Manor *18th c* **C1**
14 Race-course **E1**
15 Rottingdean *2¼ miles, toy museum* **E3**
16 Royal Pavilion *Regency exhibition, art gallery and museum* **C/D3**
17 Station **C2**
18 Sussex University *4 miles* **E1**
19 Theatre Royal **C3**
20 Volks Railway *first electric railway, on seafront* **D3**

Brighton FIAT

BRIGHTON (HOVE)   Alexandra Hotel   58%   £D/E

H Town plan A3 East Sussex
42 Brunswick Terrace
BN3 1HA
Brighton (0273) 202722
Telex 877579

Credit Access, Amex, Diners, Visa

Situated on the seafront, this pleasantly restored, comfortable hotel has an elegant Regency facade. The cosy bar is smartly decorated and adorned with lots of greenery. Bedrooms are double-glazed and have hairdryers and trouser presses. Bathrooms (two with shower only) are well maintained. Suites have balconies and mini-bars in addition. *Amenities* sauna, solarium, whirlpool bath, games room, snooker, secretarial services, laundry service.

| Rooms 63 | Direct dial Yes | Confirm by 6 | Parking Limited |
| Ensuite bath/shower 63 | Room TV Yes | Last dinner 9.30 | Room service Limited |

BRIGHTON   Bedford Hotel   65%   £C

H Town plan B3 East Sussex
King's Road BN1 2JF
Brighton (0273) 29744
Telex 878397

Credit Access, Amex, Diners, Visa

Five floors of a tower block make up a comfortable modern hotel on the seafront. Bedrooms are the subject of a gradual improvements programme that includes smart new fitted furniture and accessories such as trouser presses and hairdryers. Best rooms have sea views. Among the day rooms is a Dickensian-style bar. Guests may use the facilities of the nearby Metropole. *Amenities* terrace, in-house movies, fax, laundry service.

| Rooms 127 | Direct dial Yes | Confirm by 6 | Parking Limited |
| Ensuite bath/shower 127 | Room TV Yes | Last dinner 10.30 | Room service 24 hours |

BRIGHTON   Brighton Metropole Hotel   70%   £B/C

H Town plan C3 East Sussex
Kings Road BN1 2FU
Brighton (0273) 775432
Telex 877245

Rooms 328
Ensuite bath/shower 328
Direct dial Yes
Room TV Yes
Confirm by 6
Last dinner 10.30
Parking Ample
Room service 24 hours

Credit Access, Amex, Diners, Visa

A hotel with a prime seafront position and first-rate leisure and conference facilities. Bedrooms vary from those refurbished with modern designer fabrics and high-quality furnishings and those yet to be done, which now look rather tired and dated. All rooms boast teletext TVs, hairdryers and trouser presses, plus extensive tea-making equipment; many rooms have private balconies. Spacious public areas

include an elegant drawing room and several bars, one in pubby Victorian style. Neither reception staff nor breakfast impressed on our last visit. *Amenities* terrace, indoor swimming pool, sauna, solarium, whirlpool bath, gymnasium, hairdressing, billiards, in-house movies, secretarial services, fax, laundry service, kiosk.

BRIGHTON   China Garden Restaurant   NEW ENTRY

R Town plan B3 East Sussex
88 Preston Street
Brighton (0273) 25124

Set D from £8.95
About £35 for two
Seats 135
Parking Limited

Credit Access, Amex, Diners, Visa

A lively atmosphere, quick and friendly service and excellent food have brought this restaurant well-deserved popularity. The long and varied menu offers plenty of choice – there are even four different styles of duck to accompany spring onions, cucumber and pancakes – and the seafood is particularly good. Recommendable dishes include roast golden medallion chicken, sliced pork Szechuan style, king prawns sautéed with mange-tout and Singapore noodles.

Meals Noon–11pm

BRIGHTON (HOVE)   Courtlands Hotel   62%   £D

H Town plan A2 East Sussex
19 The Drive BN3 3JE
Brighton (0273) 731055
Telex 87574

Credit Access, Amex, Diners, Visa

New owners have acquired this quietly situated hotel, but it retains its outstanding manager, Mr Messina, and his affable assistant Mr Petrocchi. Bedrooms, mainly traditional but some more modern, are kept in A1 order, and guests relax easily in the roomy lounge and cocktail bar. *Amenities* garden, indoor swimming pool, solarium, whirlpool bath, games room, secretarial services, laundry service, children's play area.

| Rooms 58 | Direct dial Yes | Confirm by 6 | Parking Ample |
| Ensuite bath/shower 58 | Room TV Yes | Last dinner 9.30 | Room service 24 hours |

BRIGHTON (HOVE) Dudley Hotel 67% £C

H **Town plan B2** East Sussex
Lansdowne Place BN3 1HQ
Brighton (0273) 736266
Telex 87537

Credit Access, Amex, Diners, Visa

Just a stone's throw from the beach, the Dudley is a traditional hotel dating from 1900. A glass of sherry accompanies check-in, and guests have abundant lounge space in which to relax. Bedrooms are on four floors and are individual in size and style, but standard in all are remote-control TVs and good tea-making facilities. Housekeeping can be lax, and some decorative improvements are needed.
Amenities patio, laundry service.

| Rooms 80 | Direct dial Yes | Confirm by 6 | Parking Ample |
| Ensuite bath/shower 80 | Room TV Yes | Last dinner 9.45 | Room service 24 hours |

BRIGHTON (HOVE) Eaton Garden

R **Town plan A1** East Sussex
Eaton Gardens
Brighton (0273) 738921

Set L £10, Sun £11
Set D £13.25
About £40 for two
Seats 110 *Parties* 70
Parking Ample
Credit Access, Amex, Diners, Visa

For over thirty years chef John Stevens has held sway in this popular and highly professional establishment. The food is classic, consistent and precisely what the customers want. Daily-changing set menus have starters as diverse as spaghetti bolognese and fried local dabs; main courses like veal cordon bleu and duckling with apple sauce. To follow, trifle, gâteau or a savoury like soft roes on toast. 🕭 &

Lunch 12.30–2 *Dinner* 6.45–9.45, Sat 6.45–10
Closed D Sun, Good Fri & 25 Dec

BRIGHTON The Grand 78% £B

H **Town plan C3** East Sussex
Kings Road BN1 2FW
Brighton (0273) 21188
Telex 877410

Rooms 160
Ensuite bath/shower 160
Direct dial Yes
Room TV Yes
Confirm by arrang.
Last dinner 10
Parking Ample
Room service 24 hours

Credit Access, Amex, Diners, Visa

The Grand lives up to its name with resplendent public rooms that feature polished marble floors, Doric columns, finely moulded ceilings and a superb wrought-iron staircase. Many bedrooms are also spacious and sumptuous – some with private balconies – but others are more modest. Service and housekeeping still let the side down in many respects, and recent grumbles include dusty fittings, a non-closing window, poor room service, inept reception, wrong bills and a lukewarm breakfast. Management must take a much firmer hand, as this is a hotel of enormous potential. *Amenities* indoor swimming pool, sauna, solarium, whirlpool bath, gymnasium, beauty salon, hairdressing, secretarial services, fax, laundry service. &

BRIGHTON Granville Hotel 65% £C

H **Town plan B3** East Sussex
123 Kings Road BN1 2FA
Brighton (0273) 26302
Telex 878149

Credit Access, Amex, Diners, Visa

The Granville is a comfortable, stylish conversion of three seafront houses. Bedrooms vary in size and style – one room even features a water bed – and sea-facing rooms are double-glazed. Two bathrooms are fitted with whirlpool baths, and all have generous toiletries. In the basement there's a cool cocktail bar and restaurant, and a bistro/breakfast room. *Amenities* patio, solarium, secretarial services, laundry service, coffee shop (7.30am–11.30pm).

| Rooms 25 | Direct dial Yes | Confirm by arrang. | Parking Ample |
| Ensuite bath/shower 25 | Room TV Yes | Last dinner 10.30 | Room service 24 hours |

BRIGHTON Lum Thai *NEW ENTRY*

R **Town plan A3** East Sussex
196 Church Road
Brighton (0273) 772072

Thai cooking
About £26 for two
Seats 80
Parties 35
Parking Ample
Credit Access, Amex, Diners, Visa

Two black and gold statues of Thai figures add a distinctive touch to this simple Thai restaurant. Polite, friendly staff willingly advise on a choice of meat, seafood and egg dishes. Favourites include delicious fried chicken wings stuffed with pork, subtly flavoured barbecued chicken, tasty fried noodles with crunchy vegetables and prawns, chicken in a superb coconut sauce, and a salad with a delicious peanut sauce.

Lunch 12–2.30 *Dinner* 6–11.30
Closed L Sun & all Tues

BRIGHTON   La Marinade *NEW ENTRY*

R **Town plan E3** East Sussex
77 St George's Road,
Kemp Town
Brighton (0273) 600992

Set L £8.50
About £40 for two
Seats 30
Parking Limited
Credit Access, Amex, Visa

The menus at this two-storey restaurant are influenced by the Normandy and Brittany backgrounds of Yves Volant and his chef Christian Debu. Fresh produce is competently and delicately prepared, the saucing being particularly good, and presentation is delightful. Starters include an excellent feuilleté de crevettes au pernod, while main course might be saumon au beurre blanc. Decent wines: Pouilly Fumé (Bailly) '86, Ch Fombrauge St Emilion '83. ⊖

Lunch 12.15–2   *Dinner* 7.15–10
Closed D Sun, all Mon, L Sat, 25–27 Dec, 1–2 Jan & 6–19 Feb

BRIGHTON   Old Ship Hotel   69%   £C/D

HR **Town plan C3**
East Sussex
King's Road BN1 1NR
Brighton (0273) 29001
Telex 877101

Credit Access, Amex, Diners, Visa

Right on the seafront, the Old Ship offers old-world charm and hospitality, along with extensive function facilities. There's an ample choice of relaxing lounges, many with sea views, and a splendid bar in Victorian style. Refurbishment continues in the corridors (new carpets are welcome) and in the variously sized bedrooms, where decor and furnishings are both being improved. *Amenities* games room, snooker, secretarial services, fax, laundry service.

| *Rooms* 154 | *Direct dial* Yes | *Confirm by* arrang. | *Parking* Ample |
| *Ensuite bath/shower* 154 | *Room TV* Yes | *Last dinner* 9.30 | *Room service* 24 hours |

Restaurant   ♛

Set L from £9.50
About £42 for two
Seats 200

Chef Berndt Schroeter cooks consistently well in this handsome restaurant, basing his dishes whenever possible on fine fresh produce, some of it local. Cured duck breast with peppercorns, marinated monkfish on a tomato coulis, Dover sole with chive butter sauce and Southdown lamb with a sweet garlic sauce are typical offerings, and at lunchtime a cold buffet is also available. There's an excellent wine list, particularly strong in clarets, vintage ports and Armagnacs.
🍷 Well-chosen ⊖ &

Lunch 12.30–2.30, Sun 12.30–2   *Dinner* 7–9.30, Sat 7–10

BRIGHTON (HOVE)   Peking   ⁴⁄

R **Town plan B2**
9 Western Road
Brighton (0273) 722090

Chinese cooking

About £32 for two
Seats 40
Parking Limited
Credit Access, Amex, Visa

Competent cooking and swift, polite service keep the regulars happy at Mr Liu and Mr Man's little Chinese restaurant. Popular dishes on a keenly-priced menu include sweet-sour wun tun, chicken in yellow bean sauce with cashew nuts and prawns in various guises; also dumplings and one-plate noodle dishes. Simplest things are often best, and on our latest visit quick-fried prawns were excellent, shredded beef with chilli disappointing. 🍷 Well-chosen

Lunch 12–2.15   *Dinner* 6–11.30   **Closed** 25 & 26 Dec

BRIGHTON   Ramada Renaissance Hotel 83%   £A/B

HR **Town plan C3** E. Sussex
King's Road BN1 1JA
Brighton (0273) 206700
Telex 878555

Rooms 204
Ensuite bath/shower 204
Direct dial Yes
Room TV Yes
Confirm by 6
Last dinner 11
Parking Ample
Room service 24 hours

Credit Access, Amex, Diners, Visa

Luxury, comfort and the latest in high tech are features here on the seafront; staff form a commendably eager and attentive team led by effusive and very competent general manager Marie-Béatrice Lallemand. Express lifts whisk guests from the car park to the opulent open-plan public area, which includes an elegant sunken bar-lounge and a promenade coffee shop. Bedrooms, all with individual air

conditioning, well-stocked mini-bars and bedside controls for TV and radio, include a floor of Club rooms with separate check-in and a private lounge.
Amenities indoor swimming pool, sauna, solarium, whirlpool bath, gymnasium, hairdressing, in-house movies, secretarial services, fax, laundry service, coffee shop (7am–11pm), gift shop. &

La Noblesse Restaurant *NEW ENTRY* ♨

French cooking
Set L £15.50
Set D from £20
About £50 for two
Seats 56
Parties 10

In a setting of stylish opulence Belgian Filip Boyen cooks with skill and some sophistication, letting top-notch ingredients give their best in an interesting range of dishes: quail, sweetbreads and goose liver on winter leaves, fillet of lamb with braised fennel, plaited salmon and brill in a Sauternes butter, port-flavoured iced sabayon. Lunchtime brings a fixed-price menu of simpler choice. The waitresses are smartly attired in tails and wing collars. ⊖ ♿

Lunch 12–2   *Dinner* 7–11   **Closed** Sun, 26 Dec–2 Jan

BRIGHTON (HOVE)   Sackville Hotel   64%   £D/E

H **Town plan A3** East Sussex
189 Kingsway BN3 4GU
Brighton (0273) 736292
Telex 877830

Credit Access, Amex, Diners, Visa

Behind the distinctive pale green facade of this former school is a well-run and comfortable hotel. Public rooms such as the oak-panelled bar-lounge combine character with comfort. Bedrooms are individually decorated. Some have modern fitted units; others feature sturdy freestanding furniture. Many have fine sea views and all boast thoughtfully equipped ensuite bathrooms which reflect excellent housekeeping. *Amenities* laundry service.

Rooms 45	Direct dial Yes	Confirm by 6	Parking Ample
Ensuite bath/shower 45	Room TV Yes	Last dinner 9.30	Room service Limited

BRIGHTON   Sheridan Hotel   62%   £C/D

H **Town plan C3** East Sussex
64 King's Road BN1 1NA
Brighton (0273) 23221
Telex 877659

Credit Access, Amex, Diners, Visa

A seafront hotel whose new owners have the chance to make welcome improvements to the general look and decor. Best of the day rooms are a homely, comfortably furnished lounge and a bar with an Edwardian feel. Bedrooms, some with fitted furniture, others with freestanding pieces, are being refurbished with colourful carpets and fabrics. All have compact, functional bathrooms en suite. *Amenities* secretarial services, fax, laundry service.

Rooms 57	Direct dial Yes	Confirm by arrang.	Parking Difficult
Ensuite bath/shower 57	Room TV Yes	Last dinner 10.15	Room service 24 hours

Our inspectors *never* book in the name of Egon Ronay's Guides.
They disclose their identity only if they are considering an establishment
for inclusion in the next edition of the Guide.

BRIGHTON   Topps Hotel   69%   £D

HR **Town plan C3**
East Sussex
17 Regency Square BN1 2FG
Brighton (0273) 729334

Credit Access, Amex, Diners, Visa

Two Regency houses make up this charming town-centre hotel, run with great warmth and friendliness by Paul and Pauline Collins. From the cosy little reception you are shown to your bedroom, up winding stairs or via a lift to the top floor. Grandest accommodation, on the first floor, features high ceilings, private balconies and one lovely carved four-poster. All rooms are well equipped, with luxurious bathrooms. No dogs. *Amenities* laundry service.

Rooms 12	Direct dial Yes	Confirm by arrang.	Parking Ample
Ensuite bath/shower 12	Room TV Yes	Last dinner 9.30	Room service 24 hours

Bottoms Restaurant   ♨

Set D £12.50
About £34 for two
Seats 24

Delicious, imaginative yet never over-ambitious home cooking: that's Pauline Collins' recipe for success at this simply appointed basement restaurant. With husband Paul assisting front of house, she offers memorable dishes such as prawn tart made with a superb buttery pastry, and tender veal kidneys sautéed with mushrooms, onions, sausage and Madeira. Excellent al dente vegetables, alluring desserts like rich chocolate ganache cake, and first-rate espresso coffee. 🍷 Well-chosen ⊖

Dinner only 7–9.30   **Closed** Wed, Sun & 24 Dec–25 Jan

BRIGHTON (HOVE)   Whitehaven Hotel   63%   £D/E

HR **Town plan A2**
East Sussex
Wilbury Road BN3 3JP
Brighton (0273) 778355

Credit Access, Amex, Diners, Visa

Just a few minutes' walk from the busy seafront, this solidly-built villa enjoys a blissfully peaceful location. Cosy day rooms are snugly furnished in period style and there's a neat little garden at the back. Bedrooms of varying sizes are equipped with tea-makers, hairdryers, trouser presses, radio-alarms and individual heating controls. Some rooms have shower only. No dogs. No children under eight.
Amenities garden, solarium, secretarial services, laundry service. &

| Rooms 17 | Direct dial Yes | Confirm by 6 | Parking Ample |
| Ensuite bath/shower 17 | Room TV Yes | Last dinner 9.30 | Room service Limited |

Rolling Clock Restaurant

Set L £9.50
Set D £11.50
About £37 for two
Seats 40
Parties 45

A rolling clock on the mantelpiece explains the name of the place, but Lionel Roberts' skill and artistry are the reason for its popularity. Top-quality fish and shellfish play a starring role: try for example the splendidly varied seafood platter, with each component cooked and garnished in a different way. Imaginative meat dishes, too, like chicken in puff pastry with Madeira sauce. Excellent desserts and some good wines. 🍷 Well-chosen ⊘ &

Lunch 12.30–2   *Dinner* 7–9.30, Sun 7–9

We welcome bona fide complaints and recommendations
on the tear-out pages at the back of the book for readers' comment.
They are followed up by our professional team.

BRISTOL   Crest Hotel   66%   £C

H **Town plan E1** Avon
Filton Road, Hambrook
BS16 1QX
Bristol (0272) 564242
Telex 449376

Credit Access, Amex, Diners, Visa

Set in ample grounds on the A4174, near junction 1 of the M32, this low-rise, modern hotel boasts stylish public areas in its plush, open-plan reception and smart cane-furnished bar-lounge. Bedrooms have attractive modern furniture and coordinated fabrics. *Amenities* garden, indoor swimming pool, sauna, solarium, whirlpool bath, keep-fit equipment, croquet, game fishing, games room, in-house movies, secretarial services, fax, laundry service, coffee shop (7.45am–9.15pm).

| Rooms 151 | Direct dial Yes | Confirm by 6 | Parking Ample |
| Ensuite bath/shower 151 | Room TV Yes | Last dinner 9.45 | Room service 24 hours |

BRISTOL   Grand Hotel   71%   £D

H **Town plan C2** Avon
Broad Street BS1 2EL
Bristol (0272) 291645
Telex 449889

Rooms 178
Ensuite bath/shower 178
Direct dial Yes
Room TV Yes
Confirm by arrang.
Last dinner 10.30
Parking Ample
Room service 24 hours

Credit Access, Amex, Diners, Visa

Tucked away down a quiet street in the heart of the old city, the elegant Grand Hotel first opened its doors in 1869. Behind the Italianate facade there's plenty more to please the eye, from the glittering chandeliers in the foyer and the ballroom to the panelling and mirrored ceiling in the cocktail bar. Bedrooms are of average size, warm and comfortable, with attractive floral curtains and smart white furniture. All bed-

rooms have tea-makers, remote-control TVs, trouser presses and hairdryers, plus well-kept carpeted bathrooms. Work is due for completion on upgrading 90 bedrooms, building a new lounge and revamping reception.
Amenities in-house movies, secretarial services, laundry service.

BRISTOL — Hilton International Bristol 73% £B/C

H **Town plan D3** Avon
Redcliffe Way BS1 6NJ
Bristol (0272) 260041
Telex 449240

Rooms 199
Ensuite bath/shower 199
Direct dial Yes
Room TV Yes
Confirm by 6
Last dinner 10.30
Parking Ample
Room service 24 hours

Credit Access, Amex, Diners, Visa

Improvements continue at this city-centre hotel, formerly the Ladbroke Dragonara. This year it has been the turn of the public areas, where a radical shake-up has resulted in a re-sited and much-improved reception and a new-look bar-lounge. A leisure centre is also in the pipeline. Stylishly contemporary bedrooms offer remote-control TVs, tea-makers, trouser presses, hairdryers and neat tiled bathrooms. Best of all are the top-floor Plaza rooms, which include a number of suites. Breakfasts continue to disappoint, and there's also something rather depressing about the lacklustre staff and occasional lapses in housekeeping. *Amenities* in-house movies, fax, laundry service, coffee shop (7am–11pm). &

BRISTOL — Holiday Inn 70% £C

H **Town plan D2** Avon
Lower Castle Street BS1 3AD
Bristol (0272) 294281
Telex 449720

Rooms 284
Ensuite bath/shower 284
Direct dial Yes
Room TV Yes
Confirm by 6
Last dinner 11
Parking Ample
Room service 24 hours

Credit Access, Amex, Diners, Visa

Built in the 1970s, this high-rise hotel stands proudly in the centre of the city overlooking the attractive castle gardens. Checking-in is conducted efficiently in the marble-floored foyer, adjoining which is an elegant little lounge area. Above this level are the bar and sun terrace, then ten floors of well-equipped, smartly furnished bedrooms with plenty of space to work or relax. Some aspects of housekeeping and maintenance could be improved. *Amenities* indoor swimming pool, sauna, solarium, keep-fit equipment, in-house movies, secretarial services, fax, laundry service, coffee shop (11am–11pm), kiosk, children's play area. &

BRISTOL — Howards

R **Town plan A3** Avon
1a Avon Crescent, Hotwells
Bristol (0272) 262921

About £35 for two
Seats 65
Parties 26
Parking Ample
Credit Access, Visa

Booking is recommended at this friendly bistro next to Hotwells swing bridge. The customers flock in for Christopher Howard's consistently enjoyable cooking, choosing from delights such as scallops with fresh ginger in a puff pastry case, entrecôte bordelaise or breast of chicken with a lovely creamy champagne and tarragon sauce. Sweets like crème brûlée or cassis parfait sustain the pleasure level right to the end. ℮

Dinner only 7–11, Sat 7–11.30
Closed Sun, 25 & 26 Dec

BRISTOL — Restaurant Lettonie *NEW ENTRY*

R **Town plan A1** Avon
9 Druid Hill, Stoke Bishop
Bristol (0272) 686456

French cooking

Set L £9.95
Set D £16.95
About £45 for two
Seats 24
Parties 14
Parking Ample

Credit Access, Visa

Formerly Les Semailles, this comfortable little restaurant in a northern suburb of Bristol has a gifted new partnership at the helm. Exquisite presentation and the lightest of touches distinguish the cooking of Sian Williams and Martin Blunos, epitomised by our elegant lunch of pork satay with a lime and walnut oil-dressed salad, asparagus cream soup, main-course selection of fresh fish served with home-made pasta, and mouth-watering orange sabayon dessert. Noteworthy, too, are their carrot mousse with a truffle-scented sauce, guinea fowl sauced with Armagnac and prunes, and eyecatching terrine of white and bitter chocolate with a rich caramel sauce. ♟ Well-chosen ℮

Lunch 12–2 *Dinner* 7–10.30
Closed D Sun, all Mon & Bank Hols

BRISTOL

Map 4 B2
Town plan opposite

Population 391,500

The Birthplace of America–the Cabots sailed from here to discover Newfoundland in 1497. This and later voyages brought Bristol prosperity, largely in sugar, tobacco, rum and the slave trade. Architecture surviving the 1940 war damage ranges over the 13th-century Lord Mayor's Chapel, St Mary Redcliffe Church, England's oldest working theatre (Theatre-Royal–now completely renovated), and Clifton's Georgian terraces.

Annual Events
Powerboat Grand Prix *June*
Senior Citizens' Day *June*
World Wine Fair *July*
Bristol Harbour Regatta and Rally of Boats *July*
International Balloon Fiesta *August*
Bristol Maritime Carnival *August*
Bristol Flower Show *August/September*
Christmas Illuminated Water Carnival *December*

Sights Outside City
Severn Bridge, Berkeley Castle, Wells Cathedral, Cheddar Gorge, Severn Wildfowl Trust, Castle Combe Village, Bath

Tourist Information Centre
Colston House, Colston Street
Telephone Bristol 293891

Fiat Dealers
Autotrend Ltd
724–726 Fishponds Road
Bristol BS16 3UE
Tel. Bristol 659491

Bawns Ltd
168–176 Coronation Road
Bristol BS3 1RG
Tel. Bristol 631101

1 Airport *6 miles* A3
2 Arnolfini (Arts Centre) C3
3 Ashton Court Estate and Mansion *beautiful parklands* A1
4 Blaise Castle House Folk Museum *Henbury* A1
5 Bristol Industrial Museum C3
6 Bristol Cathedral *dates from 12th c* B3
7 Bristol Tapestry and Permanent Planning Exhibition D1
8 Cabot Tower *Brandon Hill, built 1897* A2
9 Central Library B3
10 Chatterton House *Chatterton's birthplace* D3
11 Christmas Steps *antique shops* C1
12 City Museum & Art Gallery *fine & applied arts* B1
13 Clifton suspension bridge A1
14 Colston Hall concert hall B2
15 Council House B2
16 Entertainment Centre B2
17 The Exploratory Hands-on-Science Centre A1
18 Georgian House *late 18th-c showpiece* B2
19 Harveys Wine Museum B2
20 Hippodrome B2
21 John Wesley Chapel *first Methodist Chapel* D1
22 Little Theatre C2
23 Lord Mayor's Chapel *13th c* B2
24 Nails and the Exchange *'pay on the nail' originated here* C2
25 National Lifeboat Museum C3
26 Norman Arch B3
27 Observatory, Clifton Down A1
28 Red Lodge *late 16th-c showpiece* B2
29 Royal York Crescent *Regency* A2
30 St Mary Redcliffe Church *dates from 13th c* D3
31 St Nicholas Church Museum C2
32 St Peter and St Paul R.C. Cathedral A1
33 S.S. 'Great Britain' *first ocean-going propeller ship, launched Bristol 1843, Great Britain Dock, Gasferry Road* A3
34 Temple Meads Station E3
35 Theatre Royal *home of the Bristol Old Vic* C2
36 Tourist Information Centre B2
37 Zoo *including flowers and rare trees* A1

Bristol F I A T

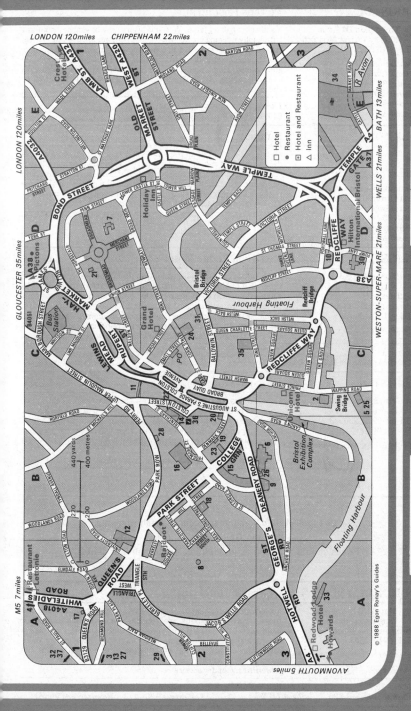

BRISTOL

Pictons Restaurant

R **Town plan D1** Avon
   46 Picton Street, Montpelier
   Bristol (0272) 47312

Set D from £6.95
About £23 for two
Seats 36
Parties 22
Parking Ample
Credit Access

Young chef-patron James West fills his friendly basement restaurant with a jolly evening crowd who like his no-nonsense cooking. Three-course set menus include dishes such as watercress and Stilton soup, smoked mackerel with cream cheese and herbs, seafood provençale and chillied pork casserole. Vegetarian main courses are always available, and a blackboard lists sweets like hot apple Bakewell or chocolate mallow mousse. ℗

Lunch parties by arrang.   *Dinner* 7–10.30
Closed Sun, 1 wk Xmas & 2 wks Aug

BRISTOL

Rajdoot

R **Town plan B2** Avon
   83 Park Street
   Bristol (0272) 291242

Indian cooking
Set L from £6
Set D from £9.50
Seats 60 *Parties* 30
Parking Limited
Credit Access, Amex, Diners, Visa

As one of the first Indian restaurants to install a clay oven, tandoori dishes featuring fish, quail and kidneys, as well as the more usual chicken and lamb, remain a speciality of this smart restaurant. Also on the menu are tasty curries subtly flavoured with fresh herbs, such as the delicious rogan josh with cashew nuts spiced with coriander. The cover charge includes chutney, papadums and hot towels.

Lunch 12–2.15   *Dinner* 6.30–11.30   *About £35 for two*
Closed L Sun, L Bank Hols & 25 & 26 Dec

BRISTOL

Redwood Lodge Hotel   69%   £C/D

H **Town plan A3** Avon
   Beggar Bush Lane,
   Failand BS8 3TG
   Bristol (0272) 393901
   Telex 444348

Credit Access, Amex, Diners, Visa

Set in wooded countryside just south of the Clifton Suspension Bridge. Open-plan public areas are smartly contemporary in style and well-equipped bedrooms (40 in a recent extension) are equally up-to-date. No dogs. *Amenities* garden, indoor & outdoor swimming pools, sauna, solarium, gymnasium, tennis, squash, badminton, games room, snooker, pool table, in-house movies, fax, cinema, laundry service, coffee shop (10am–10.30pm), 24-hour lounge service.

Rooms 112	*Direct dial* Yes	*Confirm by* arrang.	*Parking* Ample
Ensuite bath/shower 112	*Room TV* Yes	*Last dinner* 9.45	*Room service* None

BRISTOL

Unicorn Hotel   62%   £C/D

H **Town plan C3** Avon
   Prince Street BS1 4QF
   Bristol (0272) 230333
   Telex 44315

Credit Access, Amex, Diners, Visa

Guests at this modern hotel by Narrow Quay can check in, then park their cars in the multi-storey car park at the level of their bedrooms. Rooms are decorated in autumnal shades, with practical fittings and simply appointed bathrooms. Day rooms include the popular Waterfront Tavern. Here and there the hotel is beginning to show its age.
Amenities secretarial services, laundry service.

Rooms 195	*Direct dial* Yes	*Confirm by* 6	*Parking* Ample
Ensuite bath/shower 195	*Room TV* Yes	*Last dinner* 10	*Room service* 24 hours

Changes in data sometimes occur in establishments
after the Guide goes to press.
Prices should be taken as indications rather than firm quotes.

BRIXHAM

Quayside Hotel   61%   £D/E

H **Map 3 D3** Devon
   King Street TQ5 9TJ
   Brixham (080 45) 55751
   Telex 94012557

Credit Access, Amex, Diners, Visa

Six fishermen's cottages have been turned into a really charming and friendly hotel overlooking Brixham Harbour. Bedrooms, though not large, are full of character and more than comfortable, and the owners are gradually upgrading them. There's a spotless little lounge and a cosy panelled bar in nautical style, and the hotel also runs the atmospheric pub next door.
Amenities laundry service.

Rooms 30	*Direct dial* Yes	*Confirm by* 6	*Parking* Ample
Ensuite bath/shower 30	*Room TV* Yes	*Last dinner* 9.30	*Room service* Limited

BROADWAY — Broadway Hotel — 60% — £D/E

H Map 4 C1
Hereford & Worcester
The Green WR12 7AA
Broadway (0386) 852401

Credit Access, Amex, Diners, Visa

Monastic guest house, staging post, bakery and private house are the previous roles of this Cotswold-stone and half-timbered building, now a friendly hotel operated in pleasantly relaxed style. Beams, mullioned windows and log fires capture the past, and the bedrooms in the old part, with access via a minstrels' gallery above the lounge, have a good deal of character. Cross the fountained courtyard to the garden wing, where the rooms have central heating and fitted furniture. All rooms are well kept, and full marks to the affable chambermaids in their spotless uniforms. No dogs.
Amenities garden, putting.

Rooms 24	*Direct dial* Yes	*Confirm by* arrang.	*Parking* Ample
Ensuite bath/shower 22	*Room TV* Yes	*Last dinner* 9.30	*Room service* All day

BROADWAY — Collin House Hotel — 65% — £D/E

HR Map 4 C1
Hereford & Worcester
Collin Lane WR12 7PB
Broadway (0386) 858354

Credit Access, Visa
Closed 4 days Xmas

Peaceful grounds surround the 16th-century Cotswold-stone house that Judith and John Mills run with warmth and unobtrusive efficiency. Mullioned windows, log fires, antique furniture and good paintings make the public rooms charming and characterful. The traditional bedrooms have pretty wallpaper and curtains and thoughtful touches such as home-made biscuits and tissues. No children under seven. No dogs. *Amenities* garden, outdoor swimming pool, croquet.

Rooms 7	*Room phone* No	*Confirm by* arrang.	*Parking* Ample
Ensuite bath/shower 6	*Room TV* No	*Last dinner* 9	*Room service* All day

Restaurant ♀

English cooking

Set L £10.50
Set D from £12.50
About £35 *for two*
Seats 24
Parties 24

The handsome period dining room makes a delightful setting for Judith Mills' excellent meals. Her set menus offer a good choice of interesting, sensitively cooked English dishes; there's usually a home-made soup on offer and to follow: grilled loin of pork with ginger and lime or steak and kidney pie. Good traditional puds to finish. Good clarets: Ch. Gloria '82, Ch. Cantemerle '79. ♀ Well-chosen ☺ よ

Lunch Sun 12–1.30, Mon–Sat by arrang. *Dinner* 7–9
Closed D Sun to non-residents, 4 days Xmas

We welcome bona fide complaints and recommendations
on the tear-out pages at the back of the book for readers' comment.
They are followed up by our professional team.

BROADWAY — Dormy House — 71% — £C

HR Map 4 C1
Hereford & Worcester
Willersey Hill WR12 7LF
Broadway (0386) 852711
Telex 338275

Rooms 50
Ensuite bath/shower 50
Direct dial Yes
Room TV Yes
Confirm by 6
Last dinner 9.30
Parking Ample
Room service 24 hours

Credit Access, Amex, Diners, Visa

At the top of the giant Willersey Hill, overlooking Broadway, Dormy House was built as a farmhouse in the 17th century. Exposed stonework and splendid panelling (much of it original) take the eye in the main building, where there's a convivial bar, a leafy, marble-floored atrium and some comfortable, well-appointed bedrooms. Other accommodation, in outbuildings, includes two delightful cottage  suites with novel aerated baths; there are a number of rooms in a discreetly located and cleverly designed Scandinavian-style wing, which also contains conference facilities. Some bedrooms open on to little walled gardens.
Amenities garden, secretarial services, fax, laundry service, helipad.
see over

Dormy House Restaurant

Set L £11
Set D £8.50
About £60 for two
Seats 75
Parties 180

Chef Roger Chant supervises the kitchen brigade with very dependable results. In candlelit intimacy, guests enjoy a tempting variety of dishes using prime fresh produce: chicken livers and morels in a truffle and Madeira sauce, mousse of Cornish turbot, lamb with thyme, medallions of venison with a splendid sauce of ginger and gooseberries garnished with glazed chestnuts. Hard-to-resist sweets. Service works just as smoothly as the cooking. ♀ Well-chosen ℰ

Lunch 12.30–2, Sun 12–2.30   *Dinner* 7.30–9.30, Fri & Sat 7–9.30, Sun 7–9 **Closed** L Sat & 25 & 26 Dec

---

BROADWAY   Hunter's Lodge   ⌘

R Map 4 C1
Hereford & Worcester
High Street
Broadway (0386) 853247

Set L £8.50
About £50 for two
Seats 50
Parties 35
Parking Ample

Credit Access, Amex, Diners, Visa

A meal in this ivy-clad Cotswold stone house has a very personal feel. Dotti Friedli puts out the welcome mat at the door, and guests can enjoy a drink round the fire while making their choice. The dining room is delightfully intimate, with candlelight, lace and affable service by village ladies. Kurt Friedli's menus change with the seasons, making use of local produce, game and lots of fresh fish. The choice runs from crispy-fried crab pancakes and croustade of mushrooms to grilled hake with lemon and shrimp butter, roast duck with apple sauce and Madeira-sauced lamb chops. Good sweets from the sideboard. ℰ

Lunch 12.30–2   *Dinner* 7.30–9.45
Closed D Sun, all Mon, Bank Hols (exc. Good Fri), 2 wks Feb & 2 wkends Aug

---

We publish annually,
so make sure you use the current edition.
It's worth it!

BROADWAY   Lygon Arms   79%   £B

HR Map 4 C1
Hereford & Worcester
High Street WR12 7DU
Broadway (0386) 852255
Telex 338260

Rooms 66
Ensuite bath/shower 61
Direct dial Yes
Room TV Yes
Confirm by 6
Last dinner 9.15
Parking Ample
Room service 24 hours

Credit Access, Amex, Diners, Visa

A world-famous hotel which conceals behind its 600-year-old stone facade the most up-to-date facilities you could wish for. Log fires and antique furniture give plenty of character to the beamed lounges at the front of the building, while those at the rear are sympathetically modern. Nineteen bedrooms in the Orchard Wing have been lavishly refurbished with marble floors, antique furniture and new shower

units, while remaining rooms have delightful period furnishings and a wealth of thoughtful extras. Bathrooms (a few not en suite) are equipped with luxurious towels and toiletries.
Amenities garden, patio, tennis, snooker, secretarial services, fax, valeting, laundry service, shop, helipad. ⅄

Restaurant   ♔

Set L £14.75
Set D £22.50
About £65 for two
Seats 90
Parties 90

The barrel-vaulted Great Hall makes a wonderful setting in which to dine and the menu contains some interesting dishes – you might start with terrine of guinea fowl with grape salad before moving on to lamb with a tarragon and tomato sauce. Traditional puds. An absorbing, selective wine list, fine classics balanced by excellent bottles from the New World; Maximin Grunhaus (Von Schubert) '83, Chateau Tahbilk Shiraz, Victoria '84. ℰ

Lunch 12.15–2
Dinner 7.15–9.15

BROCKENHURST   Balmer Lawn Hotel   66%   £C

H Map 4 C4 Hampshire
Lyndhurst Road SO42 7ZB
Lymington (0590) 23116
Telex 477649

Credit Access, Amex, Diners, Visa

A cricket pitch with grazing ponies provides a traditional English outlook for this handsome hotel. Inside, a smart bar and lounge with a green and claret theme pleases the eye. Bedrooms boast coordinating curtains and bedcovers and decent wooden furniture; all have well-equipped bathrooms. *Amenities* garden, indoor & outdoor swimming pools, sauna, whirlpool bath, gymnasium, tennis, squash, secretarial services, fax, laundry service, 24-hour lounge service.

Rooms 58	*Direct dial* Yes	*Confirm by* 6	*Parking* Ample
Ensuite bath/shower 58	*Room TV* Yes	*Last dinner* 9.45	*Room service* All day

**Our inspectors *never* book in the name of Egon Ronay's Guides.
They disclose their identity only if they are considering an establishment
for inclusion in the next edition of the Guide.**

BROCKENHURST   Careys Manor Hotel   64%   £C/D

H Map 4 C4 Hampshire
New Forest SO42 7RH
Lymington (0590) 23551
Telex 47442

Credit Access, Amex, Diners, Visa

A characterful red-brick manor dating back to the reign of Charles II, who used it as a hunting lodge. Dark panelling and a carved oak staircase give a warmly traditional feel to the entrance hall, while the redesigned lounge, with light wood-strip floor and huge open brick fireplace, is comfortable and spacious. There's also a cheerfully decorated bar. Bedrooms vary from traditional in the main house to more modern in the garden wing. A second, recently-built extension provides 24 executive rooms with satellite TV. Bathrooms throughout are carpeted and have shower facilities. *Amenities* garden, indoor swimming pool, sauna, solarium, whirlpool bath, gymnasium, putting, croquet, in-house movies, laundry service.

Rooms 80	*Direct dial* Yes	*Confirm by* arrang.	*Parking* Ample
Ensuite bath/shower 80	*Room TV* Yes	*Last dinner* 10	*Room service* Limited

BROCKENHURST   Le Poussin   *NEW ENTRY*

RR Map 4 C4 Hampshire
57 Brookley Road
Lymington (0590) 23063

Set L from £5.95
Set D £21
About £60 for two
Seats 35
Parties 8
Parking Limited

Credit Access, Visa

Alex Aitken uses the best of local raw materials with considerable verve and skill at his smart New Forest restaurant. Sophisticated dishes like our tournedos of monkfish and tourte of lobster were outstanding, and the desserts delicious. Set lunch menus are particularly good value. Appropriate wines by the glass are a welcome option with the menu gastronomique. Very good wines include a fine choice of dessert wines from the Loire.

Lunch 12–2   *Dinner* 7–10
Closed Sun, Mon (except Bank Hols), 1 wk June & Nov & 2 wks Jan

BEDROOMS 2   £E
With bath/shower 2

Two simple but pleasant bedrooms for overnight guests with a roof garden making an ideal spot for an alfresco summer breakfast.

BROCKENHURST   Rhinefield House Hotel   69%   £C/D

H Map 4 C4 Hampshire
Rhinefield Road SO4 7QB
Lymington (0590) 22922

Credit Access, Amex, Diners, Visa

Truly in the heart of the New Forest, this mock-Elizabethan mansion is reached by a delightful driveway off the A35. The grounds are being restored to their original splendour, with formal gardens, ornamental lakes and a maze. The main building contains a leisure centre, the Grand Hall, the restaurant and the ornate Moorish bar. An attractive orangery links this with an extension that houses the lounge and the bedrooms – all of a decent size, with good bathrooms (baths can take a long time to run). Service is somewhat variable. Courtesy bus from station. No dogs. *Amenities* garden, indoor & outdoor swimming pools, sauna, steam room, solarium, whirlpool bath, gymnasium, tennis, golf practice green, croquet, laundry service.

Rooms 32	*Direct dial* Yes	*Confirm by* 6	*Parking* Ample
Ensuite bath/shower 32	*Room TV* Yes	*Last dinner* 9.30	*Room service* 24 hours

BROME   Oaksmere Country House Hotel   65%   £E

H Map 6 C2 Suffolk
Nr Eye IP23 8AJ
Eye (0379) 870326

Credit Access, Amex, Diners, Visa
Closed 25 Dec

By the junction of the A140 and B1077, this 16th-century house stands in extensive parkland and gardens that include some marvellous topiary. The old Tudor bar is large and characterful, and there's a motley collection of antiques in the lounge. The five bedrooms, all of a good size, are also furnished with antique pieces. Only one bathroom has a tub, the rest decent showers.
Amenities garden.

Rooms 5	*Room phone* No	*Confirm by* arrang.	*Parking* Ample
Ensuite bath/shower 4	*Room TV* Yes	*Last dinner* 10	*Room service* Limited

BROMLEY   Bromley Court Hotel   67%   £D

H Map 7 B5 Kent
Bromley Hill BR1 4JD
01-464 5011
Telex 896310

Credit Access, Amex, Diners, Visa

Situated on the A21, this well-run, smartly kept hotel is popular with business people and the function trade. Bedrooms have a uniform decor of brown and cream, plus fitted darkwood furniture; central heating is very efficient, and there's an excellent supply of towels in the modern bathrooms. Day rooms include a choice of bars and lounges, some newly built. *Amenities* garden, putting, in-house movies, secretarial services, fax, laundry service.

Rooms 130	*Direct dial* Yes	*Confirm by* 6	*Parking* Ample
Ensuite bath/shower 130	*Room TV* Yes	*Last dinner* 9.45	*Room service* 24 hours

BROMLEY   Peking Diner

R Map 7 B5 Kent
71 Burnt Ash Lane
01-464 7911

Chinese cooking
Set D from £8.50
About £30 for two
Seats 80 *Parties* 70
Parking Ample
Credit Access, Amex, Diners, Visa

Friendly, informative service and highly competent cooking draw the diners to this modern and sophisticated Chinese restaurant. The extensive Peking-style menu encompasses popular dishes as well as imaginative ones such as the outstanding 'Surprise of the Encircled Piglet' – pork dumplings, first steamed then grilled. Other recommendable dishes include the excellent Mongolian lamb, Peking fish, steamed scallop with black bean and garlic sauce and shredded beef. Booking is essential. &

Lunch 12–2.30   *Dinner* 6.30–11.30 (Fri & Sat till 12)
Closed Sun, 25 & 26 Dec

BROMSGROVE   Grafton Manor   70%   £B/C

HR Map 10 C4
Hereford & Worcester
Grafton Lane B61 7HA
Bromsgrove (0527) 31525

Rooms 8
Ensuite bath/shower 8
Direct dial Yes
Room TV Yes
Confirm by arrang.
Last dinner 9
Parking Ample
Room service All day

Credit Access, Amex, Diners, Visa

The Morris family maintain high standards at their lovingly restored Elizabethan manor set in delightful grounds that include a water garden bordering the lake and a chessboard pattern herb garden. Pride of the public rooms is the Great Parlour, an impressive, very comfortable room with a coat of arms over the fireplace and a bar tucked away in one corner. Antique furniture, quality fabrics and wallpaper decorate the tasteful bedrooms, which are thoughtfully equipped with fruit, sherry and toiletries as well as the usual extras. Many of the modern bathrooms boast smart corner baths. No children under seven. Kennelling for dogs. *Amenities* garden, croquet, riding, coarse fishing, secretarial services, laundry service.

Restaurant   ♔ ♙

Set L £9.85, Sun £12.75
Set D £16.75
About £45 for two
Seats 40

All the family join in here, producing and serving very good fixed-price lunches and dinners, including a well-thought-out four-course meal for vegetarians. Plaice mousse with laverbread, wine-poached skate with blackcurrant sauce and fillet of pork cooked with honey and Dijon mustard typify the dishes, which are notable for their well-balanced flavours. Super sweets (whisky steamed pudding, crème brûlée with fruit salad); good English cheeses.

Lunch 12–2   *Dinner* 7–9   **Closed** L Sat

BROMSGROVE — Perry Hall Hotel 56% NEW ENTRY £D

H Map 10 C4
Hereford & Worcester
Kidderminster Road B61 7JN
Bromsgrove (0527) 579976

Credit Access, Amex, Diners, Visa

On the A448 just outside Bromsgrove, creeper-clad Perry Hall was once a private residence. A certain homely charm remains in the main building, which is linked by a corridor to the purpose-built accommodation block. Bedrooms are fairly simple in style, with modern fitted furniture and unexceptional beige decor. Ten bathrooms have shower/WC only. 22 bedrooms are of superior Executive standard. *Amenities* garden, secretarial services, laundry service.

Rooms 55	Direct dial Yes	Confirm by 6	Parking Ample
Ensuite bath/shower 55	Room TV Yes	Last dinner 9.45	Room service Limited

BROUGHTON — Broughton Park Hotel 66% NEW ENTRY £D/E

HR Map 10 A1 Lancashire
Garstang Road,
Nr Preston PR3 5JB
Preston (0772) 864087
Telex 67180
Credit Access, Amex, Diners, Visa

Peacefully located, this extended Victorian mansion has splendid leisure facilities (a gym for each sex!) and numerous function rooms. Bedrooms are smart and well equipped, those in the newest extension being the roomiest and most attractive. No dogs.
Amenities garden, indoor swimming pool, sauna, solarium, whirlpool bath, gymnasia, hairdressing & beauty salons, satellite TV, in-house movies, fax, laundry service, coffee shop (10am–10pm). &

Rooms 98	Direct dial Yes	Confirm by 6	Parking Ample
Ensuite bath/shower 98	Room TV Yes	Last dinner 10.30	Room service 24 hours

Courtyard Restaurant ♛

About £50 for two
Seats 28
Parking Ample

Small, stylishly run restaurant with an excellent, assured chef in Paul Heathcote. Imagination abounds in menus that run from parfait de canard and consommé of smoked ham to red mullet with scallops and ratatouille, Madeira-braised pig's trotter and lamb with its sweetbread and kidneys in three different pastries (brioche, filo and puff). Good sweets and sound wines, with the odd eye-catcher: Clos de Vougeot (Faiveley) 1979. ⊗ &

Dinner only 7.30–10.30
Closed All Sun, some Bank Hols

We publish annually,
so make sure you use the current edition.
It's worth it!

BROXTED — Whitehall Hotel 76% £C/D

HR Map 6 B3 Essex
Church End CM6 2BZ
Bishop's Stortford (0279) 850603

Rooms 10
Ensuite bath/shower 10
Direct dial Yes
Room TV Yes
Confirm by arrang.
Last dinner 9.30
Parking Ample
Room service All day

Credit Access, Amex, Visa

Set in unspoilt countryside on the edge of the village, this lovely old manor house dates back to the 12th century. Gerry and Marie Keane have turned it into a delightful hotel, blending old and new in perfect harmony. Pinks and greys create a softly stylish effect in the pretty drawing room while the smart bar has a more masculine appeal with its pictures of Aston Martin cars (Gerry's passion). Antiques happily coexist with contemporary furnishings in the luxuriously appointed bedrooms, which include six fairly recent additions. Spacious deep-carpeted bathrooms offer cosseting extras like towelling robes. Excellent breakfasts. No children under five. No dogs.
Amenities garden, outdoor swimming pool, tennis. see over

Whitehall Restaurant ★   ♕ ⌇

Lunch 12.30–1.30
Dinner 7.30–9.30
Set L £14
Set D £25
About £60 for two
Seats 40
Parties 50

Closed L Sat, D Sun, all Mon,
Bank Hols & Jan (exc. to
residents)

A timbered dining room over-looking the garden and old parish church provides a classic English setting for Paula Keane's modern English cooking. Prime fresh ingredients are the starting point for all her dishes, and she has plenty of good, beautifully simple ideas – like smoked haddock flakes on a bed of French leaves or grilled red mullet sauced with orange and basil. Just occasionally sauces overpower rather than complement, and something like a stridently tart raspberry coulis will mar an otherwise perfect chocolate mousse. Good wines at fair prices, especially the white burgundies.
Specialities fillet of brill in champagne, magret duck breast on spinach, passion fruit délice. ♟ Well-chosen ℮

BUCKINGHAM   White Hart Hotel   57%   £D

H **Map 5 D1** Buckinghamshire
Market Square MK18 1NL
Buckingham (0280) 815151
Telex 934946

Credit Access, Amex, Diners, Visa

A modest but pleasant enough town-centre hotel offering acceptable overnight accommodation. Bedrooms are kept nice and warm, and all have tea-makers and remote-control TVs. The lively, popular bar has a traditional look, and there's a new lounge area with deep, well-upholstered armchairs and settees. The hotel has a white-plastered facade and a pillared portico.
Amenities secretarial services, laundry service.

Rooms 19	*Room phone* Yes	*Confirm by* 6	*Parking* Ample
Ensuite bath/shower 19	*Room TV* Yes	*Last dinner* 9.30	*Room service* All day

**If we recommend meals in a Hotel or Inn,
a separate entry is made for its restaurant.**

BUCKLAND   Buckland Manor   83%   £B

HR **Map 4 C1** Gloucestershire
Nr Broadway WR12 7LY
Broadway (0386) 852626

Rooms 11
Ensuite bath/shower 11
Direct dial Yes
Room TV Yes
Confirm by arrang.
Last dinner 8.45
Parking Ample
Room service All day

Credit Access, Visa
Closed mid Jan–1st week Feb

This truly outstanding country house hotel offers a setting that is both beautiful and peaceful, splendid service, abundant comfort, good food and fine wines. Day rooms epitomise grace and elegance, with mullioned windows affording delightful views of the countryside. Handsome furniture, much of it antique, is in evidence throughout, combining with high-quality fabrics in bedrooms that are exceptionally stylish and comfortable. Fresh fruit, mineral water and pot pourri are among many thoughtful little provisions, and bathrobes, luxury towels and excellent toiletries are supplied in the carpeted bathrooms. No children under 12. Kennels for dogs. ***Amenities*** garden, outdoor swimming pool, tennis, riding, putting, croquet, laundry service.

Restaurant   ♕

Set L Sun only £11.95
About £55 for two
Seats 32

The dining room matches the splendour of the rest of the house, and the menu holds plenty of interest. Martyn Pearn uses prime produce for dishes like home-cured duck ham with a Roquefort dressing or fillet of beef accompanied by a Madeira and mustard grain sauce. Wines are chosen with great flair: Romanée St Vivant Marey-Morge '78, Hautes Côtes de Nuits Blanc (Jayer-Gilles) '85. ▭ Outstanding ♟ Well-chosen ℮ &

Lunch 12.30–1.45   *Dinner* 7.30–8.45
Closed mid Jan–1st wk Feb

BUCKLER'S HARD — Master Builder's House Hotel £E

Map 5 D4 Hampshire
Beaulieu, Brockenhurst
SO42 7XB
Buckler's Hard (059 063) 253

Credit Access, Amex, Diners, Visa

Named after shipbuilder Henry Adams, this extended 18th-century house has grounds stretching down to the river Beaulieu and a public bar at the water's edge. The original building is full of character with its two heavily beamed oak-panelled bars a few very traditional bedrooms. Remaining accommodation is in a rear extension – bright and cheerful rooms with fitted units, shower rooms and tea-makers.
Amenities garden, laundry service.

Rooms 23	*Direct dial* Yes	*Confirm by* arrang.	*Parking* Ample
Ensuite bath/shower 19	*Room TV* Yes	*Last dinner* 9.45	*Room service* All day

BUCKLOW HILL — The Swan 62% £D

Map 10 B2 Cheshire
Nr Knutsford WA16 6RD
Knutsford (0565) 830295
Telex 666911

Credit Access, Amex, Diners, Visa

Right on the A556 and close to the motorway network, The Swan is a comfortable hotel run by helpful, efficient and friendly staff. Beams and four-posters give character to bedrooms in the original part, while rooms in the rear extension are modern, with plenty of writing space. Three Executive suites have whirlpool baths. Day rooms have been totally and elegantly refurbished.
Amenities garden, in-house movies, laundry service.

Rooms 70	*Direct dial* Yes	*Confirm by* 6	*Parking* Ample
Ensuite bath/shower 70	*Room TV* Yes	*Last dinner* 9.45	*Room service* 24 hours

BUDE — Strand Hotel 58% £E

Map 2 C2 Cornwall
The Strand EX23 8RA
Bude (0288) 3222

Credit Access, Amex, Diners, Visa

Overlooking the river Neet, this modern town-centre hotel offers simple, comfortable accommodation in a friendly atmosphere. Picture windows command fine river views in the bright third-floor lounge; there are further lounge areas downstairs, plus a rather plain bar. Neatly fitted bedrooms are light and airy with white furniture and contemporary fabrics.
Amenities games room, fax, laundry service, 24-hour lounge service.

Rooms 40	*Direct dial* Yes	*Confirm by* arrang.	*Parking* Ample
Ensuite bath/shower 40	*Room TV* Yes	*Last dinner* 9	*Room service* Limited

BURBAGE — Savernake Forest Hotel 60% £D/E

Map 4 C3 Wiltshire
Nr Marlborough SN8 3AY
Marlborough (0672) 810206

Credit Access, Amex, Diners, Visa

A pleasant Victorian building, this modest hotel continues to improve year by year. A pleasant, comfortable, pub-style bar, hung with watercolours by local artists and warmed by an open fire, offers a nice welcome and the appealing lounge has cosy chairs and sofas. Decent-sized bedrooms mostly have freestanding traditional furniture and simple decor; bathrooms are functional and in good repair.
Amenities garden, coarse fishing, laundry service.

Rooms 12	*Direct dial* Yes	*Confirm by* 6	*Parking* Ample
Ensuite bath/shower 12	*Room TV* Yes	*Last dinner* 9	*Room service* Limited

 indicates a **well-chosen** house wine

BURFORD — Bay Tree Hotel 65% £D/E

Map 4 C2 Oxfordshire
Sheep Street OX8 4LW
Burford (099 382) 3137

Credit Access, Amex, Diners, Visa
Closed 3 days Xmas

The creeper-clad Elizabethan main building has lots of character, and is equally appealing inside, with flagstoned corridors, several beamed lounges, log fires and homely old leather armchairs. The King family have made many improvements, including a larger bar with rough stone walls and pitched ceiling, and a conservatory restaurant that leads into the attractive walled garden. Bedrooms, the majority in outbuildings, vary in size and shape; what they have in common are plain white walls, nice chintzy fabrics and some mellow traditional furnishings (also bucket easy chairs). Bathrooms are up to date, with good tiling and showers above the tubs. No dogs.
Amenities garden, secretarial services, laundry service.

Rooms 22	*Direct dial* Yes	*Confirm by* arrang.	*Parking* Limited
Ensuite bath/shower 21	*Room TV* Yes	*Last dinner* 9.30	*Room service* Limited

BURGHFIELD	Knights Farm

R Map 5 D2 Berkshire
Berrys Lane, Nr Reading
Reading (0734) 572366

Set L £15
Set D £22.50
About £58 for two
Seats 46 *Parties* 25
Parking Ample
Credit Access, Amex, Diners, Visa

A small-scale country house where you can revel in Emil Forde's imaginative and talented cooking. Dishes such as baked William pear served on a mousse of mixed nuts with an orange and Stilton sauce and main course of turbot filled with crab and fresh herbs demonstrate his flair. With the change of ownership the wine list, though sound, is a shadow of its former excellence. ♀ Well-chosen ℮

Lunch 12.30–2   *Dinner* 7.30–9.30
Closed L Sat, all Sun, 2 wks Aug & 2 wks Xmas

Changes in data sometimes occur in establishments
after the Guide goes to press.
Prices should be taken as indications rather than firm quotes.

BURLEY	Burley Manor Hotel 61%	£D/E

H Map 4 C4 Hampshire
Nr Ringwood BH24 4BS
Burley (042 53) 3522
Telex 41565

Credit Access, Amex, Diners, Visa

Set in 50 acres of parkland within the New Forest, this mellow Victorian mansion retains many original features such as stained glass and oak carving in its pleasant public areas. Prettily decorated bedrooms (including nine new rooms in the converted stables and four with four-posters) all have smart bathrooms. *Amenities* garden, outdoor swimming pool, hairdressing, putting, croquet, riding, coarse fishing, hotel boat, in-house movies, laundry service.

Rooms 30	*Direct dial* Yes	*Confirm by* 6	*Parking* Ample
Ensuite bath/shower 30	*Room TV* Yes	*Last dinner* 10, Sun 9.30	*Room service* Limited

BURNHAM	Burnham Beeches Hotel 69%	£C

H Map 5 E2 Buckinghamshire
Grove Road SL1 8DP
Burnham (062 86) 3333
Telex 946240

Credit Access, Amex, Diners, Visa

Winding country lanes (check directions) lead to this remote former hunting lodge where Gray wrote his *Elegy in a Country Churchyard*. Stylishly refurbished public rooms include two elegant lounges. Some of the smartly traditional bedrooms are in a modern block. *Amenities* garden, indoor swimming pool, sauna, solarium, whirlpool bath, gymnasium, tennis, putting, croquet, games room, snooker, in-house movies, secretarial services, fax, laundry service.

Rooms 80	*Direct dial* Yes	*Confirm by* arrang.	*Parking* Ample
Ensuite bath/shower 80	*Room TV* Yes	*Last dinner* 9.30	*Room service* 24 hours

BURNHAM	Grovefield Hotel 63%	£C

H Map 5 E2 Buckinghamshire
Taplow Common Road
SL1 8LP
Burnham (062 86) 3131

Credit Access, Amex, Diners, Visa

A conservatory-lounge with chintzy settees and a bar overlooking the garden are the latest additions to this well-maintained hotel tucked away in seven acres of grounds just outside Burnham (check directions when booking). Traditional-style bedrooms with pretty decor, quilted bedspreads and useful armchairs have many thoughtful extras from fresh fruit and hairdryers to bathroom toiletries.
Amenities garden, secretarial services, laundry service.

Rooms 42	*Direct dial* Yes	*Confirm by* arrang.	*Parking* Ample
Ensuite bath/shower 42	*Room TV* Yes	*Last dinner* 9.30	*Room service* 24 hours

BURNHAM MARKET	Fishes	⑨

R Map 6 C1 Norfolk
Market Place
Fakenham (0328) 738588

Seafood

Set L £7.25, Sun £7.75
About £40 for two
Seats 42
Parking Ample

Splendidly fresh seafood cooked with unfussy care by Gillian Cape or Carole Bird is the speciality of this simple restaurant. The set lunch is excellent value, with dishes like garlicky sardines, shellfish au gratin, trout with mushrooms and Pernod or hot buttered crab with dry Martini, or you might be tempted to splash out on sole on the bone. Fine wines or delicious Norfolk cider. ♀ Well-chosen ℮

Lunch 12–2   *Dinner* 7–9 Winter, till 9.30 Summer
Closed D Sun, all Mon, 25 & 26 Dec & 3 wks Jan/Feb

BURNHAM-ON-CROUCH Contented Sole ⚐

R **Map 7 C4** Essex
80 High Street
Maldon (0621) 782139

Seafood
Set L £6.50
About £42 for two
Seats 70
Parties 30
Parking Ample

Fresh fish, some landed locally, the rest from Lowestoft or Billingsgate, is a major feature of this charming restaurant. Roy Walton applies classic skills to a good variety of dishes, including sole and salmon in various guises, scallops and scampi steamed in lettuce and the speciality seafood pancake. Meaty options run from vol-au-vents of calf's kidneys to roast duck, venison and steaks. Service is friendly and well informed. ⚐ Well-chosen ⊖ &

Lunch 12–2 *Dinner* 7–9.30 **Closed** Sun, Mon, all Bank Hols exc Good Fri, last 2 wks July & 4 wks Xmas

BURNLEY Keirby Hotel 56% £D/E

H **Map 10 B1** Lancashire
Keirby Walk BB11 2DH
Burnley (0282) 27611
Telex 63119

Credit Access, Amex, Diners, Visa

Business people will find their needs met at this purpose-built city-centre hotel. Public areas include a split level reception/lounge and a neat little cocktail bar. Bedrooms have hessian walls and functional lightwood and laminate fitted units; all are equipped with radio alarms, beverage facilities and trouser presses. Superior rooms boast teletext. The compact bathrooms are adequate. *Amenities* secretarial services, laundry service, 24-hour lounge service.

| *Rooms* 50 | *Direct dial* Yes | *Confirm by* 6 | *Parking* Ample |
| *Ensuite bath/shower* 50 | *Room TV* Yes | *Last dinner* 10 | *Room service* Limited |

BURTON UPON TRENT Brookhouse Inn 63% £D

H **Map 10 C3** Staffordshire
Brookside,
Rolleston-on-Dove DE13 9AA
Burton-on-Trent (0283) 814188
Credit Access, Amex, Diners, Visa
Closed Bank Hols, 4 days Easter & 2 wks Xmas

A well-run, attractive red-brick inn, Grade II listed as a William and Mary building. The delightful bar is welcoming in the extreme, with oak furniture, log fires, potted plants and much bric-a-brac; there is no lounge. The superb bedrooms have antique furniture, including four-posters, half-testers and brass bedsteads, excellent bathrooms, pretty fabrics and a generous array of extras. No children under ten. *Amenities* garden, laundry service.

| *Rooms* 16 | *Room phone* Yes | *Confirm by* arrang. | *Parking* Ample |
| *Ensuite bath/shower* 16 | *Room TV* Yes | *Last dinner* 9.45 | *Room service* All day |

BURTON UPON TRENT Riverside Inn £E

I **Map 10 C3** Staffordshire
Riverside Drive,
Branston DE14 3EP
Burton-upon-Trent (0283) 511234

Credit Access, Amex, Visa

A comfortable oak-furnished bar is the focal point of this well-kept inn, which enjoys a quiet, attractive location on the banks of the Trent (check directions – it's about a mile and a half south of the town centre). Bedrooms are neat and cheerful, with modern built-in units and good private facilities; many rooms overlook the river. Pleasant, friendly staff. *Amenities* garden, coarse fishing, laundry service.

| *Rooms* 21 | *Direct dial* Yes | *Confirm by* arrang. | *Parking* Ample |
| *Ensuite bath/shower* 21 | *Room TV* Yes | *Last dinner* 9.45 | *Room service* 24 hours |

We welcome bona fide complaints and recommendations
on the tear-out pages at the back of the book for readers' comment.
They are followed up by our professional team.

BURY Normandie Hotel 62% £D/E

HR **Map 10 B1**
Greater Manchester
Elbut Lane, Birtle BL9 6UT
061-764 3869

Credit Access, Amex, Diners, Visa
Closed 26 Dec–1 Jan

There are lovely vistas of the Pennine foothills from this peaceful little hotel up a winding lane off the B6222, and you can admire the view from the comfortable lounge. The best bedrooms have charming decor – with designer fabrics and well-coordinated colour schemes – as well as modern comforts, and smart bathrooms. *Amenities* garden, secretarial services.

| *Rooms* 24 | *Direct dial* Yes | *Confirm by* arrang. | *Parking* Ample |
| *Ensuite bath/shower* 24 | *Room TV* Yes | *Last dinner* 9.30 | *Room service* 24 hours |

Normandie Restaurant

Set D £15.50
About £45 for two
Seats 70
Parties 70

Stuart Beard's imaginative cooking continues to justify a detour to this elegant, out-of-the-way restaurant, but be sure to book. Menus range from a light lunch menu and à la carte to an evening menu gourmand featuring such dishes as a superb chicken liver mousse, fresh salmon en croûte and a delicious chocolate truffle gâteau. The cheeseboard is excellent, and the skilfully chosen wine list includes some fine vintage ports. ☺ ఉ

Lunch 12–2   *Dinner* 7–9.30
Closed L Sat, all Sun, Bank Hols & 26 Dec–1 Jan (ex D 31 Dec)

BURY ST EDMUNDS   Angel Hotel   71%   £C/D

H **Map 6 C2** Suffolk
Angel Hill IP33 1LT
Bury St Edmunds (0284) 753926
Telex 81630

Rooms 40
Ensuite bath/shower 40
Direct dial Yes
Room TV Yes
Confirm by arrang.
Last dinner 9.45
Parking Ample
Room service 24 hours

Credit Access, Amex, Diners, Visa

The Perry family, here since 1973, are caring owners, and their staff are smart, friendly and helpful. The Angel's fine Georgian frontage has a healthy covering of creeper, and characterful day rooms include a comfortable lounge area and a restaurant (one of two) in the 12th-century vaults. Bedrooms vary in size, shape and decor; the majority have been stylishly refurbished with quality fabrics and some  nice antiques, larger rooms having separate sitting areas. Unimproved rooms are rather plainer; all rooms have books and magazines, fresh flowers, remote-control TVs and hairdryers. Bedrooms and bathrooms are properly serviced in the evenings. Literary and musical soirées are a regular feature. *Amenities* secretarial services, laundry service.

BURY ST EDMUNDS   Butterfly Hotel   62%   £E

H **Map 6 C2** Suffolk
Symonds Road IP32 7BW
Bury St Edmunds (0284) 60884
Telex 818360

Credit Access, Amex, Diners, Visa

The sign outside proclaims 'hotel, restaurant, bar', giving a slight Continental flavour to this modern, low-rise hotel by the A45. There's a little reception area, a long bar and some lounge seating. Bedrooms have a clean simplicity, with neat lightwood units, an easy chair or settee and room to work. Bathrooms (singles with shower only) are functional and tidy. No dogs.
Amenities secretarial services.

Rooms 50	*Direct dial* Yes	*Confirm by* 6	*Parking* Ample
Ensuite bath/shower 50	*Room TV* Yes	*Last dinner* 10	*Room service* None

BURY ST EDMUNDS   Suffolk Hotel   59%   £D

H **Map 6 C2** Suffolk
38 Buttermarket IP33 1DL
Bury St Edmunds (0284) 753995

Credit Access, Amex, Diners, Visa

A well-run, town-centre hotel with friendly, obliging staff and a homely, lived-in feel. Reception and a small lounge provide seating space, supplemented by a large, cheerful bar. Bedrooms are either standard or superior, the former with fitted furniture and modern bathrooms (no showers), the latter larger, with better furniture and a few extra frills. Heating was set rather low on a coolish February visit. Missable breakfasts. *Amenities* laundry service.

Rooms 33	*Direct dial* Yes	*Confirm by* 6	*Parking* Limited
Ensuite bath/shower 33	*Room TV* Yes	*Last dinner* 9.30	*Room service* Limited

CALBOURNE   Swainston Manor Hotel   64%   £E

H **Map 5 D4** Isle of Wight
PO30 4HX
Newport (0983) 521121

Credit Access, Amex, Diners, Visa

A warm welcome and personal service are the priorities of the Woodwards, who keep their old manor spotlessly clean and pretty. Antiques grace the well-proportioned public rooms, which include an elegant lounge and relaxing bar. Bedrooms are spacious and individually furnished, mainly with period pieces, including some four-posters. *Amenities* garden, indoor swimming pool, coarse fishing, in-house movies, secretarial services, fax, laundry service.

Rooms 14	*Direct dial* Yes	*Confirm by* arrang.	*Parking* Ample
Ensuite bath/shower 14	*Room TV* Yes	*Last dinner* 10	*Room service* 24 hours

CALDBECK · Park End Restaurant · NEW ENTRY · ♦

RR **Map 13 C4** Cumbria
CA7 8HH
Caldbeck (069 98) 494

About £45 for two
Seats 20
Parties 20
Parking Ample

Judith and Michael Bulger have moved south from their Scottish country house hotel to open this comfortable restaurant with rooms. It's a fairly remote 17th-century farmhouse, reputedly the birthplace of John Peel. Guests can enjoy a drink in the rustic bar while choosing from the short, weekly-changing menu. Judith's cooking is robust and homely, with good flavours to the fore in dishes like pork terrine with home-made sage jelly, skate with black butter or jugged hare with celery and carrots in a delicious port sauce. Snackier lunches, with a roast on Sunday. ☺

Lunch 12.30–2 *Dinner* 7.30–9 **Closed** D Sun, L Tues, all Mon & mid Dec–end Feb (exc. mid-Oct–mid Dec by arrang.)

BEDROOMS 3 £E/F
With bath/shower 3

The spacious bedrooms are pleasant and well heated, with sloping floors, stripped pine furniture and decent bathrooms.

CALSTOCK · Danescombe Valley Hotel · 65% · £D/E

HR **Map 2 C3** Cornwall
PL18 9RY
Tavistock (0822) 832414

Closed Nov–23 Mar
(exc. Xmas & New Year)

This peaceful place is the perfect retreat – but ask directions or you may get lost in the surrounding woodland. Martin and Anna Smith are your hosts (and sole staff) and extend a warm welcome. The homely lounge has a log fire, and board games bid you linger in the bar. Comfy bedrooms have lots of old-fashioned extras. No children under 12. No dogs.
Amenities garden, mooring, laundry service.

Rooms 5	*Room phone* No	*Confirm by* arrang.	*Parking* Ample
Ensuite bath/shower 5	*Room TV* No	*Last dinner* 8.15	*Room service* Limited

Restaurant · ♦

Set D £16.50
About £40 for two
Seats 12
Parties 12

It's a pleasure to visit this small restaurant overlooking the Tamar. Dinner is a no-choice, 4-course set meal served in one sitting, creating a relaxed dinner-party atmosphere. A typical meal might be salmon pâté, spring chicken with lemon and herbs, a wide variety of local cheeses and walnut tart. Intelligently composed wine list under grape variety headings: note Ch. Bastor-Lamontagne Sauternes '81 and a splendid '75 Valdepenas. ♥ Well-chosen ☺

Dinner only 7.30 for 8
Closed Nov–Maundy Thurs (exc. Xmas & New Year)

CAMBERLEY · Frimley Hall Hotel · 67% · £C

H **Map 5 E3** Surrey
Portsmouth Road GU15 2BG
Camberley (0276) 28321
Telex 858446

Credit Access, Amex, Diners, Visa

Star of the day rooms at this attractively situated turn-of-the-century hotel is undoubtedly the magnificent galleried hall with its fine panelling and carved oak staircase. There are also two roomy bars. Most of the bedrooms are in practical modern style, but some rooms in the main house retain some really splendid original furnishings and fittings.
Amenities garden, secretarial services, fax, laundry service.

Rooms 66	*Direct dial* Yes	*Confirm by* 6	*Parking* Ample
Ensuite bath/shower 66	*Room TV* Yes	*Last dinner* 10	*Room service* 24 hours

---

📫 is our symbol for an **outstanding** wine list

CAMBRIDGE · Angeline

R **Town plan B3**
Cambridgeshire
8 Market Passage
Cambridge (0223) 60305

Set L £3.40, Sun £8.75
About £32 for two
Seats 48
Parking Difficult
Credit Access, Amex, Diners, Visa

A traditional English appearance is belied by the cosmopolitan flavour given by the English, French and Austrian owners of this friendly restaurant where the cooking is robust French style and most enjoyable. The menu is simple yet with some interesting flavours; starter might be smoked pigeon breast with peaches followed by lemon sole in prawn, mussel, cream and wine sauce or stuffed pheasant in Armagnac sauce. Sweets are wonderful. ☺

Lunch 12–2.30 *Dinner* 6–11 **Closed** D Sun, Bank Hols & 4 days Easter, last wk Aug & 1st 2 wks Sept

CAMBRIDGE

Map 6 B3
Town plan opposite

Population 102,300

Unexcelled as a centre of learning and research, settled by the Romans as a trading bridgehead, Cambridge was a place of scholarship even before the first college, Peterhouse, was founded. Entrance to University buildings and gardens (but not up staircases without permission) is generally allowed until dusk. Ideal punting round Backs of colleges for beauty rivalling Venice and Bruges. King's College Chapel has Britain's most celebrated boys' choir.

Annual Events
Cambridge Festival of Arts *July*
Festival of Nine Carols *Christmas Eve*
May Week *first two weeks June*

Sights Outside City
Ely Cathedral, Audley End, Grantchester, Wimpole Hall, Anglesey Abbey, American Cemetery, Cromwell Museum at Huntingdon, Wicken Fen, Imperial War Museum, Duxford

Information Centre
Wheeler Street
CB2 3QD
Telephone Cambridge 322640

Fiat Dealer
Holland Fiat Centre
315–349 Mill Road,
Cambridge CB1 3DF
Tel. Cambridge 242222

1 Arts Theatre **B3**
2 Botanic Gardens **C5**
3 Church of the Holy Sepulchre *12th-c round church* **B2**
Colleges
4 *Clare 1326* **A3**
5 *Corpus Christi 1352* **B3**
6 *Emmanuel 1584, Wren Chapel* **B/C3**
7 *King's 1441 and Chapel* **A3**
8 *Magdalene 1542* **A2**
9 *Pembroke 1347, Wren Chapel* **B3/4**
10 *Peterhouse 1284, oldest college* **B4**
11 *Queen's 1448* **A3/4**
12 *St John's 1511 and Bridge of Sighs* **A2**
13 *Trinity 1546* **A3**
14 Fitzwilliam Museum *manuscripts, statuary, tapestry and archaeology* **B4**
15 Folk Museum *furniture, cooking equipment, clothes and tools* **A2**
16 Great St Mary's Church *University Church* **B3**
17 St Bene't's Church *oldest in county* **B3**
18 Tourist Information Centre **B3**
19 University Arts Faculties **A4**

Cambridge

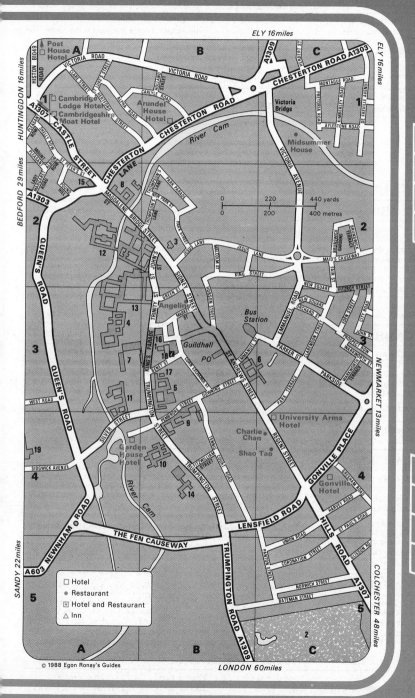

CAMBRIDGE — Arundel House Hotel   60%   £E/F

H **Town plan B1**
Cambridgeshire
53 Chesterton Road CB4 3AN
Cambridge (0223) 67701

Credit Access, Amex, Diners, Visa
Closed 25 & 26 Dec

The impressive frontage of this continually improving hotel formed
from a terrace of 19th-century houses overlooks the Cam. The
comfortable lounge area has traditional velour seating and there's a
cosy atmosphere to the basement bar. Most bedrooms have darkwood
fitted units; all have radio alarms, tea/coffee-makers and hairdryers.
Neat, clean bathrooms vary in size. No dogs.
Amenities garden, in-house movies, laundry service. &

| *Rooms* 88 | *Direct dial* Yes | *Confirm by* 6 | *Parking* Ample |
| *Ensuite bath/shower* 71 | *Room TV* Yes | *Last dinner* 9.30 | *Room service* None |

We publish annually,
so make sure you use the current edition.
It's worth it!

CAMBRIDGE — Cambridge Lodge Hotel   60%   £D/E

H **Town plan A1**
Cambridgeshire
Huntingdon Road CB3 0DQ
Cambridge (0223) 352833
Telex 817438
Credit Access, Amex, Diners, Visa
Closed 28 & 29 Dec

A reassuringly traditional atmosphere pervades this Edwardian
mock-Tudor house, set back from the A1307 west of the city. Public
rooms are pleasantly homely and include a cosy bar-lounge with
wing-back chairs. Good-sized bedrooms have pretty floral quilted
bedcovers and matching curtains, mahogany period furniture and a
couple of easy chairs. All offer tea-makers, hairdryers and radio-
alarms. *Amenities* garden, laundry service.

| *Rooms* 11 | *Direct dial* Yes | *Confirm by* 6 | *Parking* Ample |
| *Ensuite bath/shower* 8 | *Room TV* Yes | *Last dinner* 10 | *Room service* All day |

CAMBRIDGE — Cambridgeshire Moat House   63%   £C/D

H **Town plan A1**
Cambridgeshire
Bar Hill CB3 8EU
Crafts Hill (0954) 80555
Telex 817141

Credit Access, Amex, Diners, Visa

New leisure facilities have added to the attractions of this pleasant
modern hotel. The ground-floor Sportsman's Bar is popular with
golfers, while the relaxing Gallery Bar doubles as a residents' lounge.
Attractive, well-equipped bedrooms have pastel decor and light oak
furniture. *Amenities* garden, indoor swimming pool, sauna, solarium, whirlpool bath, steam room, gymnasium, tennis, squash, golf
course, pool table, secretarial services, fax, laundry service, helipad.

| *Rooms* 100 | *Direct dial* Yes | *Confirm by* 6 | *Parking* Ample |
| *Ensuite bath/shower* 100 | *Room TV* Yes | *Last dinner* 10 | *Room service* 24 hours |

CAMBRIDGE — Charlie Chan   ♀

R **Town plan C4**
Cambridgeshire
14 Regent Street
Cambridge (0223) 61763

Chinese cooking
About £40 for two
Seats 150 *Parties* 50
Parking Difficult
Credit Amex

Refurbishment has further smartened this pleasant, efficiently run
Chinese restaurant, which now boasts a small dance floor and live
music. There are good set menus, or you can choose such delights as
tasty wun tun soup with lovely fresh dumplings, tender, aromatic
crispy duck served with pancakes and plum sauce, and crunchy
mixed vegetables with oyster sauce. Crushed red bean pancake makes
an unusual sweet.

Lunch 12–2.15   *Dinner* 6–11.15
Closed 25–26 Dec

CAMBRIDGE — Garden House Hotel   68%   £C

H **Town plan A4**
Cambridgeshire
Granta Place, Mill Lane CB2 1RT
Cambridge (0223) 63421
Telex 81463

Credit Access, Amex, Diners, Visa

Pleasant riverside gardens provide a delightfully secluded setting for
this modern hotel, and most of the rooms enjoy river views. Well-kept
bedrooms remain smart if a little dated, and all have mini-bars,
hairdryers, trouser presses and remote-control TVs. Executive rooms
offer sitting areas equipped with large desks. Disappointing breakfast.
No dogs. *Amenities* garden, punting, in-house movies, secretarial
services, fax, laundry service.

| *Rooms* 117 | *Direct dial* Yes | *Confirm by* 6 | *Parking* Ample |
| *Ensuite bath/shower* 117 | *Room TV* Yes | *Last dinner* 9.30 | *Room service* 24 hours |

CAMBRIDGE Gonville Hotel 62% £D/E

H **Town plan C4**
Cambridgeshire
Gonville Place CB1 1LY
Cambridge (0223) 66611

Credit Access, Amex, Visa
Closed 4 days Xmas

A warm and friendly hotel which has been excellently run by Mrs Hooper for 16 years now. Public areas include a modern bar and a large, comfortable lounge well-equipped with easy chairs and overlooking a pretty patio. Bedrooms are simply decorated in autumn colours and have neat, practical bathrooms. High standards of housekeeping are evident throughout.
Amenities patio, laundry service, 24-hour lounge service.

| *Rooms* 62 | *Direct dial* Yes | *Confirm by* 6 | *Parking* Ample |
| *Ensuite bath/shower* 62 | *Room TV* Yes | *Last dinner* 9 | *Room service* None |

CAMBRIDGE Midsummer House ♔ ⁋

R **Town plan C1**
Cambridgeshire
Midsummer Common
Cambridge (0223) 69299
Set L from £10.50
Set D from £16.50
About £60 for two
Seats 40 *Parties* 14
Parking Difficult
Credit Access, Amex, Diners, Visa

Eat in the smart upstairs dining room or airy, plant-filled conservatory at this attractive riverside restaurant, now run by three new partners (one is the head chef). Short, fixed-price menus feature enjoyable, competently executed dishes like mille-feuilles with asparagus in a butter sauce, herby roast lamb served on a ragout of beans, or barbary duckling with cherries. Good standard of service. Some good wines on a skimpily annotated list; excellent Alsace from Gassmann and Humbrecht. ♀ Well-chosen ⊘

Lunch 12–2 *Dinner* 6.30–9.30 **Closed** L Sat, D Sun & all Mon

CAMBRIDGE Post House Hotel 68% £C/D

H **Town plan A1**
Cambridgeshire
Lakeview Bridge Road
Impington CB4 4PH
Histon (022 023) 7000
Telex 817123
Credit Access, Amex, Diners, Visa

A well-designed leisure centre is one of the attractions of this well-run modern hotel off the A45. The four bar-lounge areas range from the elegant to the luxuriously comfortable. Smart, well-kept bedrooms have neat bathrooms. Staff are friendly and efficient.
Amenities garden, indoor swimming pool, sauna, solarium, whirlpool bath, keep-fit equipment, in-house movies, secretarial services, fax, laundry service, children's playground. &

| *Rooms* 112 | *Direct dial* Yes | *Confirm by* 6 | *Parking* Ample |
| *Ensuite bath/shower* 112 | *Room TV* Yes | *Last dinner* 10.30 | *Room service* 24 hours |

CAMBRIDGE Shao Tao ⁋

R **Town plan C4**
Cambridgeshire
72 Regent Street
Cambridge (0223) 353942

Chinese cooking
Set L & D from £9.50
About £30 for two
Seats 100 *Parties* 35
Credit Access, Amex, Diners, Visa

Mr Tao's friendly, enthusiastic personality and skilful cooking guarantee an enjoyable meal at his unpretentious, informal restaurant. Quality ingredients are handled with confidence and the menu is long and tempting. Recommendable dishes include the succulent Bang Bang chicken, the plump, perfectly seasoned peppery prawns, won taon soup with delicious dumplings and the crisp-fried shredded beef with chillies and carrots. Simple fruit desserts to finish.

Lunch 12–2.30 *Dinner* 6–11, Fri & Sat till 11.30
Closed 1 wk Xmas

CAMBRIDGE University Arms Hotel 64% £D/E

H **Town plan C4**
Cambridgeshire
Regent Street CB2 1AD
Cambridge (0223) 351241
Telex 817311

Credit Access, Amex, Diners, Visa

A '60s façade hides a fine 19th-century hotel where customer comfort heads the priority list. In the Octagon lounge, gold, cream and green decor and period furniture create a cool, classical air beneath a domed ceiling with a stained glass skylight. Three cosy bars include the Whisky Galore, which offers over 100 whiskies. The comfortable, spacious bedrooms vary in style but are all well maintained.
Amenities laundry service. &

| *Rooms* 115 | *Direct dial* Yes | *Confirm by* 6 | *Parking* Ample |
| *Ensuite bath/shower* 115 | *Room TV* Yes | *Last dinner* 9.45 | *Room service* 24 hours |

Our inspectors *never* book in the name of Egon Ronay's Guides.
They disclose their identity only if they are considering an establishment
for inclusion in the next edition of the Guide.

CAMPSEA ASHE   Old Rectory   ₠

RR Map 6 **D3** Suffolk
Nr Woodbridge
Wickham Market (0728) 746524

Set D £14
About £40 for two
Seats 40
Parties 30
Parking Ample
Credit Access, Amex, Diners, Visa

Stewart Bassett cooks with flair and imagination at this peaceful old rectory. A typical meal might start with creamy smoked cod mousse, then move on to tender chicken breast sauced with herby cream cheese, lemon and mushrooms. A green salad and selection of English and French cheeses refreshingly follows, with a delicious dessert like walnut cake with sugar and cinnamon syrup to finish. Booking essential. ♥ Well-chosen ℮

Lunch by arrang.   *Dinner* 7.30–10
Closed 25, 26 & 27 Dec & 2 wks Xmas

BEDROOMS 7 **£F**
With bath/shower 7

Spacious, prettily decorated bedrooms with garden views offer flowers and magazines as well as TVs, tea-makers and private bathrooms. No children under ten. No dogs.

Changes in data sometimes occur in establishments
after the Guide goes to press.
Prices should be taken as indications rather than firm quotes.

CANTERBURY   Canterbury Hotel   58%   £E

H Town plan **E3** Kent
71 New Dover Road CT1 3DZ
Canterbury (0227) 450551
Telex 965809

Credit Access, Amex, Diners, Visa

A cheerful, friendly atmosphere is apparent as soon as you step inside the foyer-bar of this red-brick Victorian house on the outskirts of town along the A2050. Pine is much in evidence, both in the pleasant bar and in the bright bedrooms with their floral bedspreads and matching curtains. All have tea-makers, TVs and private bathrooms; about half have showers only.
Amenities secretarial services.

Rooms 27	*Direct dial* Yes	*Confirm by* 6	*Parking* Ample
Ensuite bath/shower 27	*Room TV* Yes	*Last dinner* 10	*Room service* Limited

CANTERBURY   Chaucer Hotel   61%   £C/D

H Town plan **D3** Kent
63 Ivy Lane CT1 1TT
Canterbury (0227) 464427
Telex 965096

Credit Access, Amex, Diners, Visa

Originally a Georgian house, the Chaucer is located just outside the old city wall just a few minutes' walk from the Cathedral. The hotel has no separate lounge, but guests will find ample seating in the foyer and bar. Bedrooms vary in size and furnishings, the best having smart modern pieces in dark wood. There are two mini-suites with separate sitting areas.
Amenities secretarial services, laundry service.

Rooms 45	*Room phone* Yes	*Confirm by* 6	*Parking* Ample
Ensuite bath/shower 45	*Room TV* Yes	*Last dinner* 9.45	*Room service* 24 hours

CANTERBURY   County Hotel   70%   £D

HR Town plan **C2** Kent
High Street CT1 2RX
Canterbury (0227) 66266
Telex 965076

Rooms 74
Ensuite bath/shower 74
Direct dial Yes
Room TV Yes
Confirm by 6
Last dinner 10
Parking Ample
Room service 24 hours

Credit Access, Amex, Diners, Visa

For 400 years this town-centre hostelry has been a haven for pilgrims of all persuasions. There's still plenty of old-world character in evidence with exposed beams and timbers in the foyer, coffee shop, panelled Tudor Bar and attractive first-floor lounge. Best bedrooms are the two Tudor rooms (with four-posters) and two Georgian rooms (with half-testers), all sporting good oak furniture. There's also

a single suite. Remaining rooms are gradually being upgraded, the basic fitted furniture making way for superior darkwood units. Fresh fruit, trouser presses, hairdryers and tea-makers are standard, and uncarpeted bathrooms with rather dated pink tiling are nevertheless in good order. Pleasant, helpful staff. No dogs.
Amenities valeting, laundry service, coffee shop (10.30am–11pm).

Sully's Restaurant ♛

Set L £10.50
Set D £14
About £50 for two
Seats 60
Parties 130

Good home-baked rolls and crisp fresh vegetables continue to win approval at this comfortably appointed restaurant. Best dishes such as the tasty leek broth are excellently flavoured and most enjoyable; other choices could include a pleasant but rather bland sweetbread terrine, breast of duck served nice and pink with a decent pistachio mousse, and a strawberry charlotte with a very sweet orange sauce. Good clarets. ♥ Well-chosen ℗

Lunch 12.30–2.30 *Dinner* 7–10

CANTERBURY Ebury Hotel 59% £E/F

H Town plan E3 Kent
65 New Dover Road CT1 3DX
Canterbury (0227) 68433

Credit Access, Amex, Visa
Closed 24 Dec–mid Jan

A heated pool is the latest addition to this handsome, well-maintained Victorian house just out of town on the Dover road. The spacious lounge, which overlooks the attractive garden, has plenty of relaxing armchairs and a collection of antique clocks. Good-size bedrooms have simple modern furniture and neat bathrooms.
Amenities garden, indoor swimming pool, whirlpool bath, laundry service.

Rooms 15	*Direct dial* Yes	*Confirm by* arrang.	*Parking* Ample
Ensuite bath/shower 14	*Room TV* Yes	*Last dinner* 8.30	*Room service* All day

---

CANTERBURY Falstaff Hotel £E

I Town plan B1 Kent
St Dunstan's Street CT2 8AF
Canterbury (0227) 462138
Telex 96394

Credit Access, Amex, Diners, Visa

Standing next to the old West Gate, this town-centre inn dates back to 1403 and has characterful public rooms with ancient timbers and mellow brick fireplaces. Bedrooms are mostly small and cosy, with simple decor and decent oak furniture. (Two family rooms are more spacious.) All are equipped with hairdryers, trouser presses and tea-makers. Three bathrooms have shower only. No dogs.
Amenities in-house movies.

Rooms 25	*Direct dial* Yes	*Confirm by* arrang.	*Parking* Ample
Ensuite bath/shower 24	*Room TV* Yes	*Last dinner* 9.45, Sun 8.30	*Room service* None

---

CANTERBURY Howfield Manor 70% £D/E

H Town plan B3 Kent
Chartham Hatch CT4 7HQ
Canterbury (0227) 738294

Rooms 13
Ensuite bath/shower 13
Direct dial Yes
Room TV Some
Confirm by arrang.
Last dinner 9
Parking Ample
Room service All day

Credit Access, Amex, Diners, Visa

A mellowed brick manor house set in five acres of grounds off the A28 two miles outside Canterbury. Although it was mainly built in the 19th century, the oldest part (now the kitchen) dates back to 1181, when it was a chapel. The civilised, peaceful lounges boast comfortable sofas, stylish fabrics and, in one, an inglenook fireplace. A new bar is being created in the beamed dining room. Bedrooms have pleasant fabrics and a mixture of reproduction and antique furniture; extras include chocolates, mineral water and plants. Six further bedrooms are in a new extension. Bathrooms are pleasing, with good toiletries provided. No children under ten. No dogs.
Amenities garden, croquet.

CANTERBURY Slatters Hotel 58% £D

H Town plan C2 Kent
St Margaret's Street CT1 2TR
Canterbury (0227) 463271

Credit Access, Amex, Diners, Visa

A variety of periods combine happily in this apparently modern city-centre hotel housing Tudor beams and Roman remains. Plenty of Canterbury tales are told in the handsome panelled Merchants Bar, which features a wattle-and-daub wall. Good-size bedrooms have simple, practical furnishings, remote-control TVs and tea-makers. Most have their own neat bathrooms.
Amenities laundry service.

Rooms 32	*Direct dial* Yes	*Confirm by* 6	*Parking* Limited
Ensuite bath/shower 28	*Room TV* Yes	*Last dinner* 9	*Room service* All day

CANTERBURY

Map 7 C5
Town plan opposite

Population 36,290

The Metropolitan City of the English Church (since 602), where St Augustine preached (597), and Archbishop Thomas à Becket was martyred in the Cathedral (1170). Canterbury was successfully settled by the Belgae, the Romans, the Saxons and the Normans. It has been a town of pilgrim-tourists since 1008 and the Cathedral, medieval buildings and archives well repay a lingering visit. It is strong in literary association through Chaucer and Marlowe.

Sights Outside City
Bodiam Castle, Chilham, Dover Castle, Herne Bay, Leeds Castle, Lympne Castle, Reculver Towers, Rye and Winchelsea, Walmer Castle, Whitstable Castle and Grounds

Information Office
34 St Margaret's Street
CT1 2TG
Telephone Canterbury 766567

Fiat Dealer
Martin Walter Ltd
41 St George's Place
Canterbury
Kent CT1 1UR
Tel. Canterbury 763800
Map reference D3

1 Blackfriars *13th-c Friary* C1
2 Cathedral *11th–15th c* D2
3 Christchurch Gate and Buttermarket C2
4 Conquest House C1
5 Dane John Garden *a memorial to Marlowe* C3
6 East Station B3
7 Greyfriars *first Franciscan settlement* B2
8 The Marlowe Theatre C1
9 Martyrs' Memorial *to Bloody Mary's victims* B3
10 Norman Castle *large Norman keep* B3
11 Norman Staircase *very fine roofed steps* and King's School *originally Priory hostel* D1
12 Queen Elizabeth's Guest Chamber C2
13 Roman Pavement and hypocaust C2
14 Royal Museum C2
15 St Augustine's Abbey *layered monastic remains* D2
16 St Dunstan's church *contains head of Sir Thomas More* A1
17 St George's Tower D2
18 St Martin's Church *oldest in use* E2
19 St Peter's Church *Anglo-Saxon* C2
20 St Peter's Street *typical medieval street* C2
21 St Thomas's (Eastbridge Hospital) *collection of 12th-c–17th-c buildings, beautiful Norman crypt* C2
22 Sir John Boys's House *ancient lopsided house* C1
23 The Weavers *16th-c weavers' houses* C2
24 Tower House B2
25 University and Gulbenkian Theatre A1
26 West Station B1
27 Westgate Gardens B2
28 Westgate Tower *arms and armour museum* B1

Canterbury

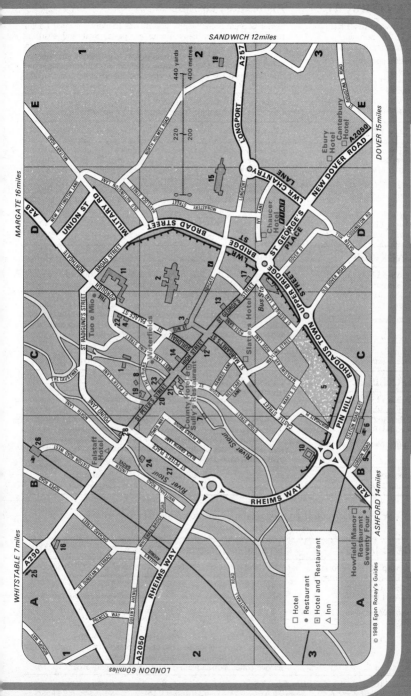

© 1988 Egon Ronay's Guides

CANTERBURY — Ristorante Tuo e Mio

R Town plan C1 Kent
16 The Borough
Canterbury (0227) 61471

Italian cooking
Set L £8
About £44 for two
Seats 40 *Parties* 25
Parking Limited
Credit Access, Amex, Diners, Visa

Signor Greggio is the helpful host at this friendly, informal Italian restaurant. A basic menu strong on pasta, veal and steak is supplemented by decently cooked daily specials like skate in tomato and pimento sauce and calf's kidneys with garlic and mushrooms. Sweets are less interesting and the wine list lacks information – but there are good bottles worth trying, such as the crisp Pinot Grigio. Book. ♥ Well-chosen ⊗ &

Lunch 12–2.30   *Dinner* 7–10.45
Closed L Tues, all Mon, 4 days Xmas & 3 days Easter

CANTERBURY — Waterfields

R Town plan C2 Kent
5a Best Lane
Canterbury (0227) 450276

Set L £8.50
About £40 for two
Seats 60
Parties 20
Parking Limited
Credit Access, Amex, Visa

Michael Waterfield handles good produce in assured style in his attractive restaurant, which was once a forge. Duck liver baked in pastry with sherry sauce or asparagus and courgette mousse with quail's eggs could be your starter, with prawn-sauced Dover sole, Indonesian-style breast of duck or rib of beef with ratatouille as a main course. Sweets include ice creams, sorbets and the popular chocolate St Emilion. ⊗ &

Lunch 12–2.30   *Dinner* 7–10.45
Closed L Mon, all Sun, Bank Hols & 1 wk Xmas

CARLISLE — Crest Hotel 55%   £C/D

H Map 13 D4 Cumbria
Kingstown CA4 0HR
Carlisle (0228) 31201
Telex 64201

Credit Access, Amex, Diners, Visa

It's easy to find this modern low-rise hotel at Junction 44 on the M6 but locating the car park is a challenge. Inside, the combined coffee shop, lounge and bar area are smartly decorated and all the bedrooms have been recently refurbished with Executive rooms offering bathrobes, trouser presses and desk space, and ironing boards in the Lady Crest rooms. *Amenities* garden, in-house movies, secretarial services, fax, laundry service, coffee shop (9am–6pm).

Rooms 94	*Direct dial* Yes	*Confirm by* 6	*Parking* Ample
Ensuite bath/shower 94	*Room TV* Yes	*Last dinner* 9.45	*Room service* 24 hours

CARLISLE — Crown & Mitre Hotel 56%   £D

H Map 13 D4 Cumbria
English Street CA3 8HZ
Carlisle (0228) 25491
Telex 64183

Credit Access, Amex, Diners, Visa

A marble staircase and chandeliered hall remain in this town-centre hotel as testimony to a grand past, while modern amenities have been installed for the present-day traveller. Public rooms include a traditional mahogany-panelled bar with memorabilia of the old Carlisle railway to gladden the hearts of train spotters. Bedrooms are well supplied with plenty of extras. *Amenities* indoor swimming pool, whirlpool bath, in-house movies, laundry service.

Rooms 98	*Room phone* Yes	*Confirm by* 6	*Parking* Limited
Ensuite bath/shower 97	*Room TV* Yes	*Last dinner* 9.30	*Room service* Limited

★ For a *discount* on next year's guide, see **An Offer for Answers**. ★

CARLISLE — Swallow Hilltop Hotel 58%   £D/E

H Map 13 D4 Cumbria
London Road CA1 2PQ
Carlisle (0228) 29255
Telex 64292

Credit Access, Amex, Diners, Visa

An extensive improvement programme has a Spring 1989 completion date at the Swallow Hilltop, which stands on the A6 south of Carlisle (leave the M6 at junction 42). The bar and restaurant have been smartly revamped and there are added and improved facilities in the leisure club. Older bedrooms are also being brought up to the general level; top-of-the-range Executive rooms have trouser presses, hair-dryers and remote-control TVs in addition to the standard radio-alarms and tea-makers. *Amenities* indoor swimming pool, sauna, solarium, whirlpool bath, keep-fit equipment, tennis, golf practice nets, putting, in-house movies, secretarial services, fax, laundry service, coffee shop (7.30am–11pm), children's play area.

Rooms 110	*Direct dial* Yes	*Confirm by* 6	*Parking* Ample
Ensuite bath/shower 97	*Room TV* Yes	*Last dinner* 9.45	*Room service* 24 hours

CARLYON BAY — Carlyon Bay Hotel — 68% — £B/C

H Map 2 B3 Cornwall
Nr St Austell PL25 3RD
Par (072 681) 2304

Credit Access, Amex, Diners, Visa

A clifftop position and 250 acres of grounds make a spectacular setting for this 1930s hotel. Inside, plentiful flower displays and a warm, friendly atmosphere give an immediately inviting impression. The comfortable bars and traditional lounges provide relaxing places in which to socialise. Bedrooms have white units and coordinating floral fabrics; most have stunning views. Bathrooms are carpeted, tiled and well maintained. Housekeeping is excellent and staff are efficient and friendly. *Amenities* garden, indoor & outdoor swimming pools, sauna, solarium, whirlpool bath, keep-fit equipment, tennis, golf course, putting, games room, snooker, in-house movies, secretarial services, fax, laundry service, children's playroom, helipad.

| Rooms 74 | Direct dial Yes | Confirm by arrang. | Parking Ample |
| Ensuite bath/shower 74 | Room TV Yes | Last dinner 9 | Room service 24 hours |

CARLYON BAY — Porth Avallen Hotel — 61% — £E

H Map 2 B3 Cornwall
Sea Road,
Nr St Austell PL25 3SG
Par (072 681) 2802

Credit Access, Amex, Diners, Visa
Closed 2 wks Xmas

A restful and homely atmosphere is to be found at this 1930s hotel overlooking Carylon Bay. Public areas include a comfortable panelled lounge, a sun lounge with sea views and a pleasant bar. Bedrooms are light and airy with pleasing decor, unfussy fabrics and neat tiled bathrooms; furniture varies from period to modern. No dogs.
Amenities garden, in-house movies, laundry service, 24-hour lounge service.

| Rooms 24 | Direct dial Yes | Confirm by arrang. | Parking Ample |
| Ensuite bath/shower 20 | Room TV Yes | Last dinner 8.30 | Room service Limited |

CARTMEL — Aynsome Manor Hotel — 60% — £C/D

H Map 13 D6 Cumbria
Nr Grange-over-Sands
LA11 6HH
Cartmel (053 95) 36653

Credit Access, Amex, Visa
Closed 1st 3 weeks Jan

A pleasant country retreat, well cared for by resident proprietors the Varley family. Most striking of the day rooms is the downstairs lounge with its two-coloured frieze, gilt-framed pictures, and porcelain figures. The upstairs drawing room is appointed in traditional style, as are the bedrooms, two of which, along with a comfortable lounge, are in a cottage across the cobbled courtyard. Half-board terms only.
Amenities garden.

| Rooms 13 | Direct dial Yes | Confirm by arrang. | Parking Ample |
| Ensuite bath/shower 12 | Room TV Yes | Last dinner 8.15 | Room service Limited |

CARTMEL — Priory Hotel — 59% — *NEW ENTRY* — £E/F

H Map 13 D6 Cumbria
The Square
Nr Grange-over-Sands
LA11 6QB
Cartmel (053 95) 36267
Credit Access
Closed Dec–Feb

Right in the heart of pretty Cartmel village, this ivy-clad hotel is a joy to stay in. Mike and Charlotte Carson are the most enthusiastic and welcoming of hosts, and the feeling throughout is one of homely comfort. The whole place gleams, from the little bar and chintzy lounge to the solidly furnished bedrooms. Excellent breakfast. No dogs in the bedrooms.
Amenities garden, laundry service, coffee shop (10.30–5.30).

| Rooms 9 | Room phone No | Confirm by arrang. | Parking Ample |
| Ensuite bath/shower 5 | Room TV Yes | Last dinner 8.30 | Room service Limited |

CARTMEL — Uplands — ⚐

RR Map 13 D6 Cumbria
Haggs Lane LA11 6HD
Cartmel (053 95) 36248

Set L £9 **Set D** £16
About £42 for two
Seats 30 *Parties* 30
Parking Ample
Credit Access, Amex

An offshoot of the Miller Howe Hotel and following the same pattern of style and cooking. Diana Peter's welcome is warm and friendly and Tom's cooking is sound and reliable, producing some interesting flavours. A typical dinner would be baked quails, fennel and almond soup, roast beef in mushroom, Marsala and cream sauce and richly flavoured Grand Marnier mousse to finish. ♥ Well-chosen ☺

Lunch 12.30 for 1   *Dinner* 7.30 for 8
Closed Mon & 2 Jan–late Feb

BEDROOMS 4   £E/F
With bath/shower 4

For dinner guests only there are four attractive, tastefully furnished bedrooms with en suite bathrooms, TVs and telephones. No children under ten.

CASTLE CARY   Bond's Hotel   63%   £E/F

HR Map 4 B3 Somerset
Ansford Hill BA7 7JP
Castle Cary (0963) 50464

Credit Access, Amex
Closed 1 wk Xmas

A civilised, well-kept little hotel, run with charm and enthusiasm by
Kevin and Yvonne Bond and their young staff. An open fire glows a
welcome in the lounge-bar, which has a comfortable, restful
atmosphere. Bedrooms are small but delightful, with pretty coordinated fabrics and furniture that is both practical and attractive.
Private bath/shower rooms, one not en suite. No children under eight.
No dogs. *Amenities* garden, laundry service.

Rooms 6	*Room phone* No	*Confirm by* arrang.	*Parking* Ample
Ensuite bath/shower 5	*Room TV* No	*Last dinner* 9	*Room service* All day

Restaurant   �

Set D £10.50
About £40 for two
Seats 22
Parties 22

Yvonne cooks with care to provide enjoyable eating in very pleasant
and relaxed surroundings. Fresh seasonal produce is put to good effect
in dishes highlighted by honest flavours and accurate seasoning.
Typical items include carrot and Jerusalem artichoke soup, mange-
tout soufflé, salmon and prawns en croûte, roast pheasant and fillet
steak with mustard and red wine glaze. Informal service led by Kevin.
🍷 Well-chosen   ℰ

Dinner only 7–9
Closed Sun–Tues to non-residents

Our inspectors *never* book in the name of Egon Ronay's Guides.
They disclose their identity only if they are considering an establishment
for inclusion in the next edition of the Guide.

CASTLE COMBE   Castle Hotel   *NEW ENTRY*   £B/C

IR Map 4 B2 Wiltshire
Nr Chippenham SN14 7HN
Castle Combe (0249) 782461

Credit Access, Amex, Visa

The Baker-Joys have done wonders in upgrading their delightful little
hotel, which stands in the centre of one of England's prettiest villages.
There are now 11 bedrooms, all en suite, with simple but very pleasing
decor of white walls contrasting with black beams, and good-quality
reproduction furniture. The best, airy rooms are at the front, while
those in the attic, nestling under 15th-century beams, are small but
full of character. The owners' personal touches are in evidence
throughout, and best use has been made of the limited ground-floor
space for a tiny reception and lounge, in addition to the large village
bar. Excellent breakfasts.
Amenities garden.

Rooms 11	*Direct dial* Yes	*Confirm by* arrang.	*Parking* Limited
Ensuite bath/shower 11	*Room TV* Yes	*Last dinner* 9.30	*Room service* Limited

Restaurant   *NEW ENTRY*

Set L £15.25, Sun £12
Set D £22.50
About £52 for two
Seats 46
Parties 26

22-year-old Ivan Reid, finalist in the 1988 Chef of the Year competition,
does a fine job in the kitchen, combining classical and modern
techniques on a menu that's full of originality. Marinated salmon with
scrambled duck's eggs, rolled fillet of lamb with kidneys and purple
basil sauce, and turban of sole and salmon with mussel sauce show the
range. The baronial-style restaurant has recently been extended into
a vaulted cellar. ℰ

Lunch 12–2
Dinner 7–9.30

Any person using our name to obtain free hospitality is a fraud.
Proprietors, please inform the police and us.

CASTLE COMBE — Manor House Hotel 72% £C

HR Map 4 B2 Wiltshire
Nr Chippenham SN14 7HR
Castle Combe (0249) 782206
Telex 449931

Rooms 32
Ensuite bath/shower 31
Direct dial Yes
Room TV Yes
Confirm by 6
Last dinner 9
Parking Ample
Room service 24 hours

Credit Access, Amex, Diners, Visa

Sweeping lawns, an Italian garden and the river Bybrook form a delightful 26-acre setting for this largely 17th-century honey-stone manor, parts of which date from the 14th century. A splendid entrance hall with panelling dating from 1664 is warmed by log fires and, in the restful lounges, fine fireplaces and attractive modern fabrics make for plenty of appeal. Bedrooms are most comfortable – some with

four-posters or testers – and are well equipped, with mini-bars, radio/intercom and direct-dial phones; many have enchanting views. All have smart bathrooms.
Amenities garden, outdoor swimming pool, tennis, croquet, game fishing, fax, helipad.

Restaurant

Set L £15.50, Sun £14.50
Set D £21.50
Seats 80

New chef Nick Evendon is producing inventive dishes graced with subtle seasoning – you might start with a delicious game terrine and follow with baby pigeon in Madeira and wild mushroom sauce. Desserts maintain a high standard. Excellent but overpriced clarets (Lynch Bages '70 £112); if you're on a budget stick to the good Riojas (Cacerès, Muga). Stylish Blagny Rouge '82 from Leflaive. 🍷 Well-chosen &

Lunch 12.30–2 Dinner 7.30–9
About £60 for two

CASTLE DONINGTON — Donington Thistle Hotel 73% £C/D

H Map 11 D3 Derbyshire
East Midlands Airport
DE7 2SH
Derby (0332) 850 700
Telex 377632

Rooms 110
Ensuite bath/shower 110
Direct dial Yes
Room TV Yes
Confirm by 6
Last dinner 10.15
Parking Ample
Room service 24 hours

Credit Access, Amex, Diners, Visa

Much thought and imagination have gone into the interior design of this low-rise modern hotel located beside the East Midlands Airport and close to junction 24 of the M1. High ceilings and pine beams contribute to the light and airy feel of the spacious stone-tiled foyer and comfortable lounge, while rugs and plenty of fresh and dried flower arrangements add the finishing touches. There's also a pine-furnished bar.

Good-sized bedrooms are neat and bright, with light decor and pretty fabrics – plus nicely tiled bathrooms and the usual accessories.
Amenities garden, indoor swimming pool, sauna, solarium, whirlpool bath, keep-fit equipment, in-house movies, secretarial services, fax, laundry service. &

CATFORD — Casa Cominetti

See under LONDON

CAVENDISH — Alfonso's ♀

R Map 6 C3 Suffolk
High Street, Nr Sudbury
Glemsford (0787) 280372

Italian cooking
Set L Sun only £9.50
About £44 for two
Seats 35 Parties 35
Parking Ample
Credit Access, Amex, Diners

Veronica Barricella is the chef in this intimate, simply decorated Italian restaurant, while Alfonso provides its congenial atmosphere. The pasta is home-made and delicious and Veronica's insistence on the best ingredients goes to ensure fine veal, fish, chicken and particularly beef dishes. Good ice creams and impeccable zabaglione to finish and the mocha-express coffee is excellent. Eat alfresco on the terrace in fine weather. 🌿 &

Lunch Sun 12–2 Dinner from 7
Closed L Mon, D Sun & L Tues–Sat exc. by arrang.

CAWSTON — Grey Gables ♧

RR Map 6 C1 Norfolk
Norwich Road
Norwich (0603) 871259

Set L £9
Set D from £12
About £35 for two
Seats 30
Parties 24
Parking Ample

Ask for directions when booking a table at this homely country restaurant. The menus offer skilfully executed, straightforward dishes such as chicken liver pâté or deep-fried mushrooms with garlic butter as starters, with perhaps roast rib of beef with Yorkshire pudding or local plaice with lemon and mushroom sauce for a main course. Flavours are excellent and saucing is good. Scrumptious sweets, generously served. ☺

Lunch by arrang.   *Dinner* 7–8.30
Closed L Sat & 25 & 26 Dec

BEDROOMS 7 **£F**
With bath/shower 7

The good-sized bedrooms are individually decorated with pretty fabrics and period furniture and fittings; all have TVs. Bathrooms are carpeted and attractive.

CHADDESLEY CORBETT — Brockencote Hall 76%   £E

HR Map 10 B4
Hereford & Worcester
Nr Kidderminster DY10 4PY
Kidderminster (056 283) 876
Telex 333431

Rooms 9
Ensuite bath/shower 9
Direct dial Yes
Room TV Yes
Confirm by 6
Last dinner 9.30
Parking Ample
Room service All day

Credit Access, Amex, Diners, Visa
Closed 3 wks Jan

Few country houses have a more gracious setting than Brockencote Hall, surrounded as it is by 70 acres of parkland. The landscape suggests spaciousness, an impression that lingers when guests enter the light and airy public rooms. Sunlight dapples the stripped pine and maple doors and panelling in the public rooms. Bedrooms of varying sizes are individually decorated. All have pretty coordinated curtains

and bedspreads, with freestanding darkwood furniture. Bathrooms have modern suites although one or two retain delightful pre-war fittings. The enthusiasm of the owners, Alison and Joseph Petitjean, is infectious. Standards of housekeeping are exemplary. *Amenities* garden, in-house movies, secretarial services, laundry service.

Restaurant ♔

French cooking
Set L £10.50
About £60 for two
Seats 35
Parties 20

Imaginative French cooking with flair is served by keen and capable staff (mainly French) in this sunny restaurant. Highlight of our memorable meal was a first-class foie gras with tiny cubes of sweet Bordeaux jelly. Fish dishes include turbot suprême and there's an earthy dish of pigs' trotters with calf's sweetbreads. Excellent crème brûlée to follow. Concise, fairly priced list of good wines: Alsace from Mure; Rhônes from Pascal. ☺ &

Lunch 12.30–2   *Dinner* 7.30–9.30, Sat till 10
Closed L Sat, D Sun & 3 wks Jan

CHAGFORD — Gidleigh Park Hotel 81%   £B/C

HR Map 3 D2 Devon
TQ13 8HH
Chagford (064 73) 2367
Telex 42643

Rooms 14
Ensuite bath/shower 14
Direct dial Yes
Room TV Yes
Confirm by arrang.
Last dinner 9
Parking Ample
Room service All day

Credit Access, Amex, Diners, Visa

Everything is on a grand scale at the Hendersons' superb mock-Tudor mansion in a beautiful and secluded setting. Immense trouble is taken to make guests comfortable, and crackling log fires in the entrance hall, bar and handsome drawing room provide the warmest of welcomes. Furnishings suggest a private country house, with antiques blending with huge traditional sofas and armchairs, and beauti-

fully arranged flowers harmonising with subtle colour schemes. Individually decorated bedrooms range from cottage-style in some of the smaller rooms to grandly elegant, with draped curtains and canopied beds. Bathrooms are equally luxurious. Half-board terms only. *Amenities* garden, tennis, croquet, laundry service.

Restaurant ★   ♔   ♙

Lunch 12.30–2
Dinner 7–9
Set L £20.77
Set D £30.47
About £80 *for two*
Seats 40
Parties 18

Shaun Hill's skilful, refined cooking ensures that a meal in this elegant restaurant is a truly memorable experience. His menus reflect the seasons and top quality produce is enhanced by delicate, subtle saucing. Highlights of our meal included a perfectly textured spinach timbale and beautifully cooked pigeon with the crispest of vegetables. The glorious wine list features such treats as Bâtard

Montrachet (Leflaive) '78 and Martha's Vineyard '77 (Heitz). No smoking. Booking essential. ***Specialities*** sautéed scallops with lentil and coriander sauce, steamed sea bass with dill and wild mushrooms, roast pigeon with herb ravioli, warm brioche with poached red fruits and cinnamon ice cream. ➢ Outstanding ♟ Well-chosen ☺ ♣

CHAGFORD   Great Tree Hotel   65%   £E

H Map 3 D2 Devon
Sandypark TQ13 8JS
Chagford (064 73) 2491

Credit Access, Amex, Diners, Visa
Closed 27 Dec–1 Feb

Set in wooded grounds just off the A382, this former hunting lodge enjoys splendid views over Dartmoor and the surrounding countryside. A carved wooden staircase leads down from reception to the raftered lounge – a comfortable, traditionally furnished room adjoining the tiny bar. Freshly refurbished bedrooms, mostly at garden level and all with lovely views, range from compact to spacious; teamakers are provided. ***Amenities*** garden.

Rooms 14	*Direct dial* Yes	*Confirm by* arrang.	*Parking* Ample
Ensuite bath/shower 14	*Room TV* Yes	*Last dinner* 9	*Room service* Limited

CHAGFORD   Mill End Hotel   63%   £D/E

HR Map 3 D2 Devon
Sandy Park TQ13 8JN
Chagford (064 73) 2282

Credit Access, Amex, Diners, Visa
Closed 10 days before Xmas

Once a flour mill, the original building dates back several centuries. There's also a 1930s extension, the whole set in delightful gardens by the river Teign. Inside all is spick and span, with plenty of inviting easy chairs in the chintzy lounges. Bedrooms, with mainly fitted furniture, are properly serviced in the evening; dimmer switches for the bedside lights are a nice touch. Some rooms have garden access. ***Amenities*** garden, game fishing.

Rooms 17	*Direct dial* Yes	*Confirm by* arrang.	*Parking* Ample
Ensuite bath/shower 16	*Room TV* Yes	*Last dinner* 9	*Room service* All day

Restaurant   ♙

Set L £13.50
Set D £14.75
About £38 *for two*
Seats 37
Parties 12

A friendly little restaurant with beams, plaster walls and crisp white linen. Fixed-price menus offer a small choice of such dishes as hot cauliflower mousse, sole with cucumber sauce, grilled lamb cutlets or chicken breasts stuffed with apricots and ground almonds. The best comes last in the shape of a splendid sweet trolley, with second helpings encouraged of delights like lemon soufflé, chocolate and rum roulade, gooseberry tart and chocolate-filled meringue gâteau. ☺

Lunch 12.30–1.30   *Dinner* 7.30–9
Closed 10 days before Xmas

CHAGFORD   Teignworthy   65%   £C

HR Map 3 D2 Devon
Frenchbeer TQ13 8EX
Chagford (064 73) 3355

Credit Access, Visa

High up on the edge of Dartmoor, this secluded country house hotel offers 1920s Lutyens-style architecture and delightful terraced gardens. Public rooms include an oak-panelled hall, a cosy bar and a homely sitting room well stocked with records and books. Prettily furnished bedrooms have smartly up-to-date bathrooms. Check directions when booking. No children under 11. No dogs. ***Amenities*** garden, sauna, solarium, tennis, croquet, in-house movies, laundry service.

Rooms 9	*Direct dial* Yes	*Confirm by* arrang.	*Parking* Ample
Ensuite bath/shower 9	*Room TV* Yes	*Last dinner* 9.30	*Room service* All day

see over

Teignworthy Restaurant

Set D £19.50
Seats 28
Parties 36

Fine ingredients and sound cooking make for highly enjoyable eating in this pleasant country dining room. David Woolfall's fixed-price menus are concise but tempting, offering delights like scallop terrine wrapped in smoked salmon and sauced with spinach, and mustard-dipped lamb noisettes served with a rich thyme jus. There's always an interesting vegetarian dish; lovely desserts too, like plum mousse and hot passion fruit soufflé. 🍷 Well-chosen 🅮 ♿

Lunch 12.30–2 by arrang.   *Dinner* 7.30–9.30
About £62 for two

CHARINGWORTH

Charingworth   75%   *NEW ENTRY*   £B
Manor Hotel

HR Map 4 C1 Gloucestershire
Nr Chipping Campden
GL55 6NS
Paxford (038 678) 555

Rooms 8
Ensuite bath/shower 8
Direct dial Yes
Room TV Yes
Confirm by arrang.
Last dinner 9.30
Parking Ample
Room service 24 hours

Credit Access, Amex, Diners, Visa
Closed 3 wks Jan–Feb

Dating from Tudor times, the manor is a listed building set in beautiful gardens and grounds. Its conversion to a high-grade hotel has kept all its period character, exemplified in the stone-flagged reception, the restful library and the elegant lounge with its chintz, painted panels and cheery fire. In the bedrooms everything has been done for guests' comfort and pleasure: sitting areas, dressing table and separate desk, telephones, trouser presses, chocolates, country wines to sample. The bathrooms are equally lavish in their appointments. Superb service sets the seal on a splendid hotel. No children under 12. *Amenities* garden, satellite TV, laundry service.

Restaurant

Set L from £14.50, Sun £15.50
Set D £17.50
About £47 for two
Seats 35
Parties 20
Parking Ample

Low-ceilinged and intimate, with rag-painted panelled walls and sturdy oak dining chairs; professional service under a very knowledgeable manager; a varied and tempting menu that makes ordering a pleasant problem; and very good cooking (especially sauces) with modern influences but by no means nouvelle portions. Raviolis of creamed vegetables in a sweet pepper and tomato dressing make a lovely starter, which you might follow with sole fillets, rolled with salmon mousse, lime and lettuce and accompanied by fresh mussels and a sabayon sauce, or maybe loin of lamb filled with a pâté of celery, thyme, mushrooms and leeks. Delicious sweets. Wines don't let the side down either: Cru de Coudelet (Perrin) '85, Clos St. Denis (Dujac) '82. 🍷 Well-chosen 🅮

Lunch noon–2   *Dinner* 7–9.30, Sat till 10   **Closed** 3 wks Jan–Feb

---

CHARLBURY

The Bell   £E

Map 4 C1 Oxfordshire
Church Street OX7 3AP
Charlbury (0608) 810278

Credit Access, Amex, Diners, Visa

The gardens at the back of this 17th-century Cotswold-stone inn run down to a little river, and inside all is spick-and-span, cosy and traditional. The bar is particularly appealing, and there's a comfortable lounge. Prettily decorated bedrooms are furnished with a mixture of antique and bamboo, with the odd white-painted piece. Neat bath/shower rooms offer a selection of toiletries.
Amenities garden, coarse fishing.

Rooms 14	Direct dial Yes	Confirm by arrang.	Parking Ample
Ensuite bath/shower 13	Room TV Yes	Last dinner 9.30	Room service All day

---

We welcome bona fide complaints and recommendations
on the tear-out pages at the back of the book for readers' comment.
They are followed up by our professional team.

...**A** little tavern in the Rue Vavin,

Chez Clémence, who makes only one dish,

but a stupendous one: *le cassoulet de Castelnaudry*...

Clémence's cassoulet has been cooking for twenty years.

She replenishes the pot...but it is always the same cassoulet.

The basis remains, and this ancient and precious substance

gives it a taste which one finds in the paintings of old

Venetian masters, in the amber flesh-tints of their women.

ANATOLE FRANCE 1844-1924
HISTOIRE COMIQUE

We may live

without poetry, music and art;

We may live without conscience and live without heart;

We may live without friends, we may live without books,

But civilised man cannot live without cooks.

OWEN MEREDITH 1831-91
LUCILE

My father was a blacksmith ...

the tender bouquets of vegetables he brought were so full

of flavour and aroma that all that was needed was the

addition of a few of the big rosy strips of pork fat which

sizzled in the big cast-iron pot.

This was the 'cuisine heureuse', which consisted of marrying

natural products with one another, of finding simple

harmonies and enhancing the flavour of each ingredient by

contact with another complementary flavour...

It is the antithesis of cooking to impress.

ROGER VERGE
CUISINE OF THE SUN
Trans. Caroline Conran (1979)

CHARLECOTE The Charlecote Pheasant 63% £E

H **Map 4 C1** Warwickshire
Nr Warwick CV35 9EN
Stratford-upon-Avon
(0789) 840200
Telex 31688

Credit Access, Amex, Diners, Visa

A 17th-century farmhouse with outbuildings both old and new makes up this friendly hotel. Public areas include a smart reception and spacious bar. Bedrooms are bright, attractive and well equipped – those in a new block featuring a double and a single bed (four with four-posters). **Amenities** garden, outdoor swimming pool, sauna, solarium, keep-fit equipment, tennis, croquet, snooker, satellite TV, secretarial services, laundry service, 24-hour lounge service. ♿

| *Rooms* 60 | *Direct dial* Yes | *Confirm by* arrang. | *Parking* Ample |
| *Ensuite bath/shower* 60 | *Room TV* Yes | *Last dinner* 10 | *Room service* Limited |

CHARNOCK RICHARD TraveLodge 57% £E

H **Map 10 A1** Lancashire
Mill Lane, Nr Chorley PR7 5LR
Coppull (0257) 791746
Telex 67315

Credit Access, Amex, Diners, Visa

A 20-year-old hotel within the service area on the northbound M6 between junctions 27 and 28 (a private road provides access for motorists on the southbound carriageway). Bedrooms are furnished and fitted in functional style, and 12 are for non-smokers. Peaceful grounds to the rear keep things generally quiet. Breakfast is served in the little restaurant/bar area.
Amenities garden.

| *Rooms* 102 | *Direct dial* Yes | *Confirm by* 6 | *Parking* Ample |
| *Ensuite bath/shower* 102 | *Room TV* Yes | *Last dinner* 9.30 | *Room service* None |

We publish annually,
so make sure you use the current edition.
It's worth it!

CHARTHAM Thruxted Oast *NEW ENTRY* £E

I **Map 7 C5** Kent
CT4 7BX
Canterbury (0227) 730080

Credit Access, Amex, Visa

Standing in picturesque countryside a short drive from the A28, this recently converted oast house is a charming and totally relaxing place to stay. The greeting from owners Tim and Hilary Derouet is warm and enthusiastic, and guests feel they are staying in a private family house. The lounge is supplied with plenty of armchairs and homely touches that include porcelain figures and a nice collection of artwork. Comfortable beamed bedrooms feature remote-control TVs, digital radio alarms, magazines and local information brochures, and bathrooms are also very well equipped, showing the attention to detail that is noticeable throughout. Breakfast is a splendid affair served in the family kitchen. **Amenities** garden, croquet, laundry service.

| *Rooms* 3 | *Room phone* Yes | *Confirm by* arrang. | *Parking* Ample |
| *Ensuite bath/shower* 3 | *Room TV* Yes | *Last dinner* 7.30 | *Room service* All day |

CHEAM Al San Vincenzo ★ ♙

R **Map 7 A5** Surrey
52 Upper Mulgrave Road
01-661 9763

Italian cooking

Lunch by arrang.
Dinner 7–9.30
Set D £15.95
About £40 for two
Seats 20
Parties 25
Parking Ample

Credit Access, Amex, Diners, Visa
Closed L Sat, all Sun, Bank Hols, 1 wk Easter, 1 wk Aug & 1 wk Xmas

There are just 20 covers at this modestly appointed suburban restaurant, so book, and enjoy some of the best Italian cooking in the land. Chef-patron Vincenzo Borgonzola is armed with endless enthusiasm, and his short menus are always packed with interest and variety: breast of duck with smoked pancetta and fennel, perfect pasta with a wonderful sauce of walnuts and mascarpone, a classic Neopolitan dish of fish and
seafood. Note, too, the Italian wines, including delicious organically grown Chianti Putto. **Specialities** baby monkfish with a light creamy cheese sauce; pork with sun-dried tomatoes; dates filled with ginger preserve with chestnut ice cream, dark chocolate sauce, cream and comb honey. 🅴 ♿

CHEDINGTON   Chedington Court   68%   £B

H **Map 4 A4** Dorset
Beaminster DT8 3HY
Corscombe (093 589) 265

Credit Amex, Visa
Closed mid Jan–mid Feb

Things to note here are the lovely quiet location, the ten acres of fabulous wooded gardens and the brooding splendour of the Jacobean-style mansion itself. Day rooms are handsomely proportioned and very comfortable: there's a vast oak-floored hallway, a superb lounge and an elegant panelled library. A wide oak staircase leads up to the bedrooms – all vast and high-ceilinged, with sturdy period furnishings and high-quality fabrics. The peace and seclusion are total, and the place lacks the convivial air of many country house hotels. Half-board terms only (the restaurant has an outstanding wine list). No dogs.
Amenities garden, putting, croquet, snooker, helipad.

Rooms 10	*Direct dial* Yes	*Confirm by* arrang.	*Parking* Ample
Ensuite bath/shower 10	*Room TV* Yes	*Last dinner* 9	*Room service* Limited

Our inspectors are our full-time employees;
they are professionally trained by us.

CHELMSFORD   Pontlands Park Country Hotel   72%   £B/C

H **Map 7 B4** Essex
West Hanningfield Road,
Great Baddow CM2 8HR
Chelmsford (0245) 76444
Telex 995256

Rooms 17
Ensuite bath/shower 17
Direct dial Yes
Room TV Yes
Confirm by 6
Last dinner 10
Parking Ample
Room service 24 hours

Credit Access, Amex, Diners, Visa
Closed 27–30 Dec

A recent extension, carefully designed in matching period style, is a welcome improvement to this Victorian country mansion. The new wing provides a large, elegantly furnished lounge – a peaceful alternative to the cosy, very traditional bar in the original building. Newer bedrooms, all with sitting areas, are particularly spacious and those on the ground floor have French windows opening out on to the garden. Decor throughout is in delicate pastel shades, and furniture (including two four-posters and one half-tester) is all top-quality. Superb, fully-tiled bathrooms have shower attachments and bidets. No dogs. *Amenities* garden, indoor swimming pool, sauna, solarium, whirlpool bath, fax, laundry service.

CHELTENHAM   Hotel de la Bere   64%   £D

H **Map 4 C1** Gloucestershire
Southam GL52 3NH
Cheltenham (0242) 37771
Telex 43232

Credit Access, Amex, Diners, Visa

Just two miles north of Cheltenham is this lovely old Cotswold-stone manor house dating from Tudor times. Mellow oak panelling, ornate plasterwork and splendidly carved fireplaces give a richly authentic feel to the finest of the public rooms. Characterful bedrooms, each named after an English king, vary in size but all rooms are well-furnished and equipped with radio-alarms, trouser presses and tea/coffee makers. Bathrooms are tiled and most have showers and heated towel rails. Good housekeeping. No dogs.
Amenities garden, outdoor swimming pool, sauna, solarium, gymnasium, tennis, squash, badminton, pitch & putt, croquet, secretarial services, fax, laundry service.

Rooms 43	*Direct dial* Yes	*Confirm by* 6	*Parking* Ample
Ensuite bath/shower 43	*Room TV* Yes	*Last dinner* 10	*Room service* 24 hours

CHELTENHAM   Le Champignon Sauvage   *NEW ENTRY*   ♀

R **Map 4 C1** Gloucestershire
24 Suffolk Road GL50 2AQ
Cheltenham (0242) 573449

About £46 for two
Seats 34
Parties 28
Parking Limited
Credit Access, Amex, Visa

Quality produce, careful saucing and capable cooking provide enjoyable results at this attractive modern-style restaurant. David Matthias' interesting, imaginative menu ranges from a wild mushroom ravioli and a hot gâteau of pigeon, black sausage and vegetables to wild rabbit stuffed with coriander in a prawn and Madeira sauce. Sweets include a superb Grand Marnier ice cream in puff pastry with a raspberry sauce. 🖵 Well-chosen

Lunch 12.30–2.30   *Dinner* 7.30–10.45
Closed L Sat, all Sun & Bank Hols

CHELTENHAM · Golden Valley Thistle Hotel · 69% · £C

H **Map 4 C1** Gloucestershire
Gloucester Road GL51 0TS
Cheltenham (0242) 32691
Telex 43410

Credit Access, Amex, Diners, Visa

Good housekeeping and smartly turned-out staff are plus factors at
this yellow-brick 1970s hotel. The interior decor is regularly refreshed
and has an attractive, up-to-date feel. Bedrooms all boast trouser
presses, hairdryers, tea-makers and remote-control TVs, with safes,
mini-bars and additional toiletries in Executive rooms.
Amenities garden, putting, croquet, in-house movies, secretarial
services, fax, laundry service, helipad.

| *Rooms* 97 | *Direct dial* Yes | *Confirm by* 6 | *Parking* Ample |
| *Ensuite bath/shower* 97 | *Room TV* Yes | *Last dinner* 10 | *Room service* 24 hours |

CHELTENHAM · The Greenway · 79% · £B/C

HR **Map 4 C1** Gloucestershire
Shurdington GL51 5UG
Cheltenham (0242) 862352
Telex 437216

Rooms 18
Ensuite bath/shower 18
Direct dial Yes
Room TV Yes
Confirm by arrang.
Last dinner 9.30
Parking Ample
Room service All day

Credit Access, Amex, Diners, Visa
Closed first 2 wks Jan

Named after the pre-Roman path
that runs beside it, this splendid
country-house hotel is set in its
own parkland just off the A46.
Luxuriously appointed day
rooms feature period furniture,
deep-cushioned sofas and fresh
flower arrangements, and there's
also a cosy club-like bar. Spacious
main-house bedrooms, furnished
in similar period style, have been
smartly refurbished using top-
quality fabrics. Coach-house

rooms are no less luxurious, and well-designed bathrooms are equally
stylish. Keen, efficient management and staff strive to make every
stay an enjoyable one, and housekeeping throughout is immaculate.
No children under seven. No dogs.
Amenities garden, croquet, secretarial services, fax, laundry service.

Dining Room · ♛

Set L £13.50
Set D £19.50
About £60 for two
Seats 45
Parties 24

An elegant restaurant with conservatory extension is the setting for
enjoyable and imaginative cooking by Tony Robson-Burrell. Working
in the modern idiom, he builds his menus around choice seasonal
produce, creating dishes to delight the eyes as well as the palate. Start
perhaps with lightly cooked scallops in filo parcels served on a bed of
leeks and red peppers; then go on to breast of duck on a cabbage and
spinach galette in a lovely, subtly flavoured jus enhanced by
redcurrant. Interesting sweets might include a chocolate mille-feuille
with fresh pineapple cream served with a coffee bean sauce. Traditional
Sunday lunch. Pleasant and professional service. Comprehensive list
of good wines. ♟ Well-chosen ⊝ ♿

Lunch 12.30–2   *Dinner* 7.30–9.30, Sun 7.30 only
Closed L Sat & first 2 wks Jan

**Our inspectors *never* book in the name of Egon Ronay's Guides.
They disclose their identity only if they are considering an establishment
for inclusion in the next edition of the Guide.**

CHELTENHAM · Queen's Hotel · 69% · £C

H **Map 4 C1** Gloucestershire
The Promenade GL50 1NN
Cheltenham (0242) 514724
Telex 43381

Credit Access, Amex, Diners, Visa

The massive white pillars of Queen's Hotel have graced the promenade
for 150 years, an anniversary that is being celebrated by a programme
of refurbishment that will enhance its period elegance. The best
bedrooms are those at the front, with huge windows and spacious
bathrooms. A bouquet for comfortable beds and pillows, but a small
brickbat for sometimes sloppy housekeeping.
Amenities garden, secretarial services, laundry service.

| *Rooms* 77 | *Direct dial* Yes | *Confirm by* 6 | *Parking* Limited |
| *Ensuite bath/shower* 77 | *Room TV* Yes | *Last dinner* 10 | *Room service* 24 hours |

CHELTENHAM　　　Redmond's ★　　　　　　　　♛ ⑨

R **Map 4 C1** Gloucestershire
12 Suffolk Road
Cheltenham (0242) 580323

Lunch Sat & Sun only 12–2
Dinner 7.15–10.30
Set L £11.50
Set D £16.50
About £45 *for two*
Seats 20
Parties 12
Parking Ample

Credit Access, Diners, Visa
Closed D Sun, all Mon, 2 wks
Aug

In two years, Redmond and Pippa Hayward have built up an enviable reputation. Pippa manages front of house with equanimity and charm, while Redmond cooks with flair and imagination. Seasonally changing menus based on top-quality produce like delights like warm salad of smoked quail, and fillet of lamb with celeriac purée and Madeira sauce. Booking essential. A model wine list, concise and expertly chosen. Riesling du Rangen (Zind Humbrecht) '82; Mercurey (Michel Juillot) '84. *Specialities* ginger ravioli stuffed with scallop mousse served with spring onion sauce, breast of maize-fed chicken with orange and vanilla sauce, hot rhubarb soufflé with honey and cinnamon cream. ♀ Well-chosen ⊝ ✿

CHELTENHAM　　　Wyastone Hotel　56%　　　　　£D/E

H **Map 4 C1** Gloucestershire
Parabola Road GL50 3BG
Cheltenham (0242) 45549
Telex 437277

Credit Access, Amex, Diners, Visa

Dutch owners run this converted Victorian house with a friendly, personal touch – though furnishings are nothing special and some areas could do with a little tidying up. Nicest bedrooms, on the first floor of the main building, are good-sized and have decent half-tiled bathrooms. Avoid the tiny ground-floor singles in the garden wing. *Amenities* garden, secretarial services, laundry service.

Rooms 13	Direct dial Yes	Confirm by arrang.	Parking Ample
Ensuite bath/shower 13	Room TV Yes	Last dinner 8.30	Room service All day

CHELWOOD　　　Chelwood House　62%　NEW ENTRY　　£E

HR **Map 4 B3** Avon
Nr Bristol BS18 4NH
Compton Dando (07618) 730
Telex 44830

Credit Access, Diners, Visa
Closed 2 wks Xmas

Over 300 years old, this friendly little family-run hotel stands on the A37. Fresh flowers and handsome period furnishings grace the tiled entrance hall, which leads to a comfortable drawing room decorated in elegant Wedgwood style. Individually appointed bedrooms are immaculately kept and offer homely touches like mineral water and home-made biscuits. Excellent private bathrooms. Splendid breakfasts. No children under 10. No dogs. *Amenities* garden, laundry service.

Rooms 8	Direct dial Yes	Confirm by 6	Parking Ample
Ensuite bath/shower 8	Room TV Yes	Last dinner 9	Room service All day

Restaurant　NEW ENTRY　　　　　　　　　　⑨

Set L Sun £12.50
About £40 *for two*
Seats 15
Parties 20

Chef-patron Rudolf Birk offers good, honest country cooking in generous portions. His short, well-balanced menus have an international flavour, ranging from fresh asparagus in a perfect hollandaise or cassoulet of seafood among starters to such tempting main courses as succulent lamb in a rosemary cream sauce, medallions of pork Parisienne or superb poached lemon sole. Delicious desserts include rhubarb and nut crunch and Bavarian apple tart. ♀ Well-chosen ⊝

Lunch Sun 12–2, Mon–Sat by arrang.　*Dinner* 7–9, Sun 7–8 (residents only)　**Closed** 2 wks Xmas

CHENIES　　　Bedford Arms Thistle Hotel　64%　　£C

H **Map 5 E2** Buckinghamshire
Nr Rickmansworth WB3 6EQ
Chorleywood (092 78) 3301
Telex 893939

Credit Access, Amex, Diners, Visa

This small redbrick hotel provides a pleasantly quiet overnight stop. The rooms are all of a good size, with pretty colour schemes and traditionally styled furniture. Remote-control TVs, hairdryers and trouser presses are standard, and there are lots of extras in the bathrooms. There's a public bar and a cosily elegant cocktail bar. Some aspects of maintenance could be improved. *Amenities* garden, in-house movies, fax.

Rooms 10	Direct dial Yes	Confirm by arrang.	Parking Ample
Ensuite bath/shower 10	Room TV Yes	Last dinner 10.30	Room service 24 hours

In the eighteenth century,
one could only eat at special cookshops or inns.
But in 1765...Boulanger, a soup-seller, called his soups
by the special name of *restaurant* - restorative.
Their sale was so successful he wanted to enlarge his menu,
but since he was not a member of the *traiteurs* corporation -
eating-house keepers - he was not permitted to serve ragouts.
Instead he offered his customers sheeps' feet in
white sauce... not a ragout. Boulanger's sheeps' feet in
white sauce became famous all over Paris.
From 1786 onwards the great cuisiniers opened restaurants,
nearly all of which were famous for a particular speciality.

PHILIPPA PULLAR
CONSUMING PASSIONS (1970)

CHESTER

Map 10 A2
Town plan opposite

Population 117,300

Nowhere in Britain are history and architectural beauty better preserved: especially this may be seen in the Roman remains, the complete two-mile circuit of medieval walls and towers, and in the shopping Rows.
Add to this the charms of the River Dee, Canal and the Castle, the Tudor buildings, and the Cathedral. Chester was once a port, but fortunately for today's tourists the mouth of the Dee silted up in the 15th century, so that Chester's sea-trade passed to Liverpool.

Annual Events
Chester Races *May, June, July*
Folk Festival *May*
Summer Musical Festival *July*

Sights Outside City
Arley Hall, *Northwich*
Beeston Castle, Chirk Castle
Boat Museum, *Ellesmere Port*
Tatton Park, *Knutsford*

Tourist Information Centre
Town Hall, Northgate Street
Chester CH1 2HF
Telephone Chester 318356 or 313126

1 Bishop Lloyd's House B4
2 Bus Exchange A3
3 Chester Castle and Regimental Museum B5
4 Chester Cathedral B3
5 Chester Heritage Centre B4
6 Chester Visitor Centre C4
7 Gamul House B4
8 Gateway Theatre A3
9 General Station C2
10 Grosvenor Museum B4
11 The Groves *for river trips* C4
12 Information Centre, Town Hall B3
13 King Charles Tower B3
14 Northgate Arena B2
15 Pied Bull Coaching Inn *17th-c* A3
16 Roman Amphitheatre C4
17 The Rows B4
18 St John's Church C4
19 St Mary's Centre B5
20 Toy Museum B4
21 Zoo A1

Fiat Dealer
Cowies, Mountview
Sealand Road, Chester CH1 4LQ
Tel. Chester 374440

Chester FIAT

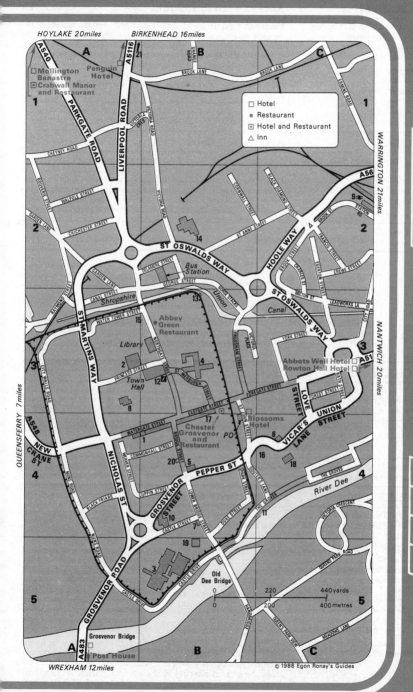

HOYLAKE 20 miles   BIRKENHEAD 16 miles

□ Mollington Banastre
□ Crabwall Manor and Restaurant

Penguin Hotel

□ Hotel
● Restaurant
⊡ Hotel and Restaurant
△ Inn

WARRINGTON 21 miles

NANTWICH 20 miles

A51

Abbots Well Hotel □
Rowton Hall Hotel □

ST OSWALDS WAY

Bus Station

Shropshire

Abbey Green Restaurant

Library

Town Hall

Chester Grosvenor and Restaurant

Blossoms Hotel

PEPPER ST

River Dee

The Groves

Old Dee Bridge

QUEENSFERRY 7 miles

GROSVENOR ROAD

Grosvenor Bridge
□ Post House

WREXHAM 12 miles

0   220   440 yards
0   200   400 metres

© 1988 Egon Ronay's Guides

CHESTER   Abbey Green Restaurant   ♋

R **Town plan B3** Cheshire
2 Abbey Green,
off Northgate Street
Chester (0244) 313251

Vegetarian cooking
About £25 for two
Seats 48 *Parties* 25
Parking Limited
Credit Access

Imaginative vegetarian food served in cosy, homely surroundings.
Ingredients are fresh, flavours harmonious on menus that change
every few weeks; our best dishes were mushrooms and cream cheese
in filo pastry with a tangy ravigote sauce and hazelnut pastry flan,
filled with whipped cream and raspberries and topped with whole
hazelnuts. The wine list is well chosen, with helpful comments and
some interesting organic wines. Alfresco summer eating. Accommodation planned (phone). ♟ Well-chosen ℮

Lunch 10–3.30, Sun 11.30–3.30 (April–Sept)   *Dinner* 6.30–10.15, Sat
6.30–11   **Closed** D Sun & Mon, 25 & 26 Dec

CHESTER   Abbots Well Hotel   61%   £D

H **Town plan C3** Cheshire
Whitchurch Road,
Christleton CH3 5QL
Chester (0244) 332121
Telex 61561

Credit Access, Amex, Diners, Visa

An angular modern hotel standing in spacious grounds on the A41,
east of Chester. Wall mosaics and medieval-style busts add character
to the day rooms, and well-equipped, good-sized bedrooms are
pleasantly modern in style. Service is friendly and well intentioned,
but not particularly efficient. A leisure complex is planned.
Amenities garden, laundry service, 24-hour lounge service.

| *Rooms* 127 | *Direct dial* Yes | *Confirm by* 6 | *Parking* Ample |
| *Ensuite bath/shower* 127 | *Room TV* Yes | *Last dinner* 9.45 | *Room service* Limited |

Changes in data sometimes occur in establishments
after the Guide goes to press.
Prices should be taken as indications rather than firm quotes.

CHESTER   Blossoms Hotel   60%   £C/D

H **Town plan B3** Cheshire
St John Street CH1 1HL
Chester (0244) 23186
Telex 61113

Credit Access, Amex, Diners, Visa

Just off one of Chester's main shopping streets, Blossoms is a popular
hotel with a quiet, relaxed ambience, friendly staff and a good standard
of housekeeping. The lofty entrance and staircase are instantly
attractive, and there are two bars and a cosy little lounge. Bedrooms
of various shapes and sizes have all recently been refurbished. Guests
may take membership of a nearby leisure centre.
Amenities in-house movies, laundry service.

| *Rooms* 72 | *Direct dial* Yes | *Confirm by* arrang. | *Parking* Ample |
| *Ensuite bath/shower* 72 | *Room TV* Yes | *Last dinner* 9.30 | *Room service* Limited |

CHESTER   Chester Grosvenor   82%   £A/B

HR **Town plan B4** Cheshire
Eastgate Street CH1 1LT
Chester (0244) 324024
Telex 61240

Rooms 87
Ensuite bath/shower 87
Direct dial Yes
Room TV Yes
Confirm by 4
Last dinner 11.30
Parking Ample
Room service 24 hours

Credit Access, Amex, Diners, Visa
Closed 25 & 26 Dec

Behind the renowned half-timbered facade it's a changed Chester Grosvenor: in place of the
traditional hall and desk is a
country house-style reception
area with small bureaux and
deep, inviting armchairs. The
handsome library-lounge doubles as a bar, and there's a striking
new brasserie and formal restaurant. Bedrooms, which range
from spacious to quite compact,
are impressively appointed, with

fine furniture and all the modern comforts. There are some lovely
suites, and the bathrooms are very well equipped. Staff are young and
keen, but for us the new-look Grosvenor has lost just a spark of its old
magic. No dogs. *Amenities* sauna, solarium, gymnasium, secretarial
services, fax, valeting, laundry service, brasserie (6.30am–11.30pm).
&

Arkle Restaurant ♕

Set L £15
Set D £32.50
About £75 for two
Seats 40

Smaller and more intimate than its grand predecessor, the Arkle keeps the services of Paul Reed, whose modern cooking is characterised by lightness of touch and considerable eye appeal. Fish is cooked with minute precision (sweet, succulent scallops served in a dry vermouth sauce with tiny vegetables) and high-quality meat dishes are exemplified by rack of lamb, cooked pink and accompanied by an admirably light puff-pastry case filled with sweetbreads. Desserts must not be missed, and there are splendid French and English cheeses. The wine list is splendid and comprehensive, with many interesting bottles: '86 Montagny 1er cru (Anthony Sarjeant), '84 Penfolds Kalimna, '66 Ch. Cos d'Estournel. Keen service is supplied by a bright, alert young team. ☻ Well-chosen ✆ ♿

Lunch 12–2.30 *Dinner* 7.30–10 **Closed** L Sat & all Sun & Bank Hols

---

CHESTER Crabwall Manor 75% £B/C

HR **Town plan A1** Cheshire
Mollington CH1 6NE
Chester (0244) 851666
Telex 61220

Rooms 32
Ensuite bath/shower 32
Direct dial Yes
Room TV Yes
Confirm by arrang.
Last dinner 9.30
Parking Ample
Room service 24 hours

Credit Access, Amex, Diners, Visa

An early 19th-century house forms the core of this professionally run country house hotel which stands in 11 acres of woodland and gardens just five minutes drive out of Chester on the A540. Chintzy, comfortable day rooms manage to be at once stylish and homely. An attractive mellow bar overlooks the grounds. Spacious bedrooms have real individuality, with a table and elegantly upholstered

armchairs adding to the sense of welcome; beds are exceptionally comfortable. Splendid bathrooms have bidets and separate shower cubicles. Staff are very friendly and efficient. No children under five. No dogs. *Amenities* garden, croquet, in-house movies, secretarial services, fax, laundry service. ♿

Restaurant ♕

Set L £12, Sun £13.50
Set D £19.50
About £80 for two
Seats 60

Service is very polished at this comfortable, split-level restaurant which also boasts excellent cooking by the talented Michael Truelove, formerly of the Box Tree Cottage. Dishes on a well-balanced, modern menu include delicious rabbit terrine, whole lobster served with memorable tortellini of diced chicken with ginger, and passion fruit bavarois. Excellent wine list, an enthusiast's collection: Chablis Vaudésir (Droin) '85, Bourgogne Pinot Noir (Henri Jayer) '85. ☻ Well-chosen ✆ ♿

Lunch 12.30–2 *Dinner* 7–9.30

CHESTER Ladbroke Hotel

See **PENGUIN HOTEL**

CHESTER Mollington Banastre Hotel 67% £C/D

H **Town plan A1** Cheshire
Parkgate Road CH1 6NN
Chester (0244) 851471
Telex 61686

Credit Access, Amex, Diners, Visa

A modernised Victorian mansion with a pub in its grounds. Public rooms are light and airy, and the best bedrooms (all are very well equipped) are the large rooms in the original part. There's a stylish leisure complex. Friendly staff. *Amenities* garden, indoor swimming pool, sauna, solarium, whirlpool bath, keep-fit equipment, beauty salon, hairdressing, squash, croquet, in-house movies, secretarial services, laundry service, 24-hour lounge service.

| *Rooms* 66 | *Direct dial* Yes | *Confirm by* 6 | *Parking* Ample |
| *Ensuite bath/shower* 66 | *Room TV* Yes | *Last dinner* 10.15 | *Room service* All day |

CHESTER   Penguin Hotel   62%   £C

H **Town plan A1** Cheshire
Backford Cross CH1 6PE
Chester (0244) 851551
Telex 61552

Credit Access, Amex, Diners, Visa

Formerly the Ladbroke, this is a purpose-built modern hotel just
north of the city at the junction of the A41 and A5117. A little
fountain plays in the stylish foyer-lounge, and there's a sleek,
streamlined cocktail bar. Bedrooms are neat and comfortable, with
hairdryers, trouser presses and functional private bathrooms. Extras
in Gold Star rooms. Brisk, cheerful staff.
Amenities in-house movies, secretarial services, fax, laundry service.

Rooms 113	*Direct dial* Yes	*Confirm by* 6	*Parking* Ample
Ensuite bath/shower 113	*Room TV* Yes	*Last dinner* 9.45	*Room service* 24 hours

CHESTER   Post House Hotel   60%   £C/D

H **Town plan A5** Cheshire
Wrexham Road CH4 9DL
Chester (0244) 680111
Telex 61450

Credit Access, Amex, Diners, Visa

A modern hotel south of the city on the A483. Bedrooms, including a
new block of 44, are smartly contemporary, with trouser presses,
hairdryers and mini-bars as standard equipment. There are two bars
and a relaxing lounge area, function facilities, plus a brand new leisure
centre. Friendly and willing staff, but lapses in housekeeping can
occur and the manager seemed short on charm.
Amenities garden, laundry service, 24-hour lounge service.

Rooms 64	*Direct dial* Yes	*Confirm by* 6	*Parking* Ample
Ensuite bath/shower 64	*Room TV* Yes	*Last dinner* 9.45	*Room service* Limited

CHESTER   Rowton Hall Hotel   62%   £D

H **Town plan C3** Cheshire
Whitchurch Road CH3 6AD
Chester (0244) 335262
Telex 61172

Credit Access, Amex, Diners, Visa

You can look across to the Welsh hills from this handsome converted
country house in eight acres of well-kept grounds just off the A41.
Pleasant public areas include a fine panelled reception hall, cosy bar,
and a sunny, plant-filled conservatory. A superb oak staircase leads to
lofty bedrooms with pretty decor and a mixture of antique and
modern furniture.
Amenities garden, croquet, secretarial services, laundry service. &

Rooms 42	*Direct dial* Yes	*Confirm by* 6	*Parking* Ample
Ensuite bath/shower 42	*Room TV* Yes	*Last dinner* 9.30	*Room service* All day

**If we recommend meals in a Hotel or Inn,
a separate entry is made for its restaurant.**

CHESTERFIELD   Chesterfield Hotel   58%   £D/E

H **Map 10 C2** Derbyshire
Malkin Street S41 7UA
Chesterfield (0246) 71141
Telex 547492

Credit Access, Amex, Diners, Visa

A restyled Victorian railway hotel, offering simple overnight
accommodation. Entrance is straight into the bar-lounge area, designed
around a nostalgic 1920s theme. Well-coordinated bedrooms – some
furnished in pine, others more modestly appointed – offer hairdryers,
trouser presses, tea-makers and (in most cases) mini-bars. Though
bathrooms are generally well kept, maintenance is not always up to
scratch. *Amenities* in-house movies, laundry service.

Rooms 61	*Direct dial* Yes	*Confirm by* 6	*Parking* Ample
Ensuite bath/shower 61	*Room TV* Yes	*Last dinner* 10	*Room service* 24 hours

CHESTER-LE-STREET   Lumley Castle Hotel   68%   £C/D

H **Map 15 B4** Co. Durham
DH3 4NX
Durham (091) 3891111
Telex 537433

Credit Access, Amex, Diners, Visa
Closed 25 & 26 Dec & 1 Jan

A proper castle, complete with courtyard, corner towers and dungeons,
sitting on top of a hill just outside town. Already 200 years old when
the Normans invaded, it now offers a splendid combination of
medieval charm and 20th-century comfort. Prettily decorated
bedrooms with stylish fabrics and some antiques range from average-
sized courtyard rooms (the majority; singles have shower/WC only)
to more characterful feature castle rooms with four-posters and neatly
concealed bathrooms. The library bar is an elegant spot to browse or
sip, and there's an attractive, cosy lounge. Staff are helpful and affable.
No dogs. *Amenities* garden, sauna, billiards, secretarial services,
laundry service.

Rooms 66	*Direct dial* Yes	*Confirm by* 6	*Parking* Ample
Ensuite bath/shower 66	*Room TV* Yes	*Last dinner* 9.45	*Room service* 24 hours

CHICHESTER | Dolphin & Anchor Hotel 63% | £C/D

H **Map 5 E4** West Sussex
West Street PO19 1QE
Chichester (0243) 785121

Credit Access, Amex, Diners, Visa

Originally two inns, this welcoming hotel stands opposite the cathedral a short walk from shops and station. The hotel's coffee shop and bar are popular with both guests and locals. Bedrooms vary from compact singles (shower/WC only) to top-of-the-range rooms with stylish modern fabrics in pretty colours. There's some current, and proposed, bedroom refurbishment.
Amenities laundry service, coffee shop (10am–10pm).

Rooms 54	*Direct dial* Yes	*Confirm by* 6	*Parking* Limited
Ensuite bath/shower 54	*Room TV* Yes	*Last dinner* 10	*Room service* 24 hours

 indicates a **well-chosen** house wine

CHIDDINGFOLD | Crown Inn | £E

I **Map 5 E3** Surrey
Nr Godalming GU8 4TX
Wormley (042 879) 2255

Credit Access, Amex, Diners, Visa

Standing by the church and village green in picture-postcard Chiddingfold, this 13th-century timbered inn is part of a typically English scene. The beamed lounge bar oozes character, and bedrooms are either delightfully original (one has a carved antique four-poster) or pleasantly modernised. Practical private bathrooms. Manager Sue Piper is a real live wire and a great asset.
Amenities secretarial services, laundry service.

Rooms 8	*Direct dial* Yes	*Confirm by* arrang.	*Parking* Ample
Ensuite bath/shower 8	*Room TV* Yes	*Last dinner* 9.30	*Room service* All day

CHIDEOCK | Chideock House Hotel 58% | £F

HR **Map 4 A4** Dorset
Main Street, Nr Bridport
DT6 6JN
Chideock (0297) 89242

Credit Access, Visa

New owners Derek and Jenny Hammond plan many improvements at their Dorset-stone roadside hotel, and new bed linen, covers and matching curtains are a good start. Bedroom furniture will be replaced, and better toiletries provided in the bathrooms. The residents' lounge is clean and bright, with a chess set and books to browse through, but the bar needs attention. The riverside gardens and terrace are attractive features.

Rooms 9	*Room phone* No	*Confirm by* arrang.	*Parking* Ample
Ensuite bath/shower 7	*Room TV* Yes	*Last dinner* 9.30	*Room service* All day

Restaurant

Set Sun L £6.75
Set D £12.50
About £36 *for two*
Seats 45
Parties 50

Chris Patterson remains as chef, but he and the Hammonds have made changes to the menus. Typical dishes run from salade niçoise and grilled scallops with smoked ham and Cointreau to chicken in apricot sauce and herby rack of lamb. The restaurant comprises two cottagy rooms with black beams, handsome fireplaces and lovely garden views. Candlelight, fresh flowers and good-quality table settings add an elegant air. ⊘

Lunch 12–2 *Dinner* 7–9.30
Closed D Sun, all Mon

CHILGROVE | White Horse Inn

R **Map 5 E3** West Sussex
High Street
East Marden (024 359) 219

Set L £14.50
Set D £17.95
About £45 *for two*
Seats 60
Parties 20
Parking Ample

Credit Access, Amex, Diners, Visa

A pretty wisteria-clad inn that's best known for its award-winning cellar. The food may not be in the same league as the wines but is perfectly competent, with menus making obvious concessions to the avocado and chicken cordon bleu brigade but also featuring imaginative options like roulade of smoked salmon filled with artichoke mousseline, and meltingly tender Aylesbury duck cooked in a rich sauce of port wine and brandied fruit conserve. Presentation is good and portions are tailored to suit country appetites. As memorable cellars go, this is the daddy of them all: probably the greatest wine list in the country bar none. ⊵ Outstanding
♉ Well-chosen ⊘

Lunch 12.30–2 *Dinner* 7–9.30
Closed Sun, Mon, 3 wks Feb & 1 wk Nov

CHIPPING CAMPDEN   Caminetto   *NEW ENTRY*   ♀

R Map 4 C1 Gloucestershire
High Street
Evesham (0386) 840934

Italian cooking
Set L £6.50
About £30 for two
Seats 45 *Parties* 45
Parking Ample
Credit Access, Visa

Customers come from miles around to eat at this agreeable Italian restaurant in a Cotswold stone building. The menu provides few surprises but plenty of choice from Sardinian-style grilled sardines and tortellini with a tasty cream and tomato sauce to liver veneziana, pepper steak and frutti di mare alla fiama – a selection of fresh fish and shellfish cooked at the table. Familiar sweets to finish. ©

Lunch 12–1.30   *Dinner* 7–10.30
Closed L Mon, all Sun, Bank Hols & 3 wks Easter

CHIPPING CAMPDEN   Cotswold House   £D/E
Hotel   70%   *NEW ENTRY*

HR Map 4 C1
Gloucestershire
The Square GL55 6AN
Evesham (0386) 840330
Telex 336810

Rooms 15
Ensuite bath/shower 15
Direct dial Yes
Room TV Yes
Confirm by arrang.
Last dinner 9.30
Parking Ample
Room service All day

Credit Access, Amex, Diners, Visa

A fine Regency house has been lovingly and tastefully converted into a most comfortable and relaxing hotel with enthusiastic owners and smiling, hardworking staff. Period elegance fills the lovely stone-floored foyer, where the armchairs are inviting and fresh flowers add splashes of colour. The adjoining drawing room is equally appealing, and the bar is a popular place for all-day snacking. A splendid staircase spirals to generously proportioned bedrooms, each with its own decorative theme (Military, Garden, Indian). Antiques and attractive fabrics abound, and all rooms have well-equipped bathrooms. Nice breakfasts. No children under eight. No dogs.
Amenities garden, secretarial services, laundry service, coffee shop (9.30am–10.30pm).

Restaurant   *NEW ENTRY*

Set L Sun £9.50
Set D £13.50
About £38 for two
Seats 35
Parties 40

Diners sit in elegant surroundings to enjoy the accomplished cooking of Serge Puyal, whose menus offer a good balance of dishes to tempt all palates. Brixham crab with prawns, yoghurt and dill or fresh asparagus in a puff pastry case could start proceedings, followed perhaps by poacher's pie, brill with shallots and red wine, veal cutlet with a mild mustard sauce or a special vegetarian main course. Brown bread ice cream, caramelised apple tart with Calvados and a duo of white and dark chocolate mousses provide plenty of incentive not to pass on the puds. Wines are carefully chosen: Cru de Coudoulet '85, Chassagne Montrachet Rouge (H. Lamy) '83. ©

Lunch Sun only 12.30–2   *Dinner* 7.15–9.30   **Closed** L Mon–Sat

---

Changes in data sometimes occur in establishments
after the Guide goes to press.
Prices should be taken as indications rather than firm quotes.

CHIPPING CAMPDEN   Kings Arms Hotel   £D/E

I Map 4 C1 Gloucestershire
Market Square GL55 6AW
Evesham (0386) 840256

Credit Access, Visa

A Cotswold-stone 16th-century inn which offers a convenient base from which to explore the surrounding countryside. Rustic appeal is to be found in the bar-lounge, with its open fireplace, simple furniture and wooden floor, while the cosy, homely TV lounge has comfortable armchairs and sofas. Bedrooms have freestanding furniture and light, traditional colour schemes and fabrics. Bathrooms, private and public, are functional and practical. *Amenities* garden.

Rooms 14	*Room phone* No	*Confirm by* arrang.	*Parking* Ample
Ensuite bath/shower 2	*Room TV* No	*Last dinner* 10	*Room service* None

CHIPPING CAMPDEN　Noel Arms Hotel　59%　£E

H Map 4 C1 Gloucestershire
High Street GL55 6AT
Evesham (0386) 840317
Telex 336810

Credit Access, Visa

Built as a coaching inn six centuries ago, this friendly little hotel retains a traditional, old-fashioned feel for hospitality. Heavy oak beams are a feature almost throughout, and in the foyer there's a fine collection of armour, weapons and trophies. Good solid furnishings, including some antique four-posters, fill the bedrooms, all of which have neatly kept private bath or shower rooms. No dogs. *Amenities* garden, bowling green.

| *Rooms* 18 | *Room phone* No | *Confirm by* 6 | *Parking* Ample |
| *Ensuite bath/shower* 18 | *Room TV* Yes | *Last dinner* 9 | *Room service* Limited |

CHIPPING NORTON　La Madonette　♧

R Map 4 C1 Oxfordshire
7 Horsefair
Chipping Norton (0608) 2320

French cooking

About £50 for two
Seats 32
Parties 30
Parking Difficult

Credit Access, Visa

Culinary triumphs are the order of the day at Alain and Patti Ritter's pretty little restaurant. Alain views cooking as nothing less than an art form and handles his raw ingredients with infinite care, using direct supply lines to ensure top quality (seafood from Cornwall, cheeses from Philippe Olivier). You might start with a hot and deliciously moist prawn and salmon mousse encased in smoked salmon, then tuck into succulent breast of pheasant cooked with button onions in red wine sauce. For a perfect ending, how about a deliquescent chocolate mousse served in a thin chocolate case on pear purée, garnished with pear slices?
🍷 Well-chosen ℗

Dinner 7.30–9.45
Closed Sun, Mon, Last wk Sept, 1st wk Oct & 1 wk Xmas

 is our symbol for an **outstanding** wine list

CHITTLEHAMHOLT　Highbullen Hotel　60%　£D/E

H Map 3 D2 Devon
Umberleigh EX37 9HD
Chittlehamholt (076 94) 561

Public rooms in this Victorian mansion enjoy splendid parkland views. Main-house bedrooms are comfortably traditional; those in outhouses are modern but equally well appointed. No children under ten. No dogs. *Amenities* garden, indoor & outdoor swimming pools, sauna, solarium, whirlpool bath, steam bath, keep-fit equipment, massage, hairdressing, indoor & outdoor tennis, squash, 9-hole golf course, croquet, game fishing, billiards, laundry service.

| *Rooms* 35 | *Direct dial* Yes | *Confirm by* arrang. | *Parking* Ample |
| *Ensuite bath/shower* 35 | *Room TV* Yes | *Last dinner* 9 | *Room service* 24 hours |

CHOLLERFORD　George Hotel　59%　£D

H Map 15 B4 Northumberland
Nr Hexham NE46 4EW
Humshaugh (043 481) 611
Telex 53168

Credit Access, Amex, Diners, Visa

Four miles north of Hexham, the George is a pleasantly run hotel with charming gardens, a long river frontage and attractive views. The bars and lounge are quite appealing, the bedrooms and bathrooms practical and fairly well kept, if a touch lacking in luxury. *Amenities* garden, indoor swimming pool, sauna, solarium, whirlpool bath, golf driving nets, putting, coarse & game fishing, pool table, secretarial services, fax, laundry service, children's play area.

| *Rooms* 54 | *Direct dial* Yes | *Confirm by* arrang. | *Parking* Ample |
| *Ensuite bath/shower* 54 | *Room TV* Yes | *Last dinner* 9.30 | *Room service* 24 hours |

CHURCH STRETTON　Stretton Hall Hotel　60%　£E

H Map 10 A4 Shropshire
All Stretton SY6 6HG
Church Stretton (0694) 723224

Credit Access, Amex, Diners, Visa

Pleasant, peaceful surroundings for a Victorian country house standing in the shadow of Long Mynd. Public rooms leading from the hall are in comfortable, traditional style, with plenty of inviting armchairs providing easy relaxation. Decent-size bedrooms – back ones overlook the garden – are furnished variously with period or modern pieces, and all have a private bath or shower. Most rooms have recently been refurbished by the new owners. *Amenities* garden, laundry service.

| *Rooms* 13 | *Room phone* Yes | *Confirm by* arrang. | *Parking* Ample |
| *Ensuite bath/shower* 13 | *Room TV* Yes | *Last dinner* 9.15 | *Room service* Limited |

CHURT   Frensham Pond Hotel   69%   £D/E

H **Map 5 E3** Surrey
Nr Farnham GU10 2QB
Frensham (025 125) 3175
Telex 858610

Credit Access, Amex, Diners, Visa

Friendly, helpful staff create a happy atmosphere at this spotlessly kept hotel, which stands by Frensham Great Pond in unspoilt countryside on the Surrey/Hampshire border. Part of the original house dates back to the 15th century, and here are to be found the comfortable, airy lounge and the clubby cocktail bar, both overlooking the pond. Here, too, are half the bedrooms, the rest being in a garden wing; the former are the more traditional, the latter spacious, modern and well equipped (you can park your car outside these rooms). More rooms planned for 1989. Good breakfasts. No dogs. *Amenities* garden, indoor swimming pool, sauna, solarium, whirlpool bath, keep-fit equipment, squash, coarse fishing, fax, laundry service.

Rooms 19	*Direct dial* Yes	*Confirm by* arrang.	*Parking* Ample
Ensuite bath/shower 19	*Room TV* Yes	*Last dinner* 9.30	*Room service* 24 hours

CIRENCESTER   Fleece Hotel   65%   £D/E

H **Map 4 C2** Gloucestershire
Market Place GL7 4NZ
Cirencester (0285) 68507

Credit Access, Amex, Diners, Visa

A part-Tudor, part-Georgian building, once a coaching inn and now a pleasant, restful base for touring the Cotswolds. Open fires keep things snug in the lounge and bar, and the courtyard is popular in summer. There's also an informal wine bar. Bedrooms, individually decorated and smartly furnished, all have private bathrooms, though four are not en suite. *Amenities* laundry service, coffee shop (10.30am–6pm, till 10pm in summer).

Rooms 25	*Direct dial* Yes	*Confirm by* 6	*Parking* Limited
Ensuite bath/shower 21	*Room TV* Yes	*Last dinner* 9.30	*Room service* Limited

CIRENCESTER   Kings Head Hotel   60%   £D/E

H **Map 4 C2** Gloucestershire
Market Place GL7 2NR
Cirencester (0285) 3322
Telex 43470

Credit Access, Amex, Diners, Visa
Closed 27–31 Dec

Standing squarely in the centre of town, the Kings Head is a former coaching inn dating back to the 14th century. Beams and panelling preserve a period feel in the day rooms, along with paintings and the odd antique. Bedrooms are modest and cheerful, with private facilities throughout. The hotel's standards of decor and housekeeping are not all they should be.
Amenities games room, laundry service, 24-hour lounge service.

Rooms 70	*Direct dial* Yes	*Confirm by* 6	*Parking* Limited
Ensuite bath/shower 70	*Room TV* Yes	*Last dinner* 9	*Room service* Limited

CIRENCESTER   Stratton House Hotel   62%   £E

H **Map 4 C2** Gloucestershire
Gloucester Road GL7 2LE
Cirencester (0285) 61761

Credit Access, Amex, Diners, Visa

A warm and friendly welcome awaits at this former wool merchant's house just north-west of Cirencester on the A417. Behind the lovely honey-coloured stone exterior are splendid public rooms like the flagstoned hall, elegant drawing room and heavily beamed bar. Main-house bedrooms are rather old-fashioned in character and could do with a facelift though smaller rooms in newer extensions are more modern.
Amenities garden, croquet, laundry service. &

Rooms 26	*Room phone* Yes	*Confirm by* 6	*Parking* Ample
Ensuite bath/shower 22	*Room TV* Yes	*Last dinner* 9.45	*Room service* All day

---

★   For a *discount* on next year's guide, see **An Offer for Answers.**   ★

CLANFIELD   Plough at Clanfield   68%   £C/D

HR **Map 4 C2** Oxfordshire
OX8 2RB
Clanfield (036 781) 222
Telex 449848

Credit Access, Amex, Diners, Visa

The Plough is a charming Elizabethan manor house with a wealth of old beams in the bar-lounge and bedrooms. Rooms have an individual appeal – here a four-poster, there a whirlpool bath, there a super king-size bed and a shower room. Staff are pleasant, and a good breakfast gets the day going. No children under 12. No dogs.
Amenities garden, in-house movies, secretarial services, laundry service.

Rooms 6	*Direct dial* Yes	*Confirm by* arrang.	*Parking* Ample
Ensuite bath/shower 6	*Room TV* Yes	*Last dinner* 9.30	*Room service* All day

Restaurant ♕

Set L £9.75, Sun £10.95
Set D from £17
About £55 for two
Seats 45
Parties 40

Fixed-price menus provide a short choice of dishes capably prepared by chef-manager Paul Barnard and his team. Some are English classics – traditional junket, roast grouse plus trimmings, rack of lamb with rosemary and thyme – others modern, like rabbit and guinea fowl terrine or veal en chemise. Among the sweets are sorbets, ices, soufflés and sultana syrup sponge pudding. There are some good Rhônes on the wine list. No smoking. ♀ Well-chosen ℮

Lunch 12–1.45
Dinner 7–9.30, Sat 7–10

**We welcome bona fide complaints and recommendations
on the tear-out pages at the back of the book for readers' comment.
They are followed up by our professional team.**

CLAWTON Court Barn Country House Hotel *NEW ENTRY* 61% £E/F

H **Map 2 C2** Devon
Nr Holsworthy EX22 6PS
North Tamerton (040 927) 219

Credit Access, Amex, Diners, Visa
Closed 1 wk Jan

The present building dates from 1853 and stands peacefully in five acres of pleasant grounds just outside the village. Susan and Robert Wood run it on personal lines, and the day rooms are cosy and relaxing. Decent-sized bedrooms are very fresh and pretty, with individual furnishings and William Morris fabrics. Tea-makers, hairdryers, radios; private bath or shower rooms, one not en suite. *Amenities* garden, badminton, pitch & putt, croquet, laundry service.

Rooms 8	*Room phone* No	*Confirm by* 7.30	*Parking* Ample
Ensuite bath/shower 7	*Room TV* No	*Last dinner* 9	*Room service* Limited

CLAYTON-LE-WOODS Pines Hotel 67% £E

H **Map 10 B1** Lancashire
Nr Chorley PR6 7ED
Preston (0772) 38551
Telex 67308

Credit Access, Amex, Diners, Visa
Closed 25 & 26 Dec

Attractive gardens surround this much-extended Victorian house. The pleasing bar, with its traditional wallpaper and comfortable easy chairs, extends into a lounge area with leather chesterfields. Standard bedrooms have decent darkwood and laminate units and easy chairs: superior rooms are larger, with stylish matching fabrics, luxurious bathrooms and plenty of extras. No dogs. *Amenities* garden, solarium, squash, pool table, secretarial services, laundry service.

Rooms 24	*Direct dial* Yes	*Confirm by* arrang.	*Parking* Ample
Ensuite bath/shower 24	*Room TV* Yes	*Last dinner* 9.30	*Room service* 24 hours

CLEARWELL Clearwell Castle 67% £D/E

H **Map 4 B2** Gloucestershire
Royal Forest of Dean GL16 8LG
Dean (0594) 32320

Credit Access, Amex, Diners, Visa

An early 18th-century Gothic Revival castle with a grand castellated exterior and stately public rooms. Chandeliers and beautifully moulded ceilings enhance the spacious hall and lounge, and there's a small clubby bar. Main-house bedrooms are attractively furnished in period style and offer extras like sherry and mineral water; two coach-house rooms are more simply appointed. No dogs. *Amenities* garden, croquet, game fishing, secretarial services, laundry service.

Rooms 12	*Direct dial* Yes	*Confirm by* arrang.	*Parking* Ample
Ensuite bath/shower 12	*Room TV* Yes	*Last dinner* 10	*Room service* All day

CLEETHORPES Kingsway Hotel 61% £D/E

H **Map 11 F2** Humberside
Kingsway DN35 0AE
Cleethorpes (0472) 601122

Credit Access, Amex, Diners, Visa
Closed 25–27 Dec

Three 1920s seaside cottages have grown out of all recognition into this comfortable and well-run hotel. Splendidly traditional lounges enjoy fine views of the Humber estuary, and the cocktail bar is handsomely appointed with oil paintings and antiques. Bedrooms range from fairly basic to smartly up-to-date, and refurbishment continues. Some rooms overlook a secluded roof garden. No dogs. *Amenities* garden, laundry service.

Rooms 54	*Room phone* Yes	*Confirm by* arrang.	*Parking* Ample
Ensuite bath/shower 50	*Room TV* Yes	*Last dinner* 9	*Room service* All day

CLIMPING — Bailiffscourt 75% — £B/C

HR **Map 5 E4** West Sussex
Littlehampton BN17 5RW
Littlehampton (0903) 723511
Telex 877870

Rooms 20
Ensuite bath/shower 20
Direct dial Yes
Room TV Yes
Confirm by 6
Last dinner 9.45
Parking Ample
Room service All day

Credit Access, Amex, Diners, Visa

'The most expensive folly in the world' is how this exquisite replica of a 13th-century courthouse has been described. Although less than 50 years old, it has been fashioned from ancient salvaged material, some from the site, the rest from old houses throughout Britain. Today it is a tranquil hotel. Public rooms include lounges with sturdy traditional furniture, and there's a small cocktail bar. Bedrooms (some in a separate thatched house that may be reached by an underground tunnel) are charming, with antiques alongside modern facilities. Bathrooms range from the practical to the palatial. No children under eight. ***Amenities*** garden, outdoor swimming pool, sauna, tennis, croquet, pool table, laundry service, helipad.

Restaurant

Set L £14.50, Sun £15.95
Set D £22.95
About £60 for two
Seats 45
Parties 30

The light from mullioned windows falls on polished oak tables decked with flowers at this unique restaurant. Garry Leaf's modern menus make good use of local produce. A typical table d'hôte choice might be gravad lax followed by baked lamb on creamed spinach with rosemary sauce. Good simple vegetables, tangy desserts. Go for the less common Italian wines on an otherwise conventional list: Venegazzu '81; Chardonnay di Appiano '86. Well-chosen

Lunch 12.30–2
Dinner 7.30–9.45, Sat 7.30–10

Any person using our name to obtain free hospitality is a fraud. Proprietors, please inform the police and us.

CLUN — Old Post Office *NEW ENTRY*

RR **Map 10 A4** Shropshire
9 The Square SY7 8JA
Clun (058 84) 687

Set D £18
About £45 for two
Seats 28
Parties 28
Parking Limited

New owners Anne and Richard Arbuthnot have made a promising start in this tiny, cosy restaurant in a former Victorian post office. Fixed price menus are based on seasonal produce and offer a handful of well-executed starters like hot scallop mousse with grapefruit sauce and main courses like pork tenderloin with marinated kumquats. An excellent selection of beautifully kept British cheeses is a highlight.

Lunch 12.30–2.30 by arrang. only *Dinner* 7.15–9.30
Closed L Tues, all Sun & Mon (exc. to residents), mid Dec–mid Mar

BEDROOMS 3 £F
With bath/shower 0

Three simply furnished bedrooms have welcoming touches like home-made biscuits, mineral water and magazines. They share a well maintained cork and tile bathroom. No dogs.

COATHAM MUNDEVILLE — Hall Garth 61% — £D

H **Map 15 B5** Co. Durham
Nr Darlington DL1 3LU
Aycliffe (0325) 300400

Credit Access, Amex, Diners, Visa
Closed 22 Dec–2 Jan

An attractively solid stone house, parts of which date back to the 16th century. Public areas include three quite pleasant lounges which have floral wallpaper and plenty of bric-a-brac. Half the bedrooms are in a stable block above the bar (which provides a certain amount of noise); these rooms are simply but decently equipped with solid lightwood furniture. Most have shower rooms. The remaining, more peaceful, bedrooms are in the main house. Here furniture is traditional, with some nice antiques and several four-posters; decor is attractive but standards of repair need attention.
Amenities garden, outdoor swimming pool, sauna, solarium, tennis, putting, croquet, laundry service, children's play area.

Rooms 21
Ensuite bath/shower 21
Direct dial Yes
Room TV Yes
Confirm by arrang.
Last dinner 9.30
Parking Ample
Room service Limited

COBHAM — Il Giardino ♨

R Map 5 E3 Surrey
221 Portsmouth Road
Cobham (0932) 63973

Italian cooking
Set L £7.45, Sun £10.50
About £45 for two
Seats 50 *Parties* 70
Parking Limited
Credit Access, Amex, Diners, Visa

Gabriele di Michele continues to cook enjoyable Italian food at this bright attractive restaurant on the old A3 just out of Cobham. The hors d'oeuvre trolley is full of good things and pasta comes in a dozen guises from tagliatelle al pesto to spaghetti pescatore. Familiar ways with chicken and veal include a decent saltimbocca and tender calf's liver with fresh sage. The house red wine (Veneto Rosso) is good, as is the properly made zabaglione. ♀ Well-chosen ☻

Lunch 12–2.15 *Dinner* 6.30–10.30
Closed L Sat, all Mon & Bank Hols

COBHAM — Hilton National Hotel 67% £B/C

H Map 5 E3 Surrey
Seven Hills Road South
KT11 1EW
Cobham (0932) 64471
Telex 929196

Credit Access, Amex, Diners, Visa

Set in wooded grounds near the junction of the A3 and A345. The newest bedrooms offer modern comforts, the best being the 12 Plaza rooms. Older rooms are being upgraded. Public areas include two attractive bars, one with natural stone arches. Dire buffet breakfast. Indifferent staff. *Amenities* garden, indoor swimming pool, sauna, whirlpool bath, keep-fit equipment, tennis, squash, in-house movies, secretarial services, fax, laundry service, helipad.

Rooms 153	*Direct dial* Yes	*Confirm by* 6	*Parking* Ample
Ensuite bath/shower 153	*Room TV* Yes	*Last dinner* 10	*Room service* 24 hours

COBHAM — Woodlands Park Hotel 65% £D

H Map 5 E3 Surrey
Woodlands Lane, Stoke
D'Abernon KT11 3QB
Oxshott (037 284) 3933
Telex 919246

Credit Access, Amex, Diners, Visa

The match-making Bryants were the original owners of this late-Victorian mansion, which stands on the A245 between Cobham and Leatherhead. The panelled hall is a striking piece of period grandeur that serves as a comfortable lounge and bar. Bedrooms of various shapes and sizes were all to be refurbished during 1988 (private bathrooms throughout, not just showers) and 30 rooms added. *Amenities* garden, tennis, clay-pigeon shooting, fax, laundry service.

Rooms 33	*Direct dial* Yes	*Confirm by* arrang.	*Parking* Ample
Ensuite bath/shower 33	*Room TV* Yes	*Last dinner* 9.30	*Room service* 24 hours

We publish annually,
so make sure you use the current edition.
It's worth it!

COGGESHALL — Peter Langan's Restaurant

R Map 6 C3 Essex
4 Stoneham Street
Coggeshall (0376) 61453

Set L £6.50
About £35 for two
Seats 76
Parties 20
Parking Ample
Credit Access, Amex, Diners, Visa

The Langan touch seems to work as well here as in town, and chef Mark Bowman's talents keep the place busy. Bare pine floors and picture-filled walls set the scene for a daily-changing selection of enjoyable dishes, from creamy mussel soup with flakes of salmon and dill to pan-fried calf's liver, chicken with saffron sauce and home-made caramel ice cream. Short list of good, reasonably priced wines. ♀ Well-chosen ☻ &

Lunch 12–2.30 *Dinner* 7.30–10 **Closed** L Sat, D Sun, all Mon, Bank Hols (exc. Good Fri) & 1st 3 wks Jan

COGGESHALL — White Hart Hotel 68% £D

HR Map 6 C3 Essex
Market End CO6 1NH
Coggeshall (0376) 61654

Credit Access, Amex, Diners, Visa
Closed Aug & 2 wks Xmas

A walkway festooned with hanging baskets ensures a pleasant arrival at this characterful hotel. Inside, the flagstoned foyer leads to an oak-beamed cocktail bar and residents' lounge, the latter with a huge stone fireplace. Bedrooms are well appointed, with fitted units and trouser presses; bathrooms vary from compact shower rooms for single rooms to palatial facilities for the larger ones. No dogs. *Amenities* patio, laundry service.

Rooms 18	*Direct dial* Yes	*Confirm by* arrang.	*Parking* Ample
Ensuite bath/shower 18	*Room TV* Yes	*Last dinner* 9	*Room service* All day

see over

White Hart Restaurant   ♛

Set L Sun only £15.50
About £58 for two
Seats 30
Parties 20

Oak beams, subdued lighting and polished silver please the eye at this honest restaurant. John Grimsby provides an extensive menu drawing on top-quality ingredients, particularly fish. Typical dishes are scallops with bacon, Mersea oysters and chargrilled gambas, while meat dishes include venison, veal, duckling and steak. Simple Sunday lunchtime menu. Exceptional wine list with a tremendous range of half-bottles.
▱ Outstanding   ♟ Well-chosen

Lunch 12.30–2   *Dinner* 7.30–9   **Closed** L Mon & Sat, D Sun to non-residents, all Fri, Aug & 2 wks Xmas

COLCHESTER   Marks Tey Hotel   55%   £E

H **Map 6 C3** Essex
Marks Tey CO6 1DU
Colchester (0206) 210001
Telex 987176

Credit Access, Amex, Diners, Visa

South of Colchester on the B1408, this purpose-built hotel is a popular choice for business meetings and conferences. Bedrooms, mainly twins, are fitted out in straightforward, functional style, and all have decent tiled bathrooms. In the bar is a mural depicting Colchester's Roman and Saxon past. The hotel is nearly 20 years old and badly needs rejuvenating.
Amenities garden, gymnasium, tennis, pool table, laundry service.

Rooms 107	*Direct dial* Yes	*Confirm by* arrang.	*Parking* Ample
Ensuite bath/shower 107	*Room TV* Yes	*Last dinner* 9.45	*Room service* 24 hours

COLCHESTER   Rose & Crown Hotel   57%   £E

H **Map 6 C3** Essex
East Street CO1 2TZ
Colchester (0206) 866677
Telex 946240

Credit Access, Amex, Diners, Visa

This is a splendid old place, full of character, and to get the best from it you should stay in the original inn rather than the annexe. Half-timbered corridors lead to the old rooms, where marvellous plank doors, old-fashioned furniture and low ceilings impart tremendous warmth and atmosphere. No less appealing are the various bars with their beams, benches, heavy chairs and copper-topped tables.
Amenities laundry service.

Rooms 29	*Direct dial* Yes	*Confirm by* arrang.	*Parking* Ample
Ensuite bath/shower 20	*Room TV* Yes	*Last dinner* 10	*Room service* 24 hours

COLEFORD   Speech House   £C/D

I **Map 4 B2** Gloucestershire
Forest of Dean GL16 7EL
Dean (0594) 22607

Credit Access, Amex, Diners, Visa

At least three ghosts and echoes of history haunt this former court house – now a friendly hotel – which stands in splendid isolation on the B4226 in the heart of the forest. A massive log fire warms the reception-lounge, and the two small informal bars are suitably beamed. Pride of the bedrooms are three rooms in antique style with splendid four-posters.
Amenities garden.

Rooms 14	*Room phone* Yes	*Confirm by* 6	*Parking* Ample
Ensuite bath/shower 3	*Room TV* Yes	*Last dinner* 9	*Room service* All day

COLERNE   Lucknam Park   81%   *NEW ENTRY*   £B

HR **Map 4 B2** Wiltshire
Nr Bath SN14 8AZ
Bath (0225) 742777
Telex 445648

Rooms 39
Ensuite bath/shower 39
Direct dial Yes
Room TV Yes
Confirm by arrang.
Last dinner 10.30
Parking Ample
Room service 24 hours

Credit Access, Amex, Diners, Visa

A mile-long driveway, lined by beech trees, leads to a magnificent Georgian country house set in its own extensive parkland of 280 acres. Fine antiques, fabrics and furnishings admirably suited to the period distinguish elegant public areas like the drawing rooms and panelled library. Bedrooms, too, are models of good taste (lovely fresh flower displays) and the marble-clad bathrooms are lavishly supplied with

toiletries and luxury towels. The turning down of beds at night typifies the caring and courteous service. First-class leisure and conference facilities. *Amenities* garden, indoor swimming pool, sauna, solarium, whirlpool bath, steam bath, gymnasium, beauty salon, hairdressing, croquet, snooker, teletext, secretarial services, laundry service.

Restaurant *NEW ENTRY* ♛♛

Set L £16.50
Set D £27.50
About £65 for two
Seats 85
Parties 100

Two lovely dining rooms overlooking immaculate lawns provide the delightful setting for Anthony Blake's skilled cooking matched by fine service. In the evening, a gourmet menu, a selection of plainer, traditional dishes and a seasonally-changing, modern carte offer an exciting variety to suit all tastes (less choice at lunchtime). Thus, a simple green salad with crisp apple and melon might be followed by succulent lamb glazed with English mustard, or chicken consommé with smoked scallops by poached turbot in a deliciously winy chervil butter sauce. Sensational sweets. Good wines with excellent Cabernet Sauvignons (Beaulieu vineyard '78, Ch. Montrose '76). 🍷 Well-chosen ⓔ ♿

Lunch 12.30–2.30   *Dinner* 7–10.30

CONGLETON   Great Moreton Hall Hotel   72%   £C/D

H Map 10 B2 Cheshire
New Road CW12 4RY
Congleton (0260) 272340
Telex 666537

Rooms 18
Ensuite bath/shower 18
Direct dial Yes
Room TV Yes
Confirm by arrang.
Last dinner 9.30
Parking Ample
Room service All day

Credit Access, Amex, Diners, Visa

This splendid piece of Victorian Gothic architecture stands surrounded by 45 acres of grounds in the heart of lovely Cheshire countryside. A sweeping staircase dominates the imposing baronial-style main lounge with its vaulted wooden ceiling and there are magnificent mouldings and a huge carved fireplace in the comfortable bar. Deep, bright colours have been used to good effect. Bedrooms vary between spacious, smartly appointed new rooms and the slightly smaller and more old-fashioned older ones; all are well maintained and have good modern bathrooms. Tea-makers, fresh fruit and mineral water are standard, and most rooms have trouser presses and mini-bars. *Amenities* garden, laundry service.

**Our inspectors *never* book in the name of Egon Ronay's Guides.
They disclose their identity only if they are considering an establishment
for inclusion in the next edition of the Guide.**

CONISTON   Coniston Sun Hotel   63%   £D/E

H Map 13 C5
Cumbria LA21 8HQ
Coniston (0966) 41248

Credit Access, Visa
Closed 2nd wk Jan–end Feb

Front rooms at this white-painted hotel with adjoining 16th-century inn look down to Coniston Water, rear ones face the Old Man, so you can hardly go wrong. Each room is individually decorated, with matching fabrics, carpeted bathrooms and thoughtful touches such as flowers and potpourri. There's a good selection of reading material and board games in the cosy lounge. No dogs. *Amenities* garden, laundry service.

| *Rooms* 11 | *Direct dial* Yes | *Confirm by* arrang. | *Parking* Ample |
| *Ensuite bath/shower* 11 | *Room TV* Yes | *Last dinner* 8 | *Room service* All day |

CONSTANTINE BAY   Treglos Hotel   66%   £D/E

HR Map 2 B3 Cornwall
Nr Padstow, St Merryn
PL28 8JH
Padstow (0841) 520727

Closed mid Nov–mid Mar

Good leisure facilities and sandy beaches close by make this a popular holiday hotel. There are fine lounges to relax in, including one with card tables and a piano, and a particularly restful bar. Bedrooms, many of them with sea views and seven with balconies, have light colour schemes and white fitted furniture. Excellent house-keeping. *Amenities* garden, indoor swimming pool, whirlpool bath, croquet, sea fishing, hotel boat, water skiing, snooker.

| *Rooms* 44 | *Direct dial* Yes | *Confirm by* arrang. | *Parking* Ample |
| *Ensuite bath/shower* 44 | *Room TV* Yes | *Last dinner* 9.30 | *Room service* All day |

Treglos Restaurant

Set L £6.95
Set D from £12.75
About £40 for two
Seats 120
Parties 120

An attractive, roomy restaurant with sea views and an abundance of locally caught seafood to guarantee enjoyment. The daily-changing à la carte menu offers dishes such as crab and cucumber mousse flavoured with tarragon as a starter, with salmon, monkfish and shellfish in a light curry sauce with ginger, pineapple and green peppers or roast lamb with Cumberland sauce to follow. The simplest dishes tend to be the best choice. 🅴

Lunch 12.30–1.30   *Dinner* 7.45–9.30
Closed mid Nov–mid Mar

COODEN	Calahonda Hotel 65% *NEW ENTRY*	£D/E

H Map 7 B6 East Sussex
Herbrand Walk TN39 4TX
Cooden (042 43) 5405

Closed Nov–end Mar

Welcoming, attentive owners Mr and Mrs Grinham have turned their home into a really delightful little hotel by the sea. The three bedrooms, two with balconies and sea views, are individually decorated and furnished in modern style, and a thoughtful range of extras runs from tissues, sewing kits and fresh fruit to radios and hairdryers. One of the carpeted bathrooms sports a whirlpool bath, and they all offer thick towels and good toiletries. The main day room is an elegant lounge with polished wooden floor, plushly inviting chairs and soft, restful lighting. There's a full-size snooker table. The hotel backs directly on to the beach. No children under 12. No dogs.
Amenities garden, sea fishing, snooker.

| *Rooms* 3 | *Direct dial* Yes | *Confirm by* arrang. | *Parking* Ample |
| *Ensuite bath/shower* 3 | *Room TV* Yes | *Last dinner* 8.30 | *Room service* All day |

COODEN	Cooden Resort Hotel 60%	£D

H Map 7 B6 East Sussex
Nr Bexhill-on-Sea TN39 4TT
Cooden (042 43) 2281
Telex 877247

Credit Access, Amex, Diners, Visa

A 1930s-style hotel sitting right on the beach, with views of Pevensey Bay and the English Channel. Day rooms are quite cosy and welcoming, and the bedrooms, all of a reasonable size, with trouser presses, hairdryers and radio-alarms, will be better for their planned refurbishment. No dogs. *Amenities* garden, indoor & outdoor swimming pools, sauna, solarium, whirlpool bath, keep-fit equipment, hairdressing, secretarial services, fax, laundry service.

| *Rooms* 36 | *Direct dial* Yes | *Confirm by* 6 | *Parking* Ample |
| *Ensuite bath/shower* 34 | *Room TV* Yes | *Last dinner* 9.30 | *Room service* 24 hours |

COOKHAM	Peking Inn	⑨

R Map 5 E2 Berkshire
High Street
Bourne End (062 85) 20900

Chinese cooking
Set L & D £14
About £40 for two
Seats 90
Parking Difficult
Credit Access, Amex, Diners, Visa

Not a restaurant to set the world alight, but a bright, busy place with reliable Peking cooking, smart staff and a particularly well-laid-out menu. Start perhaps with chilli-sauced spare ribs, crab claws or crispy 'seaweed', and progress to sizzling beef, prawns with ginger sauce or a chef's special like mussels or lobster in black bean sauce. Glazed toffee apples or bananas for a nice sticky end.

Lunch 12–2.30   *Dinner* 6–11, Sat 6–11.30
Closed 24–27 Dec

**Our inspectors are our full-time employees;
they are professionally trained by us.**

COPDOCK	Ipswich Moat House 63%	£D

H Map 6 C3 Suffolk
London Road,
Nr Ipswich IP8 3JD
Copdock (047 386) 444
Telex 987207

Credit Access, Amex, Diners, Visa

Just off the A12 south-west of Ipswich, the Moat House has completed its bedroom upgrading. Rooms are well designed, with smart modern furnishings and pretty coordinated fabrics, plus gleaming tiled bathrooms and the usual accessories. The main day room is a cool, comfortable open-plan bar-lounge. Service is helpful and friendly. An otherwise unremarkable breakfast featured excellent fresh fruit salad.
Amenities garden, secretarial services, fax, laundry service.

| *Rooms* 45 | *Direct dial* Yes | *Confirm by* 6 | *Parking* Ample |
| *Ensuite bath/shower* 45 | *Room TV* Yes | *Last dinner* 9.15 | *Room service* 24 hours |

CORFE CASTLE Morton's House Hotel 65% *NEW ENTRY* £D/E

HR **Map 4 C4** Dorset
East Street BH20 5EE
Corfe Castle (0929) 480988

Credit Access, Visa

Built in Purbeck stone around 1600, Morton's House sits in a walled garden on a hilltop. The views are splendid, and there's a new attraction in the shape of the restored Wareham–Swanage railway line (access from the garden to Corfe Castle station). Best of the day rooms is the chintzy, oak-panelled lounge; there's also a charming first floor library. Bedrooms are well provided with thoughtful personal touches, and the bathrooms offer huge towels, bathrobes and good toiletries. The four-poster suite has a whirlpool bath, while another room features a grand Victorian bath.
Amenities garden, secretarial services, laundry service.

Rooms 17	*Direct dial* Yes	*Confirm by* arrang.	*Parking* Ample
Ensuite bath/shower 17	*Room TV* Yes	*Last dinner* 10	*Room service* 24 hours

Restaurant *NEW ENTRY*

Set L £7
Set D £14
Seats 40
Parties 100

Order over a drink in the oak-panelled lounge and relax as your meal is expertly prepared to order. The four-course dinner menu offers particularly good value, and typical delights include sauté of sweetbreads with garlic, gherkins and parsley; mixed seafood salad with a dill and saffron dressing; and pleasant orange sorbet with kiwi fruit. The house white wine is an excellent New Zealand Sauvignon (Morton Estate, Hawkes Bay). Well-chosen

Lunch 12–2.30 *Dinner* 7–10
About £38 *for two*

Changes in data sometimes occur in establishments after the Guide goes to press.

Prices should be taken as indications rather than firm quotes.

CORNHILL-ON-TWEED Tillmouth Park Hotel 62% £E

H **Map 14 B2** Northumberland
TD12 4UU
Coldstream (0890) 2255

Credit Access, Amex, Diners, Visa

Fishermen are enthusiastic patrons of this imposing Victorian mansion with nine miles of salmon fishing on the Tweed. Pleasant public rooms include a handsome galleried hall and a cosy bar. Bedrooms vary in size; the best are spacious and furnished with antiques. Some bathrooms remain obstinately old-fashioned, but most are modern.
Amenities garden, coarse & game fishing, secretarial services.

Rooms 13	*Direct dial* Yes	*Confirm by* arrang.	*Parking* Ample
Ensuite bath/shower 13	*Room TV* Yes	*Last dinner* 8.45	*Room service* All day

CORSE LAWN Corse Lawn House Hotel 71% £D

HR **Map 4 B1** Gloucestershire
Nr Gloucester GL19 4LZ
Tirley (045 278) 479
Telex 437348

Rooms 10
Ensuite bath/shower 10
Direct dial Yes
Room TV Yes
Confirm by arrang.
Last dinner 10
Parking Ample
Room service All day

Credit Access, Amex, Diners, Visa

North of Gloucester on the B4211, this elegant Queen Anne building is surrounded by gardens, fields and farmland. The feeling throughout is of a civilised and lovingly cared-for country house. Day rooms are a charming blend of grandeur and intimacy. Bedrooms are spacious and very comfortable, with good pieces of period furniture, a sitting area, writing desk and canopied bed (two four-poster rooms). The usual practical accessories are supplemented by lots of thoughtful extras including exotic fruits on a silver tray. Spotless bathrooms have showers over the tubs. Service is courteous and attentive, and the day starts with a very good breakfast. ***Amenities*** garden, putting, croquet, in-house movies, laundry service, helipad.

see over

Corse Lawn House Restaurant   👑 ♬

Set L from £11.50
Set D £17.75
About £60 for two
Seats 50
Parties 20

A coolly elegant room with prints and etchings of the English countryside. Baba Hine's menus (à la carte or table d'hôte) provide a short, tempting choice typified by hot seafood in croustade, pigeon breast with red wine, bacon and foie gras and fresh figs with a fig and Armagnac sorbet. Splendid vegetables accompany main courses. The wine list includes fine clarets and exceptional old Sauternes and Cognacs. Good coffee. ☻

Lunch 12–2   Dinner 7–10

CORSHAM   Methuen Arms Hotel   £E

▌ **Map 4 B2** Wiltshire
2 High Street SN13 0HB
Corsham (0249) 714867

Credit Access, Visa
Closed 3 days Xmas

The Long family are excellent tenants at this comfortable inn with a 500-year history. They've added an extra bedroom, and four more rooms now have private facilities. Rooms in the main house have been revamped in bright, cheerful style; there's also accommodation in a cottage annexe and above the Long Bar, which features a 14th-century skittles alley. The charming walled garden is a popular spot in summer. No dogs. *Amenities* garden, laundry service.

Rooms 25	*Direct dial* Yes	*Confirm by* 6	*Parking* Ample
Ensuite bath/shower 24	*Room TV* Yes	*Last dinner* 9.30	*Room service* None

---

CORSHAM   Rudloe Park Hotel   60%   £D

H **Map 4 B2** Wiltshire
Leafy Lane SN13 0PA
Bath (0225) 810555

Credit Access, Amex, Diners, Visa

An impressive creeper-clad hotel which has recently been much improved by enthusiastic owners. Three new bedrooms have been added and the existing ones have been refurbished, all in traditional style. Trouser presses, ironing boards, sherry, mineral water, and a host of other extras are provided. Bathrooms all have new shower facilities and plenty of toiletries. No children under ten. No dogs. *Amenities* garden, croquet, secretarial services, fax, laundry service.

Rooms 11	*Direct dial* Yes	*Confirm by* arrang.	*Parking* Ample
Ensuite bath/shower 11	*Room TV* Yes	*Last dinner* 9.30	*Room service* All day

---

CORTON   Dove at Corton   ♬

R **Map 4 B3** Wiltshire
Nr Warminster
Warminster (0985) 50378

Set L £10, Sun £8.50
Set D £10
About £32 for two
Seats 20 *Parties* 12
Parking Ample
Credit Access, Visa

An immaculate, gentrified pub in a quiet Wiltshire lane, with an attractive little restaurant at one end of the bar. It's very much the personal show of Michael and Jane Rowse – he takes orders, she cooks – and the ambience is happy and relaxed. The food's straightforward, tasty and very enjoyable: crab pâté, honey duckling, local trout simply and deliciously grilled, Aberdeen Angus steak, rich puddings, decent cheeses. Booking advisable. ☻ &

Lunch 12–2, Sun 12–1.45   Dinner 7–9.30
Closed D Sun, all Mon (exc. Bank Hols), 2–3 wks Jan & 1st wk Oct

---

COVENTRY   Ansty Hall   74%   *NEW ENTRY*   £C

H **Map 10 C4** West Midlands
Ansty CV7 9HZ
Coventry (0203) 612222

Rooms 13
Ensuite bath/shower 13
Direct dial Yes
Room TV Yes
Confirm by arrang.
Last dinner 9.30
Parking Ample
Room service All day

Credit Access, Amex, Diners, Visa

Just a short distance from junction 2 of the M6, this beautifully proportioned red-brick Caroline house stands in eight acres of grounds. Enter through a wide, welcoming hall with oak panelling into a smart lounge and a library with French windows opening on to a patio. On the other side of the hall is an intimate bar where drinks are informally served from a sideboard. All bedrooms have mod-

ern, traditionally styled darkwood furniture; larger rooms have a sitting area with a settee, armchairs and small table. Thoughtful extras include fresh fruit, biscuits and potpourri. Bathrooms have quality toiletries and thick towels. Charming, helpful staff.
Amenities garden, laundry service.

COVENTRY | Chace Crest Hotel 64% | £C/D

H Map 10 C4 West Midlands
London Road,
Willenhall CV3 4EQ
Coventry (0203) 303398
Telex 311993

Credit Access, Amex, Diners, Visa

The lofty foyer-lounge with its fine panelling and period furniture makes an impressive entrance to this hotel in a Victorian building on the A423 south of the city. The comfortable, relaxing atmosphere extends to the two bars. Bedrooms in a new block are in a simple, modern style; larger rooms in the main house are traditionally furnished. *Amenities* garden, pool table, secretarial services, fax, laundry service.

Rooms 68	Direct dial Yes	Confirm by 6	Parking Ample
Ensuite bath/shower 68	Room TV Yes	Last dinner 9.45	Room service 24 hours

COVENTRY | Crest Hotel 66% | £C

H Map 10 C4 West Midlands
Hinckley Road CV2 2HP
Coventry (0203) 613261
Telex 311292

Credit Access, Amex, Diners, Visa

Excellent management and staff impart a friendly efficiency to this modern hotel on the A46. The welcoming foyer is hung with baskets of flowers, while greenery gives a summery touch to the bar-lounge. Bedrooms range from standards to Executive rooms and Lady Crest rooms with more feminine decor. *Amenities* garden, indoor swimming pool, sauna, solarium, whirlpool, games room, in-house movies, secretarial services, fax, laundry service, coffee shop (9am–5pm). ઇ

Rooms 147	Direct dial Yes	Confirm by 6	Parking Ample
Ensuite bath/shower 147	Room TV Yes	Last dinner 9.45	Room service 24 hours

COVENTRY | De Vere Hotel 70% | £C/D

H Map 10 C4 West Midlands
Cathedral Square CV1 5RP
Coventry (0203) 633733
Telex 31380

Rooms 192
Ensuite bath/shower 192
Direct dial Yes
Room TV Yes
Confirm by arrang.
Last dinner 11
Parking Ample
Room service 24 hours

Credit Access, Amex, Diners, Visa

Management and staff are conspicuously friendly and helpful at the De Vere, a large modern hotel close to Coventry Cathedral. A good impression is gained as soon as you cross the threshold into the bright, spacious foyer, and the new bar-lounge, with decor on the theme of the locally produced Daimler car, is extremely stylish. Here a pianist plays lunchtime and evenings. Bedrooms are beginning to look a little dated decoratively, but housekeeping is excellent. The rooms are of a good size and all have practical tiled bathrooms. *Amenities* in-house movies, secretarial services, fax, laundry service, coffee shop (7.30am–9pm).

COVENTRY | Herbs Restaurant | ⑪

R Map 10 C4 West Midlands
28 Lower Holyhead Road
Coventry (0203) 555654

About £28 for two
Seats 42
Parties 42
Parking Ample

A health-conscious hotel restaurant that's now really in the pink with its smart new peach-toned decor. Robert Jackson continues to create excellent vegetarian fare, ranging from deep-fried potato skins with garlicky sour cream dip to barley, mushroom, spinach and walnut roast served with fresh carrot and apricot sauce. It's genuine wholefood cooking – nothing added, nothing taken away. Nice desserts, and a couple of meat dishes too. No smoking. ℮

Dinner only 6.30–9.30
Closed Sun, Bank Hols & 2 wks Xmas

COVENTRY | Hotel Leofric 58% | £C/D

H Map 10 C4 West Midlands
Broadgate CV1 1LZ
Coventry (0203) 221371
Telex 311193

Credit Access, Amex, Diners, Visa

Part of a shopping complex (and soon to lose its most convenient car park to yet more shops), this is a modern hotel with spacious public rooms. Patio doors from the lounge bar lead to a terrace with views of the cathedral, and there are two more bars in addition. Bedrooms have vinyl-topped built-in units that have seen better days, and simple bathrooms. *Amenities* terrace, hairdressing, laundry service, coffee shop (10.30am–6pm Mon–Sat).

Rooms 91	Direct dial Yes	Confirm by 6	Parking Difficult
Ensuite bath/shower 91	Room TV Yes	Last dinner 9.45	Room service 24 hours

COVENTRY | Novotel Coventry 62% | £D/E

H **Map 10 C4** West Midlands
Wilsons Lane, Longford
CV6 6HL
Coventry (0203) 365000
Telex 31545

Credit Access, Amex, Diners, Visa

High standards of cleanliness and 24-hour room service are features that particularly appeal to business visitors at this busy hotel. Big bedrooms, all with bed-settees, are attractively furnished, with simple white units. Staff occasionally seem somewhat brusque.
Amenities patio, outdoor swimming pool, sauna, solarium, whirlpool bath, gymnasium, squash, pool table, in-house movies, secretarial services, fax, laundry service, coffee shop (6am–midnight). &

Rooms 100	*Direct dial* Yes	*Confirm by* 6	*Parking* Ample
Ensuite bath/shower 100	*Room TV* Yes	*Last dinner* midnight	*Room service* 24 hours

COVENTRY | Post House Hotel 60% | £C/D

H **Map 10 C4** West Midlands
Rye Hill, Allesley CV5 9PH
Coventry (0203) 402151
Telex 31427

Credit Access, Amex, Diners, Visa

A modern hotel on the A45, outside the city and just eight miles from Birmingham National Exhibiton Centre. Greys and pinks are the colours used in the day rooms, which include a smart foyer-lounge and bar. There's also a new conference room for 150 people. Bedrooms are well kept, and Executive rooms offer various extras beyond the standard mini-bars and tea-makers. *Amenities* garden, pool table, secretarial services, fax, laundry service.

Rooms 200	*Direct dial* Yes	*Confirm by* 6	*Parking* Ample
Ensuite bath/shower 200	*Room TV* Yes	*Last dinner* 10	*Room service* 24 hours

Our inspectors *never* book in the name of Egon Ronay's Guides.
They disclose their identity only if they are considering an establishment
for inclusion in the next edition of the Guide.

CRANBROOK | Cranes *NEW ENTRY* | ᖰ

R **Map 7 B5** Kent
2 Waterloo Road
Cranbrook (0580) 712396

About £50 for two
Seats 35
Parking Ample

Credit Access, Visa

A couple of minutes' walk from a famous windmill, Cranes is a simple but attractive restaurant with a two-fold operation. Lunchtime brings a bistro-style menu – soup and pâté, ratatouille flan, chicken casserole – while in the evening local produce is a key feature, with fish from the south coast, Hawkhurst trout, Kentish smoked meats and Wadhurst venison served with a fresh plum and damson jelly sauce. Chef-patron Jeremy Pook does fine work in the kitchen, and his wife Wendy runs front of house in friendly, knowledgeable style. There's a short, selective list of good wines: note the subtly flavoured Pouilly Fumé (Petit Soumard) and excellent Australian wines from Peter Lehmann. ♀ Well-chosen ☺

Lunch 12–2   *Dinner* 7–10
Closed D Mon & all Sun

CRANBROOK | Kennel Holt Hotel 69% | £C

HR **Map 7 B5** Kent
TN17 2PT
Cranbrook (0580) 712032

Credit Access, Amex, Diners, Visa
Closed 25 & 26 Dec

A charming Elizabethan house run very much as a private home. The delightful public rooms include a beamed and panelled library with plenty of books and a chintzy drawing room, both of which engender a feeling of homeliness and tranquillity. Bedrooms are immaculately kept and have plenty of thoughtful extras; bathrooms have luxurious bath towels and toiletries. No children under six.
Amenities garden, croquet.

Rooms 8	*Room phone* Yes	*Confirm by* arrang.	*Parking* Ample
Ensuite bath/shower 6	*Room TV* Yes	*Last dinner* 9	*Room service* All day

Changes in data sometimes occur in establishments
after the Guide goes to press.
Prices should be taken as indications rather than firm quotes.

CRATHORNE — Crathorne Hall Hotel 73% £D/E

H **Map 15 C5** Cleveland
Nr Yarm, North Yorkshire
TS15 0AR
Stokesley (0642) 700398
Telex 587426

Rooms 39
Ensuite bath/shower 39
Direct dial Yes
Room TV Yes
Confirm by arrang.
Last dinner 10
Parking Ample
Room service 24 hours

Credit Access, Amex, Diners, Visa
Closed 1 & 2 Jan

In a beautiful setting overlooking the Leven valley, this fine Edwardian mansion with its mellow sandstone facing marks a final flowering in the great tradition of English country house building. Lofty, well-lit public rooms include a magnificently proportioned drawing room featuring a carved stone fireplace, and a plush two-level bar with a very civilised club-like atmosphere. Bright and spacious bedrooms are comfortably traditional in style and many have moulded ceilings. Well-kept bathrooms are tiled and carpeted; three feature splendid old tubs, the rest have smart modern facilities (including some bidets). Executive rooms offer superior decor and more accessories. No dogs. *Amenities* garden, snooker, laundry service.

CRAWLEY — George Hotel 65% £C/D

H **Map 7 B5** West Sussex
High Street RH10 1BS
Crawley (0293) 24215
Telex 87385

Credit Access, Amex, Diners, Visa

A gallows sign identifies this 17th-century coaching inn with modern additions. Bare floorboards and beams create an authentic old-world atmosphere in the public bar, while the coffee shop across the drive is contrastingly modern. Main-house rooms remain fairly basic while those in the annexe boast smart darkwood units, attractive fabrics and accessories like trouser presses and hairdryers. *Amenities* patio, in-house movies, laundry service, coffee shop (9am–10pm).

Rooms 75	*Direct dial* Yes	*Confirm by* 6	*Parking* Ample
Ensuite bath/shower 75	*Room TV* Yes	*Last dinner* 10	*Room service* 24 hours

CRAWLEY

See also under **LONDON AIRPORTS (Gatwick)**

CRICK — Post House Hotel 64% £C

H **Map 11 D4**
Northamptonshire NN6 7XR
Crick (0788) 822101
Telex 311107

Credit Access, Amex, Diners, Visa

Just half a mile from junction 18 of the M1, this low-rise hotel offers bright, attractive accommodation ideal for the business traveller. Bedrooms have fitted units, tea-makers, mini-bars and fully tiled bathrooms, while public areas include a spacious foyer-lounge and two bars. *Amenities* garden, solarium, keep-fit equipment, pool table, laundry service, coffee shop (7am–10.30pm), 24-hour lounge service, children's play area, helipad.

Rooms 96	*Direct dial* Yes	*Confirm by* 6	*Parking* Ample
Ensuite bath/shower 96	*Room TV* Yes	*Last dinner* 10	*Room service* All day

CRICKLADE — Whites ★ ♕ ⌐

R **Map 4 C2** Wiltshire
93 High Street
Swindon (0793) 751110

Lunch 12–2
Dinner 7.30–9.30
About £50 for two
Seats 32
Parties 20
Parking Ample

Credit Access, Visa
Closed Sun & Mon

The very talented Colin White continues to impress us greatly with his cooking, which has real imagination controlled by a discipline which abhors the flashy and outlandish. Textures are delicate, flavours positive but never overwhelming. His lightness of touch is exemplified in such delights as panaché of fish with spring vegetables in a light wine, herb and cream sauce or a lovage and cucumber soup. The cheeseboard is splendid. A fine selective wine list with Chablis from Durup and an excellent Shiraz from Taltarni. *Specialities* escalope of sea trout with samphire and champagne sauce, breast of guinea fowl with a Madeira sauce, feuilleté of exotic fruits with a Gewurztraminer sabayon. Well-chosen ⊘ ♣ &

CROOK · Wild Boar Hotel · 60% · £D

H Map 13 D5 Cumbria
Nr Windermere LA23 3NF
Windermere (096 62) 5225
Telex 65464

Credit Access, Amex, Diners, Visa

There's a characterful air to the main building of this well-known old coaching inn, with ancient oak beams and stone fireplaces gracing the public rooms. Bedrooms in the original part are popular for their period appeal, while those in the new wings are notably spacious and airy; all have an impressive range of extras. Also available are four-poster rooms and two new suites with whirlpool baths.
Amenities garden, fax.

Rooms 36	*Direct dial* Yes	*Confirm by* 6	*Parking* Ample
Ensuite bath/shower 36	*Room TV* Yes	*Last dinner* 8.45	*Room service* All day

CROOKLANDS · Crooklands Hotel · 59% · £D/E

H Map 13 D6 Cumbria
Nr Kendal LA7 7NW
Crooklands (044 87) 432
Telex 94017303

Credit Access, Amex, Diners, Visa

Built in the 16th century as a croft and ale house, this much extended Lakeland building is today an attractive Lakeland building. Period charm is confined to the cottagy stone-walled public rooms. Bedrooms, all in a modern block, have bold floral wallpaper and simple fitted units. Well-kept bathrooms have good stocks of toiletries.
Amenities garden, pool table, laundry service, coffee shop (7.30am–10pm).

Rooms 15	*Direct dial* Yes	*Confirm by* 6	*Parking* Ample
Ensuite bath/shower 15	*Room TV* Yes	*Last dinner* 9.30	*Room service* All day

**We welcome bona fide complaints and recommendations
on the tear-out pages at the back of the book for readers' comment.
They are followed up by our professional team.**

CROSBY-ON-EDEN · Crosby Lodge Hotel · 66% · £D/E

HR Map 13 D4 Cumbria
High Crosby,
Nr Carlisle CA6 4QZ
Crosby-on-Eden (0228 73) 618

Credit Amex, Diners, Visa
Closed 24 Dec–late Jan

A Georgian country house with Victorian embellishments, offering an attractive pastoral setting on the B6264. The entrance hall with its rugs, antiques and welcoming open fire sets the tone for other public rooms; the atmosphere throughout is pleasantly relaxed and informal. Accommodation ranges from the best main-house bedrooms, which have half-tester beds and good antiques, to fairly basic rooms in a converted stable block. *Amenities* garden, laundry service.

Rooms 11	*Direct dial* Yes	*Confirm by* arrang.	*Parking* Ample
Ensuite bath/shower 11	*Room TV* Yes	*Last dinner* 8.45	*Room service* All day

Restaurant

Set L £11.50
Set D £18.50
About £48 for two
Seats 50

A heavily beamed ceiling and solid mahogany furniture give a distinctly Victorian feel to this spacious dining room – a traditional setting for Michael Sedgwick's good, unpretentious cooking. Fixed-price menus offer plenty of starters, from game soup to prawns thermidor, plus main dishes like roast duckling and peppered lamb noisettes. Ingredients are beautifully fresh, portions generous. Tempting sweets from the trolley, and bargain-priced fine wines. ♀ Well-chosen ☺

Lunch 12.15–1.30   *Dinner* 7.30–8.45
Closed D Sun & 24 Dec–late Jan

CROXDALE · Bridge Hotel · 58% · £E

H Map 15 B4 Co. Durham
Nr Durham DH1 3SP
Durham (091) 3780524
Telex 538156

Credit Access, Amex, Diners, Visa

The Bridge Hotel is a roadside hostelry standing on the A167 a little way south of Durham. Practical overnight accommodation is provided in motel-style rooms set around the main building; fabrics are nicely coordinated and all rooms have bright tiled bathrooms that offer ample shelf space. There's a comfortable bar with soft pink decor and plenty of sofas and settees. ⅙
Amenities laundry service, 24-hour lounge service.

Rooms 46	*Direct dial* Yes	*Confirm by* arrang.	*Parking* Ample
Ensuite bath/shower 46	*Room TV* Yes	*Last dinner* 9.45	*Room service* Limited

CROYDON | Holiday Inn 73% | £B/C

H **Map 7 B5** Surrey
7 Altyre Road CR9 5AA
01-680 9200
Telex 8956268

Rooms 214
Ensuite bath/shower 214
Direct dial Yes
Room TV Yes
Confirm by 6
Last dinner 10.30
Parking Ample
Room service 24 hours

Credit Access, Amex, Diners, Visa

A purpose-built modern hotel offering abundant comfort, good service and excellent keep-fit facilities. Generously sized bedrooms feature the usual Holiday Inn double beds, neat built-in furniture that allows ample writing and storage space, and lots of up-to-the-minute accessories, plus smart tiled bathrooms with plenty of towels. Day rooms are spacious, light and airy, with clusters of comfortable velour-clad seats. Standards of housekeeping are impressive, keeping the whole place as new.

Amenities terrace, indoor swimming pool, sauna, solarium, whirlpool bath, keep-fit equipment, squash, badminton, in-house movies, secretarial services, laundry service, coffee shop (10.30am–2am). &

CROYDON | Selsdon Park Hotel 70% | £B/C

H **Map 7 B5** Surrey
Addington Road,
Sanderstead CR2 8YA
01-657 8811
Telex 945003

Rooms 178
Ensuite bath/shower 178
Direct dial Yes
Room TV Yes
Confirm by arrang.
Last dinner 9.30
Parking Ample
Room service 24 hours

Credit Access

Standing in peaceful private parkland yet close to the M25, a substantial country mansion with excellent leisure and conference facilities. There is a new wing of chic bedrooms decorated in pinks and greys while rooms in the main house have been refurbished to a high standard of repair and comfort: all have remote-control TVs, wall safes and trouser presses. Public rooms are gracious and finely propor-

tioned, moulded ceilings and dressed stone walls a notable feature. The lounge bar is a fine antique-furnished room. Staff led by Mauro Bernese are friendly and professional. **Amenities** garden, indoor & outdoor swimming pools, sauna, solarium, whirlpool bath, keep-fit equipment, tennis, squash, snooker, fax, laundry service, helipad.

CROYDON | Tung Kum | ♀

R **Map 7 B5** Surrey
205 High Street
01-688 0748

Chinese cooking
Set L £2.50
Set D from £14 for 2
About £36 *for two*
Seats 100 *Parking* Limited
Credit Access, Amex, Diners, Visa

A spacious modern restaurant in the centre of Croydon, where chef-partner Hung Chui prepares a good range of tried-and-tested Cantonese dishes. Good duck comes in various guises – shredded with oyster sauce, sliced with orange or pineapple, diced with cashew nuts, fried with seafood sauce. Other temptations range from roast crab and many ways with king prawns to barbecued pork and beef with bean shoots. Speedy, smiling service. &

Lunch 12–2.30 *Dinner* 5–11 (Sat & Sun meals 12–11)
Closed Bank Hols, 25 & 26 Dec

If we recommend meals in a Hotel or Inn,
a separate entry is made for its restaurant.

CUCKFIELD | Jeremy's at The King's Head | ♀

R **Map 7 B6** West Sussex
South Street
Haywards Heath (0444) 454006

Set D £12.95
About £38 *for two*
Seats 30
Parties 24
Parking Difficult
Credit Access, Visa

Plain bench seating and open fires create a cosy, informal atmosphere at this popular little restaurant. Jeremy Ashpool is a skilled and imaginative chef who scores top marks for beautiful, unfussy presentation. Dishes range from good simple things like smoked fish cake or grilled spiced chicken to more sophisticated offerings such as steamed mussels with coriander or fillet of halibut with a watercress and red pepper dressing. Lovely desserts to follow. Book. ℮ &

Lunch 12.30–2 *Dinner* 7.30–10 **Closed** D Mon, all Sat, Sun & Bank Hol Mons, 2 wks Aug, 4 days Xmas & 3 days Easter

CUCKFIELD — Murray's   *NEW ENTRY*   ♈

R **Map 7 B6** West Sussex
Broad Street
Haywards Heath (0444) 455826

About £40 for two
Seats 30
Parties 20
Parking Ample

Credit Access, Amex, Visa

Several small dining rooms create a pleasing feeling of intimacy at
this cottage restaurant where Sue Murray cooks imaginative dishes
using good quality ingredients. Starters include crab pancakes, carrot
and watercress mousse and chilli stuffed peppers. Main course could
be fillet steak with oyster, cheese and garlic chicken or calf's liver with
mango. Delicious desserts. Short, good wine list: Chablis (Remon) '86.
Ch Batailley '78. 🍷 Well-chosen ℰ

Lunch 12–1.30   *Dinner* 7.15–9.30, Sat till 10.30
Closed L Sat & all Sun, 2 wks end Feb & 1st 2 wks Sept

CUCKFIELD — Ockenden Manor Hotel   71%   £C

H **Map 7 B6** West Sussex
Ockenden Lane,
Nr Haywards Heath RH17 5LD
Haywards Heath (0444) 416111

Rooms 14
Ensuite bath/shower 14
Direct dial Yes
Room TV Yes
Confirm by 6
Last dinner 9.15
Parking Ample
Room service All day

Credit Access, Amex, Diners, Visa

Sixteenth-century manor house
set back from the A272 in five
acres of gardens and woodland.
Bedrooms have individual
charm and personality; some are
very spacious, with comfortable
four-posters, others a little less
so, but all have good antique or
period furniture and plenty of
thoughtful extras, including
fresh fruit, mineral water, tea-
making facilities and reading
material. The most recent rooms
feature sumptuous marble-tiled bathrooms. Notable among the day
rooms are an inviting bar with an inglenook, an oak-panelled lounge
and a dining room with an ornate plasterwork ceiling. Breakfast on
our latest visit was nothing special in terms of either quality or service.
No children under five. *Amenities* garden, laundry service.

CUMNOR — Bear & Ragged Staff

R **Map 5 D2** Oxfordshire
Appleton Road
Oxford (0865) 862329

Set L & D £13.95
Sun L £11.95
About £47 for two
Seats 36 *Parties* 22
Parking Ample
Credit Access, Amex, Diners, Visa

The atmosphere is warm and welcoming at this 17th-century inn, and
guests can relax in the lounge while enjoying a pre-prandial drink.
Charming girls provide attentive service in the dining room, backing
up enjoyable cooking that covers a range from chicken and spinach
terrine with Cumberland sauce to poached salmon, pepper steak and
medallions of lamb with rosemary and mint. Notably good vegetables.
ℰ

Lunch 12–2   *Dinner* 7–10
Closed L Sat & D Sun

DANE END — Green End Park Hotel   63%   £D

H **Map 6 B3** Hertfordshire
Nr Ware SG12 0NY
Dane End (092 084) 344

Credit Access, Amex, Diners, Visa

Eight acres of parkland provide a peaceful and secluded setting for a
handsome 18th-century manor house. Public rooms have a Regency
opulence, with chandeliers and fine cornice work in evidence.
Bedrooms are rather less grand, though of a decent size, and are all
equipped with tea-makers, trouser presses, hairdryers and digital
radio-alarms. No dogs. *Amenities* garden, tennis, croquet, putting,
secretarial services, laundry service, 24-hour lounge service.

| *Rooms* 10 | *Direct dial* Yes | *Confirm by* arrang. | *Parking* Ample |
| *Ensuite bath/shower* 10 | *Room TV* Yes | *Last dinner* 9.30 | *Room service* All day |

DARLINGTON — Blackwell Grange Moat House   60%   £D

H **Map 15 B5** Co. Durham
Blackwell Grange DL3 8QH
Darlington (0325) 380888
Telex 587272

Credit Access, Amex, Diners, Visa

Although close to the town centre, this attractive Georgian house
enjoys a pleasant rural setting with views of the Pennines and the
moors. Most of the bedrooms are practical and modern, with the usual
accessories; 14 rooms in the original house have just been refurbished.
There is a very nice hall/lounge and two bars.
Amenities garden, tennis, pool table, in-house movies, secretarial
services, fax, laundry service.

| *Rooms* 98 | *Direct dial* Yes | *Confirm by* 6 | *Parking* Ample |
| *Ensuite bath/shower* 98 | *Room TV* Yes | *Last dinner* 9.45 | *Room service* 24 hours |

DARLINGTON King's Head Swallow Hotel 57% £D/E

H **Map 15 B5** Co. Durham
Priestgate DL1 1LW
Darlington (0325) 380222
Telex 587112

Credit Access, Amex, Diners, Visa

A large Victorian hotel sited above shops in the centre of town. Day rooms, including an agreeable bar, are on the second floor; the erstwhile residents' lounge is now part of the important function facility. Most bedrooms are good-sized with modern furnishings, trouser presses and hairdryers. Guests have free use of a nearby leisure centre. *Amenities* secretarial services, laundry service, coffee shop (10am–5.30pm).

Rooms 86	*Direct dial* Yes	*Confirm by* 6	*Parking* Ample
Ensuite bath/shower 86	*Room TV* Yes	*Last dinner* 9.30	*Room service* 24 hours

DARLINGTON St. George Hotel *NEW ENTRY* £D/E

H **Map 15 B5** Co. Durham
Teesside Airport DL2 1RH
Dinsdale (0325) 332631

Credit Access, Amex, Diners, Visa

A low, red-brick building just 200 yards from the Teesside International Airport terminal. Public areas include a spacious foyer-lounge and a pleasant bar decorated in restful pinks and greens. Half the bedrooms are now upgraded with grey-stained units, attractive fabrics and smartly tiled bathrooms; remaining rooms are rather drab by comparison. Standard accessories include hairdryers and tea-makers. *Amenities* sauna, secretarial services, laundry service.

Rooms 59	*Direct dial* Yes	*Confirm by* 6	*Parking* Ample
Ensuite bath/shower 59	*Room TV* Yes	*Last dinner* 9.45	*Room service* 24 hours

DARLINGTON Sardis *NEW ENTRY* �

R **Map 15 B5** Co Durham
196 Northgate
Darlington (0325) 461222

Italian cooking
About £35 for two
Seats 63
Parties 24
Parking Ample
Credit Access, Visa

Three galleried floors with marbled columns, fresh flowers and candlelit tables provide a pleasant, civilised setting for enjoyable, carefully-cooked Italian dishes. Portions have a North Country generosity and the choice (less at lunchtime) runs from pasta with such sauces as tomato, bolognese or smoked salmon to grilled sardines, chicken Marsala, roast venison and veal Sicilian-style (with white wine, onions and garlic). Good sweets and espresso coffee. ⊖

Lunch 12–2 *Dinner* 7.30–10.15
Closed Sun, Bank Hols

DARLINGTON Stakis White Horse Hotel 61% £C/D

H **Map 15 B5** Co. Durham
Harrowgate Hill DL1 3LD
Darlington (0325) 382121

Credit Access, Amex, Diners, Visa

North of town on the A167, this well-run hotel is a converted mock-Tudor pub. Day rooms include a smart, cane-furnished cocktail bar and a public bar decorated in plush brown. Bedrooms, in a good-looking modern block, are of a decent size, with nice solid darkwood furniture, trouser presses, hairdryers and bathrooms with tubs and showers. The state of decor and repair is excellent throughout. *Amenities* secretarial services.

Rooms 40	*Direct dial* Yes	*Confirm by* 6	*Parking* Ample
Ensuite bath/shower 40	*Room TV* Yes	*Last dinner* 10	*Room service* 24 hours

We publish annually,
so make sure you use the current edition.
It's worth it!

DARTMOUTH Bistro 33 �

R **Map 3D3** Devon
33 Lower Street
Dartmouth (080 43) 2882

Set L from £14.75
About £42 for two
Seats 30
Parties 30
Parking Difficult

The decor and atmosphere may be reminiscent of a bistro, but Richard Canfield's imaginative cooking is certainly a cut above bistro fare. His regularly changing menu is full of new ideas, from a goat's cheese soufflé with a hazelnut-scented salad to medallions of veal in a Madeira sauce garnished with sweetbreads and brains, and a superb passion fruit and mango mousse. ♀ Well-chosen

Lunch by arrang. only *Dinner* 7–10
Closed Sun, Mon, 24–26 Dec & 2–3 wks Jan–Feb

DARTMOUTH — Carved Angel ♀

R Map 3 D3 Devon
2 South Embankment
Dartmouth (080 43) 2465

Set L £17.50, Sun £20
Set D from £24
About £68 for two
Seats 35
Parties 20
Parking Limited

A location at one of England's prettiest harbours is reflected in the predominance of excellent seafood in the menus. Starters include provençale fish soup and scallops with white wine and artichokes; main course might be brill with lobster sauce or Dartmouth pie of venison, fruit and spices. Lovely wine list, especially older wines: Clos de la Roche (Rousseau) '72, Ch. Rieussec '59. ⌐ Outstanding 🍷 Well-chosen ⊗

Lunch 12.30–1.45   *Dinner* 7.30–9.30   **Closed** D Sun, all Mon, Bank Hols (exc. Good Fri), 5 days Xmas & all Jan

DARTMOUTH — Royal Castle Hotel £D/E

I Map 3 D3 Devon
The Quay TQ6 9PS
Dartmouth (080 43) 4004

Credit Access, Visa

The crenellated Regency facade overlooking the colourful harbour conceals an older coaching inn, whose original bell system survives on the stairwell as a decorative feature. The beamed lounge bar with its solid oak furniture is full of old-world charm, and there's a stylishly elegant lounge on the first floor. Flowery wallpapers and soft colour schemes characterise the tastefully furnished bedrooms; five have four-posters, all have well-equipped bathrooms.

Rooms 21	*Direct dial* Yes	*Confirm by* arrang.	*Parking* Limited
Ensuite bath/shower 21	*Room TV* Yes	*Last dinner* 9.30	*Room service* 24 hours

DEAL — Mieko's

R Map 7 D5 Kent
443 St Richard's Road
Gt Mongeham
Deal (0304) 367257

Japanese cooking
Set D £12   *About £47 for two*
Seats 42 *Parties* 42
Parking Ample
Credit Access, Visa

Brian and Mieko Morris, now assisted by chef Mr Nakamura, run this pretty Japanese restaurant adjoining a hairdressing shop (it's tucked away in a housing estate, so you'll need to ask directions when booking). Teppan dishes are the speciality, cooked on an open charcoal grill; also nabemono, a kind of do-it-yourself fondue. Other delights include soya bean soup, deep-fried tofu and whole grilled carp.

Dinner only 7–11
Closed Sun, Mon & Bank Hols

DEDHAM — Dedham Vale Hotel 67% £C

H Map 6 C3 Essex
Stratford Road,
Nr Colchester CO7 6HW
Colchester (0206) 322273

Credit Access, Amex, Diners, Visa

A creeper-clad Edwardian house with country views and a splendid mature garden. It's a hotel of great potential, but two recent visits have seen service and maintenance well below their best. Four of the bedrooms are of a good size, and all have attractive individual decor and furnishings, plus well-equipped bathrooms. Day rooms include a pleasant little lounge and a bright sunny bar. No dogs.
Amenities garden, laundry service.

Rooms 6	*Direct dial* Yes	*Confirm by* arrang.	*Parking* Ample
Ensuite bath/shower 6	*Room TV* Yes	*Last dinner* 9.30	*Room service* All day

DEDHAM — Maison Talbooth 78% £B/C

H Map 6 C3 Essex
Stratford Road,
Nr Colchester CO7 6HN
Colchester (0206) 322367
Telex 987083

Rooms 10
Ensuite bath/shower 10
Direct dial Yes
Room TV Yes
Confirm by arrang.
Last dinner 9.30
Parking Ample
Room service Limited

Credit Access, Amex, Diners, Visa

In the heart of Constable country, this traditional Victorian house stands amid attractive grounds that include a fountain and sunken garden. Principal day room is the magnificent drawing room, where guests can relax in the comfortable armchairs and enjoy the huge open fire. A baby grand, flowers and Chinese lamps complete the elegant scene. Spacious bedrooms (including a number of luxurious suites) are individ-

ually and tastefully appointed and offer thoughtful extras like fruit and a drinks tray. Excellent bathrooms offer quality toiletries and big, fluffy towels. The hotel's restaurant is the Talbooth, half a mile away: breakfast and limited room service available in rooms. No dogs.
Amenities garden, croquet, laundry service.

DEDHAM Le Talbooth ⊌⊌

R **Map 6 C3** Essex
Gun Hill
Colchester (0206) 323150

Set L £15
Set D £27.50
About £75 for two
Seats 75
Parties 20
Credit Access, Amex, Diners, Visa

Chef Steven Blake is settling in well at this elegant riverside restaurant. Dishes like terrine of sweetbreads, chicken and foie gras or brill stuffed with lobster mousse and served with a delicate morel sauce demonstrate his ability to combine excellent ingredients with skill and assurance. Seasonal fruits in a rich champagne sabayon is a delightful sweet. Friendly but discreet service. Very good wine list at realistic prices. 🍷 Well-chosen ⊖ 🎩

Lunch 12–2
Dinner 7–9.30

DENTON Old Rectory Hotel 58% £E

H **Map 10 B2**
Greater Manchester
Meadow Lane, Haughton Green
M34 1GD
061-336 7516 Telex 668615
Credit Access
Closed Bank Hols, 25 Dec–2 Jan

Check directions to this pleasant family-run hotel with a well-tended garden in a quiet residential area. Public areas include an attractive panelled bar. Compact bedrooms – in a separate block – are equipped with functional units, tea-makers, trouser presses and mini 'fridges. The decor looks a little tired, but the new annexe promises smarter accommodation. No children under six. No dogs. *Amenities* garden, laundry service. &

Rooms 32	Direct dial Yes	Confirm by 6	Parking Ample
Ensuite bath/shower 32	Room TV Yes	Last dinner 9.30	Room service None

---

Our inspectors *never* book in the name of Egon Ronay's Guides.
They disclose their identity only if they are considering an establishment
for inclusion in the next edition of the Guide.

DERBY Crest Hotel 60% £C/D

H **Map 10 C3** Derbyshire
Pastures Hill,
Littleover DE3 7BA
Derby (0332) 514933
Telex 377081

Credit Access, Amex, Diners, Visa

On the A5250 west of Derby, this is popular with visitors to Alton Towers, a 25-minute drive away. Standard bedrooms have simple built-in units with ample writing space, plus trouser presses and neatly fitted bathrooms. Executive rooms are superior in their furnishings and accessories, and there are two cottage suites in the hotel grounds. Public areas include a stylish cocktail bar. *Amenities* garden, secretarial services, fax, laundry service, children's play area. &

Rooms 67	Direct dial Yes	Confirm by 6	Parking Ample
Ensuite bath/shower 67	Room TV Yes	Last dinner 9.45	Room service 24 hours

DERBY International Hotel 62% £D

H **Map 10 C3** Derbyshire
Burton Road DE3 6AD
Derby (0332) 369321
Telex 377759

Credit Access, Amex, Diners, Visa

Located just outside the city centre is this welcoming modern hotel, where cheerful Spanish-style day rooms reflect the personal taste of owners the Flanagans. Decent-sized bedrooms are homely and well equipped, with extras ranging from trouser presses and hairdryers to mini-bars and electronic safes. *Amenities* satellite TV, in-house movies, secretarial services, laundry service, 24-hour lounge service.

Rooms 41	Direct dial Yes	Confirm by 6	Parking Ample
Ensuite bath/shower 41	Room TV Yes	Last dinner 10	Room service All day

DINNINGTON Dinnington Hall Hotel 65% *NEW ENTRY* £E

H **Map 11 D2** South Yorkshire
Falcon Way, Nr Sheffield
S31 7NY
Dinnington (0909) 569661

Credit Access, Amex, Diners, Visa

Get directions when booking at this converted Georgian manor house standing in three acres of grounds. The day rooms have a restful period feel, but the real strength is the bedrooms, all of ample size, with handsome furnishings and pretty fabrics. One room has a four-poster, another a half-tester. Welcoming touches include sherry and fresh fruit. Staff are friendly and unassuming. No children under three. *Amenities* garden, secretarial services, laundry service. &

Rooms 10	Direct dial Yes	Confirm by arrang.	Parking Ample
Ensuite bath/shower 10	Room TV Yes	Last dinner 10	Room service 24 hours

DISS   Weavers Wine Bar & Eating House   *NEW ENTRY*   ⚐

R **Map 6 C2** Norfolk
Market Hill
Diss (0379) 2411

About £28 for two
Seats 36
Parking Limited

Credit Access, Visa

Informality is the keynote at this beamed restaurant and wine bar in the old weavers' guild house. The lunchtime menu is written on a blackboard and covers such items as soup, sandwiches, lasagne and pork goulash, with some toothsome puds to round things off. In the evening Norfolk samphire with melted butter makes an unusual starter followed by a choice of main courses including pan-fried lemon sole, rack of lamb with minted peas and rump steak in a peppercorn, brandy and cream sauce. Good wholesome food, freshly prepared and enjoyably unpretentious. William Bavin is the chef and his charming wife Wilma looks after front of house. Book Friday and Saturday evenings. ⏎

Lunch 12–2   *Dinner* 7–9.30, Fri & Sat 7–10
Closed L Sat & all Sun, Bank Hols, 25 & 26 Dec & 1 Jan

Changes in data sometimes occur in establishments
after the Guide goes to press.
Prices should be taken as indications rather than firm quotes.

DONCASTER   **Danum Swallow Hotel**   63%   £D

H **Map 11 D2** South Yorkshire
High Street DN1 1DN
Doncaster (0302) 342261
Telex 547533

Credit Access, Amex, Diners, Visa

A solid, 19th-century, red-brick building, once a coaching stop, now a friendly hotel. The public bar has a railway theme and has a notably genial atmosphere, and other public areas are bright and welcoming. Best bedrooms are stylishly contemporary; the remainder are decorated in light and airy colours and have freestanding mahogany units. All have tea/coffee-makers and hairdryers.
Amenities secretarial services, fax, laundry service.

| *Rooms* 66 | *Direct dial* Yes | *Confirm by* 6 | *Parking* Ample |
| *Ensuite bath/shower* 66 | *Room TV* Yes | *Last dinner* 9.30 | *Room service* 24 hours |

DONCASTER   **Doncaster Moat House**   71%   £D

H **Map 11 D2** South Yorkshire
Warmsworth DN4 9UX
Doncaster (0302) 310331
Telex 547963

Rooms 70
Ensuite bath/shower 70
Direct dial Yes
Room TV Yes
Confirm by 6
Last dinner 10
Parking Ample
Room service 24 hours

Credit Access, Amex, Diners, Visa
Closed 1 wk Xmas

Polished marble, natural wood and light, up-to-the-minute decor make an elegant impression on travellers as they step into the foyer-lounge of this smart new hotel near the A1(M). Pastel-shaded seating areas with comfortable contemporary chairs and couches offer restful havens for the weary. Further cosy seating and plenty of greenery are to be found in the split-level bar, which is popular with residents

and locals alike. Good-sized bedrooms have quality furnishings in light pine, pale colour schemes, and attractive fabrics; all have trouser presses, tea/coffee-makers, hairdryers and tiled bathrooms. **Amenities** garden, croquet, in-house movies, secretarial services, fax, laundry service. ♿

DONCASTER   **Earl of Doncaster**   61%   £D/E

H **Map 11 D2** South Yorkshire
Bennetthorpe DN2 6AD
Doncaster (0302) 61371
Telex 547923

Credit Access, Amex, Diners, Visa

Bedrooms have been attractively refurbished at this sturdy roadside hotel not far from the racecourse. Pretty wall coverings and matching curtains please the eye, and furniture is in smart dark wood. Six Club rooms are larger and fitted with more accessories; front rooms are double-glazed. Slightly dated public areas include lounge and cocktail bar. The hotel offers a wide choice of function rooms. Friendly staff.
Amenities secretarial services, laundry service.

| *Rooms* 53 | *Direct dial* Yes | *Confirm by* 6 | *Parking* Ample |
| *Ensuite bath/shower* 53 | *Room TV* Yes | *Last dinner* 9.45 | *Room service* 24 hours |

DONCASTER   Grand St Leger Hotel   65%   *NEW ENTRY*   £D/E

HR **Map 11 D2**
South Yorkshire
Bennetthorpe DN2 6AX
Doncaster (0302) 64111

Credit Access, Amex, Diners, Visa

A white-painted hotel standing on a busy roundabout by the racecourse that is home to the St Leger. The racing connection is strongest in the bar-lounge, whose walls are lined with horsy prints. Bedrooms are comfortable and quite well equipped, with remote-control TVs, hairdryers and tea-makers, plus ample sitting and writing space. No dogs.
Amenities in-house movies, secretarial services, laundry service.

Rooms 14	Direct dial Yes	Confirm by 6	Parking Limited
Ensuite bath/shower 14	Room TV Yes	Last dinner 10	Room service All day

Restaurant   *NEW ENTRY*

Set L £7.50
Set D £10.95
About £35 for two
Seats 40
Parties 60

David Lockwood cooks in robust, dependable fashion in a smart little restaurant, and there are both à la carte and set menus. Asparagus and wild mushroom tartlet or dariole of sole and salmon could start the meal, followed perhaps by roast guinea fowl, chicken with mousseline in a golden pastry case or pork fillet with tomato and herb sauce. Service is keen, if a touch unprofessional.

Lunch 12.30–2, Sun 12–2 *Dinner* 7.30–10, Sun 7.30–9.30
Closed D 25 Dec

DORCHESTER-ON-THAMES   George Hotel   £E

I **Map 5 D2** Oxfordshire
High Street OX9 8HH
Oxford (0865) 340404
Telex 83147

Credit Access, Amex, Diners, Visa
Closed 1 wk Xmas

Innovations at this attractive old inn include fax and telex, and all bedrooms now have en suite facilities. About half the accommodation is in the main house, the rest in outbuildings. Some rooms nestle under oak beams, and most have the odd antique or traditional piece; there are two four-poster rooms. Focal point of the day rooms is a friendly beamed bar. No children under seven.
Amenities garden, laundry service.

Rooms 17	Room phone Yes	Confirm by arrang.	Parking Ample
Ensuite bath/shower 17	Room TV Yes	Last dinner 9.45	Room service Limited

DORKING   Burford Bridge Hotel   70%   £B

H **Map 5 E3** Surrey
Box Hill, Burford Bridge
RH5 6BX
Dorking (0306) 884561
Telex 859507

Rooms 48
Ensuite bath/shower 48
Direct dial Yes
Room TV Yes
Confirm by 6
Last dinner 9.30
Parking Ample
Room service 24 hours

Credit Access, Amex, Diners, Visa

Mainly 18th-century, though with a superb 16th-century tithe barn, this long, low, white-fronted hotel at the foot of Box Hill offers country charm and tranquillity. Some splendid antiques, including a fine grandfather clock, and lovely fresh flower arrangements grace the public areas, which radiate from the foyer and include a spacious lounge with green plush chairs and a relaxing cocktail bar. The

best bedrooms have been prettily refurbished with floral fabrics and smart darkwood furniture; those in the modern wing have neat decor and balconies overlooking the lawns. All have compact modern bathrooms and useful accessories. *Amenities* garden, outdoor swimming pool, secretarial services, fax, laundry service.

DORKING   White Horse Hotel   62%   £C/D

H **Map 5 E3** Surrey
High Street RH4 1BE
Dorking (0306) 881138

Credit Access, Amex, Diners, Visa

This former coaching inn, dating back to 1750, retains plenty of character in its beamed bar-lounge. Main-house rooms with modern decor and contemporary oak furniture have tea-makers and remote-control TV; remaining rooms in the garden wing are similarly appointed but are termed superior as they have slightly more space and extras like trouser presses and bath robes. *Amenities* garden, outdoor swimming pool, laundry service, 24-hour lounge service.

Rooms 68	Direct dial Yes	Confirm by 6	Parking Ample
Ensuite bath/shower 68	Room TV Yes	Last dinner 9.30	Room service Limited

DOVEDALE   Izaak Walton Hotel   59%   £D/E

H **Map 10 C3** Derbyshire
Nr Ashbourne DE6 2AY
Thorpe Cloud (033 529) 555
Telex 378406

Credit Access, Amex, Diners, Visa

Izaak Walton stayed at this 17th-century farmhouse to fish on the river Dove and no doubt enjoyed the lovely views of the surrounding hills and dales. All the bedrooms have now been updated, mostly in attractive period style, and there are three comfortable lounges. Bathrooms are generally fairly basic. *Amenities* garden, clay-pigeon shooting, game fishing, laundry service, coffee shop (10.30am–6pm summer only), 24-hour lounge service, helipad. ⟨&⟩

Rooms 34	*Direct dial* Yes	*Confirm by* 6	*Parking* Ample
Ensuite bath/shower 34	*Room TV* Yes	*Last dinner* 9.45	*Room service* All day

DOVEDALE   Peveril of the Peak Hotel   62%   £C/D

H **Map 10 C3** Derbyshire
Nr Ashbourne DE6 2AW
Thorpe Cloud (033 529) 333

Credit Access, Amex, Diners, Visa

A friendly welcome and a wonderful setting are two of the attractions of this well-run hotel. Log fires and comfortable contemporary seating make for appealing lounges and the Dove Bar looks over the secluded garden. Bedrooms vary in style, the most recently refurbished having modern designer fabrics and mahogany-style fitted units. All have plenty of thoughtful extras and fully tiled modern bathrooms. *Amenities* garden, tennis, laundry service. ⟨&⟩

Rooms 41	*Direct dial* Yes	*Confirm by* 6	*Parking* Ample
Ensuite bath/shower 41	*Room TV* Yes	*Last dinner* 9.30	*Room service* Limited

DOVER   Dover Moat House   72%   £C/D

H **Map 7 D5** Kent
Townwall Street CT16 1SZ
Dover (0304) 203270
Telex 96458

Rooms 79
Ensuite bath/shower 79
Direct dial Yes
Room TV Yes
Confirm by arrang.
Last dinner 10.15
Parking Ample
Room service Limited

Credit Access, Amex, Diners, Visa

Cross-Channel passengers are well served by this modern sea-front hotel reached by following the signs to the Eastern Docks. The favourable first impression created by the attractive foyer lounge with its terracotta tiles and comfortable leather seating is confirmed by the smart, pub-style cocktail bar and well-equipped bedrooms. Uniformly designed and surprisingly large, they have king-size beds, plenty  of writing space, thoughtful lighting, and many useful accessories including hairdryers, remote-control TVs and clock-radios. Compact bathrooms are well supplied with towels and toiletries. *Amenities* indoor swimming pool, in-house movies, secretarial services, laundry service, coffee shop (10.30am–2.30pm, 6.30pm–10.30pm).

DOVER   Crest Hotel   60%   £C/D

H **Map 7 D5** Kent
Whitfield Singledge Lane
CT16 3LF
Dover (0304) 821222
Telex 965866

Credit Access, Amex, Diners, Visa

Situated off the A2 on the outskirts of Dover (with courtesy coach for docks and station), this modern hotel has open-plan public areas and basic, yet comfortable accommodation with useful extras like trouser presses and tea-makers. The foyer lounge is contemporary, with leather-style furniture, while the garden bar features greenery and cane. No dogs. *Amenities* garden, in-house movies, secretarial services, laundry room, coffee shop (7am–11pm). ⟨&⟩

Rooms 67	*Direct dial* Yes	*Confirm by* 6	*Parking* Ample
Ensuite bath/shower 67	*Room TV* Yes	*Last dinner* 9.50	*Room service* 24 hours

DOVER   White Cliffs Hotel   62%   £D/E

H **Map 7 D5** Kent
Seafront CT17 9BW
Dover (0304) 203633
Telex 965422

Credit Access, Amex, Diners, Visa
Closed 24, 25 & 26 Dec

Immaculate housekeeping coupled with helpful staff makes staying at this solidly comfortable sea-front hotel an increasingly pleasurable experience. All bedrooms now have en-suite facilities and tea-makers. The public rooms, which include a cheerful bar and a glass-enclosed sun verandah, remain comfortable and surprisingly quiet in view of the hotel's proximity to hoverport and car ferry terminals. *Amenities* patio, laundry service.

Rooms 56	*Direct dial* Yes	*Confirm by* arrang.	*Parking* Ample
Ensuite bath/shower 56	*Room TV* Yes	*Last dinner* 9.30	*Room service* 24 hours

DRIFFIELD　　　Bell Hotel　　　　　　　　　£E

Map 15 D6 Humberside
Market Place YO25 7AP
Driffield (0377) 46661

Credit Access, Amex, Diners, Visa
Closed 2 wks Xmas

Owners George and Pat Riggs foster a friendly, welcoming atmosphere
at their town-centre inn, part of which was once the old Corn
Exchange. Bedrooms are comfortable, with traditional furnishings
and carpeted bathrooms. Three rooms for the disabled include one
specially adapted for the deaf. No children under 12. Kennels available
for dogs. *Amenities* indoor swimming pool, sauna, solarium,
whirlpool bath, squash, snooker, secretarial services, laundry service.
♿

Rooms 14	Direct dial Yes	Confirm by 6	Parking Ample
Ensuite bath/shower 14	Room TV Yes	Last dinner 9.30	Room service All day

DROITWICH SPA　　　Château Impney Hotel　76%　　　£B/C

Map 4 B1
Hereford & Worcester
WR9 0BN
Droitwich (0905) 774411
Telex 336673

Rooms 65
Ensuite bath/shower 65
Direct dial Yes
Room TV Yes
Confirm by arrang.
Last dinner 10
Parking Ample
Room service 24 hours

Credit Access, Amex, Diners, Visa

Built in 1875 in the style of a
French castle, Château Impney
stands in 60 acres of spectacular
parkland a mile from junction 5
of the M5. Day rooms have a
lofty opulence, particularly the
entrance hall with its splendid
crystal chandeliers and marble
pillars. Functions are a major
part of the hotel's trade, and there
are numerous grand suites and
smaller meeting rooms. Bedrooms in the main building range

from large to vast; those in the connected modern wing are built to a
standard design, with fitted furniture. All rooms offer trouser presses,
hairdryers, mineral water and fresh fruit. High levels of staff and
service. *Amenities* garden, sauna, solarium, gymnasium, tennis,
games room, secretarial services, fax, laundry service.

DROITWICH SPA　　　Raven Hotel　66%　　　　　£D

Map 4 B1
Hereford & Worcester
St Andrews Place WR9 8DU
Droitwich (0905) 772224
Telex 336673

Credit Access, Amex, Diners, Visa

This delightful timber-framed hotel in the town centre was once a
manor house. Much of the original carved oak panelling survives in
the public areas, where period furniture and leather chesterfields
complete the pleasantly mellow effect. A handsome staircase featuring
a fine stained glass window leads to the bedrooms – half now
attractively refurbished in traditional style, the remainder much more
functional. *Amenities* garden, fax, laundry service.

Rooms 58	Direct dial Yes	Confirm by arrang.	Parking Ample
Ensuite bath/shower 58	Room TV Yes	Last dinner 10	Room service 24 hours

**We welcome bona fide complaints and recommendations
on the tear-out pages at the back of the book for readers' comment.
They are followed up by our professional team.**

DULVERTON　　　Ashwick Country House Hotel　69%　　£D/E

HR **Map 3 D2** Somerset
TA22 9QD
Dulverton (0398) 23868

The Sherwood family's Edwardian country house is an ideal escape
for the city-dweller, a haven of peace set in beautiful countryside
above the river Barle. The atmosphere in the traditionally appointed
day rooms could not be more pleasant and restful: an open fire
banishes winter from the galleried hall, and the views from the lounge
and library are quite delightful. Good-sized bedrooms (more super
views) offer various thoughtful touches, and the talking scales in some
of the bathrooms should not deter you from the splendid breakfasts.
No children under eight. No dogs.
Amenities garden, solarium, croquet, in-house movies, laundry
service.

Rooms 6	Room phone Yes	Confirm by arrang.	Parking Ample
Ensuite bath/shower 6	Room TV Yes	Last dinner 8.30	Room service All day

see over

Ashwick Country House Restaurant

Set L Sun £7.25
Set D £11.75
Seats 35
Parties 35

Miss Bramble cooks in homely style, using the best seasonal and local produce on her nightly changing menu. Tomato and red pepper soup and Lymeswold chicken pot were alternative starters on our last visit, followed by a tasty savoury pancake, fillets of lemon sole stuffed with prawn butter and a choice of sweets or cheese. An agreeable meal ended cosily with coffee by the fire. Traditional Sunday lunch.

Lunch Mon–Sat by arrang., Sun 12.30–1.45   *Dinner* 7.15–8.30
About £30 *for two*

DULVERTON   Carnarvon Arms Hotel   60%   £D/E

H **Map 3 D2** Somerset
TA22 9AE
Dulverton (0398) 23302

Credit Access, Diners, Visa
Closed 3 wks Feb

Run by the same caring owner for 30 years, this solidly-built Victorian hotel has a delightfully warm and friendly atmosphere. Public rooms include a rustic pantry bar, cosy cocktail bar and airy sun lounge. Bedrooms have pretty wallpapers and are variously furnished.
Amenities garden, outdoor swimming pool, tennis, stabling, clay-pigeon shooting, game fishing, games room, snooker, secretarial services, laundry service, laundry room. &

Rooms 25	*Direct dial* Yes	*Confirm by* arrang.	*Parking* Ample
Ensuite bath/shower 22	*Room TV* All	*Last dinner* 8.30	*Room service* All day

DULWICH   Luigi

See under LONDON

DUNCHURCH   Dun Cow Hotel   £D/E

I **Map 11 D4** Warwickshire
The Green, Nr Rugby CV22 6NJ
Rugby (0788) 810233
Telex 94013661

Credit Access, Amex, Diners, Visa

There has been an inn since 967 on the spot where the 17th-century Dun Cow now stands. The two bars are full of character, with beams, panelling, open fires and polished brass and there's a small, traditional lounge. The homely, individually decorated bedrooms have fine period furniture and traditional fabrics; bathrooms are decorated to match each room.
Amenities garden, laundry service.

Rooms 25	*Direct dial* Yes	*Confirm by* 6	*Parking* Ample
Ensuite bath/shower 25	*Room TV* Yes	*Last dinner* 10	*Room service* 24 hours

DUNKIRK   Petty France Hotel   65%   £D

H **Map 4 B2** Avon
Nr Badminton GL9 1AF
Didmarton (045 423) 361

Credit Access, Amex, Diners, Visa

Standing by the A46, this converted Georgian mansion is a pleasant base for business or touring. There's a cosy, unhurried atmosphere throughout, and it's most agreeable to sit by a fire in the lounge browsing through books and magazines. Seven bedrooms in traditional style are in the main house, the rest in the former stable block across the courtyard. All are well equipped and very smartly kept.
Amenities garden, croquet, laundry service.

Rooms 20	*Direct dial* Yes	*Confirm by* arrang.	*Parking* Ample
Ensuite bath/shower 20	*Room TV* Yes	*Last dinner* 9.30	*Room service* All day

 indicates a **well-chosen** house wine

DUNSTABLE   Old Palace Lodge Hotel   69%   £C/D

H **Map 5 E1** Bedfordshire
Church Street LU5 4RP
Dunstable (0582) 62201
Telex 825828

Credit Access, Amex, Diners, Visa

Good standards of accommodation in a creeper-clad hotel that's popular with business people. The reception area is panelled in oak, and there's a comfortably furnished bar-cum-lounge. All the bedrooms are of a good size, and all boast hairdryers, trouser presses and smart rosewood-finish furniture. 12 rooms are large enough for a sofa as well as the standard armchairs. Excellent bathrooms.
Amenities laundry service.

Rooms 49	*Direct dial* Yes	*Confirm by* arrang.	*Parking* Ample
Ensuite bath/shower 49	*Room TV* Yes	*Last dinner* 9.45	*Room service* 24 hours

DUNSTER — Luttrell Arms 64% £C/D

H Map 3 E1 Somerset
High Street, Nr Minehead
TA24 6SG
Dunster (0643) 821555

Credit Access, Amex, Diners, Visa

Built round a 15th-century Gothic hall, this attractive, creeper-clad hotel has abundant old-world charm. The hall is now a lofty, comfortable lounge, while its kitchen has become the bar. Seven top-floor bedrooms are a little more modest than the rest, though all are very pleasant, particularly four superior rooms with four-posters. Good tiled bathrooms, remote-control TVs.
Amenities garden, laundry service.

Rooms 25	Room phone Yes	Confirm by 6	Parking Limited
Ensuite bath/shower 25	Room TV Yes	Last dinner 9.30	Room service All day

🡆 is our symbol for an **outstanding** wine list

DURHAM — Royal County Hotel 67% £D

H Map 15 B4 Co. Durham
Old Elvet DH1 3JN
Durham (091) 3866821
Telex 538238

Credit Access, Amex, Diners, Visa

Improvements are afoot at this Georgian building with a 1970s extension. The coffee shop and Piano Bar have been attractively refurbished, and the restaurant is equally smart. Bedrooms in the original part, with newly acquired oak furniture and stylish fabrics, are roomier than those in the wing.
Amenities sauna, hairdressing, in-house movies, teletext, secretarial services, fax, laundry service, coffee shop (10am–9.30pm). &

Rooms 120	Direct dial Yes	Confirm by 6	Parking Ample
Ensuite bath/shower 120	Room TV Yes	Last dinner 10.15	Room service 24 hours

DUXFORD — Duxford Lodge Hotel 66% £D/E

HR Map 6 B3 Cambridgeshire
Ickleton Road CB2 4RU
Cambridge (0223) 836444.
Telex 817438

Credit Access, Amex, Diners, Visa
Closed 1 Jan

A red-brick Victorian hotel set in well tended grounds ten miles from Cambridge, close to junction 10 of the M11. Smallish day rooms in pleasant pastel tones include a cosy lounge and comfortable bar. Main-house bedrooms feature smart darkwood furniture and mini-bars; those in a converted stable block have simple white laminate units. All are equipped with extras like tea-makers and radio-alarms.
Amenities garden, laundry service.

Rooms 16	Direct dial Yes	Confirm by arrang.	Parking Ample
Ensuite bath/shower 16	Room TV Yes	Last dinner 9.30	Room service All day

Restaurant

Set L £11.50, Sun £9.75
Set D from £14, Sun £9.75
About £47 for two
Seats 40
Parties 40

Relaxing pastel pink decor sets the scene for John Burrows' imaginative yet unfussy cooking. Tip-top ingredients, carefully prepared and nicely presented, feature in delights like mushroom-filled spinach tortelloni deliciously sauced with basil and garlic, or braised duck breast teamed with a rich fruity sauce and a duck liver tartlet. Flavours are carefully balanced and portions generous. A very good wine list. Polite, efficient service. 🍷 Well-chosen ⊖

Lunch 12–1.45 *Dinner* 7–9.30, Sun till 9
Closed L Sat, D 25 & 26 Dec, all 27 & 28 Dec & 1 Jan

EALING — New Leaf & Sinar Matahari

See under LONDON

EAST BERGHOLT — Fountain House ⌘

R Map 6 C3 Suffolk
The Street
Colchester (0206) 298232

Set L £9.95
Set D £11.95
About £34 for two
Seats 32 *Parties* 16
Parking Ample
Credit Access, Visa

A lively, welcoming restaurant where the menus are short but offer a good choice of dishes based on the best local produce. Starters include a richly filling pea soup; for a main course, try the perfectly cooked chicken livers with mushrooms in a cream and wine sauce. Good vegetables and tempting desserts. Some excellent wines in the cellar: Maximin Grunhauser (Von Schubert) '85, Zinfandel (Ridge) '80. 🍷 Well-chosen ⊖

Lunch 12.30–2 *Dinner* 7.30–10
Closed D Sun, all Mon, Bank Hols & 2 wks Feb

EAST BUCKLAND — Lower Pitt ♀

RR Map 3 D2 Devon
Barnstaple
Filleigh (059 86) 243

About £38 for two
Seats 28
Parties 24
Parking Ample

Credit Access, Amex, Visa

Ask for directions when booking a table at this secluded farmhouse restaurant where Suzanne Lyons provides home cooking of a high standard. Typical dishes include a truly excellent terrine of chicken breast with a forcemeat of chicken liver, veal and herbs, prawn and cucumber in aïoli and lamb à la grecque. Vegetables are a particular strength and there are some skilfully made desserts with which to finish. 🍷 Well-chosen 🄴

Lunch by arrang.   *Dinner* 7–9
Closed Sun, Mon, 1 Jan & 3 days Xmas

BEDROOMS 3   £E/F
With bath/shower 3

There are three double rooms, one with bath and two with showers, for dinner guests only. No under tens. No dogs.

EAST DEREHAM — King's Head Hotel £E/F

I Map 6 C1 Norfolk
Norwich Street NR19 1AD
Dereham (0362) 693842

Credit Access, Amex, Diners, Visa

Ask for directions for this side-street inn, which has been welcoming travellers for 300 years. Tubs of flowers outside the lounge bar make it a pleasant place to relax over a drink while watching the bowls players. Bedrooms in the main house, while characterful and individual in style, are noisier than those in the stable block. All, though, are comfortable and clean.
Amenities patio, tennis, bowling green.

| *Rooms* 15 | *Direct dial* Yes | *Confirm by* arrang. | *Parking* Ample |
| *Ensuite bath/shower* 15 | *Room TV* Yes | *Last dinner* 9 | *Room service* None |

EAST DEREHAM — Phoenix Hotel 59% £C/D

H Map 6 C1 Norfolk
Church Street NR19 1DL
Dereham (0362) 692276

Credit Access, Amex, Diners, Visa

A red-brick 1960s hotel with pleasant public areas comprising a comfortable foyer-lounge, an entrance hall with ornamental pool, and three cheerful bars which provide a popular meeting spot for local businessmen and farmers. Six superior, spacious rooms boast seating areas, smart darkwood furniture and luxuriously tiled bathrooms. Other rooms are more modest but have pleasing colour schemes and neat, functional bathrooms. *Amenities* laundry service.

| *Rooms* 24 | *Room phone* Yes | *Confirm by* 6 | *Parking* Ample |
| *Ensuite bath/shower* 24 | *Room TV* Yes | *Last dinner* 9.30 | *Room service* All day |

EAST GRINSTEAD — Evergreen

R Map 7 B5 West Sussex
192 London Road
East Grinstead (0342) 22078

Chinese cooking
Set D £12
About £34 for two
Seats 80 *Parties* 50
Parking Ample
Credit Access, Amex, Diners, Visa

Friendly service, good fresh ingredients and competent cooking are to be found at this small, stylish Chinese restaurant. The extensive menu is Peking-based but the chef exerts a Cantonese influence over the extensive range of enjoyable dishes. Recommendable ones include king prawns with shells, grilled dumplings, aromatic crispy duck, kuei kuo pork, aromatic crispy lamb and grilled sole Peking-style. Simple vegetables and good rice.

Lunch noon–2   *Dinner* 5.30–10.45, Sat 5.30–11
Closed L Sun & Bank Hols & 5 days Xmas

EAST GRINSTEAD — Gravetye Manor 81% £B/C

HR Map 7 B5 West Sussex
Nr East Grinstead RH19 4LJ
Sharpthorne (0342) 810567
Telex 957239

Rooms 14
Ensuite bath/shower 14
Room phone Yes
Room TV Yes
Confirm by arrang.
Last dinner 9.30
Parking Ample
Room service All day

This lovely Elizabethan manor house is an outstanding hotel with an idyllic setting, impeccable staff and a perfectionist owner whose eye for detail is eagle-sharp, even after 30 years. Public rooms are a model of country house grace, with resplendent panelling, splendid mouldings, fine paintings and fresh flowers. Everywhere there is a delightful feeling of tranquillity. Bedrooms lack for nothing in

continued ...

style and comfort. Each is named after a tree, each has beautiful antiques and every extra from books and magazines to mineral water and remote-control TVs (discreetly hidden behind tapestry screens). Sumptuous bathrooms. No children under seven. No dogs.
Amenities garden, game fishing, croquet, fax, laundry service.

Restaurant ★

Lunch 12.30–2
Dinner 7.30–9.30
Set L £16.50, Sun £20.90
Set D £20.90
About £85 *for two*
Seats 50
Parties 20

Closed D 25 Dec

Leigh Stone-Herbert has well and truly established his distinctive and self-assured style of cooking in this splendid dark-panelled restaurant. His ideas are imaginative and intriguing but often confidently simple – witness his warm salad of braised ham hock and green lentils, or beautifully sweet scallops with fresh watercress. Cheeses are of top quality, and delightful puddings include chocolate leaves filled with a tangy lime crème fraîche. Superb cellar with a powerful showing from Burgundy and Germany. Serious-minded professional service. No smoking. ***Specialities*** grilled fillet of red mullet on a bed of black noodles, breast of duck pot-roasted with fresh ginger and honey, terrine of pink grapefruit. Outstanding Well-chosen

EAST HORSLEY — Thatchers Hotel 63% £C/D

H **Map 5 E3** Surrey
Epsom Road KT24 6BT
East Horsley (048 65) 4291

Credit Access, Amex, Diners, Visa

A solid mock-Tudor building set in three acres of grounds off the A246. Comfortable facilities are offered in the roomy lounge – a very nice place to sit back with a book – and the adjoining bar. Some of the neat, attractive bedrooms are grouped round the pool, while the rest are in the main building, a new extension or a charming old cottage. No dogs.
Amenities garden, outdoor swimming pool, laundry service.

Rooms 59 | *Direct dial* Yes | *Confirm by* arrang. | *Parking* Ample
Ensuite bath/shower 59 | *Room TV* Yes | *Last dinner* 9.30 | *Room service* All day

We publish annually,
so make sure you use the current edition.
It's worth it!

EAST LANGTON — Bell Inn

R **Map 11 D4** Leicestershire
Main Street, Nr Market Harborough
East Langton (085 884) 567

French cooking
About £45 *for two*
Seats 50 *Parties* 25
Parking Ample
Credit Access, Visa

A comfortable, traditional village pub with a reputation for fresh, carefully cooked food. The neat restaurant occupies most of the available space, and a blackboard menu spells out the day's choice, with fish being something of a speciality: moules marinière, fish soup with a positive but not overpowering flavour, grey and red mullet with sauce provençale. Meaty things, including seasonal game, also meet with approval, and there are simple, enjoyable sweets.

Lunch 12–2 *Dinner* 7–10, Sat 7–10.30
Closed All Sun, 25 & 26 Dec

EAST MOLESEY — Hampton Court Brasserie

R **Map 5 E2** Surrey
3 Palace Gate Parade, Hampton Court
01-979 7891

Set L from £9.95
About £48 *for two*
Seats 120 *Parties* 80
Parking Ample
Credit Access, Amex, Diners, Visa

Chef Guy Hill and manager Carlos Simao continue in fine form at this chic two-level brasserie close to the Thames. The menu offers a good choice of imaginative yet not too ambitious dishes that are attractively presented: marinated salmon with dill and mustard sauce, roast breast of goose, medallions of beef with wild mushrooms. Short list of good wines. Evening piano, Sunday lunchtime jazz. Well-chosen

Lunch 12–3 *Dinner* 7–11, Sun 7–10
Closed 25 & 26 Dec & 1 Jan

EAST MOLESEY — Lantern ♫

R Map 5 E2 Surrey
20 Bridge Road
01-979 1531

French cooking
Set L from £12.25
Set D from £14.85
Seats 50 *Parties* 32
Parking Limited
Credit Access, Amex, Diners, Visa

Twin dining rooms (one with a pretty conservatory) house this well-established restaurant on a busy shopping street. Peter Morphew offers robust French dishes with some surprises on his fixed-price and à la carte menus. A typical set meal might be cheese pastries followed by lamb cutlets with white onion and red pepper sauce and sweets from the trolley. Vegetables of good quality are carefully cooked. ⊖

Lunch 12.30–2.15   *Dinner* 7–10.30   *About £44 for two*
Closed L Mon & Sat, all Sun, Bank Hols & Aug

EAST MOLESEY — Vecchia Roma ♫

R Map 5 E2 Surrey
57 Bridge Road
01-979 5490

Italian cooking
Set L £9.25, Sun £10.25
Set D £13.95
Seats 95 *Parties* 100
Parking Difficult
Credit Access, Diners, Visa

Excellent antipasti introduce the range of properly prepared dishes at this established, efficiently run Italian restaurant in East Molesey's main street. Main courses include calf's liver in butter and sage, marinated lamb with black cherries and sole stuffed with scampi and prawns, served with lobster and brandy sauce. Freshly made pasta is always popular. Enjoyable home-made gâteaux. ⊖

Lunch 12–2.15   *Dinner* 7–11.15   *About £47 for two*
Closed L Sat & 26 Dec

EAST STOKE — Kemps Country House Hotel   59%   £E

H Map 4 B4 Dorset
Near Wareham BH20 6AL
Bindon Abbey (0929) 462563

Credit Access, Amex, Diners, Visa

Charming new owners are maintaining the friendly atmosphere and personal style of service for which this hotel is noted. Originally a rectory, it provides plenty of room to relax with two homely lounges and a cosy cocktail bar. Bedrooms in the main building and coach house are spacious and comfortable, with easy chairs and writing desks; bathrooms are kept spotlessly clean. No dogs.
Amenities garden.

Rooms 9	*Direct dial* Yes	*Confirm by* arrang.	*Parking* Ample
Ensuite bath/shower 8	*Room TV* Yes	*Last dinner* 9.30	*Room service* All day

EASTBOURNE — Byrons ♫

R Map 7 B6 East Sussex
6 Crown Street, Old Town
Eastbourne (0323) 20171

About £40 for two
Seats 24
Parties 10
Parking Ample

Credit Amex, Diners, Visa

A delightfully intimate, personal restaurant where dedicated owners Simon and Marian Scrutton dispense excellent, simple cooking and sparkling charm. The short evening menu (lunches are by prior arrangement only) invariably features fresh local fish, while meat eaters will find plenty to delight them. Short, good wine list: try the St Véran (Pierre Ferraud) '86 and the delicious red Vigneto San Lorenzo '81. ♀ Well-chosen ⊖

Lunch by arrang.   *Dinner* 7.30–10
Closed Sun & Bank Hols

EASTBOURNE — Cavendish Hotel   73%   £C

H Map 7 B6 East Sussex
Grand Parade BN21 4DH
Eastbourne (0323) 410222
Telex 87579

Rooms 114
Ensuite bath/shower 114
Direct dial Yes
Room TV Yes
Confirm by arrang.
Last dinner 9.30
Parking Ample
Room service 24 hours

Credit Access, Amex, Diners, Visa

A familiar landmark with its whitewashed exterior and sea-front position, the Cavendish is the choice of many discriminating visitors to Eastbourne. The reception lounge has an opulent air, and there's a sunny promenade lounge. The main cocktail bar boasts plush tub seating, mirrored walls and icicle chandeliers while ornate plasterwork takes the eye in the splendid dining room. Decent-sized bed-rooms, nearly all updated, feature good-quality, sturdy furnishings and highly efficient central heating. Some 35 sea-facing rooms have small private balconies. The hotel offers extensive conference and banqueting facilities. *Amenities* snooker, games room, secretarial services, laundry service.

EASTBOURNE Grand Hotel 72% £B

H Map 7 B6 East Sussex
King Edward's Parade
BN21 4EQ
Eastbourne (0323) 412345
Telex 87332

Rooms 178
Ensuite bath/shower 178
Direct dial Yes
Room TV Yes
Confirm by arrang.
Last dinner 9.30
Parking Ample
Room service 24 hours

Credit Access, Amex, Diners, Visa

Manicured gardens and a heated pool are all that separate the gleaming white facade of this large Victorian building from the seafront. Public areas are also on a grand scale, with decor and furnishings not really doing justice to their size. Bedrooms range from suites with their own balconies to neat singles. The hotel is a popular conference venue and service for private guests can suffer accordingly. On our most recent visit only porterage worked smoothly, and breakfast was an occasion best forgotten. **Amenities** garden, indoor & outdoor swimming pools, sauna, solarium, whirlpool bath, gymnasium, beauty salon, hairdressing, putting, snooker, valeting, secretarial services, fax, laundry service, shopping arcade, children's play area.

EASTBOURNE Queen's Hotel 71% £C

H Map 7 B6 East Sussex
Marine Parade BN21 3DY
Eastbourne (0323) 22822
Telex 877736

Rooms 108
Ensuite bath/shower 108
Direct dial Yes
Room TV Yes
Confirm by 6
Last dinner 9
Parking Ample
Room service 24 hours

Credit Access, Amex, Diners, Visa

You can't miss this hotel – its imposing Victorian facade dominates the Marine Parade. Public rooms are light and spacious, with drapes and pillars flanked by Regency-style furniture. A split-level cocktail bar overlooks the sea while a basement bar creates an inner view with a display of collectable 'junk'. The hotel has good conference facilities and plenty for children, especially in summer. Spacious bedrooms, many with sea views, have smart cream furniture and good-quality drapes. Older-style rooms are plainer but all have tea-makers, TVs and direct-dial telephones. Ensuite bathrooms are smart; new ones include hairdryers, a few have shower only. **Amenities** games room, snooker, secretarial services, laundry service. ᵬ

EASTBOURNE The Wish Tower 65% £D

H Map 7 B6 East Sussex
King Edward's Parade
BN21 4EB
Eastbourne (0323) 22676

Credit Access, Amex, Diners, Visa

The whitewashed exterior of this popular seafront hotel positively gleams in the sunshine, and inside it is equally bright and cheerful. The bedrooms, all double-glazed, have been greatly improved both in decor and accessories; best are those with bay windows and sea views. Next in line for improvement are the day rooms, which include a spacious, well-furnished lounge and a cosy cocktail bar.
Amenities laundry service.

Rooms 67	Direct dial Yes	Confirm by 6	Parking Limited
Ensuite bath/shower 67	Room TV Yes	Last dinner 9	Room service 24 hours

★ For a *discount* on next year's guide, see **An Offer for Answers.** ★

EASTLEIGH Crest Hotel 65% £C

H Map 5 D3 Hampshire
Leigh Road, Passfield
Avenue SO5 5PG
Southampton (0703) 619700
Telex 47606

Credit Access, Amex, Diners, Visa

North of Southampton, close to the airport, this well-run modern hotel stands just off the A33. Bright open-plan public areas include an airy foyer and cheerful bar. Standard bedrooms have compact bathrooms and are well equipped; Executive rooms offer superior furniture and extras like bath robes; and ladies' rooms sport pretty fabrics and feminine accessories. **Amenities** in-house movies, secretarial services, laundry service, children's playroom (weekends). ᵬ

Rooms 120	Direct dial Yes	Confirm by 6	Parking Ample
Ensuite bath/shower 120	Room TV Yes	Last dinner 9.45	Room service 24 hours

EASTON GREY   Whatley Manor   75%   £C/D

HR   **Map 4 B2** Wiltshire
Malmesbury SN16 0RB
Malmesbury (0666) 822888
Telex 449380

Rooms 26
Ensuite bath/shower 26
Direct dial Yes
Room TV Yes
Confirm by arrang.
Last dinner 9
Parking Ample
Room service All day

Credit Access, Amex, Diners, Visa

Gracious country house living in a former farmhouse by the Avon. The hotel is reached by a tree-lined drive off the B4040, and guests pass under a brick archway to Cotswold-stone walls and high slate roofs covered in ivy and creeper. For relaxation the panelled lounge and library bar are hard to beat, while the energetic will head for the pool and adjacent leisure facilities. Mainhouse bedrooms are vast, with period furniture and spotless carpeted bathrooms; ten rooms in the old Court House are very secluded and do without room service.

Amenities garden, outdoor swimming pool, sauna, solarium, whirlpool bath, keep-fit equipment, game fishing, croquet, snooker, secretarial services, laundry service, 24-hour lounge service, helipad.

Restaurant

Set L £9, Sun £10.50
Set D £18
About £46 *for two*
Seats 50
Parties 50

A comfortable dining room, candlelit in the evening, with enjoyable cooking and relaxed, unhurried service. Tomato and basil soup, mushrooms Café de Paris, sole Nantua, tarragon chicken and best end cutlets with a rosemary-scented raspberry sauce typify the range, and guests are escorted to the buffet to choose their cheese or sweets. Vegetarian main dishes are available, and there's a popular Sunday buffet/carvery. ℮

Lunch 12.30–1.45
Dinner 7.30–9

EDBURTON   Tottington Manor Hotel Restaurant   *NEW ENTRY*   ⑨

R   **Map 7 B6** West Sussex
Nr Henfield
Steyning (0903) 815757

Set Sun L from £10.50
About £48 *for two*
Seats 48
Parties 20
Parking Ample
Credit Access, Amex, Diners, Visa

Unpretentious and satisfying food is to be found at this congenial restaurant. David Miller's menus offer standard fare as well as more imaginative dishes, all prepared with flair. For a starter, try the piquant tomato soup, with perhaps medallions of veal and sweetbreads to follow. Delicious sweets. Sound wines with the occasional bottle of real interest: Morgon Côte de Py (Selles) '85, Essencia Orange Muscat (California). ♀ Well-chosen ℮

Lunch 12.30–2, Sun 12–2   *Dinner* 7.30–9.45
Closed L Sat, D Sun, all Mon, 3 wks Aug

**Our inspectors *never* book in the name of Egon Ronay's Guides.
They disclose their identity only if they are considering an establishment
for inclusion in the next edition of the Guide.**

EDENBRIDGE   Honours Mill   ♕   ⑨

R   **Map 5 F3** Kent
87 High Street
Edenbridge (0732) 866757

Set L from £14.50, Sun £12.95
Set D £20.75
About £52 *for two*
Seats 38
Parties 16
Parking Ample

Credit Access, Diners, Visa

A charming restaurant which has been created from a formerly derelict mill and granary. Linen tablecloths, top quality china and stylish glasses make for an elegant setting in which to enjoy the excellent cooking of Neville Goodhew and Martin Radmall. Imaginative menus are complemented by simple yet attractive presentation, making the meals a delight. Starter might be an outstanding fish mousse, with a succulent breast of chicken with delicate pistachio filling to follow. Vegetables are masterfully cooked and presented. Pleasing sweets and a good selection of cheeses to finish. Good wines, both modest and great: Pinot Blanc (Hugel) '85, Chablis Vaulignot (Dauvissat) '86, Krug '79. ♀ Well-chosen ℮

Lunch 12.15–2   *Dinner* 7.15–10
Closed L Sat, D Sun, Mon, 2 wks Jan & 2 wks Aug

EDGWARE

Ings *NEW ENTRY* ⨍

R **Map 7 A4** Middlesex
194 Burnt Oak Broadway
01-951 5863

Chinese cooking
Set L from £3.95
Set D from £10.50
Seats 60 *Parties* 60
Parking Ample
Credit Access, Visa

Friendly Sue But and her father, chef Mr Chow, make a formidable team at this pleasantly sophisticated Chinese restaurant. The menu offers a good choice of classic Peking-style dishes, expertly prepared, with dim sum as a Sunday lunch attraction. Highlights of our meal included tasty jellyfish, superb fried prawns, succulent steamed sea bass, lovely crispy beef and squid in a flavoursome black bean sauce.

Lunch 12–2.30 *Dinner* 6–11.30 *About £30 for two*
Closed L Sat, 2 wks Jan

EGGLESTON

Three Tuns Inn ⨍

R **Map 15 B5** Co. Durham
Nr Barnard Castle
Teesdale (0833) 50289

English cooking

Set L £8.25
About £25 for two
Seats 14
Parking Ample

An appealing little pub-restaurant overlooking the village green. Genial host James Dykes takes your order in the bar while wife Christine attends to the cooking. Simple, well-prepared and largely traditional fare includes delicious home-made soups, grilled trout and pan-fried pork chasseur. Leave room for the excellent sherry trifle. Short, keenly-priced wine list with fine vintage ports. Book a day ahead. 🍷 Well-chosen

Lunch Sun only at 1 *Dinner* 7.30–9.30
Closed D Sun, all Mon & 25 Dec

**We welcome bona fide complaints and recommendations
on the tear-out pages at the back of the book for readers' comment.
They are followed up by our professional team.**

EGHAM

La Bonne Franquette ⨍

R **Map 5 E2** Surrey
5 High Street
Egham (0784) 39494

French cooking
Set L £12.50 **Set D** from £20
About £60 for two
Seats 45 *Parties* 25
Parking Ample
Credit Access, Amex, Diners, Visa

Two inter-connecting dining rooms in a converted private house make up this comfortable, pleasant restaurant with competent service by its French staff. Detailed recipes add interest to the menu which offers mostly quite ambitious dishes such as a light and nicely sauced scallop cervelas. Good sweets like apple fritters with ginger ice cream and caramel sauce. Sumptuous red burgundies on a good but pricy wine list. 🍷 Well-chosen ⊜

Lunch 12–1.45 *Dinner* 7–9.45, Sat & Sun till 10
Closed L Sat & all Bank Hols

EGHAM

Great Fosters 70% £D/E

H **Map 5 E2** Surrey
Stroude Road TW20 9UR
Egham (0784) 33822
Telex 944441

Rooms 45
Ensuite bath/shower 45
Direct dial Yes
Room TV Yes
Confirm by arrang.
Last dinner 9.15
Parking Ample
Room service 24 hours

Credit Access, Amex, Diners, Visa

Built as a royal hunting lodge nearly 400 years ago, Great Fosters became a hotel in 1930. Its period appeal is considerable, with antiques, ornate plaster-work and oak panelling much in evidence. A Jacobean fireplace graces the entrance hall, whose grand dimensions contrast with those of the charming little residents' lounge. Note, too, the rare oakwell staircase that leads to the tower. Bedrooms range from  vast suites with tapestries and antiques (two have four-posters) to some smaller singles; all have well-equipped bathrooms. The extensive grounds include a moat crossed by a Japanese bridge which leads to a sunken rose garden. No dogs.
Amenities garden, outdoor swimming pool, sauna, tennis.

EGHAM   Runnymede Hotel   70%   £C

H **Map 5 E2** Surrey
Windsor Road TW20 0AG
Egham (0784) 36171
Telex 934900

Rooms 126
Ensuite bath/shower 126
Direct dial Yes
Room TV Yes
Confirm by 6
Last dinner 9.45
Parking Ample
Room service 24 hours

Credit Access, Amex, Diners, Visa

This impressive modern business hotel combines the convenience of the M25 with a delightful location on the banks of the Thames. Continuing improvements include the refurbishing of the public areas, which include a comfortable lounge and two bars, all opening on to a splendid river terrace. Restyled bedrooms have been given smart pine furniture and coordinated furnishings, and are equipped with mini-bars, hairdryers, trouser presses, direct-dial telephones and remote-control TVs. Bathrooms now have attractive pastel tiles and non-slip floors. Staff are courteous and efficient.
Amenities garden, coarse fishing, in-house movies, secretarial services, fax, laundry service, helipad.

ELTHAM   Yardley Court Hotel

See under LONDON HOTELS under £60

ELY   Lamb Hotel   59%   £E

H **Map 6 B2** Cambridgeshire
2 Lynn Road CB7 4EJ
Ely (0353) 663574

Credit Access, Amex, Diners, Visa
Closed 25 Dec

A smartly refurbished cocktail bar is the latest improvement at this welcoming, well-run hotel close to the cathedral. The courtyard is a reminder of the days when this was a coaching inn, as is the half-timbered and brick fireplace in the lounge area. Good-sized bedrooms have pleasant coordinated colour schemes and neat fitted units, plus remote-control TVs, trouser presses and hairdryers. Back rooms are quieter. *Amenities* secretarial services, laundry service.

Rooms 32	*Direct dial* Yes	*Confirm by* arrang.	*Parking* Ample
Ensuite bath/shower 32	*Room TV* Yes	*Last dinner* 9.45	*Room service* 24 hours

ELY   Old Fire Engine House   *NEW ENTRY*

R **Map 6 B2** Cambridgeshire
St Mary's Street CB7 4ER
Ely (0353) 2582

About £25 for two
Seats 50
Parties 25
Parking Limited

Teamwork triumphs at this restaurant and art gallery. Local ladies share the cooking and both the food and the atmosphere suggest one is a welcome guest in a friend's farmhouse kitchen. We enjoyed a flavoursome lamb and vegetable soup followed by poached salmon with first-class hollandaise. Don't miss the brandy and apricot ice-cream. Absorbing, informative wine list; note the subtle Chardonnay from Northern Spain and delicious Coteaux du Layon (Baumard) '82.
🍷 Well-chosen ⊖

Lunch 12.30–2   *Dinner* 7.30–9
Closed D Sun, Bank Hols & 10 days Xmas

Changes in data sometimes occur in establishments
after the Guide goes to press.
Prices should be taken as indications rather than firm quotes.

EPPING   Post House Hotel   63%   £C/D

H **Map 7 B4** Essex
High Road, Bell Common
CM16 4DG
Epping (0378) 731370
Telex 81617

Credit Access, Amex, Diners, Visa

Part of this Post House was a 16th-century coaching inn, and there's a cosy old-world atmosphere in the foyer-lounge and bar. Bedrooms are located in motel-style wings and range from good-sized, well-appointed standard rooms to Executive Club rooms with extras such as trouser presses, hairdryers and sofas that double as extra beds.
Amenities garden, in-house movies, secretarial services, laundry service, children's play area.

Rooms 82	*Direct dial* Yes	*Confirm by* 6	*Parking* Ample
Ensuite bath/shower 82	*Room TV* Yes	*Last dinner* 10.15, Sun 9.15	*Room service* 24 hours

ESHER — Good Earth

R **Map 5 E3** Surrey
14 High Street
Esher (0372) 62489

Chinese cooking
Set L and D from £11.75
About £42 *for two*
Seats 80
Parking Limited
Credit Access, Amex, Diners, Visa

Booking is essential at this popular Chinese restaurant, where stylish new decor is matched by smart, efficient service. The menu ranges widely around the various regional cuisines, including old favourites like Peking duck and Szechuan prawns as well as less familiar dishes such as shark's fin soup with crabmeat and lettuce-wrapped crispy lamb with yellow plum sauce. There's even a Malaysian satay! All enjoyably prepared, using good-quality raw materials.

Lunch noon–2.30 *Dinner* 6–11.30
Closed 24–27 Dec

ETTINGTON — Chase Hotel 66% £E

HR **Map 4 C1** Warwickshire
Banbury Road CV37 7NZ
Stratford-upon-Avon
(0789) 740000
Credit Access, Amex, Diners, Visa
Closed 23 Dec–18 Jan

Built in 1867 in the Victorian Gothic style, the Chase provides a very comfortable stay in peaceful surroundings. Period features add to the charm of the day rooms, which include an inviting little bar-lounge. Decor in the bedrooms is soft, traditional and tasteful; housekeeping is excellent, space generous, the views delightful, and breakfast a treat. No children under eight. No dogs. ***Amenities*** garden, croquet.

Rooms 11 *Direct dial* Yes *Confirm by* arrang. *Parking* Ample
Ensuite bath/shower 11 *Room TV* Yes *Last dinner* 9 *Room service* Limited

Restaurant

English cooking
Set L £9.95
About £46 *for two*
Seats 60
Parties 65

An attractive, traditionally appointed room with fine views of garden and countryside. David Cunliffe's menus offer very enjoyable English cooking exemplified by our onion soup, best end of lamb with sprouting mustard seed sauce and poached pear with delicious almond ice cream and raspberry sauce. Steaks cater for the plain meat eater, and unpasteurised English cheeses are an alternative to a sweet. Note the thoughtful 'Befores and Afters' menu for lighter appetites. Well-chosen

Lunch 12.30–2 *Dinner* 7.30–9, Sat 7.30–9.30
Closed L Sat, D Sun & 23 Dec–18 Jan

EVERSHOT — Summer Lodge 71% £C/D

HR **Map 4 B4** Dorset
Summer Lane DT2 0JR
Evershot (093 583) 666

Rooms 17
Ensuite bath/shower 17
Direct dial Yes
Room TV No
Confirm by arrang.
Last dinner 8
Parking Ample
Room service All day
Credit Access, Visa
Closed 1st 2 wks Jan

In a wonderful setting of splendid hydrangeas and on the edge of a pretty village in the heart of Hardy country, Summer Lodge provides a haven of relaxation. The friendly Corbetts provide the personal touches which make one feel a guest in a private home – fresh flower arrangements abound throughout, and there's a delightful collection of pottery cheese dishes. French windows in the dining room open on to the garden, and there's an elegant drawing room. Bedrooms offer good toiletries, speciality teas, sewing kits and shortbread; there are six new, very spacious rooms in a converted coach house. No children under eight. ***Amenities*** garden, outdoor swimming pool, tennis, croquet, games room, laundry service.

Restaurant

Set L £10
Set D £16.50, Sat £17.50
About £45 *for two*
Seats 40
Parties 20

Friendly service, highly competent cooking and relaxing surroundings combine to make a thoroughly enjoyable meal. The dishes are mainly English in style, using good fresh ingredients and much seasonal local produce. Starters include ham and leek gougère and smoked trout mousse; main course could be beef Wellington with béarnaise sauce or poached wild salmon hollandaise. Leave room for the excellent English cheeseboard and wonderful sweets.

Lunch 12.30–1.30 *Dinner* at 8
Closed 1st 2 wks Jan

EVESHAM   Evesham Hotel   62%   £D/E

H Map 4 C1
Hereford & Worcester
Cooper's Lane, Off Waterside
WR11 6DA
Evesham (0386) 765566
Telex 339342

Credit Access, Amex, Diners, Visa
Closed 25 & 26 Dec

Built as a Tudor mansion and modernised in the Georgian period, the Evesham stands in a large garden featuring mulberry trees and a handsome Cedar of Lebanon. The Jenkinson family and their staff run the place with friendliness and a sense of fun, and the personal touch is evident throughout. Portable radios, travelling alarm clocks, board games and local information are supplied in the individually decorated bedrooms, where direct-dial telephones have now been installed. In the bathrooms you'll find shampoo, bubble bath, soap flakes and a rubber duck. Bedrooms in both old and new wings have been refurbished. *Amenities* garden, putting, croquet, secretarial services, fax, laundry service, children's play area.

Rooms 34	*Direct dial* Yes	*Confirm by* arrang.	*Parking* Ample
Ensuite bath/shower 34	*Room TV* Yes	*Last dinner* 9.30	*Room service* All day

EVESHAM   Hussains   *NEW ENTRY*

R Map 4 C1
Hereford & Worcester
13 Vine Street
Evesham (0386) 47227

Indian cooking
Set L from £7.50
Set D from £10.00
Seats 45 *Parties* 20
Credit Access, Amex, Visa

An offshoot of Hussains in Stratford, with the same high standard of cooking. Dishes are mainly of North Indian or Bangladeshi origin, and the chef's specialities include various lamb and chicken dishes, among them charcoal-cooked lamb shahi korma, served in a lovely sauce of spices, herbs, cream, butter and nuts. Also prawns and king prawns, excellent vegetables and sundries. Service could be better.

Lunch 12–2.30   *Dinner* 6–12, Fri & Sat 5.30–12.30   *About* £30 *for two*
Closed 25 Dec   *Parking* Ample

EWEN   Wild Duck Inn   £D/E

I Map 4 C2 Gloucestershire
Nr Cirencester GL7 6BY
Kemble (028 577) 364

Credit Access, Amex, Diners, Visa

Old-world charm is much in evidence at this delightful, friendly 16th-century inn in an unspoilt Cotswold village. Delights include beams, stone walls and flagstones in the bar and an Elizabethan inglenook fireplace in the cosy lounge. There are two splendid old bedrooms with four-posters, but most of the bedrooms, in a modern extension, are neatly furnished with practical units. Simple, tiled bathrooms. *Amenities* garden.

Rooms 10	*Direct dial* Yes	*Confirm by* arrang.	*Parking* Ample
Ensuite bath/shower 10	*Room TV* Yes	*Last dinner* 9.45	*Room service* All day

Any person using our name to obtain free hospitality is a fraud.
Proprietors, please inform the police and us.

EXETER   Buckerell Lodge Crest Hotel   66%   £C/D

H Map 3 D2 Devon
Topsham Road EX2 4SQ
Exeter (0392) 52451
Telex 42410

Credit Access, Amex, Diners, Visa

A comfortable, well-run hotel created from a greatly extended Regency house. The smart, tastefully decorated lounge and bar both open on to the attractive gardens and there are popular conference facilities. Standard bedrooms are pleasant, if a little old-fashioned, and have tea/coffee makers and trouser presses; superior rooms offer built-in furniture, hairdryers, good toiletries and bathrobes. *Amenities* garden, putting, croquet, secretarial services, fax, laundry service. &

Rooms 54	*Direct dial* Yes	*Confirm by* 6	*Parking* Ample
Ensuite bath/shower 54	*Room TV* Yes	*Last dinner* 9.45	*Room service* 24 hours

EXETER   Rougemont Hotel   63%   £E

H Map 3 D2 Devon
Queen Street EX4 3SP
Exeter (0392) 54982
Telex 42455

Credit Access, Amex, Diners, Visa

Major refurbishment and more bedrooms for this Victorian city-centre hotel. Original pillars and moulded ceilings grace the lofty entrance lounge, which also features a lovely stained-glass window. There are two bars. New and refurbished bedrooms are light, airy and very pleasant, with pastel colour schemes and pretty fabrics, plus trouser presses, tea-makers and fully tiled bathrooms. *Amenities* hairdressing, in-house movies, secretarial services, laundry service.

Rooms 99	*Direct dial* Yes	*Confirm by* 6	*Parking* Limited
Ensuite bath/shower 99	*Room TV* Yes	*Last dinner* 9.30	*Room service* 24 hours

EXETER White Hart Hotel 61% £E

H Map 3 D2 Devon
   South Street EX1 1EE
Exeter (0392) 79897
Telex 42521

Credit Access, Amex, Diners, Visa
Closed 3 days Xmas

The White Hart has a history going back to the 15th century, and much of its old-world charm survives. Low beams and exposed stone characterise the cosy bars, with burnished brass adding to the overall effect. There are also several homely, comfortable lounges. Main-house bedrooms are traditional, but most rooms, in cheerful, practical style, are in a modern wing. No dogs.
Amenities garden, laundry service.

Rooms 61	*Direct dial* Yes	*Confirm by* 6	*Parking* Ample
Ensuite bath/shower 61	*Room TV* Yes	*Last dinner* 9.15	*Room service* 24 hours

EXFORD Crown Hotel 63% £D

H Map 3 D1 Somerset
   Nr Minehead TA24 7PP
Exford (064 383) 554

Credit Access, Amex, Visa

It's not surprising if this 17th-century inn by the village green is a particular favourite with sports enthusiasts. Shooting and fishing can both be arranged, and you can hire a horse for hunting or hacking – or even stable your own. The comfortable lounge and rustic beamed bar have plenty of character, while pretty bedrooms are individually furnished and have good modern bathrooms. *Amenities* garden, riding, stabling, secretarial services, laundry service.

Rooms 18	*Direct dial* Yes	*Confirm by* 5.30	*Parking* Ample
Ensuite bath/shower 18	*Room TV* Yes	*Last dinner* 9.30	*Room service* Limited

EXMOUTH Imperial Hotel 60% £C/D

H Map 3 E3 Devon
   The Esplanade EX8 2SW
Exmouth (0395) 274761

Credit Access, Amex, Diners, Visa

With its super situation just seconds from the beach, the Imperial is naturally a popular choice for family holidays. The beach and the hotel's own facilities provide plenty of activity, while for gentle relaxation the pleasant day rooms and terraces come into their own. Practical overnight accommodation includes ten family rooms.
Amenities garden, outdoor swimming pool, sauna, solarium, tennis, putting, laundry service, children's playroom.

Rooms 58	*Room phone* Yes	*Confirm by* 6	*Parking* Ample
Ensuite bath/shower 58	*Room TV* Yes	*Last dinner* 9	*Room service* All day

**We welcome bona fide complaints and recommendations
on the tear-out pages at the back of the book for readers' comment.
They are followed up by our professional team.**

FAIRFORD Bull Hotel 60% £E

H Map 4 C2 Gloucestershire
   Market Place GL7 4AA
Cirencester (0285) 712535

Credit Access, Amex, Diners, Visa

A historic Cotswold-stone building, dating in part from the 15th-century and thought to have been an inn since 1745. The warmly rustic bar boasts ancient beams, fine fireplaces and simple wooden trestles and there's a homely residents' lounge. Sloping ceilings and floors make for characterful bedrooms and light, airy colours and floral fabrics add to their appeal. *Amenities* garden, coarse & game fishing, secretarial services, laundry service.

Rooms 21	*Direct dial* Yes	*Confirm by* arrang.	*Parking* Ample
Ensuite bath/shower 14	*Room TV* Yes	*Last dinner* 9.30	*Room service* All day

FAIRFORD Hyperion House Hotel 63% £E

H Map 4 C2 Gloucestershire
   London Street GL7 4AH
Cirencester (0285) 712349

Credit Access, Amex, Diners, Visa

Improvements continue at this Cotswold-stone hotel on the A417. Enthusiastic owners Peter and Gill Hands have converted seven more bedrooms out of the existing building and these, like other executive rooms, offer stylish fabrics, freestanding pine furniture and accessories such as trouser presses and hairdryers. Standard rooms are more simply appointed but all provide tea-makers. Public areas include a cosy lounge and cheerful bar. *Amenities* garden, laundry service.

Rooms 27	*Direct dial* Yes	*Confirm by* 6	*Parking* Ample
Ensuite bath/shower 27	*Room TV* Yes	*Last dinner* 9.30	*Room service* Limited

FAIRY CROSS — Portledge Hotel 64% £C/D

H Map 2 C2 Devon
Nr Bideford EX39 5BX
Horns Cross (02375) 262
Telex 265451

Credit Access, Amex, Diners, Visa

There's a genuine country-house atmosphere about this centuries-old building. A glass dome and wooden gallery feature in the lobby-lounge, together with family portraits and fine antiques. Solid, traditional furniture characterises the comfortable bedrooms and there are lovely views all round. *Amenities* garden, outdoor swimming pool, croquet, sea fishing, private beach, games room, secretarial services, fax, laundry service, coffee shop (10am–5pm).

| Rooms 25 | Direct dial Yes | Confirm by 6 | Parking Ample |
| Ensuite bath/shower 25 | Room TV Yes | Last dinner 8.45 | Room service Limited |

**Our inspectors are our full-time employees;
they are professionally trained by us.**

FALMOUTH — Bay Hotel 57% £D/E

H Map 2 B4 Cornwall
Cliff Road TR11 4NU
Falmouth (0326) 312094
Telex 45262

Credit Access, Amex, Diners, Visa
Closed end Oct–Easter

A slightly more modest sister and fairly close neighbour of the Falmouth Hotel, also Victorian and also enjoying lovely sea views. Relaxation comes easily in the day rooms, which include a pleasant, if slightly down-at-heel sun terrace, a high-ceilinged bar and a light, airy lounge. Bedrooms are light, clean and practical, with fitted furniture and carpeted bathrooms. *Amenities* garden, sauna, solarium, secretarial services, fax, laundry service.

| Rooms 28 | Direct dial Yes | Confirm by arrang. | Parking Ample |
| Ensuite bath/shower 28 | Room TV Yes | Last dinner 9.30 | Room service 24 hours |

FALMOUTH — Falmouth Hotel 62% £D

H Map 2 B4 Cornwall
Castle Beach TR11 4NZ
Falmouth (0326) 312671
Telex 45262

Credit Access, Amex, Diners, Visa
Closed 2 wks Xmas

In the same ownership for more than a century, this imposing Victorian hotel has a quiet, relaxing atmosphere and a good deal of old-fashioned charm. Sea views are a feature of the public areas, which include a roomy bar-lounge and a nice little non-smoking lounge. There's also a wine bar that opens on to a poolside patio. Some of the bedrooms have balconies to take full advantage of the setting; about half have been refurbished with smart darkwood furniture and chintzy fabrics. Bathrooms are neat and tidy, reflecting a good standard of housekeeping throughout.
Amenities garden, outdoor swimming pool, putting, snooker, in-house movies, secretarial services, fax, laundry service.

| Rooms 73 | Direct dial Yes | Confirm by arrang. | Parking Ample |
| Ensuite bath/shower 73 | Room TV Yes | Last dinner 9.30 | Room service 24 hours |

FALMOUTH — Greenbank Hotel 67% £D

H Map 2 B4 Cornwall
Harbourside TR11 2SR
Falmouth (0326) 312440
Telex 45240

Credit Access, Amex, Diners, Visa
Closed 3 wks Xmas

On a splendid site overlooking Falmouth Harbour, the Greenbank is a comfortable hotel. Picture windows make the most of the setting in the stylish lounge bar, and there are harbour views from the nicest bedrooms. These are decorated in pastels, and the larger ones have sitting areas. Rear-facing rooms are more modest. Friendly, helpful staff. *Amenities* garden, solarium, beauty salon, hairdressing, sea fishing, mooring, secretarial services, laundry service.

| Rooms 43 | Direct dial Yes | Confirm by 6 | Parking Ample |
| Ensuite bath/shower 43 | Room TV Yes | Last dinner 9.45 | Room service 24 hours |

FALMOUTH — Pandora Inn

R Map 2 B4 Cornwall
Restronguet Passage, Nr
Mylor Bridge
Falmouth (0326) 72678

About £38 for two
Seats 48
Parties 10
Parking Ample
Credit Access, Visa

Mussels with white wine and fennel, terrine of duckling with chestnuts and apricot sauce, sea bass in pastry, fillet steak medallions with shallots and burgundy glaze – all typical dishes in the cosy first-floor restaurant of a lovely thatched pub. Oysters and lobsters make special appearances, and there are some fairly wicked sweets. Good wines too, and helpful notes on the list. Go to Mylor from the A39, then to Restronguet, turning into Restronguet Passage . ☐ Well-chosen ☻

Lunch 12–2, Sun 12–1.45 (till 5 in summer)   *Dinner* 7.30–9.30
Closed Sun, 25 Dec & Mon in winter

FAREHAM   Red Lion Hotel   £D/E

Map 5 D4 Hampshire
East Street PO16 0BP
Fareham (0329) 822640
Telex 86204

Credit Access, Amex, Diners, Visa

Take junction 11 off the M27 to find this old coaching inn to the east of the town centre. Dark beams, panelling and exposed red brickwork give public areas (including three bars) a richly traditional feel, while bedrooms combine cheerful, old-fashioned furnishings with modern accessories like tea-makers, trouser presses and hairdryers. Bathrooms have shower facilities and complimentary toiletries. No dogs.
Amenities in-house movies, secretarial services, laundry service.

Rooms 33	*Direct dial* Yes	*Confirm by* 7	*Parking* Ample
Ensuite bath/shower 33	*Room TV* Yes	*Last dinner* 10	*Room service* 24 hours

**If we recommend meals in a Hotel or Inn,
a separate entry is made for its restaurant.**

FARNBOROUGH   Queen's Hotel   63%   £C

Map 5 E3 Hampshire
Lynchford Road GU14 6AZ
Farnborough (0252) 545051
Telex 859637

Credit Access, Amex, Diners, Visa

A large red-brick Edwardian building with modern extensions housing most of the bedrooms. The pleasing lounge bar has plenty of sofas and easy chairs and a mock bookcase to hide the drinks when the bar is closed. The bedrooms have soft and pretty decor, attractive curtains, quilted bedcovers and decent darkwood furniture. Remote control TVs, videos, tea/coffee-makers and radios are standard; Club rooms have trouser presses, hairdryers, teletext TV, fruit and mini-bars. Bathrooms are smart and practical.
Amenities indoor swimming pool, sauna, solarium, whirlpool bath, keep-fit equipment, in-house movies, secretarial services, fax, laundry service, coffee shop (9am–11pm), 24-hour lounge service.

Rooms 110	*Direct dial* Yes	*Confirm by* 6	*Parking* Ample
Ensuite bath/shower 110	*Room TV* Yes	*Last dinner* 10	*Room service* None

FARNHAM   Bishop's Table Hotel   59%   £D/E

Map 5 E3 Surrey
27 West Street GU9 7DR
Farnham (0252) 710222

Credit Access, Amex, Diners, Visa
Closed 26 Dec–4 Jan

An engaging little hotel of some charm and character. The owners are a friendly couple whose example is followed by their pleasant staff. Day rooms include a cheerful bar and a lounge that overlooks the garden. Bedrooms, some in the 18th-century original house, others in a modern annexe, are comfortable enough but could be better looked after. Good, well-cooked breakfasts. No dogs.
Amenities garden.

Rooms 16	*Direct dial* Yes	*Confirm by* arrang.	*Parking* Difficult
Ensuite bath/shower 14	*Room TV* Yes	*Last dinner* 9.45	*Room service* Limited

FARNHAM   Bush Hotel   63%   £C/D

Map 5 E3 Surrey
The Borough GU9 7NN
Farnham (0252) 715237
Telex 858764

Credit Access, Amex, Diners, Visa

The architecture adds interest to this rambling hotel – the residents' lounge and bar are 17th century, the restaurant is Regency and some parts appear Georgian. Public areas have a pleasingly lived-in feel. Superior bedrooms are decorated in soft modern colour schemes and have good lightwood and laminate furniture and myriad extras; standard are also modern, with decent furniture.
Amenities garden, laundry service, coffee shop (9.30am–10pm).

Rooms 65	*Direct dial* Yes	*Confirm by* 6	*Parking* Ample
Ensuite bath/shower 65	*Room TV* Yes	*Last dinner* 9.30	*Room service* None

FARNHAM   Trevena House Hotel   60%   £E

Map 5 E3 Surrey
Alton Road GU10 5ER
Farnham (0252) 716908

Credit Access, Amex, Diners, Visa
Closed 2 wks Xmas

A Victorian Gothic house standing in five acres of grounds off the A31 west of Farnham. The peaceful setting, the characterful day rooms and the friendly owner, Norman Levitt, make for a pleasant stay, and the bedrooms, of various shapes and sizes, are comfortable, practical and conspicuously well looked after. Bath/shower rooms are spick and span, too. No dogs.
Amenities garden, outdoor swimming pool, tennis, laundry service.

Rooms 20	*Direct dial* Yes	*Confirm by* arrang.	*Parking* Ample
Ensuite bath/shower 20	*Room TV* Yes	*Last dinner* 9.15	*Room service* Limited

FARRINGTON GURNEY   Old Parsonage   ♛ ⌀

RR **Map 4 B3** Avon
Nr Bristol BS18 5UB
Temple Cloud (0761) 52211

Set L Sun £9
About £32 for two
Seats 26
Parties 12
Parking Ample

A 17th-century manor house which has been restored to its former glory to create a civilised restaurant. Marina Gofton-Watson is a cook of great natural talent and her menus offer simple, competently cooked dishes such as pheasant in Cumberland sauce. Vegetables are fresh and delicious and sweets are superb. Good, short wine list at keen prices; note the Rouge Homme Cabernet Sauvignon from Australia. ☙ Well-chosen ☙

Lunch 12.30–2   *Dinner* 7–9.30
Closed D Sun, all Mon, Bank Hols, 5 days Xmas & 3 wks Autumn

BEDROOMS 3   £E
With bath/shower 3

The bedrooms are good-sized, with sturdy traditional furnishings and en suite bathrooms. A homely TV lounge is, like other rooms, spotlessly clean. No dogs.

FAUGH   String of Horses   £E

Map 13 D4 Cumbria
Heads Nook, Nr Carlisle
CA4 9EG
Hayton (022 870) 297

Credit Access, Amex, Diners, Visa
Closed 25 & 26 Dec

Old-world charm is not in short supply at this 17th-century village inn where rustic beamed bars do not prepare the visitor for the sumptuous bedrooms, one with a splendid four-poster. Gold-plated Hollywood-style bathrooms are equally unexpected. *Amenities* patio, outdoor swimming pool, sauna, solarium, whirlpool bath, keep-fit equipment, in-house movies, laundry service.

Rooms 14	*Room phone* Yes	*Confirm by* arrang.	*Parking* Ample
Ensuite bath/shower 14	*Room TV* Yes	*Last dinner* 10.30	*Room service* All day

FAVERSHAM   Read's ★   ⌀

R **Map 7 C5** Kent
Painter's Forstal
Faversham (0795) 535344

French cooking

Lunch 12–2
Dinner 7–10
Set L from £10
About £45 for two
Seats 36
Parking Ample

Credit Amex, Diners, Visa
Closed Sun, 26 dec & 1 Jan

Fine French cooking, superb wines and stylish, civilised surroundings are hallmarks of David and Rona Pitchford's splendid restaurant. David shows classic skills including mastery of the saucier's art, in dishes that include refined, up-dated versions of classics like chicken liver parfait, blanquette of veal and coq au vin à la bouguignonne. Serving staff are right on the ball, and it's a typical

Pitchford touch to provide a special menu for children (guaranteed no fish fingers!). A really fine, comprehensively annotated wine list is especially strong in burgundy – note the delicious 1978 Pernand Vergelesses from Roland Rapet.
Specialities fruits de mer façon bouillabaisse, coq au vin, médaillons de deux saumons-sauce Newburg.

We publish annually,
so make sure you use the current edition.
It's worth it!

FAWKHAM   Brandshatch Place 68%   £C

H **Map 7 B5** Kent
Ash Green DA3 8NQ
Ash Green (0474) 872239

Credit Access, Amex, Diners, Visa
Closed 24–30 Dec

Despite its proximity to the Brands Hatch circuit, this extended Georgian house is a peaceful haven. Public rooms include a relaxing book-lined bar-library. Simple, attractive bedrooms have carpeted en suite bathrooms. The adjacent leisure centre is a major attraction. No dogs. *Amenities* garden, indoor swimming pool, sauna, solarium, whirlpool bath, gymnasium, tennis, squash, badminton, snooker, secretarial services, laundry service, children's play area. ♿

Rooms 30	*Direct dial* Yes	*Confirm by* arrang.	*Parking* Ample
Ensuite bath/shower 30	*Room TV* Yes	*Last dinner* 9.30	*Room service* All day

FELIXSTOWE Brook Hotel 66% £D

H **Map 6 D3** Suffolk
Orwell Road IP11 7PF
Felixstowe (0394) 278441
Telex 987674

Credit Access, Amex, Diners, Visa

Behind the facade of this extended detached house there's quite a lot of style: the splendid reception-lounge with its chintz, greenery and abundant comfort, the relaxing bar and the individually styled bedrooms, furnished in solid pine, well lit and thoughtfully equipped. Executive rooms have separate sitting areas, and all rooms have compact bathrooms. Mediocre breakfast, but the restaurant opens out onto a pretty paved patio. No dogs. *Amenities* laundry service.

Rooms 25	*Direct dial* Yes	*Confirm by* noon	*Parking* Ample
Ensuite bath/shower 25	*Room TV* Yes	*Last dinner* 9.30	*Room service* 24 hours

FELIXSTOWE Orwell Moat House 69% £D/E

H **Map 6 D3** Suffolk
Hamilton Road IP11 7DX
Felixstowe (0394) 285511
Telex 987676

Credit Access, Amex, Diners, Visa

A gabled, red-brick building with a '60s extension. You enter through the old part, where ornate painted ceilings are an attractive feature, and beyond this there's a large, dated-looking lounge and various bars. Bedrooms, with smart cane furniture and well-coordinated colour schemes, are of a reasonable size, with armchairs and good desk/dressing table space. Bathrooms are quite basic in their appointments. *Amenities* garden, hairdressing, laundry service.

Rooms 60	*Direct dial* Yes	*Confirm by* arrang.	*Parking* Ample
Ensuite bath/shower 60	*Room TV* Yes	*Last dinner* 9.45	*Room service* 24 hours

We publish annually,
so make sure you use the current edition.
It's worth it!

FERNDOWN Dormy Hotel 71% £B/C

H **Map 4 C4** Dorset
New Road BH22 8ES
Bournemouth (0202) 872121
Telex 418301

Rooms 132
Ensuite bath/shower 132
Direct dial Yes
Room TV Yes
Confirm by arrang.
Last dinner 9.30
Parking Ample
Room service 24 hours

Credit Access, Amex, Diners, Visa

Set in wooded gardens alongside a golf course, this smart, efficiently run hotel is especially popular with sports enthusiasts and conference organisers. Of the two bedroom wings, one is new, the other refurbished to the same luxurious standard – all using coordinated soft furnishings and providing extras like trouser presses, hairdryers and remote-control TVs. Rooms in the main building are more traditional but

perfectly comfortable. One bar is currently being updated; the other retains its golfing theme. *Amenities* garden, indoor swimming pool, sauna, solarium, whirlpool bath, keep-fit equipment, tennis, squash, golf practice nets, putting, games room, snooker, pool table, secretarial services, fax, valeting, laundry service, coffee shop (10am–10pm).

FINDON Findon Manor 62% £E

H **Map 5 E4** West Sussex
High Street BN14 0TA
Findon (090 671) 2733
Telex 879877

Credit Access, Amex, Diners, Visa
Closed 1 wk Xmas

Parts of this former rectory, in a pretty village famous for its racing connections, date back to 1584. Inside, day rooms like the cosy beamed lounge and pubby bar provide plenty of period atmosphere. Comfortable, tasteful bedrooms (some with four-posters, whirlpool baths and garden views) offer colour TVs, tea-makers and direct-dial telephones. Smartly tiled modern bathrooms throughout. *Amenities* garden, whirlpool bath, croquet, secretarial services, laundry service.

Rooms 11	*Direct dial* Yes	*Confirm by* arrang.	*Parking* Ample
Ensuite bath/shower 11	*Room TV* Yes	*Last dinner* 9.15	*Room service* All day

FLITWICK   Flitwick Manor   79%   £B/C

HR **Map 5 E1** Bedfordshire
Church Road MK45 1AE
Flitwick (0525) 712242
Telex 825562

Rooms 16
Ensuite bath/shower 16
Direct dial Yes
Room TV Yes
Confirm by arrang.
Last dinner 9.30
Parking Ample
Room service All day

Credit Access, Amex, Diners, Visa
Closed 24–27 Dec

Major improvements are now
completed at this delightful country house hotel. The flagstoned
entrance hall with its welcoming
log fire remains as before, but
there's a new, supremely comfortable lounge-cum-bar, created
out of a conservatory and featuring elegant, strikingly coordinated furnishings. The former
bar is now a meeting room, and
the library doubles as an additional meeting room and bar.

Eight stunning new bedrooms (two with whirlpool baths) rival the
original rooms in their bold use of colour, lovely fabrics and fine
antiques; all offer a vast range of extras. Exemplary housekeeping.
No dogs. **Amenities** garden, tennis, putting, croquet, bicycles,
secretarial services, fax, laundry service, helipad. ⅙

Restaurant ♕

Set L from £12.80, Sun £14.50
Set D from £12.80
About £64 *for two*
Seats 55
Parties 16

Concentrating mainly on seafood, Geoffrey Welch offers a selection
that includes baked Helford oysters in a caviar butter sauce, fresh
scallop and Jerusalem artichoke soup, and pastry-wrapped lobster
sauced with brandy and truffles. Meat and game also put in an
appearance, and there are vegetarian choices too. Decent desserts like
raspberry brûlée. Considering the highish prices, service – though
friendly – could be more professional. Excellent burgundies.
♀ Well-chosen ☺ ⅙

Lunch 12–2   *Dinner* 7.30–9.30, Sun till 9
Closed 24–27 Dec

FOLKESTONE   Burlington Hotel   60%   £E

H **Map 7 C5** Kent
Earls Avenue CT20 2HR
Folkestone (0303) 55301
Telex 966389

Credit Access, Amex, Diners, Visa

The large, old-fashioned, comfortable lounge sets the tone of this
sturdy Victorian hotel near the seafront. A spectacular stained-glass
window dominates the attractive wooden staircase, which leads to
bedrooms of varying shapes and sizes which are gradually being
refurbished and upgraded. Basic, simply carpeted bathrooms.
Amenities garden, putting, secretarial services, laundry service.

Rooms 59	*Direct dial* Yes	*Confirm by* 6	*Parking* Ample
Ensuite bath/shower 59	*Room TV* Yes	*Last dinner* 9.30	*Room service* 24 hours

FOLKESTONE   Paul's   ⅾ

R **Map 7 C5** Kent
2a Bouverie Road West
Folkestone (0303) 59697

About £34 *for two*
Seats 44
Parties 55
Parking Limited

Credit Access, Visa

A light and airy restaurant in a converted modern house. Paul
Hagger's menus change weekly and his cooking is imaginative and
enjoyable – though some might find his use of cream excessive (herring
fillets baked in cream and white port is a typical starter). Subtle use of
spices distinguishes dishes like diced lamb with mild chillies topped
by Cheddar wholemeal crumble. Wife Penny makes the excellent
trolley sweets. ☺

Lunch 12.30–2   *Dinner* 7.30–9.30
Closed Sun, Bank Hols, 2 wks Xmas, 1 wk winter & 2 wks summer

FOLKESTONE   La Tavernetta   ⅾ

R **Map 7 C5** Kent
Leaside Ct, Clifton Gdns
Folkestone (0303) 54955

Italian cooking
Set L £7.30
About £38 *for two*
Seats 55 *Parties* 25
Parking Limited
Credit Access, Amex, Diners, Visa

Traditional Italian cooking in a comfortable and long-established
restaurant near the promenade. There are few surprises on the clearly
presented menus, but old favourites like minestrone, spaghetti
bolognese, trout with almonds, pepper steak and saltimbocca are well
prepared from good-quality raw materials by joint-owner Mr. Puricelli.
The set lunch at £7.30 provides excellent value for money. Service is
correct, friendly and on the ball. ☺

Lunch 12.30–2.30   *Dinner* 6–10.30
Closed Sun & Bank Hols

FOSSEBRIDGE — Fossebridge Inn — £E

Map 4 C2 Gloucestershire
Nr Cheltenham GL54 3JS
Fossebridge (028 572) 721

Credit Access, Amex, Diners, Visa

A mellow Cotswold-stone inn standing in extensive grounds beside the river Coln. The five-hundred-year-old bar is delightfully authentic, with its rough-stone walls and low oak beams, and the elegant drawing room has homely touches like fresh flower arrangements and ornaments. Bedrooms with attractively coordinated decor and period-style furniture have splendid carpeted bathrooms. *Amenities* garden, coarse and game fishing, secretarial services, laundry service.

Rooms 14	*Direct dial* Yes	*Confirm by* 6	*Parking* Ample
Ensuite bath/shower 14	*Room TV* Yes	*Last dinner* 9.30	*Room service* All day

FOWEY — Food for Thought — *NEW ENTRY*

Map 2 C3 Cornwall
Town Quay
Fowey (072 683) 2221

Set D £13.95
About £47 *for two*
Seats 35
Parking Difficult

Credit Access, Visa

A pretty little restaurant in a 600-year-old building on the quayside. Fish features strongly on the menus, typical items including garlicky grilled mussels, warm scallop salad, salmon in puff pastry, sole and lobster. Also some meat choices (duck à l'orange, veal with pasta). Martin Billingsley cooks, while Caroline supervises the attentive service.

Dinner only 7–9.30
Closed Sun, 23 Dec–end Feb

FRAMLINGHAM — Crown Hotel — 61% — £D

Map 6 D2 Suffolk
Market Hill IP13 9AN
Framlingham (0728) 723521

Credit Access, Amex, Diners, Visa

A well-run, town-centre inn tracing back to the 16th century. Beams and timbers characterise the day rooms, with the odd antique emphasising the period charm. Bedrooms are mostly of a good size, and solidly furnished; two particularly spacious rooms have sitting areas. Three 'standard rooms', though acceptable, are less appealing than the rest. Smart bathrooms have showers above the tubs. A good leisurely breakfast starts the day. *Amenities* laundry service.

Rooms 14	*Room phone* Yes	*Confirm by* arrang.	*Parking* Ample
Ensuite bath/shower 14	*Room TV* Yes	*Last dinner* 9	*Room service* None

FRAMLINGHAM PIGOT — The Old Feathers — *NEW ENTRY*

Map 6 C2 Norfolk
Fox Road, Nr Norwich
Framlingham Earl (050 86) 2445

About £45 *for two*
Seats 45
Parties 8
Parking Ample

Credit Access, Visa

Pretty curtains, silver salvers and an air of relaxation arouse happy anticipation in the diner at this restaurant and sure enough the food is a delight. Paul Courtney's skilful touch produces truly excellent meals; try asparagus with salmon and cream cheese, followed by a wonderful mélange of seafood in a pink champagne and fresh dill sauce. Desserts are outstanding. Decent wine list: Ch. Crissac '81, Auxey Duresses (Poulet) '82.

Lunch 12–2.30 *Dinner* 7–9.30, Sat till 10.30
Closed Sun

FRESHFORD — Homewood Park — 80% — £B/C

Map 4 B3 Avon
Nr Bath BA3 6BB
Limpley Stoke (022 122) 3731
Telex 444937

Rooms 15
Ensuite bath/shower 15
Direct dial Yes
Room TV Yes
Confirm by arrang.
Last dinner 9.30
Parking Ample
Room service All day

Credit Access, Amex, Diners, Visa
Closed 23 Dec–6 Jan

A wonderfully unpretentious and comfortable Victorian hotel enjoying ten acres of gardens and woodland by the lovely ruin of 13th-century Hinton Priory off the A36. Stephen and Penny Ross run it with pride and immense enthusiasm; their personal touch is evident in the exquisite furnishings and delightful ornaments in the elegant, well-proportioned public rooms. The bedrooms are sumptuously ap-

pointed and individually decorated in excellent taste and have such homely touches as fresh flowers and books; two have recently been upgraded to an even higher standard. Bathrooms are luxuriously equipped and are among the best in the country. No dogs. *Amenities* garden, tennis, croquet, fax.

see over

Homewood Park Restaurant ★ ♛ ♧

Lunch 12–1.30
Dinner 7–9.30
Set L £15.50
Set D from £19.50
About £60 for two
Seats 50
Parties 44

Closed 23 Dec–6 Jan

In the handsome two-roomed restaurant Stephen Ross and his talented team provide highly enjoyable food using the very best seasonal produce available. Fish is delivered regularly from Cornwall and you may find John Dory feuilleté or sole in a subtle tomato sauce on the menu. Typical first course might be hot pastry of scallops and sweetbreads with a chervil and vermouth sauce. Very good cellar with some delicious mature bottles; Volnay (Ampeau) '72, Ch. d'Angludet '70. **Specialities** Provençale soup; terrine of Cornish crab wrapped in smoked salmon with tomato & fresh basil sauce; best end of spring lamb with a charlotte of aubergines, courgettes & tomatoes; three passion-fruit puddings. Well-chosen ☺ ♿

FRESHWATER   Farringford Hotel   57%   £D/E

H **Map 4 C4** Isle of Wight
   Bedbury Lane PO40 9PE
Isle of Wight (0983) 752500
Telex 477575

Credit Access, Amex, Diners, Visa
Closed Jan & Feb

Peacefully situated in its own grounds, this 18th-century mansion was once the home of Lord Tennyson. Gothic arched doorways and windows are a feature of the public rooms, yet furnishings are modest. Bedrooms too are fairly basic, with padded headboards, candlewick bedspreads, radios and tea-makers. **Amenities** garden, outdoor swimming pool, tennis, 9-hole golf course, putting, bowling green, croquet, games room, snooker, laundry service, children's playground.

Rooms 20	*Direct dial* Yes	*Confirm by* arrang.	*Parking* Ample
Ensuite bath/shower 20	*Room TV* Yes	*Last dinner* 9.30	*Room service* Limited

 indicates a **well-chosen** house wine

FRESSINGFIELD   Fox & Goose ★   ♧

R **Map 6 C2** Suffolk
   Nr Eye
Fressingfield (037 986) 247

Lunch 12–1.30
Dinner 7–9
Set L from £14
Set D from £14
About £47 for two
Seats 26
Parties 30
Parking Ample

Credit Access, Amex, Diners, Visa
Closed D Sun (Sept–Mar), all Tues & 8 days Xmas

A 16th-century village inn provides a simple rustic setting for this appealing country restaurant. But there's nothing unsophisticated about Adrian Clarke's skilful and imaginative cooking. Fish and seafood are a speciality, and intensely flavoured well judged sauces a particularly strong point. Lobster, oysters, scallops, prawns and langoustines tossed in noodles

with a creamy lobster sauce makes a perfect starter and could lead to quail sauced with Madeira followed by an outstanding chocolate marquise. **Specialities** fresh mussels grilled in garlic butter, halibut in cream and saffron sauce with langoustines, breast of wild duck in green peppercorn sauce, hot raspberry soufflé. ⌦ Outstanding 🍷 Well-chosen ☺

FROME   Mendip Lodge Hotel   61%   £D/E

H **Map 4 B3** Somerset
   Bath Road BA11 2HP
Frome (0373) 63223
Telex 44832

Credit Access, Amex, Diners, Visa

Views of the Mendip Hills are a feature here, and the garden setting is quite attractive. Day rooms are in the main part – originally a private residence – and include a cosy lounge and pleasant little bar. Covered walkways connect to two motel-style accommodation blocks, where most of the rooms enjoy the views.
Amenities garden, secretarial services, laundry service, 24-hour lounge service.

Rooms 40	*Direct dial* Yes	*Confirm by* arrang.	*Parking* Ample
Ensuite bath/shower 40	*Room TV* Yes	*Last dinner* 9.30	*Room service* All day

FROME | Selwood Manor 68% | £C/D

H Map 4 B3 Somerset
BA11 3NL
Frome (0373) 63605

Credit Access, Amex, Diners, Visa

Selwood Manor is a beautifully maintained Jacobean building set in 14 acres of unspoilt Somerset countryside off the A362. Owners Valerie and John Chorley have sacrificed none of its charm and character in creating a wonderfully relaxing hotel; open fires warm the elegantly furnished lounges and comfort is in generous supply. There are just five bedrooms, all featuring fine fabrics and period furnishings, and two with exposed beams. In the large bathrooms are thick towels and good-quality toiletries. Splendid breakfasts. No children under 12. No dogs.
Amenities garden, outdoor swimming pool, coarse fishing, croquet, clay-pigeon shooting, laundry service.

Rooms 5	*Room phone* No	*Confirm by* arrang.	*Parking* Ample
Ensuite bath/shower 4	*Room TV* Yes	*Last dinner* 9	*Room service* Limited

➦ is our symbol for an **outstanding** wine list

GARFORTH | Hilton National Hotel 63% | £C/D

H Map 11 D1 West Yorkshire
Wakefield Road,
Nr Leeds LS25 1LH
Leeds (0532) 866556
Telex 556324

Credit Access, Amex, Diners, Visa

The leisure centre is proving popular at this modern hotel east of Leeds at the junction of the A63 and A642. Receptionists have a smile and a warm welcome, and relaxation is easy in the intimate bar. Recent improvements in the bedrooms include pretty pastels and brass light fittings. **Amenities** garden, indoor swimming pool, sauna, keep-fit equipment, games room, in-house movies, secretarial services, fax, laundry service, 24-hour lounge service, helipad.

Rooms 143	*Direct dial* Yes	*Confirm by* arrang.	*Parking* Ample
Ensuite bath/shower 143	*Room TV* Yes	*Last dinner* 10	*Room service* Limited

GATESHEAD | Springfield Hotel 63% | £C/D

H Map 15 B4 Tyne & Wear
Durham Road NE9 5BT
Tyneside (091) 477 4121
Telex 538197

Credit Access, Amex, Diners, Visa

A young manager and friendly staff create a pleasant atmosphere in this convivial 1930s hotel on the A6127. One of the bars is in period style, while the other, a fresh, bright cocktail bar, has just acquired a conservatory extension. Bedrooms are of three types: 20 rather small and dated and due for refurbishment in summer 1989, another 20 slightly roomier and brighter and 20 in a brand new block.
Amenities garden, secretarial services, fax, laundry service.

Rooms 60	*Direct dial* Yes	*Confirm by* arrang.	*Parking* Ample
Ensuite bath/shower 60	*Room TV* Yes	*Last dinner* 9.30	*Room service* 24 hours

GATESHEAD | Swallow Hotel Gateshead 60% | £D/E

H Map 15 B4 Tyne & Wear
High West Street NE8 1PE
Tyneside (091) 477 1105
Telex 53534

Credit Access, Amex, Diners, Visa

A modern high-rise hotel in the town centre, with a lock-up garage, smart day rooms, extensive conference facilities and a leisure complex. Bedrooms, though certainly not large, are practical and quite comfortable, the best being those on the top floor. Mezzanine rooms, though a bit larger than some, are beginning to look tired and dated. **Amenities** indoor swimming pool, sauna, solarium, whirlpool bath, keep-fit equipment, fax, laundry service, coffee shop (10am–10pm).

Rooms 106	*Direct dial* Yes	*Confirm by* 6	*Parking* Ample
Ensuite bath/shower 106	*Room TV* Yes	*Last dinner* 10	*Room service* 24 hours

GERRARDS CROSS | Bull Hotel 63% | £C

H Map 5 E2 Buckinghamshire
Oxford Road SL9 7PA
Gerrards Cross (0753) 885995
Telex 847747

Credit Access, Amex, Diners, Visa

The 17th and 20th centuries meet at this former coaching inn by the A40. The facade, beamed bar and a few bedrooms have a degree of old-fashioned charm, while the purpose-built bedroom block is smart and modern. Here the rooms have yew veneered furniture, trouser presses and hairdryers. Older bedrooms are more basic, but refurbishment will improve things.
Amenities garden, in-house movies, laundry service.

Rooms 98	*Direct dial* Yes	*Confirm by* 6	*Parking* Ample
Ensuite bath/shower 98	*Room TV* Yes	*Last dinner* 9.30	*Room service* 24 hours

GILLINGHAM

HR Map 4 B3 Dorset
Wyke SP8 5NR
Gillingham (074 76) 3626

Rooms 6
Ensuite bath/shower 6
Direct dial Yes
Room TV Yes
Confirm by arrang.
Last dinner 9
Parking Ample
Room service All day

Credit Access, Visa
Closed 1 wk June & mid Dec–mid Jan

Stock Hill House Hotel   70%   £B

Peter and Nita Hauser are most affable and generous hosts and they will only make such bedrooms available to guests as have reached their high standards of decor and comfort. Quality wallpapers and fabrics are de rigueur and the growing selection of antique furniture includes a splendid hand-carved four-poster and an intricate ironwork bed which once belonged to a Spanish princess. Bathrooms are equally

delightful, with modern units and good toiletries, and thoughtful extra touches abound. Public rooms are relaxed and informal, with comfortable furnishings of varying styles. Half-board terms only. No children under seven. No dogs. *Amenities* garden, indoor swimming pool, keep-fit equipment, croquet.

Restaurant ★   ♀

Lunch 12.30–2
Dinner 7.30–9
Set L £14
Set D £20
About £50 *for two*
Seats 24

Closed D Sun, all Mon, 1 wk June & mid Dec–mid Jan

Well-spaced tables in a smartly decorated room, a silver-bordered dinner service and gleaming silverware combine to make a delightful ambiance in which to savour Peter Hauser's dedicated, enthusiastic cooking. His short, fixed-price menus are classically inspired, with dishes from his native Austria featuring strongly, while presentation is artistic in modern style. Flavours and seasonings throughout the

meal keep the tastebuds titillated and the sweets are a high point.
Specialities wood-smoked haddock on a nettle and dill butter; medallions of tenderloin of pork in a light cream and curry sauce; roasted John Dory larded with bay leaves; elderflower fritters with strawberry coulis and blackcurrant coulis.   ♀ Well-chosen ℮

Our inspectors *never* book in the name of Egon Ronay's Guides.
They disclose their identity only if they are considering an establishment
for inclusion in the next edition of the Guide.

GITTISHAM

H Map 3 E2 Devon
Nr Honiton EX14 0AD
Honiton (0404) 2756

Rooms 12
Ensuite bath/shower 12
Direct dial Yes
Room TV Yes
Closed early Jan–end Feb
Confirm by arrang.
Last dinner 9.30
Parking Ample
Room service All day

Credit Access, Amex, Diners, Visa

Combe House Hotel   75%   £D

Peaceful green pastures surround this Elizabethan manor and as you enter the striking entrance hall with its panelling, Dutch-tiled fireplace and deep, chintzy seating you begin to feel you are arriving at a grand but homely private house. Ancestral portraits look down from the panelled walls of the relaxing main lounge, while a smaller room has deep-red walls and plum coloured chesterfields. Bedrooms are generally spacious,

with good reproduction furniture (and some genuine pieces), high-quality, tasteful fabrics and some attractive murals handpainted by owner Thérèse Boswell. Bathrooms (three with showers only) are carpeted, well appointed and have luxury toiletries.
Amenities garden, game fishing, laundry service.

GLASTONBURY — George & Pilgrims Hotel   62%   £E

H Map 4 A3 Somerset
1 High Street BA6 9DP
Glastonbury (0458) 31146
Telex 46625

Credit Access, Amex, Diners, Visa

A handsome town-centre inn with a history going back more than 500 years. Beams, flagstones and sturdy old furnishings are much in evidence in the public rooms, and the Pilgrims Bar, which sports some lovely 18th-century Dutch tiles, is particularly appealing. Main-house bedrooms share the old-world feel (a few have four-posters) while the others are more modern.
Amenities patio, laundry service.

Rooms 14	*Direct dial* Yes	*Confirm by* 6	*Parking* Limited
Ensuite bath/shower 12	*Room TV* Yes	*Last dinner* 9.30	*Room service* Limited

GLASTONBURY — No 3   *NEW ENTRY*

RR Map 4 A3 Somerset
Magdalene Street BA6 9EW
Glastonbury (0458) 32129

Set L Sun £12
Set D from £19
About £50 *for two*
Seats 30
Parties 40
Parking Ample

Credit Amex, Visa

A restaurant with rooms set in a splendid Georgian building next to the ruins of Glastonbury Abbey. John Tynan is front of house, while his wife Anne takes care of the cooking. Subtle sauces and seasoning enhance high-quality ingredients, and typical dishes on the fixed-price menu could include plump Cornish scallops in sauce smitaine, lobster from the restaurant's tank, and loin of Somerset lamb with an orange and ginger sauce. There's a good pudding list including splendid home-made ice creams. Skilfully chosen wine; note the delicious halves of Ch. Bastor Lamontagne Sauternes '81.   ♀ Well-chosen   ᴇ

Lunch Sun 12.30–1.30, Mon–Sat by arrang.   *Dinner* 7.30–9.30
Closed D Sun, all Mon, Bank Hols & 26 Dec–end Jan

BEDROOMS 3   £E/F
With bath/shower 3

Smart, spacious bedrooms have antique furniture and modern bathrooms and there's a fine Victorian-style residents' lounge. No dogs.

GLEMSFORD — Barretts   ♔ ♀

R Map 6 C3 Suffolk
31 Egremont Street, Nr
Sudbury
Glemsford (0787) 281573

Set L Sun only £9.95
About £55 *for two*
Seats 18
Parties 18
Parking Ample

Credit Access, Visa

At the Barretts' comfortable, intimate restaurant, Diane is impressively efficient at front of house while Nicholas' skilled and sure cooking has swiftly attracted a steady following. Starters are superb, particularly the warm herb tartlets – the lightest pastry imaginable with a delicate filling and a subtle tomato and red pepper sauce – and the outstanding scallops with wine. Main dishes include tender cubes of lamb with thyme sauce and fresh noodles, grilled saddle of monkfish and halibut poached in red burgundy and tarragon. Sumptuous sweets to finish – try the white and dark chocolate ice cream. Skilfully chosen wines: St Aubin Blanc (Prudhon) '85, Ch. Palmer '78.   ♀ Well-chosen   ᴇ

Lunch Sun 12–2, Tues–Sat by arrang. only   *Dinner* 7–9.30
Closed D Sun, all Mon, Bank Hols, 1–10 Jan

GLEN PARVA — Glen Parva Manor Restaurant   *NEW ENTRY*

R Map 11 D4 Leicestershire
The Ford, Little Glen Road
Leicester (0533) 774604

Set L £9.50
Set D £14.50
About £55 *for two*
Seats 90 *Parties* 30
Parking Ample
Credit Access, Amex, Diners

A spacious restaurant with views over magnificent gardens. Service is very professional, and young Martin Zalesny is a chef of developing talents. His chicken liver pâté with a cold port wine sauce and home-made brioche was a fine dish by any standards, though pheasant with green apples and chestnut purée was a little less well conceived. Good vegetables, decent sweets and a sound wine list with the odd gem.   ᴇ

Lunch 12.30–2.30, Sun 11–4   *Dinner* 7.30–10
Closed L Sat, D Sun, 26–28 Dec

GLOUCESTER — Blazers   *NEW ENTRY*

R Map 4 B1 Gloucestershire
38 Worcester Street
Gloucester (0452) 300772

Set L £7.95
Set D £12.95
About £50 *for two*
Seats 55 *Parties* 25
Parking Limited
Credit Access, Amex, Diners, Visa

Fresh produce is treated with proper respect at this smart, town-centre restaurant. Sauces are a strong point of Hugh Wright's capable cooking and, as well as simple fixed-price menus, he produces more adventurous à la carte dishes such as a delicious sole, crab and avocado mousse, sea bass wrapped in lettuce and veal with a vodka and strawberry sauce. Tempting sweets too.   &

Lunch 12–2   *Dinner* 7–10
Closed L Sat, D Mon, all Sun, 26 Dec & 1 Jan

GLOUCESTER   Crest Hotel   63%   £C

H Map 4 B1 Gloucestershire
Crest Way, Barnwood
GL4 7RX
Gloucester (0452) 613311
Telex 437273

Credit Access, Amex, Diners, Visa

A modern hotel on the A417 close to Gloucester. Exposed brickwork is a feature in the day rooms – recently refurbished – and in the well-kept bedrooms, where dark fabrics combine with lightwood furniture. Executive rooms have superior furnishings and accessories. ***Amenities*** garden, indoor swimming pool, sauna, solarium, whirlpool bath, keep-fit equipment, in-house movies, secretarial services, fax, laundry service, 24-hour lounge service, children's play area. ♿

Rooms 100	*Direct dial* Yes	*Confirm by* 6	*Parking* Ample
Ensuite bath/shower 100	*Room TV* Yes	*Last dinner* 10	*Room service* All day

GLOUCESTER   Hatton Court   76%   £C/D

H Map 4 B1 Gloucestershire
Upton Hill,
Upton St Leonards GL4 8DE
Gloucester (0452) 617412
Telex 437334

Rooms 53
Ensuite bath/shower 53
Direct dial Yes
Room TV Yes
Confirm by 6
Last dinner 10
Parking Ample
Room service 24 hours

Credit Access, Amex, Diners, Visa

Improvements continue to be made at this elegant Cotswold manor overlooking the Severn valley. Public rooms have a traditional country house appeal with their period-style furniture and striking floral drapes, while spacious bedrooms in both the original building and sympathetically constructed new wing offer every comfort. Smart darkwood furniture (including a number of four-posters, brass and canopied

beds) and attractive fabrics are individually combined to stylish effect; thoughtful extras range from hairdryers and trouser presses to bathrobes and lavish toiletries in the splendid bathrooms (many with whirlpool baths). No dogs. ***Amenities*** garden, outdoor swimming pool, in-house movies, secretarial services, laundry service.

Changes in data sometimes occur in establishments
after the Guide goes to press.
Prices should be taken as indications rather than firm quotes.

GOATHLAND   Mallyan Spout Hotel   60%   £E/F

H Map 15 C5 North Yorkshire
Whitby YO22 5AN
Whitby (0947) 86206

Credit Amex, Diners, Visa

A characterful ivy-clad hotel well run by the charming Heslops. Hand-carved oak furniture graces the entrance hall and bar, while the cosy lounge has traditionally upholstered seating and plenty of books and magazines. Half the bedrooms have been recently refurbished with Laura Ashley fabrics and pine furniture; the remainder have laminate fitted units. One room has a splendid half-tester, two have brass bedsteads. ***Amenities*** garden, secretarial services.

Rooms 22	*Room phone* No	*Confirm by* arrang.	*Parking* Ample
Ensuite bath/shower 22	*Room TV* Yes	*Last dinner* 8.30	*Room service* All day

GODALMING   Inn on the Lake   £D/E

I Map 5 E3 Surrey GU7 1RH
Godalming (048 68) 5575

Credit Access, Amex, Diners, Visa

Martin Cummings is proud to be an innkeeper and it is the personal attention of himself and his wife Joy that makes this country house such a splendid establishment. Attention to detail shows in the charming, individually decorated bedrooms whose extras include magazines, trouser presses and sewing kits. Good-quality carpeting extends to the bathrooms, the newer of which (in an extension) have whirlpool baths and bidets. There's no reception area (you check in in your room) but there is a small rustic bar and plush lounge. ***Amenities*** garden.

Rooms 19	*Direct dial* Yes	*Confirm by* arrang.	*Parking* Ample
Ensuite bath/shower 16	*Room TV* Yes	*Last dinner* 10	*Room service* All day

*N*ovelty ! It is the prevailing cry;

it is imperiously demanded by everyone ...

What feats of ingenuity have we not been forced

to perform ... to meet our customers' wishes? ...

I have ceased counting the nights spent in the attempt

to discover new combinations, when,

completely broken with fatigue of a heavy day,

my body ought to have been at rest.

G. A. ESCOFFIER 1847-1935
A GUIDE TO MODERN COOKERY (1907)

Gastronomy...

the intelligent knowledge of whatever

concerns man's nourishment.

BRILLAT-SAVARIN 1755-1826
PHYSIOLOGIE DU GOÛT

'**C**uisine' means that

Things taste just like what they are!

CURNONSKY 1872-1956
' To Melanie Rouat '

Strange to say

how a good dinner and feasting

reconciles everybody.

SAMUEL PEPYS 1633-1703
DIARY

GOLANT — Cormorant Hotel 62% £E

H Map 2 C3 Cornwall
Nr Fowey PL23 1LL
Fowey (072 683) 3426

Credit Access, Visa

There are delightful panoramic views of the Fowey Estuary from every window of this friendly family-run hotel perched on a hillside above the river. You can admire the view from the spacious lounge, or draw up a couch in front of the fire if it's chilly. Warm, comfortable bedrooms with neat bathrooms are pleasantly furnished; two have been upgraded.
Amenities garden, indoor swimming pool, keep-fit equipment.

| Rooms 11 | Direct dial Yes | Confirm by arrang. | Parking Ample |
| Ensuite bath/shower 11 | Room TV Yes | Last dinner 8.45 | Room service All day |

GOODWOOD — Goodwood Park Hotel 66% £C

H Map 5 E4 West Sussex
Chichester PO18 0QB
Chichester (0243) 775537
Telex 869173

Credit Access, Amex, Diners, Visa

A 15th-century inn which has been much extended and modernised and is now popular with the conference trade. Comfortable public areas include a spacious bar and relaxing lounge. Bedrooms in the new wings are spacious, with good-quality coordinating fabrics and plenty of writing space; those in the main building, including one with a four-poster, are more characterful. *Amenities* garden, snooker, secretarial services, fax, laundry service, 24-hour lounge service. &

| Rooms 49 | Direct dial Yes | Confirm by 6 | Parking Ample |
| Ensuite bath/shower 49 | Room TV Yes | Last dinner 9.30 | Room service Limited |

GOUDHURST — Star & Eagle £E

I Map 7 B5 Kent
High Street TN17 1AL
Goudhurst (0580) 211512

Credit Access, Amex, Diners, Visa

Old beams are much in evidence throughout this delightful half-timbered inn, and in winter open fires add to the charm of the characterful bars and chintzy lounge. Prettily decorated, pine-furnished bedrooms offer radio-alarms and tea-makers. The honeymoon suite boasts a four-poster and antiques, and many rooms enjoy fine country views. No dogs.
Amenities garden, in-house movies.

| Rooms 11 | Room phone Yes | Confirm by arrang. | Parking Ample |
| Ensuite bath/shower 9 | Room TV Yes | Last dinner 9.30 | Room service Limited |

Our inspectors *never* book in the name of Egon Ronay's Guides.
They disclose their identity only if they are considering an establishment
for inclusion in the next edition of the Guide.

GRANTHAM — Barkston House

RR Map 11 E3 Lincolnshire
Barkston NG32 2NH
Loveden (0400) 50555

Set L Sun only £7.50
About £40 for two
Seats 34
Parties 28
Parking Ample

Credit Access, Amex, Diners, Visa

Fronted by a broad expanse of lawn, this pleasant Georgian farmhouse restaurant offers a short unfussy menu with the emphasis on English cooking. Everything from wholemeal rolls to biscuits served with coffee is home-made. Raw materials are of good quality. Main courses might include a delicious fish pie or cassoulet of lamb. Abundant vegetables are perfectly cooked. Short, skilfully chosen wine list including Chablis from Durup, Beaujolais from Sylvain Fessy.
🍷 Well-chosen 🕒 &

Lunch 12–2, Sun at 1 *Dinner* 7.30–9.15
Closed L Sat, D Sun & Mon, Bank Hols exc. Good Fri & 5 days Xmas

BEDROOMS 2 £E
With bath/shower 2

Guests are accommodated in two immaculate bedrooms, each with TV. The decor is soft and muted, with pretty fabrics. No dogs.

If we recommend **meals** in a Hotel or Inn,
a separate entry is made for its restaurant.

GRASMERE   Michael's Nook   79%   £A

HR **Map 13 C5** Cumbria
Nr Ambleside LA22 9RP
Grasmere (096 65) 496
Telex 65329

Rooms 11
Ensuite bath/shower 11
Direct dial Yes
Room TV Yes
Confirm by arrang.
Last dinner 8
Parking Ample
Room service All day

The garden and the wonderful views are just two of the attributes of this fine Victorian house. Friendly staff are another, and the whole place has a fair measure of country house civility, with open fires, impressive flower displays, handsome antiques and homely touches like magazines and board games. There are plenty of thoughtful extras in the bedrooms – two with four-posters – and bathrooms. But there are niggles, too, including some let-downs in terms of housekeeping. Guests may use the facilities of the nearby Wordsworth Hotel. Half-board only. No dogs.
Amenities garden, laundry service, secretarial services.

Restaurant   ♕

Set D £28
Seats 26
Parties 30

Candlelight adds a warm glow to dinner here, and the daily-changing menus provide plenty of quality and variety. Spinach-wrapped seafood terrine makes a super starter which you could follow with halibut, venison or maybe loin and sweetbreads of veal. Sweets are not to be missed, and chef Andrew Eastick is very keen on high-class British cheeses. Friendly, well-informed staff. ☙

Lunch by arrang.   *Dinner* 7.30 for 8, Sat 7 for 7.15 (9 for 9.15 Fri & Sat in summer)   *About £70 for two*

**We welcome bona fide complaints and recommendations
on the tear-out pages at the back of the book for readers' comment.
They are followed up by our professional team.**

GRASMERE   Swan Hotel   65%   £C

H **Map 13 C5** Cumbria
Nr Ambleside LA22 9RF
Grasmere (096 65) 551

Credit Access, Amex, Diners, Visa

An ancient coaching inn where many a traveller en route to Keswick must have stopped for fortification before tackling Dunmail Raise. Public areas are charming, with wing chairs, copper jugs, brass ornaments and fresh flowers. Twelve plush bedrooms boast floral drapes and festoon blinds, brass lamp fittings and lots of extras; standard rooms are very acceptable. Bathrooms are well equipped with good toiletries. *Amenities* garden, laundry service.

Rooms 36	*Room phone* Yes	*Confirm by* 6	*Parking* Ample
Ensuite bath/shower 36	*Room TV* Yes	*Last dinner* 9	*Room service* All day

GRASMERE   White Moss House   68%   £B/C

HR **Map 13 C5** Cumbria
Rydal Water LA22 9SE
Grasmere (096 65) 295

Closed mid Nov–mid Mar

A Lakeland stone house north of Rydal on the Ambleside–Grasmere road. Homely charm is much in evidence, typified by the restful lounge full of deep armchairs, antiques and books and warmed by an open fire. In the comfortable bedrooms similar standards apply and thoughtful extras include hairdryers, trouser presses, magazines, guide books and flowers. Bathrooms are small but modern, with good toiletries. For unparalleled peace and quiet, there's a two-bedroom cottage perched 600 feet above on the edge of a wood, reached by a steep scramble or about a mile's drive along a single track. Half-board terms only. No children under eight. No dogs.
Amenities garden, coarse & game fishing, laundry service.

Rooms 6	*Direct dial* Yes	*Confirm by* arrang.	*Parking* Ample
Ensuite bath/shower 6	*Room TV* Yes	*Last dinner* 8	*Room service* All day

Restaurant ★ 🍷

English cooking

Dinner only 7.30 for 8
Set D £17.95
About £45 for two
Seats 20

Closed Sun (except Easter) &
mid Nov–mid Mar

Peter Dixon plans his five-course set menus with great attention to complementary flavours and textures and guests congregate for dinner at eight with happy anticipation. Excellent raw ingredients are cooked in an unpretentious fashion but with the liberal use of fresh herbs and seasonings. Local produce is used to create such dishes as soufflé of Rydal Water pike and dill, and there's an excellent cheeseboard

with a range of unusual English cheeses including Cumberland farmhouse and Ribblesdale goat cheese.

Specialities soufflé of smoked fish with fennel; fillet of venison with juniper and Pomerol sauce; mallard with a plum and Pinot Noir sauce; guardsman's pudding. 🍷 Well-chosen 🥂

GRASMERE Wordsworth Hotel 72% £C/D

HR **Map 13 C5** Cumbria
Nr Ambleside LA22 9SW
Grasmere (096 65) 592
Telex 65329

Rooms 38
Ensuite bath/shower 38
Direct dial Yes
Room TV Yes
Confirm by arrang.
Last dinner 9
Parking Ample
Room service 24 hours

Credit Access, Amex, Diners, Visa

A solid Victorian mansion offering traditional comfort and service: bags are whisked to your room, tea trays arrive promptly, beds are turned down, and all done willingly and cheerfully. The lounges have a lived-in country house look, with inviting sofas and wing chairs, lamps, plants and some handsome pieces of furniture. There are two contrasting bars, one with a sunny conservatory, the other a slate-

floored 'local'. Bedrooms, most of them recently refurbished, are appointed with style and taste; one bathroom is splendidly original, while the rest have modern fittings. No dogs.

Amenities garden, indoor swimming pool, keep-fit equipment, hairdressing, snooker, secretarial services, laundry service.

Prelude Restaurant

Set L Sun only £8.50
Set D £17.50
About £50 for two
Seats 65
Parties 120

Pleasant, efficient service complements excellent cooking that combines classical and modern elements. Seafood is well represented (terrine of crab with a lovely mild garlic sauce, salmon and turbot poached with saffron), while meaty treats are typified by nuggets of tender lamb, topped with a herb mousse and presented with a coulis of red peppers. Sweets like chocolate moussecake on a feathered lime sauce emphasise Bernard Warne's meal-long culinary skills. 🥂 ♿

Lunch 12.30–2
Dinner 7–9, Sat 7–9.30

★ For a *discount* on next year's guide, see **An Offer for Answers.** ★

GRAYSHOTT Woods 🍷

R **Map 5 E3** Hampshire
Headley Road, Nr Hindhead
Hindhead (042 873) 5555

About £50 for two
Seats 30
Parking Limited

Credit Access, Amex, Diners, Visa

Dana and Eric Norregen run a friendly, informal operation in this characterful converted butcher's shop. In full view of diners, Eric conjures up interesting and sometimes ambitious combinations, usually with enjoyable results. You might start with a pastry case of quail's eggs on mushroom purée, topped by hollandaise, and go on to chicken breast stuffed with crabmeat and pike, accompanied by a lobster sauce. Finish with a superb soufflé – perhaps hot lemon with sabayon. ♿

Dinner only 7–11.30 **Closed** Sun, Mon & 1 wk Xmas

GREAT AYTON   Ayton Hall   74%   £C/D

H **Map 15 C5** North Yorkshire
Low Green,
Nr Middlesbrough TS9 6BW
Great Ayton (0642) 723595

Rooms 6
Ensuite bath/shower 6
Direct dial Yes
Room TV Yes
Confirm by arrang.
Last dinner 9.30
Parking Ample
Room service All day

Credit Access, Amex, Visa

Originally the country home of the Earls of Westmorland, this Grade II listed building stands amid six acres of landscaped gardens. Now a characterful hotel, it offers superb accommodation and it seems that every need is catered for; the bedrooms, while simply furnished, have everything from videos and chess boards to fully equipped stationery bureaux. Four more atmospheric rooms have four-posters. Public areas include a cosy, Moroccan style foyer-bar and a traditional lounge with period-style seating, fine oil paintings and a grand piano (with pianist in the evenings). No children under 11. No dogs. *Amenities* garden, tennis, croquet, clay-pigeon shooting, in-house movies, secretarial services, laundry service.

Changes in data sometimes occur in establishments
after the Guide goes to press.
Prices should be taken as indications rather than firm quotes.

GREAT DUNMOW   Saracen's Head Hotel   59%   £C/D

H **Map 6 B3** Essex
High Street CM6 1AG
Great Dunmow (0371) 3901

Credit Access, Amex, Diners, Visa

The black-and-white Georgian facade hides earlier origins, and the lounge and bar, both popular local meeting places, have a very traditional look with beams and panelling. Three bedrooms are in the old part, while the rest, with a practical, modern appeal, are in separate buildings across the courtyard. Public area refurbishment and 29 new bedrooms are proposed for 1989.
Amenities laundry service.

Rooms 24	*Room phone* Yes	*Confirm by* 6	*Parking* Ample
Ensuite bath/shower 24	*Room TV* Yes	*Last dinner* 9.30	*Room service* 24 hours

GREAT DUNMOW   Starr

RR **Map 6 B3** Essex
Market Place CM6 1AX
Great Dunmow (0371) 4321

Set L £13, Sun £16.50
Set D £22, Sat £25
About £60 *for two*
Seats 60
Parties 30
Parking Ample

Credit Access, Amex, Diners, Visa

A public house for 500 years, the Starr is now a very civilised, high-quality restaurant, run by the affable Brian Jones. Susan Andrews and her youthful kitchen team do a first-class job producing delightful dishes that range from scallops beurre blanc and pigeon-breast salad to grilled calf's liver, duck breast with prunes, and Bakewell tart. The wine list is wholly admirable – attractively laid out, with accurate, pithy comments on vintages: note the delicious, keenly priced Ch. l'Etoile (Graves) '85 and the spectacular dessert Late Harvest '82 (de Bortoli) from Australia. ➲ Outstanding ♀ Well-chosen ℮
THREE BEDROOMS WILL BE READY AFTER WE GO TO PRESS.

Lunch 12–2   *Dinner* 7–9.30
Closed L Sat, D Sun, 3 wks Aug & 1 wk Xmas

We publish annually,
so make sure you use the current edition.
It's worth it!

GREAT MILTON Le Manoir aux Quat' Saisons 86% £B

HR **Map 5 D2** Oxfordshire
Church Street OX9 7PD
Great Milton (084 46) 8881
Telex 837552

Rooms 10
Ensuite bath/shower 10
Direct dial Yes
Room TV Yes
Confirm by arrang.
Last dinner 10
Parking Ample
Room service 24 hours

Credit Access, Amex, Diners, Visa
Closed 23 Dec–20 Jan

Although not far from junction 7 of the M40, the modern world seems blissfully remote once you enter the delightful grounds of this 15th-century manor house with tall Tudor chimneys and stone-mullioned windows. Within, magnificent flower arrangements abound, especially in the two elegantly comfortable lounges, where drinks are served (there's no bar). Bedrooms want for nothing, with antique furniture, canopied beds, and an impressive range of extras from a decanter of Madeira (champagne in the suites) to fresh fruit, hairdryers, trouser presses and sewing kits. Bathrooms are equally impressive. Dogs in kennels only. No children under 7 years. *Amenities* garden, outdoor swimming pool, tennis, croquet, riding, game fishing, laundry service.

Restaurant ★★★ ♕♕ ⌇

French cooking

Lunch 12.15–2.30
Dinner 7.15–10.15
Set L from £19.50
Set D £40
About £130 *for two*
Seats 55
Parties 30

Closed L Tues, all Mon & 23 Dec–20 Jan

Restrained luxury is the keynote of the elegant twin dining rooms that provide a charming setting for chef Raymond Blanc's talent. In a year by no means without its problems, Raymond and his team were rarely anything but magnificent, creating exquisite dishes, from delicious hors d'oeuvre to pigeon baked in a salt crust, served with a delicate truffle juice sauce, and the assiette gourmand – a selection of five heavenly sweets. There's a great cellar, especially strong in burgundies. *Specialities* terrine de bouillabaisse à la vinaigrette de safran; pavé de saumon fumé à chaud et soufflé au raifort; caille des Dombes farcie, sauce au Pineau des Charentes et écorces de pamplemousse; trio de chocolats. ▭ Outstanding ♀ Well-chosen

See INSPECTOR FOR A DAY

GREAT SNORING Old Rectory 60% £D/E

H **Map 6 C1** Norfolk
Nr Fakenham NR21 0HP
Fakenham (032 872) 597

Credit Amex, Diners
Closed 25 & 26 Dec

Tucked away in a tiny village sleepy by name and nature, this delightful old house makes an ideal country retreat. Antique pieces in the restful drawing room emphasise the private house atmosphere also apparent in the individually furnished bedrooms with their pretty ornaments, fresh flowers, books and magazines. Shutters keep out the cold night air and draw attention to the lovely views. No dogs. *Amenities* garden.

| *Rooms* 7 | *Direct dial* Yes | *Confirm by* arrang. | *Parking* Ample |
| *Ensuite bath/shower* 7 | *Room TV* Yes | *Last dinner* 8 | *Room service* All day |

 is our symbol for an **outstanding** wine list

GREAT YARMOUTH   Carlton Hotel   62%   £E

H Map 6 D1 Norfolk
Marine Parade NR30 3JE
Great Yarmouth (0493) 855234
Telex 975642

Credit Access, Amex, Diners, Visa

Refurbishment continues at this friendly seafront hotel. The redecorated cocktail bar looks very smart with its gilded grand piano, and the restaurant is being given a royal look with prints and photographs of the Windsors. Upgraded bedrooms are colour-coordinated in conservative fabrics and equipped with trouser presses, hairdryers, and well-kept bathrooms. Excellent housekeeping throughout.
Amenities satellite TV, secretarial services, laundry service.

Rooms 97	*Direct dial* Yes	*Confirm by* 6	*Parking* Ample
Ensuite bath/shower 68	*Room TV* Yes	*Last dinner* 9.30	*Room service* 24 hours

GREAT YARMOUTH   Seafood Restaurant

R Map 6 D1 Norfolk
85 North Quay
Great Yarmouth (0493) 856009

Seafood
About £50 for two
Seats 40 *Parties* 40
Parking Limited

Credit Access, Amex, Diners, Visa

Sip an aperitif in the recently refurbished bar of this plush family-run restaurant and admire the selection of superbly fresh fish cushioned on crushed ice in the cool cabinet. The choice may include sole, plaice, monkfish, salmon, trout, seabass and turbot, and a lobster tank promises further delights. Cooking is consummate. Desserts include an excellent pavlova. Some very good wines: Pouilly Fumé (Pabiot) '86; Puligny Montrachet 1er Cru (Latour) '85. ♀ Well-chosen

Lunch 12–2   *Dinner* 7–10.45
Closed L Sat, all Sun, Bank Hols & 2 wks Xmas

GREENWICH   Gachons

See under LONDON HOTELS under £60

GRETA BRIDGE   Morritt Arms Hotel   55%   £E

H Map 15 B5 Co. Durham
Rokeby, Nr Barnard Castle
DL12 9SE
Teesdale (0833) 27232

Credit Access, Amex, Diners, Visa

A splendidly traditional though modest hotel, with strong Dickensian associations. The great man stayed here in 1838 and there's a Gilroy mural in the cheerful bar depicting characters from his novels. The lounge too has plenty of old-world charm, with its deep armchairs and roaring log fires in winter. Simply furnished bedrooms are equipped with tea-makers and trouser presses. Good breakfasts.
Amenities garden, coarse fishing.

Rooms 26	*Room phone* No	*Confirm by* arrang.	*Parking* Ample
Ensuite bath/shower 16	*Room TV* Yes	· *Last dinner* 8.45	*Room service* All day

Any person using our name to obtain free hospitality is a fraud.
Proprietors, please inform the police and us.

GRIMSBY   Crest Hotel   55%   £C/D

H Map 11 F1 Humberside
St James' Square DN31 1EP
Grimsby (0472) 59771
Telex 527741

Credit Access, Amex, Diners, Visa
Closed 10 days Xmas

Right in the centre of town, the Crest is a purpose-built hotel dating from the early 1970s. Standard bedrooms, including about 20 for non-smokers, are practical if a little dated; the seven Lady Crest rooms are more up-to-date in terms of decor. There's a public bar in modern rustic style, a cocktail bar and a coffee shop.
Amenities sauna, secretarial services, fax, laundry service, coffee shop (9.30am–5.30pm Mon–Sat).

Rooms 131	*Direct dial* Yes	*Confirm by* 6	*Parking* Ample
Ensuite bath/shower 131	*Room TV* Yes	*Last dinner* 10	*Room service* Limited

GRIMSBY   Humber Royal Crest Hotel   64%   £C/D

H Map 11 F1 Humberside
Littlecoates Road DN34 4LX
Grimsby (0472) 50295
Telex 527776

Credit Access, Amex, Diners, Visa

Overlooking a golf course on the outskirts of town, this 20-year-old hotel provides decent overnight accommodation in friendly, peaceful surroundings. Bedrooms (some with balconies) are neatly kept, with trouser presses, hospitality trays and well-equipped bathrooms. There are two bars, one with a terrace, and good conference facilities. Check directions as it's not easy to find. *Amenities* garden, golf course, pool table, secretarial services, fax, laundry service.

Rooms 52	*Direct dial* Yes	*Confirm by* arrang.	*Parking* Ample
Ensuite bath/shower 52	*Room TV* Yes	*Last dinner* 10	*Room service* 24 hours

GRIMSTHORPE — Black Horse Inn — £E

IR Map 11 E3 Lincolnshire
Nr Bourne PE10 0LY
Edenham (077 832) 247

Credit Access, Amex, Visa
Closed 1 wk Xmas

In a hollow of the rolling countryside you'll find the little village of Grimsthorpe and this neatly-kept black-and-white 18th-century inn. Guests are attentively cared for by the Fishers and their friendly, hard-working staff. Public rooms have a cottage, homely atmosphere; likewise the bedrooms with pretty fabrics, comfortable beds and many thoughtful touches. Really delicious breakfasts, including the best lemon curd around. *Amenities* garden.

Rooms 4	*Room phone* No	*Confirm by* arrang.	*Parking* Ample
Ensuite bath/shower 4	*Room TV* No	*Last dinner* 9.30 (10.30 Sat)	*Room service* All day

Restaurant ⚘

English cooking

Set D £11.95
About £35 *for two*
Seats 45
Parties 40

Traditional English cooking in the most English of settings. Joyce Fisher's four-course meals use high-quality ingredients, and favourite dishes include crispy fish pancakes, Stilton, celery and herb pâté, monkfish mornay, rack of lamb and beefsteak, kidney and mushroom pie. Super sweets include honey meringues with whipped cream. A really delightful restaurant – relaxed, friendly and charming. No children under 8 at dinner. ☻ &

Lunch 12–1.45 *Dinner* 7–9.30, Sat 7–10.30
Closed Sun & 1 wk Xmas

GRIMSTON — Congham Hall — 75% — £C/D

H Map 6 B1 Norfolk
Nr King's Lynn PE32 1AH
Hillington (0485) 600250
Telex 81508

Rooms 11
Ensuite bath/shower 11
Direct dial Yes
Room TV Yes
Confirm by arrang.
Last dinner 9.30
Parking Ample
Room service 24 hours

Credit Access, Amex, Diners, Visa

This pleasant Georgian mansion, set in grounds that include paddocks, gardens and a cricket pitch, is run in friendly, personal style by Christine and Trevor Forecast. Public rooms have lots of comfortable armchairs and magazines and local guides to browse through. The bar is furnished in summery cane, and in warm weather chairs are set out on the lawn. Furniture in the bedrooms is in various styles;  there are two four-posters and a mahogany half-tester, the last being handsome but not very long. Lots of little extras. Good breakfasts. No children under 12. Kennelling for dogs.
Amenities garden, outdoor swimming pool, tennis, whirlpool bath, croquet, stabling, secretarial services, laundry service, helipad.

GRINDLEFORD — Maynard Arms Hotel — £E

I Map 10 C2 Derbyshire
Main Road S30 1HP
Hope Valley (0433) 30321

Credit Access, Amex, Diners, Visa

An early-Victorian stone-built inn which has been tastefully refurbished to provide comfortable and pleasant accommodation. Public areas include an attractive hall with stained-glass windows and a most appealing residents' lounge. Three superior bedrooms have four-posters and Stag or antique furniture, other rooms have nice fabrics and wallcoverings and decent laminate furniture. All have smart tiled bathrooms. Housekeeping is excellent. *Amenities* garden.

Rooms 13	*Direct dial* Yes	*Confirm by* arrang.	*Parking* Ample
Ensuite bath/shower 11	*Room TV* Yes	*Last dinner* 9.30, 10 Fri & Sat	*Room service* Limited

GRIZEDALE — Grizedale Lodge Hotel — 60% — £E/F

HR Map 13 D5 Cumbria
Nr Hawkshead LA22 0QL
Hawkshead (096 66) 532

Credit Access, Visa
Closed 3 Jan–9 Feb

The Lambs have created a super little hotel and due to its much-deserved popularity you must book well in advance. A rare Victorian sideboard is a feature of the homely, spotlessly kept lounge and guests can enjoy sunsets from a west-facing balcony. Bedrooms are immaculate, with floral decor and plenty of extras such as potpourri and sewing kits. Four have showers only. No dogs. *Amenities* garden.

Rooms 6	*Room phone* No	*Confirm by* arrang.	*Parking* Ample
Ensuite bath/shower 6	*Room TV* Yes	*Last dinner* 8.30	*Room service* All day

see over

Restaurant in the Forest   ♵

Set D £11.50
About £32 for two
Seats 35
Parties 36

Margaret Lamb is an acknowledged expert in Cumbrian cooking, with a Border TV series under her belt. Her five-course fixed-price menus offer a small choice of mainly English dishes, all cooked to a consistently high standard. Start perhaps with carrot and orange soup following with chicken and Stilton roulade or Esthwaite trout in oatmeal. Lovely puds such as warm chocolate fudge cake to finish. Booking essential.

Dinner only 7–8.30
Closed 3 Jan–9 Feb

GUILDFORD   Angel Hotel   62%   £C/D

H Map 5 E3 Surrey
High Street GU1 3DR
Guildford (0483) 64555

Credit Access, Amex, Diners, Visa

The cobbled courtyard and 12th-century vault conjure up the past at the Angel, where the nicest public room is the galleried lounge with its chintzes and pastels. The bedrooms, reached by a maze of corridors, come in all shapes and sizes, and most have recently been attractively refurbished with smart darkwood furniture and prettily coordinating fabrics.
Amenities laundry service, coffee shop (7.30am–10pm).

Rooms 27	*Direct dial* Yes	*Confirm by* 6	*Parking* Difficult
Ensuite bath/shower 27	*Room TV* Yes	*Last dinner* 10	*Room service* 24 hours

GUILDFORD   Rumwong

R Map 5 E3 Surrey
16 London Road
Guildford (0483) 36092

Thai cooking

Set D £12
About £30 for two
Seats 50
Parties 20
Parking Limited

Credit Access, Visa

In a parade of shops opposite the Civic Hall, Rumwong is a civilised Thai restaurant serving much above average food. Khanom cheeb is an exemplary starter – lovely light dim sum-style dumplings filled with minced beef and served with a soy sauce made piquant with tiny pickled chillis. Fish is especially good: try crispy fried prawns in a garlic and pepper sauce or cod mixed with green beans. Barbecued beef quenelles and roast duck with pickled ginger are among the favourite meat dishes. In the evening you can try the set dinner menu served on low tables or stay with the extensive carte. Delightful service by gracious Thai ladies. Drink jasmine tea.

Lunch 12–2.45   *Dinner* 6–10.45, Sun 6–10.30
Closed Mon, 1st 2 wks Aug, 3 days Xmas & 2 days New Year

GUILDFORD   University Post House Hotel   68%   £C

H Map 5 E3 Surrey
Egerton Road GU2 5XZ
Guildford (0483) 574444
Telex 858572

Credit Access, Amex, Diners, Visa

An 'upmarket' Post House opened in June 1987, just off the A3 with views across to the Cathedral and close to the University grounds. Impressive public rooms include a marble-floored foyer, a spacious lounge adorned with flower prints and tapestries, a clubby bar and a coffee shop. Bedrooms, of uniform design, are tailored to the needs of the business traveller, with excellent writing surfaces, good lighting, mini-bars and remote-control TVs. Club rooms offer various extras, and all rooms have well-equipped bathrooms. Staff let the side down somewhat.
Amenities terrace, indoor swimming pool, sauna, solarium, laundry service, coffee shop (6.30am–11pm). ♿

Rooms 121	*Direct dial* Yes	*Confirm by* 6	*Parking* Ample
Ensuite bath/shower 121	*Room TV* Yes	*Last dinner* 10.15	*Room service* 24 hours

GUIST   Tollbridge Restaurant

R Map 6 C1 Norfolk
Nr Fakenham
Foulsham (036 284) 359

Set L £7.80
About £38 for two
Seats 50
Parties 50
Parking Ample
Credit Visa

An attractive restaurant with a delightful position on the river Wensum, which provides the pike for a delicious mousseline. Other starters include feuilleté of herring roe and watercress soup, while main course might be fricassée of brill or pork in Norfolk cider sauce. Nice home-made sweets to finish. Impeccably chosen wines at keen prices: note the delicious Mountadam Chardonnay (Wynn) '85 from Australia. ☑ Well-chosen ⊖ ♿

Lunch 12–1.30   *Dinner* 7.30–9.15
Closed Sun, Mon, 3 days Xmas, 1st 3 weeks Jan & 1st week Oct

GULWORTHY | Horn of Plenty ⑼

RR Map 2 C3 Devon
Tavistock PL19 8JD
Tavistock (0822) 832528

Set L £12.50
Set D £17.50
About £52 *for two*
Seats 60 *Parties* 60
Parking Ample
Credit Access, Amex, Visa

The views are splendid, and the menu offers a selection of favourites old and new. In the former category come crab soufflé and sorrel-sauced Tamar salmon, in the latter green ribbon pasta with salsa di noci and casseroled duck with a rich burgundy sauce. Not everything is a total success, but there's an absorbing wine list with fine burgundies back to Grands Echezeaux (Mongeard) '79 and the delicious Château Loupiac-Gaudiet '83. ⑤

Lunch 12–2 *Dinner* 7–9.30
Closed Thurs, L Fri & all 25 & 26 Dec

BEDROOMS 6 £D
With bath/shower 6

Six super bedrooms feature attractive contemporary fabrics, pine furniture, well-fitted bathrooms and balconies that provide lovely views.

GWEEK | Mellanoweth Restaurant *NEW ENTRY* ⑼

R Map 2 B3 Cornwall
Helston
Mawgan (032 622) 271

About £38 *for two*
Seats 26
Parking Ample

Credit Access, Visa

Former publican Colin Funnell makes diners very welcome at this cottage restaurant at the Lizard peninsula. His wife Hazel takes care of culinary matters, producing a variety of enjoyable, straightforward dishes. Seafood specials change daily (baked crab à la crème, salmon in red wine sauce, sea bass with herbs and wine) and there's also plenty of choice for meat-eaters. Sweets include boozy sorbets. Summer eating in the courtyard. ⓔ

Dinner only 7.30–9
Closed Sun, Mon (in winter), 26 Dec, 1 Jan & 2 wks winter

HACKNESS | Hackness Grange Country Hotel 69% £C

H Map 15 D6 North Yorkshire
Nr Scarborough YO13 0JW
Scarborough (0723) 82345
Telex 527667

Credit Access, Amex, Diners, Visa

A traditionally appointed Victorian hotel in a very beautiful riverside setting with only ducks to disturb the peace. Embossed wallpaper and heavily patterned carpets adorn the public areas, where space, warmth and solid comfort are the order of the day. Spotlessly kept bedrooms – again with plenty of space – have decent modern furniture, easy chairs, hairdryers, mini-bars and fresh fruit. A number are in a splendid old coach house across the garden. Service is caring and very friendly. No children under four.
Amenities garden, indoor swimming pool, tennis, pitch & putt, croquet, game fishing, in-house movies, laundry service, helipad.

| *Rooms* 26 | *Direct dial* Yes | *Confirm by* arrang. | *Parking* Ample |
| *Ensuite bath/shower* 26 | *Room TV* Yes | *Last dinner* 9 | *Room service* All day |

HADLEIGH | Weavers Restaurant ⑼

R Map 6 C3 Suffolk
23 High Street
Hadleigh (0473) 827247

About £34 *for two*
Seats 50
Parties 26
Parking Ample

Credit Access, Visa

Robust French cooking is the order of the day at Jean-Jacques Pons' delightful beamed restaurant. You can start with authentic onion soup or Burgundy snails before progressing to game pie Madeira, lamb provençale, or halibut with a lime and lemon mousseline. Vegetables are crisp and flavourful, and there are tempting puds. Sound wine list includes Chablis (Durup) '86 and Ch. Chasse Spleen '79. ⓔ

Dinner only 7–9.30
Closed Sun & Mon

HADLEY WOOD | West Lodge Park 65% £C

H Map 7 B4 Hertfordshire
Cockfosters Road,
Nr Barnet EN4 0PY
01-440 8311
Telex 24734

Credit Access, Amex, Diners, Visa

A much-extended William IV mansion set in 34 acres of manicured grounds on the A111. Standard bedrooms, especially the singles, are fairly compact, but others are larger, including a number with four-posters. Bathrooms range from moderately functional to quite elaborate Victorian style. Day rooms, particularly the lounge, have a stylish, traditional air. No dogs.
Amenities garden, putting, croquet, fax, laundry service, helipad.

| *Rooms* 50 | *Direct dial* Yes | *Confirm by* arrang. | *Parking* Ample |
| *Ensuite bath/shower* 50 | *Room TV* Yes | *Last dinner* 9.30 | *Room service* 24 hours |

HALIFAX　　Holdsworth House　71%　　£D

H **Map 10 C1**
West Yorkshire
Holdsworth, Nr Halifax HX2 9TG
Halifax (0422) 240024
Telex 51574

Rooms 40
Ensuite bath/shower 40
Direct dial Yes
Room TV Yes
Confirm by arrang.
Last dinner 9.45
Parking Ample
Room service 24 hours

Credit Access, Amex, Diners, Visa
Closed 25 & 26 Dec & 1 Jan

The original house dates back to 1633 and the extensions have been designed to match it in style. Inside, exposed stone walls, well-polished antiques, a grandfather clock and fresh flowers create an elegant and welcoming feel. Sage green velour wing chairs and soft, muted colours create a pleasant lounge area and, in the bar, stone-mullioned windows and an open hearth give lots of charm. Bedrooms are in the extensions and are good-sized and smartly traditional with period-style free-standing furniture; sherry, remote-control TVs and radios, dressing gowns and sewing kits are supplied. Bathrooms are carpeted and have shower facilities.
Amenities garden, snooker, laundry service. &

*If we recommend **meals** in a Hotel or Inn,
a separate entry is made for its restaurant.*

HANDFORTH　　Belfry Hotel　71%　　£C/D

HR **Map 10 B2** Cheshire
Stanley Road, Nr
Wilmslow SK9 3LD
061-437 0511
Telex 666358

Rooms 90
Ensuite bath/shower 90
Direct dial Yes
Room TV Yes
Confirm by 6
Last dinner 10
Parking Ample
Room service 24 hours

Credit Access, Amex, Diners, Visa

For over 25 years the Beech family have been running their pleasant hotel with high standards of professionalism and efficiency. The welcoming foyer, with its pink marble floor and fresh floral displays, leads to a relaxing lounge with green leather button-backed seating, an intimate cocktail bar and the beamed Belfry Bar, which is now mainly used in conjunction with the extensive banqueting and conference facilities. The bedrooms feature coordinating Sanderson fabrics and freestanding mahogany furniture; the more basic bathrooms have compact shower/baths, half-tiled walls and the usual extras. Housekeeping is excellent. Courtesy coach to airport. No dogs.
Amenities garden, teletext, secretarial services, laundry service. &

Restaurant

Set L from £8.50
Set D from £9.50
About £52 for two
Seats 100
Parties 180

Superbly professional service and consistently skilled cooking guarantee an enjoyable meal here. The lengthy à la carte menu is supplemented by the daily table d'hôte and a list of specials to provide an abundance of choices; typical dishes are terrine de ris de veau as a starter and roast wild duck with plum and Armagnac sauce to follow. Good classic cellar strong in Bordeaux and vintage ports.
🍷 Well-chosen ℗

Lunch 12.30–2　*Dinner* 7–10
Closed 26 Dec, 1 Jan & Good Friday

HARLOW　　Harlow Moat House　60%　　£D

H **Map 7 B4** Essex
Southern Way CM18 7BA
Harlow (0279) 22441
Telex 81658

Credit Access, Amex, Diners, Visa

Near junction 7 of the M11, this low-rise modern hotel has extensive and very popular conference facilities. The bedrooms, smartly revamped in sage, beige and peach, pack all the usual up-to-date accessories into their average dimensions, and all have neat, compact bathrooms. Public areas include a bar in traditional pub style, with round tables, bucket chairs and fruit machines.
Amenities garden, in-house movies, fax, laundry service.

Rooms 120	*Direct dial* Yes	*Confirm by* 6	*Parking* Ample
Ensuite bath/shower 120	*Room TV* Yes	*Last dinner* 10	*Room service* Limited

HAROME | Pheasant Hotel 68% | £C/D

H **Map 15 C6** North Yorkshire
Nr Helmsley YO6 5JG
Helmsley (0439) 71241

Closed all Jan & Feb

Quietly situated overlooking the village pond, this charming hotel was created from a smithy, a shop and two cottages. The interior is a happy blend of old and new, from the relaxing chintzy lounge to the cosy beamed bar complete with inglenook fireplace. Large, well-kept bedrooms have plain painted walls, floral fabrics and up-to-date bathrooms. Half-board terms only. No children under twelve.
Amenities garden, laundry service. ♿

Rooms 13	*Direct dial* Yes	*Confirm by* arrang.	*Parking* Ample
Ensuite bath/shower 13	*Room TV* Yes	*Last dinner* 8.15	*Room service* Limited

HAROME | Star Inn

R **Map 15 C6** North Yorkshire
Nr Helmsley
Helmsley (0439) 70397

About £38 *for two*
Seats 36
Parties 36
Parking Ample

Credit Access, Amex, Diners, Visa

Enjoyable, unfussy food, capably cooked, is on offer at this cosy, beamed pub restaurant. Straightforward starters include soup of the day, home-made terrine or mushrooms and prawns in garlic butter; main courses may range from grilled sole, chicken Antigua, and duck bigarade to pork fillet with Stilton and port wine. Finish with oranges in caramel or home-made meringues. ♀ Well-chosen ⊖

Dinner only 7–9.30
Closed Sun, Mon, 24 & 25 Dec & all Jan

HARPENDEN | Glen Eagle Hotel 64% | £C/D

H **Map 5 E2** Hertfordshire
1 Luton Road AL5 2PX
Harpenden (058 27) 60271
Telex 825828

Credit Access, Amex, Diners, Visa

Recent improvements at this pleasantly staffed red-brick hotel have focused on the day rooms, which are now quite stylish and elegant. Standard bedrooms are of a decent size, decorated in peach and cream, with light cherrywood furniture, double glazing and the usual up-to-date accessories. De luxe rooms are larger and similarly equipped, but a bit gloomy and dated. The flowery patio is nice in summer.
Amenities garden, fax, laundry service.

Rooms 51	*Direct dial* Yes	*Confirm by* 6	*Parking* Ample
Ensuite bath/shower 51	*Room TV* Yes	*Last dinner* 9.30	*Room service* 24 hours

HARPENDEN | Harpenden Moat House Hotel 65% | £C/D

H **Map 5 E2** Hertfordshire
Southdown Road AL5 1PE
Harpenden (058 27) 64111
Telex 826938

Credit Access, Amex, Diners, Visa
Closed 1 wk Xmas

A comfortable, well-kept hotel located just off the A1081, overlooking Harpenden East Common. The main building was originally a convent, and the public rooms retain many features from the Georgian period. Bedrooms range from simply furnished singles in the old part to the very smart newest rooms with stylish Italian pine furniture. All rooms are equipped with tea-makers, trouser presses and hairdryers.
Amenities garden, secretarial services, fax, laundry service.

Rooms 53	*Direct dial* Yes	*Confirm by* 6	*Parking* Ample
Ensuite bath/shower 53	*Room TV* Yes	*Last dinner* 9.45	*Room service* 24 hours

---

Our inspectors *never* book in the name of Egon Ronay's Guides.
They disclose their identity only if they are considering an establishment
for inclusion in the next edition of the Guide.

HARROGATE | Burdekins

R **Town plan B2**
North Yorkshire
21 Cheltenham Crescent
Harrogate (0423) 502610
Set D £7.95
About £35 *for two*
Seats 40 *Parties* 40
Parking Limited
Credit Access, Amex, Visa

Tim and Kath Burdekin work hard for the success of their stylish restaurant, and Stewart Barker does a capable job in the kitchen. His seasonal menu offers a decent choice, from vegetarian pancake and hot creamed shrimps to monkfish provençal, guinea fowl and saddle of hare with a green peppercorn sauce. Vegetables are very good, and puddings are a great feature – try sticky toffee pie or spotted dick with custard.

Dinner only 6.30–9.30
Closed Sun (exc. during trade shows) & 25 & 26 Dec

HARROGATE

Map 15 C6
Town plan opposite

Population 67,000

The Tewit Well in Harrogate was found to have healing properties in 1571 and the town developed into a spa resort as further chalbeyate and sulphur springs were discovered. Its popularity in the Victorian era is reflected in its architecture. The Royal Baths Assembly Rooms, formerly the main hydro-therapy centre, now houses traditional Turkish baths and modern sauna and solarium facilities. As well as being a historically famous spa resort, Harrogate is now a cosmopolitan conference venue.

Annual Events
International Youth Music Festival *15th-22nd April*
Spring Flower Show *23rd–25th April*
Great Yorkshire Show *14th–16th July*
Harrogate International Festival (music and drama) *29th July–12th August*
Great Autumn Flower Show *18th–19th September*

Sights Outside Town
Fountains Abbey
Ripley Castle
Newby Hall
Knaresborough
Ripon
Pateley Bridge
Brimham Rocks

Tourist Information Office
Royal Baths Assembly Rooms
Crescent Road HG1 2RR
Telephone Harrogate 525666

1 Art Gallery and Public Library **C3**
2 Conference Centre *incorporating a 2000-seat auditorium* **B1**
3 Exhibition Centre *six halls comprising 10,000 square metres* **B2**
4 Harrogate Theatre **B2**
5 Royal Baths Assembly Rooms *originally a hydro-therapy centre, now housing the Tourist Information Centre and Turkish baths* **B2**
6 Royal Hall *when opened in 1903, an entertainment venue for those taking the waters, now a theatre* **B2**
7 Royal Pump Room Museum *containing local historical material* **B2**
8 St John's Well **E2**
9 Sun Colonnade **A2/3**
10 Tourist Information Office **B2**
11 Valley Gardens **A2**

Fiat Dealer
Croft & Blackburn Ltd
Leeds Road
Pannal
Harrogate HG3 1EP
Tel. Harrogate 879236

Harrogate $F/I/A/T$

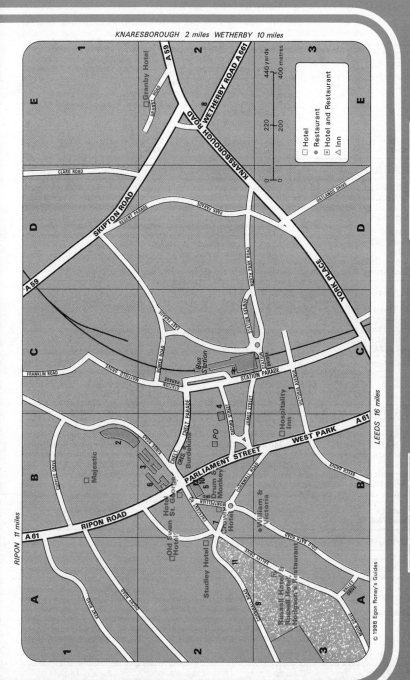

KNARESBOROUGH 2 miles WETHERBY 10 miles

RIPON 11 miles

LEEDS 16 miles

□ Hotel
● Restaurant
▣ Hotel and Restaurant
△ Inn

440 yards
400 metres
220
200
0

Granby Hotel
GRANBY ROAD
A 59
WETHERBY ROAD A 661
KNARESBOROUGH ROAD
8
OATLANDS DRIVE
CLARO ROAD
SKIPTON ROAD
REGENT PARADE
PARK PARADE
A 59
EAST PARADE
NORTH PARK ROAD
YORK PLACE
STATION AVENUE
FRANKLIN ROAD
MAYFIELD GROVE
BOWER ROAD
STATION PARADE
Bus Station
STATION BRIDGE
STATION PARADE
VICTORIA AVENUE
CHELT. PARADE
□ PO
4
OXFORD STREET
JAMES STREET
□ Hospitality Inn
KINGS ROAD
CHELT. CRES.
Burdekins
5
PARLIAMENT STREET
WEST PARK
A 61
BEECH GROVE
Majestic
2
3
6
10
Drum &
Monkey
MONTPELLIER
CORNWALL ROAD
● William &
Victoria
Old Swan Hotel □
Hotel St. George
Crown
Hotel
RIPON ROAD
A 61
RIPON ROAD
Studley Hotel □
11
MONTPELLIER
Russell Hotel/
Russell Hotel
Hodgson's Restaurant
9
DUCHY ROAD
CORNWALL ROAD
SOUTH PARK ROAD
OTLEY ROAD
VALLEY DRIVE

© 1988 Egon Ronay's Guides

HARROGATE   Crown Hotel   66%   £C/D

H **Town plan B2**
North Yorkshire
Crown Place HG1 2RZ
Harrogate (0423) 67755
Telex 57652

Credit Access, Amex, Diners, Visa

The Crown is a pleasant period building standing in the heart of Harrogate next to the historic Pump Room. The large reception lounge has the appeal of chintz, well-worn leather and brass chandeliers; there's a neat cocktail bar, a peaceful reading room and a fine marble-pillared restaurant. Good-sized bedrooms have lightwood fitted furniture, armchairs, coffee tables and writing space. All the suites and many of the bedrooms have recently been refurbished, and a similar programme is improving the hitherto fairly basic bathrooms. Guests have full use of the facilities (including a health and fitness club) of the Majestic.
Amenities garden, games room, fax.

Rooms 122	*Direct dial* Yes	*Confirm by* 6	*Parking* Ample
Ensuite bath/shower 122	*Room TV* Yes	*Last dinner* 9.30	*Room service* 24 hours

HARROGATE   Drum & Monkey

R **Town plan B2**
North Yorkshire
5 Montpellier Gardens
Harrogate (0423) 502650

Seafood
About £36 for two
Seats 48
Parking Difficult
Credit Access, Visa

Booking is essential at this extremely popular seafood restaurant. Raw materials are first class and cooked with care in simple and composite dishes that range from grilled sole to sweet and sour prawn and fish roulade. The lunch menu includes several salads and to follow there's a choice of sorbets, ices and more indulgent desserts. 🅮

Lunch 12–2.30   *Dinner* 7–10.15
Closed Sun & 9 days Xmas

HARROGATE   Granby Hotel   58%   £D

H **Town plan E2**
North Yorkshire
Granby Road HG1 4SR
Harrogate (0423) 506151
Telex 57423

Credit Access, Amex, Diners, Visa

The handsome proportions remain, but not much of the grandeur of this former spa hotel overlooking the Stray. The foyer-lounge has a fine plasterwork ceiling, but decor is generally unsympathetic. Upgrading is planned for some 25 bedrooms, which all have tea-makers and remote-control TVs. Front-facing rooms will have additional accessories. **Amenities** garden, snooker, in-house movies, secretarial services, laundry service. ₺

Rooms 93	*Direct dial* Yes	*Confirm by* 6	*Parking* Ample
Ensuite bath/shower 93	*Room TV* Yes	*Last dinner* 9.30	*Room service* 24 hours

HARROGATE   Hospitality Inn   66%   £D/E

H **Town plan B3**
North Yorkshire
West Park, Prospect Place
HG1 1LB
Harrogate (0423) 64601
Telex 57530
Credit Access, Amex, Diners, Visa

Part of a smart Georgian terrace in the town centre, the Hospitality Inn provides neat, up-to-date accommodation. Decent-sized bedrooms are equipped with the usual accessories including hairdryers and trouser presses, and there's reasonable desk/dressing table space. The hotel also has five self-catering apartments. The bar and small lounge have an agreeably traditional air. No dogs.
Amenities in-house movies.

Rooms 71	*Direct dial* Yes	*Confirm by* 6	*Parking* Limited
Ensuite bath/shower 71	*Room TV* Yes	*Last dinner* 10	*Room service* 24 hours

HARROGATE   Majestic   69%   £C

H **Town plan B1**
North Yorkshire
Ripon Road HG1 2HU
Harrogate (0423) 68972
Telex 57918

Credit Access, Amex, Diners, Visa

Built on the grand scale in 1900, the Majestic now only partly lives up to its name. The potential is still there – magnificently proportioned public areas, pillars, lots of marble, grand floral displays – but something seems lacking in style and service, and it has a rather 'conferency' feel. Refurbished bedrooms are spacious and of a good decorative standard but there were minor irritations on our visit such as threadbare towels and only basic toiletries. Let's hope that these little problems can quickly be ironed out.
Amenities garden, indoor swimming pool, sauna, solarium, whirlpool bath, tennis, squash, games room, snooker, secretarial services, laundry service.

Rooms 156	*Direct dial* Yes	*Confirm by* 6	*Parking* Ample
Ensuite bath/shower 156	*Room TV* Yes	*Last dinner* 9.45	*Room service* 24 hours

HARROGATE — Old Swan Hotel 68% £C

Town plan A2
North Yorkshire
Swan Road HG1 2SR
Harrogate (0423) 500055
Telex 57922

Credit Access, Amex, Diners, Visa

Though traditional in looks – it's an ivy-clad 18th-century building of considerable charm – the Old Swan is thoroughly up to date in its appeal. Proximity to the International Conference and Exhibition Centre makes it a popular business choice, and staff are kept very busy with the large throughput of custom. Day rooms are on a grand scale, and bedrooms range from compact singles to spacious suites; all have desk/dressing table space and decent lighting, with armchairs and coffee tables in the larger rooms. Functional private facilities throughout. A general refurbishment programme is under way.
Amenities garden, tennis, putting, croquet, in-house movies, secretarial services, fax, laundry service.

Rooms 137	*Direct dial* Yes	*Confirm by* 6	*Parking* Ample
Ensuite bath/shower 137	*Room TV* Yes	*Last dinner* 10.30	*Room service* 24 hours

HARROGATE — Russell Hotel 62% £E

Town plan A3
North Yorkshire
Valley Drive HG2 0JN
Harrogate (0423) 509866

Credit Access, Amex, Diners, Visa

In a residential area overlooking the Valley Gardens, the Russell is a Victorian hotel with a friendly, relaxing appeal. The Hodgson brothers make everyone feel very welcome, and the main bar is a favourite with many locals. Bedrooms are comfortable and decently sized, the largest and most traditional being those at the front. Housekeeping is not always immaculate. **Amenities** garden, game fishing, laundry service, 24-hour lounge service.

Rooms 34	*Direct dial* Yes	*Confirm by* 6	*Parking* Limited
Ensuite bath/shower 34	*Room TV* Yes	*Last dinner* 10	*Room service* All day

Hodgson's Restaurant ♔ ∮

Set D £11.25
About £46 for two
Seats 65
Parties 30

A fairly sombre setting for the capable and sometimes innovative cooking of Richard Hodgson. Some dishes are familiar favourites – game terrine with Cumberland sauce, for example – while others are much more unusual, like mallard with a sauce of peach, orange and stem ginger. Sweets can sometimes disappoint. Good list of classic and New World wines: note Merlot Clos du Val from California.
⊃ Outstanding ♟ Well-chosen

Dinner only 7–10
Closed Sun & Mon to non-residents & 24–30 Dec

HARROGATE — Hotel St George 65% £C/D

Town plan B2
North Yorkshire
Ripon Road HG1 2SY
Harrogate (0423) 61431
Telex 57995

Credit Access, Amex, Diners, Visa

A location opposite the exhibition centre makes this hotel convenient for business travellers. There is a vast foyer-cum-lounge furnished with period-style seating and two bars. Good-sized, well-equipped bedrooms have contemporary furniture and pretty fabrics; family rooms have ingenious bunk beds built into cupboards.
Amenities garden, indoor swimming pool, sauna, solarium, whirlpool bath, keep-fit equipment, secretarial services, fax, laundry service.

Rooms 85	*Direct dial* Yes	*Confirm by* 6	*Parking* Ample
Ensuite bath/shower 85	*Room TV* Yes	*Last dinner* 9.15	*Room service* 24 hours

 indicates a **well-chosen** house wine

HARROGATE — Studley Hotel 66% £D

Town plan A2
North Yorkshire
28 Swan Road HG1 2SE
Harrogate (0423) 60425
Telex 57506

Credit Access, Amex, Diners, Visa

The compactness of the public rooms here is more than made up for by the friendly family atmosphere. In the cosy lounge, a mixture of traditional seating creates a relaxed ambience; there's also a new residents' lounge and bar and a room for private parties. Well-equipped, pretty bedrooms have tea/coffee-makers, hairdryers, trouser presses and modern, carpeted bathrooms. No children under eight.
Amenities patio, in-house movies, laundry service.

Rooms 36	*Direct dial* Yes	*Confirm by* arrang.	*Parking* Ample
Ensuite bath/shower 36	*Room TV* Yes	*Last dinner* 10.30	*Room service* 24 hours

HARROGATE | William & Victoria Restaurant

R **Town plan B3**
North Yorkshire
6 Cold Bath Road
Harrogate (0423) 521510

Set D from £10
About £28 for two
Seats 50 Parties 25
Parking Limited
Credit Access

Robin Straker's smart yet informal restaurant is located above his popular wine bar. Blackboard menus provide plenty of choice, suggesting tempting starters like creamed prawns in lobster sauce or chicken liver and green peppercorn pâté, and imaginative main dishes like pork escalope with brandy and tarragon or beef casserole with horseradish dumplings. Cooking is careful and accomplished and desserts are first-class. Wine list includes some exciting New World labels. ♀ **Well-chosen** ℮

Dinner only 6–10 **Closed** Sun, 26 Dec, 1st wk Jan & last wk Aug

 is our symbol for an **outstanding** wine list

HARROW WEALD | Mansion House at Grim's Dyke   59%   £C/D

H **Map 5 E2** Middlesex
Old Redding HA3 6SH
01-954 4227
Telex 94014082

Credit Access, Amex, Diners, Visa
Closed 3 days Xmas

A ten-acre garden in dense woodland is the setting for the former home of Sir William Gilbert (his splendid galleried music room is now the restaurant). The panelled entrance hall leads to a cheerful library bar-lounge, and a fine staircase climbs to the original bedrooms, which have traditional furnishings and quite basic bathrooms. Main-house decor needs attention. Most bedrooms are in a separate modern block.
Amenities garden, croquet, laundry service.

Rooms 47	*Direct dial* Yes	*Confirm by* arrang.	*Parking* Ample
Ensuite bath/shower 47	*Room TV* Yes	*Last dinner* 9.30	*Room service* 24 hours

HARTLEPOOL | Grand Hotel   60%   £D

H **Map 15 C5** Cleveland
Swainson Street TS24 8AA
Hartlepool (0429) 266345

Credit Access, Amex, Diners, Visa

Closed 25 & 26 Dec, 1 Jan

Built at the turn of the century, this imposing red-brick hotel retains a certain grandeur, notably in the recently redecorated ballroom. The bar, which also serves as a lounge, has a suitably Victorian air. Bedrooms, generally lofty and spacious, combine touches of old-fashioned comfort (real eiderdowns) with modern accessories like trouser presses and hairdryers. Disco Thursday–Sunday.
Amenities secretarial services, laundry service. &

Rooms 41	*Direct dial* Yes	*Confirm by* arrang.	*Parking* Limited
Ensuite bath/shower 29	*Room TV* Yes	*Last dinner* 10	*Room service* 24 hours

HARWICH | Pier at Harwich

RR **Map 6 D3** Essex
The Quay
Harwich (0255) 241212

Seafood

Set L £7.25, Sun £10.50
About £47 for two
Seats 128 Parties 80
Parking Ample
Credit Access, Amex, Diners, Visa

Take a pre-prandial drink in the bright, nautically themed bar before venturing up to the first-floor restaurant, which is equally resplendent with seafaring mementos, brassy artefacts and captain's chairs. Ferries and freighters sail by as you tuck into sparklingly fresh fish dishes based on the day's catch. It's best to stick to simple things – pan-fried plaice, sole and cod, all served with excellent chips – for sauces are less successful. However, there's a good moules marinière to satisfy even the heartiest appetite. ♀ **Well-chosen** ℮

Lunch 12–2   *Dinner* 6–9.30, Sat 6–10
Closed D 25 Dec & all 26 Dec

BEDROOMS 6 **£E**
With bath/shower 6

Light, pleasantly decorated bedrooms are on the top floor and have harbour views, modern en suite bathrooms, TVs and tea-makers.

HASLEMERE | Lythe Hill Hotel   67%   £B/C

H **Map 5 E3** Surrey
Petworth Road GU27 3BQ
Haslemere (0428) 51251
Telex 858402

Credit Access, Amex, Diners, Visa

A fine old timbered farmhouse and outbuildings tucked into a slope of the Surrey Hills makes a most attractive hotel. Public areas are due to be refurbished, and half the annexe bedrooms have already been given a smart modern look. The five in the old part are particularly luxurious, with antiques and handsome period bathrooms. No dogs.
Amenities garden, sauna, tennis, croquet, laundry service.

Rooms 38	*Direct dial* Yes	*Confirm by* arrang.	*Parking* Ample
Ensuite bath/shower 38	*Room TV* Yes	*Last dinner* 9.45	*Room service* 24 hours

HASLEMERE — Morels ★ ♛ ዿ

R **Map 5 E3** Surrey
23 Lower Street
Haslemere (0428) 51462

French cooking

Lunch 12.30–2
Dinner 7–10
Set L £12
Set D £15
About £60 *for two*
Seats 45
Parking Limited

Credit Access, Amex, Diners, Visa
Closed L Sat, all Sun & Mon,
Bank Hols (exc. Good Fri), last 2
wks Sept & 2 wks Feb

A light, attractive restaurant that's home to the subtle and thoughtful cooking of Jean-Yves Morel, a chef steeped in classical skills but always receptive to new ideas. The two elements combine triumphantly in lovely dishes like yellow and green courgettes, their flowers filled with a chicken and basil mousse, served with a classy sauce vierge, or braised boned oxtail stuffed with morels. End with the gorgeous assiette du chef – four desserts served in miniature. Very good wines, chosen with real discernment: especially fine burgundies, delicious Bruno Paillard champagne, lots of half-bottles. ♀ Well-chosen

Specialities andouillette de moules aux aromates, ris de veau aux carottes et jus de cardamone, assiette du chef. ☞ ♿

See INSPECTOR FOR A DAY

HASLEMERE — Shrimpton's

R **Map 5 E3** Surrey
Midhurst Road,
Kingsley Green
Haslemere (0428) 3539

Set L £9.50 **Set D** £16.50
About £38 *for two*
Seats 38 *Parties* 20
Parking Ample
Credit Access, Amex, Diners, Visa

A popular beamed restaurant standing in pretty countryside on the Midhurst road. The atmosphere is very jolly (though the canned music can be intrusive) and the menu of familiar favourites is well handled by sunny Canary Islander Jose Afonso. Some typical dishes: pâté-stuffed mushrooms, spaghetti bolognese, trout meunière, fillet of beef with béarnaise sauce. Treacle tart is a good pud. Staff are welcoming and commendably professional. Book. ☞

Lunch 12.30–2 *Dinner* 6.30–9.45
Closed L Sat, all Sun, 26 Dec & 1 Jan

HASELEY — Haseley House Hotel 62% NEW ENTRY £E

H **Map 10 C4** Warwickshire
Nr Hatton CV35 7LS
Haseley Knob (092 687) 227

Credit Access, Amex, Diners, Visa

A fine old Georgian mansion in an attractive rural setting near the A41. A cosy, friendly atmosphere is apparent on entering the foyer, and the lounge is a nice spot for a drink. Bedrooms, divided between the main house and a building across the car park, are decorated in gentle colours and furnished in traditional style. The four-poster room has a whirlpool bath.
Amenities garden, secretarial services, fax, laundry service.

Rooms 20	*Direct dial* Yes	*Confirm by* arrang.	*Parking* Ample
Ensuite bath/shower 16	*Room TV* Yes	*Last dinner* 9.30	*Room service* None

★ For a *discount* on next year's guide, see **An Offer for Answers**. ★

HASTINGLEIGH — Woodmans Arms Auberge ዿ

RR **Map 7 C5** Kent
Hassell Street, Ashford
TN25 5JE
Elmsted (023 375) 250

Set L from £13.50
Set D £16
About £41 *for two*
Seats 10
Parties 10
Parking Ample

Actor Gerald Campion and his wife Susan live in an isolated 17th-century house on the North Downs. Its tiny dining room exudes old-world charm and Gerald (for many years alias Billy Bunter) is a most entertaining host. Susan's imaginative no-choice menus feature tasty soups like curried parsnip and interesting appetisers like beetroot roulade. Main courses such as navarin of new season's lamb give a starring role to local meat, fish and game. Nice puddings and a cleverly chosen wine list with good clarets (Ch. Cissac '75, Les Forts de Latour '70). Book. ♀ Well-chosen ☞

Lunch by arrang. only *Dinner* 7.30 for 8, Sun 7 for 7.30
Closed 1 wk May & first 3 wks Sept

BEDROOMS 3 £E
With bath/shower 3

Pretty bedrooms all have TVs. Excellent breakfasts. No children. No dogs. No smoking anywhere.

HASTINGS   Rösers   ♀

R **Map 7 C6** East Sussex
64 Eversfield jPlace,
St Leonards
Hastings (0424) 712218

Set L from £13.20
About £50 for two
Seats 40
Parties 30
Parking Ample

Credit Access, Amex, Diners, Visa

Mild-mannered Gerald Röser is the driving force behind this well-run seafront restaurant, where Basil, a voluble African Grey parrot, continues in top form. Fish is perhaps what he (Gerald) is best known for, his careful, confident cooking enhancing the fine fresh flavours. Dover sole, sea bass, turbot and king prawns are some of the favourites, and our starter was a delicately flavoured pike soufflé accompanied by a dill cream sauce with smoked salmon. Romney Marsh lamb, seasonal game and steaks are popular meaty choices, and sweets include a really lovely chocolate mousse. Good wines, with clarets back to Ch. Latour 1952 and a choice of half a dozen fine Chablis.
♟ Well-chosen ☙

Lunch 12–2   *Dinner* 7–10
Closed L Sat, all Sun & Bank Hols, 26 Dec & 2½ wks Jan

HATCH BEAUCHAMP   Farthings Country House Hotel   70%   £C/D

H **Map 3 E2** Somerset
Nr Taunton TA3 6SG
Hatch Beauchamp (0823) 480664

Rooms 6
Ensuite bath/shower 6
Room phone Yes
Room TV Yes
Confirm by arrang.
Last dinner 9.30
Parking Ample
Room service All day

Credit Access, Visa
Closed 2 wks Jan

Peace and tranquillity are in good supply at this well-maintained Georgian house in a quiet village setting. Public rooms are comfortable and inviting – the lounge offering deep sofas and plenty of magazines for leisurely reading, the pretty little bar providing blue bucket-style armchairs for a relaxing drink. Individually appointed bedrooms are mostly large, light and spacious. Two have spiral staircases lead-

ing up (or down) to private bathrooms; another features 'his and hers' bathrooms; two more are in cottage style with flowery wallpaper and pine furniture. All are equipped with tea-making facilities, radio-alarms, mineral water and good toiletries.
Amenities garden, laundry service.

HATFIELD   Comet Hotel   61%   £C/D

H **Map 7 B4** Hertfordshire
301 St Albans Road West
AL10 9RH
Hatfield (070 72) 65411

Credit Access, Amex, Diners, Visa

Built in the 1930s, this popular hotel near the A1 derives its original shape from the renowned contemporary Comet racer, which was built nearby. It's an unpretentious place appealing principally to business people, and the neat, standardised bedrooms have practical furnishings that include good writing surfaces, and very clean, functionally modern bathrooms with decent shelf space. 12 Executive rooms are much better equipped.   *Amenities* garden, laundry service.

| *Rooms* 57 | *Direct dial* Yes | *Confirm by* 6 | *Parking* Ample |
| *Ensuite bath/shower* 54 | *Room TV* Yes | *Last dinner* 10 | *Room service* 24 hours |

HATFIELD HEATH   Down Hall Hotel   72%   *NEW ENTRY*   £C

H **Map 7 B4** Essex
Bishops Stortford
Bishops Stortford (0279) 731441
Telex 81609

Rooms 45
Ensuite bath/shower 45
Direct dial Yes
Room TV Yes
Confirm by arrang.
Last dinner 9.30
Parking Ample
Room service 24 hours

Credit Access, Amex, Diners, Visa

Set in beautiful, landscaped grounds and rebuilt in the 1870s as an Italian-style mansion, Down House is now a luxury hotel. Pride of the elegant public rooms is the magnificent pillared lounge with its handsome stone fireplace and glittering chandeliers. Bedrooms are in Executive style, with smart darkwood furniture, good-size desks and trouser presses, while the stylish marble bathrooms have a good

range of accessories. Service lacks the personal touch, and breakfast was disappointing.   *Amenities* garden, indoor swimming pool, sauna, solarium, whirlpool bath, keep-fit equipment, tennis, putting, croquet, games room, snooker, secretarial services, fax, laundry service.

HATHERLEIGH — George Hotel — £E/F

Map 3 D2 Devon
Market Street,
Nr Okehampton EX20 3JN
Okehampton (0837) 810454

Credit Access, Visa

Dating from 1450, this thatched inn was originally a monks' retreat and it has been allowed to retain much of its period character – the beamed reception area boasts a huge inglenook fireplace and the Jubilee Bar oozes old-world charm. Bedrooms are simple yet comfortable, with pretty fabrics and period furniture; there are two four-posters and one half-tester. *Amenities* garden, outdoor swimming pool, pool table, laundry service.

| *Rooms* 11 | *Direct dial* Yes | *Confirm by* 8 | *Parking* Ample |
| *Ensuite bath/shower* 9 | *Room TV* Yes | *Last dinner* 9.30 | *Room service* All day |

HAVANT — Bear Hotel 59% — £D/E

Map 5 D4 Hampshire
East Street PO9 1AA
Portsmouth (0705) 486501
Telex 869136

Credit Access, Amex, Diners, Visa

Old blends with new at this former coaching inn, which was recently extended to provide a conference room and further accommodation. Public areas are pleasantly traditional while bedrooms – some with fresh, light colour schemes, others in darker, warmer tones – provide accessories like remote-control teletext TVs, trouser presses, hairdryers and tea-makers. Bathrooms have shower facilities and are equally well equipped. *Amenities* in-house movies, laundry service.

| *Rooms* 42 | *Direct dial* Yes | *Confirm by* 6 | *Parking* Ample |
| *Ensuite bath/shower* 42 | *Room TV* Yes | *Last dinner* 10.30 | *Room service* 24 hours |

HAVANT — Post House Hotel 62% — £C/D

Map 5 D4 Hampshire
Northney Road,
Hayling Island PO11 0NQ
Hayling Island (0705) 465011
Telex 86620

Credit Access, Amex, Diners, Visa

A hotel in a pretty setting overlooking Langstone harbour. Inside, lounge space is confined to the hall and foyer and the bar and coffee shop are upstairs. Superior rooms have reasonable soft furnishings and coordinated colours; standard have orange candlewick bedspreads and curtains. *Amenities* garden, indoor swimming pool, sauna, solarium, whirlpool bath, keep-fit equipment, games room, secretarial services, laundry service, coffee shop (10am–10pm), 24-hour lounge service, helipad.

| *Rooms* 96 | *Direct dial* Yes | *Confirm by* 6 | *Parking* Ample |
| *Ensuite bath/shower* 96 | *Room TV* Yes | *Last dinner* 10 | *Room service* Limited |

**Changes in data sometimes occur in establishments
after the Guide goes to press.
Prices should be taken as indications rather than firm quotes.**

HAWKCHURCH — Fairwater Head Hotel 64% — £D

Map 3 E2 Devon
Nr Axminster EX13 5TX
Hawkchurch (029 77) 349

Credit Access, Amex, Diners, Visa
Closed 20 Dec–1st wk Mar

The beautiful country setting is a great feature of this splendid Edwardian house run with great charm and friendliness by resident family owners. Day rooms have a peaceful, traditional atmosphere, and the view along the Axe Valley from the little sun lounge ·is something special. Bedrooms, including four in a garden wing, are neat, bright and comfortable, with up-to-date carpeted bathrooms. *Amenities* garden, badminton, croquet, snooker, laundry service.

| *Rooms* 18 | *Direct dial* Yes | *Confirm by* arrang. | *Parking* Ample |
| *Ensuite bath/shower* 18 | *Room TV* Yes | *Last dinner* 8.30 | *Room service* All day |

HAWKHURST — Tudor Arms Hotel 64% — £D/E

Map 7 C6 Kent
Rye Road TN18 5DA
Hawkhurst (058 05) 2312

Credit Access, Amex, Diners, Visa

A substantial red-brick hotel on the A268. The lounge is a cheerful mix of chintz and green leather armchairs and sofas, and more chintz carries the country feel into the half-panelled public bar. Decent-sized bedrooms, again with flowery fabrics, combine traditional with modern furniture. All have tea-makers, radio-alarms and trouser presses – hairdryers on request. Well-kept carpeted bathrooms. *Amenities* garden, putting, secretarial services, children's play area.

| *Rooms* 14 | *Direct dial* Yes | *Confirm by* arrang. | *Parking* Ample |
| *Ensuite bath/shower* 12 | *Room TV* Yes | *Last dinner* 9.15 | *Room service* All day |

HAWKSHEAD   Field Head House   67%   £E/F

HR **Map 13 D5** Cumbria
Outgate LA22 0PY
Hawkshead (096 66) 240
Telex 64117

Credit Diners, Visa
Closed last 2 wks Jan

The hills of Beatrix Potter and Wordsworth country provide a
delightful setting for this former shooting lodge off the B5286. Wood-
burning stoves warm the inviting lounges stocked with books and
records, and the bedrooms, most with charming views, offer homely
comforts. The splendidly hospitable Dutch owners, who are slowly
restoring the house and gardens, prepare superb breakfasts.
Amenities garden, croquet, laundry service.

Rooms 8	*Room phone* No	*Confirm by* arrang.	*Parking* Ample
Ensuite bath/shower 8	*Room TV* Yes	*Last dinner* 8	*Room service* All day

Restaurant   ♛ ♌

Set D £15
About £38 *for two*
Seats 12
Parties 12

Bob van Gulik's five-course dinner menus (no choice, and non-
residents must book) rely on fresh local produce and a splendid
vegetable garden. Delicately flavoured air-dried ham remains the
favourite starter, followed by a creamy soup and perhaps trout with
grapes and walnuts and imaginatively cooked vegetables. Finish with
home-made ice cream or sticky toffee pudding. Interesting cheeses
and a small, excellent value wine list. ♟ Well-chosen ℰ

Lunch by arrang.   *Dinner* at 8
Closed D Tues, last 2 wks Jan

HAWORTH   Weaver's   *NEW ENTRY*   ♌

R **Map 10 C1** West Yorkshire
15 West Lane
Haworth (0535) 43822

English cooking
Set L Sun £7.95
Set D £9.95 (Before 8)
About £32 *for two*
Seats 60 *Parties* 14
Credit Access, Amex, Diners, Visa

A delightful English restaurant and café-bar in the home town of the
Brontës. A cosy, relaxing atmosphere puts guests in the perfect mood
for sampling Jane Rushworth's enjoyable, unpretentious cooking.
Crab and haddock fritters and spicy vegetable parcels are typical
starters while main courses include pies, stews, roasts and fish dishes.
Sticky toffee pudding is a winner. Super home-baked bread. ℰ

Lunch Sun (Oct–Easter only) 12.30–1.30   *Dinner* 7–9.30
Closed D Sun, all Mon, Bank Hols, 1st 2 wks Jul & 1 wk Xmas
Parking Ample

**We welcome bona fide complaints and recommendations
on the tear-out pages at the back of the book for readers' comment.
They are followed up by our professional team.**

HAYDOCK   Post House Hotel   65%   £C

H **Map 10 B2** Merseyside
Lodge Lane,
Newton-le-Willows WA12 0JG
Wigan (0942) 717878
Telex 677672

Credit Access, Amex, Diners, Visa

Haydock's Post House stands by the racecourse close to junction 23
of the M6. It offers extensive facilities for functions, and a new health
and fitness club was under orders for October 1988. Bedrooms are
bright, airy and practical and among the day rooms a pleasant
foyer-lounge and a small bar. *Amenities* garden, indoor swimming
pool, sauna, whirlpool bath, gymnasium, in-house movies, fax, laundry
service, 24-hour lounge service.

Rooms 99	*Direct dial* Yes	*Confirm by* 6	*Parking* Ample
Ensuite bath/shower 99	*Room TV* Yes	*Last dinner* 10.30	*Room service* Limited

HAYTOR   Bel Alp House   67%   £C

H **Map 3 D3** Devon
Nr Bovey Tracey TQ13 9XX
Haytor (036 46) 217

Credit Access, Visa
Closed Jan, Feb & Dec exc. by
arrang.

Roger and Sarah Churnock are friendly and concerned hosts at their
elegant Edwardian house on the Haytor road out of Bovey Tracey.
Antiques feature throughout, and the drawing rooms invite a sojourn
with their deep-cushioned chairs and selection of books and magazines.
Bedrooms are also thoughtfully equipped, and many have been very
attractively redecorated and furnished. Two bathrooms keep their
splendid original fittings. *Amenities* garden, snooker.

Rooms 9	*Direct dial* Yes	*Confirm by* arrang.	*Parking* Ample
Ensuite bath/shower 9	*Room TV* Yes	*Last dinner* 8.30	*Room service* All day

HEATON MOOR — Jade Garden

R Map 10 B2 Cheshire
29 Shaw Road, Stockport
061-442 0143

Chinese cooking
Set L from £3.50
Set D from £8
Seats 50 *Parties* 50
Parking Ample
Credit Access, Amex, Visa

A comfortable and attractive Chinese restaurant in a suburban shopping arcade. The Cantonese-influenced menu is long and a light hand in the kitchen ensures some highly enjoyable, natural flavours. Hong Kong roast duck has a very good black bean sauce, and specials include sea bass and lobster in various guises. Note also Kun Bo sliced chicken and fillet steak with ginger and spring onion. Friendly service.

Lunch 12–2   *Dinner* 5–11.30, Sat 5–1.45am, Sun 2–11.30
About £30 for two   **Closed** L Sat, Bank Hols & 25 Dec

**We publish annually,
so make sure you use the current edition.
It's worth it!**

HELFORD — Riverside ♀

RR Map 2 B4 Cornwall
Nr Helston
Manaccan (032 623) 443

Set L £12.50
Set D £28
About £68 for two
Seats 40
Parking Ample

Fresh fish is much in evidence on the menu of the Darrells' delightful cottage restaurant at the entrance to Helford village. Fish soup, salmon with ginger and currants, turbot with lobster sauce all appear on the imaginative fixed-price menus. Our delicious poached sea bass came with an excellent aïoli, new potatoes and a crisp salad, and there were well-presented cheeses with home-baked biscuits, walnuts and dried apricots. 🍷 Well-chosen ⊝ ♿

Lunch 12.30–2   *Dinner* 7.30–9.30
Closed Nov–mid Mar

BEDROOMS 6   £C/D
With bath/shower 6

Six pretty rooms with pine furniture and charming soft furnishings are all equipped with TVs and tea-makers. No dogs.

HELLAND BRIDGE — Tredethy Country Hotel 58% £D/E

H Map 2 B3 Cornwall
Nr Bodmin PL30 4QS
St Mabyn (020 884) 262

Credit Access, Visa

New owners have refurbishment plans for this predominantly Victorian building, some of whose bedrooms have already been brightened up. The best is a light, spacious room with a Tudor barrel ceiling, decent darkwood furniture and an enormous bathroom with a whirlpool bath. Other rooms are simpler but all are neat and tidy. The entrance hall combines with a bar and book-lined lounge. No dogs. *Amenities* garden, outdoor swimming pool, laundry service.

Rooms 11	Direct dial Yes	Confirm by arrang.	Parking Ample
Ensuite bath/shower 11	Room TV Yes	Last dinner 8.30	Room service Limited

---

HELMSLEY — Black Swan Hotel 70% £C

H Map 15 C6 North Yorkshire
Market Place YO6 5BJ
Helmsley (0439) 70466

Rooms 37
Ensuite bath/shower 37
Direct dial Yes
Room TV Yes
Confirm by 6
Last dinner 9.30
Parking Ample
Room service 24 hours

Credit Access, Amex, Diners, Visa

Three adjoining houses – Tudor, Georgian and Edwardian – present an unusual facade on the market square. The Black Swan is a country inn of great character, and years of care have given it a luxurious, lived-in feel. There are numerous lounges, the most attractive being the low-ceilinged Tudor room with large lamps, comfortable sofas and huge open fire. Note also the garden lounge, another with

beams and books and chintz, and a quaint panelled bar. Bedrooms are individually decorated, thoughtfully furnished and well lit; older rooms have the added charm of beams, sloping floors and locally crafted furniture. Good bathrooms with robes and choice toiletries. *Amenities* garden, croquet, secretarial services, laundry service.

HELMSLEY   Feversham Arms Hotel   65%   £E

H Map 15 C6 North Yorkshire
1 High Street YO6 5AG
Helmsley (0439) 70766

Credit Access, Amex, Diners, Visa

Long-standing family owners make constant improvements to this pleasant stone-built hotel in the centre of town. It has two comfortable bars, one with glass doors leading directly onto a secluded patio. Bedrooms in traditional style are nicely coordinated and offer trouser presses, hairdryers and wall safes; good carpeted bathrooms with showers and bidets feature gold-plated fittings.
Amenities garden, outdoor swimming pool, tennis.

Rooms 19	*Direct dial* Yes	*Confirm by* 4	*Parking* Ample
Ensuite bath/shower 19	*Room TV* Yes	*Last dinner* 9	*Room service* All day

HEMEL HEMPSTEAD   Post House Hotel   60%   £C/D

H Map 5 E2 Hertfordshire
Breakspear Way HP2 4UA
Hemel Hempstead (0442) 51122
Telex 826902

Credit Access, Amex, Diners, Visa

Just by junction 8 of the M1, this was Britain's first Post House. Bedrooms are on three sides of a garden; all are quite spacious, and standard features include mini-bars and remote-control TVs. Fully tiled bathrooms have good-sized towels. Lobby, lounge and bar are open-plan, and there's a cheerful coffee shop.
Amenities garden, secretarial services, laundry service, coffee shop (10am–10.30pm).

Rooms 107	*Direct dial* Yes	*Confirm by* 6	*Parking* Ample
Ensuite bath/shower 107	*Room TV* Yes	*Last dinner* 10	*Room service* 24 hours

HENLEY-IN-ARDEN   Yew Trees Hotel   69%   £D/E

H Map 10 C4 West Midlands
154 High Street B95 5BN
Henley-in-Arden (05642) 4636

Credit Access, Amex, Diners, Visa

On the High Street, this handsome 15th-century half-timbered hotel has attractive gardens to the rear. Public rooms include a pleasant entrance hall and lounge with linenfold panelling and painted floorboards. Beyond is a bar with access to the terrace and garden. Bedrooms are traditional with modern facilities and carpeted bathrooms – some with bidets – are well maintained. Excellent staff. No dogs. *Amenities* garden, patio, fax, laundry service.

Rooms 11	*Direct dial* Yes	*Confirm by* arrang.	*Parking* Ample
Ensuite bath/shower 11	*Room TV* Yes	*Last dinner* 9.30	*Room service* All day

HENLEY-ON-THAMES   Red Lion Hotel   56%   £D

H Map 5 D2 Oxfordshire
Hart Street RG9 2AR
Henley-on-Thames
(0491) 572161
Telex 83343

Credit Access, Amex, Visa

Standing right next to the river, this ancient hostelry affords bird's-eye views of that major sporting and social event, the Henley Royal Regatta. A few dark beams lend character to the lounge and there are a couple of cosy bars. Bedrooms (three with lovely old timbers) are variously furnished and acceptably maintained though carpets look rather tired. Decent bathrooms, both old and new.
Amenities laundry service.

Rooms 26	*Room phone* Yes	*Confirm by* 6	*Parking* Ample
Ensuite bath/shower 20	*Room TV* Yes	*Last dinner* 9.45	*Room service* All day

Our inspectors *never* book in the name of Egon Ronay's Guides.
They disclose their identity only if they are considering an establishment
for inclusion in the next edition of the Guide.

HEREFORD   Fat Tulip   *NEW ENTRY*

R Map 4 A1
Hereford & Worcester
The Old Wye Bridge,
2 St. Martin's St.
Hereford (0432) 275808

About £35 for two
Seats 35 *Parties* 20
Parking Ample
Credit Access, Amex, Visa

A delightful city centre bistro with fresh, simple decor and a pleasant, informal atmosphere. Susan Poweles provides charming service while husband Kevin works single-handed in the basement kitchen, turning top-quality produce into tasty, well presented dishes like brochette of river prawns in garlic butter, roast best end of spring lamb served with a classic soubise sauce, and fresh mango parfait with strawberry coulis. Booking is recommended.

Lunch 12–2   *Dinner* 7–10
Closed Sun, some Bank Hols & 10 days Xmas

HEREFORD | Green Dragon Hotel 68% | £D

H Map 4 A1
Hereford & Worcester
Broad Street HR4 9BG
Hereford (0432) 272506
Telex 35491

Credit Access, Amex, Diners, Visa

The name has been around since Norman times, and the present Green Dragon boasts a fine Georgian facade. The chandeliered foyer has an elegant air, and there's a spacious lounge (popular for morning coffee), a cocktail bar and a handsome oak-panelled restaurant. Bedrooms and bathrooms are well equipped and smartly maintained: more are being brought up to the standard of the superior front rooms.
Amenities secretarial services, laundry service.

Rooms 88	*Direct dial* Yes	*Confirm by* 6	*Parking* Ample
Ensuite bath/shower 88	*Room TV* Yes	*Last dinner* 9.30	*Room service* 24 hours

HEREFORD | Hereford Moat House 61% | £D/E

H Map 4 A1
Hereford & Worcester
Belmont Road HR2 7BF
Hereford (0432) 354301

Credit Access, Amex, Diners, Visa
Closed 1 wk Xmas

A steeply pitched red-tiled roof all but envelops the main building of this modern hotel on the A465 Abergavenny road. Inside, a starkly simple foyer leads to function rooms and to a bright and comfortable bar-lounge overlooking an ornamental pool. Chalet-style blocks house practical, decent-sized bedrooms – all with fitted units, tea-makers, radio-alarms and smart, well-maintained bathrooms.
Amenities garden, secretarial services, laundry service.

Rooms 32	*Room phone* Yes	*Confirm by* arrang.	*Parking* Ample
Ensuite bath/shower 32	*Room TV* Yes	*Last dinner* 9.45	*Room service* 24 hours

Any person using our name to obtain free hospitality is a fraud.
Proprietors, please inform the police and us.

HERNE BAY | L'Escargot

R Map 7 C5 Kent
22 High Street
Herne Bay (0227) 372876

French cooking
Set L £7.80 **Set D** £8.60
About £36 *for two*
Seats 36 *Parties* 40
Parking Ample
Credit Access, Visa

Alain Bessemoulin cooks single-handed in his tiny kitchen while wife Joyce provides a friendly welcome front-of-house. Classic and modern influences intermingle in the simple set menu and, where ingredients are carefully chosen, results can be most enjoyable. Flavoursome moules marinière is a popular starter and to follow there are dishes like tender-pink calf's liver with garlic butter, and chicken breast sauced with Armagnac and tarragon. Portions are generous.

Lunch 12.30–2 *Dinner* 7–10 **Closed** L Sat, Sun & Mon, also D Sun in winter, also L Bank Hols & 2 days Xmas

HERSHAM | The Dining Room

R Map 7 A5 Surrey
10 Queens Road,
The Village Green
Walton on Thames (0932) 231686

English cooking
Set L £9.95
About £35 *for two*
Seats 65 *Parking* Limited
Credit Access, Amex, Diners, Visa

Described as 'a very English restaurant', this charming four-roomed establishment serves solidly traditional dishes like devilled lamb kidneys in Yorkshire pudding alongside Cumberland sausage, beef and oyster pie and nursery puddings like spotted dick. Booking advised. Good short wine list including Macon Clessé (Dananchet) '86 and the exceptional Chianti Classico Riserva '83 (Rampolla).
♣ Well-chosen ⊛

Lunch 12–2, Sun till 2.30 *Dinner* 7–10.30
Closed L Sat, D Sun, all Mon & Bank Hols & 2wks Xmas

HERSTMONCEUX | Sundial

R Map 7 B6 East Sussex
Gardner Street
Herstmonceux (0323) 832217

French cooking
Set L from £12.50
Set D £17.50
About £50 *for two*
Seats 50
Parties 60
Parking Ample

Credit Amex, Diners, Visa

For 20 years now, Giuseppe and Laurette Bertoli have run their charmingly cottagy restaurant with great pride and professionalism. Nothing is too much trouble for a dedicated chef like Giuseppe; he takes great pains to select the best possible raw materials and uses skill and imagination in their careful preparation. Menus offer a quite staggering choice, ranging from classic dishes like poached fillet of turbot with sauce mousseline to freestyle modern creations like breast of wild duck sauced with blackcurrant. Among the desserts, an exemplary crème brûlée. Splendid classic wines to match the serious cooking include Vosne Romanée '78 and Ch. Gloria '70.
▷ Outstanding ♣ Well-chosen ⊛ &

Lunch 12.30–2.30 *Dinner* 7–10, Sat 7.30–10
Closed D Sun, all Mon, Bank Hols, 10 Aug–5 Sept, Xmas–mid Jan

HERTINGFORDBURY   White Horse Inn   61%   £C/D

H Map 7 B4 Hertfordshire
Hertingfordbury Road
SG14 2LB
Hertford (0992) 586791

Credit Access, Amex, Diners, Visa

Once the local manor house, the White Horse lies in a quaint village about a mile from Hertford. Bedrooms in modern extensions include 12 spacious doubles or twins classed as superior, with pleasant pastel decor and stylish fitted units. All rooms have neat, well-maintained bathrooms with plenty of towels on heated rails. There's a comfortable bar-lounge with garden views. Friendly, professionally concerned manager. *Amenities* garden.

Rooms 42	Direct dial Yes	Confirm by 6	Parking Ample
Ensuite bath/shower 42	Room TV Yes	Last dinner 9.30	Room service All day

HETHERSETT   Park Farm Hotel   65%   £E

H Map 6 C2 Norfolk
Nr Norwich NR9 3DL
Norwich (0603) 810264

Credit Access, Amex, Diners, Visa
Closed 24–29 Dec

A Georgian house fronts a hotchpotch of architectural styles and there is even a working farm here. The public areas are smart and relaxing. The bedrooms are extremely comfortable and well equipped; ten new rooms have individually made furniture, four-posters, whirlpool baths, record decks and trouser presses. *Amenities* garden, indoor swimming pool, sauna, solarium, tennis, putting, croquet, games room, pool table, fax, laundry service, helipad.

Rooms 32	Direct dial Yes	Confirm by arrang.	Parking Ample
Ensuite bath/shower 32	Room TV Yes	Last dinner 9	Room service All day

HETTON   Angel Inn   ♀

R Map 15 B6 North Yorkshire
Nr Skipton
Cracoe (075 673) 263

Set L £8.50
Set D £12.95
About £35 for two
Seats 36 Parties 40
Parking Ample
Credit Access

A warm, cosy restaurant with a blazing fire on winter evenings; and delightfully informal but efficient service. Chefs Denis Watkins and John Topham provide a daily-changing four-course fixed-price menu of carefully cooked and prettily presented dishes. A typical meal might include terrine of fresh salmon and halibut, breast of pheasant coated in ground almonds served with Madeira sauce, and apricot chiffon pie or lemon tart for dessert. ⊡ &

Lunch Sun only 12–2   *Dinner* 7–10
Closed L Mon–Sat, D Sun & some Bank Hols

HEXHAM   Beaumont Hotel   58%   £E/F

H Map 15 B4 Northumberland
Beaumont Street NE46 3LT
Hexham (0434) 602331

Credit Access, Amex, Diners, Visa

In the centre of town overlooking the abbey, the Beaumont has smart day rooms that include a foyer-lounge and bar on the ground floor and a cosy cocktail bar on the first floor. Bedroom refurbishment continues, with solid freestanding furniture replacing more basic units, and decor changing for the brighter. All rooms have private facilities, but only three boast bath tubs. No dogs.
Amenities laundry service.

Rooms 20	Direct dial Yes	Confirm by arrang.	Parking Limited
Ensuite bath/shower 20	Room TV Yes	Last dinner 9.45	Room service Limited

Changes in data sometimes occur in establishments
after the Guide goes to press.
Prices should be taken as indications rather than firm quotes.

HIGH WYCOMBE   Crest Hotel   65%   £C

H Map 5 E2 Buckinghamshire
Crest Road, Handycross
HP11 1TL
High Wycombe (0494) 442100
Telex 83626

Credit Access, Amex, Diners, Visa

A modern low-rise hotel by junction 4 of the M40, with bright, spacious day rooms and good accommodation. Standard bedrooms are comfortable and quite well equipped, but better still are the Lady Crest and Executive rooms, including the smart new study Executive rooms with memory phones and other gadgets to make a practical and stylish working base. *Amenities* garden, in-house movies, secretarial services, fax, laundry service, coffee shop (7am–9pm). &

Rooms 111	Direct dial Yes	Confirm by 6	Parking Ample
Ensuite bath/shower 111	Room TV Yes	Last dinner 10.15	Room service 24 hours

HILLINGDON — Master Brewer Motel 58% £D

H Map 5 E2 Middlesex
Western Avenue,
Hillingdon Circus UB10 9BR
Uxbridge (0895) 51199

Credit Access, Amex, Diners, Visa

A well-maintained modern motel on the A40. A pleasant foyer with green bamboo furniture doubles as a lounge area and there's a smart, cosy bar. Bedrooms are built around a garden with an ornamental pool and most ground floor rooms have doors opening on to a small patio. All are newly decorated and are equipped with trouser presses and hairdryers. *Amenities* garden, in-house movies, laundry service, children's playground. &

Rooms 106	*Direct dial* Yes	*Confirm by* 6	*Parking* Ample
Ensuite bath/shower 106	*Room TV* Yes	*Last dinner* 11	*Room service* Limited

HINTLESHAM — Hintlesham Hall 82% £C/D

HR Map 6 C3 Suffolk
Nr Ipswich IP8 3NS
Hintlesham (047 387) 268
Telex 98340

Rooms 17
Ensuite bath/shower 17
Direct dial Yes
Room TV Yes
Confirm by arrang.
Last dinner 9.30
Parking Ample
Room service All day

Credit Access, Amex, Diners, Visa

From the rear this is a mellow red-brick Elizabethan mansion, but the house was significantly altered in the 18th century and it's a handsome Georgian facade that greets visitors. The public rooms offer grace and luxury, with many antiques, paintings and fine architectural features; the same is true of most of the bedrooms, whose extras run from iced water to books, magazines, hairdryers and teletext TVs. Six

rooms are smaller, with a more contemporary look. Well-equipped bathrooms. Friendly, obliging staff are another plus, and an excellent breakfast starts the day. No dogs.
Amenities garden, tennis, croquet, riding, games room, snooker, secretarial services, fax, valeting, laundry service.

Restaurant ♕

Set L £13.95
Set D £23
About £58 *for two*
Seats 54
Parties 60

Two elegant panelled dining rooms are the inviting setting for Robert Mabey's sophisticated cooking. The seasonal carte and daily menu gastronomique provide a splendid choice, from chicken mousseline with a mustard and cream sauce to sautéed scallops with wild rice and ginger butter, herby home-bred lamb and hot raspberry soufflé. The wine list here was always good, now it's great: exquisite clarets (Trotanoy '62, Latour '55), peerless white burgundies (Puligny Les Pucelles '83 from Leflaive) and a delicious Sauvignon Blanc '86 (Woodstock) from Australia. No smoking. No children under ten in the evening. ⌒ Outstanding ⚑ Well-chosen ⌾

Lunch 12.15–1.45 *Dinner* 7–9.30
Closed L Sat

HOCKLEY HEATH — Nuthurst Grange 74% £B/C

HR Map 10 C4 Warwickshire
Nuthurst Grange Lane
B94 5NL
Lapworth (056 43) 3972
Telex 333485

Rooms 8
Ensuite bath/shower 8
Direct dial Yes
Room TV Yes
Confirm by arrang.
Last dinner 9.30
Parking Ample
Room service All day

Credit Access, Amex, Diners, Visa
Closed 1 wk Xmas

A charming welcome by Darryl Randolph and her young staff aptly conveys the relaxing, informal atmosphere of this inviting Edwardian country house set in landscaped gardens and woodland just off the A34. There are plenty of deep sofas and armchairs in the elegant entrance and comfortable lounge, where drinks are served in the absence of a bar. Spacious bedrooms are individually decorated in excel-

lent taste, and the host of thoughtful extras ranges from mineral water and fresh fruit to books and playing cards. Carpeted bathrooms are equally well equipped, with bidets, telephones, and luxury toiletries. No dogs. *Amenities* garden, croquet, secretarial services, laundry service, helipad.

see over

Nuthurst Grange Restaurant ★　　　♛ ♧

Lunch 12.30–2
Dinner 7–9.30
Set L £13.90
Set D £19.50 & £24.50
About £64 *for two*
Seats 45
Parties 20

Closed L Sat & D Sun, Bank Hol
Mons & 1 wk Xmas

Intimate elegance is the keynote of this delightful dining room. David Randolph is a most talented chef, and his fixed-price menus offer some memorable dishes, from a marvellous mousseline of scallops and lobster with a subtle dill sauce to the tenderest roast lamb. Vegetables are impeccable, and sweets include a superb passion fruit soufflé. The wine list, with some very good burgundies, is thoughtfully laid out with helpful, unsnobbish comments. *Specialities* raw wild salmon, John Dory and mackerel marinated in coriander and lime; mousseline of scallops and lobster; fillet of lamb with a lemon balm quenelle and Madeira wine sauce; orange and walnut pudding with toffee sauce. ➪ Outstanding 🍷 Well-chosen ℮ ও

We welcome bona fide complaints and recommendations
on the tear-out pages at the back of the book for readers' comment.
They are followed up by our professional team.

HOLBETON　　　Alston Hall Hotel　73%　　　£D/E

H **Map 3 D3** Devon
Battisborough Cross,
Nr Plymouth PL8 1HN
Holbeton (075 530) 259

Rooms 9
Ensuite bath/shower 9
Direct dial Yes
Room TV Yes
Confirm by arrang.
Last dinner 9.30
Parking Ample
Room service All day

Credit Access, Amex, Diners, Visa

A beautifully maintained Edwardian country house situated in an area of outstanding natural beauty between Dartmoor and the sea. The oak-panelled entrance hall is most impressive, with its minstrels' gallery, stained glass and mullioned windows, rich red carpet, deep leather armchairs and sofas, and open log fire. The bar, too, is rich in oak, and there's an elegant, antique-furnished drawing room overlooking the pool. Individually decorated bedrooms feature traditional furnishings and vary greatly in size but all provide extras ranging from hairdryers and radios to fresh fruit and bath robes. Good carpeted bathrooms and impeccable housekeeping. No dogs.
Amenities garden, outdoor swimming pool, tennis, laundry service.

HOLLINGBOURNE　　Great Danes Hotel　70%　　　£C/D

H **Map 7 C5** Kent
Ashford Road ME17 1RE
Maidstone (0622) 30022
Telex 96198

Rooms 126
Ensuite bath/shower 126
Direct dial Yes
Room TV Yes
Confirm by arrang.
Last dinner 11
Parking Ample
Room service 24 hours

Credit Access, Amex, Diners, Visa

A solid, 18th-century country house which has been much extended but still retains some character. The foyer boasts a splendid marble floor and attractive furniture in pastel colours while in the elegant lounge there are velour chairs and sofas, light-wood tables, plenty of table lamps and a view into a small inner garden. The bedrooms have fitted furniture and discreetly patterned wallpaper; all have tea/coffee makers and radios. *Amenities* garden, indoor swimming pool, sauna, solarium, whirlpool bath, hairdressing, tennis, pitch & putt, croquet, coarse fishing, games room, snooker, pool table, in-house movies, laundry service, coffee shop (10am–11pm), kiosk, children's playground, helipad. ও

HOPE Poachers Arms Hotel £E

Map 10 C2 Derbyshire
Castleton Road S30 2RD
Hope Valley (0433) 20380

Credit Access, Amex, Diners, Visa

A friendly inn offering simple, pleasant accommodation. There's no residents' lounge, but the bar areas are spacious, with dark green plush seating and copper-topped tables. Bedrooms vary in size and style, some having white woodchip walls and others patterned wallpaper; the furniture ranges from utilitarian white laminate to antique pieces. Bathrooms are smart and modern, with good towelling; some boast bidets and separate showers. *Amenities* laundry service.

Rooms 7	*Direct dial* Yes	*Confirm by* arrang.	*Parking* Ample
Ensuite bath/shower 7	*Room TV* Yes	*Last dinner* 9.30	*Room service* All day

HOPE COVE Cottage Hotel 56% £C/D

Map 3 D3 Devon
Nr Kingsbridge TQ7 3HJ
Kingsbridge (0548) 561555

Closed 2–31 Jan

The Irelands are welcoming hosts at their cosy hotel set in attractive grounds looking out to sea. The roomy main lounge is warmed by cheerful fires, and guests can enjoy a drink in a snug little cabin built from timbers salvaged from local shipwrecks. Bedrooms are generally fairly modest, but seven rooms designated de luxe are more stylish and better equipped. Inclusive terms only.
Amenities garden, games room, laundry room.

Rooms 36	*Direct dial* Yes	*Confirm by* arrang.	*Parking* Ample
Ensuite bath/shower 19	*Room TV* Some	*Last dinner* 8.30	*Room service* Limited

HOPE COVE Lantern Lodge Hotel 59% £E

Map 3 D3 Devon
Nr Kingsbridge TQ7 3HE
Kingsbridge (0548) 561280

Credit Amex, Visa

A clifftop setting overlooking the cove makes the Lantern Lodge a popular holiday spot. Friendly staff create a warm and welcoming feel, and guests can browse through books and magazines in the cosy lounge or enjoy a tipple in the little bar. Well-kept bedrooms have a variety of furnishings, including a few four-posters; six rooms enjoy sea views. No children under eight. No dogs.
Amenities garden, indoor swimming pool, sauna, solarium, putting.

Rooms 14	*Room phone* No	*Confirm by* arrang.	*Parking* Ample
Ensuite bath/shower 14	*Room TV* Yes	*Last dinner* 8.30	*Room service* Limited

**Our inspectors are our full-time employees;
they are professionally trained by us.**

HORNDON ON THE HILL Hill House *NEW ENTRY*

RR **Map 7 B4** Essex
High Road
Stanford-le-Hope (0375) 642463

About £47 for two
Seats 24
Parties 24
Parking Ample

Credit Access, Visa

BEDROOMS 10 £F
With bath/shower 10

Just 24 covers at this pretty little restaurant, where Marcus Springett presents an interesting modern menu. His cooking is very capable, if sometimes rather elaborate, and among typical dishes are guinea fowl pâté with wild mushrooms and truffles; smoked fillet of lamb with scallops and horseradish and tarragon sauce; and chocolate terrine with coffee sauce. Good British cheeses. ⊖ &

Lunch 12–2 *Dinner* 7.30–10
Closed L Sat, all Sun & Mon, Bank Hols & 10 days Xmas

Some bedrooms boast splendid oak beams and all have teletext TVs, trouser presses and tea-makers. Two bathrooms offer the luxury of whirlpool baths. No dogs.

HORSHAM Cisswood House Hotel 65% £D

HR **Map 5 E3** West Sussex
Sandy Gate Lane,
Lower Beeding RH13 6NF
Lower Beeding (040 376) 216

Credit Access, Amex, Diners, Visa
Closed 2 wks Xmas

A 1920s-built house that takes its name from former owners, Sir Woodman Burbidge and his wife Cissily. Now a friendly and well-run hotel, it offers comfortable accommodation and the use of a simple bar-lounge. Attractively furnished bedrooms (four with four-posters) provide mini-bars, tea-makers and radio-alarms. Good carpeted bathrooms (two with whirlpool baths). No children under 12. No dogs.
Amenities garden, sauna, croquet, fax, laundry service.

Rooms 18	*Direct dial* Yes	*Confirm by* arrang.	*Parking* Ample
Ensuite bath/shower 18	*Room TV* Yes	*Last dinner* 9.30	*Room service* All day

see over

Cisswood House Restaurant

Set Sun L £12.50
Set Sun D £15.75
About £50 for two
Seats 80
Parties 80

Austrian-born owner-chef Othmar Illes scours the London markets for fresh produce to use in his straightforward and unpretentious cooking. Enjoyable starters might include Parma ham and melon with onion confit, or calf's sweetbreads and kidneys in a light pastry with red wine sauce. Equally well-prepared main dishes range from simple sauced grills to daily specials like pan-fried scallops with bacon. Sweets from the trolley. ☺

Lunch 12–2.30   *Dinner* 7–9.30, Sat till 10, Sun till 9
Closed 2 wks Xmas

If we recommend **meals** in a Hotel or Inn,
a separate entry is made for its restaurant.

HORTON   French Partridge   ⁊

R Map 5 D1 Northamptonshire
  Nr Northampton
Northampton (0604) 870033

Set D £16.50, Sat £17
About £45 for two
Seats 40
Parties 24
Parking Ample

Dinner is a leisurely and most agreeable four-course affair at this comfortable country restaurant. Dishes selected from a wide repertoire are mostly simple, but accurately cooked and attractively presented. You might start with the delicious gravlax before enjoying fillet of lemon sole with a well-made herb and cream sauce, then tender stuffed lamb, and wonderfully rich amaretti schokoladentorte to finish. Some excellent burgundies. 🍷 Well-chosen ☺ &

Dinner only 7.30–9
Closed Sun & Mon, 2 wks Easter & Xmas & 3 wks July/Aug

HORTON-CUM-STUDLEY   Studley Priory Hotel   65%   £D/E

H Map 5 D2 Oxfordshire
  OX9 1AZ
Stanton St John (086 735) 203
Telex 23152

Credit Access, Amex, Diners, Visa
Closed 2–9 Jan

Set in 13 acres and overlooking beautiful countryside, the exterior of this mellowed building has changed little since the days of Queen Elizabeth I. Inside, there is a comfortable, elegant drawing room with fine period furniture and a smaller lounge. Six bedrooms in the main house are traditional, those in the Georgian wing are more modern. No dogs. *Amenities* garden, tennis, croquet, clay-pigeon shooting, secretarial services, laundry service.

Rooms 19	*Direct dial* Yes	*Confirm by* arrang.	*Parking* Ample
Ensuite bath/shower 19	*Room TV* Yes	*Last dinner* 9.15	*Room service* Limited

---

HOUGHTON BRIDGE   'Quins

R Map 5 E4 West Sussex
  Nr Amberley
Bury (0798) 831790

Set L from £7.50, Sun £11.50
About £41 for two
Seats 34
Parties 34
Parking Ample
Credit Access, Amex, Diners, Visa

In the summer you can eat outside on the terrace of this attractive restaurant on the banks of the Arun. Co-owner Marianne Walker is Swiss and specialities from her homeland, such as rösti and butterleberli, often feature in the menus. Starter might be a light salmon terrine with perhaps suprême of duckling in an orange and ginger sauce to follow. Finish with a fresh meringue with yoghurt and caramelised sugar. ☺

Lunch 12.15–2.30   *Dinner* 7.30–9.30   **Closed** D Sun, all Mon & Tues, Bank Hols excl. Good Fri & Boxing Day, 1 wk Apr & 2 wks Oct

---

HOVE

See under BRIGHTON

HUDDERSFIELD   George Hotel   60%   £D

H Map 10 C1 West Yorkshire
  St George's Square HD1 1JA
Huddersfield (0484) 515444

Credit Access, Amex, Diners, Visa

A handsome Victorian building on the main square by the railway station. There's a period feel to the pillared foyer, adjoining which is a quiet cocktail bar. In the livelier main bar a plaque commemorates the inaugural meeting of the Rugby League, which took place here in 1895. Bedrooms vary in style and furnishings, the best being refurbished with contemporary fabrics and fittings. Courteous staff. *Amenities* secretarial services, laundry service.

Rooms 59	*Direct dial* Yes	*Confirm by* 6	*Parking* Limited
Ensuite bath/shower 40	*Room TV* Yes	*Last dinner* 10	*Room service* 24 hours

HUDDERSFIELD   Pennine Hilton National   62%   £C

H Map 10 C1 West Yorkshire
Ainley Top HD3 3RH
Huddersfield (0422) 75431
Telex 517346

Credit Access, Amex, Diners, Visa
Closed 27–31 Dec

Next to junction 24 of the M62, the Pennine Hilton National (formerly the Ladbroke) is a modern low-rise hotel convenient for business people and motorists. Day rooms are in open-plan style, and decent-sized bedrooms include some superior Gold Star rooms. 60 rooms were due to be upgraded by the time we published. There are conference facilities for up to 400. *Amenities* garden, in-house movies, secretarial services, fax, laundry service.

Rooms 119	*Direct dial* Yes	*Confirm by* 6	*Parking* Ample
Ensuite bath/shower 119	*Room TV* Yes	*Last dinner* 10 (Sun 9)	*Room service* Limited

We publish annually,
so make sure you use the current edition.
It's worth it!

HULL   Ceruttis   ⑤

R Map 11 E1 Humberside
10 Nelson Street
Hull (0482) 28501

Seafood
About £50 for two
Seats 36
Parties 25
Parking Ample
Credit Access, Visa

Seafood comes in rich variety at this friendly family-run restaurant, which stands on the harbour front overlooking the Humber. Scampi and scallops are each available three ways as starter or main course, and other choices run from fish cakes and mussels provençale to sole, halibut and excellent poached brill with a sauce of creamed spinach. Steaks for the carnivorous.
🍷 Well-chosen ⓔ

Lunch 12–2   *Dinner* 7–9.30
Closed L Sat, all Sun, Bank Hols & 10 days Xmas

HULL   Crest Hotel (Humber Bridge)   62%   £C/D

H Map 11 E1 Humberside
Ferriby High Road HU14 3LG
Hull (0482) 645212
Telex 592558

Credit Access, Amex, Diners, Visa

A comfortable, modern hotel overlooking the stunning Humber suspension bridge. Public areas are stylishly decorated in pastel shades with plenty of bedrooms have pine fitted units, trouser presses and tiled bathrooms; Lady Crest rooms have many extras, including good toiletries. *Amenities* garden, pool table, in-house movies, secretarial services, fax, laundry service, coffee shop (9am–10pm), 24-hour lounge service, children's play area (weekends).

Rooms 102	*Direct dial* Yes	*Confirm by* 6	*Parking* Ample
Ensuite bath/shower 102	*Room TV* Yes	*Last dinner* 10	*Room service* Limited

HULL   Marina Post House Hotel   69%   *NEW ENTRY*   £C/D

HR Map 11 E1 Humberside
Castle Street HU1 2BX
Hull (0482) 225221
Telex 592777

Credit Access, Amex, Diners, Visa

A brand new hotel in the exciting redevelopment of Hull's old docks. The link with the sea is strongest in the bar-lounge with its paintings and sailors' knots. Comfortable bedrooms, some with balconies, boast all the usual up-to-the-minute accessories, and bathrooms are also very well equipped. Decent breakfast, but room service was a trifle tardy on our visit. *Amenities* terrace, indoor swimming pool, sauna, solarium, gymnasium, secretarial services, laundry service. ♿

Rooms 99	*Direct dial* Yes	*Confirm by* 7	*Parking* Ample
Ensuite bath/shower 99	*Room TV* Yes	*Last dinner* 10.30	*Room service* 24 hours

Club House Restaurant   *NEW ENTRY*   ♔

Set L from £8.95
Set D £11.95
About £50 for two
Seats 120
Parties 100

Smartly set tables and marina views in this agreeable restaurant, where John Richardson heads a very competent kitchen brigade. A la carte and set menus provide a splendid choice, with some dishes from the repertoire of international classics and others a little different, like salmon and vegetable terrine with yoghurt and chives, or collops of beef with a lobster and herb butter. The cheeseboard and fruit bowl are popular finales. Friendly, proficient waitress service. ⓔ ♿

Lunch 12.30–2.30   *Dinner* 7–10.30

HULL   Waterfront Hotel   60%   £E

H **Map 11 E1** Humberside
Dagger Lane, Old Town
HU1 2LS
Hull (0482) 227222

Credit Access, Visa
Closed 25 & 26 Dec

Clever conversion has transformed a Victorian warehouse into a hotel
with a character all of its own. In the foyer-lounge, assorted
memorabilia and deep leather seating add to the atmosphere given by
the bare brick walls and flagstoned floor; a selection of bars includes
a cellar bar with brick arched ceiling. Bedrooms have pine fitted units,
shagpile carpets and tea/coffee-makers.
Amenities solarium, secretarial services, laundry service.

Rooms 32	*Direct dial* Yes	*Confirm by* 6	*Parking* Limited
Ensuite bath/shower 25	*Room TV* Yes	*Last dinner* 10	*Room service* 24 hours

HUNGERFORD   Bear at Hungerford   66%   £D/E

HR **Map 4 C2** Berkshire
Charnham Street RG17 0EL
Hungerford (0488) 82512

Credit Access, Amex, Diners, Visa

Steeped in history, including ownership by Henry VIII, the Bear is an
inn of great renown. Exposed beams are everywhere, but the period
feel is combined with good modern facilities. Day rooms are inviting,
and the bedrooms have solid, comfortable furnishings, well-equipped,
up-to-date bathrooms and lots of extras. There's a four-poster room
and several suites.
Amenities terrace, laundry service, 24-hour lounge service. &

Rooms 32	*Direct dial* Yes	*Confirm by* 6	*Parking* Ample
Ensuite bath/shower 32	*Room TV* Yes	*Last dinner* 9.30	*Room service* All day

Restaurant   ♔

Set L £12.95
Set D £14.95
About £55 *for two*
Seats 55
Parties 60

Mellow beams and rich red decor anticipate a tempting choice of
seasonal fare. Dishes may include leek and potato soup, lamb sweetbreads with tomato sauce, herb-stuffed trout, jugged hare and vegetarian
dishes. Outstanding English farmhouse cheeses are matched in the cellar
by an impeccable catholic selection of the world's best wines: Mercurey
(Michel Juillot) '84, Bandol Mas de la Rouvière '82, Alpine Chardonnay
(Oregon) '86. ⊃ Outstanding ♀ Well-chosen ☕ &

Lunch 12.30–2   *Dinner* 7.30–9.30, Fri & Sat till 10
Closed 24, 25 & 26 Dec

HUNSTRETE   Hunstrete House   83%   £B

HR **Map 4 B3** Avon
Chelwood, Bristol BS18 4NS
Compton Dando (076 18) 578
Telex 449540

Rooms 24
Ensuite bath/shower 24
Direct dial Yes
Room TV Yes
Confirm by 6
Last dinner 9.15
Parking Ample
Room service All day

Credit Access, Amex, Diners, Visa

Old walled gardens, an orchard
and deer park make a lovely
setting for this handsome Georgian stone manor house. Owners
Thea and John Dupays con-
verted the place into a hotel some
ten years ago, but have cleverly
retained the feel of an English
country house by filling the
rooms with fine antiques, paintings and objets d'art. Elegant
drapes and open fires contribute
to the gracious ambience of the

hall, library and drawing room, while bedrooms in both the main
house and the Italianate courtyard are equally luxurious, with
sumptuous bathrooms to match. Delicious breakfasts. No children
under nine. No dogs. *Amenities* garden, outdoor swimming pool,
tennis, croquet, laundry service. &

Restaurant   ♔

Set L £17.25, Sun £23
Set D £28.75
About £75 *for two*
Seats 70
Parties 50

Robert Elsmore is an enthusiastic and imaginative young chef who
sets great store by the fresh vegetables, herbs and fruit he obtains
from the kitchen gardens. Red mullet mousse might be served with a
herb and shallot butter sauce, rack of lamb with a mustard and
tarragon sauce and baby vegetables. Delicious desserts like plum
fritters. Excellent wine list with fabulous old clarets and burgundies.
No smoking. ⊃ Outstanding ♀ Well-chosen

Lunch 12.30–2
Dinner 7.30–9.15

HUNTINGDON   Brampton Hotel   58%   £D

H **Map 6 A2** Cambridgeshire
Brampton PE18 8NH
Huntingdon (0480) 810434

Credit Access, Amex, Diners, Visa

Motorway travellers welcome the convenience of this handily placed, friendly hotel situated on the A1/A604 crossroads between Huntingdon and St Neots. Public areas offer old-fashioned, rustic comfort that includes a beamed bar. Identically furnished bedrooms, all with neat bathrooms, are well kept and equipped with tea-makers and hairdryers.
Amenities patio, laundry service.

Rooms 17	*Room phone* Yes	*Confirm by* 6	*Parking* Ample
Ensuite bath/shower 17	*Room TV* Yes	*Last dinner* 9.45	*Room service* 24 hours

**We welcome bona fide complaints and recommendations
on the tear-out pages at the back of the book for readers' comment.
They are followed up by our professional team.**

HUNTINGDON   George Hotel   59%   £C/D

H **Map 6 A2** Cambridgeshire
George Street PE18 6AB
Huntingdon (0480) 432444

Credit Access, Amex, Diners, Visa

Kings and highwaymen are among the past patrons of this reliable town-centre Stuart inn with a galleried inner courtyard where Shakespeare plays are staged in summer. An elegant staircase leads from the comfortable open-plan public rooms to pleasantly decorated bedrooms with fitted units, remote-control TVs and neat bathrooms. Best rooms are on the top floor.
Amenities patio, laundry service.

Rooms 24	*Direct dial* Yes	*Confirm by* 6	*Parking* Ample
Ensuite bath/shower 24	*Room TV* Yes	*Last dinner* 9.30	*Room service* All day

HUNTINGDON   Old Bridge Hotel   70%   £C/D

HR **Map 6 A2** Cambridgeshire
1 High Street PE18 6TQ
Huntingdon (0480) 52681
Telex 32706

Rooms 27
Ensuite bath/shower 27
Direct dial Yes
Room TV Yes
Confirm by 6
Last dinner 10.30
Parking Ample
Room service 24 hours

Credit Access, Amex, Diners, Visa

This handsome Georgian house with gardens running down to the river Ouse skilfully preserves period charm while keeping thoroughly up to date. An impressively equipped business centre merges into the fabric of the original building, while the Terrace Lounge with its slender white columns, light cane furniture and plentiful greenery is a happy blend of old and new.

Comfort harmonises with period detail in the original lounge, and the bar is reassuringly traditional. Bedrooms are all stylishly decorated but most attractive of all are six luxurious rooms overlooking the river. Bathrooms throughout have deep-pile carpets, Italian tiling and luxury toiletries. *Amenities* garden, coarse fishing, secretarial services, fax, laundry service.

Restaurant   ♛

Set L Sun £13.25
Seats 60

Good traditional cooking is this restaurant's strength and it's best to go for deliciously simple things like pan-fried calf's sweetbreads and roast sirloin of beef. Other stalwarts might include roast pheasant or – a touch more adventurous – rack of lamb with lavender. The cellar goes from strength to strength: a catholic range, impeccably chosen, from the magnificent Ch. Ausone '76 to the remarkable New Zealand Sauvignon '86 (Collard Bros). ⌷ Outstanding ♀ Well-chosen ℮

Lunch 12.30–2.30   *Dinner* 7.30–10.30
About £47 for two

HUNTSHAM | Huntsham Court   70% | £D

HR **Map 3 E2** Devon
Huntsham EX16 7NA
Clayhanger (039 86) 210

Rooms 15
Ensuite bath/shower 15
Room phone No
Room TV No
Confirm by arrang.
Last dinner by arrang.
Parking Ample
Room service Limited

Credit Visa
Closed mid Jan–mid Feb

A large rambling Victorian Gothic mansion with an unusual off-beat appeal. Features include marble columns and a huge stone fireplace in the main hall, while furniture is a bewildering hot-potch of varying periods and quality. Guests are encouraged to dip into the huge record collection provided – or just to help themselves to drinks in the bar. Good-sized bedrooms lack up-to-date amenities but offer

reliable pre-war radios and spacious bathrooms with large old-fashioned tubs. Informality is the keynote here, with service and housekeeping both somewhat erratic. No dogs. **Amenities** garden, sauna, solarium, keep-fit equipment, tennis, croquet, shooting, sea & coarse fishing, bicycles, billiards, snooker, laundry service.

Restaurant   ♛

English cooking

Set D £17.50
About £45 *for two*
Seats 24
Parties 45

The setting is an elegantly proportioned dining room with a single long candlelit table, the atmosphere that of a convivial country house party. Guests first select their wine from the cellar, then settle down to a five-course no-choice dinner of good unpretentious fare like local smoked trout with horseradish, flavoursome watercress soup, tasty roast duck, French and English cheeses, and deliciously rich crème brûlée with cherries. Booking essential. ♟ Well-chosen ℰ

Lunch by arrang. only   *Dinner* 8–9.30
Closed mid Jan–mid Feb

 indicates a **well-chosen** house wine

HURLEY | Ye Olde Bell Hotel   64% | £D

H **Map 5 D2** Berkshire
High Street,
Nr Maidenhead SL6 5LX
Littlewick Green (062 882) 5881
Telex 847035

Credit Access, Amex, Diners, Visa

Ye Olde Bell is among the most venerable of English inns, dating from 1135, when it was built as a guest house for a Benedictine monastery. Beyond the Norman porch there's a lot of character, notably in the mellow beamed bar where brasses gleam and comfortable old chairs beckon. Bedrooms are in period or more modern style and seven have recently been refurbished to Club standard.
Amenities garden, secretarial services, fax, laundry service.

| *Rooms* 25 | *Direct dial* Yes | *Confirm* by arrang. | *Parking* Ample |
| *Ensuite bath/shower* 25 | *Room TV* Yes | *Last dinner* 10 | *Room service* 24 hours |

HURSTBOURNE TARRANT | Esseborne Manor   72% | £C/D

HR **Map 4 C3** Hampshire
Nr Andover SP11 0ER
Hurstbourne Tarrant
(026 476) 444

Rooms 12
Ensuite bath/shower 12
Direct dial Yes
Room TV Yes
Confirm by arrang.
Last dinner 9.30
Parking Ample
Room service All day

Credit Access, Amex, Diners, Visa
Closed 2 wks Xmas

Friendly personal service and stylish decor make a lasting impression at this delightful Victorian country house hotel surrounded by peaceful farmland. A few nice antiques lend character to the entrance hall and appealing lounge, while a log fire brings cheer to the cosy bar. Spacious individually furnished bedrooms in various tasteful styles have thoughtful extras such as books and magazines as well as portable

radios and remote-control TVs. Bathrooms too are of a good size and well equipped right down to bath toys. Attentive room service extends to shoe cleaning. No children under ten. No dogs.
Amenities garden, tennis, croquet, golf practice net, laundry service.
&

Restaurant

About £46 for two
Seats 24

An elegant and tasteful restaurant where Philip Harris is an efficient master of ceremonies while Peter Birnie and Belinda Watson maintain cooking standards in the kitchen. Imaginative, enjoyable dishes range from rabbit and apricot pie to chicken breast subtly flavoured with scampi, coconut, lemon and coriander. Impeccable vegetables, good English cheeses, and marvellous sweets. Good value, skilfully chosen wines, with excellent half-bottles. 🍷 Well-chosen ⊖ ♿

Lunch 12.30–2   *Dinner* 7.30–9.30
Closed L Sat, all Sun & 2 wks Xmas

HYTHE | Fredericks Hotel   69% | £C/D

HR **Map 7 C6** Kent
Seabrook Road CT21 5QY
Hythe (0303) 67279

Credit Access, Amex, Diners, Visa

A warm welcome awaits at this well-run Edwardian hotel. Spacious, well-appointed bedrooms feature extras like mini-bars, chocolates and exotic fresh fruits. Some rooms enjoy sea views and those facing the road are double-glazed. Compact, fully tiled bathrooms are equally luxurious. Public areas include a relaxing cocktail bar and well-stocked reading room. *Amenities* garden, in-house movies, laundry service, coffee shop (11am–11pm).

| Rooms 9 | Direct dial Yes | Confirm by arrang. | Parking Ample |
| Ensuite bath/shower 9 | Room TV Yes | Last dinner 11 | Room service 24 hours |

Restaurant

Set L Sun £10.75
About £50 for two
Seats 30
Parties 30

Elegant table settings and the soothing sounds of a grand piano combine to create a sophisticated setting for Freddie Jones' accomplished cooking. Seasonally changing, classically inspired menus feature ambitious combinations like marinated scallops layered with smoked salmon, topped by caviar and a cream chive sauce; and beef, pork and veal fillet sandwiched with chicken mousse in puff pastry. Some dishes are perhaps a little too complex, but the excellent desserts are beyond reproach.

Lunch 12.30–2.30   *Dinner* 6.30–11   **Closed** D Sun & all Mon

---

HYTHE | Hythe Imperial Hotel   73% | £C

H **Map 7 C6** Kent
Princess Parade CT21 6AE
Hythe (0303) 67441
Telex 965082

Rooms 83
Ensuite bath/shower 83
Direct dial Yes
Room TV Yes
Confirm by 6
Last dinner 9
Parking Ample
Room service 24 hours

Credit Access, Amex, Diners, Visa

Standing in its own grounds, this impressive Victorian seafront hotel combines pleasant, well-appointed public rooms (including an attractive lounge for non-smokers and two recently refurbished bars) with an extensive leisure centre and refreshment area. Good-sized bedrooms with either garden or sea views are individually decorated. All have ensuite carpeted bathrooms and extras include tea-makers, radios, hairdryers and trouser presses. *Amenities* garden, indoor swimming pool, sauna, solarium, gymnasium, beauty salon, hairdressing, tennis, squash, 9-hole golf course, putting, bowling green, croquet, games room, snooker, pool table, secretarial services, fax, laundry service.

HYTHE | Stade Court Hotel   62% | £D/E

H **Map 7 C6** Kent
West Parade CT21 6DT
Hythe (0303) 68263

Credit Access, Amex, Diners, Visa

Solid, comfortable accommodation is a great strength at this 1930s seafront hotel. Neatly fitted bedrooms (best at the front with fine sea views) all have tea-makers and functional modern bathrooms. Public areas include a foyer-lounge and bar decorated in autumnal shades. Guests may use the leisure facilities of nearby sister hotel Hythe Imperial.
Amenities garden, laundry service, 24-hour lounge service.

| Rooms 39 | Direct dial Yes | Confirm by arrang. | Parking Ample |
| Ensuite bath/shower 39 | Room TV Yes | Last dinner 9 | Room service Limited |

IDE   Old Mill   ♀

R Map 3 D2 Devon
20 High Street
Exeter (0392) 59480

Set L £7.35
Set D £10.95
About £40 for two
Seats 36 *Parties* 50
Parking Ample
Credit Access, Amex, Diners, Visa

John Cruwys combines careful cooking with a flair for presentation in his appealing little restaurant. A daily list of fish specials supplements an interesting menu typified by such dishes as crispy crab beignets with a tangy lemon mayonnaise, poussin in dark ale, steak stuffed with mushroom pâté and marinated noisettes of lamb with redcurrants and capers. Mousses and ice creams among the sweets. Pleasant, cheerful service. ☺

Lunch 12–1.30   *Dinner* 7–9.30
Closed Sun & 25 & 26 Dec

We publish annually,
so make sure you use the current edition.
It's worth it!

ILKLEY   Box Tree Restaurant   ★   ♕

R Map 10 C1 West Yorkshire
Church Street
Ilkley (0943) 608484

French cooking

Dinner 7.30–9.45, Sun only
12.30–3
Set L Sun only £12.95
Set D £16.95
About £70 for two
Seats 45
Parties 25
Parking Ample

Credit Access, Amex, Diners, Visa
Closed all Mon, L Tues–Sat, D Sun, 25 & 26 Dec & 1 Jan

Now in its twenty-sixth year, the Box Tree retains all its highly individual charm and appeal, and the pleasures of the table are enhanced by notably friendly and smooth-running service. Chef and co-director Edward Denny's menus make fine use of top-quality seasonal produce, and many of his dishes are distinguished by splendid sauces. There are some real stars in a well-balanced cellar: Mas de Daumas Gassac 1985, Opus 1 1982, Taylors 1963. *Specialities* zéphyr de fruits de mer chaud, filets de lièvre aux petits oignons et trompettes de mort, émincé de boeuf et sa garniture de courgette, assiette de grand dessert chocolatier. ⊃ Outstanding
🍷 Well-chosen ☺

ILKLEY   Craiglands Hotel   58%   £D

H Map 10 C1 West Yorkshire
Cowpasture Road LS29 8RQ
Ilkley (0943) 607676

Credit Access, Amex, Diners, Visa

A Victorian building with a modern extension, the ivy-clad Craiglands Hotel stands on the edge of Ilkley Moor. The restaurant has been smartly refurbished, and the lobby-lounge would benefit from similar treatment. There's a simple but cosy cocktail bar. Best bedrooms have a comfortable contemporary feel, but others look rather dated.
Amenities garden, tennis, putting, croquet, games room, secretarial services, laundry service, 24-hour lounge service, children's play area.

Rooms 70	*Direct dial* Yes	*Confirm by* arrang.	*Parking* Ample
Ensuite bath/shower 50	*Room TV* Yes	*Last dinner* 9.30	*Room service* All day

INGATESTONE   Heybridge Moat House Hotel   68%   £D

H Map 7 B4 Essex
Roman Road CM4 9AB
Ingatestone (0277) 355355
Telex 995186

Credit Access, Amex, Diners, Visa

Ancient and modern coexist happily in this well-run hotel off the A12 north of Chelmsford. The old part dates from 1494 and houses an oak-panelled cocktail bar and restaurant. The reception area is in the newer section, facing a modest residents' bar-lounge with sofas and winged armchairs. Spacious bedrooms have darkwood units, trouser presses and good bathrooms. No dogs.
Amenities garden, secretarial services, laundry service. ♿

Rooms 22	*Direct dial* Yes	*Confirm by* arrang.	*Parking* Ample
Ensuite bath/shower 22	*Room TV* Yes	*Last dinner* 10.30, Sat 11	*Room service* 24 hours

IPSWICH — Belstead Brook Hotel 68% £C/D

H Map 6 C3 Suffolk
Belstead Road IP2 9HB
Ipswich (0473) 684241
Telex 987674

Credit Access, Amex, Diners, Visa

Ask directions to this country hotel set in peaceful, attractive grounds on the outskirts of the city. Public rooms and a honeymoon suite are in a creeper-clad Jacobean building, while the other bedrooms are in rear extensions and a garden block. The last are perhaps the best, having sitting areas, mostly antique furniture, little patios and smart bathrooms with corner whirlpool baths. Some rooms are rather dated, but a refurbishment programme is improving them. Tea-makers, hairdryers, trouser presses and remote-control TVs in all rooms. No dogs.
Amenities garden, secretarial services, laundry service.

Rooms 33	*Direct dial* Yes	*Confirm by* arrang.	*Parking* Ample
Ensuite bath/shower 33	*Room TV* Yes	*Last dinner* 9.30	*Room service* 24 hours

IPSWICH — Marlborough Hotel 64% £C/D

H Map 6 C3 Suffolk
Henley Road IP1 3SP
Ipswich (0473) 57677

Credit Access, Amex, Diners, Visa

Smartly turned-out staff provide attentive service at this converted Victorian house north of the town centre. Bedrooms vary in size and style, but all have good accessories and some personal touches. The foyer-lounge has just been refurbished, and there's an attractive bar. The Marlborough is in the same ownership as the Angel at Bury St. Edmunds.
Amenities garden, laundry service.

Rooms 22	*Direct dial* Yes	*Confirm by* arrang.	*Parking* Ample
Ensuite bath/shower 22	*Room TV* Yes	*Last dinner* 9.30	*Room service* 24 hours

IPSWICH — Post House Hotel 63% £C/D

H Map 6 C3 Suffolk
London Road IP2 0UA
Ipswich (0473) 690313
Telex 987150

Credit Access, Amex, Diners, Visa

The starkly modern exterior of this hotel on the A1214 belies the attractive interior. Public areas include a smart foyer and lounge with chic fabrics and a stylish cocktail bar. Most of the spacious bedrooms have pleasant darkwood units and pretty quilted bedspreads; executive rooms have trouser presses, hairdryers and potted plants.
Amenities garden, outdoor swimming pool, laundry service, coffee shop (10am–10pm), children's play area. &

Rooms 118	*Direct dial* Yes	*Confirm by* 6	*Parking* Ample
Ensuite bath/shower 118	*Room TV* Yes	*Last dinner* 10	*Room service* Limited

Our inspectors *never* book in the name of Egon Ronay's Guides. They disclose their identity only if they are considering an establishment for inclusion in the next edition of the Guide.

IXWORTH — Theobald's Restaurant *NEW ENTRY* ⌁

R Map 6 C2 Suffolk
68 High Street
Pakenham (0359) 31707

Set L £8.50, Sun £8.95
About £45 for two
Seats 36
Parties 25
Parking Ample

Credit Access, Visa

A roaring log fire and ancient exposed beams convey some of the character of Simon and Geraldine Theobald's comfortably converted shop. Simon has struck a winning formula with his emphasis on fresh seasonal produce and his confident, imaginative style of cooking. Classic flavour combinations – hare sauced with port and redcurrant, pork with apples and Calvados – are treated with great respect, while thoughtfully devised original creations might include a rich yet light twice-baked cheese soufflé with a crisp cheese top, delicately poached scallops sautéed with mushrooms and served in a rich champagne sauce, and fillet of lamb cooked with bacon and tarragon and sauced with Madeira. 🍷 Well-chosen ℮

Lunch 12.15–2, Sun 12.30–2.30   *Dinner* 7.15–10
Closed L Sat & Mon, D Sun & all Bank Hols

JERVAULX — Jervaulx Hall Hotel   71%   £D/E

H Map 15 B6
North Yorkshire
Nr Masham, Ripon HG4 4PH
Bedale (0677) 60235

Rooms 8
Ensuite bath/shower 8
Room phone No
Room TV No
Confirm by arrang.
Last dinner 8
Parking Ample
Room service Limited

Closed mid Nov–mid Mar

John and Shirley Sharp make guests very welcome at their delightful 19th-century house set in lovely gardens overlooking the picturesque ruins of Jervaulx Abbey. Peace and tranquillity reign throughout the house, from the characterful entrance hall with its fresh flowers and handsome rugs on a gleaming polished floor to the comfortable, antique-filled lounge where guests can unwind over a drink. Spacious

bedrooms are individually decorated in pastel shades set off by pretty floral fabrics, and stylishly furnished with period or modern pieces. Thoughtful extras range from fresh fruit and tissues to sewing kits; the neat carpeted bathrooms are also well equipped. Half-board terms only. *Amenities* garden, croquet, laundry service. &

JEVINGTON — Hungry Monk

R Map 7 B6 East Sussex
Nr Polegate
Polegate (032 12) 2178

Set L Sun only £13.80
About £40 for two
Seats 40
Parties 15
Parking Ample

The strains of a nickelodeon from one of the lounges might greet diners at this characterful and friendly restaurant. Blackboard menus provide good simple fare like parsnip and cumin soup, rack of English lamb with garlic and rosemary sauce, and deliciously gooey banoffi pie – also more imaginative choices like spiced beef pancake with Gruyère. Interesting wines, St Aubin Blanc '84, Raige Honme, Cabernet Sauvignon '84. Booking essential throughout. 🍷 Well-chosen

Lunch Sun 12–2.30, Mon–Sat by arrang.   *Dinner* 7–10.30
Closed 25 & 26 Dec

Our inspectors *never* book in the name of Egon Ronay's Guides.
They disclose their identity only if they are considering an establishment
for inclusion in the next edition of the Guide.

KENDAL — Woolpack Hotel   59%   £D/E

H Map 13 D5 Cumbria
Stricklandgate LA9 4ND
Kendal (0539) 23852

Credit Access, Amex, Diners, Visa

The Woolpack dates back 300 years, and its popular Crown Bar used to be Kendal's wool auction rooms. Bedrooms in the old building have a lot of period feel, especially those with low beams and drunken floors, while those in the linked annexe have a modern appeal, with lightwood fitted furniture, good lighting and plenty of desk/dressing table space. Refurbishment has much improved the accommodation. Besides the main bar there's a small but stylish cocktail bar, a coffee shop and a lounge area.
Amenities in-house movies, secretarial services, laundry service, coffee shop (10am–9pm, till 4 in winter). &

Rooms 57	*Direct dial* Yes	*Confirm by* 6	*Parking* Ample
Ensuite bath/shower 57	*Room TV* Yes	*Last dinner* 9.30	*Room service* 24 hours

KENILWORTH — Restaurant Bosquet

R Map 10 C4 Warwickshire
97a Warwick Road
Kenilworth (0926) 52463

French cooking
Set D £13
About £50 for two
Seats 26 *Parties* 30
Parking Ample
Credit Amex, Visa

Bernard and Jane Lignier have won many friends at their excellent restaurant on the main road. Bernard's cooking is French, and his menus pose pleasant dilemmas for diners with delights like red mullet terrine, Madeira-sauced loin of veal, partridge St Hubert and salmon with a cream and herb sauce. A fine, selective wine list includes such excellent lesser known items as Madiran Rouge '83, Coteaux du Layon '67. 🍷 Well-chosen

Dinner only 7–10
Closed Sun, Mon, Bank Hols, 10 days Xmas & 3 wks July/Aug

KENILWORTH | Clarendon House Hotel 61% | £E

H Map 10 C4 Warwickshire
Old High Street CV8 1LZ
Kenilworth (0926) 57668
Telex 311240

Credit Access, Visa

In the centre of the Kenilworth Conservation Area, the house dates back to 1430. Owner-manager Martyn Lea has made a good job of restoration, and the chief feature of the public rooms is a collection of Cromwellian armour. Bedrooms in the main house, some on the small side, are traditionally furnished – one has a splendid four-poster; those in the wing are modern.
Amenities secretarial services, laundry service.

Rooms 31	*Direct dial* Yes	*Confirm by* arrang.	*Parking* Ample
Ensuite bath/shower 26	*Room TV* Yes	*Last dinner* 9.30	*Room service* All day

KENILWORTH | De Montfort Hotel 62% | £C/D

H Map 10 C4 Warwickshire
The Square CV8 1ED
Kenilworth (0926) 55944
Telex 311012

Credit Access, Amex, Diners, Visa

The modern, brightly lit foyer of this purpose-built hotel leads to a comfortable, contemporary lounge and a simple cocktail bar. Nearly half the bedrooms have been completely refurbished and equipped with hairdryers, trouser presses and remote-control TVs; the remaining rooms await the same treatment. Bathrooms are small and functional.
Amenities patio, pool table, in-house movies, secretarial services, fax, laundry service, coffee shop (10am–9pm), 24-hour lounge service.

Rooms 96	*Direct dial* Yes	*Confirm by* arrang.	*Parking* Ample
Ensuite bath/shower 96	*Room TV* Yes	*Last dinner* 9.45	*Room service* Limited

KENILWORTH | Restaurant Diment *NEW ENTRY*

R Map 10 C4 Warwickshire
121 Warwick Road
Kenilworth (0926) 53763

Set L £6.95
About £35 for two
Seats 40
Parties 40
Parking Ample
Credit Access, Amex, Diners, Visa

Gimmickry and pretentiousness have no place in this friendly restaurant, which occupies a corner spot on the town's main street. Fine, fresh raw materials are capably handled to produce tasty, easy-to-enjoy dishes such as brochette of scampi and scallops with a lemon butter, sirloin of beef béarnaise or chicken breast filled with chicken mousse and accompanied by an asparagus sauce and garnish. ☙

Lunch 12–2 *Dinner* 7–10
Closed L Sat, all Sun & Mon, Bank Hols, 1 wk Easter & 3 wks Aug

KENILWORTH | Romano's | ⚐

R Map 10 C4 Warwickshire
60 Waverley Road
Kenilworth (0926) 57473

Italian cooking
Set L £6.80
About £34 for two
Seats 26 *Parties* 40
Parking Limited
Credit Visa

Anna and Romano Goldoni run their friendly restaurant on the basis of sound, unpretentious cooking in pleasant, unassuming surroundings. Anna does the cooking while Romano translates the more adventurous items on the menu and the daily specials. Starter might be tasty lamb sweetbreads in a white wine sauce, with chicken in breadcrumbs and a lovely devilled sauce to follow. Finish with a simple sweet such as Italian trifle or zabaglione. ☙

Lunch 12.30–2 *Dinner* 7.30–10.30 **Closed** L Sat, all Sun, Bank Hols (excl. 25 Dec, 1 Jan & 1st Mon in May) & Aug

▷ is our symbol for an **outstanding** wine list

KESWICK | Keswick Hotel 62% | £C/D

H Map 13 C5 Cumbria
Station Road CA12 4NQ
Keswick (076 87) 72020
Telex 64200

Credit Access, Amex, Diners, Visa

An imposing Victorian hotel set in pleasant grounds. The decor throughout the public rooms is kept largely in period and there is an air of some elegance. Most atmospheric is the plant-filled conservatory where afternoon tea is served. Bedrooms are spacious, with fitted furniture and compact modern bathrooms. Guests have free use of the adjacent Keswick Spa Leisure Pool. ***Amenities*** garden, putting, croquet, secretarial services, laundry service.

Rooms 64	*Direct dial* Yes	*Confirm by* 6	*Parking* Ample
Ensuite bath/shower 64	*Room TV* Yes	*Last dinner* 9	*Room service* 24 hours

KESWICK | Underscar Hotel

See under APPLETHWAITE

KIDDERMINSTER   Stone Manor Hotel   63%   *NEW ENTRY*   **£C/D**

H Map 10 B4 Worcestershire
Stone DY10 4PJ
Chaddesley Corbett (056 283) 555
Telex 335661

Credit Access, Amex, Diners, Visa

Built in mock-Tudor style in 1926, this well-run hotel stands in 25 attractive acres on the A448, three miles from Kidderminster. Timbers and lattice windows are much in evidence, and wing chairs invite occupation in the bar and quiet oak-panelled lounge. Bedrooms (30 more to open as we publish) are in keeping with the country character of the house. **Amenities** garden, outdoor swimming pool, tennis, secretarial services, laundry service.

Rooms 23	*Direct dial* Yes	*Confirm by* noon	*Parking* Ample
Ensuite bath/shower 23	*Room TV* Yes	*Last dinner* 10 (Sun 9)	*Room service* 24 hours

KILDWICK   Kildwick Hall   69%   **£C/D**

H Map 10 C1 North Yorkshire
Nr Keighley BD20 9AE
Crosshills (0535) 32244

Credit Access, Amex, Diners, Visa

Overlooking Airedale, with fine valley views, this is a splendid Jacobean manor house. The new owners continue to make improvements and all the lounges and five of the bedrooms have recently been refurbished. Fine panelling, an inglenook fireplace, beamed ceilings and tapestries help to recreate a more leisured age, while bedrooms twin traditional furnishings with modern comforts. **Amenities** garden, in-house movies, secretarial services, laundry service.

Rooms 14	*Direct dial* Yes	*Confirm by* arrang.	*Parking* Ample
Ensuite bath/shower 11	*Room TV* Yes	*Last dinner* 10.30	*Room service* 24 hours

KILSBY   Hunt House   ♧

R Map 11 D4 Warwickshire
Main Road, Nr Rugby
Crick (0788) 823282

Set D £13.50
About £40 *for two*
Seats 40
Parties 30
Parking Ample
Credit Access, Amex, Diners, Visa

A husband and wife team runs this pleasant country restaurant. Ian Geggie is the charming host, his wife Jan the talent in the kitchen. Monthly-changing menus, based on top-quality ingredients, are always full of interest, with dishes ranging from mange tout soufflé and scallops in tempura to plaice fillets stuffed with lettuce and smoked salmon, and loin of veal with Gruyère and creamy noodles. Well-made sweets from the trolley. ⊖ &

Dinner only 7.15–10, Sat 7.15–10.30
Closed Sun, Mon & 2 wks Xmas

KILVE   Meadow House   72%   **£D**

HR Map 3 E1 Somerset
Sea Lane, Nr Bridgwater
TA5 1EG
Holford (027 874) 546

Rooms 6
Ensuite bath/shower 5
Direct dial Yes
Room TV Yes
Confirm by arrang.
Last dinner 8
Parking Ample
Room service All day

Credit Access, Visa
Closed 2 wks Xmas

Take the narrow Sea Lane off the A39 to reach this lovely Georgian house, surrounded by attractive countryside and only minutes from a quiet beach. The hotel is run on friendly, personal lines by David and Marion MacAuslan, and guests will find true home-from-home comfort in the elegant, restful day rooms. Bedrooms lack nothing in comparison, their attractions including pretty, individual decor,

well-chosen period or contemporary furniture, pleasant views and a goodly number of extras, plus well-equipped bathrooms (all private, one not en suite). No children under 12. No dogs.
Amenities garden, croquet, billiards, laundry service.

Restaurant   ♧

Set D £17
About £45 *for two*
Seats 14

Non-residents must book, as Marion only caters for set numbers. Her dinners (no choice except main course) make fine use of top produce in accomplished dishes like smoked salmon parcels with avocado cream cheese, Dover sole véronique or lamb topped with an onion and mint purée. Superb cheeses and an inspired selection of great wines, from the rarely seen Morgon Charmes 1985 (Marcel Vincent) to Hermitage La Chapelle 1961 and Gigondas 1967 (P. Jaboulet). ⊑ Outstanding ♀ Well-chosen ⊖

Dinner only at 8
Closed 2 wks Xmas

KINGHAM — Mill House Hotel 66% £C

HR Map 4 C1 Oxfordshire
Nr Chipping Norton
OX7 6UH
Kingham (060 871) 8188
Telex 849041

Credit Access, Amex, Diners, Visa

High standards are found at this sympathetically converted Cotswold-stone mill. Pretty pine-furnished bedrooms offer extras like pot-pourri and sewing kits as well as hairdryers and tea-makers. Good toiletries are provided in carpeted modern bathrooms. Downstairs, the flagstoned foyer, beamed bar and elegant, chintzy lounge have a smart country appeal. No children under five. No dogs. *Amenities* garden, croquet, game fishing, secretarial services, laundry service.

Rooms 21	*Direct dial* Yes	*Confirm by* arrang.	*Parking* Ample
Ensuite bath/shower 21	*Room TV* Yes	*Last dinner* 9.30	*Room service* All day

Restaurant

Set L £10.95
Set D £15.95
About £40 for two
Seats 65
Parties 70

Young French chef Pascal Pommier offers an attractively presented selection of interesting dishes at this pleasant restaurant. Good fresh ingredients are the basis of such tempting dishes as sauté of langoustines sauced with tarragon and tomato on a bed of courgettes, fillet of beef with marrow or flavoursome hare in puff pastry. Vegetables are particularly good, sweets light and delicious. Fine clarets and burgundies: Ch. d'Angludet '78, Morey St Denis (Roumier) '80. ♟ Well-chosen ⊘

Lunch 12.30–2   *Dinner* 7–9.30

KING'S LYNN — Butterfly Hotel 63% £E

H Map 6 B1 Norfolk
Beveridge Way PE30 4NB
King's Lynn (0553) 771707
Telex 818313

Credit Access, Amex, Diners, Visa

Comfortable and pleasant accommodation is on offer at this purpose-built hotel east of the town centre. Abundant dried flower displays, pastel colour schemes and plenty of greenery make the public areas light and welcoming. Bedrooms range from singles with showers only to twin- and double-bedded rooms, all having well-coordinated pastel colours and fabrics, pine furniture and contemporary artwork. No dogs. *Amenities* garden, secretarial services, laundry service.

Rooms 50	*Direct dial* Yes	*Confirm by* 6	*Parking* Ample
Ensuite bath/shower 50	*Room TV* Yes	*Last dinner* 10	*Room service* Limited

KING'S LYNN — Duke's Head 64% £C/D

H Map 6 B1 Norfolk
Tuesday Market Place
PE30 1JS
King's Lynn (0553) 774996
Telex 817349

Credit Access, Amex, Diners, Visa

There's no mistaking the fine late 17th-century facade of this pleasant market-place hotel with a spacious lounge and oak-panelled bar. Bedrooms continue to be refurbished, and most now have handsome darkwood units and well-coordinated colour schemes as well as smart bathrooms. Rooms in a more functional, dated wing are adequate for a short stay. Small dogs only.
Amenities laundry service, coffee shop (10am–10pm).

Rooms 72	*Direct dial* Yes	*Confirm by* 6	*Parking* Ample
Ensuite bath/shower 72	*Room TV* Yes	*Last dinner* 9.30	*Room service* Limited

KINGSBRIDGE — Buckland-Tout-Saints Hotel 70% £C/D

HR Map 3 D3 Devon
Goveton TQ7 2DS
Kingsbridge (0548) 3055
Telex 42513

Rooms 12
Ensuite bath/shower 12
Direct dial Yes
Room TV Yes
Confirm by arrang.
Last dinner 9
Parking Ample
Room service All day

Credit Access, Amex, Diners, Visa
Closed 2 wks early Jan

The lush pastures of the South Hams surround the lovely grounds of this William and Mary manor house. Inside, you are greeted by a striking panelled foyer-lounge, which leads to a quiet reading room and a bar with green and brown leather chesterfields. Bedrooms vary in size and are individually decorated with flowered, stippled or striped wallpaper which coordinates with the soft furnishings;  one has a mahogany four-poster and there are two extremely stylish suites. Attic rooms are somewhat small. Ultra-modern bathrooms are individually styled to match each bedroom. No children under eight. No dogs. *Amenities* garden, putting, bowling green, croquet, secretarial services, laundry service, helipad. *see over*

Queen Anne Restaurant

Set L £14
Set D £19.75
About £52 for two
Seats 30
Parties 14

An elegant panelled dining room provides a delightful setting in which to sample Alastair Carter's enjoyable cooking. His menus take advantage of excellent local produce, which is very capably handled, and there are some tempting dishes. Tasty ones to try are Pithiviers of sweetbreads and pan-fried calf's liver with butter and raspberry vinegar and there's a super choice of well-kept local cheeses.
🍷 Well-chosen ✆

Lunch 12.30–2, by arrang. only   *Dinner* 7.30–9
Closed 2 wks early Jan

KINGTON

Penrhos Court Restaurant ⚘

R **Map 4 A1** Herefordshire
Lyonshal[1]
Kington (0544) 230720

Set L Sun £8
About £48 for two
Seats 40
Parties 80
Parking Ample

Daphne Lambert has nearly a dozen successful years behind her at this charmingly rustic restaurant in old buildings next to a splendid Elizabethan manor house. Her cooking is highly enjoyable over a range of dishes such as cream of fennel soup, smoked quail and walnut salad, salmon with sorrel, wild boar with black cherry sauce and brown-bread ice cream. A traditional lunch is served on Sunday. Note no credit cards. 🍷 Well-chosen ✆

Lunch Sun only 12.30–2   *Dinner* 7.30–10
Closed D Sun, all Mon & Tues, 25 & 26 Dec & 5 Jan–end Feb

KINTBURY

Dundas Arms £E

IR **Map 4 C2** Berkshire
Nr Newbury DY7 6HG
Kintbury (0488) 58263

Credit Access, Amex, Diners, Visa
Closed 1 wk Xmas

A friendly late-18th-century inn on the Kennet and Avon canal. The bar-reception is splendidly traditional with its solid wooden settles and display of blue and white china, and there's a pretty, chintzy residents' lounge. Comfortable, well-appointed bedrooms, in a converted stable block, have solid old-fashioned furniture, pleasant modern bathrooms and access to a waterside terrace. No dogs.
Amenities garden.

Rooms 5	*Direct dial* Yes	*Confirm by* arrang.	*Parking* Ample
Ensuite bath/shower 5	*Room TV* Yes	*Last dinner* 9.15	*Room service* None

Restaurant ⚘

Set L £9.75
Set D £16.50
About £47 for two
Seats 36

The Dalzell-Piper family are building up quite a reputation in their long galley-style restaurant. Tip-top ingredients are lovingly handled to produce interesting dishes like scallop mousse with ginger sauce, quail stuffed with pâté and lentils, and fillet of veal with wild mushroom sauce. Superb, keenly-priced wine list includes inspired choice of burgundies (Chablis from Raveneau, Clos Vougeot from Grivot). ➣ Outstanding 🍷 Well-chosen ✆ &

Lunch 12.30–1.30   *Dinner* 7.30–9.15
Closed Sun, Mon, Bank Hol Mons & 1 wk Xmas

Changes in data sometimes occur in establishments
after the Guide goes to press.
Prices should be taken as indications rather than firm quotes.

KINVER

Berkleys Restaurant, Piano Room ⚘

R **Map 10 B4** Staffordshire
High Street, Nr. Stourbridge
Kinver (0384) 873679

Set D £17
About £45 for two
Seats 40
Parties 40
Parking Ample
Credit Access, Amex, Diners, Visa

On Friday and Saturday nights you dine to live piano music at Andrew Mortimer's smart first-floor restaurant. His four-course menu, short and imaginative, changes every couple of months and features lots of fresh seasonal produce. Tomato and pepper soup, mussels with shallot and dill sauce, chicken with orange, and venison with red cabbage are typical choices, with pavlova and home-made ices among the sweets. ✆

Dinner only 7–10
Closed Sun & Bank Hols

KIRKBY FLEETHAM Kirkby Fleetham Hall 75% £D

HR Map 15 B5
North Yorkshire
Nr Northallerton DL7 0SU
Northallerton (0609) 748226

Rooms 15
Ensuite bath/shower 15
Direct dial Yes
Room TV Yes
Confirm by arrang.
Last dinner 9
Parking Ample
Room service Limited

Credit Amex, Diners, Visa

The hall dates back to 1600 but was later enlarged into a square William and Mary building. Set in 30 acres of magnificent landscaped grounds next to a 12th-century church, it's a very tranquil spot. A high-ceilinged entrance hall sets an elegant tone and the various lounges and drawing rooms are made for relaxation with their log fires, comfortable period furnishings, delightful fabrics and flower arrangements. Spacious bedrooms are boldly decorated and handsomely furnished, some with four-posters, others with ornamental brass beds. Little extras abound in the bedrooms and in the warm, carpeted bathrooms, which also have splendid brass fittings. Good breakfasts are another plus. *Amenities* garden, laundry service.

Restaurant ♕

Set L £11.50
Set D £19
About £50 *for two*
Seats 36
Parties 16

Open fires, gilt-framed watercolours and handsome mahogany tables add up to a splendid setting for Raymond Sharp's talented cooking. Dinner starts with soup, followed perhaps by guinea fowl roulade with walnuts, or spinach and Swaledale cheese soufflé. Main courses such as breast of duck with raspberry sauce or herby rack of lamb come with a variety of home-grown vegetables, and there are some tempting sweets. Good wines, with some fine clarets in half-bottles. ℮

Lunch Sun only 12.30–2   *Dinner* 7–9

**We welcome bona fide complaints and recommendations
on the tear-out pages at the back of the book for readers' comment.
They are followed up by our professional team.**

KNAPTON Knapton Hall 64% *NEW ENTRY* £E

H Map 6 D1 Norfolk
The Street NR28 0SB
Mundesley (0263) 720405

Credit Access, Amex, Visa
Closed 2 days after Xmas

Ask for directions as this secluded hotel stands back from the road in two and a half acres of grounds. The charming Laverys extend a warm welcome and the cosy bar and lounge reinforce the homely feeling. The individually furnished, simply decorated bedrooms have a tasteful blend of antique and modern pieces; bathrooms are clean and functional. No children under twelve. *Amenities* garden, outdoor swimming pool, sauna, bowling green, in-house movies.

Rooms 9	*Room phone* Yes	*Confirm by* arrang.	*Parking* Ample
Ensuite bath/shower 9	*Room TV* Yes	*Last dinner* 9.30	*Room service* All day

KNARESBOROUGH Dower House 62% £E

H Map 15 C6 North Yorkshire
Bond End HG5 9AL
Harrogate (0423) 863302

Credit Access, Amex, Diners, Visa
Closed 25 Dec

The main building dates from Tudor times, though the facade is Georgian and the original elegance has largely been lost to the modern extension. It's a popular place with both conference visitors and holidaymakers, being handy for Harrogate and the Dales. Bedrooms vary in size and style, some being modern, with built-in furniture, others having a comfortably old-fashioned feel; one of the best rooms boasts a mass of exposed beams. There's a little bar and a long lounge that features a handsome Georgian staircase. A leisure centre, conference room and more bedrooms are planned.
Amenities garden, secretarial services, laundry service, 24-hour lounge service.

Rooms 21	*Direct dial* Yes	*Confirm by* 6.30	*Parking* Ample
Ensuite bath/shower 19	*Room TV* Yes	*Last dinner* 9.15	*Room service* All day

KNARESBOROUGH   Schwaller's   ♀

R **Map 15 C6** North Yorkshire
6 Bond End
Harrogate (0423) 863899

Set D from £17.90
About £45 for two
Seats 30
Parties 44
Parking Difficult
Credit Access, Visa

Fresh produce dictates Martin Schwaller's daily-changing five-course
dinner menus at this characterful restaurant where the evening begins
with drinks and canapés in the lounge. Choice ranges from starters
like salmon quenelles and steamed mussels to duck with apricots,
saltimbocca and coriander pheasant. Exuberant hostess Caroline
Schwaller describes the superb sweets. Some gems to be found among
the wines. No smoking. ♀ Well-chosen ℮

Dinner only 7–9.30
Closed Tues & 24 Dec–30 Jan

KNOWLE   Grays Country Restaurant   *NEW ENTRY*   ♔ ♀

R **Map 3 E3** Devon
Nr Braunton
Braunton (0271) 812809

Set D £13.95
About £35 for two
Seats 30
Parties 20
Parking Ample
Credit Access, Visa

Colin Gray's menus are full of interest, and his culinary ability does
full justice to some excellent produce. Stilton and apple strudel or
salmon mousse could be your starter, followed perhaps by chicken
breast stuffed with apricots, in a ginger wine sauce. Good fresh
vegetables. A tempting range of puddings. The twin dining rooms are
quite stylish, and there's a delightful sitting area with inviting sofas.
Book.

Dinner only 7–8.45
Closed Sun, Mon, Bank Hols & 2 wks end Oct

★ For a *discount* on next year's guide, see **An Offer for Answers**. ★

KNUTSFORD   La Belle Epoque   ♔

RR **Map 10 B2** Cheshire
60 King Street WA16 2DT
Knutsford (0565) 3060

French cooking
About £53 for two
Seats 65
Parties 85
Parking Ample

Credit Access, Amex, Diners, Visa

A fanciful turn-of-the-century Italianate building houses this characterful Art Nouveau restaurant – an appropriately extravagant setting
for Yvonne Holt's elaborate and sometimes over-the-top assemblages.
Imagination runs riot in dishes like snails casseroled in green
chartreuse with cèpes and hazelnuts or roast quails stuffed with game
mousseline and wrapped in filo, but there are plainer offerings too,
like duck terrine with onion marmalade and breast of guinea fowl
with lime sauce. Pleasant desserts might include a well-made chocolate
praline gâteau and there's an excellent cheeseboard. ℮

Dinner only 7.30–10
Closed Sun, Bank Hols & 1st wk Jan

BEDROOMS 5 **£E/F**
With bath/shower 5

Prettily decorated bedrooms, with white-painted French-style furniture, have TVs and spacious modern bathrooms. No children. No dogs.

KNUTSFORD   The Cottons Hotel   65%   £C/D

H **Map 10 B2** Cheshire
Manchester Road WA16 0SU
Knutsford (0565) 50333
Telex 669931

Credit Access, Amex, Diners, Visa

Just outside Knutsford on the A50, this long, low building was recently
extended to include a smart new lounge area and 26 more bedrooms
– four with whirlpool baths. New additions to the leisure facilities are
a floodlit tennis court and full-scale gymnasium.
Amenities terrace, indoor swimming pool, sauna, solarium, whirlpool bath, gymnasium, tennis, in-house movies, secretarial services,
fax, laundry service, 24-hour lounge service. ♿

Rooms 86	*Direct dial* Yes	*Confirm by* arrang.	*Parking* Ample
Ensuite bath/shower 86	*Room TV* Yes	*Last dinner* 9.45	*Room service* Limited

KNUTSFORD   David's Place

R **Map 10 B2** Cheshire
10 Princess Street
Knutsford (0565) 3356

Set D £12
About £48 for two
Seats 70
Parties 35
Parking Limited
Credit Access, Amex, Diners, Visa

David and Arlette Molloy set you quickly at ease in their busy town-
centre restaurant, where Philip Hill's cooking is shown to best
advantage on the more ambitious evening menu. Nicely sauced pasta,
duck with red wine and kumquats, lamb with olives and well-hung
fillet steak are justly popular dishes, and the wine list is chosen with
flair and care, from fine half-bottles of claret to interesting New World
wines. ♀ Well-chosen ℮

Lunch 12.30–2 *Dinner* 7.15–10, Fri & Sat till 10.30
Closed Sun, Bank Hols & 3 days Xmas

LACOCK · Sign of the Angel · £D

IR **Map 4 B2** Wiltshire
Nr Chippenham SN15 2LA
Lacock (024 973) 230

Credit Access, Visa
Closed 22 Dec–1 Jan

Built for a wool merchant in the 15th century, this is a delightful little inn with oodles of charm exemplified in heavy beams, sloping floors, log fires and antique furniture. Bedrooms are quaint, old-fashioned and intimate, with massive wardrobes and not many right angles. There's a splendid panelled residents' lounge on the first floor. Breakfast is freshly prepared and very good. No children under 12. No dogs.
Amenities garden.

Rooms 8	*Direct dial* Yes	*Confirm by* 5.30	*Parking* Limited
Ensuite bath/shower 8	*Room TV* No	*Last dinner* 8.15	*Room service* Limited

Restaurant ♀

English cooking
Set L £15, Sun £20
Set D £20
About £50 *for two*
Seats 30
Parties 20

Lorna Levis cooks in straightforward style using notably fresh ingredients, including eggs from the family hens, vegetables from the garden and meat from an excellent local butcher. A traditional roast is the centrepiece of her dinners, on our last visit a very good leg of lamb with a slice of stuffed loin, preceded by grilled sole or soup and followed by a very commendable crème caramel. Wines are taken seriously, with some fine bottles at keen prices: Pommard Clos les Epeneause 1980, Ch. Lascombes 1978. Local ladies serve with real charm and efficiency, making diners feel instantly at home. ℰ

Lunch Mon–Fri by arrang., Sun at 1 *Dinner* 7.30–8.15
Closed L Sat & Bank Hols, D Sun to non-residents & all 22 Dec–1 Jan

---

Changes in data sometimes occur in establishments
after the Guide goes to press.
Prices should be taken as indications rather than firm quotes.

LAMORNA COVE · Lamorna Cove Hotel 67% · £B/C

H **Map 2 A4** Cornwall
Nr Penzance TR19 6XH
Penzance (0736) 731411

Credit Access, Amex, Visa

A wooded valley above the cove makes a delightful setting for a well laid-out hotel. Three restful lounges include one with picture windows on to the swimming pool and the sea and there's also a cosy, attractive bar. The light, pleasant bedrooms are individually decorated and many have marvellous sea views. Bathrooms are modern and functional. *Amenities* garden, outdoor swimming pool, sauna, secretarial services, laundry service.

Rooms 18	*Direct dial* Yes	*Confirm by* arrang.	*Parking* Ample
Ensuite bath/shower 18	*Room TV* Yes	*Last dinner* 9.30	*Room service* All day

LANCASTER · Post House Hotel 69% · £C

H **Map 13 D6** Lancashire
Waterside Park,
Caton Road LA1 3RA
Lancaster (0524) 65999
Telex 65363

Credit Access, Amex, Diners, Visa

Good leisure pursuits, including fishing in the River Lune, are a feature of this modern red-brick hotel. Day rooms are attractive, and many of the well-equipped bedrooms have river views.
Amenities garden, indoor swimming pool, sauna, solarium, whirlpool bath, gymnasium, clay-pigeon shooting, in-house movies, secretarial services, laundry service, coffee shop (7am–10.30pm), children's playground. ৬

Rooms 117	*Direct dial* Yes	*Confirm by* 6	*Parking* Ample
Ensuite bath/shower 117	*Room TV* Yes	*Last dinner* 10.30	*Room service* 24 hours

---

♀ indicates a **well-chosen** house wine

LANGDALE　　　　Langdale Hotel　72%　　　　£C

H **Map 13 C5** Cumbria
Nr Ambleside LA22 9JB
Langdale (096 67) 302
Telex 65188

Rooms 50
Ensuite bath/shower 50
Direct dial Yes
Room TV Yes
Confirm by 6
Last dinner 10
Parking Ample
Room service 24 hours

Credit Access, Amex, Diners, Visa

Accommodation is spread over a
number of blocks at an attractive
modern hotel and leisure centre
in an extensive woodland setting
in the heart of the Lake District.
Public areas include an open plan
bar-lounge and restaurant that
features a bubbling millstream,
and a traditional pub with slate
walls and a log fire. The most
desirable bedrooms have been
refurbished with pretty chintz
and boast Edwardian-style bath-
rooms with whirlpool baths. *Amenities* garden, indoor swimming
pool, sauna, solarium, whirlpool bath, gymnasium, beauty salon,
hairdressing, squash, coarse & game fishing, hotel yacht, games room,
snooker, satellite TV, secretarial services, fax, laundry service, coffee
shop (10am–10pm), children's playroom.

LANGHO　　　　Northcote Manor　66%　　　　£E

HR **Map 10 B1** Lancashire
Northcote Road,
Nr Blackburn BB6 8BE
Blackburn (0254) 40555
Credit Access, Amex, Diners, Visa
Closed Bank Hol Mons, 25 & 26
Dec & 1 Jan

Affable owner-manager Craig Bancroft and young, keen staff provide
excellent service at this converted Victorian manor house just off the
A59. The setting is very peaceful, and log fires crackle a welcome in
the cosy day rooms. Bedrooms, which feature some rather splendid
antiques, offer ample comfort and various thoughtful extras. Mr.
Bancroft prepares an excellent repast to enjoy in the breakfast room.
Amenities garden.

Rooms 6	*Direct dial* Yes	*Confirm by* 6	*Parking* Ample
Ensuite bath/shower 6	*Room TV* Yes	*Last dinner* 9.30	*Room service* All day

Restaurant　　　♕

Set L £8.25
About £50 *for two*
Seats 45
Parties 20

Youthful skill and imagination abound in the kitchen, so a meal here
is always an occasion to savour. Pan-fried local wild duckling and
pigeon served on juices of raspberries and morels is a delicious
centrepiece which you might surround with smoked trout and
profiterole swans. Note a lovely savoury speciality – poached quail's
eggs and bacon on wholemeal croûtons topped with hollandaise sauce.
Good wines.

Lunch 12–1.30　*Dinner* 7–9.30, Sat 7–10, Sun 7–9
Closed L Sat, all Bank Hol Mons, 25 & 26 Dec & 1 Jan

LANGLEY-ON-TYNE　Langley Castle　67%　*NEW ENTRY*　£D/E

H **Map 15 B4** Northumberland
Nr Haydon Bridge NE47 5LU
Haydon Bridge (0434 84) 8888

Credit Access, Amex, Diners, Visa

Modern comforts combine with medieval charm in a splendidly
restored 14th-century castle set in wooded grounds. Superb stained
glass windows dominate the impressive drawing room with its seven-
foot-thick stone walls. Bare stone also features in some of the bedrooms,
which are furnished with antiques. All have modern bathrooms, some
with their own sauna or whirlpool bath. Housekeeping could be
improved. *Amenities* garden, secretarial services, laundry service.

Rooms 8	*Direct dial* Yes	*Confirm by* arrang.	*Parking* Ample
Ensuite bath/shower 8	*Room TV* Yes	*Last dinner* 9.30	*Room service* 24 hours

LANREATH　　　　Punch Bowl Inn　　　　£F

I **Map 2 C3** Cornwall
Nr Looe PL13 2NX
Lanreath (0503) 20218

Credit Access, Visa

A working inglenook fireplace, antiques and gleaming horse brasses
give the lounge bar of this 17th-century village inn a good deal of
character. Upstairs, a bright residents' lounge overlooks the garden.
Charming main-house bedrooms have solid furniture (including three
four-posters) and those without en suite bathrooms have basins;
rooms in the modern extension have plain fitted furniture.
Amenities garden, pool table.

Rooms 18	*Room phone* No	*Confirm by* arrang.	*Parking* Ample
Ensuite bath/shower 14	*Room TV* Yes	*Last dinner* 9.30	*Room service* Limited

LAVENHAM | The Great House *NEW ENTRY*

RR Map 6 C3 Suffolk
Market Place
Lavenham (0787) 247431

French cooking
Set L from £6.90
Set D from £10.75
About £45 for two
Seats 38
Parking Ample
Credit Access, Amex, Visa

A Georgian facade hides earlier origins evident in the dining room which features a large redbrick inglenook and a massive central oak beam. Régis Crépy's menus offer hugely enjoyable French and English dishes typified by Scotch salmon in pastry, creamy avocado soup, medallions of lamb with a red and green pepper sauce and some mouthwatering gâteaux and ice creams. Intelligently planned cellar – from the delicious Gaillac house wines to the superb 1985 Gewürztraminer Grand Cru Golbert. 🍷 Well-chosen ⊖

Lunch 12–2.30 *Dinner* 7.30–10.30
Closed L Mon in winter, 3 wks Jan

BEDROOMS 3 **£E**
With bath/shower 3

The three delightful bedrooms (two full suites) have the character of old timbers and beams, antique furniture and pretty fabrics.

LAVENHAM | Swan Hotel 71% | £C/D

HR Map 6 C3 Suffolk
High Street,
Nr Sudbury CO10 9QA
Lavenham (0787) 247477
Telex 987198

Rooms 48
Ensuite bath/shower 48
Direct dial Yes
Room TV Yes
Confirm by arrang.
Last dinner 9.30
Parking Ample
Room service 24 hours

Credit Access, Amex, Diners, Visa

A delightful hotel comprising several 14th- and 15th-century buildings and charming gardens. There is much to please here, including the quality of the service (porterage, shoe cleaning, proper room service) and the care and sympathy with which renovations and improvements have been made. Public rooms are quite extensive, with lots of old beams, comfortable seating areas and an inviting, traditional

feel. Creature comforts abound in the solidly furnished bedrooms, from hairdryers and trouser presses to huge towels and ample toiletries. There are two suites. A good breakfast, freshly cooked and properly served, starts the day on the right note.
Amenities garden, fax, valeting, laundry service.

Restaurant *NEW ENTRY*

Set L from £8.95
Set D from £14.50
About £56 for two
Seats 70
Parties 40
Parking Ample

A pianist accompanies dinner in this appealing restaurant with tall timbered ceiling and minstrels' gallery. The menus span dishes both plain and more elaborate, from omelettes and cold meat platters to truffled goose liver with port aspic, délice of turbot and excellent veal steak with Sauternes and wild mushrooms. Good classic wines include the occasional gem: Corton Charlemagne Bonneau du Martray '83, Lynch-Bages '61. Attentive service from smartly dressed staff. ⊖

Lunch 12.30–2, Sun 12.15–2.15 *Dinner* 7–9.30
Closed D 25 Dec

LEAMINGTON SPA | Mallory Court 81% | £A/B

HR Map 10 C4 Warwickshire
Harbury Lane,
Tachbrook Mallory CV33 9QB
Leamington Spa (0926) 30214
Telex 317294

Rooms 10
Ensuite bath/shower 10
Direct dial Yes
Room TV Yes
Confirm by arrang.
Last dinner 9.30
Parking Ample
Room service All day

Credit Access, Amex, Diners, Visa

A really handsome country house hotel, built in 1910 and standing in ten acres of beautifully landscaped gardens that are a match for the quite splendid interior. Pastel-pink sofas and pretty flower displays grace the lounge, and there's a more masculine drawing room and a delightful little suntrap of a conservatory. The ten bedrooms have a perfection of proportion, each individually appointed

with the finest fabrics, period furnishings and every cosseting extra. Staff are relaxed yet attentive, housekeeping impeccable, and everything combines to provide the perfect formula for civilised country living. No children under 12. No dogs. *Amenities* garden, outdoor swimming pool, tennis, squash, croquet, valeting, laundry service.
see over

Mallory Court Restaurant   ★   ♛♛ ⊈

Lunch 12.30–1.45
Dinner 7.30–9.30, Sun till 8.30
Set L £15.95
Set D £29.50
About £74 for two
Seats 50
Parties 30

Anthony Wright has taken over the culinary reins, and standards remain admirably high in this most elegant panelled restaurant. The menu shows great flair and imagination, and results do not disappoint: our mille-feuille of potatoes, turnips and foie gras was a delightful harmony of textures and flavours, and roast partridge with noodles and a light orange and champagne sauce was equally successful.

Service is the height of discretion, and there's an excellent cellar, best in classic burgundies and Bordeaux. *Specialities* terrine of lobster and veal sweetbreads; sea bass with spinach and a light tomato sauce; veal tournedos with foie gras and chive cream sauce; gâteau of caramelised rice with fresh figs and plums. ♟ Well-chosen ℮

LEAMINGTON SPA   Regent Hotel   63%   £D/E

H **Map 10 C4** Warwickshire
The Parade CV32 4AX
Leamington Spa (0926) 27231
Telex 311715

Credit Access, Amex, Diners, Visa

Old-world courtesy and excellent housekeeping are strong suits at this reassuringly traditional hotel managed by Vernon May for 34 years. A fine Regency building dating from 1819, it retains splendid original features like stained-glass windows, elegant ceilings and a handsome staircase. Bedrooms are currently being upgraded with slightly more feminine furnishings. Adequate bathrooms. *Amenities* garden, games room, fax, laundry service, 24-hour lounge service.

Rooms 80	*Direct dial* Yes	*Confirm by* arrang.	*Parking* Ample
Ensuite bath/shower 80	*Room TV* Yes	*Last dinner* 10.45	*Room service* All day

---

Any person using our name to obtain free hospitality is a fraud.
Proprietors, please inform the police and us.

LEDBURY   Feathers Hotel   59%   £D/E

H **Map 4 B1**
Hereford & Worcester
High Street HR8 1DS
Ledbury (0531) 2600

Credit Access, Amex, Diners

A much-loved landmark in the town centre, this Elizabethan half-timbered inn is rich in old-world charm. There's a pretty lounge with period furnishings, and a splendidly traditional bar sporting plenty of exposed beams and horse brasses. Bedrooms too are thoroughly authentic, with sloping floors and sturdy furniture; all are well-equipped and have decent modern bathrooms, and those facing the High Street are double-glazed. *Amenities* squash, laundry service.

Rooms 11	*Direct dial* Yes	*Confirm by* arrang.	*Parking* Ample
Ensuite bath/shower 11	*Room TV* Yes	*Last dinner* 9.30	*Room service* All day

---

LEDBURY   Hope End Country House Hotel   70%   £B

HR **Map 4 B1**
Hereford & Worcester
Hope End HR8 1JQ
Ledbury (0531) 3613

Rooms 9
Ensuite bath/shower 9
Room phone Yes
Room TV Some
Confirm by arrang.
Last dinner 8.30
Parking Ample
Room service Limited

Credit Access, Visa
Closed Mon & Tues nights &
Dec–end Feb

The Hegartys run this delightful little hotel set in 40 acres of wooded parkland with exemplary care and taste. Once the childhood home of Elizabeth Barrett Browning, it has been completely renovated and today provides a marvellously peaceful retreat. A library has joined the two original sitting rooms, where antiques and leather chesterfields blend harmoniously with an attractive modern decor. Bed-

rooms include three splendid new rooms featuring magnificent exposed beams and joists. The six older rooms are smaller but equally appealing with their pine furnishings and tweedy Welsh fabrics. All have immaculate private bathrooms. Half-board terms only. No children under 14. No dogs. *Amenities* garden, terrace.

Restaurant ♀

English cooking

Set D £20
About £50 *for two*
Seats 24
Parties 6

Talented and enthusiastic chef Patricia Hegarty cooks in the English country tradition at this pristine restaurant, making excellent use of the fruit, vegetables and herbs she grows in her 18th-century walled garden. Her short, fixed-price dinner menus change daily and offer a well balanced selection of dishes. Flavoursome leek and crab soup might precede robust beef and Guinness casserole served with wonderfully fresh vegetables. A crisp, refreshing salad (perhaps orange and chicory) follows, then superb British cheeses and tempting sweets like demerara meringues with black and redcurrant sauce. Wonderful burgundies. ⌦ Outstanding ♀ Well-chosen ℗

Dinner only 7.30–8.30
Closed Mon & Tues & Dec–end Feb

We publish annually,
so make sure you use the current edition.
It's worth it!

LEEDS | Crest Hotel 55% | £C/D

H Town plan B3
West Yorkshire
The Grove, Oulton LS26 8EJ
Leeds (0532) 826201
Telex 557646

Credit Access, Amex, Diners, Visa

Pleasant motel-style accommodation is on offer at this modern hotel at the junction of the A642 and A639, five miles south of the city centre. Bedrooms, all with tiled bathrooms, have thoughtful extras such as mineral water and bedside radios. Public rooms are in a separate block and include a small foyer-lounge and two bars.
Amenities garden, secretarial services, fax, laundry service.

| *Rooms* 40 | *Direct dial* Yes | *Confirm by* 6 | *Parking* Ample |
| *Ensuite bath/shower* 40 | *Room TV* Yes | *Last dinner* 9.45 | *Room service* Limited |

LEEDS | Hilton International Hotel 71% | £B/C

H Town plan B3
West Yorkshire
Neville Street LS1 4BX
Leeds (0532) 442000
Telex 557143

Rooms 234
Ensuite bath/shower 234
Direct dial Yes
Room TV Yes
Confirm by 6
Last dinner 10
Parking Limited
Room service 24 hours

Credit Access, Amex, Diners, Visa

Close to the city centre, this modern high-rise hotel offers excellent accommodation, good service and a wide range of meeting and function facilities. Lifts take guests from the ground floor to reception, which also comprises a comfortable lounge and a little coffee shop, all in bright open-plan design. On the same (first-floor) level is the bar, its walls hung with photographs of famous guests. Air-conditioned bedrooms, each floor with its own colour scheme, feature pretty contemporary fabrics and smart darkwood furnishings. Hairdryers and trouser presses are standard.
Amenities in-house movies, secretarial services, fax, laundry service, coffee shop (10am–10pm), kiosk. ♿

LEEDS | Merrion Hotel 63% | £C/D

H Town plan C1
West Yorkshire
Merrion Centre LS2 8NH
Leeds (0532) 439191
Telex 55459

Credit Access, Amex, Diners, Visa

A purpose-built hotel in the city centre, linked by a covered walkway to a multi-storey car park. Reception is on the ground floor, while above is a bar with a music hall theme. Two other bars with trendy decor and pop videos are in an adjacent building. Bedrooms, all with functional bathrooms, have remote-control teletext TVs.
Amenities in-house movies, laundry service, 24-hour lounge service.

| *Rooms* 120 | *Direct dial* Yes | *Confirm by* 6 | *Parking* Ample |
| *Ensuite bath/shower* 120 | *Room TV* Yes | *Last dinner* 10.30 | *Room service* All day |

LEEDS

Map 11 D1
Town plan opposite

Population 748,000

Originally Loidis, a Celtic settlement, it was given its industrial send-off by a 13th-century community of monks, who practised the crafts that made the town great–notably cloth-spinning and coal-mining but the big leap came between 1775 (population 17,000) and 1831 (population 123,000).

It has taken gargantuan efforts to eliminate the excesses of unplanned industrial and population growth, but its post-war housing and roads record and industrial mix are making Leeds a prouder city. Today it can boast as much of its University and Poly, its shopping areas, parks and new estates as it has always done of its choir, cricket, rugby league, soccer and fish and chips.

Yet it is as true today as when Henry VIII's Librarian first stated it, that 'the town stondith most by clothing'.

Information Centre
19 Wellington Street
Leeds LS1 4DE
Telephone Leeds 462453/4

Fiat Dealers
JCT 600
Spence Lane
Leeds LS12 1AG
Tel. Leeds 431843

Whitehead & Hinch Ltd
South Bradgate Lane
Horsforth, Leeds LS18 4AG
Tel. Horsforth 585056

1 Adel Church *St John the Baptist 12th c* **B1**
2 Airport *Yeadon 8 miles* **B1**
3 Central Library **C2**
4 City Art Gallery **C2**
5 City Museum **C2**
6 City Station **B/C3**
7 City Varieties *'Good Old Days'* **C2**
8 Civil Theatre **C2**
9 Grand Theatre **C2**
10 International Pool **A2**
11 Kirkstall Abbey *12th c* **A2**
12 Kirkstall Abbey House Folk Museum **A2**
13 Leeds Industrial Museum **A2**
14 Leeds Parish Church **D3**
15 Leeds United F.C. *Elland Road* **C3**
16 Middleton Colliery Railway *1785, oldest in world* **C3**
17 Playhouse **B1**
18 Queen's Hall *Exhibitions* (Leeds Exhibition Centre) **C3**
19 Roman Catholic Cathedral **C2**
20 Roundhay Park **E1**
21 Rugby League and Cricket *Headingley* **B1**
22 Temple Newsam House *15th c and Park, home of Darnley, husband of Mary Queen of Scots; outstanding furniture collection* **E2**
23 Tourist Information Centre **B3**
24 University **A/B1**

Leeds F I A T

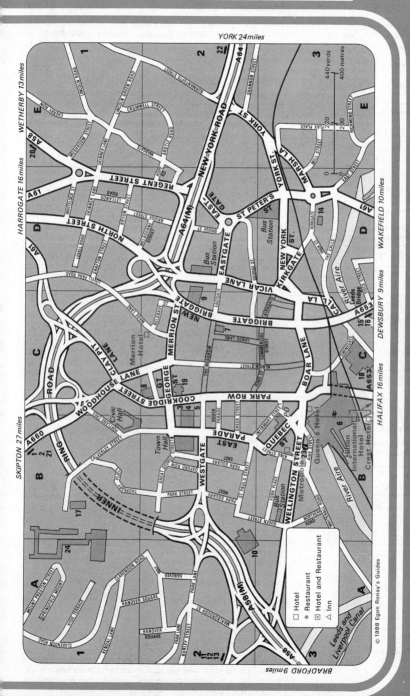

YORK 24 miles

WETHERBY 13 miles

HARROGATE 16 miles

SKIPTON 27 miles

BRADFORD 9 miles

WAKEFIELD 10 miles

DEWSBURY 9 miles

HALIFAX 16 miles

440 yards
400 metres

Legend:
- □ Hotel
- ● Restaurant
- ⊡ Hotel and Restaurant
- △ Inn

© 1988 Egon Ronay's Guides

LEEDS   Metropole   57%   £C/D

H **Town plan B3**
West Yorkshire
King Street LS1 2HQ
Leeds (0532) 450841
Telex 557755

In the city centre near the main railway station, the Metropole is a late-Victorian hotel with an imposing terracotta facade. Inside, the splendour has faded a little, but lofty public rooms like the pillared foyer and Gaslight Bar are comfortable enough. Tea-makers and remote-control TVs are provided in the bedrooms, all of which are planned to have bathrooms en suite by spring 1989.

Credit Access, Amex, Diners, Visa   *Amenities* fax, laundry service, 24-hour lounge service.

Rooms 114	*Direct dial* Yes	*Confirm by* 6	*Parking* Limited
Ensuite bath/shower 78	*Room TV* Yes	*Last dinner* 10	*Room service* Limited

LEEDS   Queen's Hotel   67%   £C

H **Town plan C3**
West Yorkshire
City Square LS1 1PL
Leeds (0532) 431323
Telex 55161

Refurbishment continues at this white Portland stone hotel overlooking City Square, gradually restoring it to its former grandeur. The impressive foyer leads to an informal lounge and the lively Harlequin Bar. Spacious bedrooms – all with en suite bathrooms – are mainly in traditional style. Redecorated rooms have attractive, well-coordinated decor.

Credit Access, Amex, Diners, Visa   *Amenities* secretarial services, laundry service.

Rooms 186	*Direct dial* Yes	*Confirm by* 6	*Parking* Ample
Ensuite bath/shower 186	*Room TV* Yes	*Last dinner* 10	*Room service* 24 hours

LEICESTER   Belmont Hotel   64%   £D/E

H **Map 11 D4** Leicestershire
De Montfort Street LE1 7GR
Leicester (0533) 544773
Telex 34619

Credit Access, Amex, Diners, Visa

Quietly situated not far from the city centre, the Belmont is a traditionally run, well-maintained and friendly hotel. The lounges and residents' bar have a homely, restful appeal, while the mood is livelier in the bright basement bar. Well-lit bedrooms offer desk and dressing table space, armchairs and coffee tables, plus neat, up-to-date bathrooms. Executive rooms are generally larger, with more extras. *Amenities* garden, laundry service.

Rooms 55	*Direct dial* Yes	*Confirm by* 6	*Parking* Limited
Ensuite bath/shower 55	*Room TV* Yes	*Last dinner* 10	*Room service* Limited

LEICESTER   Grand Hotel   67%   £C/D

H **Map 11 D4** Leicestershire
Granby Street LE1 6ES
Leicester (0533) 555599
Telex 342244

Credit Access, Amex, Diners, Visa
Closed 25 & 26 Dec

A spacious marble-floored foyer greets guests at this Victorian city-centre hotel. Comfortable sofas furnish the lounge area, where a skylight illuminates hanging baskets. Two smart bars create contrasting moods. Bedrooms now come up to scratch, with new furniture and fittings plus hairdryers, trouser presses and tea-makers. Friendly and efficient staff. *Amenities* secretarial services, fax, laundry service, coffee shop (9am–10pm).

Rooms 92	*Direct dial* Yes	*Confirm by* 6	*Parking* Ample
Ensuite bath/shower 92	*Room TV* Yes	*Last dinner* 9.30	*Room service* 24 hours

LEICESTER   Holiday Inn   75%   £C/D

H **Map 11 D4** Leicestershire
St Nicholas Circle LE1 5LX
Leicester (0533) 531161
Telex 341281

Rooms 188
Ensuite bath/shower 188
Direct dial Yes
Room TV Yes
Confirm by 6
Last dinner 10.15
Parking Ample
Room service 24 hours

Credit Access, Amex, Diners, Visa

A multi-storey hotel on one of the main arterial roads leading into the city centre. There's an attractive reception area with salmon-pink seating arranged round a central 'open' artificial log fire. Pink also predominates in the softly lit lounge area, while the bar sports wine-coloured decor, copper-topped tables and fake exposed timbers. Standard bedrooms offer two double beds, fitted units, good modern bath-

rooms, trouser presses and mini-bars. Executive rooms pamper with bathrobes and superior toiletries, and there are several impressive suites. Two floors are reserved for non-smokers. *Amenities* indoor swimming pool, sauna, gymnasium, in-house movies, secretarial services, fax, laundry service, coffee shop (10am–10pm), kiosk. ♿

LEICESTER — Ladbroke Hotel

See under PENGUIN HOTEL

LEICESTER — Leicester Forest Moat House 58% £D/E

H Map 11 D4 Leicestershire
Hinckley Road LE3 3GH
Leicester (0533) 394661

Credit Access, Amex, Diners, Visa

New owners have completely refurbished this low-rise modern hotel which stands close to the M1 beside the A47. Attractive multi-coloured settees and glass-topped tables make a pleasant lounge area in the entrance hall. There are three bars, including the popular public bar. Sprucely fitted bedrooms offer fresh fruit, remote-control TVs, tea-making facilities and hairdryers. Friendly, pleasant staff.
Amenities garden, putting, laundry service.

| Rooms 34 | Direct dial Yes | Confirm by 6 | Parking Ample |
| Ensuite bath/shower 34 | Room TV Yes | Last dinner 9.45 | Room service 24 hours |

LEICESTER — Penguin Hotel 61% £D

H Map 11 D4 Leicestershire
Humberstone Road LE5 3AT
Leicester (0533) 20471
Telex 341460

Credit Access, Amex, Diners, Visa

Formerly the Ladbroke Hotel but now under new ownership, this high-rise building stands on the edge of the city centre. The spacious foyer-lounge is bright and airy and the main bar is a lively spot, popular with residents and locals alike. Standard bedrooms offer practical overnight accommodation and compact bathrooms. Superior rooms have extras like hairdryers. *Amenities* in-house movies, secretarial services, laundry service, coffee shop (11am–10.30pm).

| Rooms 215 | Direct dial Yes | Confirm by 6 | Parking Limited |
| Ensuite bath/shower 215 | Room TV Yes | Last dinner 10.30 | Room service None |

LEICESTER — Post House Hotel 61% £C/D

H Map 11 D4 Leicestershire
Braunstone Lane East
LE3 2FW
Leicester (0533) 896688
Telex 341009

Credit Access, Amex, Diners, Visa

Leave the M1 at junction 21 and you'll find the Post House a mile or so into Leicester. It's a low-rise modern building with cheerful, popular public areas, good conference facilities and neat, reasonably spacious accommodation. Bedrooms are well lit, with armchairs, desk/dressing table space, mini-bars and compact bathrooms. Many rooms are family-size. *Amenities* garden, secretarial services, laundry service, coffee shop (7am–10pm), 24-hour lounge service.

| Rooms 172 | Direct dial Yes | Confirm by 6 | Parking Ample |
| Ensuite bath/shower 172 | Room TV Yes | Last dinner 10 | Room service Limited |

LEICESTER — Hotel Saint James 64% £D/E

H Map 11 D4 Leicestershire
Abbey Street LE1 3TE
Leicester (0533) 510666
Telex 342434

Credit Access, Amex, Diners, Visa

New owners have changed the name of this city centre hotel and refurbished it throughout. There's now a smart, up-to-date reception leading to a pleasant lounge with contemporary seating and a clubby library bar. The well-equipped bedrooms, 48 of which are small singles, have light wallcoverings, smart fitted furniture and fashionable fabrics; bathrooms are attractively tiled and have shower facilities.
Amenities secretarial services, fax, laundry service.

| Rooms 73 | Direct dial Yes | Confirm by 6 | Parking Ample |
| Ensuite bath/shower 73 | Room TV Yes | Last dinner 10 | Room service 24 hours |

**Our inspectors are our full-time employees;
they are professionally trained by us.**

LEIGH — Greyhound Hotel 56% £D

H Map 10 B2
Greater Manchester
Warrington Road WN7 3XQ
Leigh (0942) 671256

Credit Access, Amex, Diners, Visa

Functional accommodation is on offer at this modern hotel, popular with business visitors, fronted by a refurbished pub at a roundabout on the A580. Public areas include two lively bars, one named after Hector, the greyhound of the original inn on this site. Compact bedrooms, in a three-storey block, have tea-makers and neat bathrooms. Service lacks a smile.
Amenities laundry service.

| Rooms 54 | Direct dial Yes | Confirm by 6 | Parking Ample |
| Ensuite bath/shower 54 | Room TV Yes | Last dinner 9.45 | Room service 24 hours |

LEIGH-ON-SEA   Christine's Restaurant   *NEW ENTRY*   ♨

R **Map 7 C4** Essex
56 The Broadway
Southend (0702) 76411

Set L £11.95
Set D from £14.95
About £45 for two
Seats 40
Parties 36
Parking Ample

Credit Access, Visa

Wayne Hawkins' annual holiday is a gastronomic trip to France, and visitors to his restaurant, sited on a parade of shops, reap the benefit of his dedication and enthusiasm. His raw materials include the pick of the London markets, and the end product shows high culinary skills and an artist's eye for presentation. Some typical delights: cauliflower soup with cheese; terrine of trout and brill with a light tomato coulis; venison liver with wild mushrooms; best end of lamb with shallots, bacon and lentil sauce; a marvellous chocolate mousse with a biscuit base and a lovely crème anglaise. Fine food is complemented by carefully chosen wines. 🍷 Well-chosen ⊘ ♿

Lunch 12.30–2, Sun 12.30–2.30   *Dinner* 7.30–10
Closed D Sun, L Tues & Sat, all Mon, Bank Hols 4 days Xmas, 1st wk Jan & 2 wks Sept

LEIGHTON BUZZARD   Swan Hotel   60%   £D/E

HR **Map 5 E1** Bedfordshire
High Street LU7 7EA
Leighton Buzzard (0525) 372148

Credit Access, Amex, Diners, Visa

In the centre of town, the Swan is a handsome coaching inn dating back to 1710. The lounge, with its velour-clad settees, oil paintings and potted plants, has a comfortable, traditional character, and the adjacent Hunter's Bar is equally appealing. Bedrooms are neat and bright, with freestanding pine furniture (some mahogany); four courtyard suites have their own kitchens.
Amenities secretarial services, laundry service.

Rooms 38	*Direct dial* Yes	*Confirm by* 6	*Parking* Limited
Ensuite bath/shower 38	*Room TV* Yes	*Last dinner* 9.30	*Room service* 24 hours

Restaurant

Set L £10
Set D £11
About £42 for two
Seats 65
Parties 50

A pretty restaurant with a conservatory that overlooks a plant-filled patio. Candlelight enhances the romantic setting, and a varied and imaginative dinner menu tempts with the likes of Camembert parcels, roast duck with Chinese plum sauce or beef medallions with whisky sauce and a ragout of tomato and basil. Roast beef is a favourite on the simpler luncheon menu, and both sessions offer vegetarian main courses. ♿

Lunch 12–2.30   *Dinner* 7–9.30, Fri & Sat 7.30–10, Sun 7–9

Our inspectors *never* book in the name of Egon Ronay's Guides.
They disclose their identity only if they are considering an establishment
for inclusion in the next edition of the Guide.

LENHAM   Chilston Park   75%   £C

H **Map 7 C5** Kent
Boughton Malherbe ME17 2BE
Maidstone (0622) 859803
Telex 966154

Rooms 42
Ensuite bath/shower 41
Direct dial Yes
Room TV Yes
Confirm by arrang.
Last dinner 9.30
Parking Ample
Room service 24 hours

Credit Access, Amex, Diners, Visa

A 17th-century house which has been extensively restored, the hotel offers impressive features, including a treasure trove of antiques which encompasses all styles from Chippendale to Jacobean. On the walls are oils, watercolours and etchings and in the immense drawing room two roaring fires and deep leather and chintz sofas add to the luxury. The Renaissance hall boasts Tudor panelling and a superb

wooden staircase which sweeps up to the bedrooms, where there are further antiques and log fires. Most notable is the secluded and oak-beamed Tudor Suite. Bathrooms are sumptuously appointed.
Amenities garden, tennis, croquet, clay-pigeon shooting, coarse fishing, billiards, secretarial services, fax, laundry service, helipad.

LETCHWORTH Broadway Hotel 59% £E

H **Map 6 A3** Hertfordshire
The Broadway SG6 3NZ
Letchworth (0462) 480111
Telex 82425

Credit Access, Amex, Diners, Visa

An extensive programme of refurbishment has meant the loss of two bedrooms at this popular hotel, but all rooms now boast ensuite facilities, smart modern built-in furniture and coordinated soft furnishings. Trouser presses and tea-makers are standard (so are biscuits!). On the ground floor are two bars – a traditional pub and a spacious bar-lounge with bamboo furniture. No dogs.
Amenities secretarial services, laundry service.

| *Rooms* 35 | *Direct dial* Yes | *Confirm by* arrang. | *Parking* Ample |
| *Ensuite bath/shower* 35 | *Room TV* Yes | *Last dinner* 10 | *Room service* None |

LEWDOWN Fox's Earth, Lewtrenchard Manor 66% £C/D

HR **Map 2 C2** Devon
Nr Okehampton EX20 4PN
Lewdown (056 683) 256

Credit Access, Amex, Visa

American owners continue their painstaking refurbishment of this lovely 17th-century manor house, once the home of the Rev Sabine Baring-Gould who not only wrote the hymn 'Onward Christian Soldiers' but also had a passion for architectural embellishment – hence the ornate plaster ceilings and splendidly carved wood panelling in evidence throughout the building. Antique furniture and open fires add to the charm of the public rooms, while individually appointed bedrooms – also featuring period furniture, including three four-posters – have a nice homely feel. All but one have en suite bathrooms with showers. No children under 12. *Amenities* garden, croquet, shooting, clay-pigeon shooting, coarse fishing, laundry service, helipad.

| *Rooms* 8 | *Direct dial* Yes | *Confirm by* arrang. | *Parking* Ample |
| *Ensuite bath/shower* 7 | *Room TV* Yes | *Last dinner* 9.30 | *Room service* All day |

Restaurant ♔

Set L Sun £13.50
Set D £21.50
About £60 for two
Seats 40
Parties 50

The candlelit dining room with its mullioned windows and dark panelling is as attractive as ever, and the emphasis on ultra-fresh produce remains an overriding priority, but a change of chef has brought about a slight shift in emphasis – from simple cooking methods and light saucing to more ambitious assemblies and richer flavour combinations. Current offerings could include mille-feuilles of potato and turnip interlaced with foie gras, teamed with wild mushrooms in a sherry sauce; artichoke soup spiced with root ginger, presented in a crusted wholemeal bowl; and herb-stuffed fillet of brill sauced with champagne, leeks and truffles. Desserts, too, seem more elaborate. Carefully selected wines. ♟ Well-chosen ❧

Lunch Sun only 12.30–2 *Dinner* 7.30–9.30
Closed L Mon–Sat

LEWES Kenwards ♙

R **Map 7 B6** East Sussex
Pipe Passage,
151a High Street
Lewes (0273) 472343

About £42 for two
Seats 28
Parking Limited

Credit Access, Amex, Diners, Visa

A raftered, 15th-century building with simple pine tables and a pretty garden for pre-dinner drinks. John Kenward's enthusiastic, enjoyable cooking draws on fresh local produce and his menus offer two fish dishes, one vegetarian and three meat (including game in winter). An admirable cellar, reasonably priced, features many fine wines in half bottles. The lovely Quarts de Chaume '71 (Jean Baumard) is a perfect pudding wine. ♟ Well-chosen ❧

Lunch by arrang. *Dinner* 7.30–9.30, Sat 7–10
Closed Sun, Mon & 25 & 26 Dec

LEWES Light of Bengal

R **Map 7 B6** East Sussex
32 Lansdown Place
Lewes (0273) 472493

Indian cooking
About £28 for two
Seats 34
Parking Limited

Credit Access, Visa

Consistently competent cooking explains why the Light of Bengal has never been extinguished. The tandoori oven is responsible for delicious tikkas and seekh kebabs, and curries range from the subtle kormas to the spirited Bangalore phal. The nan is excellent, as is the pulao rice. Finish with delicious almond or pistachio kulfi. Service is friendly and efficient.

Lunch 12–2.30 *Dinner* 6–11.30
Closed 25 & 26 Dec

LEWES   Shelleys Hotel   66%   £C/D

H Map 7 B6 East Sussex
High Street BN7 1XS
Lewes (0273) 472361

Credit Access, Amex, Diners, Visa

A fine period house, covered in creeper, with a correspondingly elegant, comfortable interior. Entrance is via a handsome pillared hall and there's a spacious, well-proportioned lounge with a charming writing room at one end; the attractive bar is hung with oil paintings. Bedrooms range from huge bay-windowed rooms with antique furniture to compact, well-equipped singles. All have neat modern bathrooms. *Amenities* garden, croquet, laundry service.

Rooms 21	*Direct dial* Yes	*Confirm by* arrang.	*Parking* Ample
Ensuite bath/shower 21	*Room TV* Yes	*Last dinner* 9.15	*Room service* 24 hours

LEWES   Trumps   ♀

R Map 7 B6 East Sussex
19 Station Street
Lewes (0273) 473906

Set L £15.95, Sun £8.95
Set D £15.95
About £45 for two
Seats 36 *Parties* 45
Parking Limited
Credit Access, Visa

The McGowns work hard to make a success of their town-centre restaurant. Both are accomplished cooks, Lesley deputising for Neil when he goes in search of game to enhance the well-balanced set menus. Anyone not wanting a full meal may select a single dish: Scotch salmon with crayfish sauce, perhaps, venison with sherry and cream, or trout with a cucumber and prawn sauce.

Lunch 12–2, Sun 12–3   *Dinner* 7–10.30, Fri & Sat 7–11, Sun 7.30–9.30   **Closed** L Thurs & Sat, all Wed, Bank Hols, D 25 Dec, 26–30 Dec & 2wks autumn

---

Changes in data sometimes occur in establishments
after the Guide goes to press.
Prices should be taken as indications rather than firm quotes.

LEYLAND   Penguin Hotel   65%   £D

H Map 10 A1 Lancashire
Leyland Way PR5 2JX
Leyland (0772) 422922
Telex 677651

Credit Access, Amex, Diners, Visa

A friendly smile and a glass of sherry greet guests at this modern business hotel, and easy relaxation is available in the leafy, pine-furnished bar-lounge. Bedrooms range from decent-sized singles to ten Gold Star executive rooms with luxury touches like hairdryers and teletext. All rooms have tea-makers and remote-control TVs. *Amenities* pool table, in-house movies, secretarial services, laundry service. &

Rooms 93	*Direct dial* Yes	*Confirm by* arrang.	*Parking* Ample
Ensuite bath/shower 93	*Room TV* Yes	*Last dinner* 10	*Room service* 24 hours

LICHFIELD   George Hotel   60%   £D

H Map 10 C3 Staffordshire
Bird Street WS13 6PR
Lichfield (0543) 414822

Credit Access, Amex, Diners, Visa

Once a coaching inn, this charming hotel still conveys a quiet aura of Regency elegance. The comfortable foyer provides instant peace after the bustle of the main street, and the lounge is cosy and inviting. Bedroom furniture is in attractive dark wood, fabrics in pleasant pastel shades. All rooms have tea-makers, and there are many extras in the five Executive rooms. No dogs. *Amenities* patio, laundry service.

Rooms 39	*Direct dial* Yes	*Confirm by* 6	*Parking* Ample
Ensuite bath/shower 39	*Room TV* Yes	*Last dinner* 9.30	*Room service* 24 hours

LIFTON   Arundell Arms   62%   £D/E

H Map 2 C2 Devon
PL16 0AA
Lifton (0566) 84666

Credit Access, Amex, Diners, Visa
Closed 5 days Xmas

One of the best-known fishing hotels in Britain, with 20 miles of its own water on the Tamar and its tributaries. They also run fishing courses from beginners to advanced. Behind the creeper-clad frontage guests can relax in the comfort of the lounge, or swap fishy tales in the bar. Bedrooms are of a reasonable size, with restful decor and mostly pine furniture. *Amenities* garden, game fishing, games room, laundry service.

Rooms 29	*Direct dial* Yes	*Confirm by* arrang.	*Parking* Ample
Ensuite bath/shower 29	*Room TV* Yes	*Last dinner* 9	*Room service* All day

LIMEHOUSE — Good Friends

See under LONDON

LINCOLN — D'Isney Place Hotel — NEW ENTRY — £E

PH Map 11 E2 Lincolnshire
Eastgate LN2 4AA
Lincoln (0522) 538881

Credit Access, Amex, Diners, Visa

Built in 1735 for John d'Isney, this comfortable little hotel is close to the cathedral. A couple of bedrooms are small, fairly basic singles, but most are quite luxurious, with well-chosen fabrics and decent period furniture. There are several four-poster rooms, a double suite and some rooms with whirlpool baths. Fresh fruit, fresh milk, good-quality toiletries and fluffy bathrobes. No day rooms.
Amenities garden, badminton.

Rooms 18	*Direct dial* Yes	*Confirm by* arrang.	*Parking* Limited
Ensuite bath/shower 18	*Room TV* Yes		*Room service* All day

LINCOLN — Eastgate Post House Hotel — 65% — £C

H Map 11 E2 Lincolnshire
Eastgate LN2 1PN
Lincoln (0522) 20341
Telex 56316

Credit Access, Amex, Diners, Visa

A comfortable modern hotel facing the splendid cathedral and ideally situated for the pretty shops and restaurants of old Lincoln. Refurbishment keeps things smart in the bedrooms, all of which have well-equipped bathrooms en suite. There's a spacious, airy lobby-lounge, a popular coffee shop and a choice of bars. The buffet breakfast served is better than average. Pleasant, polite staff. *Amenities* garden, secretarial services, laundry service, coffee shop (10am–10pm).

Rooms 71	*Direct dial* Yes	*Confirm by* 6	*Parking* Ample
Ensuite bath/shower 71	*Room TV* Yes	*Last dinner* 10	*Room service* 24 hours

LINCOLN — Harvey's Cathedral Restaurant — NEW ENTRY

R Map 11 E2 Lincolnshire
1 Exchequergate,
Castle Square
Lincoln (0522) 21886

Set L from £5.75
Set D from £13.95
Seats 55
Parties 50
Parking Difficult

Credit Access, Visa

Jovial Bob Harvey and his professional team provide an interesting choice of good eating in a stylish, welcoming restaurant near the cathedral. Chicken liver parfait could get your meal under way, followed perhaps by warm Brie tart and then prawn gumbo, Chinese-style duck or loin of lamb with herb butter. There are some excellent cheeses, and sweets include ice creams, chocolate pot and an irresistible squidgy orange and almond pudding. Fixed-price four-course menu; à la carte and short set menu at lunchtime. The keenly priced wine list has been chosen with great flair – white burgundies are especially attractive. Also some excellent half-bottles. ♀ Well-chosen ⊗

Lunch 12–2.30 *Dinner* 7–10
About £38 *for two*

LINCOLN — Moor Lodge Hotel — 58% — £D/E

H Map 11 E2 Lincolnshire
Sleaford Road, Branston
LN4 1HU
Lincoln (0522) 791366

Credit Access, Amex, Diners, Visa

The hotel is a modernised and much extended Edwardian house on the B1188 some three miles from the city centre. The Lancaster Bar, warmed by a central hooded fire, is a nice spot for a drink, and there's a comfortable, well-furnished lounge done out in pretty pastel shades. Bedrooms are neat and modern, with compact, carpeted bathrooms. A popular hotel for conferences and functions.
Amenities garden, laundry service. ₺

Rooms 25	*Direct dial* Yes	*Confirm by* arrang.	*Parking* Ample
Ensuite bath/shower 25	*Room TV* Yes	*Last dinner* 9.30	*Room service* All day

LINCOLN — White Hart Hotel — 69% — £C

HR Map 11 E2 Lincolnshire
Bailgate LN1 3AR
Lincoln (0522) 26222
Telex 56304

Credit Access, Amex, Diners, Visa

Exemplary service makes every guest feel especially welcome at this venerable city-centre hotel located between the cathedral and castle. There's been an inn here since 1460 but the present building dates back to 1710. Its dignified public rooms positively glow with antiques and old-world charm, while the spacious, elegant bedrooms – also featuring antiques – sport sitting areas (or sitting rooms) and luxurious bathrooms. *Amenities* secretarial services, fax, laundry service.

Rooms 48	*Direct dial* Yes	*Confirm by* 6	*Parking* Ample
Ensuite bath/shower 48	*Room TV* Yes	*Last dinner* 10	*Room service* 24 hours

see over

White Hart Restaurant   *NEW ENTRY*

Set L from £7.55, Sun £8.95
Set D £12.95
About £42 for two
Seats 70
Parties 65
Parking Ample

A gracefully proportioned Georgian dining room is the setting for carefully prepared, well balanced dishes based on top-quality ingredients. Light, refreshing starters might range from mackerel mousse in a herby mayonnaise to vegetable terrine in a red pepper coulis while simple, straightforward main courses could include stir-fried scampi with almonds or loin of venison in port wine sauce. The cellar offers some fine mature clarets and burgundies. Excellent service. 🍷 Well-chosen ⓔ

Lunch 12.30–2.15   *Dinner* 7–10, Sun 7.00–9.30

**If we recommend meals in a Hotel or Inn,
a separate entry is made for its restaurant.**

LINTON   Wood Hall   82%   *NEW ENTRY*   £C

HR Map 10 C1
West Yorkshire
Nr Wetherby LS22 4JA
Wetherby (0937) 67271
Telex 557660

Rooms 22
Ensuite bath/shower 22
Direct dial Yes
Room TV Yes
Confirm by arrang.
Last dinner 9.30
Parking Ample
Room service 24 hours

Credit Access, Amex, Diners, Visa

An impressive Georgian house set in 100 acres of peaceful parkland. Owner Jonathan Wix spent two years restoring the house to its former glory, and the result is a hotel of great comfort and luxury, which he and his staff run with justified pride and enthusiasm. Floral displays grace the entrance hall, setting the tone for rooms like the sumptuously furnished lounge and elegant panelled bar. Individually designed bedrooms feature eye-catching floral wallpapers, hand-painted furniture, seating areas, modern accessories and many thoughtful extras. Bathrooms are equally pleasing. **Amenities** garden, indoor swimming pool, sauna, solarium, shooting, clay-pigeon shooting, coarse fishing, snooker, secretarial services, fax, laundry service. ♿

Restaurant   *NEW ENTRY*

Set L £12.95
Set D from £22, Sun £12.95
About £65 for two
Seats 65
Parties 28

Michael Riley has an impressive pedigree, and the elegant surroundings are a fine backdrop for his talents. His style is modern British, with superb sauces enhancing distinct, natural flavours: puff pastry pillow of roast quail with wild mushrooms, steamed monkfish on a subtle cream chervil sauce, beef medallions with bone marrow and a rich thyme juice, lovely Armagnac parfait with an orange and caramel sauce. Excellent wines, too, the house wines in particular being scrupulously chosen. 🍷 Well-chosen ⓔ ♿

Lunch 12.30–2   *Dinner* 7–9.30, Sun till 8.30

LISKEARD   The Well House   74%   £D

HR Map 2 C3 Cornwall
St Keyne PL14 4RN
Liskeard (0579) 42001

Rooms 7
Ensuite bath/shower 7
Direct dial Yes
Room TV Yes
Confirm by arrang.
Last dinner 9
Parking Ample
Room service All day

Credit Access, Amex, Visa

Follow the signs to St Keyne Well, off the B3254 three miles south of Liskeard, to find this delightful hotel set in well-tended grounds amid some glorious Cornish countryside. Welcoming owner Nicholas Wainford has created a quiet and relaxing atmosphere for his guests throughout attractive public areas like the lovely foyer with its original tiled floor, the sumptuously comfortable lounge and

bright, up-to-date little bar. Individually decorated and furnished bedrooms are stylishly contemporary and all offer excellent private bathrooms as well as remote-control TVs, direct-dial telephones and trouser presses. Helpful, efficient service. **Amenities** garden, outdoor swimming pool, tennis, croquet, laundry service.

Restaurant ♕

Set L £13.50
Set D £18.50
About £48 for two
Seats 36
Parties 36

David Pope cooks with confidence in an imaginative, modern style at this elegantly contemporary restaurant. Prime local produce features throughout his monthly-changing menus, which might include vegetable and foie gras terrine followed by, say, pinkly tender beef with aubergines and tarragon sauce or monkfish with mixed peppers and herbs. Tempting sweets like apple and Calvados tart to finish. Booking essential. ♟ Well-chosen ⊖

Lunch 12.30–2 *Dinner* 7.30–9
Closed Mon eve to non-residents

LITTLE WYMONDLEY Redcoats Farmhouse Hotel 57% £E

H **Map 6 A3** Hertfordshire
Redcoats Green,
Nr Hitchin SG4 7JR
Stevenage (0438) 729500

Credit Access, Amex, Diners, Visa
Closed 24 Dec–2 Jan

Dating in part from the middle of the 15th century, this former farmhouse offers splendidly informal and very characterful accommodation. Main-house bedrooms are old-fashioned, with sturdy, traditional furniture, while the others, in a converted stable block, are in modern motel style; all are comfortable and decently sized. There's a marvellous bar with beams and old country furnishings, and a chintzy, lived-in lounge. No dogs. *Amenities* garden.

Rooms 16	*Direct dial* Yes	*Confirm by* arrang.	*Parking* Ample
Ensuite bath/shower 11	*Room TV* Yes	*Last dinner* 9	*Room service* Limited

---

We welcome bona fide complaints and recommendations
on the tear-out pages at the back of the book for readers' comment.
They are followed up by our professional team.

LIVERPOOL Armadillo *NEW ENTRY*

R **Town plan C3** Merseyside
20 Mathew Street
051-236 4123

About £35 for two
Seats 60
Parties 60
Parking Ample

Credit Access

Stylish decor creates a pleasant ambience at this friendly restaurant where imaginative and capably cooked dishes are on offer. Starters are particularly good – try the home-made soups served with outstanding fresh bread or blinis with sour cream. Main courses range from steak to roast pheasant. Very good, wide-ranging wine list: Moss Wood Pinot Noir '83, St Joseph (Chapoutier) '78, Alfred Gratien Crémant '76. ♟ Well-chosen ⊖

Lunch 12–3 *Dinner* 7.30–10.30
Closed D Mon, all Sun & 2 days Xmas

LIVERPOOL Atlantic Tower Hotel 70% £C/D

H **Town plan B3** Merseyside
Chapel Street L3 9RE
051-227 4444
Telex 627070

Rooms 226
Ensuite bath/shower 226
Direct dial Yes
Room TV Yes
Confirm by 6
Last dinner 10.30
Parking Ample
Room service 24 hours

Credit Access, Amex, Diners, Visa

There are fine views across the Mersey from this strikingly designed hotel, whose lines are reminiscent of a great ship's bows. Friendly receptionists greet guests in the large lobby-lounge, where a ceiling-suspended bronze is a prominent feature. The plush public bar has a nautical theme, while the carvery bar is done out like a Pullman car. There's also a cosy little cocktail bar. Bedrooms, many

recently upgraded, include a floor of suites and a lot more Executive rooms (the latter have mini-bars in addition to the standard hairdryers, trouser presses and remote-control TVs). Neat, compact bathrooms throughout.
Amenities in-house movies, secretarial services, laundry service.

F I A T Liverpool

SOUTHPORT 20miles

□ Hotel
● Restaurant
⊡ Hotel and Restaurant
△ Inn

Princes Dock

BATH STREET

KING EDWARD STREET

GREAT HOWARD ST A565

LEEDS ST

LEEDS STREET

B5182 PALL MALL

A5038 VAUXHALL ROAD

NAYLOR STREET

OLD LEEDS STREET

EAST STREET

PALL MALL

OLD HALL STREET

BROOK STREET

EDMUND STREET

ORMOND STREET

TITHEBARN STREET

VERNON STREET

MOORFIELDS

Tunnel Exit Atlantic Tower Hotel

CHAPEL STREET

Town Hall

EXCHANGE S

DALE STREET

NORTH JOHN ST

ST NICHOLAS PL

WATER STREET

CASTLE STREET

COOK STREET

VICTORIA

Armadillo

Royal Liver Building

THE STRAND

BRUNSWICK STREET

FENWICK STREET

JAMES STREET

HARRINGTON STREET

NTH JOHN ST

SOUTH JOHN STREET

RIVER MERSEY

Bus Sta

7

Cunard Building

19

Port of Liverpool Building

GORE

MANN ISLAND

STRAND STREET

CANNING PLACE

Canning Dock

CANNING PLACE

WAPPING

A5036

5

0   220   440 yards
0   200   400 metres

15

25   Albert Dock   3

Salthouse Dock

A   B   C

© 1988 Egon Ronay's Guides

LIVERPOOL

Map 10 A2
Town plan on preceding page

Population 509,981

Since King John granted its Charter in 1207, Liverpool has taken increasing advantage of its sheltered Merseyside position to become England's leading Atlantic port and an industrial magnet, while the Arts are as vigorously pursued as football. The Royal Liverpool Philharmonic Orchestra, the Walker Art Gallery, the University's music-making, and the city's five theatres are at least as important to it as pop.

Annual Events
Grand National at Aintree *April*
City of Liverpool Parade *May*
Mersey River Festival *June*
Orange Day Parade *July*
Beatle Convention *August*

Sights Outside City
Aintree, Hoylake, Chester, New Brighton, Southport

Information Office
Lime Street
Liverpool 1
Telephone 051–709 3631

Fiat Dealers
Stanley Motors Ltd
243 East Prescot Road
Liverpool L14 5NA
Tel. 051–228 9151

Crosby Park Garage Ltd
2 Coronation Road, Crosby
Liverpool L23 3BJ
Tel. 051–924 9101

Lambert Autos Ltd
Custom House
Brunswick Business Park
Liverpool L3 4BJ
Tel. 051–708 8224

1 Aintree Race-course **E1**
2 Airport **D5**
3 Albert Dock, *Shopping, business, conference centre* **B5**
4 Anglican Cathedral *20th-c Gothic, complete after 75 years* **F5**
5 Birkenhead Tunnel Entrance **D2**
6 Cavern Walks site of Beatles' Cavern Club **C3**
7 Cunard Building, Dock Company Office and Royal Liverpool Building *waterfront landmarks* **B4**
8 Empire Theatre **E2**
9 Everton Football Club **E1**
10 Everyman Theatre **F4**
11 Festival Gardens and Otterspool Promenade **C5**
12 Library and Museum *Hornby Library has outstanding prints and first editions. Museum houses aquarium, ivories, jewellery, birds, shipping gallery* **E2**
13 Lime Street Station **E/F3**
14 Liverpool Football Club **E1**
15 Maritime Museum **B4/5**
16 Museum of Labour History **E2**
17 Neptune Theatre **D4**
18 Philharmonic Hall **F5**
19 Pier Head **A4**
20 Playhouse Theatre **D3**
21 Roman Catholic Cathedral *space-age architecture* **F4**
22 Royal Court Theatre **E3**
23 St George's Hall *former Assize Courts and Concert Hall* **E3**
24 Speke Hall *Elizabethan house with beautiful gardens on the Mersey* **D5**
25 Tate Gallery Liverpool **B5**
26 Tourist Information Centre **E3**
27 Walker Art Gallery *England's largest collection outside London* **E2**

LIVERPOOL — Britannia Adelphi Hotel — 69% — £C

H Town plan E4 Merseyside
Ranelagh Place L3 5UL
051-709 7200
Telex 629644

Credit Access, Amex, Diners, Visa

Day rooms at this impressively-proportioned hotel span various moods and styles: a palatial lounge with Doric columns and chandeliers, an Edwardian-style bar with moulded plasterwork ceiling, the somewhat dated American Bar and basement night clubs and the well-equipped leisure centre. Changes are due by publication date, including two new restaurants and a coffee shop (plus, we hope, better housekeeping). Size and appointments of the bedrooms vary, but some refurbishment has taken place and all rooms have clock radios and tea-makers. *Amenities* indoor swimming pool, sauna, solarium, whirlpool bath, gymnasium, hairdressing and beauty salon, squash, satellite TV, secretarial services, fax, laundry service.

Rooms 344	*Direct dial* Yes	*Confirm by* 8	*Parking* Ample
Ensuite bath/shower 314	*Room TV* Yes	*Last dinner* 10.30	*Room service* 24 hours

LIVERPOOL — Crest Hotel, Liverpool City — 58% — £C/D

H Town plan F3 Merseyside
Lord Nelson Street L3 5QB
051-709 7050
Telex 627954

Credit Access, Amex, Diners, Visa

A modern grey-brick hotel right by Lime Street station. Simple, practical bedrooms include 45 designated non-smoking, Lady Crest rooms and a couple of suites designed with the business executive in mind. There's a good-sized bar-lounge and a friendly pub, the *Stamp & Whistle*, attached to the hotel. The large car park is a great asset. *Amenities* pool table, secretarial services, fax, laundry service, 24-hour lounge service.

Rooms 160	*Direct dial* Yes	*Confirm by* 6	*Parking* Ample
Ensuite bath/shower 160	*Room TV* Yes	*Last dinner* 9.30	*Room service* Limited

LIVERPOOL — Liverpool Moat House — 67% — £C/D

H Town plan D4 Merseyside
Paradise Street L1 8JD
051-709 0181
Telex 627270

Credit Access, Amex, Diners, Visa
Closed 4 days Xmas

A central location, free parking in the adjacent NCP, leisure facilities and stylishly revamped day rooms are pluses at this modern hotel. Bedrooms, on seven floors, are all of a good size, with individual heating and air conditioning, huge open wardrobe areas and armchair or sofa seating. The decor, which was beginning to look rather dated, was the subject of a major refurbishment programme due to end as we published. Housekeeping is generally good. Poor breakfasts. *Amenities* garden, indoor swimming pool, sauna, solarium, whirlpool bath, gymnasium, in-house movies, secretarial services, fax, laundry room & service, coffee shop (11am–10.30pm), kiosk. &

Rooms 258	*Direct dial* Yes	*Confirm by* 6	*Parking* Ample
Ensuite bath/shower 258	*Room TV* Yes	*Last dinner* 10	*Room service* 24 hours

LIVERPOOL — St George's Hotel — 63% — £C/D

H Town plan E3 Merseyside
St John's Precinct,
Lime Street L1 1NQ
051-709 7090
Telex 627630

Credit Access, Amex, Diners, Visa

A modern hotel built as part of the St John's Precinct development near Lime Street Station in the early 1970s. Views across the city are a feature of the bedrooms, which have oak-stained fitted furniture and smallish bathrooms; some rooms are double-glazed. Among the day rooms are a spacious second-floor lounge and bar; there are also extensive function facilities. Poor breakfasts. *Amenities* laundry service, coffee shop (8am–8pm).

Rooms 155	*Direct dial* Yes	*Confirm by* 6	*Parking* Ample
Ensuite bath/shower 155	*Room TV* Yes	*Last dinner* 10	*Room service* 24 hours

LODDISWELL — Lavinia's

R Map 3 D3 Devon
Nr Kingsbridge
Kingsbridge (0548) 550306

Set D from £12.50
About £50 for two
Seats 30
Parties 40
Parking Ample
Credit Access, Visa

Follow the signs down little country lanes just north of Loddiswell to find this delightfully civilised farmhouse restaurant. The journey's well worth it, as Lavinia Davies is a most accomplished chef who uses top-quality ingredients in such delightful dishes as gougère of crab and mushrooms, wild rabbit and venison pie with a puff-pastry top, and veal with a cream and sorrel sauce. Super sweets, too.
🍷 Well-chosen 🕏

Lunch by arrang. only   *Dinner* 7.30–9.30
Closed Sun, Mon, Bank Hols & Nov–Mar

LOFTUS · Grinkle Park Hotel   71%   £D

H **Map 15 C5** Cleveland
Easington
Nr Saltburn-by-the-Sea TS13 4UB
Guisborough (0287) 40515

Rooms 20
Ensuite bath/shower 20
Direct dial Yes
Room TV Yes
Confirm by 6
Last dinner 9
Parking Ample
Room service All day

Credit Access, Amex, Diners, Visa

A long rhododendron-lined drive leads up to a fine Victorian mansion surrounded by wide lawns and mature trees. The whole place was completely transformed a couple of years ago, and the day rooms have all been tastefully redecorated and refurbished. Notable are the fine billiards room and the Camellia room with its picture windows, ruffled curtains, wicker seating and flowering camellias growing up through the floor. Good-sized bedrooms are individually and stylishly decorated, and nice touches include mineral water, magazines, pot-pourri and plants. Single rooms have showers/WC only. Smart, friendly staff. *Amenities* garden, tennis, croquet, game fishing, clay-pigeon shooting, billiards, secretarial services, laundry service.

LONG MELFORD · Black Lion Hotel   68%   £E/F

HR **Map 6 C3** Suffolk
The Green CO10 9DN
Sudbury (0787) 312356

Credit Access, Visa

Luke and Amelia Brady have transformed their old coaching inn into a place of great atmospheric charm. In the lounge, antique furnishings, groaning book shelves and antique artwork provide homely relaxation, while the bar has old prints and russet walls. Bedrooms have pretty floral fabrics, antique freestanding furniture and thoughtful touches such as pot-pourri and reading material; well-equipped bathrooms boast good toiletries. *Amenities* garden, laundry service.

Rooms 10	*Direct dial* Yes	*Confirm by* arrang.	*Parking* Ample
Ensuite bath/shower 10	*Room TV* Yes	*Last dinner* 9.30 (9 in winter)	*Room service* All day

Restaurant

Set L Sun only £7
About £35 for two
Seats 45
Parties 50

Simple, homely decor and good-quality food prepared from prime ingredients combine to make a successful formula. The imaginative, concise menu encompasses such unusual delights as pancakes filled with sweetbreads and chicken in a sorrel, mushroom and brandy sauce, saddle of monkfish in rosé wine sauce with tomato and basil and veal medallions in Madeira and truffle sauce. Good, selective wine list: Givry Baron Thérard '83. ♀ Well-chosen ♿

Lunch 12.30–2.15, Sun till 2.30   *Dinner* 7.30–9.30, till 9 in winter
Closed D Sun to non-residents

LONG MELFORD · Bull Hotel   64%   £C/D

H **Map 6 C3** Suffolk
Nr Sudbury CO10 9JG
Sudbury (0787) 78494

Credit Access, Amex, Diners, Visa

Originally the home of a wool merchant, the Bull has a history stretching back some 500 years. Refurbishment is under way: new carpets, curtains and armchairs in the splendid beamed lounge, and a complete facelift for the bedrooms, which include two atmospheric Tudor suites. The bar is full of character, and there's a quiet writing room. Breakfast, judged on our last visit, is an event to be missed. *Amenities* laundry service.

Rooms 27	*Direct dial* Yes	*Confirm by* 6	*Parking* Ample
Ensuite bath/shower 27	*Room TV* Yes	*Last dinner* 9.30	*Room service* Limited

LONG MELFORD · Chimneys

R **Map 6 C3** Suffolk
Hall Street
Sudbury (0787) 79806

Set L £10.50, Sun £11.50
About £50 for two
Seats 50
Parties 40
Parking Ample
Credit Access, Visa

You can be sure of a good meal at this quaint beamed restaurant where imaginative menus change every month and a typical starter is a flavoursome oxtail broth with medallions of monkfish poached in vermouth, tomato and cream to follow. Excellent desserts. Interesting wine list with some fine bottles: '85 St Aubin Rouge (Roux), '64 Coteaux du Layon (Moulin de Tigne), Quinta do Noval '31. ☺ ♿

Lunch 12–2   *Dinner* 7.30–9.30
Closed D Sun, all Mon & Bank Hols

LONGHAM   The Bridge House   60%   *NEW ENTRY*   £D

H **Map 4 C4** Dorset
2 Ringwood Road,
Nr Wimborne BH22 9AN
Bournemouth (0202) 578828
Telex 418484

Credit Access, Amex, Visa

There's a Mediterranean flavour to this Greek-owned hotel perched on the banks of the Stour and boasting a waterside patio and island garden. Cheerful public rooms include a reception lounge and a busy bar with a self-service food counter. Good-size bedrooms – some with river views – have tasteful decor and compact tiled bathrooms. No dogs. *Amenities* garden, coarse fishing, laundry service, children's play area.

Rooms 36	*Direct dial* Yes	*Confirm by* arrang.	*Parking* Ample
Ensuite bath/shower 36	*Room TV* Yes	*Last dinner* 9.30	*Room service* Limited

LONGHORSLEY   Linden Hall Hotel   81%   *E*   £C/D

H **Map 14 B3** Northumberland
Nr Morpeth NE65 8XF
Morpeth (0670) 516611
Telex 538224

Rooms 45
Ensuite bath/shower 45
Direct dial Yes
Room TV Yes
Confirm by 6
Last dinner 10
Parking Ample
Room service 24 hours

Credit Access, Amex, Diners, Visa

A long rhododendron-lined drive leads to a handsome Georgian mansion set in beautiful gardens and parkland. Elegant public rooms are immaculately kept, and the inner hall, with its leather armchairs, gilt-framed oils and fine cantilevered staircase, is particularly splendid. There's a small bar, and in the grounds a stone-walled pub converted from an old granary. Bedrooms are standard or superior, the latter being

larger; individually and tastefully decorated, they all have well-equipped private bathrooms. Staff do their jobs well. *Amenities* garden, sauna, solarium, hairdressing, tennis, putting, croquet, clay-pigeon shooting, games room, snooker, in-house movies, secretarial services, fax, laundry service, children's playroom & playground. &

We welcome bona fide complaints and recommendations on the tear-out pages at the back of the book for readers' comment. They are followed up by our professional team.

LOOE   Talland Bay Hotel   67%   £D/E

HR **Map 2 C3** Cornwall
Talland Bay PL13 2JB
Polperro (0503) 72667

Credit Access, Amex, Diners, Visa
Closed Jan–mid Feb

Guests return here year after year to enjoy the glorious scenery and splendid, old-fashioned standards of service. It's a quietly situated hotel, dating from the 16th century but now much extended, with two simply furnished lounges – one non-smoking and both overlooking the swimming pool, garden and sea beyond – plus a cosy little bar. Good-sized bedrooms are attractively furnished in traditional style and most have cushioned window seats to make the most of the lovely views. Neat, modern bathrooms (one shared). Five rooms are in a nearby annexe.
Amenities garden, outdoor swimming pool, sauna, solarium, putting, croquet, games room, snooker, secretarial services. &

Rooms 23	*Direct dial* Yes	*Confirm by* arrang.	*Parking* Ample
Ensuite bath/shower 21	*Room TV* Yes	*Last dinner* 9	*Room service* All day

Restaurant

Set D £11.50
About £38 *for two*
Seats 55

A mellow oak-panelled dining room with sea views is the setting for John Tyldesley's enjoyable cooking. Beautifully fresh seafood is the obvious choice here – from whiting and lemon sole to prawns, scampi, oysters, crab and lobster – though meat-eaters and vegetarians are not forgotten. To finish, delicious home-made ice creams or sweets from the trolley. In summer there's a popular buffet lunch by the pool. &

Lunch 12.30–2, Sun 12.45–1.30   *Dinner* 7.15–9
Closed Jan–mid Feb

LOSTWITHIEL | Carotel Motel　55% | £E

H **Map 2 C3** Cornwall
20 Castle Hill PL22 0DD
Lostwithiel (0208) 872223

Credit Access, Amex, Diners, Visa

A friendly welcome and modest comforts are offered by this well-run motel on the A390 in the town centre. Simple public areas include a relaxing lounge and a pleasant bar. Practical, unfussy bedrooms – due to be refurnished with darkwood fitted units – have tea-makers and private facilities.
Amenities garden, outdoor swimming pool, solarium, satellite TV, laundry room.

Rooms 32	*Direct dial* Yes	*Confirm by* arrang.	*Parking* Ample
Ensuite bath/shower 32	*Room TV* Yes	*Last dinner* 9.30	*Room service* Limited

LOUGHBOROUGH | Kings Head Hotel　58% | £D

H **Map 11 D3** Leicestershire
High Street LE11 2QL
Loughborough (0509) 233222

Credit Access, Amex, Diners, Visa

Check directions when booking at this comfortable town-centre hotel. Public areas are quite smart, with contemporary patterned carpeting and period-style furniture. Bedrooms are attractively decorated, some in pale beige and cream tones, others in pretty floral prints. All are of a good size and offer tea-makers. Bathrooms are modern, with cork floors and basic toiletries.
Amenities games room, laundry service.

Rooms 86	*Direct dial* Yes	*Confirm by* 6	*Parking* Ample
Ensuite bath/shower 78	*Room TV* Yes	*Last dinner* 9.15	*Room service* 24 hours

LOUGHBOROUGH | Restaurant Roger Burdell | ♧

R **Map 11 D3** Leicestershire
The Manor House,
Sparrow Hill
Loughborough (0509) 231813

Set L from £9
Set D from £19.50
Seats 70 *Parties* 32
Parking Limited
Credit Access, Amex, Visa

A fine old manor house makes a splendid venue for Roger Burdell's pleasing cooking. Top-quality fresh produce is expertly handled, saucing being particularly strong, and presentation is eye-catching. Typical dishes are warm salad of pigeon breast with bacon and croûtons followed by fillet of brill with braised fennel. Sound wine list; drink the delicious Rosemount Chardonnay '87 and the St Joseph Rouge '83 (P. Jaboulet Aîné). ♀ Well-chosen ⊖

Lunch 12.30–2　*Dinner* 7.30–9.15　*About* £55 *for two*
Closed L Mon, all Sun, 26 Dec & 1 Jan

LOWER BEEDING | South Lodge　76% | £C

HR **Map 5 E3** West Sussex
London Road RH13 6PS
Lower Beeding (040 376) 711
Telex 877765

Rooms 34
Ensuite bath/shower 34
Direct dial Yes
Room TV Yes
Confirm by 6
Last dinner 10.30
Parking Ample
Room service 24 hours

Credit Access, Amex, Diners, Visa

Glorious views of the South Downs, grounds ablaze with flowering shrubs, and a superb rock garden all add up to a delightful setting for this Victorian country house. Public rooms are on a grand scale, with high ornate ceilings, wood panelling and open fires. Spacious bedrooms are prettily (if a little impractically) furnished in period style and have splendidly opulent bathrooms (though the  inefficient hot water system causes a few grumbles). Some bedrooms at the top of the house are smaller and more cottage in style, and further accommodation is becoming available with the conversion of a stable block. *Amenities* garden, tennis, croquet, riding, clay-pigeon shooting, game fishing, fax, laundry service.

Restaurant ♔

Set L £12.50, Sun £13.50
Set D from £21.50
Seats 36

A fine, half-panelled dining room sets the scene for James Hayward's exciting cooking. He's a chef of considerable talent and great enthusiasm who strikes a careful balance between classical and modern ideas in dishes like beef consommé with foie gras dumplings. Just occasionally imagination oversteps the mark and too many flavours jostle for attention, as in salmon with Sauternes, chives and mint. Service is patchy. Vegetarian menu. ♀ Well-chosen ⊖

Lunch 12–2.30　*Dinner* 7–10.30
About £75 *for two*

LOWER SLAUGHTER Lower Slaughter Manor 73% £C

H **Map 4 C1** Gloucestershire
GL54 2HP
Cotswold (0451) 20456
Telex 437287

Rooms 21
Ensuite bath/shower 21
Direct dial Yes
Room TV Yes
Confirm by arrang.
Last dinner 9.30
Parking Ample
Room service Limited

Credit Access, Amex, Visa
Closed 2 wks Jan–Feb

Its setting, in delightful gardens in a picturesque village, gives this 17th-century Cotswold-stone manor a head start. Inside, the tone is set by the cosy, welcoming entrance hall, with its fine period furniture, oil paintings and open fire, and continued in the small, elegant lounges. Bedrooms in the main house are traditional in style, with period pieces and floral fabrics; those in the converted coach house are more contemporary. All have good carpeted bathrooms and plenty of extras such as mineral water, sherry, tissues and sewing kits. No children under eight. No dogs.
Amenities garden, indoor swimming pool, sauna, tennis, croquet, laundry service, 24-hour lounge service.

LOWER SWELL Old Farmhouse Hotel £E

I **Map 4 C1** Gloucestershire
Stow-on-the-Wold GL54 1LF
Cotswold (0451) 30232

Credit Access, Amex, Diners, Visa
Closed 1 month Xmas

Spotless housekeeping and friendly, attentive service are valued assets at this village hotel run with care and pride by Rosemary and Rollo Belsham. Bedrooms are individually decorated and furnished; some are in the stable block, others – generally smaller but with more character – in the main house. Top of the price range are the two four-poster rooms. There's a cosy bar and a quiet lounge with plenty of reading matter. *Amenities* garden.

Rooms 13	*Room phone* No	*Confirm by* arrang.	*Parking* Ample
Ensuite bath/shower 11	*Room TV* Yes	*Last dinner* 9.15	*Room service* All day

 indicates a **well-chosen** house wine

LUDLOW Feathers Hotel 71% £D

H **Map 10 A4** Shropshire
Bull Ring SY8 1AA
Ludlow (0584) 5261
Telex 35637

Rooms 36
Ensuite bath/shower 36
Direct dial Yes
Room TV Yes
Confirm by arrang.
Last dinner 9
Parking Ample
Room service Limited

Credit Access, Amex, Diners, Visa

Justly famous for its richly carved facade, this historic timber-framed inn has stood in the town centre for more than 300 years. The first-floor lounge is wonderfully authentic with its ornate plasterwork ceiling and magnificent Jacobean mantelpiece, and there's also plenty of genuine old-world character in the two bars and cosily panelled writing room. Best bedrooms are spacious, with four-poster beds and prettily coordinated furnishings. Some of the smaller doubles were recently converted into large singles. All rooms offer fully-tiled bathrooms (most with bidets) and extras ranging from fresh fruit and mineral water to bath robes and hairdryers. No dogs.
Amenities patio, laundry service, 24-hour lounge service.

LUTON Chiltern Hotel 63% £C

H **Map 5 E1** Bedfordshire
Waller Avenue,
Dunstable Road LU4 9RU
Luton (0582) 575911
Telex 825048

Credit Access, Amex, Diners, Visa

A modern three-storey block midway between the M1 and the town centre. Downstairs there's an attractive foyer-lounge with polished pink marble floor, and a smart cane-furnished bar. Bright and cheerful bedrooms have tea-makers, trouser presses and neat bathrooms. Executive rooms offer darkwood furniture, reclining armchairs and extras like hairdryers and trouser presses. *Amenities* garden, in-house movies, secretarial services, fax, laundry service.

Rooms 99	*Direct dial* Yes	*Confirm by* 6	*Parking* Ample
Ensuite bath/shower 99	*Room TV* Yes	*Last dinner* 10	*Room service* 24 hours

LUTON · Crest Hotel · 58% · £C/D

H Map 5 E1 Bedfordshire
641 Dunstable Road LU4 8RQ
Luton (0582) 575955
Telex 826283

Credit Access, Amex, Diners, Visa

Business people are regular patrons of this pleasant hotel at junction 11 of the M1. First-floor public rooms include a reception-lounge and roomy bar. Bedrooms with well-coordinated decor, fitted units and good writing space, have tea-makers and bedside controls for TV and radio; but single rooms are on the small side.
Amenities garden, games room, secretarial services, fax, laundry service, 24-hour lounge service.

Rooms 133	*Direct dial* Yes	*Confirm by* 6	*Parking* Ample
Ensuite bath/shower 133	*Room TV* Yes	*Last dinner* 9.45	*Room service* None

LUTON · Leaside Hotel · 54% · £E

H Map 5 E1 Bedfordshire
72 New Bedford Road
LU3 1BT
Luton (0582) 417643

Credit Access, Amex, Diners, Visa
Closed 25 & 26 Dec

A friendly, unassuming little hotel converted from a Victorian house. It's not far from the town centre and is a popular overnight stop for business people. Bedrooms, ten of them singles, are quite simply appointed and all have their own shower rooms, apart from one with a bathroom. There's a cosy panelled bar and a lounge/club room with a snooker table. Very pleasant staff.
Amenities garden, laundry service.

Rooms 13	*Direct dial* Yes	*Confirm by* arrang.	*Parking* Ample
Ensuite bath/shower 13	*Room TV* Yes	*Last dinner* 9.30	*Room service* All day

LUTON · Strathmore Thistle Hotel · 66% · £C/D

H Map 5 E1 Bedfordshire
Arndale Centre LU1 2TR
Luton (0582) 34199
Telex 825763

Credit Access, Amex, Diners, Visa

Limited free parking is a useful bonus at this modern town-centre hotel. Marble floors and lofty pillars give a luxurious feel to the spacious foyer-lounge, and there's a choice of two bars. Best bedrooms are reasonably sized, with modern (though ageing) dark wood furniture. Hairdryers, trouser presses and tea-makers are standard.
Amenities in-house movies, secretarial services, fax, laundry service, coffee shop (10am–11pm Mon–Sat). &

Rooms 151	*Direct dial* Yes	*Confirm by* 6	*Parking* Limited
Ensuite bath/shower 151	*Room TV* Yes	*Last dinner* 10	*Room service* 24 hours

We publish annually,
so make sure you use the current edition.
It's worth it!

LUTTERWORTH · Denbigh Arms Hotel · 68% · £D

H Map 11 D4 Leicestershire
High Street LE17 4AD
Lutterworth (045 55) 3537
Telex 342545

Credit Access, Amex, Diners, Visa

A fine Georgian coaching inn with a traditional frontage and a modern but fairly harmonious rear extension. Comfortable and stylish accommodation is provided in decent-sized, well-lit bedrooms with standard pine furnishings, armchairs, tea-making facilities and carpeted bathrooms with showers over the tubs. There's a welcoming reception-lounge and a smart bar with panelled counter area. No dogs.
Amenities secretarial services, laundry service.

Rooms 34	*Direct dial* Yes	*Confirm by* arrang.	*Parking* Ample
Ensuite bath/shower 34	*Room TV* Yes	*Last dinner* 9.30	*Room service* 24 hours

LYDDINGTON · Marquess of Exeter · £E

I Map 11 E4 Leicestershire
Nr Uppingham LE15 9LT
Uppingham (0572) 822477

Credit Access, Amex, Diners, Visa

Set in lovely countryside, this thatched village inn dates from the 16th century. The stone-floored reception area leads to a rambling bar lounge (which comprises four rooms) with beamed ceilings and rough stone walls. Cross the car park to an annexe where bedrooms are pretty and well equipped with TVs, direct-dial telephones and carpeted ensuite bathrooms. No dogs.
Amenities garden, fax, laundry service.

Rooms 20	*Direct dial* Yes	*Confirm by* arrang.	*Parking* Ample
Ensuite bath/shower 20	*Room TV* Yes	*Last dinner* 9.45	*Room service* Limited

LYME REGIS Alexandra Hotel 58% £D

H **Map 3 E2** Dorset
Pound Street DT7 3HZ
Lyme Regis (029 74) 2010

Credit Access, Amex, Diners, Visa
Closed 18 Dec–3 Feb

The Haskins family continue to improve this former dower house which they run with such care. Among the public rooms is a prettily furnished, tranquil sun lounge, equipped with tables and parasols in summer. Front bedrooms overlook the lovely garden and the famous Cobb; three ground floor rooms have easy access for the disabled. Full board terms only, although allowance can be made if dinner is not taken. *Amenities* garden, croquet.

Rooms 24	*Direct dial* Yes	*Confirm by* 6	*Parking* Limited
Ensuite bath/shower 21	*Room TV* Yes	*Last dinner* 8.30	*Room service* All day

LYME REGIS Mariners Hotel 54% £E

H **Map 3 E2** Dorset
Silver Street DT7 3HS
Lyme Regis (029 74) 2753

Credit Access, Amex, Diners, Visa
Closed Jan & 1st 2 wks Feb

A hilltop location gives this 17th-century inn stunning views over Lyme Bay and Chesil Beach. Old timbers and brickwork are displayed to advantage in the reception and lounge, while the bar is more traditional in decor. The newly arrived Prestons plan much-needed refurbishment of all the bedrooms and their new luxury suite is certainly handsome, with period furniture, a half-tester and generous extras. No dogs. *Amenities* garden.

Rooms 17	*Direct dial* Yes	*Confirm by* arrang.	*Parking* Ample
Ensuite bath/shower 13	*Room TV* Yes	*Last dinner* 9	*Room service* Limited

LYMINGTON Passford House Hotel 70% £C

H **Map 4 C4** Hampshire
Mount Pleasant Lane SO41 8LS
Lymington (0590) 682398
Telex 47502

Rooms 54
Ensuite bath/shower 54
Direct dial Yes
Room TV Yes
Confirm by arrang.
Last dinner 9
Parking Ample
Room service 24 hours

Credit Access, Amex, Visa

Set in attractive grounds overlooking the New Forest, this splendidly relaxing hotel offers plenty of space to unwind in its three comfortably traditional lounges – one with oak panelling and open fire, another with French windows opening on to a patio and ornamental pool. There's also an elegant cocktail bar in period style. Good-sized bedrooms are bright and airy, with pretty decor and mostly white furniture – plus extras like hairdryers, trouser presses and tea-makers. Carpeted bathrooms have shower facilities, scales and nice toiletries. *Amenities* garden, indoor & outdoor swimming pools, sauna, solarium, whirlpool bath, keep-fit equipment, tennis, putting, croquet, games room, snooker, laundry service, children's play area.

LYMINGTON Provence ★ ⌘

RR **Map 4 C4** Hampshire
Gordleton Mill, Silver Street, Hordle
Lymington (0590) 682219

French cooking

Set L £10.50, Sun from £11.90
Set D from £17.50
About £65 for two
Seats 25
Parties 14
Parking Ample

Credit Access, Amex, Diners, Visa

Provence is a truly delightful restaurant with rooms in an old creeper-covered mill house on the banks of Avon Water. Claire Novi is the charming hostess and her husband Jean-Pierre does exceptional work in the kitchen. His cooking is very French and bursting with subtle, complex flavours; a recent meal was an unqualified success, from grilled langoustines with béarnaise and Madeira sauce to goose sausage,

lamb with artichokes and a warm apple tart. The coffee and petits fours kept standards high right to the end. *Specialities* jambon de canard aux figues fraîches, homard au muscat de Beaumes de Venise, carré d'agneau pané à l'artichaut, glace à la menthe dans sa coque au chocolat. ♀ Well-chosen ⌘

Lunch 12.30–2 *Dinner* 7.30–10 **Closed** D Sun, all Mon & Jan

BEDROOMS 5 £D/E
With bath/shower 5

Bedrooms are quite pretty, with pine furniture, remote-control TVs, direct-dial phones and lots of extras. No children under eight. No dogs.

LYMINGTON　　　Stanwell House Hotel　65%　　　　　£D

H Map 4 C4 Hampshire
High Street SO41 9AA
Lymington (0590) 77756

Credit Access, Amex, Visa

New owners have brought a fresh, attractive look to this solid 18th-century hotel. Pale blue decor, chintzy sofas and antique bric-a-brac make for a cosy lounge, and the cocktail bar gleams with burnished copper. 20 bedrooms in the main house have pretty fabrics and modern bathrooms; those in the extension are pleasingly cottagy in style. Housekeeping is excellent. No dogs.
Amenities garden, secretarial services, fax, laundry service.

Rooms 35	*Direct dial* Yes	*Confirm by* arrang.	*Parking* Difficult
Ensuite bath/shower 35	*Room TV* Yes	*Last dinner* 9.30	*Room service* 24 hours

LYMPSHAM　　　Batch Farm Country Hotel　56%　　　£E/F

H Map 3 E1 Somerset
Nr Weston-super-Mare
BS24 0EX
Edingworth (093 472) 371

Credit Access, Visa
Closed 10 days Xmas

A hundred acres of surrounding farmland make this extended farmhouse a haven of tranquillity and provide panoramic views from all the windows. Exposed beams contribute to the rustic charm of the homely public rooms, while the bedrooms are simple and cosy. Families are made very welcome, with separate children's rooms in three of the bedrooms. Housekeeping is excellent. No dogs.
Amenities garden, croquet, coarse fishing, games room, pool table.

Rooms 8	*Room phone* No	*Confirm by* 6	*Parking* Ample
Ensuite bath/shower 8	*Room TV* Yes	*Last dinner* 8.30	*Room service* All day

LYMPSTONE　　　River House　　　　　　　　　　　　　　⚘

RR Map 3 E3 Devon
The Strand
Exmouth (0395) 265147

Set L & D from £17.75
About £50 for two
Seats 35
Parties 50
Parking Difficult

Credit Access, Amex, Visa

The river Exe washes the walls of this friendliest of restaurants, and the views across to Powderham Castle are quite something. Shirley Wilkes cooks with care and skill to provide enjoyable, unpretentious eating. Fish is a speciality – seafood tartlet, paupiettes of smoked trout, spinach-wrapped sole with a cream and cheese sauce – but meat-eaters are certainly not forgotten. Fresh vegetables are served copiously, and sweets include delicious home-made ices. Michael Wilkes is a most amiable host. ♀ Well-chosen ⊗ ♿

Lunch 12–1.30　*Dinner* 7–9.30, Sat 7–10.30　**Closed** D Sun, all Mon, Bank Hols (except Good Fri), 25 & 27 Dec & 1 & 2 Jan

BEDROOMS 2　£D/E
With bath/shower 2

The two bedrooms (no children under 16, no dogs) are spotless and well equipped.

🢒 is our symbol for an **outstanding** wine list

LYNDHURST　　　Crown Hotel　63%　　　　　　　　　　£D

H Map 4 C4 Hampshire
High Street SO43 7NF
Lyndhurst (042 128) 2922

Credit Access Amex, Diners, Visa

A warm and friendly atmosphere greets you as you step into the simple reception of this town-centre hotel. A variety of lounges, some with garden views, offer comfortable armchairs and plenty of reading matter while a log fire crackles in the cosy bar. Bedrooms, generally of a good size, vary in standards of decor, but the best have nice period furniture. Bathrooms are functional. No dogs.
Amenities garden, games room.

Rooms 43	*Direct dial* Yes	*Confirm by* 6	*Parking* Ample
Ensuite bath/shower 43	*Room TV* Yes	*Last dinner* 9.30	*Room service* 24 hours

LYNDHURST　　　Lyndhurst Park Hotel　64%　　　　　£D/E

H Map 4 C4 Hampshire
High Street SO43 7NL
Lyndhurst (042 128) 3923
Telex 477802

Credit Access, Amex, Diners, Visa

Secluded grounds surround this sprawling hotel of Victorian origins. Public areas are smart and pleasant, and the cocktail bar has French windows to the garden. Bedrooms (some balconied) have radio alarms, hairdryers, trouser presses and compact bathrooms; 28 have recently been completely refurbished. *Amenities* garden, outdoor swimming pool, tennis, golf practice net, bicycles, games room, snooker, in-house movies, secretarial services, laundry service.

Rooms 59	*Direct dial* Yes	*Confirm by* arrang.	*Parking* Ample
Ensuite bath/shower 59	*Room TV* Yes	*Last dinner* 10	*Room service* 24 hours

LYNDHURST Parkhill Hotel 57% £E

H **Map 4 C4** Hampshire
Beaulieu Road SO4 7FZ
Lyndhurst (042 128) 2944

Credit Access, Amex, Diners, Visa

A Georgian building in an attractive setting outside Lyndhurst. The public areas and some bedrooms had already received attention before the previous owners left, and more improvements would be welcome – some bedrooms were looking a bit dismal on our last visit. 15 rooms are in the main part, the rest in outbuildings. There's a bright, airy lounge, a library and a lounge-bar, all with garden views.
Amenities garden, outdoor swimming pool, coarse fishing.

Rooms 20	*Direct dial* Yes	*Confirm by* arrang.	*Parking* Ample
Ensuite bath/shower 18	*Room TV* Yes	*Last dinner* 9	*Room service* Limited

Our inspectors *never* book in the name of Egon Ronay's Guides.
They disclose their identity only if they are considering an establishment
for inclusion in the next edition of the Guide.

LYNMOUTH Tors Hotel 56% £E

H **Map 3 D1** Devon
EX35 6NA
Lynton (0598) 53236

Credit Access, Amex, Diners, Visa
Closed Jan & Feb

Five acres of woodland surround this imposing hotel overlooking Lynmouth Bay. The light, airy public areas all offer panoramic views which cannot fail to thrill. Bedrooms, some with views, have light colour schemes and simple modern units; most have seating areas. Some refurbishment and extra staff are needed to make the most of this stunning site. *Amenities* garden, outdoor swimming pool, pool table, laundry service.

Rooms 36	*Direct dial* Yes	*Confirm by* arrang.	*Parking* Ample
Ensuite bath/shower 34	*Room TV* Yes	*Last dinner* 8.45	*Room service* All day

LYNTON Hewitt's 65% *NEW ENTRY* £E

HR **Map 3 D1** Devon
North Walk EX35 6HJ
Lynton (0598) 52293
Telex 265871

Credit Access, Amex, Diners, Visa

Built at the end of the last century, Hewitt's enjoys splendid sea views from its lofty perch. Much of the 19th-century feel has survived, particularly in the panelled entrance hall and homely lounge with its Victorian parlour atmosphere. Bedrooms are mostly of a good size, light and airy, and the best boast some handsome antiques.
Amenities garden, clay-pigeon shooting, secretarial services, laundry service.

Rooms 12	*Direct dial* Yes	*Confirm by* arrang.	*Parking* Ample
Ensuite bath/shower 7	*Room TV* Yes	*Last dinner* 9	*Room service* All day

Restaurant *NEW ENTRY*

Set D £13.50
About £50 *for two*
Seats 24
Parties 50

Chef David Lamprell's menus are both interesting and well conceived, and he makes particular use of local produce. Stir-fried marinated chicken, moules marinière or a coarse liver terrine could be your starter, with trout en papillote, pork with juniper berries or maybe Somerset duck with cassis and pink grapefruit to follow. Vegetarian dishes; super sweets include a wonderful lemon tart. Pleasant, informal service. No smoking. ℗ ♿

Lunch by arrang.
Dinner 7–9

LYNTON Lynton Cottage Hotel 62% £D/E

H **Map 3 D1** Devon
North Walk EX35 6ED
Lynton (0598) 52342

Credit Access, Amex, Diners, Visa
Closed Jan

A friendly, well-run hotel with a continuing programme of improvements. Its position, 500 ft above Lynmouth Bay, gives wonderful views and the interiors, too, are pleasing to the eye. The tasteful lounge has comfortable armchairs, period furnishings and a profusion of plants, and there's a warm and convivial bar. Bedrooms have attractive colour schemes, modern furniture and neat bathrooms. No children. *Amenities* garden, laundry service.

Rooms 18	*Direct dial* Yes	*Confirm by* arrang.	*Parking* Ample
Ensuite bath/shower 17	*Room TV* Yes	*Last dinner* 8.45	*Room service* All day

LYTHAM	Bennett's Bistro *NEW ENTRY*

R **Map 10 A1** Lancashire
15 Park St
Lytham (0253) 739265

About £28 for two
Seats 50
Parking Ample

Capable cooking, swift service and a friendly, relaxed atmosphere combine to make this a pleasant spot for a meal. Jolly menus run from lunchtime snacks such as 'Egg Head' (boiled egg filled with asparagus and cream cheese coated in a mild curried mayonnaise) to principal dinner dishes like 'Frank's Fury' (marinated lamb kebabs with a devilled sauce and rice) or 'Gingeroo' (veal escalope with ginger, sherry and sharon fruit).

Lunch 12–2.30   *Dinner* 7–10.30
Closed Sun, Mon & all Bank Hols

LYTHAM	Wade & Fryer's *NEW ENTRY* ♀

R **Map 10 A1** Lancashire
74A Clifton Street
Lytham (0253) 794 258

About £45 for two
Seats 24
Parking Ample

Credit Access, Visa

The long-established partnership of Steve Fryer and Patricia Wade works well at this cosy first-floor restaurant, where a model of an old shrimping boat is a point of interest. Pat's menus change monthly, and her assurance and skill turn top-notch produce into delightfully different dishes: plump scallops with a basil-scented tomato coulis, salmon with ginger and raisins in a pastry case and Barbary duckling served very generously and nicely pink with a delicate gin and juniper sauce. Vegetables are excellent, and to round things off there are some super home-made sorbets and ice creams. Service by Steve is both friendly and helpful. ♀ Well-chosen ⊘

Dinner only 7–11
Closed All Sun & Mon, Bank Hols

LYTHAM ST ANNE'S	Clifton Arms Hotel 64% **£D**

H **Map 10 A1** Lancashire
West Beach, Lytham FY8 5QJ
Lytham (0253) 739898
Telex 677463

Credit Access, Amex, Diners, Visa

A glass of sherry welcomes guests to this red-brick Victorian hotel on the Ribble estuary. The lounge and cocktail bar are pleasant spots to relax, and Gershwin's Piano Bar is popular with residents and outsiders alike. Bedrooms, all with trouser presses and hairdryers, run from standard singles to Executive and the top-of-the-range Directors rooms with lounge areas. *Amenities* sauna, solarium, whirlpool bath, secretarial services, laundry service.

Rooms 45	*Direct dial* Yes	*Confirm by* 6	*Parking* Ample
Ensuite bath/shower 45	*Room TV* Yes	*Last dinner* 9.45	*Room service* 24 hours

We publish annually,
so make sure you use the current edition.
It's worth it!

MACCLESFIELD	Sutton Hall **£D/E**

I **Map 10 B2** Cheshire
Bullocks Lane, Sutton SK11 0HE
Sutton (026 05) 3211

Credit Access, Amex, Visa

Built as a baronial home in the early 16th century and until recently a convent, this is now a splendidly atmospheric inn. The comfortable bars with their open fires and fine pieces of furniture are very welcoming and friendly. All the bedrooms have four-poster beds and good oak pieces, and some have oak panelling as well. Tea-makers and trouser presses are standard and neat modern bathrooms are clean and carpeted. *Amenities* garden, fax, laundry service.

Rooms 9	*Direct dial* Yes	*Confirm by* arrang.	*Parking* Ample
Ensuite bath/shower 9	*Room TV* Yes	*Last dinner* 10	*Room service* All day

Any person using our name to obtain free hospitality is a fraud.
Proprietors, please inform the police and us.

MAIDEN NEWTON — Maiden Newton House — 73% — £D

HR Map 4 B4 Dorset
Nr Dorchester DT2 0AA
Maiden Newton (0300) 20336

Rooms 7
Ensuite bath/shower 7
Direct dial Yes
Room TV Yes
Confirm by arrang.
Last dinner 8
Parking Ample
Room service All day

Credit Access, Visa
Closed Jan

Peace and tranquillity are in generous supply at this splendid old manor house, where Elizabeth and Bryan Ferriss are on hand to see to the needs of their guests. The feeling throughout is one of a private house, and comfort is the keynote in the day rooms. In the bedrooms, standards of decor, furnishings and cleanliness are beyond reproach; fluted red and blue drapes match seat coverings and bedspreads.

Each room is stocked with a wide selection of books and magazines, along with a host of other thoughtful extras, from hairdryers and sewing kits to heart-shaped shortbreads. A splendid breakfast features prime Dorset and West Country produce.
Amenities garden, game fishing, shooting, croquet, laundry service.

Restaurant ♔ ♂

Set D £16
About £48 *for two*
Seats 16
Parties 40

Dinner is served at 8 o'clock in a splendidly elegant room. Elizabeth arrives from the kitchen with the evening's choice; seasonal produce figures prominently, and much of the fruit and vegetables comes from the garden. Courgette and herb soup, pasta shells with smoked salmon, tarragon chicken and gooseberry fool exemplify the fare, and our rogan josh was an enjoyably different centrepiece. Good selection of Dorset cheeses. Booking is essential. 🖥 Well-chosen ⊖ &

Dinner only at 8
Closed Jan

MAIDENCOMBE — Orestone Manor House — 64% *NEW ENTRY* — £E

H Map 3 D3 Devon
Rockhouse Lane,
Nr Torquay TQ1 4SX
Torquay (0803) 38098

Credit Access, Amex, Diners, Visa
Closed Jan & Feb

John and Janet Flude are welcoming hosts at their gabled Georgian lodge, which enjoys a really beautiful setting in gardens overlooking the sea. The main lounge – note the unusual pitch pine ceiling – takes full advantage of the views, and there's a very cosy little bar. Good-sized bedrooms are light and airy, with bright modern furniture and neat bathrooms. *Amenities* garden, outdoor swimming pool, putting, games room, fax.

Rooms 20	*Direct dial* Yes	*Confirm by* arrang.	*Parking* Ample
Ensuite bath/shower 20	*Room TV* Yes	*Last dinner* 8.45	*Room service* All day

**Our inspectors *never* book in the name of Egon Ronay's Guides.
They disclose their identity only if they are considering an establishment
for inclusion in the next edition of the Guide.**

MAIDENHEAD — Crest Hotel — 66% — £C

H Map 5 E2 Berkshire
Manor Lane SL6 2RA
Maidenhead (0628) 23444
Telex 847502

Credit Access, Amex, Diners, Visa

A large modern hotel near junction 8/9 of the M4. There's ample room to relax in the day rooms, and bedrooms also offer plenty of space, plus the usual accessories. Bidets in all bathrooms. Repair and housekeeping are good, staff smart if not particularly jolly.
Amenities garden, indoor swimming pool, sauna, solarium, whirlpool bath, keep-fit equipment, squash, snooker, pool table, in-house movies, fax, coffee shop (8am–9pm), children's play area. &

Rooms 189	*Direct dial* Yes	*Confirm by* 6	*Parking* Ample
Ensuite bath/shower 189	*Room TV* Yes	*Last dinner* 9.45	*Room service* 24 hours

MAIDENHEAD

Fredrick's Hotel   77%   £B

HR **Map 5 E2** Berkshire
Shoppenhangers Road
SL6 2PZ
Maidenhead (0628) 35934
Telex 849966

Rooms 38
Ensuite bath/shower 38
Direct dial Yes
Room TV Yes
Confirm by arrang.
Last dinner 9.45
Parking Ample
Room service All day

Credit Access, Amex, Diners, Visa
Closed 26–30 Dec

Public rooms at this handsome
red-brick hotel are particularly
appealing, and in the entrance
hall a welcoming glass of champagne boosts the general feeling
of luxury. The Winter Garden
lounge is a most pleasant spot,
and there's a very civilised cocktail bar. Bedrooms are furnished
in pleasing traditional style, but,
though well equipped (mini-bars,
hairdryers, remote-control TVs),
they're short on personal touches.

Bathrooms, six or so with shower only, have excellent towelling and
toiletries. The few bedrooms that face the road can suffer from traffic
noise. Staff are friendly, but not invariably efficient. No dogs.
Amenities garden, croquet, in-house movies, secretarial services,
fax, laundry service, 24-hour lounge service.

Restaurant   ♔

Set L from £19.50
Set D £29.50
About £77 for two
Seats 60
Parties 100

Service is exemplary in an elegant dining room with panelled walls,
chandeliers, crisp linen and garden views. Brian Cutler's menus
provide abundant variety, from brains and sweetbreads on toast with
a wine, mushroom and fennel sauce to seafood lasagne, lamb steak
with fresh herbs and a nice silky chocolate mousse. Not everything
succeeds – witness our undistinguished stuffed oxtail in savoy cabbage.
There's a sound list of mature classic wines.   ℮

Lunch 12–2   *Dinner* 7–9.45, Sun 7–9
Closed L Sat & D 25–30 Dec

MAIDSTONE

Boxley House Hotel   56%   £E

H **Map 7 B5** Kent
Boxley ME14 3D7
Maidstone (0622) 692269

Credit Access, Amex, Diners, Visa

Situated close to both the M2 and the M20, yet in a tranquil village,
Boxley House is a modernised and extended building whose 17th-
century origins are revealed in some fine panelling and a minstrel's
gallery. It's a well-run, friendly hotel and everywhere is spotlessly
clean. Bedrooms are individually decorated with simple, plain
furniture and functional, carpeted bathrooms.
Amenities garden, outdoor swimming pool.

Rooms 18	*Direct dial* Yes	*Confirm by* 6	*Parking* Ample
Ensuite bath/shower 18	*Room TV* Yes	*Last dinner* 9	*Room service* All day

MAIDSTONE

Larkfield Hotel   62%   £C/D

H **Map 7 B5** Kent
London Road,
Larkfield ME60 6HJ
West Malling (0732) 846858
Telex 957420

Credit Access, Amex, Diners, Visa

Five miles west of Maidstone on the A20 you'll find pleasant
accommodation at this old rectory. The oak dado-panelled bar and
the lounge have comfortable seating, stylish fabrics and attractive
prints on the walls. Bedrooms, in a modern wing, have freestanding
furniture, brass light fittings and tea/coffee-makers; executive rooms
have trouser presses, hairdryers, fruit and mini-bars.
Amenities garden, secretarial services, laundry service.

Rooms 52	*Direct dial* Yes	*Confirm by* 6	*Parking* Ample
Ensuite bath/shower 52	*Room TV* Yes	*Last dinner* 10	*Room service* 24 hours

MAIDSTONE

Mandarin Chef   *NEW ENTRY*   ♟

R **Map 7 B5** Kent
35 Lower Stone Street
Maidstone (0622) 55917

Chinese cooking
Set L & D from £8.50
About £35 for two
Seats 70
Parking Limited
Credit Access, Amex, Diners, Visa

A cut above your average Chinese eatery, this recently restyled
restaurant offers smart modern decor, attentive service and some
really sophisticated cooking. Old favourites like crispy duck are
reliably and enjoyably prepared but you might prefer to explore less
familiar offerings such as moist and juicy grilled pork dumplings, or
fried bean curd in a good, rich chilli sauce with crunchy vegetables.
Seafood choices may include baked lobster.

Lunch 12–2   *Dinner* 5.30–11.30
Closed 3 days Christmas

MALDON — Blue Boar Hotel 60% £D

H Map 7 C4 Essex
3 Silver Street CM9 7QE
Maldon (0621) 52681

Credit Access, Amex, Diners, Visa

Just off the High Street, the Blue Boar hides 14th-century origins behind a Georgian facade. Beams and panelling feature in the cosy day rooms, and there's a pleasant paved beer garden. After the refurbishment programme is completed, all bedrooms will have decent furniture, much smarter decor and the usual up-to-date accessories. Heating and breakfast didn't shine on our last visit.
Amenities laundry service.

Rooms 28	*Room phone* Yes	*Confirm by* 6	*Parking* Ample
Ensuite bath/shower 28	*Room TV* Yes	*Last dinner* 9.30	*Room service* Limited

MALDON — Francine's ♀

R Map 7 C4 Essex
1a High Street
Maldon (0621) 56605

About £40 for two
Seats 26
Parties 26
Parking Limited

Credit Access, Visa

The Brothertons have taken over this simple little bistro, John in the kitchen and Sara out front. Most items on John's short, monthly-changing menu are successful (suprême of turbot with red peppers and stem ginger, cooked in whisky and orange juice) but not all – creamy smoked salmon mousse was fine but the accompanying pear vinaigrette tasted too sharp and acidic. Ile flottante is a lovely finale.

Lunch 12–2 *Dinner* 7.30–9.15
Closed Sun, Mon, Bank Hols, 2 wks Jan & 2 wks Aug

MALMESBURY — Old Bell Hotel 63% £D

H Map 4 B2 Wiltshire
Abbey Row SN16 0BW
Malmesbury (0666) 822344

Credit Access, Amex, Visa

Next to Malmesbury Abbey, the Old Bell is an ancient inn with oodles of character and a history tracing back to the reign of King John. New owners are making a number of improvements while being careful not to lose the hotel's period appeal. Bedrooms in the main house are generally of a decent size (a few singles are rather small), individually decorated and furnished, cosy and comfortable. 16 new bedrooms are housed in the former stable block. The oak-beamed 16th-century bars are mellow and inviting, and the walled garden with its gazebo remains a delight. No dogs.
Amenities garden, secretarial services, fax, laundry service.

Rooms 35	*Direct dial* Yes	*Confirm by* arrang.	*Parking* Ample
Ensuite bath/shower 32	*Room TV* Yes	*Last dinner* 9.30	*Room service* All day

MALVERN — Abbey Hotel 64% £D

H Map 4 B1
Hereford & Worcester
Abbey Road
Great Malvern WR14 3ET
Malvern (0684) 892332
Telex 335008

Credit Access, Amex, Diners, Visa

Splendid in late summer with its copper-red ivy coat, the Abbey Hotel stands peacefully in the grounds of the magnificent old Benedictine Priory. Pride of place among the day rooms goes to the picture-windowed lounge; there's also a pleasant bar and several conference suites. Three floors of modern bedrooms in a new wing have been considerably upgraded with high-quality fabrics, good chairs and writing desks, radio-alarms, trouser presses and bright tiled bathrooms. Main-house rooms are more traditional and generally large, though some singles are very small. The poor buffet breakfast was our only disappointment.
Amenities garden, in-house movies, secretarial services, fax.

Rooms 107	*Direct dial* Yes	*Confirm by* 6	*Parking* Ample
Ensuite bath/shower 107	*Room TV* Yes	*Last dinner* 8.30	*Room service* 24 hours

MALVERN — Anupam *NEW ENTRY*

R Map 4 B1
Hereford & Worcester
85 Church Street
Malvern (068 45) 3814

Indian cooking
Set L £4.95 (not Fri & Sat)
Seats 46 *Parties* 50
Parking Limited
Credit Access, Amex, Diners, Visa

Keep your eyes peeled for this Indian restaurant tucked away down a little alley off Church Street. Decor is fashionable pinks and greens, service more than polite, cooking most acceptable over a range of tandoori dishes and curries mild, medium and hot. Most are familiar treatments of chicken, lamb and prawns, but note also tandoori mackerel. Kulfi comes in three flavours, and the yoghurt-based drink, lassi, is a cool accompaniment to the curries.

Lunch 12–2.30 *Dinner* 6–midnight *About £28 for two*
Closed 25 Dec

MALVERN	Colwall Park Hotel 62%	£E

H **Map 4 B1**
Hereford & Worcester
Colwall WR13 6QG
Colwall (0684) 40206
Telex 335626

Credit Access, Amex, Visa

Behind its mock-Tudor facade all is neat and tidy at this little family-run hotel in a village some three miles from Malvern. The bar has a village-inn atmosphere, and there's a cosy residents' lounge. Bedrooms, all double-glazed, are furnished with good-quality pieces and equipped with radios and tea-makers. Top-floor rooms, including one suite, are particularly attractive.
Amenities garden, croquet, fax.

Rooms 20	*Direct dial* Yes	*Confirm by* arrang.	*Parking* Ample
Ensuite bath/shower 20	*Room TV* Yes	*Last dinner* 9.30	*Room service* All day

> **Changes in data sometimes occur in establishments
> after the Guide goes to press.
> Prices should be taken as indications rather than firm quotes.**

MALVERN	Cottage in the Wood Hotel 63%	£D/E

H **Map 4 B1**
Hereford & Worcester
Holywell Road,
Malvern Wells WR14 4LG
Malvern (068 45) 3487

Credit Access, Visa

A handsome Georgian dower house high in the Malvern Hills, two miles south of Malvern off the A449. Magazines abound in the comfortable, period-style lounge and there's a warmly decorated cocktail bar with an open fire and an attractive conference room. Bedrooms in the main house are furnished in pleasingly traditional style, some having four-poster beds. Dogs are not allowed in the main house. ***Amenities*** garden, snooker.

Rooms 20	*Room phone* Yes	*Confirm by* arrang.	*Parking* Ample
Ensuite bath/shower 20	*Room TV* Yes	*Last dinner* 9	*Room service* All day

MALVERN	Croque-en-Bouche ★	

R **Map 4 B1**
Hereford & Worcester
221 Wells Road, Malvern Wells
Malvern (068 45) 65612

French cooking

Dinner only 7.30–9.15
Set D £23
About £55 *for two*
Seats 22
Parties 8
Parking Ample

Credit Access, Visa
Closed Sun & Tues

Marion Jones' superb French cooking goes from strength to strength, rock solid in its consistent excellence. Our dinner this year was a memorable feast of beautifully judged flavours. Game soup with pheasant and rabbit was a lovely amalgam of root vegetables, identifiable flesh and rich game consommé; crêpe of avocado, crabmeat and ginger presented a fine medley of tastes, delicately sauced. Cheeses were

exceptional for range and prime condition; and crème brûlée was a model of its kind. Robin Jones' cellar is exquisite, a real labour of love. ***Specialities*** soup au pistou, salmon with marsh samphire and chive sauce, chocolate mousse cake with orange sauce. ⟿ Outstanding
℗

MALVERN	Foley Arms Hotel 61%	£D/E

H **Map 4 B1**
Hereford & Worcester
14 Worcester Road,
Great Malvern WR14 4QS
Malvern (068 45) 3397
Telex 437269
Credit Access, Amex, Diners, Visa
Closed 25–31 Dec

Built as a coaching inn in 1810, and enlarged to accommodate visitors to the spa, this comfortable hotel retains many period features. Of particular interest is the bar, with its arches in local stone, and stained-glass windows. Individually decorated bedrooms (some traditional, others modern) have carpeted ensuite bathrooms. Some have fine views of the Severn Valley, an aspect which is echoed in the spacious lounge. Refurbishment of public areas in progress. ***Amenities*** garden, secretarial services, laundry service.

Rooms 28	*Direct dial* Yes	*Confirm by* 6	*Parking* Ample
Ensuite bath/shower 28	*Room TV* Yes	*Last dinner* 9.15	*Room service* 24 hours

Changes in data sometimes occur in establishments
after the Guide goes to press.
Prices should be taken as indications rather than firm quotes.

MANCHESTER	**Britannia Hotel 69%**	**£B/C**

H **Town plan E3**
Greater Manchester
Portland Street M1 3LA
061-228 2288
Telex 665007

Credit Access, Amex, Diners, Visa

Originally a cotton warehouse, this handsome building has been a hotel since 1982. Public rooms start with the grand foyer, resplendent in royal blue, with its gilt columns, magnificent cantilever staircase and huge chandeliers. There are bars, restaurants and discothéques, a health club and numerous function rooms. Smartly furnished bedrooms, reached by rather dismal corridors, range from smallish singles to spacious split-level suites; all are well equipped. Staff did not shine on our last visit, and the buffet breakfast was eminently missable. *Amenities* indoor swimming pool, sauna, solarium, whirlpool bath, gymnasium, beauty salon, hairdressing, satellite TV, secretarial services, fax, laundry service, coffee shop (11am–2am, midnight Sun).

Rooms 362	*Direct dial* Yes	*Confirm by* 6	*Parking* Difficult
Ensuite bath/shower 362	*Room TV* Yes	*Last dinner* 2am	*Room service* 24 hours

---

MANCHESTER	**Copthorne Hotel 69%**	**£C/D**

H **Town plan A4**
Greater Manchester
Clippers Quay, Salford Quays
M5 3DL
061-873 7321
Telex 669090
Credit Access, Amex, Diners, Visa

A brick-built hotel opened in May 1987 in the Salford Docks redevelopment area. Bedrooms are of a decent size, double-glazed and smartly furnished, with remote-control TV/radios, trouser presses, hairdryers and neatly disguised mini-bars. Day rooms include a stylish little cocktail bar. No dogs. *Amenities* indoor swimming pool, sauna, solarium, whirlpool bath, gymnasium, in-house movies, secretarial services, fax, laundry service. &

Rooms 166	*Direct dial* Yes	*Confirm by* 6	*Parking* Ample
Ensuite bath/shower 166	*Room TV* Yes	*Last dinner* 10.45	*Room service* 24 hours

---

MANCHESTER	**Grand Hotel 58%**	**£C**

H **Town plan E3**
Greater Manchester
Aytoun Street M1 3DR
061-236 9559
Telex 667580

Credit Access, Amex, Diners, Visa

Well sited in the centre of the city, the Grand is a mid-Victorian hotel offering decent overnight accommodation. Furnishings are mainly quite simple, and all bedrooms have remote-control TVs, tea-makers and private bath or shower. There are two bars, a coffee shop and a three-table snooker room. The hotel is showing some signs of wear and tear. *Amenities* solarium, keep-fit equipment, snooker, laundry service, coffee shop (10am–10.30pm).

Rooms 146	*Room phone* Yes	*Confirm by* 6	*Parking* Ample
Ensuite bath/shower 146	*Room TV* Yes	*Last dinner* 10	*Room service* 24 hours

---

MANCHESTER	**Holiday Inn 78%** *NEW ENTRY* **Crowne Plaza**	**£B/C**

H **Town plan C3**
Greater Manchester
Peter Street, M60 2DS
061–236 3333
Telex 667550

Rooms 303
Ensuite bath/shower 303
Direct dial Yes
Room TV Yes
Confirm by 6
Last dinner 11
Parking Ample
Room service 24 hours

Credit Access, Amex, Diners, Visa

Built in 1903 as the Midland, and the scene, a year later, of the historic first meeting between Mr Rolls and Mr Royce. The new owners have spared no expense in bringing back its splendour, particularly among the very elegant and spacious day rooms. Bedrooms, reached by wide corridors, are generally of a good size and all very well equipped: king-size beds, hairdryers, trouser presses, mini-bars, remote-control TVs and individual controls for heating and air conditioning. Bathrooms are sumptuous with expensive toiletries and plenty of thick towels. *Amenities* indoor swimming pool, sauna, solarium, whirlpool bath, gymnasium, beauty salon, hairdressing, squash, in-house movies, secretarial services, fax, valeting, laundry service. &

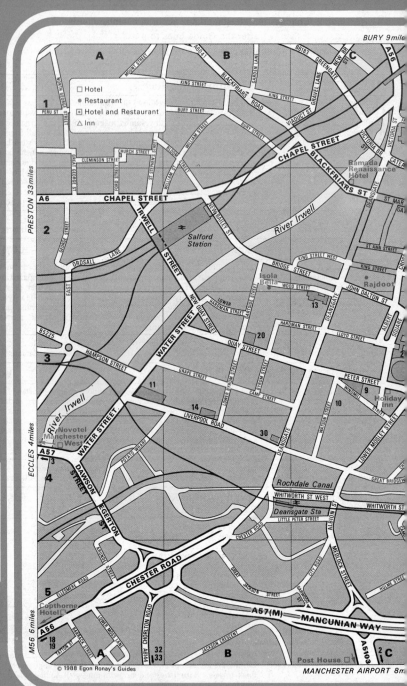

FIAT Manchester

FIAT

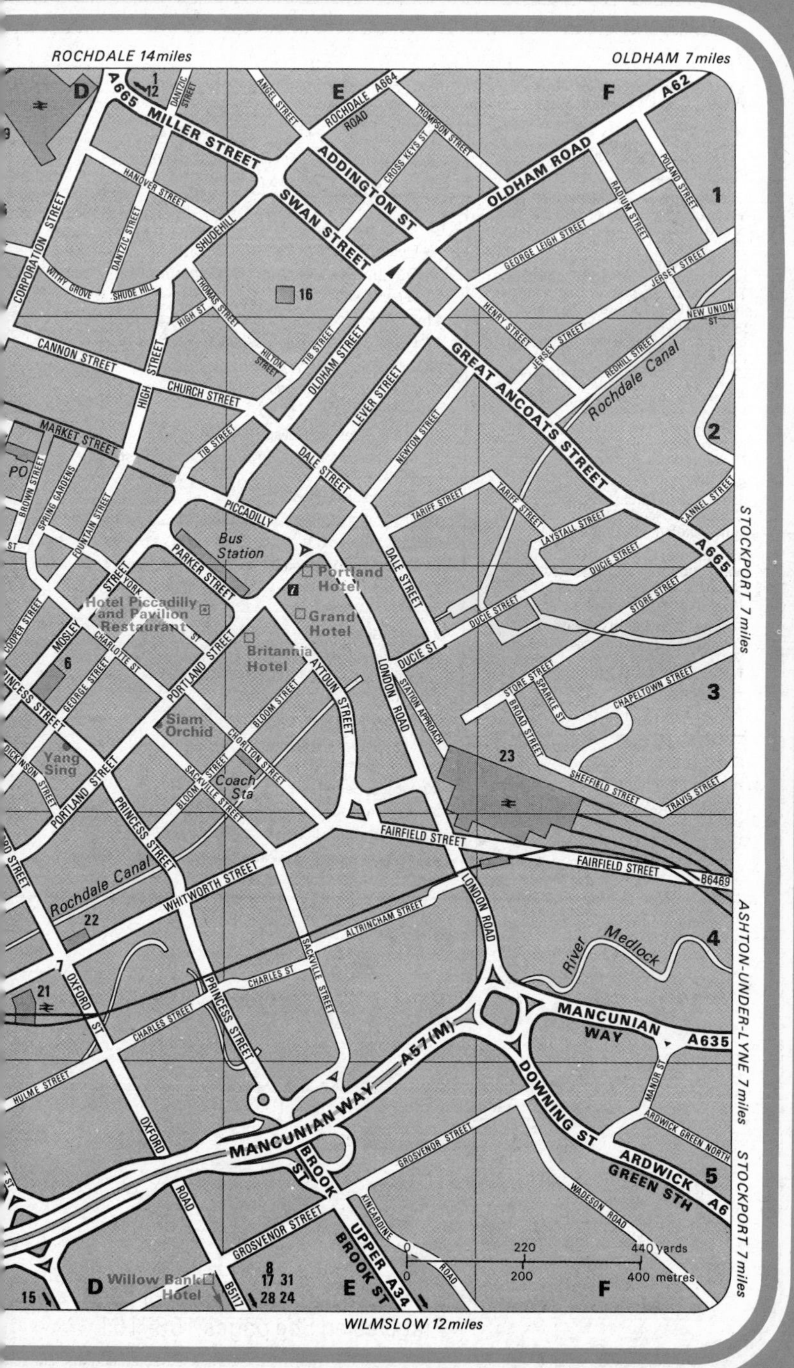
ROCHDALE 14 miles
OLDHAM 7 miles
STOCKPORT 7 miles
ASHTON-UNDER-LYNE 7 miles
STOCKPORT 7 miles
WILMSLOW 12 miles
D
E
F
1
2
3
4
5
A665 MILLER STREET
ADDINGTON ST
SWAN STREET
OLDHAM ROAD
A62
A664
ROCHDALE ROAD
ANGEL STREET
THOMPSON STREET
CROSS KEYS ST
DANTZIC STREET
HANOVER STREET
SHUDEHILL
WITHY GROVE
SHUDE HILL
CORPORATION STREET
POLAND STREET
RADIUM STREET
GEORGE LEIGH STREET
JERSEY STREET
NEW UNION ST
HENRY STREET
REDHILL STREET
Rochdale Canal
GREAT ANCOATS STREET
THOMAS STREET
HIGH ST
HILTON STREET
TIB STREET
OLDHAM STREET
LEVER STREET
NEWTON STREET
CANNON STREET
CHURCH STREET
HIGH STREET
MARKET STREET
PO
BROWN STREET
SPRING GARDENS
FOUNTAIN STREET
DALE STREET
PICCADILLY
Bus Station
PARKER STREET
TARIFF STREET
LAYSTALL STREET
CANNEL STREET
DUCIE STREET
STORE STREET
A665
Portland Hotel
Grand Hotel
Britannia Hotel
Hotel Piccadilly and Pavilion Restaurant
YORK STREET
MOSLEY STREET
CHARLOTTE ST
COOPER STREET
GEORGE STREET
PRINCESS STREET
PORTLAND STREET
AYTOUN STREET
BLOOM STREET
LONDON ROAD
STATION APPROACH
DUCIE ST
BROAD STREET
SPARKLE ST
CHAPELTOWN STREET
Siam Orchid
Yang Sing
DICKINSON STREET
CHORLTON STREET
SACKVILLE STREET
Coach Sta
23
SHEFFIELD STREET
TRAVIS STREET
FAIRFIELD STREET
B6469
WHITWORTH STREET
ALTRINCHAM STREET
River Medlock
22
21
7
6
16
OXFORD ST
CHARLES ST
CHARLES STREET
MANCUNIAN WAY
A635
A57(M)
DOWNING ST
MANOR ST
ARDWICK GREEN NORTH
ARDWICK GREEN STH
A6
HULME STREET
OXFORD ROAD
BROOK ST
GROSVENOR STREET
WADESON ROAD
KINCARDINE ROAD
UPPER BROOK ST
A34
B5117
Willow Bank Hotel
0
220
440 yards
200
400 metres
8
17 31
28 24
15

MANCHESTER

Map 10 B2
Town plan on preceding page

Population 458,600

Established 38 BC as Mancenion, the 'place of tents', a Roman fortification centre. Became a free market town in 1301. Opened Manchester Ship Canal in 1894 leading to Manchester becoming Britain's third inland seaport. The textile trade prepared it for the Industrial Revolution and the city prospered with engineering skills brought to its cotton industry. Apart from night-spot entertainment the city is noted for the Hallé Orchestra.

Annual Events
Manchester Parade *June*
Hallé Summer Proms *June–July*
Manchester Festival *September*
Northern Motor Show *April*

Sights Outside City
Jodrell Bank, Tatton Hall, Chatsworth House, Haddon Hall, Little Moreton Hall, Bramall Hall

Manchester City Council Promotion and Tourism St James's Buildings, Oxford Street, Manchester M1 6FL
Telephone 061–234 1343

Tourist Information Offices
PO Box 532, Town Hall, Manchester M60 2LA
Telephone 061–234 3157/8

Theatre Information
Telephone 061–234 3156

Fiat Dealer
D. C. Cook (Manchester) Ltd
Midland Street Garage
Ashton Old Road
Manchester M12 6LB
Tel. 061–273 4411

1 Abraham Moss Centre *leisure facilities* D1
2 Airport *8 miles* C5
3 Barton Aqueduct *swing trough bridge* A4
4 Cathedral *mainly 15th-c. fine carvings* C1
5 Central Library *houses 11 libraries* C3
6 City Art Gallery *mostly early British art* D3
7 Cornerhouse Art Gallery & Cinema D4
8 Fletcher Moss Museum & Art Gallery E5
9 Free Trade Hall *home of Hallé Orchestra* C3
10 G-Mex Centre C3/4
11 Greater Manchester Museum of Science & Industry A3
12 Heaton Hall *Georgian museum* D1
13 John Rylands Library *rare books* C3
14 Manchester Air & Space Gallery B3
15 Manchester City F.C. D5
16 Manchester Craft Village E1
17 Manchester Museum *Egyptology, natural history; coins; stamps* E5
18 Manchester United F.C. A5
19 Old Trafford Cricket Ground A5
20 Opera House B3
21 Oxford Road Station D4
22 Palace Theatre D4
23 Piccadilly Station F3
24 Platt Hall *Gallery of English Costume* E5
25 Schools Library *Europe's oldest public library; part of the 13th-c Chetham Hospital School* D1
26 Tourist Information Centre C3
27 Town Hall *Gothic revival* C3
28 University Theatre E5
29 Victoria Station D1
30 Visitors Centre B4
31 Whitworth Art Gallery *paintings; textiles* E5
32 Wythenshawe Forum *leisure facilities* A5
33 Wythenshawe Hall *Elizabethan manor and art gallery* A5

MANCHESTER — Isola Bella

R Town plan B2
Greater Manchester
Dolefield, Crown Square
061-831 7099

Italian cooking
About £44 for two
Seats 70
Parking Limited
Credit Access, Diners, Visa

Evandro Barbieri has moved his popular restaurant to smart new premises – suitably Italian in style with white marble floor and beige-toned decor. Food remains straightforward and traditional, ranging from eggs florentine and bean and pasta soup to grilled sole and peppered steak, with a couple of daily specials. It's all reliably prepared, using good fresh ingredients, and there are enjoyable home-made sweets from the trolley. ℮

Lunch 12.30–2.15   *Dinner* 7–11
Closed Sun & Bank Hols

MANCHESTER — Novotel Manchester West   62%   £D/E

H Town plan A4
Greater Manchester
Worsley Brow, Worsley M28 4YA
061-799 3535
Telex 669586

Credit Access, Amex, Diners, Visa

A practical overnight stop set in landscaped grounds on the slip road from junction 13 of the M62. Bedrooms are located in six wings and all have triple glazing to keep out motorway noise. Beds are king size, with sofa beds providing extra scope for families. Compact bathrooms have separate toilets.
Amenities garden, outdoor swimming pool, in-house movies, secretarial services, fax, laundry service, coffee shop (6am–midnight). &

Rooms 119	*Direct dial* Yes	*Confirm by* 7	*Parking* Ample
Ensuite bath/shower 119	*Room TV* Yes	*Last dinner* 12	*Room service* All day

We welcome bona fide complaints and recommendations
on the tear-out pages at the back of the book for readers' comment.
They are followed up by our professional team.

MANCHESTER — Hotel Piccadilly   75%   £B

HR Town plan D3
Greater Manchester
Piccadilly Plaza M60 1QR
061-236 8414
Telex 668765

Rooms 255
Ensuite bath/shower 255
Direct dial Yes
Room TV Yes
Confirm by 6
Last dinner 11
Parking Ample
Room service 24 hours

Credit Access, Amex, Diners, Visa

A drab city-centre shopping arcade is the unlikely setting for this luxurious high-rise modern hotel. Marble floors and columns give an impressive feel to spacious and extensive public areas. Bedrooms, though fairly compact, are very well equipped with everything from bedside controls and radio-alarms to hairdryers and tea-makers. Nicely fitted bathrooms provide telephone extensions and radio loudspeakers. Executive rooms throw in extras like bathrobes, while nine executive suites are the height of luxury with air conditioning, whirlpool baths, bidets and teletext TV. Good room service. *Amenities* beauty salon, hairdressing, in-house movies, secretarial services, fax, laundry service, coffee shop (7am–11pm), kiosk. &

Pavilion Restaurant   ♕

Set L £16
Set D £22
About £68 for two
Seats 46
Parties 20

All-round sophistication is the achievement here, with smart, attentive staff and stylish table settings providing a fitting accompaniment to exciting, inventive dishes that are very much in the modern idiom. A typically interesting starter might be cheese roulade on Kirsch-soaked pineapple glazed under a light basil soufflé. To follow, perhaps salmon escalope filled with sole and dill mousse, served on a cucumber and champagne sauce. ℮

Lunch 12.30–2.30   *Dinner* 7–10.30
Closed L Sat & Mon, all Sun, Bank Hols, 2 wks Aug & 25 Dec–3 Jan

MANCHESTER Portland Thistle Hotel 73% £B/C

H **Town plan E3**
Greater Manchester
Piccadilly Gardens M1 6DP
061-228 3400
Telex 669157

Rooms 208
Ensuite bath/shower 208
Direct dial Yes
Room TV Yes
Confirm by 6
Last dinner 10.30
Parking Limited
Room service 24 hours

Credit Access, Amex, Diners, Visa

The smart leisure spa is a major asset of this comfortable hotel in the heart of the city. There are two bars and a large lobby (the last beginning to look a little tired), plus extensive conference facilities. Overnight accommodation runs from smallish standard singles with hairdryers and trouser presses to club rooms (more space and comfort, plus mini-bars) and the luxurious top-of-the-range Executive Club rooms and suites. Staff are not always as efficient as they might be.
Amenities indoor swimming pool, whirlpool bath, keep-fit equipment, in-house movies, secretarial services, fax, laundry service.

MANCHESTER Post House Hotel 60% £C

H **Town plan C5**
Greater Manchester
Palatine Road, Northenden
M22 4FH
061-998 7090 Telex 669248

Credit Access, Amex, Diners, Visa

Comfortable overnight accommodation is provided at this 15-year-old high-rise hotel, which stands about five miles south of the city centre just off junction 9 of the M63. All rooms have tea-makers and mini-bars, with extras in Executive rooms. Staff are ready with a smile, especially jovial assistant manager Harry Fenna. Cosy day rooms.
Amenities garden, laundry service, coffee shop (10.30am–10.30pm).

Rooms 200 *Ensuite bath/shower* 200 *Direct dial* Yes *Room TV* Yes *Confirm by* 6.30 *Last dinner* 10.30 *Parking* Ample *Room service* 24 hours

★ For a *discount* on next year's guide, see **An Offer for Answers.** ★

MANCHESTER Rajdoot

R **Town plan C2**
Greater Manchester
St James' House
South King Street
061-834 2176

Indian cooking
About £36 for two
Seats 110 *Parking* Difficult
Credit Access, Amex, Diners, Visa

In a city-centre office block, a ground-floor establishment with stylish Oriental decor. Part of a chain of restaurants, all sharing the same menu, it offers a good choice of familiar favourites, from keema peas and lamb pasanda to king prawn masalla and chicken moghlai. The set meals are particularly attractive, providing the opportunity to sample a wide variety of reliably prepared dishes, including some typical Indian sweets.

Lunch 12–2.30 *Dinner* 6.30–11.30 **Closed** L Sun & L Bank Hols
Set L from £6.75 **Set D** from £10.50

MANCHESTER Ramada Renaissance Hotel 78% *NEW ENTRY* £B/C

H **Town plan C2**
Greater Manchester
Blackfriars Street M3 2EQ
061-835 2555
Telex 669699

Rooms 205
Ensuite bath/shower 205
Direct dial Yes
Room TV Yes
Confirm by 6
Last dinner 11
Parking Ample
Room service 24 hours

Credit Access, Amex, Diners, Visa

A spanking new luxury hotel in the heart of the city, very near the Arndale Centre. Day rooms, including the Deansgate Bar next to the lobby, are particularly stylish and comfortable, and there are numerous function and meeting rooms. Bedrooms boast pretty pastel colour schemes and accessories large and small, from mini-bars, trouser presses and remote-control TVs to plastic ducks in the bathrooms. Spy holes and special magnetic keys are security features. The top three floors are Renaissance Club rooms with many extras and their own lounge set apart from other public areas.
Amenities satellite TV, in-house movies, secretarial services, fax, shop, laundry service. ♿

MANCHESTER   Siam Orchid   NEW ENTRY

R **Town plan D3**
Greater Manchester
54 Portland Street
061-236 1388

Thai cooking
Set L from £3.50
Set D from £12
Seats 55 *Parking* Ample
Credit Access, Diners, Visa

Capable cooking, simple decor and friendly service from waitresses in national costume are features of this Thai restaurant where the head chef is a lady. Her best dishes include those that make authentically liberal use of coconut cream and chilli. Try the chicken, coconut cream and lemon grass soup, followed by spicy stir-fries and perhaps a curry; cool down with mango pudding.

Lunch 11.30–2.30   *Dinner* 6.30–11.30   *About* £35 *for two*
Closed L Sun & 2 days Xmas

MANCHESTER   Willow Bank Hotel   56%   £E

H **Town plan D5**
Greater Manchester
340 Wilmslow Road,
Fallowfield M14 6AF
061-224 0461
Telex 668222
Credit Access, Amex, Diners, Visa

A popular business hotel some three miles outside the city centre. Day rooms include an airy lounge and a contemporary-style bar with rustic features, while a large modern extension – quite out of character with the original Victorian building – provides most of the accommodation. Good-sized bedrooms are bright and airy, with simple fitted units and compact bathrooms. Plentiful parking is a major attraction. *Amenities* laundry service.

Rooms 124	*Direct dial* Yes	*Confirm by* 6	*Parking* Ample
Ensuite bath/shower 122	*Room TV* Yes	*Last dinner* 10.15	*Room service* 24 hours

MANCHESTER   Yang Sing   ⏣

R **Town plan D3**
Greater Manchester
34 Princess Street
061–236 2200

Chinese cooking

About £38 *for two*
Seats 140
Parties 220
Parking Limited

Credit Access, Amex

So popular is the Yeung family's Chinese restaurant that even the larger premises they moved into a couple of years ago often seem likely to burst at the seams. It's a bustling, noisy and easy-going place, and booking's essential. Home-prepared dim sum are particularly good – try roast pork bun, or chicken and rice in lotus leaves. Other choices among 250 items on a mainly Cantonese menu cater for both conservative and more adventurous palates – for the latter, perhaps quick-fried chicken gizzards with cashew nuts or ox tripe with pickled cabbage. Go on a Sunday and join Chinese families on their traditional weekly outing.

Meals 12–11
Closed 25 Dec

We publish annually,
so make sure you use the current edition.
It's worth it!

MANCHESTER AIRPORT   Excelsior Hotel   69%   £C

H **Map 10 B2**
Greater Manchester
Ringway Road, Wythenshawe
M22 5NS
061-437 5811 Telex 668721
Credit Access, Amex, Diners, Visa

Passengers can check up on the latest flight information on a screen in the foyer of this well-run, modern hotel. Most bedrooms are quite stylish, with darkwood furniture and smart furnishings. Executive rooms have the usual extras and nicer bathrooms. Public areas include a leisure centre. *Amenities* indoor swimming pool, sauna, solarium, whirlpool bath, keep-fit equipment, secretarial services, fax, laundry service, coffee shop (10am–midnight).

Rooms 300	*Direct dial* Yes	*Confirm by* 6	*Parking* Ample
Ensuite bath/shower 300	*Room TV* Yes	*Last dinner* 10.15 (Sun 10)	*Room service* 24 hours

Our inspectors are our full-time employees;
they are professionally trained by us.

MANCHESTER AIRPORT   Hilton International Hotel   72%   £B

H **Map 10 B2**
Greater Manchester
Outwood Lane, Ringway M22 5WP
061-436 4404
Telex 668361

Rooms 165
Ensuite bath/shower 165
Direct dial Yes
Room TV Yes
Confirm by 6
Last dinner 10.30
Parking Ample
Room service 24 hours

Credit Access, Amex, Diners, Visa

This modern brick-built hotel started life as the Ladbroke International but now celebrates its second birthday with a new name. A major bedroom extension is under way, and other improvements include more bar space and extra conference facilities. A screen provides flight information in the spacious tiled foyer, which leads via a small bridge over a stream to the main public areas. Existing bedrooms have attractive pale grey stained wood furniture, quilted bedcovers with matching curtains, smartly appointed bathrooms and plenty of extras. Transport for airport. *Amenities* indoor swimming pool, sauna, whirlpool bath, keep-fit equipment, in-house movies, secretarial services, fax, laundry service, coffee shop (8am–11pm). &

MANCHESTER AIRPORT   Moss Nook   ♛ ♧

R **Map 10 B2**
Greater Manchester
Ringway Road
061-437 4778

Set L & D from £16.50
About £55 *for two*
Seats 50
Parking Ample

Credit Access, Amex, Diners, Visa

A mile or so from the airport on the Cheshire border, Moss Nook is a comfortable, stylish restaurant with a sumptuous Edwardian look. The menu is full of intriguing and inventive combinations that really work, thanks to the talents of Robert Thornton: laver bread with shellfish in a pancake; ginger and a sweet-sour sauce with maize-fed breast of chicken; delicious celery and apple soup. Sauces are a particular strength, vegetables deserve a special mention and sweets include home-made ice cream. Main courses are served under silver cloches and the whole meal is very attractively presented. Correct service from charming girls in black waistcoats and bow ties.

Lunch 12–2   *Dinner* 7–9.30
Closed L Sat, all Sun & Mon, Bank Hols & 2 wks Xmas

MARKET HARBOROUGH   Three Swans Hotel   £E

H **Map 11 D4** Leicestershire
21 High Street LE16 7HJ
Market Harborough (0858) 66644

Credit Access, Amex, Diners, Visa

Major improvements are well under way at the Three Swans, a town-centre hotel graded as an inn in our 1988 Guide. The new owners' scheme includes a brand new reception area, along with a new cocktail bar, plus a residents' lounge and bar. Bedrooms will be increased from 18 to 35; existing rooms are bright and comfortable, and two have four-posters. No dogs.
Amenities laundry service. &

Rooms 35	*Direct dial* Yes	*Confirm by* arrang.	*Parking* Ample
Ensuite bath/shower 35	*Room TV* Yes	*Last dinner* 10	*Room service* None

MARKINGTON   Hob Green Hotel   71%   £D

H **Map 15 B6** North Yorkshire
Nr Harrogate HG3 3PJ
Harrogate (0423) 770031
Telex 57780

Rooms 12
Ensuite bath/shower 12
Direct dial Yes
Room TV Yes
Confirm by arrang.
Last dinner 9.30
Parking Ample
Room service All day

Credit Access, Amex, Diners, Visa

Set in lovely rolling countryside, this mellow stone-built house enjoys peaceful views on all sides. Splendid floral displays and fine antiques set the tone of comfort and elegance in the hall and drawing room, and in winter there are welcoming open fires. In summer you might prefer to relax in the garden room where fresh green and white decor, bamboo furniture and picture windows create a stylish conservatory effect.

Spacious bedrooms are individually decorated to a high standard and offer extras like electric blankets, tea-coffee makers, remote-control TVs, radios and mini-bars. Nice bathrooms, with plenty of toiletries. Courteous, attentive staff.
Amenities garden, putting, croquet, laundry service.

MARLBOROUGH Ivy House 64% *NEW ENTRY* £C/D

H **Map 4 C2** Wiltshire
High Street SN8 1HJ
Marlborough (0672) 55333

Credit Access, Amex, Diners, Visa

Fishing rights are rare in a town-centre hotel, but Ivy House, an extended Georgian building, has its own rods on the Kennet. Bedrooms are a strong point, spotlessly clean and individually decorated, with tasteful contemporary fabrics, freestanding furniture, neat bathrooms and good accessories. Pretty flowers decorate the entrance hall, lounge and bar. No children under 12. *Amenities* coarse fishing, satellite TV, in-house movies, secretarial services, fax, laundry service.

Rooms 35	*Direct dial* Yes	*Confirm by* 6	*Parking* Ample
Ensuite bath/shower 35	*Room TV* Yes	*Last dinner* 9.30	*Room service* All day

MARLOW Compleat Angler Hotel 77% £B

HR **Map 5 E2**
Buckinghamshire
Marlow Bridge SL7 1RG
Marlow (062 84) 4444
Telex 848644

Rooms 46
Ensuite bath/shower 46
Direct dial Yes
Room TV Yes
Confirm by arrang.
Last dinner 10
Parking Ample
Room service 24 hours

Credit Access, Amex, Diners, Visa

Nestling in a picturesque curve of the Thames, this famous hotel takes its name from Izaak Walton's classic work, written here in 1653. It's an elegant, sophisticated place, with comfortable day rooms leading from the marble-floored entrance hall. Ornaments, colourful, chintzy fabrics and traditional furnishings give a homely charm to the bedrooms, where sherry and chocolates are among the welcoming touches. Best

rooms have river views. Bathrooms are excellent, too, with good towels and toiletries. All bedrooms were due to have been refurbished by August 1988. There's an extensive buffet selection for breakfast, but hot items can be disappointing. *Amenities* garden, tennis, croquet, coarse fishing, secretarial services, fax, laundry service, helipad.

Valaisan Restaurant ♕

French cooking

Set L from £16.50, Sun £22
About £72 for two
Seats 130
Parties 130

An elegant and spacious room where chef Marc Legros offers classical menus with imaginative touches. Foie gras heads the list, which also includes sole Souvaroff, veal provençale and sautéed fillet of lamb with an excellent garlic and mustard sauce. Among the sweets there is a light, delicious chocolate mousse gâteau. Safe, conventional wine list with the odd gem such as Ch. Lynch-Bages 1961. Some of the otherwise excellent French staff have only halting English. ℮

Lunch 12.30–2.30, Sun 12.30–3
Dinner 7.30–10, Sat 7.30–10.30

See INSPECTOR FOR A DAY

MATLOCK Riber Hall 71% £C/D

HR **Map 10 C2** Derbyshire
Riber DE4 5JU
Matlock (0629) 2795

Rooms 11
Ensuite bath/shower 11
Direct dial Yes
Room TV Yes
Confirm by arrang.
Last dinner 9.30
Parking Ample
Room service All day

Credit Access, Amex, Diners, Visa

High above the town, this Elizabethan manor house makes a very fine hotel. The building dates from the 15th century and there are plenty of reminders of this in the heavy oak beams spanning thick stone walls. There's only one public room (apart from the dining room), a delightful bar-lounge with comfy sofas and chairs grouped around a carved oak fireplace. Bedrooms in a separate converted stable block are indi-

vidually decorated. The best have seating areas, capacious whirlpool baths, skirt and trouser presses and thoughtful extras including books, mini-bars, fruit and truffles. Bathrooms – all with bidets – are excellent. No children under ten. No dogs. *Amenities* garden, tennis, secretarial services, fax laundry service. *see over*

Riber Hall Restaurant 👑

Set L £11
About £60 for two
Seats 45
Parties 34

Booking is essential for lunch and dinner at this elegant restaurant, a testimony to the excellence of Jeremy Brazelle's cooking. Innovative touches transform a superficially conservative menu. Ingredients are first class, seasonings subtle and sauces carefully composed. We relished mousseline of scallops and lobster and venison medallions with port wine sauce. Some very good wines: Beaujolais Crus from Trenel and superb Petaluma Chardonnay '84 and Penfolds Grange Hermitage '80 from Australia. 🍷 Well-chosen 🅮 🍴

Lunch 12–1.30   *Dinner* 7–9.30

MATLOCK BATH   New Bath Hotel   60%   £C/D

🇭 **Map 10 C2** Derbyshire
New Bath Road DE4 3PX
Matlock (0629) 583275

Credit Access, Amex, Diners, Visa

Swimming pools fed by a thermal spring are one of the attractions of this Georgian house hotel overlooking the River Derwent. Best bedrooms, in a modern wing overlooking the outdoor pool, are comfortable and spacious with smart Italian furniture. Some are due for much needed refurbishment, as are the bar and lounge.
Amenities   garden, indoor & outdoor swimming pools, sauna, solarium, tennis, games room, pool table, laundry service.

Rooms 55	*Direct dial* Yes	*Confirm by* 6	*Parking* Ample
Ensuite bath/shower 55	*Room TV* Yes	*Last dinner* 9.30	*Room service* 24 hours

---

Our inspectors *never* book in the name of Egon Ronay's Guides.
They disclose their identity only if they are considering an establishment
for inclusion in the next edition of the Guide.

MAWNAN SMITH   Budock Vean Hotel   65%   £B

🇭 **Map 2 B4** Cornwall
Nr Falmouth TR11 5LG
Falmouth (0326) 250288

Credit Access, Amex, Diners, Visa
Closed Jan–mid Feb

An 18th-century mansion set in delightful countryside has been extended over the years into a comfortable and relaxed hotel. Best of the day rooms is a cane-furnished sun lounge, and there are other lounges and two bars. The majority of bedrooms are fairly plain in decor and furnishings, while eight have been pleasantly refurbished.
Amenities   garden, indoor swimming pool, tennis, 9-hole golf course, coarse fishing, snooker, laundry service.

Rooms 53	*Direct dial* Yes	*Confirm by* arrang.	*Parking* Ample
Ensuite bath/shower 53	*Room TV* Yes	*Last dinner* 9	*Room service* 24 hours

---

MAWNAN SMITH   Meudon Hotel   69%   £C/D

🇭 **Map 2 B4** Cornwall
Nr Falmouth TR11 5HT
Falmouth (0326) 250541
Telex 45478

Credit Access, Diners, Visa
Closed Jan & Dec

Lovingly tended sub-tropical gardens, originally laid out by Capability Brown, surround this much extended hotel which has its own private beach and a livery stable. The main building contains a lounge in classical style, with wing chairs, an open fire and a pleasing pink and green colour scheme, a tiny cocktail bar and two further comfortable lounges, one a sunny room linking a modern wing. The bedrooms are neat and pleasantly decorated, with matching curtains and bedspreads in stripes or floral prints and functional furniture; all have radios, remote-control TVs and clean, carpeted bathrooms. No under fives.
Amenities   garden, terrace, hairdressing, stabling, sea fishing, private beach, secretarial services, fax, laundry service.

Rooms 30	*Direct dial* Yes	*Confirm by* arrang.	*Parking* Ample
Ensuite bath/shower 30	*Room TV* Yes	*Last dinner* 8.45	*Room service* 24 hours

---

 For a *discount* on next year's guide, see **An Offer for Answers.**

Thought depends
absolutely on the stomach, but in spite of that,
those who have the best stomachs
are not the best thinkers.

VOLTAIRE 1694-1778
Letter To D'Alembert,
20 August 1770

I know about details,
and if I have introduced or perfected a hundred
details in my time, I shall be content.
After all, no chef has even invented a hundred dishes.

CHARLES RITZ
Cited by Stephen Watts in
THE RITZ (1963)

A recipe

is not meant to be followed exactly -

it is a canvas on which you can embroider.

Improvise and invent. Add the zest of this,

a drop of that, a tiny pinch of the other...

ROGER VERGE
CUISINE OF THE SUN
Trans. Caroline Conran (1979)

According to the Spanish proverb,

four persons are wanted to make a good salad (dressing):

a spendthrift for oil, a miser for vinegar,

a counsellor for salt and a madman to stir it all up.

ABRAHAM HAYWARD 1801-84
THE ART OF DINING

MAWNAN SMITH Nansidwell Country House 71% NEW ENTRY £C/D

H **Map 2 B4** Cornwall
Nr Falmouth TR11 5HU
Falmouth (0326) 250340

Rooms 15
Ensuite bath/shower 12
Direct dial Yes
Room TV Yes
Confirm by arrang.
Last dinner 9.30
Parking Ample
Room service Limited

Credit Access, Amex, Diners, Visa
Closed Jan

The setting is pure delight, in lovely gardens and grounds looking across to the sea. Felicity and Jamie Robertson opened their doors to guests in February 1988, after a careful programme of restoration which has created a most peaceful and relaxing refuge from the hurly-burly of city life. Period furnishings, pictures, ornaments and fresh flowers grace the entrance hall and lounge, and copious books and magazines provide pleasant browsing. Bedrooms are of a good size and individually decorated, with mainly pine or period furniture, remote-control TVs, tea-makers and tidy bathrooms stocked with good-quality toiletries. Service is keen, if not particularly polished.
Amenities garden, laundry service.

MELBOURN Pink Geranium

R **Map 6 B3** Hertfordshire
Station Road, Nr Royston
Royston (0763) 60215

Set L £11.95
About £52 for two
Seats 55 *Parties* 40
Parking Ample
Credit Access, Amex, Visa

A 16th-century thatched cottage with a pink-washed picture-postcard appeal. Inside, beams, chintz and candlelight make an intimate setting for a meal served and presented with style. The cooking is a bit variable (maybe the chef – new since the last Guide – is still settling in) and it could be that simpler things like grilled Dover sole or rack of English lamb are the best bets. Reasonably priced wines, with many half-bottles. ℮

Lunch 12–2.30 *Dinner* 7–10 **Closed** D Sun & L Mon

MELKSHAM King's Arms Hotel £E/F

I **Map 4 B3** Wiltshire
Market Place SN12 6EX
Melksham (0225) 707272

Credit Access, Amex, Diners, Visa

Set back from the main street of a Wiltshire market town, the King's Arms is a traditional inn providing modest accommodation in well-kept, individually appointed bedrooms. The four singles share facilities but all the twins and doubles have private bathrooms en suite, with tubs, showers and hairdryers. The lounge is well supplied with easy chairs, and there's a pleasant bar supplemented by courtyard seating in summer.

| *Rooms* 14 | *Direct dial* Yes | *Confirm by* arrang. | *Parking* Ample |
| *Ensuite bath/shower* 10 | *Room TV* Yes | *Last dinner* 9 | *Room service* Limited |

MELLOR Millstone Hotel £D/E

I **Map 10 B1** Lancashire
Church Lane, Nr Blackburn
BB2 7JR
Mellor (025 481) 3333
Telex 635309

Credit Access, Amex, Diners, Visa

A roadside inn offering very comfortable accommodation close to the M6. The lounge bar has oak-panelled walls, velour seating and polished wood tables and there's an intimate, alcoved lounge. Bedrooms have lightwood furniture, tea/coffee-makers and trouser presses; Executive rooms also offer fruit, dressing gowns and teletext TV. All have carpeted bathrooms with good quality toiletries. Three new suites are individually styled. *Amenities* laundry service.

| *Rooms* 19 | *Direct dial* Yes | *Confirm by* 6 | *Parking* Ample |
| *Ensuite bath/shower* 19 | *Room TV* Yes | *Last dinner* 9.45 | *Room service* All day |

MELTON MOWBRAY George Hotel 57% £E

H **Map 11 D3** Leicestershire
High Street LE13 0TR
Melton Mowbray (0664) 62112

Credit Access, Amex, Diners, Visa

The George was once a coaching inn, and the former coach entrance is now the busy reception area. Prints of horses decorate the walls here and in the two cheerful bars. Bedrooms vary in size and are individually furnished (four with four-posters). Decor is reassuringly old-fashioned and bathrooms are well kept. Tea-makers are provided and there is double glazing throughout.
Amenities coffee shop (10am–10pm).

| *Rooms* 20 | *Room phone* Yes | *Confirm by* 6 | *Parking* Limited |
| *Ensuite bath/shower* 20 | *Room TV* Yes | *Last dinner* 10 | *Room service* Limited |

MELTON MOWBRAY Harboro' Hotel   57%   £E

H **Map 11 D3** Leicestershire
Burton Street LE13 1AF
Melton Mowbray (0664) 60121
Telex 341713

Credit Access, Amex, Diners, Visa

An easily spotted black-and-white inn on the edge of town, by the
A606 to Oakham. Staff are pleasant and helpful, though some tasks,
like servicing rooms and cooking breakfast, could be performed better.
Seven bedrooms are compact singles, the rest of a decent size;
furnishings vary from traditional to fairly modern. Jolliest of the day
rooms is a cosy panelled bar.
Amenities laundry service.

Rooms 28	*Direct dial* Yes	*Confirm by* 6	*Parking* Ample
Ensuite bath/shower 28	*Room TV* Yes	*Last dinner* 10	*Room service* Limited

MELTON MOWBRAY   Stapleford Park   86%   *NEW ENTRY*   £B/C

H **Map 11 D3** Leicestershire
Stapleford,
Nr Melton Mowbray LE14 2EF
Melton Mowbray (057 284) 522
Telex 342319

Rooms 30
Ensuite bath/shower 30
Direct dial Yes
Room TV Yes
Confirm by arrang.
Last dinner 11
Parking Ample
Room service 24 hours

Credit Access, Amex, Diners, Visa

Ebullient Bob Payton and his wife Wendy have restored a marvellous
16th-century house to rather more than its former splendour. 15
renowned designers have created rooms of differing style and
character, with no expense spared on antiques and fabrics. Luxury
prevails, each room having at least two comfortable armchairs, all the
expected accessories, marble-floored bathrooms and lovely views.
Day rooms are of magnificent proportions, lofty, elegant and
beautifully appointed. A great hotel for sportsmen, with a wide variety
of activities available on site or locally by arrangement. Very relaxed,
friendly staff. No children under ten. Kennels for dogs. *Amenities*
garden, tennis, badminton, putting, croquet, riding, stabling, shooting,
coarse fishing, secretarial services, fax, laundry service.

**We welcome bona fide complaints and recommendations
on the tear-out pages at the back of the book for readers' comment.
They are followed up by our professional team.**

MERE   Old Ship Hotel   £E/F

I **Map 4 B3** Wiltshire
Castle Street BA12 6JE
Mere (0747) 860258

Credit Access, Visa

A handsome old town-centre inn that was once the home of Sir John
Coventry, MP. There are three characterful bars, one panelled, the
others beamed, and the peaceful residents' lounge is made for relaxing.
Main-house bedrooms are traditional, annexe rooms modern and
practical. Staff are friendly and efficient, and breakfast is very decent
– go for the excellent home-cooked ham.
Amenities garden.

Rooms 22	*Direct dial* Yes	*Confirm by* arrang.	*Parking* Ample
Ensuite bath/shower 17	*Room TV* Yes	*Last dinner* 9	*Room service* All day

MERIDEN   Manor Hotel   64%   £D

H **Map 10 C4** West Midlands
Main Road CV7 7NH
Meriden (0676) 22735
Telex 311011

Credit Access, Amex, Diners, Visa

Changes continue behind the Georgian facade of this converted country
residence. There is a smart new reception area, and a new look is
planned for the lounge and cocktail bar. Bedrooms, too, are being
gradually updated, using attractive fabrics and good-quality lightwood
units. Upgraded bathrooms have attractive tiling and vanity units. 42
additional bedrooms are due by December 1988. *Amenities* garden,
outdoor swimming pool, secretarial services, fax, laundry service.

Rooms 32	*Direct dial* Yes	*Confirm by* arrang.	*Parking* Ample
Ensuite bath/shower 32	*Room TV* Yes	*Last dinner* 10	*Room service* 24 hours

MICKLETON Three Ways Hotel 60% £E

H **Map 4 C1** Gloucestershire
Nr Chipping Campden
GL55 6SB
Mickleton (0386) 438429
Telex 337242

Credit Access, Amex, Diners, Visa

Standing in the centre of the village, just off the A46, this lovely
Cotswold-stone hotel has built up a reputation for friendliness and
efficiency. Day rooms include a welcoming bar and pleasantly homely
lounge. Main-house bedrooms provide ample space and have carpeted
bathrooms; others, in a modern extension, are more compact, with
fully-tiled bathrooms. All have tea-makers.
Amenities garden, fax, laundry service.

Rooms 40	*Direct dial* Yes	*Confirm by* arrang.	*Parking* Ample
Ensuite bath/shower 40	*Room TV* Yes	*Last dinner* 9	*Room service* 24 hours

We publish annually,
so make sure you use the current edition.
It's worth it!

MIDDLE WALLOP Fifehead Manor 61% £D/E

HR **Map 4 C3** Hampshire
Nr Stockbridge SO20 8EG
Andover (0264) 781565

Credit Access, Amex, Diners, Visa
Closed 1 wk Xmas

Established gardens frame this small, mellow manor house. The
entrance hall, which doubles as the bar, leads to a small lounge with
limited seating. Best bedrooms are in a new extension. These are
spacious and attractively furnished and should not be confused with
the smaller annexe rooms. Bedrooms in the main house are homely,
with pleasant furnishings and acceptable bathrooms. *Amenities*
garden, croquet, secretarial services, laundry service. &

Rooms 16	*Direct dial* Yes	*Confirm by* 6	*Parking* Ample
Ensuite bath/shower 16	*Room TV* Yes	*Last dinner* 9.30	*Room service* All day

Restaurant

Set L £9
Set D £17
About £50 *for two*
Seats 35
Parties 40

Nicholas Ruthven-Stuart's light touch continues to delight at this
rustic dining room. Raw materials of outstanding quality are carefully
cooked and interestingly combined in such dishes as Stilton mousse
on a bed of chicory, apple and watercress, and salmon with saffron
and ginger in filo pastry. A sensible à la carte menu is supplemented
by daily-changing fixed-price set lunches and dinners. Sauces are very
good indeed and desserts are well made. ❤

Lunch 12–2.30 *Dinner* 7.30–9.30
Closed 1 wk Xmas

MIDDLECOMBE Periton Park 66% *NEW ENTRY* £D

HR **Map 3 D1** Somerset
Periton Road,
Nr Minehead TA24 8SW
Minehead (0643) 6885
Telex 42513
Credit Access, Amex, Diners, Visa
Closed 2 wks Nov

Tony and Valerie Wright's delightful Victorian house stands in lovely
woodland and gardens on the fringe of Exmoor. Informality is the
watchword, and in the splendid drawing room, guests can browse
through the books, turn a hand of cards or enjoy a drink. Bedrooms
are individually furnished with period pieces. Good breakfasts. No
children under 12. *Amenities* garden, croquet, riding, snooker,
secretarial services, laundry service.

Rooms 7	*Direct dial* Yes	*Confirm by* arrang.	*Parking* Ample
Ensuite bath/shower 7	*Room TV* Yes	*Last dinner* 8	*Room service* All day

Restaurant *NEW ENTRY* ∜

Set D £15
Seats 14
Parties 18

Valerie's cooking is enjoyably unpretentious, and her no-choice menus
can be relied upon to provide a tasty, well-prepared meal. King
prawns mayonnaise or smoked mackerel gratinée could get things
under way, followed perhaps by poached salmon, leg of lamb or roast
beef. Sweets may include poached pear or plum pudding finishing
with a choice of well-kept cheeses. Service is delightfully friendly and
informal. ❤

Dinner only at 8
About £40 *for two*

MIDDLESBROUGH   Hotel Baltimore   65%   £E

H **Map 15 C5** Cleveland
250 Marton Road TS4 2EZ
Middlesbrough (0642) 224111
Telex 58517

Credit Access, Amex, Diners, Visa

A red-brick hotel just south of the city centre, on the A172. The exterior with its bay windows and pediments may be solidly traditional but inside, apart from some button-back armchairs and settees in the foyer-lounge, all is brightly contemporary. Light and airy bedrooms (largest at the front) have pleasant pastel decor and simple white furniture. *Amenities* garden, solarium, in-house movies, secretarial services, laundry service, 24-hour lounge service.

Rooms 31	*Direct dial* Yes	*Confirm by* arrang.	*Parking* Ample
Ensuite bath/shower 31	*Room TV* Yes	*Last dinner* 10.45	*Room service* All day

MIDDLESBROUGH   Dragonara Hotel   63%   £D

H **Map 15 C5** Cleveland
Fry Street TS1 1JH
Middlesbrough (0642) 232000
Telex 58266

Credit Access, Amex, Diners, Visa

A high-rise hotel which offers comfortable, town-centre accommodation. Public areas include a popular split-level public bar with music and a cosy residents' bar. Bedrooms are decorated in pastel shades and pleasing coordinated fabrics of varying styles and have smart fitted furniture, tea/coffee makers and functional bathrooms; Gold Star rooms have extras such as hairdryers and trouser presses. *Amenities* solarium, in-house movies, secretarial services, laundry service.

Rooms 140	*Direct dial* Yes	*Confirm by* arrang.	*Parking* Limited
Ensuite bath/shower 140	*Room TV* Yes	*Last dinner* 10	*Room service* Limited

MIDDLETON IN TEESDALE   Teesdale Hotel   59%   £E

H **Map 15 B5** Co. Durham
DL12 0QG
Teesdale (0833) 40264

Credit Access, Visa

A pleasant family-run hotel that keeps some of the charm of coaching days. Flowers add a cheerful touch to the little foyer and bar, where there are plenty of comfortable seats. Bedrooms, reached via corridors with elaborate gold wallpaper, are kept in good order and include a family room. There are some holiday cottages in the courtyard. The majority of rooms have en suite facilities.

Rooms 18	*Direct dial* Yes	*Confirm by* arrang.	*Parking* Ample
Ensuite bath/shower 11	*Room TV* Yes	*Last dinner* 8.30	*Room service* Limited

MIDDLETON STONEY   Jersey Arms   £D/E

I **Map 5 D1** Oxfordshire
Nr Bicester OX6 8SE
Middleton Stoney (086 989) 234

Credit Access, Amex, Diners, Visa

Brass, beams and a fine inglenook fireplace bolster the rustic charm of this 16th-century coaching inn. Standing on the busy A43, and under the enthusiastic control of the owner, the hotel offers a choice of accommodation. Rooms in the main house are traditional, courtyard rooms have pine furnishings and there are also luxury suites. Mineral water and hairdryers are standard in all rooms. Excellent housekeeping. No dogs. *Amenities* garden.

Rooms 14	*Direct dial* Yes	*Confirm by* arrang.	*Parking* Ample
Ensuite bath/shower 14	*Room TV* Yes	*Last dinner* 9.30	*Room service* Limited

Our inspectors *never* book in the name of Egon Ronay's Guides.
They disclose their identity only if they are considering an establishment
for inclusion in the next edition of the Guide.

MIDHURST   Spread Eagle Hotel   65%   £D/E

H **Map 5 E3** West Sussex
South Street GU29 9NH
Midhurst (073 081) 6911
Telex 86853

Credit Access, Amex, Diners, Visa

A wig powder closet is just one of many period features of this picturesque 15th-century hostelry. Public rooms include an atmospheric beamed lounge, a comfortable lounge bar with a huge inglenook and a pubby cellar bar. Most bedrooms in the old hotel are traditional. The new annexe (which adjoins the hotel) is modern with efficient insulation and heating. *Amenities* garden, secretarial services, laundry service.

Rooms 41	*Direct dial* Yes	*Confirm by* arrang.	*Parking* Ample
Ensuite bath/shower 37	*Room TV* Yes	*Last dinner* 9.15	*Room service* 24 hours

MILFORD-ON-SEA   South Lawn Hotel   66%   £D/E

H **Map 4 C4** Hampshire
Lymington Road SO41 0RF
Lymington (0590) 43911

Credit Access, Visa
Closed 1 month Xmas

Standing just outside the village, about a mile from the sea, this black and white half-timbered building was once a dower house but is now a well-maintained, family-run hotel. Comfortable wing chairs with pretty floral covers give the spacious bar-lounge an attractive country feel while good-sized bedrooms, with restful creamy beige decor, have well-appointed bathrooms. No children under seven. No dogs. *Amenities* garden, secretarial services, laundry service. ⅙

Rooms 24	*Direct dial* Yes	*Confirm by* arrang.	*Parking* Ample
Ensuite bath/shower 24	*Room TV* Yes	*Last dinner* 8.30	*Room service* All day

MILTON DAMEREL   Woodford Bridge Hotel   66%   £D/E

H **Map 2 C2** Devon
Nr Holsworthy EX22 7LL
Milton Damerel (040 926) 481

Credit Access, Visa

High standards prevail at this charming 15th-century coaching inn on the A388 Holsworthy to Bideford road. Cosy, homely public rooms boast plenty of panelling and attractively upholstered seating. Bedrooms vary in size and style but are all simply decorated with white-painted walls and have period furniture and tiled bathrooms. *Amenities* garden, indoor swimming pool, sauna, solarium, keep-fit equipment, tennis, squash, coarse fishing, games room, fax.

Rooms 14	*Direct dial* Yes	*Confirm by* arrang.	*Parking* Ample
Ensuite bath/shower 11	*Room TV* No	*Last dinner* 8.30	*Room service* Limited

MINSTER LOVELL   Old Swan Hotel   £E

I **Map 4 C2** Oxfordshire
Nr Witney OX8 5RN
Witney (0993) 75614

Credit Access, Amex, Diners, Visa

Cotswold stone and half timbering combine delightfully at this 600-year-old inn close to the Windrush river. Open fires, low-beamed ceilings and flagstoned floors characterise the three cosy little lounges. Super bedrooms feature smart darkwood furniture and richly autumnal fabrics; all have modern carpeted bathrooms, as well as tea-makers, trouser presses and hairdryers. Enthusiastic new managers. No children under 12. No dogs. *Amenities* garden.

Rooms 10	*Direct dial* Yes	*Confirm by* arrang.	*Parking* Ample
Ensuite bath/shower 10	*Room TV* Yes	*Last dinner* 9.30	*Room service* All day

Changes in data sometimes occur in establishments
after the Guide goes to press.
Prices should be taken as indications rather than firm quotes.

MONK FRYSTON   Monk Fryston Hall   64%   £D/E

H **Map 11 D1** North Yorkshire
Nr Leeds LS25 5DU
South Milford (0977) 682369
Telex 556634

Credit Access, Amex, Visa

An ancient and historic manor house, now transformed into a highly characterful hotel. Dark oak panelling and fine oil paintings cover the walls of the public rooms and wine-coloured velour upholstered seating blends well with antique pieces. An oak staircase and gallery lead to bright, sunny bedrooms with traditional freestanding furniture. All have tea/coffee-makers, radios, trouser presses and two easy chairs. *Amenities* garden, laundry service. ⅙

Rooms 29	*Direct dial* Yes	*Confirm by* arrang.	*Parking* Ample
Ensuite bath/shower 29	*Room TV* Yes	*Last dinner* 9.30	*Room service* 24 hours

MONTACUTE   King's Arms Inn   £E

I **Map 3 F2** Somerset
TA15 6UU
Martock (0935) 822513

Credit Access, Amex, Visa
Closed 25 Dec

New resident owners have no major changes planned for their mellow stone-built inn standing opposite the village church. Exposed stone walls feature in the public areas, which include a small, elegant lounge bar with comfortable chintzy sofas. Accommodation ranges from a spacious and stylish suite at the front and de luxe rooms with quality furnishings, to rather more ordinary rooms at the back. Decent modern bathrooms. *Amenities* garden.

Rooms 11	*Direct dial* Yes	*Confirm by* arrang.	*Parking* Ample
Ensuite bath/shower 11	*Room TV* Yes	*Last dinner* 9	*Room service* All day

MORETON-IN-MARSH   Manor House Hotel   69%   £D/E

H **Map 4 C1** Gloucestershire
High Street GL56 0LJ
Moreton-in-Marsh (0608) 50501
Telex 837151

Credit Access, Amex, Diners, Visa

The Fentum family and their staff provide a warm welcome at this lovely Cotswold-stone manor house dating from the 16th century. Day rooms include a long foyer-lounge warmed by log fires in winter, and a bar (currently being refurbished) overlooking the garden. Characterful main-house bedrooms, some with four-posters and fine period furniture, are individually styled using well-coordinated colour schemes; annexe rooms have simple white furniture and attractive contemporary decor. All rooms are equipped with thoughtful extras. Bathrooms throughout are fairly basic. No children under 12. No dogs. *Amenities* garden, indoor swimming pool, sauna, whirlpool bath, tennis, putting, in-house movies, secretarial services, laundry service.

Rooms 38	*Direct dial* Yes	*Confirm by* arrang.	*Parking* Ample
Ensuite bath/shower 35	*Room TV* Yes	*Last dinner* 9	*Room service* 24 hours

MORETON-IN-MARSH   Redesdale Arms Hotel   £E

I **Map 4 C1** Gloucestershire
High Street GL56 0AW
Moreton-in-Marsh (0608) 50308
Telex 837928

Credit Access, Amex, Visa

Eighteenth-century charm blends with modern comforts at this characterful old inn, once a staging post on the Lincoln to Bath coach run. Improvements include a new reception and a cane-furnished conservatory lounge. Good-sized bedrooms are smartly furnished in period style and all now have en suite bathrooms. Tea-makers, trouser presses, hairdryers and radio-alarms are provided. No dogs. *Amenities* patio, secretarial services, fax, laundry service.   ⅄

Rooms 18	*Direct dial* Yes	*Confirm by* arrang.	*Parking* Ample
Ensuite bath/shower 18	*Room TV* Yes	*Last dinner* 9.30	*Room service* All day

---

**Changes in data sometimes occur in establishments
after the Guide goes to press.
Prices should be taken as indications rather than firm quotes.**

MORETONHAMPSTEAD   Manor House Hotel   67%   £C

H **Map 3 D3** Devon
TQ13 8RE
Moretonhampstead (0647) 40355
Telex 42794

Credit Access, Amex, Diners, Visa

Two hundred acres of lovely Devon countryside are the setting for this imposing manor house on the B3212. The interior retains some charming features, notably fine panelling in the bar and splendid lounge. Well-equipped bedrooms are furnished variously with traditional or more modern pieces. Service is not the strongest point. *Amenities* garden, tennis, squash, golf, putting, pitch & putt, croquet, game fishing, games room, snooker, pool table, laundry service.

Rooms 69	*Direct dial* Yes	*Confirm by* arrang.	*Parking* Ample
Ensuite bath/shower 69	*Room TV* Yes	*Last dinner* 9	*Room service* 24 hours

MORETONHAMPSTEAD   White Hart Hotel   £E

I **Map 3 D3** Devon
The Square TQ13 8NF
Moretonhampstead (0647) 40406

Credit Access, Amex, Diners, Visa

A sculptured white hind keeps graceful watch over the portico of this historic town-centre inn. Inside, good old-fashioned furnishings complement the reassuringly solid facade, and there's a huge open fire in the lounge. Dark traditional furniture and floral papers and fabrics give individually decorated bedrooms a charming country appeal, while dedicated owner Peter Morgan ensures high standards of service and housekeeping throughout. *Amenities* snooker, laundry service.

Rooms 23	*Room phone* No	*Confirm by* arrang.	*Parking* Ample
Ensuite bath/shower 23	*Room TV* Yes	*Last dinner* 8.30	*Room service* Limited

---

**Any person using our name to obtain free hospitality is a fraud.
Proprietors, please inform the police and us.**

MOTTRAM ST ANDREW Mottram Hall Hotel 70% £C

H **Map 10 B2** Cheshire
Wilmslow Road,
Nr Prestbury SK10 4QT
Prestbury (0625) 828135
Telex 668181

Rooms 95
Ensuite bath/shower 95
Direct dial Yes
Room TV Yes
Confirm by 5
Last dinner 10
Parking Ample
Room service 24 hours

Credit Access, Amex, Diners, Visa

A fine red-brick Georgian mansion standing in 270 acres of
parkland, including a delightful
lake (complete with swans) and
well-tended ornamental gardens.
Day rooms include a handsome
bar with an original Adam
moulded ceiling and a club-like
panelled lounge. All the bedrooms have now been refurbished and have extras such as
hairdryers, trouser presses and
satellite TVs. There are several

De Luxe suites in a new block, and all rooms have modern facilities.
Staff are friendly and helpful. Plans for 1989 include a golf course.
Amenities garden, indoor swimming pool, sauna, solarium, whirlpool bath, tennis, squash, putting, croquet, games room, snooker, in-
house movies, secretarial services, fax, laundry service. &

MOULTON Black Bull Inn Restaurant

R **Map 15 B5** North Yorkshire
Nr Richmond
Barton (032 577) 289

Set L £7.75
About £37 for two
Seats 100
Parties 30
Parking Ample
Credit Access, Amex, Diners, Visa

A popular village pub with a very varied appeal. The lunchtime bar
restaurant becomes a seafood restaurant at night, and you can also
dine in a converted *Brighton Belle* Pullman coach or a pretty
conservatory. Fish cookery is the star attraction – straightforward
classic fare based on local catches and ranging from lobster bisque to
sole mornay. No reservations are taken for the seafood restaurant,
otherwise you'll need to book. ♥ Well-chosen ℮

Lunch 12–2   *Dinner* 7–10.15
Closed L Sat, all Sun & 24 Dec–31 Dec

MOUSEHOLE Lobster Pot 56% £D/E

H **Map 2 A4** Cornwall
Nr Penzance TR19 6QX
Penzance (0736) 731251

Credit Access, Amex, Visa
Closed 1st Sun in Jan to mid Mar

The Lobster Pot seems almost to cling to the harbour wall and inside
is a jumble of little rooms with lots of character. Day rooms, steep
steps up from the tiny reception, are cosy and chintzy, and there's a
popular glassed-in verandah. Neatly repainted bedrooms are another
flight up, and it's a nearly vertical climb to the Crow's Nest, a lovely,
spacious room under the eaves.
Amenities sea fishing, fax.

Rooms 26	*Direct dial* Yes	*Confirm by* 6	*Parking* Difficult
Ensuite bath/shower 23	*Room TV* Yes	*Last dinner* 9.45	*Room service* Limited

MUCH BIRCH Pilgrim Hotel 64% £D/E

H **Map 4 A1**
Hereford & Worcester
Hereford HR2 8HJ
Golden Valley (0981) 540742
Telex 35332

Credit Access, Amex, Diners, Visa

A red-stone hotel with wonderful views over parkland and Golden
Valley. The atmospheric bar is a delight, with exposed stone walls and
polished oak tables, and there's a peaceful, chintzy lounge. Bedrooms
have well-coordinated decor, modern soft furnishings and lots of
extras such as mineral water and biscuits. Bathrooms (two with
shower only) are simple and modern, with plentiful towels and soaps.
Amenities garden, pitch & putt, croquet, laundry service.

Rooms 19	*Direct dial* Yes	*Confirm by* arrang.	*Parking* Ample
Ensuite bath/shower 19	*Room TV* Yes	*Last dinner* 9.45, Sun 8.45	*Room service* All day

MUDEFORD Avonmouth Hotel 59% £C

H **Map 4 C4** Dorset
Christchurch BH23 3NT
Bournemouth (0202) 483434

Credit Access, Amex, Diners, Visa

Christchurch harbour provides an attractive setting for this pleasant
waterside hotel with its own moorings and jetty. Picture windows in
the cosy lounge-bar make the most of the view. Best bedrooms also
have sea views and comfortable sitting areas; the rest are nice enough,
with fitted units and tea-makers. Most have showers.
Amenities garden, outdoor swimming-pool, putting, games room,
snooker, pool table, laundry service.

Rooms 41	*Direct dial* Yes	*Confirm by* 6	*Parking* Ample
Ensuite bath/shower 41	*Room TV* Yes	*Last dinner* 9	*Room service* 24 hours

MULLION   Polurrian Hotel   57%   £D

H **Map 2 B4** Cornwall
Helston TR12 7EN
Mullion (0326) 240421
Telex 94015906

Credit Access, Amex, Diners, Visa
Closed mid Dec–1 Mar

Excellent leisure facilities and a position high on the rugged coastline make this friendly hotel a popular spot. Splendid views are to be had from the large, comfortable lounge bar with its traditional seating and there is also a peaceful writing room. The bedrooms mainly have simple furnishings but offer direct dial phones and a welcoming sherry; three larger rooms boast smart furniture and matching fabrics. Bathrooms are adequate. *Amenities* garden, indoor & outdoor swimming pools, sauna, solarium, whirlpool bath, keep-fit equipment, beauty salon, tennis, squash, badminton, putting, croquet, sea fishing, boating, games room, snooker, pool table, in-house movies, secretarial services, fax, laundry service, children's playground.

Rooms 41	*Direct dial* Yes	*Confirm by* arrang.	*Parking* Ample
Ensuite bath/shower 39	*Room TV* Yes	*Last dinner* 9.30	*Room service* 24 hours

---

**We welcome bona fide complaints and recommendations
on the tear-out pages at the back of the book for readers' comment.
They are followed up by our professional team.**

NANTWICH   Rookery Hall   85%   £B

HR **Map 10 B3** Cheshire
Worleston CW5 6DQ
Nantwich (0270) 626866

Rooms 11
Ensuite bath/shower 11
Direct dial Yes
Room TV Yes
Confirm by arrang.
Last dinner 9.15
Parking Ample
Room service All day

Credit Access, Amex, Diners, Visa
Closed 4 Jan–28 Jan

Enjoying a tranquil setting amidst extensive gardens and wooded parkland fringing the river Weaver, this lovely château-style mansion is the perfect place to unwind. Sumptuously elegant day rooms enhanced by antiques, log fires and inviting sofas are wonderfully comfortable and relaxing, while individually decorated bedrooms, too, breathe style and taste, from their lavish fabrics and carpets to their beautifully upholstered furniture. Luxurious extras range from exotic fruits, chocolates and champagne to bathrobes and hairdryers in the chic bathrooms. Excellent polished and unobtrusive service. No children under ten. No dogs.
Amenities garden, tennis, putting, croquet, clay-pigeon shooting, laundry service, helipad.

Restaurant ★   ♔ ♔ ♔

Lunch 12.15–1.45
Dinner 7–9.15, Sat 7–9.45
Set L from £12.95
Set D £25
About £65 *for two*
Seats 55
Parties 40

Closed 4 Jan–28 Jan

Highly polished panelling, a splendidly ornate ceiling and fine table settings provide the dazzling backdrop for Stephen Ferenczy's assured and skilful cooking. Seasonally changing dishes based on old English recipes and executed with a light, modern touch offer such imaginative combinations as baked brill with a herb crust and dill sauce, and succulent veal served with noodles, leeks and a delicious chervil sauce. Beautifully presented sweets are equally delightful, and lovely home-made breads accompany outstanding British cheeses. Magnificent wine list, very strong in Bordeaux, burgundies and first-rate Californians (Jordan). ☞ Outstanding ♚ Well-chosen ☺

NEASHAM — Newbus Arms Hotel 64% £D

H Map 15 B5 Co. Durham
Nr Darlington DL2 1PE
Darlington (0325) 721071
Telex 58664

Credit Access, Amex, Diners, Visa

Guests can look forward to being cosseted at this small country house hotel not far from Teesside airport. A welcoming glass of sherry awaits you in the pretty, traditional-style bedrooms, and comforts include hot-water bottles for cold nights. Public rooms range from a panelled lounge and smart bar to a handsome bistro where afternoon tea is served. *Amenities* garden, secretarial services, laundry service.

Rooms 15	*Direct dial* Yes	*Confirm by* arrang.	*Parking* Ample
Ensuite bath/shower 15	*Room TV* Yes	*Last dinner* 10.15	*Room service* 24 hours

NEEDINGWORTH — Pike & Eel £E/F

I Map 6 B2 Cambridgeshire
Overcote Lane, Huntingdon
PE17 3TW
St Ives (0480) 63336

Credit Access, Amex, Diners, Visa
Closed 2 days Xmas

Boats moor on the banks of the Ouse in front of this friendly inn. Flanking the lively bar with its copper-topped tables and comfortable seats are two cosy lounges and upstairs the residents' lounge offers books and a small writing desk. Well-kept bedrooms – all with washbasins (three with bathrooms) – include TVs, tea-makers and writing areas. Public bathrooms are clean and functional. No dogs. *Amenities* garden, coarse fishing, mooring.

Rooms 9	*Room phone* No	*Confirm by* arrang.	*Parking* Ample
Ensuite bath/shower 3	*Room TV* Yes	*Last dinner* 10	*Room service* Limited

NEW MILTON — Chewton Glen Hotel 88% £A

HR Map 4 C4 Hampshire
BH25 6QS
Highcliffe (042 52) 5341
Telex 41456

Rooms 46
Ensuite bath/shower 46
Direct dial Yes
Room TV Yes
Confirm by arrang.
Last dinner 9.30
Parking Ample
Room service 24 hours

Credit Access, Amex, Diners, Visa

Beautifully kept grounds surround this handsome country house on the edge of the New Forest. Public areas are decorated in impeccable taste, including the delightfully light, airy main sitting room giving onto the garden and the cosy inner lounge with its marble fireplace. Bedrooms feature antiques, attractive painted furniture and luxurious fabrics, as well as discreetly hidden modern essentials like trouser presses, hairdryers and TVs. Extras such as sherry decanters, ice, chocolate and magazines abound, and bathrooms offer the finest toiletries. Service is outstanding. No children under seven. No dogs. *Amenities* garden, outdoor swimming pool, 9-hole golf course, putting, croquet, snooker, in-house movies, secretarial services, fax, valeting, laundry service, helipad.

Marryat Room ★ ♛♛

French cooking

Lunch 12.30–2
Dinner 7.30–9.30
Set L from £12.50
Set D £27.50
About £75 for two
Seats 100
Parties 100

A new conservatory extension lends extra space to a comfortable, tastefully appointed dining room. Cooking is very sound and professional, though not every dish sets the taste buds tingling; the seasonally changing menu makes tempting reading, with dishes like courgette flower stuffed with crab or our subtly smoked duck's breast served with a potato galette. There's a splendid selection of perfectly kept cheeses. First-rate sommelier Gérard Basset will advise you on the excellent cellar.

Specialities ravioli de morilles au fumet des cèpes, mille-feuilles de langoustines et épinards à la graine de moutarde, gratin d'abricots aux amandes et son sorbet au cognac. ▷ Outstanding
♟ Well-chosen ☺

NEWARK-ON-TRENT   Grange Hotel   56%   £F

H **Map 11 D3** Nottinghamshire
73 London Road NG24 1RZ
Newark (0636) 703399

Credit Access, Visa
Closed 10 days Xmas

A warm, friendly feel is generated throughout this converted Victorian house. Bedrooms include three delightful attic rooms with modern bathrooms and a couple of smallish singles that share facilities. Duvets are standard, but blankets are available on request; all rooms have tea-makers and radio-alarms. The main day room is a comfortable, old-fashioned bar. No children under 12. No dogs.
Amenities garden.

Rooms 8	Room phone No	Confirm by arrang.	Parking Ample
Ensuite bath/shower 6	Room TV Yes	Last dinner 9	Room service All day

NEWBURY   Chequers Hotel   63%   £C/D

H **Map 5 D2** Berkshire
Oxford Street RG13 1JB
Newbury (0635) 38000
Telex 849205

Credit Access, Amex, Diners, Visa

Once a coaching inn, this old building retains a feel of the past in its brass chandeliers and scattered antiques. The public areas are pleasant, with comfortable seating. Bedrooms vary in size and style; some have lightwood fitted units, while refurbished rooms offer Italian darkwood freestanding furniture. The latter have attractive matching fabrics and tiled bathrooms; older bathrooms are adequate. All provide tea/coffee-makers. *Amenities* garden, laundry service.

Rooms 60	Direct dial Yes	Confirm by 6	Parking Ample
Ensuite bath/shower 60	Room TV Yes	Last dinner 9.30	Room service 24 hours

NEWBURY   Elcot Park Hotel   69%   £D/E

HR **Map 5 D2** Berkshire
Nr Newbury RG16 8NJ
Kintbury (0488) 58100
Telex 846448

Credit Access, Amex, Diners, Visa

Five miles west of Newbury off the A4, this handsome Georgian mansion stands in a fine position overlooking the Kennet Valley. The central hall/lounge area features a rather splendid art nouveau fireplace that was made for the Paris Exhibition of 1900. There's a cocktail bar, a conservatory and a number of small meeting rooms. Seven bedrooms in the mews wing, including two with private patios, are particularly attractive, with soft colour schemes, ruffled curtains and high-quality reproduction furniture. Main-house bedrooms are traditionally appointed. There are four full suites and four rooms with four-posters. Excellent bathrooms throughout. *Amenities* garden, tennis, secretarial services, fax, laundry service, helipad.

Rooms 37	Direct Dial Yes	Confirm by arrang.	Parking Ample
Ensuite bath/shower 37	Room TV Yes	Last dinner 9.30	Room service Limited

Restaurant   NEW ENTRY

Set L £12.50
Set D £15.50
About £55 *for two*
Seats 55
Parties 70

David Evans and his brigade offer a well-balanced selection of dishes to enjoy in an elegantly proportioned dining room. Skewered langoustines with sole mousse and pigeon consommé under a puff-pastry lid are typical starters, while principal dishes could include salmon with chive butter or lamb cutlets with a tarragon and tomato sauce. Tempting sweets, farmhouse cheeses and good wines: Château Fonroque St. Emilion 1983, Anjou Moulin Touché 1959.
♑ Well-chosen ☪

Lunch 12–2   *Dinner* 7.30–9.30

Any person using our name to obtain free hospitality is a fraud.
Proprietors, please inform the police and us.

NEWBY BRIDGE   Swan Hotel   61%   £D/E

H **Map 13 D6** Cumbria
LA12 8NB
Newby Bridge (053 95) 31681
Telex 65108

Credit Access, Amex, Diners, Visa
Closed 10 days Jan

Attractively situated by the river Leven, the Swan is a modernised coaching inn. The beamed reception area keeps a comfortable, traditional look, and there's a neat TV lounge and two bars. Bedrooms are exceptionally well kept, with plenty of storage and writing space, remote-control TVs, trouser presses and compact carpeted bathrooms. Four de luxe rooms have balconies. No dogs. *Amenities* garden, coarse fishing, mooring, in-house movies, laundry service.

Rooms 36	Direct dial Yes	Confirm by 6	Parking Ample
Ensuite bath/shower 36	Room TV Yes	Last dinner 9.30	Room service Limited

NEWBY WISKE   Solberge Hall   69%   £D/E

H Map 15 C6 North Yorkshire
Nr Northallerton DL7 9ER
Northallerton (0609) 779191

Credit Access, Amex, Diners, Visa

A handsomely proportioned hotel with splendid views of the Hambleton Hills through the tall windows. Step through a pillared portico to a panelled hall, leading to an elegant bar and lounge and a billiard room with an antique slate table. Bedrooms range from spacious to vast, with luxurious beds, good darkwood furniture and excellent bathrooms, the majority with bidets. *Amenities* garden, croquet, clay-pigeon shooting, snooker, fax, laundry service.

Rooms 15	*Direct dial* Yes	*Confirm* by arrang.	*Parking* Ample
Ensuite bath/shower 15	*Room TV* Yes	*Last dinner* 9.30	*Room service* All day

NEWCASTLE-UNDER-LYME   Clayton Lodge Hotel   61%   £C/D

H Map 10 B3 Staffordshire
Clayton Road ST5 4AF
Newcastle-under-Lyme
(0782) 613093
Telex 36547

Credit Access, Amex, Diners, Visa

Set back from the busy A519 is this period house with modern wings. Most of the ground floor is given over to conference suites with their own private bars. Other guests can choose between an attractive lounge bar and the hotel's own adjoining pub, the Copeland Arms. Recently refurbished bedrooms are equipped with trouser presses, tea-makers and remote-control TVs. Neat tiled bathrooms. *Amenities* garden, secretarial services, laundry service.

Rooms 54	*Direct dial* Yes	*Confirm* by 6	*Parking* Ample
Ensuite bath/shower 54	*Room TV* Yes	*Last dinner* 10	*Room service* 24 hours

NEWCASTLE-UNDER-LYME   Post House Hotel   62%   £C/D

H Map 10 B3 Staffordshire
Clayton Road ST5 4DL
Newcastle-under-Lyme
(0782) 717171
Telex 36531

Credit Access, Amex, Diners, Visa

Close to junction 15 of the M6, this is a modern hotel with informal, open-plan public rooms. Baskets of ferns give a fresh feeling, and walls and display cabinets feature prints of old Newcastle and examples of the local potter's art. Good-sized bedrooms are bright and comfortable, with tea-makers, mini-bars and sparkling bathrooms. *Amenities* garden, laundry service, coffee shop (10.30am–10.30pm), children's playground.

Rooms 126	*Direct dial* Yes	*Confirm* by 6	*Parking* Ample
Ensuite bath/shower 126	*Room TV* Yes	*Last dinner* 10	*Room service* Ample

NEWCASTLE UPON TYNE   Blackgate Restaurant

R Town plan B4 Tyne & Wear
The Side
Tyneside (091) 261 7356

Set L & D £6.95
About £40 for two
Seats 70 *Parties* 80
Parking Difficult

Credit Access, Amex, Diners, Visa

An attractive, relaxing restaurant where you can find interesting modern dishes. Tasty starters include sautéed chicken livers with Stilton, and smoked salmon bavarois with orange cream; main course might be guinea-fowl with vegetable timbale and shallot sauce or breast of chicken filled with crab mousse. Top-quality ingredients are capably handled to create an enjoyable meal and service is friendly. ♀ Well-chosen ☺

Lunch 12–3   *Dinner* 7.30–10.30
Closed L Sat, D Mon, all Sun & Bank Hols

NEWCASTLE UPON TYNE   County Thistle Hotel   71%   £C/D

H Town plan A5
Tyne & Wear
Neville Street NE99 1AH
Tyneside (091) 232 2471
Telex 537873

Rooms 115
Ensuite bath/shower 115
Direct dial Yes
Room TV Yes
Confirm by arrang.
Last dinner 10.15
Parking Limited
Room service Limited

Credit Access, Amex, Diners, Visa

Conveniently located opposite the railway station, this splendid mid-Victorian hotel continues to benefit from recent improvements. On the first floor there's a very elegant cocktail bar – its panelled walls, leather armchairs and button-back settees suggesting the style of an exclusive late 19th-century club. In the basement is the livelier Boston Bean Company bar, with bright and modern decor. Bedrooms have

soft colour schemes, prettily coordinated fabrics, attractive pine or mahogany furniture and brass light fittings – plus tea-makers, trouser presses and hairdryers. Smart, fully-tiled bathrooms throughout. *Amenities* in-house movies, secretarial services, fax, laundry service, coffee shop (11am–11.30pm), 24-hour lounge service.

NEWCASTLE UPON TYNE

Map 15 B4
Town plan opposite

Population 272,914

Newcastle was founded in Roman times and later became a fortress against the Scots. Its commercial influence began with the mining of coal, but today rests on engineering and other industries. The coast and hinterland of Northumberland are areas of outstanding natural beauty. The theatres, Northern Sinfonia Orchestra, and the University, provide some of the many cultural activities.

Annual Events
The Hoppings (travelling fair) *last full week in June*
Great North Run *June*
Newcastle Festival *July*

Sights Outside City
Hadrian's Wall, Hexham Abbey, Durham Cathedral, Alnwick, Seaton Delaval, Northumberland National Park

City Information Service
Central Library, PO Box 1DX, Princess Square
Newcastle upon Tyne NE99 1DX
Telephone Tyneside 2610691

Fiat Dealer
Benfield Motors Ltd
Railway Street
Newcastle upon Tyne
NE4 7AD
Tel. Tyneside 2732131

1 Airport A1
2 Bessie Surtees House *fine 17th-c timbered house* B5
3 Blackfriars Heritage and Interpretation Centre A4
4 Castle, Black Gate Museum B5
5 Central Library and Information Bureau B3
6 Central Station A5
7 Civic Centre *outstanding modern architecture including Carillon Tower* B2
8 Cloth Market B4
9 Gosforth Park Racecourse B1
10 Grey Monument B3
11 Guildhall *17th-c with Georgian facade* B5
12 Hancock Museum *natural history of area* B1/2
13 Jesmond Dene Park C1
14 John George Joicey Museum *history, furniture, Northumberland Fusiliers Museum* C4
15 Laing Art Gallery B3
16 Museum of Science and Engineering *exhibits of Newcastle's Great engineers* A5
17 Newcastle Playhouse Theatre A2
18 Newcastle United F.C. *St James's Park* A3
19 Northumberland County C.C. B1
20 Quayside *open-air market on Sunday mornings* C4/5
21 St Nicholas's Cathedral *mainly 14th & 15th-c* B4
22 Theatre Royal B4
23 Town Moor *nearly 1,000 acres of free grazing, sport and recreation* A1
24 Tyne Bridge C5
25 Tyne Theatre & Opera House A4
26 University and Museum of Antiquities A2

Newcastle upon Tyne

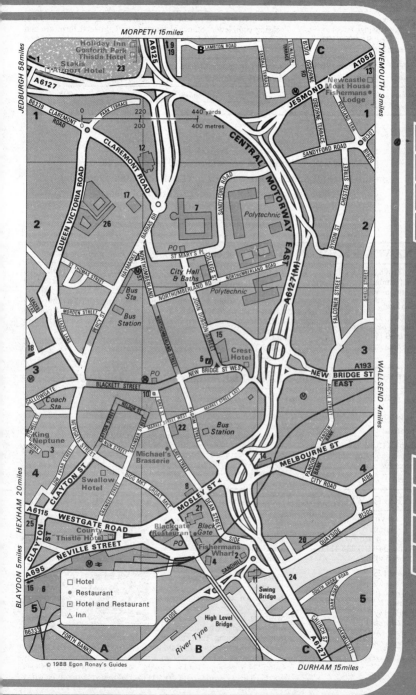

© 1988 Egon Ronay's Guides

NEWCASTLE UPON TYNE   Crest Hotel   59%   £C/D

H **Town plan B3** Tyne & Wear
New Bridge Street NE1 8BS
Tyneside (091) 232 6191
Telex 53467

Credit Access, Amex, Diners, Visa

A red-brick city-centre hotel where upgrading of accommodation is nearing completion. Standard rooms have lightwood furniture and usual accessories like tea-makers. Executive rooms sport darkwood furniture, bolder decor and additional accessories while pretty Lady Crest rooms offer extras like spyholes and magazines. Complete reorganisation and restyling of public areas is also well underway. *Amenities* sauna, solarium, in-house movies, fax, laundry service.

Rooms 178	*Direct dial* Yes	*Confirm by* 6	*Parking* Ample
Ensuite bath/shower 178	*Room TV* Yes	*Last dinner* 11.30	*Room service* 24 hours

**We welcome bona fide complaints and recommendations
on the tear-out pages at the back of the book for readers' comment.
They are followed up by our professional team.**

NEWCASTLE UPON TYNE   Fishermans Lodge   *NEW ENTRY*

R **Town plan C1** Tyne & Wear
Jesmond Dene, Jesmond
Tyneside (091) 281 3281

Seafood
Set L £11.50
About £55 for two
Seats 60 *Parties* 40
Parking Ample
Credit Access, Amex, Diners, Visa

Attractively situated by a stream in Jesmond Dene public park is this well-established fish restaurant. Consult the hand-written part of the menu for the pick of the catch, much of it local. Sautéed scallops, fricassee of turbot with lobster and cucumber, grilled halibut with garden herbs are typical of the enjoyable range. Meat and poultry dishes are also available and good sweets. Service is cheerful and attentive. ☺ 🍴

Lunch 12–2   *Dinner* 7–11
Closed L Sat, all Sun and Bank Hols

NEWCASTLE UPON TYNE   Fishermans Wharf   *NEW ENTRY*

R **Town plan B5** Tyne & Wear
15 The Side
Tyneside (091) 232 1057

Seafood

Set L £10.50
About £55 for two
Seats 40

Credit Access, Amex, Diners, Visa

Almost underneath the Newcastle side of the Tyne Bridge, this is a sister restaurant to Fishermans Lodge and the staff are equally pleasant and friendly. The menu is similar, too, making sound use of fresh fish in dishes both classic (moules marinière, sole Walewska, skate with black butter) and more adventurous. Carnivores are not forgotten here either, and there's an attractive choice of sweets. ☺

Lunch 12–2   *Dinner* 7–11
Closed L Sat, all Sun and Bank Hols

NEWCASTLE UPON TYNE   Gosforth Park Thistle Hotel   75%   £B

H **Town plan A1**
Tyne & Wear
High Gosforth Park NE3 5HN
Tyneside (091) 236 4111
Telex 53655

Rooms 178
Ensuite bath/shower 178
Direct dial Yes
Room TV Yes
Confirm by 6
Last dinner 11
Parking Ample
Room service 24 hours

Credit Access, Amex, Diners, Visa

Willing porters create a good first impression at this splendid modern hotel in wooded parkland off the A1. Stylish day rooms include an elegant foyer-lounge and several bars, and there are first-class conference and leisure facilities. Good-sized bedrooms have been attractively refurbished, and are well equipped, with spacious bathrooms. Executive rooms have bathrobes and mini-bars among their extras.

There are luxury suites and studios too. *Amenities* garden, indoor swimming pool, sauna, solarium, whirlpool bath, gymnasium, beauty salon, hairdressing, tennis, squash, pool table, in-house movies, secretarial services, fax, laundry service, children's playroom, courtesy car, helipad. ♿

NEWCASTLE UPON TYNE   Holiday Inn   70%   £C

H **Town plan A1**
Tyne & Wear
Great North Road, Seaton Burn
NE13 6BP
Tyneside (091) 2365432
Telex 53271

Rooms 150
Ensuite bath/shower 150
Direct dial Yes
Room TV Yes
Confirm by 6
Last dinner 10.30
Parking Ample
Room service 24 hours

Credit Access, Amex, Diners, Visa

A modern low-rise hotel some five miles north of the city at the junction of the A1 and A6125. Public areas are in a good state of repair and decoration: the lounge has cushioned cane chairs set around a canopied fire, and there's similar seating in the bar that overlooks the indoor pool. Bedrooms offer plenty of space, large beds and good accessories, though their decor and furnishings are functional rather than attractive. King Leisure rooms are smarter and more stylishly furnished, and all rooms have good-sized, well-fitted bathrooms.
Amenities garden, indoor swimming pool, sauna, solarium, whirlpool bath, gymnasium, pool table, in-house movies, secretarial services, fax, laundry service, coffee shop (7am–11pm). ⓑ

NEWCASTLE UPON TYNE   King Neptune   *NEW ENTRY*

R **Town plan A4** Tyne & Wear
34 Stowell Street NE1 4XB
Tyneside
(091) 261 6657

Chinese cooking
Set L from £3.80 **Set D** £10.50
Seats 120 *Parties* 70
Parking Ample
Credit Access, Amex, Diners, Visa

Newcastle is developing its own Chinatown based around Stowell Street, and King Neptune is one of its newer and better restaurants. The menu covers a wide range of Peking and seafood dishes, and also offers a special vegetarian section. Cooking is more than acceptable – crispy duck and garlicky prawns both particularly good – and service is quite attentive and professional under the Mak family, first generation Geordie Chinese.

Lunch 12–2, Sun 12.30–2   *Dinner* 6.30–11, Sat 6–11.15
About £21 *for two*   **Closed** 23 Dec–1 Jan

NEWCASTLE UPON TYNE   Michaels Brasserie   *NEW ENTRY*

R **Town plan B4** Tyne & Wear
2 High Bridge Court,
High Bridge
Tyneside (091) 2320056

Set L £6.95
About £42 *for two*
Seats 32
Parking Difficult
Credit Access, Visa

Bare brick walls, white lattice work and varnished floorboards make a modest but welcoming setting for the excellent and enthusiastic cooking of Clive Imber. Fresh ingredients are used whenever possible and the enticing menus change every three or four weeks. Mousseline of sole with prawn sauce, pan-fried calf's liver and marinated poussin, grilled and served with wine-braised onions and apricots, show the range. Good vegetables, too, and tempting sweets. ⓟ

Lunch noon–2   *Dinner* 7–10.45
Closed L Sat, all Sun & 25 Dec

See INSPECTOR FOR A DAY

NEWCASTLE UPON TYNE   Newcastle Moat House   66%   £D/E

H **Town plan C1** Tyne & Wear
Coast Road,
Wallsend NE28 9HP
Tyneside (091) 262 8989
Telex 53583
Credit Access, Amex, Diners, Visa
Closed 25 & 26 Dec

The A1/A1058 intersection runs past this modern hotel just north of the Tyne Tunnel and five miles east of the city centre. The foyer-lounge and bars have comfortable seating and a relaxing atmosphere. Bedrooms, with floor-to-ceiling windows, are bright, nicely furnished and well-equipped. All have smart tiled bathrooms. Leisure complex planned for 1989. *Amenities* garden, in-house movies, secretarial services, fax, laundry service, 24-hour lounge service.

Rooms 172	*Direct dial* Yes	*Confirm by* arrang.	*Parking* Ample
Ensuite bath/shower 172	*Room TV* Yes	*Last dinner* 9.45	*Room service* All day

We publish annually,
so make sure you use the current edition.
It's worth it!

NEWCASTLE UPON TYNE   Swallow Hotel   65%   £D

H **Town plan A4**
Tyne & Wear
2 Newgate Arcade NE1 5SX
Tyneside (091) 232 5025
Telex 538230

Credit Access, Amex, Diners, Visa

Ask for directions to the car park which leads straight into the contemporary foyer of this modern hotel. A bright, attractive terrace coffee shop doubles as a bar at night; there is a fine lounge bar with dark panelling and pleasing drapes. Bedrooms have smart modern units, light colour schemes, tea/coffee-makers, trouser presses, hair-dryers and compact bathrooms. *Amenities* secretarial services, coffee shop (9.30am–5pm), laundry service.

Rooms 94	*Direct dial* Yes	*Confirm by* 6	*Parking* Ample
Ensuite bath/shower 94	*Room TV* Yes	*Last dinner* 10	*Room service* All day

NEWCASTLE UPON TYNE   Stakis Airport Hotel   62%   £C/D

H **Town plan A1**
Tyne & Wear
Woolsington NE13 8DJ
Ponteland (0661) 24911
Telex 537121

Credit Access, Amex, Diners, Visa

It's only a short walk from the terminal to this popular modern hotel with a welcoming contemporary-style foyer-lounge, spacious bar and conference facilities. Attractive bedrooms – all with double glazing – are comfortably furnished and equipped with tea-makers, hairdryers and trouser presses. Fresh fruit and a morning paper are thoughtful extras. *Amenities* garden, in-house movies, secretarial services, laundry service.

Rooms 100	*Direct dial* Yes	*Confirm by* arrang.	*Parking* Ample
Ensuite bath/shower 100	*Room TV* Yes	*Last dinner* 10	*Room service* 24 hours

Our inspectors are our full-time employees;
they are professionally trained by us.

NEWGATE STREET   Gable House   *NEW ENTRY*   ♔

RR **Map 7 B4** Hertfordshire
Nr Cuffley SG13 8RA
Potters Bar (0707) 873899

Set L £8.50
Set D £13.50
Seats 50
Parties 32
Parking Ample
Credit Access, Amex, Diners, Visa

A steeply gabled house in a pleasant Hertfordshire village is the setting for a discreetly luxurious restaurant with rooms. Chef Stanley Matthews and sous-chef Mark make a fine team, using tip-top ingredients in delicious dishes like cured salmon with a brandy and mustard sauce, grilled sea bass on an onion purée or casseroled lamb's kidneys with noodles. Wines are thoughtfully selected with an eye to quality and value. 🍷 Well-chosen 🅴

Lunch 12–12.30   *Dinner* 7–10
About £55 *for two*

BEDROOMS 2 £E
With bath/shower None

The comfortable bedrooms are smartly rustic, with sturdy furnishings, remote-control TVs and a shared luxury bathroom. Breakfasts are excellent.

NEWINGTON   Newington Manor Hotel   55%   £E

H **Map 7 C5** Kent
Callaways Lane,
Nr Sittingbourne ME9 7LU
Newington (0795) 842 053

Credit Access, Amex, Diners, Visa
Closed 4 days Xmas

Massive chimney breasts and a wealth of old beams recall the Tudor past of this authentic half-timbered house, and there's a nice old stone fireplace in the bar. Characterful main-house bedrooms have good solid antique oak furniture (including two four-posters). Remaining rooms, in a modern building at the back, are rather more basic and functional. Bathrooms are due for refurbishment. No dogs. *Amenities* garden, laundry service.

Rooms 12	*Direct dial* Yes	*Confirm by* arrang.	*Parking* Ample
Ensuite bath/shower 12	*Room TV* Yes	*Last dinner* 9.45	*Room service* All day

NEWLYN   Higher Faugan Hotel   62%   £D/E

H **Map 2 A4** Cornwall
Nr Penzance TR18 5NS
Penzance (0736) 62076

Credit Access, Amex, Diners, Visa

An attractive, well-kept stone house built at the turn of the century. It stands in ten acres of grounds two miles south of Penzance on B3315. Best of the bedrooms are spacious, with good sturdy furniture and nice views; others have more everyday fitted units. Pleasant day rooms include a tiny nautical-style bar. No dogs. *Amenities* garden, outdoor swimming pool, tennis, putting, croquet, games room, snooker.

Rooms 12	*Direct dial* Yes	*Confirm by* arrang.	*Parking* Ample
Ensuite bath/shower 12	*Room TV* Yes	*Last dinner* 8.30	*Room service* Limited

NEWMARKET — Newmarket Moat House 62% — £D/E

H **Map 6 B2** Suffolk
Moulton Road CB8 8DY
Newmarket (0638) 667171

Credit Access, Amex, Diners, Visa

Just away from the town centre and overlooking the Heath, the Newmarket Moat House used to be a block of flats. Overnight accommodation is comfortable and quite spacious, with darkwood fitted furniture, remote-control TVs, hairdryers and trouser presses. Lighting is good, bathrooms neat and tidy. Among the day rooms are a large, well-appointed bar and a quiet residents' lounge. Pleasant, helpful staff. *Amenities* laundry service, in-house movies.

Rooms 49	Direct dial Yes	Confirm by 6	Parking Ample
Ensuite bath/shower 49	Room TV Yes	Last dinner 9.45	Room service 24 hours

NEWMARKET — White Hart Hotel 60% — £E

H **Map 6 B2** Suffolk
High Street CB8 8JP
Newmarket (0638) 663051

Credit Access, Visa

Refurbishment has smartened up this high-street hotel across the road from the Jockey Club. All the bedrooms, smallish but pleasantly decorated and comfortable, now have en suite facilities, and two new rooms include one with a four-poster and whirlpool bath. Day rooms comprise a cosy little lounge and cocktail bar, and a large public bar with racing photographs.
Amenities in-house movies.

Rooms 23	Direct dial Yes	Confirm by 6	Parking Ample
Ensuite bath/shower 23	Room TV Yes	Last dinner 9	Room service Limited

NEWPORT — Lugleys

See under WOOTTON COMMON

NEWPORT PAGNELL — Welcome Lodge 57% — £E

H **Map 5 E1** Buckinghamshire
Service Area 3,
M1 Motorway MK16 8DS
Newport Pagnell (0908) 610878
Telex 826186

Credit Access, Amex, Diners, Visa

This well-run hotel is part of the Newport Pagnell service area between junctions 14 and 15 of the M1. Day rooms include a smart bar-lounge and a comfortable restaurant. Motel-style bedrooms – many with car parking space at the front – are equipped with drinks trays, tea-makers, and neat bathrooms; Executive rooms have various extras. &

Rooms 96	Direct dial Yes	Confirm by 6	Parking Ample
Ensuite bath/shower 96	Room TV Yes	Last dinner 10	Room service None

**If we recommend meals in a Hotel or Inn,
a separate entry is made for its restaurant.**

NEWQUAY — Atlantic Hotel 58% — £D/E

H **Map 2 B3** Cornwall
Dane Road TR7 1EN
Newquay (0637) 872244

Credit Access, Amex, Visa
Closed Jan & Feb

A solidly built hotel with a friendly and relaxed atmosphere. Public rooms include two lounges, one overlooking the sea and the other the indoor pool. Bedrooms are equipped with tea/coffee-makers, trouser presses, hairdryers and compact bathrooms. *Amenities* garden, indoor & outdoor swimming pools, sauna, solarium, keep-fit equipment, tennis, squash, 9-hole golf course, games room, snooker, in-house movies, laundry service, coffee shop (11am–6pm), children's play area.

Rooms 86	Direct dial Yes	Confirm by arrang.	Parking Ample
Ensuite bath/shower 60	Room TV Yes	Last dinner 8.30	Room service 24 hours

NEWQUAY — Hotel Bristol 64% — £D/E

H **Map 2 B3** Cornwall
Narrowcliff TR7 2PQ
Newquay (0637) 875181

Credit Access, Amex, Diners, Visa

The Young family have run their seafront hotel for 60 years, and it's been known as long for its friendliness and excellent housekeeping. Day rooms offer plenty of space to relax, and the bedrooms – also of a good size – vary from functionally modern to more traditional, with solid old beds. All are bright, and front ones enjoy sea views.
Amenities indoor swimming pool, sauna, solarium, beauty salon, hairdressing, billiards, in-house movies, laundry room.

Rooms 97	Direct dial Yes	Confirm by arrang.	Parking Ample
Ensuite bath/shower 73	Room TV Yes	Last dinner 8.30	Room service 24 hours

NEWQUAY   Hotel Riviera   63%   £D/E

H Map 2 B3 Cornwall
Lusty Glaze Road TR7 3AA
Newquay (0637) 874251

Credit Access, Amex, Visa

Splendid sea views, neat gardens and a pleasant sun patio enhance this well-maintained hotel. Despite its modern appearance, it's run along good old-fashioned lines, and housekeeping is immaculate. Day rooms include a quiet lounge and three bars. Compact, well-fitted bedrooms are bright and airy, and most have tiled, carpeted bathrooms. *Amenities* garden, outdoor swimming pool, sauna, hairdressing, squash, games room, snooker, in-house movies, laundry room.

Rooms 50	*Direct dial* Yes	*Confirm by* 6	*Parking* Ample
Ensuite bath/shower 42	*Room TV* Yes	*Last dinner* 8.30	*Room service* 24 hours

NEWTON SOLNEY   Newton Park Hotel   67%   £C/D

H Map 10 C3 Derbyshire
Nr Burton upon Trent
DE15 0SS
Burton-upon-Trent
(0283) 703568
Credit Access, Amex, Diners, Visa
Closed 3 days Xmas

A sympathetically designed bedroom extension adds to the charm of this 17th-century mansion. Set in a pretty garden, the hotel has some interesting period pieces, including a handsome staircase and stained-glass windows. The comfortable bar is oak panelled and there's a colourful moulded ceiling in the restaurant. Bedrooms have attractive colour schemes and modern facilities. Tiled bathrooms have over-the-tub showers. *Amenities* garden, laundry service.

Rooms 47	*Direct dial* Yes	*Confirm by* 6	*Parking* Ample
Ensuite bath/shower 47	*Room TV* Yes	*Last dinner* 9.30	*Room service* 24 hours

We publish annually,
so make sure you use the current edition.
It's worth it!

NORTH CAVE   Sundial   ⚲

R Map 11 E1 Humberside
18 Westgate
North Cave (043 02) 2537

About £36 for two
Seats 45
Parties 48
Parking Ample

Credit Access, Amex, Diners, Visa

Traditional British food, enjoyably and carefully prepared, is Jane Marsden's forte, and she has built up quite a reputation for her pretty little village restaurant. The menu is not overly ambitious but is thoroughly authentic, drawing on carefully researched historical sources for inspiration. Start perhaps with a fluffy salmon mousse, then choose an old favourite like herby beef olives in a good rich gravy, and finish with a warming upside-down pudding. 🐨 ♿

Lunch by arrang.   *Dinner* 7.30–9.30
Closed Sun, Mon, Bank Hols, 2 wks Feb & 2 wks Aug

NORTH HUISH   Brookdale House   72%   £D/E

HR Map 3 D3 Devon
Nr South Brent TQ10 9NR
Gara Bridge (054 882) 402

Rooms 8
Ensuite bath/shower 8
Direct dial Yes
Room TV Yes
Confirm by arrang.
Last dinner 9
Parking Ample
Room service Limited

Credit Access, Visa
Closed 23 Dec–23 Jan

Originally a rectory, this Tudor Gothic-style house has an appropriately calm and peaceful air. Charles Trevor-Roper extends a warm welcome, and guests quickly feel at home in the comfortable drawing room or quaint panelled bar. Bedrooms are particularly pleasing, with a variety of furnishings (some antiques), chintzy fabrics and plenty of sitting space. Modern conveniences include remote-control TVs, radio-alarms and trouser presses, and there are lots of smaller personal touches. Smart bathrooms boast huge, fluffy towels, bathrobes and quality toiletries. Rooms are properly serviced in the evening, and morning brings an excellent breakfast. No children under ten. No dogs. *Amenities* garden, croquet, secretarial services.

Restaurant ♨ �

Set D £17.50
About £45 for two
Seats 24
Parties 8

The elegant, well-proportioned dining room provides a very apt setting for the enjoyment of Carol Trevor-Roper's highly accomplished cooking. Local produce figures prominently on menus that are interesting without being gimmicky: Stilton, apple and celery soup, potted Salcombe crab served with toasted walnut bread, guinea fowl with mushrooms and bacon, best end of lamb with tarragon, a lemon tart with just the right amount of zip. The wine list is a model of masterly selection with not a single slip: note Oregon Pinot Noir (Eyrie) 1984, Puligny Montrachet Les Pucelles (Leflaive) 1981. Smokers must hold fire until coffee in the lounge. ⊃ Outstanding ☺

Dinner only 7.30–9
Closed 23 Dec– 23 Jan

NORTH PETHERTON   Walnut Tree Inn   64%   £E

Ⓗ **Map 3 E2** Somerset
Fore Street TA6 6QA
North Petherton (0278) 662255
Telex 46529

Credit Access, Amex, Diners, Visa

The Gouldens no longer manage this hotel, but remain in residence and continue to play a large part in the continuation of its success. Once a modest coaching inn, now a charming little hotel, it has an attractive reception area, plush bar and well-appointed bedrooms with solid darkwood furniture. Four Executive rooms have trouser presses and hairdryers. No dogs.
Amenities garden, secretarial services, fax, laundry service.

Rooms 20	*Direct dial* Yes	*Confirm by* 6	*Parking* Ample
Ensuite bath/shower 20	*Room TV* Yes	*Last dinner* 10	*Room service* All day

---

Our inspectors *never* book in the name of Egon Ronay's Guides.
They disclose their identity only if they are considering an establishment
for inclusion in the next edition of the Guide.

NORTH STIFFORD   Stifford Moat House   61%   £D

Ⓗ **Map 7 B4** Essex
High Road, North Stifford,
Nr Grays RM16 1UE
Grays Thurrock (0375) 390909
Telex 995126
Credit Access, Amex, Diners, Visa
Closed 25 & 26 Dec

Situated just off the A13 north of the Dartford Tunnel, this Georgian house makes an attractive hotel and conference centre. The classically-proportioned entrance hall leads to a lounge whose French doors invite a tour of the 6½-acre grounds. Along a short corridor is a wood-panelled bar overlooking an inner courtyard. All bedrooms have compact tiled bathrooms. No dogs. **Amenities** garden, tennis, croquet, secretarial services, fax, laundry service.

Rooms 64	*Direct dial* Yes	*Confirm by* 6	*Parking* Ample
Ensuite bath/shower 64	*Room TV* Yes	*Last dinner* 9.40	*Room service* 24 hours

---

NORTH STOKE   Springs Hotel   75%   £B/C

Ⓗ **Map 5 D2** Oxfordshire
Wallingford Road OX9 6BE
Wallingford (0491) 36687
Telex 849794

Rooms 34
Ensuite bath/shower 34
Direct dial Yes
Room TV Yes
Confirm by 6
Last dinner 10
Parking Ample
Room service 24 hours

Credit Access, Amex, Diners, Visa

A long, low, mock-Tudor building overlooking a pretty lake. The lounge area is warm and inviting, with dark wood panelled-leather chesterfields and open fire, and there's a pleasant bar in similar traditional style. Bed-rooms, mostly of a good size, have pretty matching fabrics, darkwood freestanding furniture and thoughtful little extras like fresh flowers and mineral water. Club rooms provide mini-bars,

and there are four nice suites – two traditional, two more contemporary in style. Spacious, well-fitted bathrooms (some with bidets, whirlpool baths and separate showers) are a high point throughout.
Amenities garden, outdoor swimming pool, sauna, tennis, pitch & putt, croquet, bicycles, secretarial services, valeting, laundry service.

NORTHAMPTON · Northampton Moat House · 65% · £C/D

H **Map 5 D1** Northamptonshire
Silver Street NN1 2TA
Northampton (0604) 22441
Telex 311142

Credit Access, Amex, Diners, Visa
Closed 26 Dec

A modern city-centre hotel with a basement leisure centre, the Moat House has spacious public rooms, including a panelled bar and stylish lounge bar with couches and cane chairs. Attractive bedrooms with fitted units have small en suite bathrooms.
Amenities garden, sauna, solarium, whirlpool bath, keep-fit equipment, in-house movies, secretarial services, fax, laundry service, coffee shop (7am–10pm).

Rooms 134	Direct dial Yes	Confirm by 6	Parking Ample
Ensuite bath/shower 134	Room TV Yes	Last dinner 10.30	Room service Limited

NORTHAMPTON · Swallow Hotel · 74% · £C/D

H **Map 5 D1** Northamptonshire
Eagle Drive NN4 0HN
Northampton (0604) 768700
Telex 31562

Rooms 122
Ensuite bath/shower 122
Direct dial Yes
Room TV Yes
Confirm by arrang.
Last dinner 10.30
Parking Ample
Room service 24 hours

Credit Access, Amex, Diners, Visa

A modern hotel with a difference – the decor is both up-to-the-minute and also highly individual. Typically striking is the small reception lounge, which has black contemporary seating with red cushions set against a white background. Stylish bedrooms again make the best use of the new; all have modern lamps and light, grey fitted units, while contemporary prints adorn the walls. Refrigerators, tea/coffee-makers, irons and two telephones are standard. Bright, well-equipped bathrooms have hairdryers. *Amenities* garden, indoor swimming pool, sauna, solarium, whirlpool bath, steam room, keep-fit equipment, massage parlour, 9-hole golf course, in-house movies, secretarial services, fax, laundry service, restaurant (7am–10.30pm). &

NORTHAMPTON · Westone Moat House · 59% · £D/E

H **Map 5 D1** Northamptonshire
Ashley Way, Weston Favell
NN3 3EA
Northampton (0604) 406262
Telex 312587
Credit Access, Amex, Diners, Visa
Closed 28–30 Dec

Find this hotel in a residential area off the A4500 by following signs for Weston Favell. Both the comfortable bar and the lounge have attractive leaded windows overlooking the gardens. Bedrooms in the main building are slightly larger than those in a separate modern block; all have simple practical furnishings and bathrooms with showers. *Amenities* garden, sauna, solarium, keep-fit equipment, putting, croquet, in-house movies, laundry service.

Rooms 67	Direct dial Yes	Confirm by 6	Parking Ample
Ensuite bath/shower 67	Room TV Yes	Last dinner 9.45	Room service 24 hours

NORTHLEACH · Old Woolhouse · ♛ ♉

R **Map 4 C2** Gloucestershire
The Square
Northleach (045 160) 366

French cooking
Set D £25
About £60 for two
Seats 18
Parties 18
Parking Ample

Originally used for storing fleeces, this unobtrusive little restaurant stands on the main square. Inside all is set for some really good eating – Limoges plates, silver cutlery, engraved glasses, napkins bearing the owners' initials. Jenny Astic recites the day's menu, and Jacques in the kitchen produces the goods: lightly cooked stuffed trout, crab and monkfish soup with scallops, chicken with champagne, pork in a red wine sauce. Ask about the classic wines. ℗

Lunch by arrang. only   *Dinner* at 8.15
Closed Sun, Mon & 1 wk Xmas

NORTHWICH · Hartford Hall Hotel · 62% · £D

H **Map 10 B2** Cheshire
School Lane, Hartford
CW8 1PW
Northwich (0606) 75711
Credit Access, Amex, Diners, Visa
Closed 1 wk after Xmas

Just off the A556, Hartford Hall is a gabled 16th-century house with a charming garden. The major improvement of late has been in the bedrooms, all refurbished in pleasing contemporary style and all with good private bathrooms. Nicest of the public rooms is the mellow beamed bar; there's also a small TV room and a banquet/conference facility. Staff are efficient and helpful, though personal service is not emphasised. *Amenities* garden, in-house movies.

Rooms 21	Direct dial Yes	Confirm by 6	Parking Ample
Ensuite bath/shower 21	Room TV Yes	Last dinner 10	Room service Limited

NORWICH — Green's Seafood

R Map 6 C1 Norfolk
82 Upper St Giles Street
Norwich (0603) 623733

Seafood
About £40 for two
Seats 50
Parking Limited

Credit Access, Visa

There's an appropriately nautical flavour to the decor of this popular seafood restaurant. From the comfortable bar you can study the splendid assortment of such fish as turbot or sea bass bought from Lowestoft and displayed in an ice cabinet to await Dennis Crompton's sound cooking. Starter might be fresh sardines in garlic butter, and to follow, poached salmon with prawn sauce or monkfish with pimento. Simple, enjoyable sweets.

Lunch 12–2.30   Dinner 7–11
Closed L Sat, all Sun, Bank Hols & 2 wks Xmas

NORWICH — Maid's Head Hotel   64%   £D/E

H Map 6 C1 Norfolk
Tombland NR3 1LB
Norwich (0603) 72111
Telex 975080

Credit Access, Amex, Diners, Visa

For over 700 years guests have been made welcome at this hospitable hotel opposite the Cathedral. Uneven floors, sloping ceilings, leaded lights and exposed beams add character to rooms of all shapes and sizes. Well-equipped bedrooms, smartly decorated with quality coordinated fabrics, all have modern, well-kept bathrooms. *Amenities* patio, in-house movies, secretarial services, laundry service, coffee shop (10.30am–10.30pm).

| Rooms 83 | Direct dial Yes | Confirm by arrang. | Parking Ample |
| Ensuite bath/shower 83 | Room TV Yes | Last dinner 9.45 | Room service 24 hours |

NORWICH — Marco's

R Map 6 C1 Norfolk
17 Pottergate
Norwich (0603) 624044

Italian cooking
Set L £10
About £40 for two
Seats 40 Parties 10
Parking Difficult
Credit Access, Amex, Diners, Visa

A charming, intimate restaurant consisting of two small but elegant dining rooms. The charming Marco Vessalio takes a personal interest in all his guests; his cooking, using the very finest ingredients, is superb. The short menu offers such delicious dishes it's hard to make a choice, but for a starter don't miss the outstanding gnocchi alla Marco, sautéed with mushrooms, garlic, tomato, cream and parmesan. ♀ Well-chosen

Lunch 12.30–2   Dinner 7.30–10
Closed Sun, Mon, Bank Hols & mid Aug–mid Sept

**Changes in data sometimes occur in establishments
after the Guide goes to press.
Prices should be taken as indications rather than firm quotes.**

NORWICH — Hotel Nelson   65%   £D/E

H Map 6 C1 Norfolk
Prince of Wales Road NR1 1DX
Norwich (0603) 760260
Telex 975203

Credit Access, Amex, Diners, Visa

Enthusiastic staff generate a pleasant, energetic atmosphere at this well-run, modern riverside hotel. Picture windows in the cheerful lounge take full advantage of the view; the nautical Cannon Bar commemorates local hero Nelson. Bright bedrooms include a number of State Rooms with extra luxuries and superior bathrooms; many also have balconies. No dogs. *Amenities* garden, sauna, keep-fit equipment, mooring, secretarial services, fax, laundry service.

| Rooms 122 | Direct dial Yes | Confirm by arrang. | Parking Ample |
| Ensuite bath/shower 122 | Room TV Yes | Last dinner 9.45 | Room service 24 hours |

NORWICH — Hotel Norwich   64%   £D/E

H Map 6 C1 Norfolk
121 Boundary Road NR3 2BA
Norwich (0603) 787260
Telex 975337

Credit Access, Amex, Diners, Visa

A modern hotel bursting with civic pride; local maps abound in the public rooms and the Rouen restaurant, named after Norwich's twin town, is designed to resemble a Rouen street. In the popular Gates bar, board games are available. The bright bedrooms have attractive contemporary fabrics, hairdryers, tea/coffee-makers and well-fitted bathrooms. No dogs. *Amenities* satellite TV, secretarial services, fax, laundry service, coffee shop (11am–6.45pm).

| Rooms 102 | Direct dial Yes | Confirm by 6 | Parking Ample |
| Ensuite bath/shower 102 | Room TV Yes | Last dinner 9.45 | Room service None |

NORWICH · Post House Hotel · 63% · £D

H Map 6 C1 Norfolk
Ipswich Road NR4 6EP
Norwich (0603) 56431
Telex 975106

Credit Access, Amex, Diners, Visa

Business people are well catered for at this friendly modern hotel on the A140. There are good leisure facilities, and refreshments are available all day in the spacious public rooms. Comfortable bedrooms – all with neat, well-equipped bathrooms – have a good range of extras including mini-bars. *Amenities* garden, indoor swimming pool, sauna, solarium, whirlpool bath, keep-fit equipment, putting, secretarial services, fax, laundry service, coffee shop (10.30am–10pm).

| *Rooms* 116 | *Direct dial* Yes | *Confirm by* 6 | *Parking* Ample |
| *Ensuite bath/shower* 116 | *Room TV* Yes | *Last dinner* 10 | *Room service* 24 hours |

NOTTINGHAM · Albany Hotel · 71% · £C

H Map 11 D3 Nottinghamshire
St James' Street NG1 6BN
Nottingham (0602) 470131
Telex 37211

Rooms 138
Ensuite bath/shower 138
Direct dial Yes
Room TV Yes
Confirm by 6
Last dinner 11
Parking Ample
Room service 24 hours

Credit Access, Amex, Diners, Visa

Don't miss going right to the top to enjoy the spectacular view of the city from this modern high-rise hotel near the castle. Handsome plants bring a touch of greenery to the elegant foyer with its red leather chesterfields; there are plants also grouped round the fountain in the smart cocktail lounge, which features live music in the evening. For something more boisterous, try the lively basement bar. Standard bedrooms are most acceptable, but the Executive rooms on the top four floors have better views, superior decor and furniture, and many extras from mini-bars to chocolates.
Amenities pool table, secretarial services, laundry service.

NOTTINGHAM · Novotel · 62% · £D

H Map 11 D3 Nottinghamshire
Bostock Lane,
Long Eaton NG10 4EP
Nottingham (0602) 720106
Telex 377585

Credit Access, Amex, Diners, Visa

A popular and well-equipped modern hotel less than a mile from the M1 (junction 25). Plants provide an extra touch of freshness in the day rooms, which include a comfortable lounge and smart bar. Bedrooms, uniform in size and decor, offer practical comforts, and all have bright, tiled bathrooms with separate WCs. *Amenities* garden, outdoor swimming pool, putting, pitch & putt, in-house movies, coffee shop (6am–midnight), children's playground, helipad. &

| *Rooms* 110 | *Direct dial* Yes | *Confirm by* 6 | *Parking* Ample |
| *Ensuite bath/shower* 110 | *Room TV* Yes | *Last dinner* midnight | *Room service* All day |

NOTTINGHAM · Pagoda

R Map 11 D3 Nottinghamshire
31 Greyfriars Gate
Nottingham (0602) 580745

Chinese cooking
About £30 for two
Seats 70 *Parties* 90
Parking Limited

Credit Access, Amex, Diners, Visa

On Sundays, Nottingham's Chinese community get together for lunchtime dim sum at the Pagoda. Book, and join them for a splendid selection of these tasty snacks and a good range of other, mainly Cantonese fare: soups, lots of composite rice and noodle dishes, seafood, poultry, pork, beef, vegetables and bean curd. Less choice of dim sum and sweets during the week.

Lunch 12–3, Sun noon–midnight   *Dinner* 6.30–11.30
Closed 25 Dec

NOTTINGHAM · Post House Hotel · 62% · £C/D

H Map 11 D3 Nottinghamshire
Bostocks Lane,
Sandiacre NG10 5NJ
Nottingham (0602) 397800
Telex 377378

Credit Access, Amex, Diners, Visa

A residential area ensures a quiet setting for this well-run modern hotel only seconds from the M1 (junction 25). The inviting foyer-lounge overlooks an ornamental pool, and there's a friendly, comfortable bar. Bedrooms, in an adjoining block, are smart and spacious, with tea-makers, mini-bars and remote-control TVs.
Amenities garden, laundry service, coffee shop (10am–10.30pm), 24-hour lounge service.

| *Rooms* 107 | *Direct dial* Yes | *Confirm by* 6 | *Parking* Ample |
| *Ensuite bath/shower* 107 | *Room TV* Yes | *Last dinner* 9.45 | *Room service* Limited |

NOTTINGHAM — Royal Moat House International 71% £C/D

Map 11 D3 Nottinghamshire
Wollaton Street NG1 5RH
Nottingham (0602) 414444
Telex 37101

Rooms 201
Ensuite bath/shower 201
Direct dial Yes
Room TV Yes
Confirm by 6
Last dinner 11
Parking Ample
Room service 24 hours

Credit Access, Amex, Diners, Visa
Closed 25 & 26 Dec

The penthouse bar of this city-centre hotel enjoys panoramic views over Nottingham, and on the first floor there's a magnificent glass-roofed arcade with a wealth of tropical plants and trees. Reception is equally striking, all fitted out in black marble, with a sunken lounge area. Standard rooms are of a decent size and have fitted wooden units, coffee tables, easy chairs and mini-bars; bathrooms are equipped with plenty of toiletries. Executive rooms offer extras like newspapers, mineral water, bathrobes and superior toiletries. Bright, alert staff. No dogs. *Amenities* gymnasium, hairdressing, squash, in-house movies, secretarial services, fax, laundry service, coffee shop (10am–6.30pm), kiosk.

NOTTINGHAM — Savoy Hotel 64% £D/E

Map 11 D3 Nottinghamshire
Mansfield Road NG5 2BT
Nottingham (0602) 602621
Telex 377429

Credit Access, Amex, Diners, Visa

A large modern hotel on the A60, north of the city centre. It's a bustling, business-orientated place with comfortably appointed bedrooms that include a number of decent-sized singles. Most striking of the day rooms are the conservatory bar lounge, with lots of greenery hanging from the ceiling, and the adjoining snack bar where cheerful ladies serve a decent breakfast. No dogs.
Amenities in-house movies, fax, laundry service.

Rooms 173	*Direct dial* Yes	*Confirm by* 6	*Parking* Ample
Ensuite bath/shower 173	*Room TV* Yes	*Last dinner* 11	*Room service* 24 hours

NOTTINGHAM — Shôgun

Map 11 D3 Nottinghamshire
95 Talbot Street
Nottingham (0602) 475611

Japanese cooking
Set L £5 Set D from £10.90
About £32 for two
Seats 50 *Parties* 50
Parking Limited
Credit Access, Amex, Diners, Visa

Nottingham's only Japanese restaurant is a converted warehouse with light, space and the minimum of decor. Cooking is very capable while presentation is simple and effective on striking crockery, and the waitresses are very clued up on the menus. Sushi, sashimi, pot dishes and tempura are the most familiar dishes, but there's plenty more besides. Drink sake, with green tea and fresh fruit to finish.

Lunch 12–2   *Dinner* 7–11
Closed L Mon, all Sun, 25 & 26 Dec & 1 Jan

NOTTINGHAM — Stakis Victoria Hotel 63% £D

Map 11 D3 Nottinghamshire
Milton Street NG1 3PZ
Nottingham (0602) 419561
Telex 37401

Credit Access, Amex, Diners, Visa

Reception staff do a brisk, efficient job here, and the foyer-lounge is a good spot to relax. The gloomy breakfast room and the meal served therein are less appealing, however. Standard bedrooms are comfortable, if not very large, while Executive rooms tend to be more spacious, with extra accessories. Some rooms are unfortunately within earshot of a droning air-conditioning unit.
Amenities in-house movies, secretarial services, fax, laundry service.

Rooms 166	*Direct dial* Yes	*Confirm by* 6	*Parking* Difficult
Ensuite bath/shower 166	*Room TV* Yes	*Last dinner* 10	*Room service* 24 hours

NOTTINGHAM — The Strathdon Thistle Hotel 65% £C/D

Map 11 D3 Nottinghamshire
Derby Road NG1 5FT
Nottingham (0602) 418501
Telex 377185

Credit Access, Amex, Diners, Visa

On the Derby side of town, the Strathdon Thistle is a business hotel offering good service and comfort. The reception lounge has a solid, welcoming feel, and there are two pleasant places for a drink, the Western-style Boston Bean Company Bar and the leafy cocktail bar/conservatory. Well-fitted bedrooms, all double-glazed, have neat, modern bathrooms (showers only in singles).
Amenities in-house movies, secretarial services, fax, laundry service.

Rooms 69	*Direct dial* Yes	*Confirm by* 6	*Parking* Difficult
Ensuite bath/shower 69	*Room TV* Yes	*Last dinner* 10.30	*Room service* 24 hours

OAKHAM   Hambleton Hall 82%   £C

HR Map 11 E3 Leicestershire
Hambleton LE15 8TH
Oakham (0572) 56991
Telex 342888

Rooms 15
Ensuite bath/shower 15
Direct dial Yes
Room TV Yes
Confirm by arrang.
Last dinner 9.30
Parking Ample
Room service All day

Credit Access, Amex, Diners, Visa

The setting, by Rutland Water, is peaceful and beautiful, and the style, service and comforts offered make guests feel they're staying at the finest private country house. Young staff work with smiles and dedication, and there's a great feeling of warmth and ease. The reception hall, dominated by a magnificent open fire, has abundant inviting armchairs and the drawing room, with its objets d'art and stunning flower displays, is sheer elegance. Striking fabrics, antique and reproduction furniture, prints and cosseting extras distinguish the bedrooms, which all have sumptuous bathrooms. Nine rooms with lake views are the biggest and sunniest. Super breakfasts. No children under ten.
Amenities garden, tennis, secretarial services, laundry service.

Restaurant ★   ♛

Lunch 12–1.30
Dinner 7–9.30
Set L £15.50
Set D from £25
About £70 for two
Seats 55
Parties 20

Double doors link two elegant rooms, one decorated in yellow, the other sporting bold striped wallpaper. Brian Baker's strength is in letting prime ingredients speak for themselves, and his menus always offer something out of the ordinary, like teal with a sauce based on its liver, poached fillet of gurnard or the marvellous toasted rice pudding encircled with mango and autumn berries. Staff are absolutely on the ball – witness an erudite explanation of the superb cheeseboard. There's a magnificent quality cellar. *Specialities* terrine of hare and pork with an orange and chestnut salad; pan-fried calf's liver and kidneys on a bed of Jerusalem artichokes; hot sabayon soufflé of quince and apple. ⌦ Outstanding ♟ Well-chosen ⊜ ♥

We welcome bona fide complaints and recommendations
on the tear-out pages at the back of the book for readers' comment.
They are followed up by our professional team.

OAKHAM   The Whipper-In Hotel 72% *NEW ENTRY* £D

HR Map 11 E3 Leicestershire
The Market Place LE15 6DT
Oakham (0572) 56971
Telex 8950511

Rooms 24
Ensuite bath/shower 24
Direct dial Yes
Room TV Yes
Confirm by arrang.
Last dinner 9.45
Parking Ample
Room service 24 hours

Credit Access, Amex, Diners, Visa

Major restoration has brought this 17th-century town-centre hotel up to the same high standard as its sister establishment, The Feathers at Woodstock. Antiques and lovely displays of fresh flowers take the eye in the day rooms, where comfortable chairs and log fires invite the guest to linger. Delightful bedrooms have been individually decorated and furnished with care and no little style: pleasing colour schemes harmonize with good-quality fabrics, handsome period furniture is used throughout and most rooms have seating areas; there are two four-poster rooms. Bathrooms are also very appealing, with pretty walls and supplies of de luxe toiletries. Staff are young, friendly and efficient. *Amenities* terrace, fax, laundry service.

Restaurant *NEW ENTRY*

Set L £8.50, Sun £10.50
Set D £14.95
About £50 for two
Seats 35
Parties 50

Paul Cherrington cooks with skill and care, and his attention to detail pays off in some really delightful dishes. Salmon and lobster terrine or collops of duck on a crisp salad bed could start the meal, with thyme-sauced quail, grilled calf's liver or roast fillet of lamb with kidneys and sweetbreads coated in a dark, rich Madeira sauce for a main course. Passion fruit mousse makes a memorable ending. Service is first-class. Good wines. ☙

Lunch 12.15–2 *Dinner* 7.30–9.45

OAKHILL — Oakhill House

RR **Map 4 B3** Somerset
Bath Road BA3 5AQ
Oakhill (0749) 840180

Set L £8.75
About £44 for two
Seats 35
Parties 25
Parking Ample

Credit Access, Amex, Diners, Visa

The Long tradition of hospitality embraces Ian as host, Ann as chef-patron and their daughter Suzanne who serves at this Georgian restaurant. Ann is an inventive and able cook, who executes with ease such starters as pancakes with smoked salmon and caviar, and main courses like medallions of veal on rhubarb purée or pheasant breasts flavoured with wine and herbs, baked with chestnuts and served with redcurrant sauce. Home-made puddings to follow, with coffee served in the bar. ☙ ♿

Lunch 12.30–1.45 *Dinner* 7.30–9.30
Closed L Sat, D Sun, all Mon & 2–3 weeks Jan/Feb

BEDROOMS 3 £E/F
With bath/shower 3

Dinner guests may be accommodated in traditionally furnished rooms with TVs, tea-makers and smart, well-equipped bathrooms. No children under 12. No dogs.

OCKLEY — King's Arms Restaurant

RR **Map 5 E3** Surrey
Stane Street
Dorking (0306) 711224

Set L Sun £7.50
About £40 for two
Seats 40
Parking Ample

Credit Access, Amex, Diners, Visa

A mellow, traditional pub restaurant offering good food and cheerful, bustling service. Melvin Halliday's repertoire runs from starters like chicken and pork terrine or gravad lax (served here with minted yoghurt) to straightforward grills and more ambitious dishes such as fillet of lamb in puff pastry with a watercress hollandaise. Crisp vegetables, enjoyable sweets; only the wine list needs improving. Set lunch Sunday. ☙ ♿

Lunch 12–1.45, Sun 12–1.30 *Dinner* 7–9.30
Closed D Sun, 25 & 26 Dec

BEDROOMS 5 £E/F
With bath/shower 3

Two of the well-kept bedrooms are in the main house – traditionally appointed rooms sharing a pretty little bathroom. The others are in an extension and have their own practical bath or shower rooms. No children. No dogs.

ODIHAM — La Forêt

R **Map 5 D3** Hampshire
High Street
Odiham (025 671) 2697

Set D from £13.95
About £45 for two
Seats 56
Parties 40
Parking Ample
Credit Access, Amex, Diners, Visa

Troughs of greenery outside and hanging plants within justify the name of this agreeable high-street restaurant, whose menu prices include half a bottle of wine. Crudités, dips, hot bread, pâté and salamis start the meal, with an optional course – perhaps leek tart or seafood profiteroles – preceding a main course such as confit de canard with cassis, grilled langoustines or tournedos with a peppercorn sauce. Home-made ices, French cheeses. ☙

D only 7–10
Closed Sun, Bank Hol Mons & 1 wk Xmas

ODIHAM — George Hotel £E

▌**Map 5 D3** Hampshire
High Street RG25 1LP
Odiham (025 671) 2081
Telex 858797

Credit Access, Diners, Visa

In the middle of a very attractive village, the George is a 15th-century inn with many original features. Old stonework, beams and fireplaces keep the period feel in the bars and residents' lounge, and the restaurant was once the local assize court. Bedrooms – beams also much in evidence – are solidly furnished in traditional style; central heating and double glazing make for comfort and there are four new rooms in an extension. *Amenities* garden, laundry service.

Rooms 15	*Direct dial* Yes	*Confirm by* arrang.	*Parking* Ample
Ensuite bath/shower 15	*Room TV* Yes	*Last dinner* 10	*Room service* All day

OLD HARLOW | Green Man Hotel 62% | £C/D

H Map 7 B4 Essex
Mulberry Green CM17 0ET
Harlow (0279) 442521
Telex 817972

Credit Access, Amex, Diners, Visa

Check directions when booking for this old-town hotel overlooking the village green. Public areas – in a 600-year-old listed building – include a flagstoned entrance hall leading to two pleasant beamed bars. Bedrooms, in a separate block, have smart darkwood units, modern comforts, and good tiled bathrooms.
Amenities laundry service.

Rooms 55	*Direct dial* Yes	*Confirm by* 6	*Parking* Ample
Ensuite bath/shower 55	*Room TV* Yes	*Last dinner* 10	*Room service* 24 hours

OLNEY | Dhaka Dynasty *NEW ENTRY*

R Map 6 A3 Buckinghamshire
2 Stanley Court,
Weston Road
Bedford (0234) 713179

Indian cooking
About £30 for two
Seats 54
Parking Ample
Credit Access, Amex, Diners, Visa

In an attractive setting close to the town centre, this bright restaurant offers very enjoyable Indian cooking. Flavours are excellent throughout a tempting range of dishes, from shami kebab and delicious mixed vegetable pakoras to Bengal-style prawns, chicken jalfrezi and lamb makhani flavoured with fenugreek, tomatoes and subtle spices. Interesting tandoori variants include trout and duck. Try mango-flavoured lassi, a yoghurt drink. Sunday buffet lunch. Service lags behind cooking.

Lunch 12–3   *Dinner* 6–11.30
Closed 25, 26 Dec & L on Moslem Religious Holidays

ORMESBY ST MARGARET | Ormesby Lodge Hotel 60% | £E/F

H Map 6 D1 Norfolk
Decoy Road NR29 3LG
Great Yarmouth (0493) 730910

Credit Access, Amex, Diners, Visa
Closed 25 & 26 Dec

Located on Decoy Road, off the road from Ormesby St Margaret to Hemsby, this sturdy family-run Victorian hotel offers a very friendly welcome and comfortable, sparkling-clean accommodation. A period staircase connects convivial public rooms with the cosy bedrooms. All have carpeted bathrooms with generous towels. Delicious Yarmouth haddock with poached eggs for breakfast. No dogs.
Amenities garden, outdoor swimming pool, laundry service.

Rooms 11	*Room phone* Yes	*Confirm by* arrang.	*Parking* Ample
Ensuite bath/shower 11	*Room TV* Yes	*Last dinner* 10.30	*Room service* All day

We publish annually,
so make sure you use the current edition.
It's worth it!

OSWESTRY | Sweeney Hall Hotel 55% | £E

H Map 10 A3 Shropshire
Morda SY10 9EU
Oswestry (0691) 652450

Credit Access, Visa

Set in eight acres of grounds alongside the A483, Sweeney Hall is a handsome Georgian building with a Jacobean-style east wing. On the ground floor are the old-fashioned entrance hall and cheerful bar, above them (reached by a sweeping stone staircase) the roomy lounge and the bedrooms, some of which are very spacious and traditional, others more compact and modern.
Amenities garden, putting, helipad.

Rooms 9	*Room phone* No	*Confirm by* 6	*Parking* Ample
Ensuite bath/shower 6	*Room TV* No	*Last dinner* 9	*Room service* None

OSWESTRY | Wynnstay Hotel 57% | £D

H Map 10 A3 Shropshire
Church Street SY11 2SZ
Oswestry (0691) 655261

Credit Access, Amex, Diners, Visa

Upgrading of the bedrooms is under way at this pleasant Georgian hotel. Those which have received attention have light colour schemes, pretty, traditional fabrics and modern fitted furniture. Tiled, functional bathrooms have a good range of toiletries. Public areas include a light, spacious lounge bar, an attractive and popular wine bar and a cosy lounge. *Amenities* garden, bowling green, laundry service, coffee shop (10am–4pm Mon–Thur, 10am–5pm Fri–Sat).

Rooms 26	*Direct dial* Yes	*Confirm by* 6	*Parking* Ample
Ensuite bath/shower 26	*Room TV* Yes	*Last dinner* 9.30	*Room service* All day

OTLEY — Chevin Lodge 65% £D

H **Map 10 C1** West Yorkshire
Yorkgate LS21 3NU
Otley (0943) 467818
Telex 51538

Credit Access, Amex, Visa

Set in acres of woodland high above Otley, this Scandinavian-style building is reflected in the man-made lake at its foot. Public areas are small and cosy, the warm colours of the upholstery complementing the natural pine walls. Bedrooms are spacious, comfortable and equipped with stereo radios, tea/coffee makers and carpeted bathrooms. ***Amenities*** garden, sauna, solarium, whirlpool bath, coarse fishing, in-house movies, secretarial services, laundry service. ♿

Rooms 43 | *Direct dial* Yes | *Confirm by* arrang. | *Parking* Ample
Ensuite bath/shower 43 | *Room TV* Yes | *Last dinner* 9.30 | *Room service* 24 hours

OTTERBURN — Percy Arms Hotel 59% £E

H **Map 14 B3** Northumberland
NE19 1NR
Otterburn (0830) 20261

Credit Access, Amex, Diners, Visa

A long, low, pebbledash building on the main road through town. The new owners are making some changes, including upgrading existing bars, creating a cocktail bar and moving reception into an enlarged lobby. The chintzy lounges will stay much as they are. Bedrooms, some more stylish than others, are furnished with traditional or more modern pieces. ***Amenities*** garden, coarse & game fishing, croquet, games room, secretarial services, laundry service.

Rooms 30 | *Direct dial* Yes | *Confirm by* arrang. | *Parking* Ample
Ensuite bath/shower 30 | *Room TV* Yes | *Last dinner* 9 | *Room service* All day

OTTERY ST MARY — The Lodge

R **Map 3 E2** Devon
17 Silver Street
Ottery St Mary (040 481) 2356

Set L & D £19.50
About £48 for two
Seats 20
Parties 20
Parking Limited
Credit Amex, Diners, Visa

Drinks in a small sitting room make a cosy prelude to the delicious seasonal food served in Diane Shenton's spacious, prettily decorated restaurant. Starters include tasty mushrooms topped with bacon and laverbread, grilled mussels, and smoked mallard, while main courses range from duck with a kumquat and wine sauce to lamb en croûte and an old English pigeon and quail pie. Vegetables are superb, and there are nice sweets.

Lunch by arrang. only *Dinner* 7–9.30
Closed D Sun, all Mon, Bank Hols

Our inspectors *never* book in the name of Egon Ronay's Guides. They disclose their identity only if they are considering an establishment for inclusion in the next edition of the Guide.

OUNDLE — Talbot Hotel 61% £C/D

H **Map 6 A2** Northamptonshire
New Street PE8 4EA
Oundle (0832) 73621
Telex 32364

Credit Access, Amex, Diners, Visa

A splendid gabled building dating back to 1666 which contains a staircase descended by Mary Queen of Scots on the way to her execution. Weaponry, engravings and relics lend plenty of character. Public rooms include an extensive business complex, a cosy bar and a lounge with log fire. Bedrooms are comfortable and unfussy and have well-fitted bathrooms; five Club rooms are more spacious, with updated furnishings. ***Amenities*** garden, fax, laundry service. ♿

Rooms 39 | *Direct dial* Yes | *Confirm by* arrang. | *Parking* Ample
Ensuite bath/shower 39 | *Room TV* Yes | *Last dinner* 10 | *Room service* 24 hours

OXFORD — Café Français

R **Town plan C4** Oxfordshire
146 London Road,
Headington
Oxford (0865) 62587

French cooking
Set L from £7.95 **Set D** £10.95
Seats 60 *Parties* 35
Parking Difficult
Credit Access, Amex, Visa

Victorian photographs, candlelight and fresh flowers set the scene at this agreeable restaurant in the eastern suburbs. Fixed-price menus provide a well-balanced choice of largely familiar French dishes, from Mediterranean fish soup and chicken liver mousse to trout with almonds, pork fillet Vallée d'Auge and sirloin steak with green and black peppercorn sauce. Apple tartlet with whipped cream makes a delightful conclusion.

Lunch 12–2.15 *Dinner* 7–10.30
About £35 for two

OXFORD

Map 5 D2
Town plan opposite

Population 114,200

Despite the encroachment of industry, Oxford remains incomparable–except with Cambridge–as a centre of learning for 800 years, interrupted only by the disturbance of the Civil War siege in the 1640s. No city has more to offer the sightseer in its own architectural glories and the beauty of its surroundings–the Thames Valley, the Cotswolds and so much besides.

Annual Events
St Giles Fair *September*
Eights Week (5th week of University term)
Sheriff's Races *summer*

Sights Outside City
Blenheim Palace
Burford Village
Dorchester-on-Thames
Chipping Campden
Cogges Farm Museum
Cotswold Wild Life Park
Sulgrave Park
Waddesdon Manor

Information Centre
St Aldate's, Oxford OX1 1DY
Telephone Oxford 726871

Fiat Dealer
J. D. Barclay Ltd
Barclay House
Botley Road
Oxford OX2 0HQ
Tel. Oxford 722444

1 Apollo Theatre **B3**
2 Ashmolean Museum *art and archaeology treasures* **B3**
3 Bate Collection of Historical Musical Instruments **B4**
4 Botanic Garden *one of the oldest in the country* **C4**
5 Carfax Tower *viewpoint open in summer* **B4**
6 Christ Church Meadow **C5**
7 Coach Park **A4**
8 Divinity School *15th-c fine vaulted ceiling* **B3**
9 Folly Bridge **B5**
10 Martyrs' Memorial **B3**
11 Museum of History of Science **B3**
12 Museum of Oxford **B4**
13 Oxford Ice Rink **A4**
14 Oxford Information Centre **B4**
15 Oxford Story **B3**
16 Pitt Rivers Museum of Ethnology **B1/C2**
17 Playhouse **B3**
18 Sheldonian Theatre *Wren building for conferment of degrees* **B3**
19 Station **A3**
20 Town Hall **B4**
21 University Museum **B2**
22 University Parks **B/C1/2**

Oxford F I A T

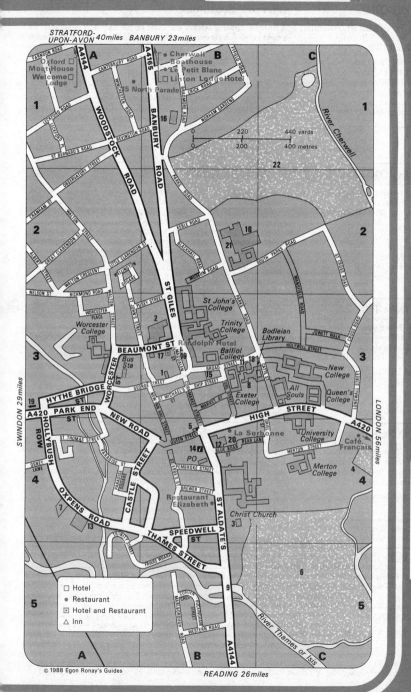

STRATFORD-UPON-AVON 40miles BANBURY 23miles

A4144 **A4165**

A Oxford Moat House Welcome Lodge
Farndon Road
Canterbury Road
Winchester Road

B Cherwell Boathouse
Le Petit Blanc
Linton Lodge Hotel
5 North Parade

C River Cherwell

Patrick Road
Crick Road
Norham Gardens

16

Bevington Road
St Bernard's Road

Woodstock Road
Banbury Road
Parks Road

1

Leckford Road
Leckford Road

0   220   440 yards
0   200   400 metres

22

2

Observatory Street
Kingston Road

Keble Road

16
21
South Parks Road

Museum Road

St Cross Road

2

Cranham St
Walton Street
Little Clarendon St
Great Clarendon St

Blackhall Road

Mansfield Road

Adelaide Street
Walton Crescent
Wellington Square

St Giles

St John's College

3

Nelson St
Richmond Road
Worcester Place

St John Street
Pusey Street

Trinity College

Bodleian Library

Jowett Walk

Longwall Street

Worcester College

Beaumont St
17 19 2
Randolph Hotel

Balliol College

Holywell Street

New College

3

Bus Sta
Worcester Street

George Street
New Inn Hall St
St Michael's St
Cornmarket St

Broad   5
St   11 18
Turl St   8

Exeter College

All Souls

Queen's College

A4420

Hythe Bridge St
Park End St
New Road
Swindon 29miles

Hollybush Row
St Thomas Street
Paradise St
Osney Lane

Castle Street

Queen St
Market St
St Aldate's

5
14 7 12 20
PO   Blue Boar
Bear Lane

High   Street

London 56miles

La Sorbonne

University College

Café Français

Merton Street

4

Oxpens Road
7
13

Trinity St
Pembroke Street
Brewer Street
Restaurant Elizabeth

Merton College

4

Speedwell St
Thames Street
3
Christ Church

Friars Wharf

5

☐ Hotel
● Restaurant
☑ Hotel and Restaurant
△ Inn

Corpus Marlborough Road
Buckingham Street
Western Road

9

6

River Thames or Isis

5

© 1988 Egon Ronay's Guides

READING 26miles

A4144

A   **B**   **C**

OXFORD — Cherwell Boathouse

R **Town plan B1** Oxfordshire
Bardwell Road
Oxford (0865) 52746

Set Sun L £11.50
Set D £11.50
About £30 for two
Seats 45
Parties 50
Parking Ample

Credit Access, Amex, Diners, Visa

A leisurely punting session will build up the right sort of appetite for a meal in this converted riverside boathouse. The menu offers a choice of just two dishes per course, some traditional, others modern: a marvellous cream onion tart, fish stew with aïoli *and* rouille, lamb with mushrooms and rice, duck with an unusual but very successful accompaniment of lemon, mustard, shallots and wine. Sweets like brandy sorbet or bread and butter pudding keep up the good work, and in the cellar there's a beautiful selection of the best wines from the best growers: Morgon (Jacky Janodet) '86, Pouilly Fuissé (Ch. de Fuissé) '83, Bonnezeaux Ch. des Gauliers '47. Staff are delightfully relaxed and friendly. ☞ Outstanding ☺ ⓑ

Lunch 1–2.30   *Dinner* 7.30–10
Closed D Sun & 1 wk Xmas

OXFORD — Restaurant Elizabeth   ♕

R **Town plan B4** Oxfordshire
85 St Aldate's
Oxford (0865) 242230

Set L £12
About £55 for two
Seats 45
Parties 40
Parking Difficult

Credit Access, Amex, Diners, Visa

A 16th-century building houses the two dining rooms, one oak panelled, the other spanned by an elaborately moulded Elizabethan ceiling. Caring owner Antonio Lopez continues to supervise a classic menu that includes such dishes as pipérade, avgolemono, beef stroganoff, châteaubriand, sorbet and syllabub. Honest cooking, generous portions. One of the great cellars with some exquisite old bottles: four vintages of Vega Sicilia, Ch. Branaire Ducru '61, Chambertin (Rousseau) '69. ☞ Outstanding ♚ Well-chosen ☺

Lunch 12.30–2.30   *Dinner* 6.30–11, Sun 7–10.30
Closed Mon, Good Fri & 1 wk Xmas

OXFORD — 15 North Parade   ♖

R **Town plan A1** Oxfordshire
15 North Parade,
off Banbury Road
Oxford (0865) 513773

Set L £9.75
About £55 for two
Seats 55
Parking Difficult
Credit Access, Visa

A coolly elegant restaurant with a regularly changing menu offering a short but imaginative selection of carefully prepared and attractively presented dishes. A typical meal might be rich Mediterranean fish soup with garlic mayonnaise and croûtons, followed by excellent noisettes of venison with a port and celeriac sauce or roast guinea fowl breast with a sherry sauce, accompanied by good and plentiful vegetables. Book. ♚ Well-chosen ☺ ⓑ

Lunch 12–2   *Dinner* 7–10.30
Closed Sun, 1 wk Xmas & 2 wks Aug

OXFORD — Linton Lodge Hotel   66%   £C

H **Town plan B1** Oxfordshire
Linton Road OX2 6UJ
Oxford (0865) 53461
Telex 837093

Credit Access, Amex, Diners, Visa

A friendly hotel which bustles with conference delegates. A modern foyer leads to a small lounge with attractive cane seating and to the simple but inviting Dragon Bar, from which you can take your drink into the spacious garden. Some bedrooms have been refurbished with pleasing freestanding furniture and light colour schemes and fabrics. Bathrooms are compact and modern. *Amenities* garden, pool table, in-house movies, secretarial services, fax, laundry service. ⓑ

Rooms 71	*Direct dial* Yes	*Confirm by* 6	*Parking* Ample
Ensuite bath/shower 71	*Room TV* Yes	*Last dinner* 9.30	*Room service* 24 hours

OXFORD — Oxford Moat House   60%   £C/D

H **Town plan A1** Oxfordshire
Wolvercote Roundabout
OX2 8AL
Oxford (0865) 59933
Telex 837926

Credit Access, Amex, Diners, Visa

Located at the junction of the A40 and A34, near the city centre, this contemporary hotel combines excellent leisure facilities with spacious open-plan public rooms, an intimate bar and generously equipped bedrooms. *Amenities* garden, indoor swimming pool, sauna, solarium, whirlpool bath, keep-fit equipment, hairdressing, squash, pitch & putt, clay-pigeon shooting, games room, snooker, in-house movies, secretarial services, fax, laundry service, coffee shop (7am–midnight), 24-hour lounge service.

Rooms 155	*Direct dial* Yes	*Confirm by* 6	*Parking* Ample
Ensuite bath/shower 155	*Room TV* Yes	*Last dinner* 9.45	*Room service* Limited

OXFORD   Le Petit Blanc ★   ♕

R **Town plan B2** Oxfordshire
61a Banbury Road
Oxford (0865) 53540

French cooking

Lunch 12.15–2.15
Dinner 7.15–10.15
Set L £12.50, Sun £15.50
About £60 *for two*
Seats 62
Parties 65
Parking Difficult

Credit Access, Visa
Closed Tues, 2 wks Xmas & 2
wks Aug/Sept

Not too far from the centre of the city, Le Petit Blanc is set in a very splendid Victorian conservatory. Bruno Loubet is master of the kitchen, turning out dishes that are notable for their superb flavours and fine sauces. The menu tempts at every turn with delights such as breast of wild pigeon poached in a beetroot consommé, set in a beetroot jelly and garnished with young pickled vegetables, or lightly smoked rib of beef, charcoal grilled and served with a red wine fumet. Good list of youngish French wines at highish prices. *Specialities* terrine de volailles 'Bourgeoise'; morue fraîche au four, jus de volailles, ragoût de fèves à la sariette; moussaka et petit sauté d'agneau à la tapenade; charlotte fondante de chocolat praliné. 🍷 Well-chosen ℮

OXFORD   Randolph Hotel   70%   £C

H **Town plan B3** Oxfordshire
Beaumont Street OX1 2LN
Oxford (0865) 247481
Telex 83446

Rooms 109
Ensuite bath/shower 109
Direct dial Yes
Room TV Yes
Confirm by 6
Last dinner 9.45
Parking Ample
Room service 24 hours

Credit Access, Amex, Diners, Visa

Built in 1864, the Randolph stands close to the Ashmolean Museum in the centre of the city. Public areas, recently expanded in terms of lounge space, retain some nice architectural features, including Gothic arches and windows, attractive cornice work and a fairly grand staircase. Bedrooms are mainly of a good size, with stylish fabrics, Italian freestanding furniture, easy chairs and useful room to work. Executive rooms get trouser presses, hairdryers and pleasant views; there are several suites with handsome reproduction antiques. Good porterage. Residents are now guaranteed a parking space in the hotel's garage.
Amenities laundry service, coffee shop (10am–10pm).

★ For a *discount* on next year's guide, see **An Offer for Answers.** ★

OXFORD   La Sorbonne   ⸸

R **Town plan B4**
Oxfordshire
130A High Street
Oxford (0865) 241320

French cooking
Set L & D £16
Seats 60 *Parties* 30
Parking Difficult
Credit Access, Amex, Diners, Visa

A handsome building dated 1637 houses this classical French restaurant where chef-patron André Chavagnon has been cooking for 22 years. He has trained such famous pupils as Raymond Blanc over the years and M. Chavagnon's accomplishments and admirably unfussy style are well illustrated in a simple meal consisting of fresh asparagus, poached turbot with béarnaise sauce, and crème brûlée. Wines include fine clarets and burgundies. 🍷 Well-chosen ℮

Lunch 12–2.30 *Dinner* 7–11 *About* £50 *for two*
Closed Bank Hols & 1 wk Xmas

OXFORD   Welcome Lodge   56%   £D/E

H **Town plan A1** Oxfordshire
Peartree R/about,
Woodstock Road OX2 8JZ
Oxford (0865) 54301
Telex 83202

Credit Access, Amex, Diners, Visa

Next to a service area at the junction of the A34 and A43, this is a handy overnight stop for the motorist. Most of the rooms are in two blocks, with parking spaces outside; all rooms have fairly basic laminate units, but there's ample well-lit writing space. Repair falls down in little ways, in both bedrooms and bathrooms. Bar, lounge and carvery.
Amenities garden, outdoor swimming pool, fax, laundry service.

Rooms 100	*Direct dial* Yes	*Confirm by* 6	*Parking* Ample
Ensuite bath/shower 100	*Room TV* Yes	*Last dinner* 10	*Room service* None

PADSTOW — Seafood Restaurant

RR Map 2 B3 Cornwall
Riverside
Padstow (0841) 532485

Seafood

Set D £16.50
About £50 for two
Seats 75
Parking Ample

Credit Access, Amex, Diners, Visa

Booking is essential at Richard and Jill Stein's cane-furnished quayside restaurant, where the menu is interesting and the cooking very competent. The delights of the deep dominate, with classics like skate and black butter or the mighty shellfish platter standing alongside modern dishes such as sliced raw fish with horseradish or grilled prawns with lemon grass and chilli. Also sirloin steaks and, among the sweets, strawberry shortbread flan, fresh fruit with sorbets and an exemplary crème brûlée. ♟ Well-chosen ✆

Dinner only 7–9.30
Closed Sat, all Sun, 1 May & 13 Dec–early Mar

BEDROOMS 10   **£E/F**
With bath/shower 8

Centrally heated bedrooms have simple light decor, antiques, TVs and views of harbour, town or garden.

Any person using our name to obtain free hospitality is a fraud.
Proprietors, please inform the police and us.

PAIGNTON — Palace Hotel   60%   £C/D

H Map 3 D3 Devon
Esplanade Road TQ4 6BJ
Paignton (0803) 555121

Credit Access, Amex, Diners, Visa

There's plenty to do for young and old at this popular holiday hotel opposite the pier. Day rooms have a comfortably traditional air, and picture windows provide fine views. Best and largest bedrooms are designated superior; all rooms are light and airy, with neat, practical bathrooms. **Amenities** garden, outdoor swimming pool, sauna, solarium, whirlpool bath, keep-fit equipment, beauty salon, tennis, squash, games room, laundry service, children's play area.

Rooms 54	Room phone Yes	Confirm by 6	Parking Ample
Ensuite bath/shower 54	Room TV Yes	Last dinner 9	Room service 24 hours

PAIGNTON — Redcliffe Hotel   59%   £D/E

H Map 3 D3 Devon
Marine Drive TQ3 2NL
Paignton (0803) 526397

Credit Access, Amex, Visa

An Indian palace inspired the architecture of this pleasant holiday hotel with a private tunnel leading to the beach. Relaxation comes easily in the day rooms, nicest of which is the main lounge with views over the bay. Bedrooms, most of them also affording sea views, are practical and well looked after. No dogs.
Amenities garden, outdoor swimming pool, hairdressing, putting, sea fishing, games room, secretarial services, laundry service.

Rooms 63	Direct dial Yes	Confirm by arrang.	Parking Ample
Ensuite bath/shower 63	Room TV Yes	Last dinner 8.30	Room service 24 hours

PAINSWICK — Painswick Hotel   67%   £D/E

H Map 4 B2 Gloucestershire
Kemps Lane GL6 6YB
Painswick (0452) 812160
Telex 43605

Credit Access, Amex, Diners, Visa

This handsome stone-built hotel was once a vicarage and is now run with great charm and efficiency by a family team of mother and daughter. The richly panelled bar has a welcoming log fire and leaded windows, and there's a cosy lounge upstairs with a baby grand. Bedrooms of varying sizes, some in a modern extension, are all comfortably furnished and well equipped.
Amenities garden, croquet, snooker, laundry service.

Rooms 15	Direct dial Yes	Confirm by arrang.	Parking Ample
Ensuite bath/shower 15	Room TV Yes	Last dinner 9.30	Room service All day

PANGBOURNE — Copper Inn   66%   £D

HR Map 5 D2 Berkshire
Church Road RG8 7AR
Pangbourne (073 57) 2244
Telex 849041

Credit Access, Amex, Diners, Visa

Behind the timbered facade of this 19th-century coaching inn are elegantly furnished public areas, combining style with comfort. A beamed bar, popular with locals, complements the smart cocktail lounge. Bedrooms vary in style with those in the garden wing being light and airy with delightful garden views. Bathrooms throughout are well equipped. Service, from well-motivated staff, is friendly and efficient. No dogs. **Amenities** garden, laundry service.

Rooms 21	Direct dial Yes	Confirm by 6	Parking Ample
Ensuite bath/shower 21	Room TV Yes	Last dinner 9.30	Room service All day

Restaurant

Set L from £11.95
Set D from £15.95
About £60 for two
Seats 40
Parties 50

French windows overlook the garden in this pleasant pine-ceilinged restaurant with very attentive service. The seasonally changing menu offers English food cooked in modern style, with very tasty results. Typical items are matelote of market fish in Noilly Prat, local pheasant with a crumble of woodland mushrooms, and an excellent vegetarian mousseline of parsnip and leek on a bed of noodles. There are some interesting desserts and a good English cheeseboard. ℮

Lunch 12.30–2   *Dinner* 7.30–9.30, Fri & Sat till 10, Sun till 9

PARKGATE   Ship Hotel   57%   £E

H Map 10 A2 Cheshire
The Parade, Wirral L64 6SA
051-336 3931

Credit Access, Amex, Diners, Visa

From the bleak, windswept street you step into a warm welcome at this modest hotel overlooking the marshy flats of the Dee estuary. The staff are very enthusiastic, and a programme of general refurbishment is keeping standards up. Spotless bedrooms feature pretty pastels and good modern lightwood furnishings. Two first-floor rooms facing the front are more stylish than the rest.
Amenities laundry service.

Rooms 26	Room phone Yes	Confirm by 6	Parking Ample
Ensuite bath/shower 26	Room TV Yes	Last dinner 9.30	Room service Limited

---

PARKHAM   Penhaven Country House   64%   *NEW ENTRY*   £D/E

H Map 2 C2 Devon
Nr Bideford EX39 5PL
Horns Cross (023 75) 711

Credit Access, Amex, Diners, Visa

Alan and Maxine Wade dispense charm and relaxed hospitality at their delightful old rectory transformed into a peaceful and informal hotel. In the cosy bar-lounge, a large stone fireplace catches the eye and there's a variety of comfortable seating. The light, airy bedrooms have modern freestanding furniture, pleasant floral wallcoverings and tiled bathrooms with shower fittings. Friendly, helpful staff.
Amenities garden, in-house movies, laundry service.

Rooms 12	Direct dial Yes	Confirm by arrang.	Parking Ample
Ensuite bath/shower 12	Room TV Yes	Last dinner 9.30	Room service All day

---

Changes in data sometimes occur in establishments
after the Guide goes to press.
Prices should be taken as indications rather than firm quotes.

PENDOGGETT   Cornish Arms   £F

IR Map 2 B3 Cornwall
St Kew,
Nr Port Isaac PL30 3HH
Bodmin (0208) 880263

Credit Access, Amex, Diners, Visa
Closed 25 & 26 Dec

Blackened woodwork and slate floors worn shiny with age create a delightful old-world atmosphere in the bars of this inn on the B3314. Bedrooms are warm and comfortable, with good solid white-painted furniture, and there's a cosy upstairs residents' lounge. Despite its out-of-the-way location, this is quite a lively place – the public bar providing plenty of activity until closing time. No children under 14.
Amenities garden.

Rooms 7	Room phone No	Confirm by arrang.	Parking Ample
Ensuite bath/shower 5	Room TV No	Last dinner 8.45	Room service Limited

---

Restaurant

Set Sun L £6
About £32 for two
Seats 30

Fresh fish and local game in season make a visit to this tiny dining room worthwhile. But it's definitely not a place for sophisticates: brightly lit and plainly furnished, the setting is as unaffected as the homely cooking. Go for simple dishes like home-made soup, baked crab, smoked mackerel and grilled sole and steak. And finish with lovely ice cream or treacle tart. Traditional Sunday lunch. Booking essential. ℮

Lunch Sun only 12.30–1.45   *Dinner* 7.15–8.45
Closed 25 & 26 Dec

PENRITH

North Lakes Gateway Hotel   74%   £C/D

Map 13 D5 Cumbria
Ullswater Road CA11 8QT
Penrith (0768) 68111
Telex 64257

Rooms 85
Ensuite bath/shower 85
Direct dial Yes
Room TV Yes
Confirm by 6
Last dinner 9.45
Parking Ample
Room service 24 hours

Credit Access, Amex, Diners, Visa

Guests will find their needs well catered for at this expertly planned and smoothly run hotel. In the open-plan bar and lounge, massive railway sleeper beams dominate the decor, while a louvred peephole window amid the subtropical foliage in reception provides an irresistible view of the pretty pool. Bedrooms include family rooms with foldaway beds and Executive rooms with raised seating areas, large writing desks, sofa beds, teletext, drinks trays and telephone and radio extensions in the bathrooms.

Amenities garden, indoor swimming pool, sauna, solarium, whirlpool bath, gymnasium, squash, snooker, satellite TV, in-house movies, secretarial services, fax, laundry service, coffee shop (9am–9pm). &

We welcome bona fide complaints and recommendations
on the tear-out pages at the back of the book for readers' comment.
They are followed up by our professional team.

PENZANCE

Abbey Hotel   67%   £D/E

Map 2 A4 Cornwall
Abbey Street TR18 4AR
Penzance (0736) 66906

Every room is a delight at the Abbey, a pretty little hotel tucked away in a narrow street near the harbour. Antiques, paintings and well-chosen fabrics blend in comfortable harmony, the sofas are deep, loose-covered and very inviting, books and magazines abound – in short, a picture of English country house living, with Jean Cox the inspiration for it all. Bedrooms – some of them very large, all with excellent heating – continue the style, and their bathrooms range from compact (shower/WC only) in corner rooms to very roomy in old-fashioned style. There's a very smart suite with two bedrooms, sitting room and magnificent bathroom. No children under five.
Amenities garden.

Rooms 7	*Room phone* No	*Confirm by* arrang.	*Parking* Limited
Ensuite bath/shower 7	*Room TV* Yes	*Last dinner* 8.30	*Room service* None

Restaurant

Set D £12.95
About £34 for two
Seats 20
Parties 20

The 17th-century dining room has great charm, with antique tables and chairs, white-painted panelling and a huge open fire. Candles and fresh flowers grace each table, and local girls serve nicely prepared dishes like squid in tomato and garlic, vegetable soup, rack of lamb and chicken cooked with yoghurt, chilli, spices and herbs. Sweets are of the hard-to-resist traditional variety. Mainly residents only, though some outside bookings are taken. €

Dinner only 7.30–8.30

PENZANCE

Berkeley

Map 2 A4 Cornwall
Abbey Street TR18 4AW
Penzance (0736) 62541

Set D from £14
About £38 for two
Seats 30
Parties 30
Parking Limited
Credit Access, Amex, Visa

Thirties decor and music create a nostalgic atmosphere at this attractive restaurant. Ian Morris's cooking is sound and he provides some interesting pasta dishes such as tortelloni filled with meat, mortadella and herbs and home-made tagliatelle in a cream and mushroom sauce. Classics include steak and kidney pie and coquilles St Jacques à la bretonne. A good dark chocolate mousse features among the pleasing sweets.

Dinner only 7.30–10.30
Closed Sun, also Mon–Wed Oct–mid June & 25 & 26 Dec

PENZANCE — Harris's ♖

R **Map 2 A4** Cornwall
46 New Street
Penzance (0736) 64408

About £42 for two
Seats 35
Parties 40
Parking Limited

Credit Access, Amex, Diners, Visa

A tiny, informal restaurant tucked away down a lane off the main street. Roger Harris's menus change every few weeks, offering simple dishes such as avocado with fresh crab mayonnaise or pâté maison as a starter, with perhaps breast of chicken stuffed with mushroom and tarragon in cream and sherry sauce to follow. Beautifully cooked vegetables accompany and there are delicious sweets to finish. Light lunches except by prior arrangement. Book.

Lunch 12–1.45   *Dinner* 7–10   **Closed** Sun, also Mon Nov–1 May, Bank Hols exc Good Fri & Easter Mon, 1 wk April & 2 wks Nov

---

PENZANCE — Higher Faugan Hotel

See under NEWLYN

PETERBOROUGH — Crest Hotel   60%   £C/D

H **Map 6 A2** Cambridgeshire
Great North Road, Norman
Cross PE7 3TB
Peterborough (0733) 240209
Telex 32576

Credit Access, Amex, Diners, Visa

Conveniently situated at the Norman Cross roundabout on the A1, this low-rise hotel is constructed of the same pale yellow brick that is a feature of the functional foyer. There are a few sofas in the foyer; the only other seating is in the bar. Best bedrooms are in a recently refurbished block and are all well equipped.
Amenities games room, pool table, in-house movies, fax, laundry service. ₺

Rooms 97	Direct dial Yes	Confirm by 6	Parking Ample
Ensuite bath/shower 97	Room TV Yes	Last dinner 10	Room service 24 hours

---

PETERBOROUGH — Peterborough Moat House   64%   £D/E

H **Map 6 A2** Cambridgeshire
Thorpe Wood PE3 6SG
Peterborough (0733) 260000
Telex 32708

Credit Access, Amex, Diners, Visa

Friendly, helpful staff provide the character at this modern hotel, where 1988 brought a leisure complex and a new wing of bedrooms. These rooms and fourth-floor rooms in the original wing are the best, but all are practical and well kept. Teletext keeps business people informed in the lounge, and there are two bars. *Amenities* indoor swimming pool, sauna, solarium, whirlpool bath, keep-fit equipment, in-house movies, secretarial services, fax, laundry service. ₺

Rooms 131	Direct dial Yes	Confirm by arrang.	Parking Ample
Ensuite bath/shower 131	Room TV Yes	Last dinner 10	Room service 24 hours

---

PETERSFIELD — Langrish House   63%   £E

H **Map 5 D3** Hampshire
Langrish GU32 1RN
Petersfield (0730) 66941

Credit Access, Amex, Diners

A nice old Tudor mansion in a peaceful parkland setting. Basement vaults (reputedly excavated by Royalist prisoners during the Civil War) provide most of the public areas, leaving part of the ground floor free for accommodation. Rooms here and on the first floor are spacious, those above much smaller. Note the prettily coordinated wall panels, curtains and bedcovers. Well-kept bathrooms throughout. No dogs. *Amenities* garden, laundry service.

Rooms 18	Direct dial Yes	Confirm by arrang.	Parking Ample
Ensuite bath/shower 18	Room TV Yes	Last dinner 9.30	Room service All day

---

Our inspectors are our full-time employees;
they are professionally trained by us.

PETTS WOOD — Ming   *NEW ENTRY*   ♖

R **Map 7 B5** Kent
23 Station Square
Orpington (0689) 20427

Chinese cooking
Set L from £3.50
Set D £11
Seats 75 *Parties* 22
Parking Ample
Credit Access, Amex, Diners, Visa

A Chinese restaurant with simple modern decor and lots of greenery. Mrs Yip and her staff look after guests very well, while Mr Yip prepares a range of enjoyable dishes on a mainly Peking menu: aromatic duck or mutton, garlicky mussels or paper-wrapped prawns to start, then perhaps deep-fried squid, grilled sole, lemon chicken or one of the sizzling dishes. Capable cooking, with good use of spices and seasoning. ₺

Lunch 12–2.30, Sun 1–2.30   *Dinner* 6–11   *About £35 for two*
Closed 25 & 26 Dec

PETWORTH

Shanghai Cottage *NEW ENTRY* ♀

R **Map 5 E3** West Sussex
Petworth
Petworth (0798) 43949

Chinese cooking
Set L & D from £8
About £30 for two
Seats 24 *Parties* 20
Parking Limited
Credit Access, Amex, Visa

Snowy table linen, fresh flowers and elegant wine glasses create a
stylish air in this intimate Chinese restaurant. Peking, Szechuan and
Shanghai dishes feature on the menu and Peter Deng prepares them
with loving care. Delicious dishes to try include Szechuan dumplings
in hot red pepper sauce, Shanghai fried beef with carrots in a chilli
sauce, and aubergine in ginger and garlic sauce. Book well in advance.

Lunch 12.30–2.30   *Dinner* 6.30–11
Closed 3 days Xmas

PLUMTREE

Perkins Bar Bistro ♀

R **Map 11 D3** Nottinghamshire
Station Road
Plumtree (060 77) 3695

About £30 for two
Seats 70
Parties 24
Parking Ample

Credit Access, Amex

You'll find a warm welcome and dependable cooking at this
thoughtfully converted and characterful old railway station. The
blackboard menu changes regularly, depending on availability of
produce from local suppliers. Starters might include cheese, nut and
brandy pâté, German salad with smoked fish or chicken liver and
pork terrine. Main course could be wood pigeon casserole or pot roast
chicken chasseur. Carefully chosen wines. Book. ♀ Well-chosen ℮

Lunch 12–2   *Dinner* 7–9.45
Closed Sun, Mon, 25 & 26 Dec, 1 Jan & 1 wk Autumn

Our inspectors *never* book in the name of Egon Ronay's Guides.
They disclose their identity only if they are considering an establishment
for inclusion in the next edition of the Guide.

PLYMOUTH

Astor Hotel 58%   £D/E

H **Map 2 C3** Devon
14 Elliott Street,
The Hoe PL1 2PS
Plymouth (0752) 225511
Telex 45652

Credit Access, Amex, Diners, Visa

Converted from five Victorian houses, this white-painted hotel stands
close to Plymouth Hoe within easy walking distance of the city centre.
The foyer-lounge is crowned by a handsome moulded ceiling, and
there's a modest but comfortable bar with a cheery, relaxed feel.
Decent-sized bedrooms are decorated in traditional style, with quite
simple furnishings. Some redecoration is in progress. No dogs.
Amenities laundry service.

Rooms 56	*Direct dial* Yes	*Confirm by* 6	*Parking* Ample
Ensuite bath/shower 56	*Room TV* Yes	*Last dinner* 9.30	*Room service* 24 hours

PLYMOUTH

Chez Nous ★   ♀

R **Map 2 C3** Devon
13 Frankfort Gate
Plymouth (0752) 266793

French cooking

Set L & D £17
About £50 for two
Seats 30
Parties 30
Parking Limited

Credit Access, Amex, Diners, Visa
Closed Sun, Mon, Bank Hols, 1st
2 wks Feb & 1st 2 wks Sept

French posters and a blackboard
menu give a bistro feel to Jacques
and Suzanne Marchal's unobtrusive little restaurant tucked
away in a shopping precinct.
Booking is essential since word
has spread about Jacques' culinary talents. His fish dishes are
justly popular, and meat dishes
to try include pheasant with
apricots and sweetbreads in a
rich mushroom sauce. Don't miss
the marvellous marble gâteau.

Good wine list has some fine burgundies such as a Volnay Clos des
Chênes (Fontaine-Gagnard) '82. **Specialities** coquilles St Jacques au
gingembre et julienne de légumes, filets de St Pierre à l'orange et au
coulis de carottes, filet de boeuf à la moelle et porto, la tranche de
chocolat aux deux sauces. ♀ Well-chosen ℮

PLYMOUTH · Copthorne Hotel · 71% · £C/D

H Map 2 C3 Devon
Armada Centre,
Armada Way PL1 1AR
Plymouth (0752) 224161
Telex 45756

Rooms 135
Ensuite bath/shower 135
Direct dial Yes
Room TV Yes
Confirm by 6
Last dinner 10.30
Parking Ample
Room service 24 hours

Credit Access, Amex, Diners, Visa

Enjoying a central position near the town's major facilities, Plymouth's Copthorne offers high standards of comfort and service. Bill Clifford is an excellent manager; his staff are smartly turned out and good at their jobs. The first-floor foyer-lounge is a light, elegant and relaxing room, and there's a stylish bar with Victorian prints and marble-topped tables. Bedrooms, many interconnectable to make suites, are furnished in pleasant contemporary style, and all have plenty of seating and writing space. All the usual up-to-the-minute extras are provided, and the bathrooms have good showers as well as baths.
Amenities plunge pool, sauna, solarium, keep-fit equipment, pool table, in-house movies, secretarial services, fax, laundry service. &

PLYMOUTH · Duke of Cornwall Hotel · 56% · £E

H Map 2 C3 Devon
Millbay Road PL1 3LG
Plymouth (0752) 266256
Telex 45424

Credit Access, Amex, Diners, Visa
Closed 24–27 Dec

Purpose-built in 1863, the Duke of Cornwall retains much of its Victorian Gothic decor and design, though the bar, with barrel seats, tartan carpet and stag's head, has a strong Scottish theme. There's another bar (in the basement) and a cosy panelled lounge. Bedrooms in various sizes and styles are modest but quite comfortable, with simple tiled bath or shower rooms.
Amenities secretarial services, laundry service.

Rooms 70	*Direct dial* Yes	*Confirm by* arrang.	*Parking* Ample
Ensuite bath/shower 70	*Room TV* Yes	*Last dinner* 9.30	*Room service* 24 hours

**If we recommend meals in a Hotel or Inn,
a separate entry is made for its restaurant.**

PLYMOUTH · Holiday Inn · 70% · £C

H Map 2 C3 Devon
Armada Way PL1 2HJ
Plymouth (0752) 662866
Telex 45637

Rooms 217
Ensuite bath/shower 217
Direct dial Yes
Room TV Yes
Confirm by 6
Last dinner 10.30
Parking Ample
Room service 24 hours

Credit Access, Amex, Diners, Visa

Overnight accommodation is roomy and comfortable at this modern high-rise hotel overlooking the Hoe and Plymouth Sound. All rooms offer generous space for sitting, working and storage, and picture windows add to the feeling of size. Decor is unfussily contemporary, furnishings are practical and accessories include trouser presses and hairdryers. The foyer is large and welcoming (pleasant, efficient reception staff) and there are two attractive bars, one on the top floor with fairly spectacular views. Our buffet breakfast was nothing to write home about. *Amenities* patio, indoor swimming pool, sauna, solarium, keep-fit equipment, games room, pool table, in-house movies, secretarial services, fax, laundry service, coffee shop (7am–10pm). &

PLYMOUTH · Mayflower Post House Hotel · 65% · £C/D

H Map 2 C3 Devon
Cliff Road, The Hoe PL1 3DL
Plymouth (0752) 662828
Telex 45442

Credit Access, Amex, Diners, Visa

A tallish modern hotel with good views from the vantage point of the Hoe. Two bars and a comfortable, good-sized foyer-lounge provide ample space to relax, and there's a bright coffee shop. Bedrooms range from practically appointed standards to luxury penthouse suites; nearly all look to sea. *Amenities* garden, outdoor swimming pool, secretarial services, fax, coffee shop (7am–10.30pm), 24-hour lounge service, laundry service, children's play area.

Rooms 106	*Direct dial* Yes	*Confirm by* 6	*Parking* Ample
Ensuite bath/shower 106	*Room TV* Yes	*Last dinner* 10.30	*Room service* Limited

PLYMOUTH   Novotel   62%   £D/E

H Map 2 C3 Devon
Marsh Mills
Roundabout PL6 8HN
Plymouth (0752) 221422
Telex 45711

Credit Access, Amex, Diners, Visa

Sited by a roundabout on the A38 at the entrance to the city, the 1980s-built Novotel is a practical place for an overnight stop, appealing to both business and leisure visitors. Public areas are roomy and relaxing, and practical bedrooms all have double and single beds, plus private bathrooms with separate WCs. *Amenities* garden, outdoor swimming pool, pool table, in-house movies, laundry service, coffee shop (6am–midnight), children's play area. &

Rooms 101	*Direct dial* Yes	*Confirm by* 7	*Parking* Ample
Ensuite bath/shower 101	*Room TV* Yes	*Last dinner* 12	*Room service* Limited

---

Any person using our name to obtain free hospitality is a fraud.
Proprietors, please inform the police and us.

POCKLINGTON   Feathers Hotel   £E/F

I Map 11 E1 Humberside
Market Place YO4 2UN
Pocklington (0759) 303155

Credit Access, Amex, Diners, Visa

An inn has stood on the same town-centre site since Elizabethan times, and the present pebbledashed incumbent makes a good overnight stop. The six bedrooms in the main house have a traditional look, while the others, across the car park, are in chalet style; all rooms have hairdryers, trouser presses and tea-makers. There is a roomy bar and a TV lounge. Staff seem a bit listless. No dogs.
Amenities patio.

Rooms 12	*Direct dial* Yes	*Confirm by* arrang.	*Parking* Ample
Ensuite bath/shower 12	*Room TV* Yes	*Last dinner* 9.30	*Room service* None

---

POLPERRO   Kitchen at Polperro   ⊄

R Map 2 C3 Cornwall
Fish Na Bridge
Polperro (0503) 72780

Set L from £5.95
Set D from £8.95
About £38 for two
Seats 24 *Parties* 20
Parking Ample
Credit Access, Amex, Diners, Visa

A delightful little restaurant near the centre of Polperro (park in the village car park). Ian Bateson offers a wide selection of menus, including a vegetarian one, and daily specials feature mainly seafood. His cooking is confident and enjoyable and, with the friendly service, a pleasant meal is assured. A typical meal might be mushroom and coriander pâté followed by a flavoursome crab filo, with strawberry toffee flan to finish.

Lunch Mar–Oct 12.30–2 exc. Sat, Nov–Mar 12.30–2 Sun only
Dinner Mar–Oct 6.30–10, Nov–Mar 7.30–10 Fri & Sat only

POOL-IN-WHARFEDALE   Pool Court   ★   ♕♕

RR Map 10 C1
West Yorkshire
Nr Otley LS21 1EH
Arthington (0532) 842288

Set D £10
About £60 for two
Seats 65
Parties 30
Parking Ample

Credit Access, Amex, Diners, Visa

Twenty one years have not dimmed Michael and Hanni Gill's enthusiasm for their elegant restaurant, and in Melvin Jordan (14 years service) they have a chef of outstanding ability. His menus change regularly to reflect what's best in the markets, and his dishes are always bursting with fine natural flavours, enhanced by spot-on seasoning and super sauces. They are rightly accompanied by an impeccable

selection of wines, as strong in Alsace and California as in classics: Riesling Muenchberg (André Ostertag) '83, Cabernet Sauvignon (Jordan) '80. *Specialities* platter of various marinaded fish; wild mushroom consommé; roast partridge with rösti-style bacon and potato cake and a truffle gravy; cashew nut and butterscotch slice.
⊳ Outstanding   ♥ Well-chosen ☺

Lunch by arrang. only   *Dinner* 7–10
Closed Sun, Mon, last wk July, 1st wk Aug & 10 days Xmas

BEDROOMS 6   £C
With bath/shower 6

The six immaculate bedrooms are decorated and furnished with great taste and include many extras, from sewing kits and board games to drinks bars and wall safes. No dogs.

POOLE

Hospitality Inn, The Quay 70% £D

H
Map 4 C4 Dorset
The Quay BH15 1HD
Poole (0202) 666800
Telex 418374

Rooms 68
Ensuite bath/shower 68
Direct dial Yes
Room TV Yes
Confirm by 6
Last dinner 10
Parking Ample
Room service 24 hours

Credit Access, Amex, Diners, Visa

Major refurbishment, a new wing of bedrooms and (perhaps) a leisure complex are major events for 1989 at this modern low-rise hotel by the quay. There are panoramic views of the bay from the pleasant lounge and octagonal restaurant. Views can be enjoyed, too, from many of the bedrooms, which are of a good size, with ample seating and writing space. Hairdryers and trouser presses are standard, and all rooms have spotless, well-equipped bathrooms. Ten ground-floor rooms have proper wheelchair access, with a lift to the lounge, where the toilets are fully adapted. Smart, friendly staff.
Amenities patio, in-house movies, secretarial services, laundry service. ♿

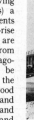

POOLE

Mansion House 74% £C/D

HR
Map 4 C4 Dorset
Thames Street BH15 1JN
Poole (0202) 685666
Telex 41495

Rooms 19
Ensuite bath/shower 19
Direct dial Yes
Room TV Yes
Confirm by arrang.
Last dinner 10.
Parking Ample
Room service All day

Credit Access, Amex, Diners, Visa
Closed 10 days Xmas

A fine Georgian town house whose interior reflects the building's elegant proportions. The characterful Members Bar on the ground floor has dark oak beams, exposed brickwork and oak furniture, all of which establish a cosy, intimate atmosphere. A beautiful sweeping staircase leads to a comfortable and stylish residents' lounge with deep, chintzy sofas and antiques. The charming bedrooms are decorated and furnished to a high standard and a long list of extras including books, trouser presses, hairdryers, fresh fruit, sherry and potted plants gives a feeling of cosseted luxury. Bathrooms are well-equipped with good quality toiletries and further thoughtful extras.
Amenities secretarial services, laundry service.

Restaurant ♕

Set L £13.75
Set D from £19
About £52 for two
Seats 80
Parties 32

A formal restaurant which is open to non-members for a cover charge of £3 per head; jackets and ties are essential. Tony Parsons produces superb dishes from a long, traditional menu – starter might be scallop mousseline with beurre blanc and sorrel, followed by pheasant in port wine sauce. Standard sweets to finish. Good, fairly priced Bordeaux include Chx. Thieuley '83, Pavie '75 and Haut-Batailley '70. Book. 🍷 Well-chosen ⓔ

Lunch 12.30–2 *Dinner* 7.30–10
Closed L Sat & 10 days Xmas

🍷 indicates a **well-chosen** house wine

PORLOCK

The Oaks Hotel 65% *NEW ENTRY* £E/F

HR
Map 3 D1 Somerset
Somerset TA24 8ES
Porlock (0643) 862265

Tim and Anne Riley warmly welcome guests at their Edwardian country house, which overlooks the village and the waters of Porlock Bay. Day rooms, heated by open fires in winter, are very cosy and relaxing, and the individually styled bedrooms have plenty of thoughtful extras to add to the comfort. All rooms have private bath or shower room, one not en suite.
Amenities garden.

Rooms 11	*Direct dial* Yes	*Confirm by* arrang.	*Parking* Ample
Ensuite bath/shower 10	*Room TV* Yes	*Last dinner* 8.45	*Room service* All day

see over

The Oaks Restaurant   *NEW ENTRY*   ♫

Set D £11
Seats 26
Parties 15

An admirably unpretentious menu cooked by Anne Riley and served
by Tim in pleasant, homely surroundings. Carrot soup, pipérade or
smoked mackerel pâté could get dinner under way, followed perhaps
by fresh salmon with a cream sauce, liver and onions or venison steak
with Cumberland sauce. Simple sweets like chocolate mousse round
things off. Good choice of wines. Booking preferred. ☺

Lunch by arrang.   *Dinner* 7–8.45
About £30 *for two*

PORTLOE   Lugger Hotel   59%   £D/E

H **Map 2 B3** Cornwall
Nr Truro TR2 5RD
Truro (0872) 501322

Credit Access, Amex, Diners, Visa
Closed mid Nov–early Mar

A pleasant holiday hotel standing right at the water's edge in a quiet
Cornish fishing village. The building dates from the 17th century, and
period appeal remains to some degree in the day rooms. Seven cosily
traditional bedrooms are in the main house, the rest, larger and
smartly up-to-date, in an annexe. Half-board terms only. No children
under 12. No dogs.
Amenities sauna, solarium, fax, laundry service.

| *Rooms* 20 | *Direct dial* Yes | *Confirm* by arrang. | *Parking* Ample |
| *Ensuite bath/shower* 20 | *Room TV* Yes | *Last dinner* 9 | *Room service* All day |

PORTSMOUTH   Crest Hotel   64%   £D

H **Map 5 D4** Hampshire
Pembroke Road,
Southsea PO1 2TA
Portsmouth (0705) 827651
Telex 86397

Credit Access, Amex, Diners, Visa

Follow signs for the Isle of Wight hovercraft to locate this modern
red-brick hotel. Reception rooms include two bars and there's also a
comfortable foyer-lounge. Bedrooms are different in decor: women's
rooms have hairdryers and fresh flowers; executives gain a drinks
tray and fruit platter. Bathrooms are compact. *Amenities* patio,
whirlpool bath, games room, in-house movies, secretarial services, fax,
laundry service, coffee shop (10am–10pm in summer). ♿

| *Rooms* 163 | *Direct dial* Yes | *Confirm* by 6 | *Parking* Ample |
| *Ensuite bath/shower* 163 | *Room TV* Yes | *Last dinner* 9.45 | *Room service* 24 hours |

PORTSMOUTH   Holiday Inn   77%   £C

H **Map 5 D4** Hampshire
North Harbour, Cosham
PO6 4SH
Portsmouth (0705) 383151
Telex 86611

Rooms 170
Ensuite bath/shower 170
Direct dial Yes
Room TV Yes
Confirm by 6
Last dinner 10.45
Parking Ample
Room service 24 hours

Credit Access, Amex, Diners, Visa

North of the city centre and
adjacent to the M27 and A3,
Portsmouth's Holiday Inn is a
modern brick and glass hotel of
great appeal to both travellers
and business executives. The major public areas are all under one
great roof in the Holidome: reception, cocktail bar, lounge, restaurant and leisure facilities.
Bedrooms are splendidly designed and well maintained, with
lots of storage space and writing
surfaces, smart walnut-style fitted furniture, large beds and the usual
up-to-the-minute accessories. Courtesy coach. *Amenities* garden,
indoor swimming pool, sauna, solarium, whirlpool bath, gymnasium,
squash, games room, in-house movies, secretarial services, fax, laundry
service, coffee shop (7am–11pm), children's play area. ♿

PORTSMOUTH   Hospitality Inn   64%   £D

H **Map 5 D4** Hampshire
South Parade,
Southsea PO4 0RN
Portsmouth (0705) 731281
Telex 86719

Credit Access, Amex, Diners, Visa

A handsome, bay-windowed building right on the esplanade, with
views of the Solent. In the imposing public rooms, glittering chandeliers
and elaborate mouldings complement furniture that is comfortably
contemporary. Most of the spacious bedrooms are traditionally
furnished and have tea-makers, hairdryers, trouser presses and
functional bathrooms. More luxurious rooms have smart lightwood
units and up-to-date bathrooms. *Amenities* sea fishing, secretarial
services, laundry service.

| *Rooms* 115 | *Direct dial* Yes | *Confirm* by 6 | *Parking* Limited |
| *Ensuite bath/shower* 115 | *Room TV* Yes | *Last dinner* 9.45 | *Room service* 24 hours |

PORTSMOUTH   Pendragon Hotel   59%   £C/D

H Map 5 D4 Hampshire
Clarence Parade, Southsea
POS 2HY
Portsmouth (0705) 823201
Telex 86376

Credit Access, Amex, Diners, Visa

A sunny, south-facing position overlooking the Solent is one of the attractions of this gradually improving hotel. The front-facing bedrooms are spacious and bright, while the totally upgraded superior and Executive rooms to the rear have smart, modern Italian furniture, well-chosen contemporary decor and shower units in the bathrooms. Older rooms have built-in light pine units and simpler bathrooms. *Amenities* laundry service.

Rooms 49	*Room phone* Yes	*Confirm by* 6	*Parking* Limited
Ensuite bath/shower 49	*Room TV* Yes	*Last dinner* 9	*Room service* 24 hours

---

Our inspectors *never* book in the name of Egon Ronay's Guides.
They disclose their identity only if they are considering an establishment
for inclusion in the next edition of the Guide.

POWBURN   Breamish House Hotel   69%   £E

HR Map 15 B3
Northumberland
Nr Alnwick NE66 4LL
Powburn (066 578) 266

Closed Jan–mid Feb

Maintenance and housekeeping both shine at Breamish House, an attractive Georgian building in a peaceful country setting. The inviting, comfortable lounge offers a log fire burning in the marble hearth, plenty of relaxing sofas and chairs, fresh flowers and a porcelain collection. Pleasantly decorated bedrooms are supplied with a multitude of little extras, including chocolates, mineral water and sewing kits. Bathrooms sparkle. Good breakfasts. *Amenities* garden.

Rooms 10	*Room phone* Yes	*Confirm by* arrang.	*Parking* Ample
Ensuite bath/shower 9	*Room TV* Yes	*Last dinner* 8	*Room service* Limited

Restaurant   ⚑ ⌇

English cooking

Set L £9
Set D £15.50
About £40 for two
Seats 30

Fresh flowers and candlelight create a most agreeable setting for a five-course meal that starts at 8 o'clock. Good honest flavours are enhanced by accurate seasoning in straightforward dishes like crab salad, watercress soup, tarragon chicken and loin of pork dijonnaise. Plentiful vegetables, and a choice of four or five sweets. Aperitifs and coffee are taken in the lounge; no smoking in the dining room.

Lunch Sun only at 1   *Dinner* 7.30 for 8
Closed Jan–mid Feb

PRESTBURY   Bridge Hotel   £D

I Map 10 B2 Cheshire
New Road, Nr Macclesfield
SK10 4DQ
Prestbury (0625) 829326

Credit Access, Amex, Diners, Visa

The several cottages that make up this handsome village inn date back as far as 1626, and some of the original wattle and daub may still be seen in the comfortably traditional lounge. Bedrooms combine beamed, cottage appeal with adequate modern comforts; en suite facilities are mainly shower/WC only. Staff, many of very long standing, provide very pleasant and courteous service. No dogs. *Amenities* garden, laundry service.

Rooms 6	*Room phone* Yes	*Confirm by* arrang.	*Parking* Ample
Ensuite bath/shower 6	*Room TV* Yes	*Last dinner* 9.45	*Room service* All day

---

PRESTON   Crest Hotel   63%   £C/D

H Map 10 A1 Lancashire
The Ringway PR1 3AU
Preston (0772) 59411
Telex 677147

Credit Access, Amex, Diners, Visa

A town-centre, multi-storey hotel which offers convenient accommodation. Conference facilities are good and other public areas include a disco-themed bar. The compact, well-designed bedrooms have good quality wooden units and attractive drapes, while a plush suite boasts a mirrored spa bathroom. Non-smoking and Lady Crest rooms are available.
Amenities in-house movies, secretarial services, fax, laundry service.

Rooms 126	*Direct dial* Yes	*Confirm by* 6	*Parking* Limited
Ensuite bath/shower 126	*Room TV* Yes	*Last dinner* 10	*Room service* 24 hours

PRESTON   Novotel   62%   £D/E

H Map 10 A1 Lancashire
Reedfield Place,
Walton Summit PR5 6AB
Preston (0772) 313331
Telex 677164

Credit Access, Amex, Diners, Visa

Conveniently situated close to junction 29 on the M6, this modern
hotel has spacious, well-planned public rooms including a restaurant
where breakfasts are served overlooking the pool. Large bedrooms
have generous writing space, practical furnishings and excellent
bathrooms (each with bidet, shower and separate WC).
Amenities garden, outdoor swimming pool, pool table, laundry
service, coffee shop (6am–midnight), 24-hour lounge service.   &

Rooms 100	*Direct dial* Yes	*Confirm by* 6	*Parking* Ample
Ensuite bath/shower 100	*Room TV* Yes	*Last dinner* Midnight	*Room service* All day

Changes in data sometimes occur in establishments
after the Guide goes to press.
Prices should be taken as indications rather than firm quotes.

PUDDINGTON   Craxton Wood Hotel   70%   £D/E

HR Map 10 A2 Cheshire
Parkgate Road,
South Wirral L66 9PB
051-339 4717

Rooms 14
Ensuite bath/shower 14
Room phone Yes
Room TV Yes
Confirm by arrang.
Last dinner 10
Parking Ample
Room service Limited

Credit Access, Amex, Diners, Visa
Closed 2 wks end of Aug

Thirty-six peaceful acres of garden and woodland surround this
white-painted hotel, and the air
of calm is enhanced by discreet,
well-mannered staff, some of
whom have been with Mr. Pe-
tranca for as long as 16 years.
Housekeeping is exemplary, and
refurbishment keeps the whole
place in tip-top condition. The
bar and lounge look out over the
garden, and both are particularly
comfortable and sunny. The bar

has a contemporary pastel look, and the lounge features the handsome
darkwood furniture that is also used in the bedrooms. Rooms are of a
decent size, with bright bathrooms. No dogs.
Amenities garden, fax, laundry service.

Restaurant

About £48 for two
Seats 80
Parties 36

Sauces are a particular strength of Scotsman James Minnis, chef at
this bright, airy restaurant with lovely country views. Dishes much
enjoyed on a recent visit included marinated salmon with dill and
cream, chicken breast and lobster poached in white wine, served with
a delicate sherry and butter sauce, and strips of fillet of beef cooked in
ginger, mustard and orange zest laced with cream and sherry. The
imaginative menu is simply described in French and English. Service
is polite and efficient, if occasionally a little overzealous. Among the
carefully chosen list of serious wines are some fine clarets at 'gift'
prices (Ch. La Dominique '78, Ch. Montrose '76).   ♥ Well-chosen   ℗

Lunch 12.30–2   *Dinner* 7.30–10
Closed Sun, Bank Hols, 2 wks end of Aug

PULBOROUGH   Chequers Hotel   60%   £E

H Map 5 E3 West Sussex
Church Place RH20 1AD
Pulborough (079 82) 2486
Telex 67596

Credit Access, Amex, Diners, Visa

Built partly during the reign of Queen Anne, this hotel is run by a
delightful, welcoming family. Tea is offered on your arrival as you
make yourself at home in the cosy, deep-carpeted lounge with its open
fire in winter. The public areas have recently been redecorated in
keeping with the old-fashioned feel, while the pretty, cottage bedrooms
have a home-from-home appeal.
Amenities garden, fax.

Rooms 9	*Room phone* No	*Confirm by* arrang.	*Parking* Ample
Ensuite bath/shower 8	*Room TV* Yes	*Last dinner* 8	*Room service* All day

PULBOROUGH · Stane Street Hollow Restaurant 🍴

R Map 5 E3 West Sussex
Codmore Hill
Pulborough (079 82) 2819

Set L £5.50
About £42 for two
Seats 32
Parties 20
Parking Ample

At this charming Sussex stone cottage on the A29 you can find some of the most delicious and unpretentious cooking you could wish for. René Kaiser's dishes are Swiss in style, utterly dependable and bursting with flavour. His menus change with the season and all the offerings are a delight. You might start with potage de gibier and move on to meltingly tender medallions of venison with a brandy, bacon, mushroom and cream sauce. The desserts are scrumptious. Super wines – keenly priced – include a fine Swiss Pinot Noir, Ch. la Dominique '80 (a vineyard to watch) and the wonderful Gewürztraminer Rangen from Zind-Humbrecht. 🍷 Well-chosen ⊖

Lunch 12.30–1.15   *Dinner* 7.30–9.15
Closed L Sat & Tues, all Sun & Mon, 10 days Xmas, 2 wks end Oct & 3 wks end May

We welcome bona fide complaints and recommendations
on the tear-out pages at the back of the book for readers' comment.
They are followed up by our professional team.

QUORN · Quorn Country Hotel 74% £C/D

H Map 11 D3 Leicestershire
Charnwood House,
66 Leicester Road LE12 8BB
Loughborough (0509) 415050
Telex 347166

Rooms 19
Ensuite bath/shower 19
Direct dial Yes
Room TV Yes
Confirm by arrang.
Last dinner 10
Parking Ample
Room service 24 hours

Credit Access, Amex, Diners, Visa

In the centre of the village, surrounded by neat, well laid out grounds, is this delightful country hotel, splendidly maintained and efficiently run by a really dedicated team. Comfort is the keynote everywhere, from the welcoming reception hall with blazing fire and gleaming oak panelling to the elegant lounge with floral-patterned armchairs and complementary flower arrangements. Bedrooms are even  more stylish, with pretty coordinating colour schemes and fine reproduction furniture. They're spacious and well equipped, too, with extras like mini-bars and hairdryers. Modern tiled bathrooms are kept spotlessly clean. Suites and specially designated ladies' rooms are available. *Amenities* garden, coarse fishing, laundry service, helipad.

RAMSBOTTOM · Village Restaurant *NEW ENTRY* 🍴

R Map 10 B1
Greater Manchester
Market Place
Ramsbottom (070 682) 5070

Set D £19.50
About £55 for two
Seats 20 *Parties* 14
Parking Ample
Credit Access, Visa

Husband and wife Chris Johnson and Ros Hunter run their quaint little restaurant with great enthusiasm. Their daily-changing, no-choice set menu offers a feast of quality local produce from garden-fresh vegetables to superb cheeses. Our main course was pinkly perfect roast lamb, accompanied by tender vegetables and an excellent rhubarb, ginger and cranberry conserve. Delightful sweets. House wines are selected to accompany each course. 🍷 Well-chosen ⊖

Dinner only at 8.30
Closed Sun to Tues & all Bank Hols

RAVENSTONEDALE · Black Swan *NEW ENTRY* £E

I Map 13 D5 Cumbria
Nr Kirby Stephen CA17 4NG
Newbiggin on Lune (058 73) 204

Credit Amex, Visa
Closed Jan & Feb

Christopher and Alison Davy and their cheerful local staff make it a real pleasure to stay in this turn-of-the-century village inn. No TVs or telephones intrude in the neat bedrooms, where the only noise is the gentle bubble of the beck that borders the garden. There's a comfortable, gleaming lounge bar and a residents' sitting room. Super breakfasts.
Amenities garden, game fishing, laundry service.

Rooms 9	*Room phone* No	*Confirm by* 6	*Parking* Ample
Ensuite bath/shower 7	*Room TV* No	*Last dinner* 8.30	*Room service* Limited

READING   Caversham Hotel   77%   *NEW ENTRY*   £B/C

HR **Map 5 D2** Berkshire
Caversham Bridge,
Richfield Avenue RG1 8BD
Reading (0734) 391818
Telex 846933

Rooms 120
Ensuite bath/shower 120
Direct dial Yes
Room TV Yes
Confirm by 6
Last dinner 10.30
Parking Ample
Room service 24 hours

Credit Access, Amex, Diners, Visa

A newly opened riverside hotel with handsome red-brick exterior. Open-plan split-level public areas include a bright and spacious foyer-lounge and a stylishly furnished cocktail bar, and there's also the Edwardian-themed Three Men in a Boat pub, offering public river mooring. Attractively designed bedrooms range from decent-sized standards to large suites with spacious, river-facing balconies. All are well equipped and have compact, fully tiled bathrooms. When we visited, service and housekeeping were still suffering teething problems; more attention to detail, please! No dogs. *Amenities* patio, indoor swimming pool, sauna, solarium, keep-fit equipment, snooker, in-house movies, teletext, fax, laundry service. ♿

Bridge Restaurant   *NEW ENTRY*   ♛

Set L £14.50, Sun £18.50
Set D £22
About £85 *for two*
Seats 75
Parties 200

John McGeever's imaginative ideas and artistic presentation make for delightful eating in this airy, glass-domed restaurant. Top-quality raw materials (including faultlessly fresh fish) enhance excellent combinations like salad of spiced vegetables with couscous and tomato, saffron-scented sweetbreads and crayfish ravioli, breast of chicken filled with morels and parsnips, served on a rich white port sauce, and honey bavarois sauced with coconut. Patchy service. Non-smoking area.
♿

Lunch 12.30–2.30   *Dinner* 7.30–10.30

READING   Post House Hotel   64%   £C

H **Map 5 D2** Berkshire
500 Basingstoke Road RG2 0SL
Reading (0734) 875485
Telex 849160

Credit Access, Amex, Diners, Visa

A modern single-storey hotel near junction 11 of the M4. There are two bars and a coffee shop, nicer places to relax than the lounge with its very low easy chairs. The leisure centre is a major feature. Decent-sized bedrooms have remote-control TVs, mini-bars and toasters for the room service breakfast bread. *Amenities* indoor swimming pool, sauna, solarium, whirlpool bath, gymnasium, secretarial services, coffee shop (7am–11pm), children's play area.

Rooms 143	*Direct dial* Yes	*Confirm by* 6	*Parking* Ample
Ensuite bath/shower 143	*Room TV* Yes	*Last dinner* 10.30	*Room service* Limited

▷ is our symbol for an **outstanding** wine list

READING   Ramada Hotel   76%   £C

H **Map 5 D2** Berkshire
Oxford Road RG1 7RH
Reading (0734) 586222
Telex 847785

Rooms 200
Ensuite bath/shower 200
Direct dial Yes
Room TV Yes
Confirm by 6
Last dinner 11.30
Parking Limited
Room service 24 hours

Credit Access, Amex, Diners, Visa

A good-looking, modern hotel in the centre of town. Overnight accommodation is very comfortable and well designed: king-size beds in decent-sized bedrooms, easy chairs, a table of writing height, mini-bars, neatly fitted bathrooms with the usual toiletries. Public areas leading from the pillared foyer are on several levels and include two bars, one with an evening pianist, the other in pub style. The coffee shop is open long hours, and there are excellent facilities for conferences and keeping fit. Service is OK, nothing more. No dogs. *Amenities* indoor swimming pool, sauna, solarium, whirlpool bath, steam bath, keep-fit equipment, beauty salon, hairdressing, secretarial services, fax, coffee shop (7am–11.30pm), kiosk. ♿

REDBOURN | Aubrey Park Hotel 56% | £D

H **Map 5 E2** Hertfordshire
Hemel Hempstead Road
AL3 7AF
Redbourn (058 285) 2105
Telex 82195

Credit Access, Amex, Diners, Visa

Six acres of gardens and lawns provide the setting for Aubrey Park Hotel, where the most important recent development has been a new wing of bedrooms. These 21 rooms are of a much higher standard than the rest, with whirlpool baths among the touches of luxury. The hotel has a cheerful bar and lounge, plus several function and meeting rooms. *Amenities* garden, outdoor swimming pool, games room, laundry service.

| *Rooms* 102 | *Direct dial* Yes | *Confirm by* arrang. | *Parking* Ample |
| *Ensuite bath/shower* 102 | *Room TV* Yes | *Last dinner* 10 | *Room service* All day |

**We publish annually,
so make sure you use the current edition.
It's worth it!**

REIGATE | La Barbe

R **Map 7 B5** Surrey
71 Bell Street
Reigate (0737) 241966

French cooking
Set L £13.75 **Set D** £22.50
About £40 *for two*
Seats 55 *Parties* 30
Parking Ample
Credit Access, Amex, Diners, Visa

The decor is simple but pleasing at this cheerful little bistro-style restaurant and the menus offer classic French dishes, confidently cooked. Starters might include puff pastry with mussels and truffle duxelles; main course could be lamb in garlic sauce or duck suprême with turnips and a celery sauce. Good selection of sweets to round off an enjoyable meal. Sound wines: try the Fleurie Château de Grand Pré (Ferraud) '86.

Lunch 12–2 *Dinner* 7–10, Sat 7 till 10.30
Closed L Mon, all Sun & Bank Hols

REIGATE | Bridge House Hotel 58% | £C/D

H **Map 7 B5** Surrey
Reigate Hill RH2 9RP
Reigate (0737) 246801
Telex 268810

Credit Access, Amex, Diners, Visa

In a fine position on Reigate Hill, this modern hotel overlooks the town. The relative strength of this place is the accommodation, all bedrooms being comfortable and well equipped, and most having little balconies to take best advantage of the views. Bathrooms are good, too, with tubs and powerful shower units (singles shower only). Public areas extend to an inviting bar and bright restaurant. No dogs. *Amenities* laundry service.

| *Rooms* 30 | *Direct dial* Yes | *Confirm by* arrang. | *Parking* Ample |
| *Ensuite bath/shower* 30 | *Room TV* Yes | *Last dinner* 10.30 | *Room service* Limited |

RENISHAW | Sitwell Arms Hotel 59% | £E

H **Map 11 D2** Derbyshire
Nr Eckington S31 9WE
Eckington (0246) 435226
Telex 547303

Credit Access, Amex, Diners, Visa

Management standards have been allowed to slide at this old stone inn, which is a pity because most of the staff are cheerful and public rooms comfortable and pleasantly refurbished. Bedrooms, in an extension, have darkwood fitted units and dark fabrics. Bathrooms (showers only in singles) are adequate. Good breakfasts are a plus. Avoid the two rooms opposite the entrance to the first-floor function room. *Amenities* garden, laundry service.

| *Rooms* 32 | *Direct dial* Yes | *Confirm by* 6 | *Parking* Ample |
| *Ensuite bath/shower* 32 | *Room TV* Yes | *Last dinner* 9.30 | *Room service* 24 hours |

RICHMOND | Lichfields | 🍴

R **Map 5 E2** Surrey
Lichfield Terrace
Sheen Road
01-940 5236

Set L £16.50
About £58 *for two*
Seats 40 *Parties* 40
Parking Limited
Credit Access, Visa

New chef-patron Gerald Haslegrave has made an impressive start at this striking restaurant in a modern parade of shops. Well-judged menus display his impressive talents to the full, with such sophisticated offerings as lobster and basil raviolis with shellfish butter sauce, barbary duck served with noodles and a delicious wild mushroom sauce, plus some truly stunning desserts and fine British farmhouse cheeses. 🍷

Lunch 12–2.30 *Dinner* 7–10.30
Closed L Sat, D Sun, all Mon, Bank Hols, & 1 wk Xmas

RICHMOND | Petersham Hotel   64% | £C

H **Map 5 E2** Surrey
Nightingale Lane,
Richmond Hill TW10 6RP
01-940 7471
Telex 928556

Credit Access, Amex, Diners, Visa

The best of the bedrooms at this imposing Victorian hotel enjoy views over a magnificent bend of the Thames between Richmond and Kingston. Most rooms have been totally refurbished with handsome darkwood pieces and pretty coordinated colour schemes that demonstrate the owner's daughter's flair for interior design; for many of the bathrooms there's a stylish new Italian look. The entrance hall – now with a marble floor – features a fine staircase, and there's an elegant lounge and bar. Staff are smart, friendly and efficient, and a full room service menu operates all day. No dogs.
Amenities garden, secretarial services, laundry service, 24 hour lounge service.

| *Rooms* 54 | *Direct dial* Yes | *Confirm by* arrang. | *Parking* Ample |
| *Ensuite bath/shower* 54 | *Room TV* Yes | *Last dinner* 9.45 | *Room service* All day |

RICHMOND | Richmond Gate Hotel   63% | £C/D

H **Map 5 E2** Surrey
Richmond Hill TW10 6RP
01-940 0061
Telex 928556
Credit Access, Amex, Diners, Visa
Closed 3 days Easter & 1 wk Xmas

A fine-looking Georgian hotel at the top of Richmond Hill. Public rooms have some character and personality, as in the charming lounge with its winged armchairs and numerous prints. Accommodation ranges from five large, handsome rooms in the main building to more modern rooms with nicely coordinated colour schemes and fabrics. No meals except breakfast. No dogs.
Amenities garden, secretarial services, fax, laundry service.

| *Rooms* 51 | *Direct dial* Yes | *Confirm by* 6 | *Parking* Ample |
| *Ensuite bath/shower* 51 | *Room TV* Yes | *Last dinner* None | *Room service* All day |

RICHMOND | Cannizaro House

See under LONDON

RICHMOND | Café Mamma

See under LONDON RESTAURANTS under £30

RIDGEWAY | The Old Vicarage   *NEW ENTRY*   ♨ ♀

R **Map 11 D2** Derbyshire
Ridgeway Moor, Nr Sheffield
Sheffield (0742) 475814

Set L Sun £11.50
Set D £15.50
About £55 for two
Seats 55 *Parties* 30
Parking Ample
Credit Access, Visa

Two acres of delightful gardens surround the charming old stone vicarage where Tessa Bramley and her team cook admirable meals. The ambitious menu contains inventive dishes, prepared with infinite care. Poached scallops with oysters in puff pastry is an excellent starter, with perhaps quails stuffed with lemon compote to follow. Desserts are delicious. Splendid cellar; note the superb Alsace wines of Rolly Gassmann. ▱ Outstanding ♀ Well-chosen ⊘

Lunch Sun 12.15–2.30, Mon-Sat by arrang.   *Dinner* 7–10
Closed D Sun & Mon, 2 wks from 27 Dec & last 2 wks Aug

 indicates a **well-chosen** house wine

RIPLEY | Michels' | ♀

R **Map 5 E3 Surrey**
Portsmouth Road
Guildford (0483) 224777

French cooking

Set L £12.50
Set D £12.50 except Sat
About £53 for two
Seats 50
Parties 12
Parking Limited

Credit Access, Amex, Diners, Visa

Erik Michel, artist turned chef, and his charming wife Karen have now completed restoring the original Georgian style of their restaurant. Erik's very reasonable fixed-price menus are interesting and imaginative; parcels of pasta filled with crab, and mussels served with saffron pasta garnished with beans, shallots and tomato are among the starters, and main courses range from lamb stuffed with ratatouille and goat cheese to venison with Madeira sauce garnished with sweet and sour red cabbage. Tempting sweets include a biscuit tulip filled with a velvety chocolate mousse. Fine wine list includes a Vosne Romanée (Henri Jayer) '81 and a Ch. Léoville Barton '70. ♀ Well-chosen ⊘

Lunch 12.30–2   *Dinner* 7.30–9, Sat 7–10
Closed L Sat, D Sun, all Mon & 26–30 Dec

Cooking in Italy . . .

consists of serving something exquisitely fresh,

with the least amount of modification

in the process of preparation.

ANONYMOUS
Cited in
THE TUSCAN COOKBOOK (1979)

Many excellent cooks

are spoilt by going into the arts.

PAUL GAUGUIN 1848-1903

In Cournos'
MODERN PLUTARCH

I don't see why people make
such a to-do about choosing a new cook.
There is only one thing that is absolutely essential.
I always ask at once, 'Do you drink?',
and if she says 'No!', I bow politely and say that I am
very sorry but I fear she will not suit.
All *good* cooks drink.

J. A. McNEILL WHISTLER 1834-1903
Attributed in
LIFE WAS WORTH LIVING

Some people have a foolish way of
not minding, or pretending not to mind what they eat.
For my part, I mind my belly very studiously,
and very carefully; for I look upon it, that he who does not
mind his belly, will hardly mind anything else.

SAMUEL JOHNSON 1709-84
Boswell's
LIFE OF JOHNSON

RIPON | Ripon Spa Hotel 62% | £E

H **Map 15 C6** North Yorkshire
Park Street HG4 2BU
Ripon (0765) 2172
Telex 57780

Credit Access, Amex, Diners, Visa

Most bedrooms at this Edwardian hotel have recently been refurbished, with pretty floral fabrics adding a fresh, bright look. Hairdryers, trouser presses, tea-makers and remote-control TVs are standard, and bathrooms are smartly tiled. Day rooms like the entrance hall, lounge and bars retain a traditional feel. The hotel stands in seven acres of well-tended grounds. Leisure centre planned for 1989.
Amenities garden, laundry service, children's play area.

Rooms 40	*Direct dial* Yes	*Confirm by* 6.	*Parking* Ample
Ensuite bath/shower 40	*Room TV* Yes	*Last dinner* 9.30	*Room service* 24 hours

**Changes in data sometimes occur in establishments
after the Guide goes to press.
Prices should be taken as indications rather than firm quotes.**

ROADE | Roadhouse Restaurant *NEW ENTRY* ⌐

R **Map 5 D1** Northamptonshire
16 High Street
Roade (0604) 863372

Set L £9
About £45 *for two*
Seats 32
Parties 36
Parking Ample
Credit Access, Amex, Visa

The pace is gentle and leisurely at the Kewleys' cottage roadhouse, a homely setting in which to enjoy Christopher's skilled, imaginative cooking. Our delightful meal began with flavourful celery and leek soup with lovely home-baked bread, followed by ravioli stuffed with a ham mousse, and the freshest brill filled with succulent spinach scented with sorrel in a superb lemon sauce. Excellent vegetables and delicious sweets. Good, selective wine list. 🍷 Well-chosen 🕯

Lunch 12–2   *Dinner* 7–10
Closed L Sat, all Sun, Bank Hol Mons, 1 wk Xmas & 2 wks Aug

ROBERTSBRIDGE | Bough House ⌐

R **Map 7 B6** East Sussex
43 High Street
Robertsbridge (0580) 880440

Set L £7.50
Set D £12.50
About £37 *for two*
Seats 30 *Parties* 25
Parking Ample
Credit Access, Amex, Diners, Visa

John and Martine Taylor are working wonders at this cosy beamed restaurant. Martine is the charmingly Gallic hostess, John the enthusiastic and very competent chef. Interesting, monthly-changing menus include enjoyable dishes like veal and bacon terrine and guinea fowl in red wine as well as real triumphs like saddle of venison served with a delicate orange and redcurrant sauce. Desserts might feature an excellent chocolate bavarois. ❤

Lunch 12–1.30   *Dinner* 7–10.30
Closed L Sat & Mon, all Sun, 1 wk Feb & 1 wk Sept

ROCHESTER | Crest Hotel 62% | £C

H **Map 7 B5** Kent
Rochester Airport,
Maidstone Road ME5 9SF
Medway (0634) 687111
Telex 965933

Credit Access, Amex, Diners, Visa

A well-run modern hotel offering comfortable, unpretentious accommodation. The spacious public areas include a pleasant bar with rattan furniture and quiet, intimate corners. Bedrooms are well-designed and have modern units and simple decor. Room prices are negotiable at quiet times, especially weekends. *Amenities* garden, croquet, in-house movies, secretarial services, fax, laundry service, 24-hour lounge service, nanny, children's play area (weekends). ♿

Rooms 105	*Direct dial* Yes	*Confirm by* 6	*Parking* Ample
Ensuite bath/shower 105	*Room TV* Yes	*Last dinner* 10, Sun 9.30	*Room service* Limited

ROCKLEY | Loaves & Fishes ⌐

R **Map 4 C2** Wiltshire
Rockley Chapel
Nr Marlborough
Marlborough (0672) 53737

Set L £15.50
Set D £16.50
About £34 *for two*
Seats 28 *Parties* 10
Parking Ample

A converted Victorian chapel is the setting for Angela Rawson's enjoyable cooking, and wild flowers, candlelight and classical music create a pleasant, relaxing ambience. Her set menu changes daily, and starters like curried egg mayonnaise or avocado and lovage mousse could precede the single main course choice, perhaps chicken in a champagne and lemon sauce. Simple sweets, fairly ordinary cheeses, home-baked bread, no licence (take your own wine).

Lunch Sun only 12.30–1.15   *Dinner* 7.30–8.30
Closed D Sun, all Mon & Tues, Bank Hols, 31 Dec & 3 wks Jan

ROMALDKIRK   Rose & Crown Hotel   £E

Map 15 B5 Co. Durham
Nr Barnard Castle DL12 9EB
Teesdale (0833) 50213

Credit Access, Amex, Diners, Visa

Right next door to the ancient village church, this lovely old stone inn has welcomed travellers since the 18th century. Beams, horse brasses and a stag's head lend plenty of character to the two lively bars. Bedrooms in the original building (including three impressive suites) are traditional in style; those in a courtyard annexe are more modern. All have tea-makers and private bath/shower.
Amenities laundry service.

Rooms 11	*Direct dial* Yes	*Confirm by* arrang.	*Parking* Ample
Ensuite bath/shower 11	*Room TV* Yes	*Last dinner* 9	*Room service* Limited

ROMSEY   Old Manor House ★

Map 4 C3 Hampshire
21 Palmerston Street
Romsey (0794) 517353

Lunch 12–2
Dinner 7–9.30
Set L from £7.95
Set D £21
About £50 *for two*
Seats 45
Parties 24
Parking Limited

Credit Access, Visa
Closed D Sun, all Mon, last 3 wks
Aug & 1 wk Xmas

Old-world charm combines with modern cooking to splendid effect at this delightful 16th-century house, where chef-patron Mauro Bregoli smokes his own meats in the giant open fireplace. Game dominates the short, tempting menus in winter, fish in summer, with typical offerings including wonderfully aromatic lobster bisque, entrecôte steak served with three mustard sauces and red bream sauced with sorrel. Excellent sweets and cheeses to finish. A good rather than great cellar. The list of clarets and burgundies is more impressive for length than for quality. *Specialities* home-made green and white noodles, marinated venison with onion confit and spiced fruit, turbot with cream and chive sauce, mousse aux fruits composés. 🍷 Well-chosen ℮

ROMSEY   White Horse Hotel   63%   £C/D

Map 4 C3 Hampshire
Market Place SO5 8ZJ
Romsey (0794) 512431

Credit Access, Amex, Diners, Visa

Parts of this town-centre hotel predate the smart Georgian facade, the oldest being the Elizabethan lounge with old beams and murals and a mellow brick fireplace. There's a second lounge, and a little bar. Bedrooms in the main building have smart Italian furniture and quite stylish coordinating fabrics, plus fully tiled modern bathrooms. Seven rooms, larger but a little less attractive, are in a motel-style annexe.
Amenities garden, laundry service.

Rooms 33	*Room phone* Yes	*Confirm by* 6	*Parking* Ample
Ensuite bath/shower 33	*Room TV* Yes	*Last dinner* 9.45	*Room service* All day

ROSEDALE ABBEY   Milburn Arms Hotel   £E/F

Map 15 C5 North Yorkshire
Nr Pickering YO18 8RA
Lastingham (075 15) 312

Credit Access, Visa

A new extension has added eight bedrooms to this charming inn. All are individually styled, with antique pine furniture (plus one oak four-poster) and pretty floral drapes. The original rooms have been refurbished and all now have en suite facilities. Public rooms include a homely lounge with comfy sofas and piles of books, and a bar that doubles as the village local.
Amenities garden, games room, satellite TV.

Rooms 14	*Room phone* No	*Confirm by* arrang.	*Parking* Ample
Ensuite bath/shower 14	*Room TV* Yes	*Last dinner* 9	*Room service* Limited

ROSS-ON-WYE   Chase Hotel   59%   £C/D

Map 4 B1
Hereford & Worcester
Gloucester Road HR9 5LH
Ross-on-Wye (0989) 763161
Telex 35658

Credit Access, Amex, Diners, Visa

Major refurbishment is under way at this characterful Victorian mansion, peacefully set in extensive grounds yet only a few minutes' walk from the town centre. An elegant white portico frames the entrance to the columned hall, which in turn leads to a comfortable lounge and spacious bar. Main-house bedrooms are larger than those in the wing; bathrooms throughout are being smartly upgraded. No dogs. *Amenities* garden, secretarial services, fax, laundry service.

Rooms 41	*Direct dial* Yes	*Confirm by* 6	*Parking* Ample
Ensuite bath/shower 41	*Room TV* Yes	*Last dinner* 9.45	*Room service* 24 hours

ROSS-ON-WYE Pengethley Manor Hotel 65% £C

H **Map 4 B1**
Hereford & Worcester
Harewood End HR9 6LL
Harewood End (098 987) 211
Telex 35332

Credit Access, Amex, Diners, Visa

This magnolia-coloured Georgian building is set in attractive grounds on the A49, north of Ross. Original panelling graces the entrance hall and the library and main-house bedrooms are handsomely proportioned and traditionally appointed. There are some smaller, cottagey rooms in the annexe, and two newly converted courtyard suites. *Amenities* garden, outdoor swimming pool, pitch & putt, croquet, snooker, secretarial services, laundry service. ♿

| *Rooms* 20 | *Direct dial* Yes | *Confirm by* arrang. | *Parking* Ample |
| *Ensuite bath/shower* 20 | *Room TV* Yes | *Last dinner* 9.30 | *Room service* All day |

ROTHERHAM Rotherham Moat House 73% £E

H **Map 11 D2** South Yorkshire
Moorgate Road S60 2BG
Rotherham (0709) 364902
Telex 547810

Rooms 64
Ensuite bath/shower 64
Direct dial Yes
Room TV Yes
Confirm by 6
Last dinner 9.45
Parking Ample
Room service 24 hours

Credit Access, Amex, Diners, Visa

Just south of the town centre on the A618 you will find comfortable, relaxing accommodation at this attractive modern hotel. An air of elegance pervades the public rooms: a fountain enlivens the foyer, the open-plan lounge area has smartly contemporary upholstered cane chairs and sofas, and the Pavilion Bar features an unusual tented ceiling. Bedrooms have deep carpeting, co-ordinating fabrics and free-

standing darkwood or white furniture; tea-makers, trouser presses, hairdryers and mini-bars are all standard. Bathrooms are small but fully tiled and well provided with toiletries.
Amenities garden, sauna, solarium, whirlpool bath, keep-fit equipment, pool table, in-house movies, secretarial services, laundry service.

ROTHERWICK Tylney Hall Hotel 81% £C

HR **Map 5 D3** Hampshire
Nr Hook,
Basingstoke RG27 9AJ
Hook (025 672) 4881
Telex 859864

Rooms 90
Ensuite bath/shower 90
Direct dial Yes
Room TV Yes
Confirm by arrang.
Last dinner 9.30
Parking Ample
Room service 24 hours

Credit Access, Amex, Diners, Visa

Excellent service is a major plus at this mellow mansion set in 66 acres of lovely landscaped grounds. The richly panelled entrance hall with its black-and-white chequered marble floor sets the striking tone for equally impressive day rooms like the Italianate lounge (which features a gilded carved oak ceiling) and wonderfully restful Grey lounge. Spacious, comfortable bedrooms (including new rooms in the

stylishly converted stable blocks) boast handsome reproduction furnishings and luxurious carpeted bathrooms. No dogs. *Amenities* garden, indoor & outdoor swimming pools, sauna, whirlpool bath, gymnasium, tennis, croquet, clay-pigeon shooting, coarse fishing, boating, snooker, secretarial service, fax, laundry service.

Restaurant ♨♨

Set L from £9
Set D £19
About £70 for two
Seats 84
Parties 40

Stephen Hine presents an imaginative and appealing selection of modern dishes at this elegant glass-domed restaurant. Top-quality ingredients are handled with assurance and sauces are particularly fine: note hot asparagus spears served in puff pastry with carrot purée and a deliciously light almond butter sauce, baked sea bass and mussels with saffron sauce and English lamb presented on a basil cream sauce. Delectable desserts. ♀ Well-chosen ⊘

Lunch 12.30–2.30, Sun 12–3
Dinner 7.30–9.30, Sat 7.30–10

**If we recommend meals in a Hotel or Inn,
a separate entry is made for its restaurant.**

ROTHLEY　　　　Rothley Court　68%　　　£D/E

H Map 11 D3 Leicestershire
Westfield Lane LE7 7LG
Leicester (0533) 374141

Credit Access, Amex, Diners, Visa

A lovely old manor house in an utterly romantic landscaped setting. Carved panelling, polished wood floor, leather armchairs and ticking grandfather clock all contribute to the appeal of the coffee lounge, and there's a comfortable bar and splendid drinks terrace. Bedrooms range from functional and modern (in the stable block) to sumptuous and atmospheric (in the main house) and bathrooms are equally varied. *Amenities* garden, fax, laundry service.

Rooms 35	*Direct dial* Yes	*Confirm by* arrang.	*Parking* Ample
Ensuite bath/shower 32	*Room TV* Yes	*Last dinner* 9.30	*Room service* 24 hours

ROWSLEY　　　　Peacock Hotel　65%　　　£D

H Map 10 C2 Derbyshire
Nr Matlock DE4 2EB
Matlock (0629) 733518

Credit Access, Amex, Diners, Visa

There's plenty of atmosphere at this stone-mullioned 17th-century establishment. Antique tables and settles in the lounge are complemented by well-chosen sofas and armchairs, while the bar, with its exposed stone walls and ancient timbers, boasts 'Mousey Thompson' oak tables. Bedrooms in the main house have stylish fabrics and plenty of antiques; those in a separate building have Stag furniture and more ordinary decor. *Amenities* garden, game fishing.

Rooms 20	*Direct dial* Yes	*Confirm by* 6	*Parking* Ample
Ensuite bath/shower 15	*Room TV* Yes	*Last dinner* 9	*Room service* 24 hours

★　For a *discount* on next year's guide, see **An Offer for Answers**.　★

RUCKHALL　　　The Ancient Camp Inn　*NEW ENTRY*　　£F

I Map 4 A1
Hereford & Worcester
Nr Eaton Bishop, Hereford
HR2 9QX
Golden Valley (0981) 250449

Credit Access, Visa

A most delightful little country inn in a position of remarkable natural beauty above the river Wye. The setting is not only scenic but particularly quiet and secluded, though Hereford is only five miles away. The bars are cosily rustic, and there's a lovely terrace with sweeping views of the river, and an upstairs lounge with plenty of reading material. The three comfortable bedrooms are prettily decorated and spotlessly kept; two have modern shower rooms, the third (really a mini-suite) a well-equipped bathroom. No children under eight. No dogs. *Amenities* garden, coarse & game fishing.

Rooms 3	*Room phone* Yes	*Confirm by* arrang.	*Parking* Ample
Ensuite bath/shower 3	*Room TV* Yes	*Last dinner* 9.30	*Room service* Limited

RUGBY　　　　Three Horse Shoes Hotel　56%　　　£E

H Map 11 D4 Warwickshire
Sheep Street CV21 3BX
Rugby (0788) 544585
Telex 311794

Credit Access, Amex, Diners, Visa

Period touches like beams and oak panelling lend charm to an 18th-century inn set in a modern shopping precinct. Day rooms are on a fairly small scale, offering only reasonable comfort, while bedrooms have the practical appeal of modern fitted furniture, trouser presses, hairdryers and even telephones in some of the bathrooms. A hotel of potential which needs some money spent on it. *Amenities* in-house movies, laundry service.

Rooms 31	*Direct dial* Yes	*Confirm by* 6	*Parking* Limited
Ensuite bath/shower 29	*Room TV* Yes	*Last dinner* 10	*Room service* 24 hours

RUNCORN　　　　Crest Hotel　62%　　　£C

H Map 10 A2 Cheshire
Wood Lane, Beechwood
WA7 3HA
Runcorn (0928) 714000
Telex 627426

Credit Access, Amex, Diners, Visa

Proximity to the M56 and extensive conference facilities make this modern hotel popular with business clientele. A fish pond and greenery enliven the foyer and the two bars are tastefully furnished. Bedrooms have neat fitted units, coordinating fabrics and compact bathrooms; some are for non-smokers and there are six Lady Crest rooms. *Amenities* garden, games room, pool table, in-house movies, secretarial services, fax, laundry service, 24-hour lounge service, helipad.

Rooms 127	*Direct dial* Yes	*Confirm by* 6	*Parking* Ample
Ensuite bath/shower 127	*Room TV* Yes	*Last dinner* 9.45	*Room service* Limited

RUSPER | Ghyll Manor 71% | £C/D

H Map 5 E3 West Sussex
High Street,
Nr Horsham RH12 4PX
Rusper (029 384) 571
Telex 877557

Rooms 28
Ensuite bath/shower 28
Direct dial Yes
Room TV Yes
Confirm by 6
Last dinner 9.30
Parking Ample
Room service 24 hours

Credit Access, Amex, Diners, Visa

Well tended lawns, fine specimen trees, a lake and a cloistered courtyard provide a charming setting for this fine Elizabethan manor house. It's easy to unwind in the cosy library-lounge, panelled in limed oak, or enjoy a quiet drink in the little cocktail bar overlooking the garden. There are eight period-style bedrooms in the main house. The rest are in various extensions; some of the nicest, with modern furniture and pretty fabrics, are in the stable block. All rooms have many thoughtful extras, and bathrooms, too, are well equipped. Staff could be more welcoming and attentive.
Amenities garden, outdoor swimming pool, sauna, solarium, tennis, croquet, riding, fax, laundry service.

RYDE | Hotel Ryde Castle 57% | £C/D

H Map 5 D4 Isle of Wight
Esplanade PO33 1JA
Ryde (0983) 63755

Credit Access, Visa

There's no mistaking the crenellated battlements of this creeper-clad hotel on the seafront with splendid views across the Solent. Plenty of red plush strikes a cheerful note in the public areas, which include a popular lounge. Pretty pink bedrooms – all doubles with modern four-posters – have double glazing, hairdryers, and direct-dial telephones.
Amenities garden, in-house movies.

| Rooms 17 | Direct dial Yes | Confirm by 6 | Parking Ample |
| Ensuite bath/shower 17 | Room TV Yes | Last dinner 9.45 | Room service All day |

RYE | George Hotel 61% | £C/D

H Map 7 C6 East Sussex
High Street TN31 7JP
Rye (0797) 222114

Credit Access, Amex, Diners, Visa

The Georgian facade fronts a 400-year-old coaching inn at the centre of a popular tourist town. Oak beams characterise the foyer and public bar, and there's a roomy residents' lounge, a little cocktail lounge and – surprising in a small hotel – a rather splendid galleried ballroom. Bedrooms of various shapes and sizes are all thoughtfully equipped and the more dated rooms are to be revamped.
Amenities laundry service.

| Rooms 16 | Direct dial Yes | Confirm by 6 | Parking Limited |
| Ensuite bath/shower 16 | Room TV Yes | Last dinner 9 | Room service All day |

RYE | Landgate Bistro | ♙

R Map 7 C6 East Sussex
5 Landgate
Rye (0797) 222829

About £34 for two
Seats 34
Parties 38
Parking Ample

Credit Access, Amex, Diners, Visa

Popular bistro with good interesting food and swift service. Local produce features strongly on the seasonally changing menu. Typical dishes run from watercress soup, artichoke hollandaise, garlicky braised squid to hearty fish stew, tarragon-sauced chicken, liver with apple juice and beef in pastry with sauce béarnaise. Home-made ices and other good puds. Note Moulin à Vent (Ferraud) '85 and Ch. Labégorce-Zédé Margaux '83 on a good wine list. ℰ
Dinner only 7–9.30
Closed Sun, Mon, Bank Hols, 2 wks Oct, 1 wk Xmas & 1 wk June

RYE | Mermaid Inn 60% | £D

H Map 7 C6 East Sussex
Mermaid Street TN31 7EU
Rye (0797) 223065
Telex 957141

Credit Access, Amex, Diners, Visa

A Tudor half-timbered facade, Norman cellars and a history of smuggling connections give this ancient building a unique charm. Sloping floors and deep armchairs contribute to the warm, romantic feel. Bedrooms boast antique furniture, including richly carved four-posters, and attractive drapes frame leaded windows. Most have en suite bathrooms, six with shower only. No under eights. No dogs.
Amenities secretarial services, laundry service.

| Rooms 28 | Direct dial Yes | Confirm by 6 | Parking Limited |
| Ensuite bath/shower 25 | Room TV No | Last dinner 9.15 | Room service 24 hours |

SAFFRON WALDEN　　Saffron Hotel　59%　　　　　£E

HR Map 6 B3 Essex
High Street CB10 1AY
Saffron Walden (0799) 22676
Telex 81653

Credit Access, Visa

Three separate buildings, the oldest dating from about 1600, were merged into this town-centre hotel, which the Craddock family run with great warmth and style. Bedrooms, not surprisingly, come in various shapes and sizes, but all are pleasant and comfortable, and the beamed attic rooms have lots of character. There's a convivial lounge-bar (note the collection of old bottles) and a pretty, flowery patio. *Amenities* laundry service.

| Rooms 21 | Direct dial Yes | Confirm by 6 | Parking Limited |
| Ensuite bath/shower 16 | Room TV Yes | Last dinner 9.30 | Room service Limited |

Restaurant　　　　　　　　　　♀

Set L & D £12.95, Sun L £9.95
About £40 for two
Seats 28
Parties 18

The dining room is cosily appointed, and local ladies serve in friendly fashion. The food is decent, fresh and well prepared, and you won't go far wrong with straightforward dishes like chicken noodle and saffron soup, grilled sole with parsley butter and sirloin steak served either sauced or plain with tomatoes and mushrooms or topped with Stilton. Bread and butter pudding is an excellent choice among a good variety of sweets. ☺

Lunch 12–2　*Dinner* 7–9.30
Closed L Sat, D Sun & all Bank Hols

ST ALBANS　　　　Noke Thistle Hotel　75%　　　　£C

H Map 5 E2 Hertfordshire
Watford Road AL2 3DS
St Albans (0727) 54252
Telex 893834

Rooms 57
Ensuite bath/shower 57
Direct dial Yes
Room TV Yes
Confirm by 6
Last dinner 10
Parking Ample
Room service 24 hours

Credit Access, Amex, Diners, Visa

A white-painted early Victorian house, The Noke enjoys excellent motorway connections: it's just north of junction 6 of the M1 and junction 21A of the M25. It's still scoring points for a recent major refurbishment in which – among other things – the lounge and bar were elegantly redesigned, using prettily coordinated fabrics and comfortable traditional furniture. Neat, compact bedrooms have smart pastel decor and  darkwood units, plus remote-control teletext TVs, hairdryers, tea-makers and trouser presses; well-fitted bathrooms provide towelling robes and bathtime luxuries. There's also a stylish American themed bar-cum-coffee shop. *Amenities* garden, in-house movies, secretarial services, fax, laundry service, coffee shop (9am–9pm).

ST ALBANS　　　　St Michael's Manor Hotel　63%　　£D

H Map 5 E2 Hertfordshire
Fishpool Street AL3 4RY
St Albans (0727) 64444

Credit Access, Amex, Diners, Visa
Closed 27–30 Dec

Terraced gardens and an ornamental lake provide a peaceful outlook for this much extended manor house. Public rooms are mainly traditional in character, though the cosy bar has a more contemporary feel. Neat, attractively decorated bedrooms (four with four-posters and most with smart darkwood furniture) have hairdryers, trouser presses and remote-control TV. Modern bathrooms, seven with shower only. *Amenities* garden, secretarial services, laundry service.

| Rooms 26 | Direct dial Yes | Confirm by arrang. | Parking Ample |
| Ensuite bath/shower 26 | Room TV Yes | Last dinner 8.30 (Sat 9) | Room service 24 hours |

ST ALBANS　　　　Sopwell House Hotel　65%　　　　£D

H Map 5 E2 Hertfordshire
Cottonmill Lane AL1 2HQ
St Albans (0727) 64477

Credit Access, Amex, Diners, Visa

A converted 18th-century house standing in pleasant, mature grounds off the A1081 (best to check directions). Eye-catching public areas include a fountained inner hall and a splendid conservatory that contains a fine sunken lounge, a little bar and a restaurant (where our breakfast was a big let-down). Bedrooms, though not large, are comfortable and quite stylish; eight have four-posters. *Amenities* garden, croquet, laundry service.

| Rooms 32 | Direct dial Yes | Confirm by arrang. | Parking Ample |
| Ensuite bath/shower 32 | Room TV Yes | Last dinner 10 | Room service 24 hours |

ST AUSTELL — White Hart Hotel £F

Map 2 B3 Cornwall
Church Street PL25 4AT
St Austell (0726) 72100

Credit Access, Amex, Diners, Visa
Closed 25 & 26 Dec

Originally the family home of a local landowner, this greystone hostelry in the centre of town offers pleasant, homely accommodation. Cosily traditional public rooms include a comfortable lounge and two bars. Most of the bedrooms are simply furnished, but two have been attractively upgraded. Planned refurbishment will include the installation of en suite facilities; at present some rooms have foldaway showers. *Amenities* laundry service.

Rooms 20	*Room phone* No	*Confirm by* arrang.	*Parking* Difficult
Ensuite bath/shower 6	*Room TV* Yes	*Last dinner* 8.30	*Room service* All day

**We welcome bona fide complaints and recommendations
on the tear-out pages at the back of the book for readers' comment.
They are followed up by our professional team.**

ST IVES — Slepe Hall Hotel 63% £E

Map 6 B2 Cambridgeshire
Ramsey Road PE17 4RB
St Ives (0480) 63122

Credit Access, Amex, Diners, Visa

Closed 25 & 26 Dec

The Stapletons obviously enjoy running this welcoming little hotel in a former Victorian girls' school. Public rooms have pretty floral decor and the cosy bar is ideal for a quiet drink. Good-size bedrooms with sitting areas include some with brass or four-poster beds. Most have private bathrooms with pine accessories. Good breakfasts served with a smile.
Amenities garden, fax, laundry service.

Rooms 13	*Room phone* Yes	*Confirm by* arrang.	*Parking* Ample
Ensuite bath/shower 9	*Room TV* Yes	*Last dinner* 9.45	*Room service* All day

ST IVES — Boskerris Hotel 58% £D/E

Map 2 A3 Cornwall
Carbis Bay TR26 2NQ
Penzance (0736) 795295

Credit Diners, Visa
Closed Oct–Easter

New owners have brightened up this neat, homely hotel overlooking the sea, the most obvious improvements being new carpets in the public areas and redecoration of the bedrooms. Most of the rooms have compact bathrooms en suite, and the best enjoy sea views. These views are shared by the comfortable lounge/cocktail bar, while another room provides views for TV-watchers.
Amenities garden, outdoor swimming pool, putting, games room.

Rooms 19	*Room phone* No	*Confirm by* arrang.	*Parking* Ample
Ensuite bath/shower 15	*Room TV* No	*Last dinner* 8	*Room service* Limited

ST IVES — Garrack Hotel 61% £D/E

Map 2 A3 Cornwall
Burthallan Lane TR26 3AA
Penzance (0736) 796199

Credit Access, Amex, Diners, Visa

Well-tended gardens and magnificent sea views enhance this creeper-clad hotel overlooking St Ives. Day rooms full of books, games and ornaments are bright and homely. Bedrooms in the original house are traditionally furnished and vary in size; those in a modern extension are spacious, with en suite bathrooms and sea views.
Amenities garden, indoor swimming pool, sauna, solarium, whirlpool bath, laundry service, coffee shop (11am–10pm).

Rooms 21	*Direct dial* Yes	*Confirm by* arrang.	*Parking* Ample
Ensuite bath/shower 14	*Room TV* Yes	*Last dinner* 8.30	*Room service* Limited

ST IVES — Tregenna Castle Hotel 65% £C/D

Map 2 A3 Cornwall
TR26 2DE
Penzance (0736) 795254
Telex 45128

Credit Access, Amex, Diners, Visa

A miniature castle perched high above the bay and offering excellent leisure facilities. Public rooms include several spacious lounges and a cheerful cocktail bar. Best bedrooms have white fitted furniture, sitting areas and sea views; others are more modest. Bathrooms are adequate, with old-fashioned suites and lino floors. *Amenities* garden, outdoor swimming pool, tennis, squash, badminton, golf course, putting, croquet, pool table, secretarial services, laundry service.

Rooms 82	*Direct dial* Yes	*Confirm by* 6	*Parking* Ample
Ensuite bath/shower 69	*Room TV* Yes	*Last dinner* 9	*Room service* Limited

ST KEVERNE   The Laden Table   *NEW ENTRY*   ♀

R **Map 2 B3** Cornwall
St Keverne (0326) 280090

Set D £15.50
About £40 for two
Seats 30
Parking Ample

Tony Gulliford's latest Laden Table (he had one in Bath a few years back) is a cottagy restaurant with plastered stone walls and simple, attractive wooden tables. Local girls serve dinner, three courses offering a regularly changing variety of tempting dishes, from cucumber fritters and Provençal fish soup to pork with prunes, sauté of guinea fowl and rib of beef for two. Home-made ices among the sweets. ⊖

Dinner 7.30–9.30
Closed Sun, Mon, Tue, 28 Mar–30 May & mid-Nov–Mar

We publish annually,
so make sure you use the current edition.
It's worth it!

ST MARGARET'S AT CLIFFE   Wallett's Court   57%   £F

HR **Map 7 D5** Kent
West Cliffe, Dover
CT15 6EW
Dover (0304) 852424

Closed 3 days Xmas

Peace and comfort surround guests at this lovingly restored 17th-century manor house where Chris and Lea Oakley offer the warmest welcome imaginable. The spacious lounge boasts carved oak beams, an inglenook fireplace and antique furniture. Bedrooms in the main house have mahogany-style units, those in the converted barn modern pine furniture; all are equipped with many thoughtful extras. No dogs. *Amenities* garden, games room, laundry service.

Rooms 7	*Room phone* No	*Confirm by* arrang.	*Parking* Ample
Ensuite bath/shower 7	*Room TV* Yes	*Last dinner* 9	*Room service* Limited

Restaurant   ♀

Set D £15.50, Sat £22
About £38 for two, Sat about £50
Seats 30
Parties 30

The restaurant is mainly for residents, with the exception of private parties and gourmet dinners on Saturday evenings. A unique atmosphere prevails, induced by the baronial setting of oak beams, whitewashed walls and sturdy oak tables. Chris Oakley's cooking is equally unpretentious and he uses excellent local produce to create some stunning dishes. Good short wine list: Muscadet Soleil Nantais '86, Ch. La Croix Pomerol '79. 🍷 Well-chosen ⊖

Lunch Sun only by arrang.   *Dinner* 7–9, Sat at 8
Closed L Mon–Sat, D Sun & 3 days Xmas

ST MARY'S   Hotel Godolphin   60%   £D

H **Map 2 A2** Isles of Scilly
(Cornwall) Church Street
TR21 0JR
Scillonia (0720) 22316

Credit Access, Visa
Closed mid Oct–mid Mar

Mr & Mrs Mumford are approaching 20 years at their well-kept holiday hotel, whose attractions include a pretty, sub-tropical garden. A friendly feeling is all around, and the little bar is a particularly cheerful spot; the lounge features a fireplace in Italian marble, and there's a delightful conservatory. Bedrooms, most with private facilities, are in simple, modern style. Half-board terms only. No dogs. *Amenities* garden, sauna, games room.

Rooms 31	*Direct dial* Yes	*Confirm by* arrang.	*Parking* No cars
Ensuite bath/shower 27	*Room TV* Yes	*Last dinner* 8	*Room service* Limited

---

ST MARY'S   Tregarthen's Hotel   60%   £D

H **Map 2 A2** Isles of Scilly
(Cornwall) TR21 0PP
Scillonia (0720) 22540

Credit Access, Amex, Diners, Visa
Closed 1 Nov–mid Mar

A well-managed holiday hotel in a position overlooking the harbour and boasting sea views from most of the bedrooms and from the sun lounge section of the spacious lounge-reception. Bedrooms have lightwood Scandinavian furniture, candlewick bedspreads and bucket chairs; those without en suite facilities share several clean and functional public bathrooms. All have tea-makers and clock radios. Half-board only. No dogs. *Amenities* garden.

Rooms 33	*Direct dial* Yes	*Confirm by* 7	*Parking* Limited
Ensuite bath/shower 26	*Room TV* Yes	*Last dinner* 8, Sat 8.45	*Room service* All day

ST MAWES   Idle Rocks Hotel   62%   £C/D

H **Map 2 B4** Cornwall
Tredenham Road TR2 5AN
St Mawes (0326) 270771

Credit Access, Amex, Diners, Visa
Closed Nov–early Mar

In the centre of St Mawes, the Idle Rocks enjoys a super setting alongside the harbour, and the long terrace is a fine place to soak up the sun and drink in the views. The hotel generally is cosy, relaxed and well kept, both in the traditional lounge and intimate cocktail bar, and in the light, airy bedrooms, all of which are named after sea birds. Half-board terms only. No children under six.
Amenities terrace.

Rooms 24	*Room phone* No	*Confirm by* 5	*Parking* Difficult
Ensuite bath/shower 22	*Room TV* Yes	*Last dinner* 9.15	*Room service* None

ST MAWES   Rising Sun Inn   62%   £D/E

H **Map 2 B4** Cornwall
The Square TR2 5DJ
St Mawes (0326) 270233

Credit Access, Amex, Diners, Visa

Harbour views and a flower-filled terrace add to the charms of this friendly, well-run inn. The main bar is a popular meeting place for local people and has a warm and lively atmosphere. For residents who favour a quieter, more peaceful place to relax, there's also a comfortable lounge. Smallish bedrooms have soft colour schemes, traditional furniture and tea-making facilities. No children under nine.
Amenities terrace, laundry service.

Rooms 12	*Direct dial* Yes	*Confirm by* arrang.	*Parking* Difficult
Ensuite bath/shower 9	*Room TV* Yes	*Last dinner* 9	*Room service* All day

ST MAWES   Hotel Tresanton   69%   £C

H **Map 2 B4** Cornwall
Lower Castle Road TR2 5DR
St Mawes (0326) 270544
Telex 45117
Credit Access, Amex, Diners, Visa
Closed Nov–Mar (exc. 1 wk Xmas)

A white-painted hotel with a splendid sun terrace and sub-tropical garden. The foyer-lounge is in the original house, while other day rooms are in a separate building, elevated to give fine views. Bedrooms, mainly of a good size, are comfortable and well maintained; they have light colour schemes, pretty fabrics and period-style furniture. Seven bathrooms are en suite, the rest are opposite their bedrooms. No children under ten. *Amenities* garden.

Rooms 21	*Direct dial* Yes	*Confirm by* arrang.	*Parking* Ample
Ensuite bath/shower 7	*Room TV* Yes	*Last dinner* 9	*Room service* All day

**Our inspectors *never* book in the name of Egon Ronay's Guides.
They disclose their identity only if they are considering an establishment
for inclusion in the next edition of the Guide.**

SALCOMBE   Marine Hotel   69%   £C/D

H **Map 3 D3** Devon
Cliff Road TQ8 8JH
Salcombe (054 884) 2251
Telex 42513

Credit Access, Amex, Diners, Visa

Sweeping views over the estuary give a bright and airy feel to this comfortable waterside hotel, where stylishly modern public areas include an attractive lounge decorated in restful pinks and greens. Simply furnished bedrooms provide thoughtful extras like mineral water, fresh fruit and flowers. No dogs. *Amenities* garden, indoor swimming pool, sauna, solarium, whirlpool bath, keep-fit equipment, beauty salon, hairdressing, games room, fax, laundry service. &

Rooms 51	*Direct dial* Yes	*Confirm by* arrang.	*Parking* Ample
Ensuite bath/shower 51	*Room TV* Yes	*Last dinner* 9.30	*Room service* 24 hours

SALCOMBE   Soar Mill Cove Hotel   65%   £E

HR **Map 3 D3** Devon
Soar Mill Cove TQ7 3DS
Kingsbridge (0548) 561566

Credit Access, Visa
Closed 29 Dec–14 Feb

In a remote and beautiful setting down country lanes, this modern hotel has welcoming owners (Keith and Norma Makepeace) and first-class staff. Picture windows provide splendid sea views in the relaxing day rooms, and bedrooms – many with private terraces – are light, bright and well looked after, with modern furnishings and thickly carpeted bathrooms. Good breakfasts. *Amenities* garden, indoor & outdoor swimming pools, tennis, putting, games room, laundry service.

Rooms 14	*Direct dial* Yes	*Confirm by* arrang.	*Parking* Ample
Ensuite bath/shower 14	*Room TV* Yes	*Last dinner* 9.30	*Room service* All day

see over

Soar Mill Cove Restaurant

Set D £19
About £48 for two
Seats 40

A pleasant restaurant offering enjoyable cooking and capable, friendly service. Fixed-price dinner menus include such tasty dishes as yoghurt-dressed chicken liver salad, crab and lobster bisque, brill and prawns with fennel and fillet of pork with walnuts and Roquefort sauce. The sweet trolley displays tempting goodies like gâteau Pithiviers, flummery and strawberry cheesecake. Local and English cheeses. Lighter lunches. No smoking. 🍷 Well-chosen ⊖

Lunch 12–2.30   *Dinner* 7.30–9.30
Closed 29 Dec–14 Feb

SALCOMBE   South Sands Hotel   63%   £C/D

H Map 3 D3 Devon
South Sands TQ8 8LL
Salcombe (054 884) 3741

Credit Access, Amex, Diners, Visa

A modern hotel right on the beach. Public areas are bright and roomy, with fine views of the bay. Bedrooms, too, are of a good size, and family suites have lounges with balconies. Friendly owners and staff create a pleasant, relaxed atmosphere.
Amenities indoor swimming pool, solarium, whirlpool bath, steam room, sea fishing, mooring, hotel boat, in-house movies, laundry service, coffee shop (noon–8pm, 9pm high season).

Rooms 29	*Direct dial* Yes	*Confirm by* arrang.	*Parking* Ample
Ensuite bath/shower 29	*Room TV* Yes	*Last dinner* 9.30	*Room service* All day

---

SALCOMBE   Tides Reach Hotel   72%   £B

H Map 3 D3 Devon
South Sands TQ8 8LJ
Salcombe (054 884) 3466

Rooms 42
Ensuite bath/shower 42
Direct dial Yes
Room TV Yes
Confirm by arrang.
Last dinner 10
Parking Ample
Room service All day

Credit Access, Amex, Diners, Visa
Closed Nov–early Mar

Splendid views, excellent leisure facilities and friendly staff are some of the attractions of the Tides Reach, which sits in a delightful cove by the beach. Day rooms, including a lovely sun lounge, have an elegant, relaxing feel, and picture windows make the most of the picturesque setting. Bedrooms, many with private balconies, are light, bright and spacious, with seating areas and carpeted bathrooms. Conscientious housekeeping and decent breakfasts are further pluses. No children under eight. **Amenities** garden, indoor swimming pool, sauna, solarium, whirlpool bath, keep-fit equipment, beauty salon, hairdressing, squash, mooring, sailing, water-skiing, snooker, satellite TV, 24-hour lounge service.

SALISBURY   Crustaceans   *NEW ENTRY*   🦞

R Map 4 C3 Wiltshire
2 Ivy Street
Salisbury (0722) 333948

Seafood
About £40 for two
Seats 48
Parties 20
Parking Ample
Credit Access, Visa

Roy Thwaites obtains his fish from all over Britain – salmon, sea trout, turbot and bass from Devon, shellfish from Poole, langoustines from Scotland and crawfish from the Scilly Isles – and cooks them with skill, saucing being a strong point. Particularly recommendable is his John Dory with hollandaise. Good wines strong in Alsace, burgundy and the Loire: Pouilly Fumé '86 (D. Pabiot) a model of its kind. 🍷 Well-chosen ⊖

Dinner only 7–10.30
Closed Sun, 25 & 26 Dec & Jan

SALISBURY   Rose & Crown Hotel   56%   £C/D

H Map 4 C3 Wiltshire
Harnham Road,
Harnham SP2 8JQ
Salisbury (0722) 27908
Telex 47224

Credit Access, Amex, Diners, Visa

The building dates back to 1380, and period character is the Rose and Crown's strong suit, along with a picturesque setting by the river Avon. Bedrooms are divided between the old inn – creaking timbers, sloping floors, even a four-poster room complete with ghost – and a red-brick extension, where the rooms are generally larger, with the best views. The bars feature Cotswold stone, oak beams and log fires. **Amenities** garden, laundry service. &

Rooms 28	*Direct dial* Yes	*Confirm by* 4	*Parking* Ample
Ensuite bath/shower 28	*Room TV* Yes	*Last dinner* 9.30	*Room service* All day

SALISBURY White Hart Hotel 65% £C/D

H **Map 4 C3** Wiltshire
1 St John Street SP1 2SD
Salisbury (0722) 27476

Credit Access, Amex, Diners, Visa

A convenient city-centre hotel with extensive private car parking. A large log fire cheers the foyer-lounge, where two antique mahogany desks serve as the reception point. There's a newly decorated bar and a variety of conference/function rooms. Comfortable guest accommodation is divided between refurbished rooms in the Georgian-style main house and larger rooms in a two-storey wing. **Amenities** garden, secretarial services, laundry service, 24-hour lounge service.

Rooms 68	*Direct dial* Yes	*Confirm by* 6	*Parking* Ample
Ensuite bath/shower 68	*Room TV* Yes	*Last dinner* 9.30	*Room service* Limited

SAMLESBURY Swallow Trafalgar Hotel 59% £D/E

H **Map 10 B1** Lancashire
Preston New Road PR5 0UL
Samlesbury (077 477) 351
Telex 677362

Credit Access, Amex, Diners, Visa

Practical overnight accommodation, plus leisure and conference facilities, in a modern hotel situated alongside the A677 (leave the M6 at junction 31). Day rooms include a choice of bars, and bedrooms provide accessories such as hairdryers and trouser presses. Singles have shower cubicles, while doubles offer bath and shower. **Amenities** garden, indoor swimming pool, solarium, squash, satellite TV, in-house movies, secretarial services, fax, laundry service, helipad.

Rooms 78	*Direct dial* Yes	*Confirm by* 6	*Parking* Ample
Ensuite bath/shower 78	*Room TV* Yes	*Last dinner* 9.45	*Room service* 24 hours

SAMLESBURY Tickled Trout Hotel 60% £D/E

H **Map 10 B1** Lancashire
Preston New Road,
Preston PR5 0UJ
Samlesbury (077 477) 671
Telex 677625
Credit Access, Amex, Diners, Visa

A modern hotel on the banks of the rushing river Ribble, just off junction 31 of the M6 and precisely halfway between London and Glasgow. Day rooms include an attractively beamed lounge with picture windows. Bedrooms, many recently refurbished, are spacious and well equipped, bathrooms compact. **Amenities** garden, indoor swimming pool, sauna, solarium, keep-fit equipment, coarse fishing, satellite TV, in-house movies, laundry service.

Rooms 66	*Direct dial* Yes	*Confirm by* 6	*Parking* Ample
Ensuite bath/shower 66	*Room TV* Yes	*Last dinner* 10	*Room service* Limited

We welcome bona fide complaints and recommendations
on the tear-out pages at the back of the book for readers' comment.
They are followed up by our professional team.

SANDBACH Chimney House Hotel 61% £D/E

H **Map 10 B2** Cheshire
Congleton Road CW11 0ST
Crewe (0270) 764141
Telex 367323

Credit Access, Amex, Diners, Visa

Set in eight acres of grounds close to junction 17 of the M6 is this half-timbered building – once a country rectory, now a comfortable hotel. Contemporary decor in warm, well-coordinated colour schemes sets the tone of the open-plan public areas. Prettily decorated bedrooms are well equipped and have good modern bathrooms. No dogs. **Amenities** garden, sauna, solarium, putting, in-house movies, secretarial services, laundry service. &

Rooms 52	*Direct dial* Yes	*Confirm by* 7	*Parking* Ample
Ensuite bath/shower 52	*Room TV* Yes	*Last dinner* 10	*Room service* Limited

SANDOWN Melville Hall Hotel 57% £D/E

H **Map 5 DA** Isle of Wight
Melville Street PO36 9DH
Isle of Wight (0983) 406526

Credit Access, Visa

Attractive gardens surround this pleasant, modest hotel where you can find comfortable accommodation. Public areas include a large, cheerful bar, a dance floor and entertainment most evenings. Bedrooms vary in size from average to family-sized, and have modern units and well-maintained bathrooms. No dogs. **Amenities** garden, outdoor swimming pool, putting, games room, satellite TV, in-house movies, laundry service, coffee shop (10.30am–midnight).

Rooms 36	*Direct dial* Yes	*Confirm by* arrang.	*Parking* Ample
Ensuite bath/shower 36	*Room TV* Yes	*Last dinner* 8.30	*Room service* All day

SAUNTON   Saunton Sands Hotel   67%   £D

H **Map 2 C1** Devon
Nr Braunton EX33 1LQ
Croyde (0271) 890212

Credit Access, Amex, Diners, Visa

Overlooking miles of beach and dunes, this 1930s hotel enjoys one of the finest situations on the Devon coast. It's a splendid holiday base, with excellent leisure facilities supplementing the delights of beach and countryside. Flowers deck the lobby, and the lounge bar is an ideal place to drink in the lovely views. Bedrooms, all recently upgraded, are comfortable, light and airy, with pretty fabrics and smart white furnishings; all have good tiled bathrooms. Housekeeping is assiduous, staff look the part and on our last visit only breakfast was a disappointment. No dogs. *Amenities* garden, indoor swimming pool, sauna, solarium, whirlpool bath, hairdressing, tennis, squash, putting, snooker, laundry service, children's playroom.

Rooms 93	*Direct dial* Yes	*Confirm by* arrang.	*Parking* Ample
Ensuite bath/shower 93	*Room TV* Yes	*Last dinner* 9	*Room service* 24 hours

Changes in data sometimes occur in establishments
after the Guide goes to press.
Prices should be taken as indications rather than firm quotes.

SCARBOROUGH   Crown Hotel   65%   £D/E

H **Map 15 D6** North Yorkshire
Esplanade YO11 2AG
Scarborough (0723) 373491
Telex 52277

Credit Access, Amex, Diners, Visa

There has been a massive programme of improvements at this Victorian hotel on the seafront. A grand piano, marble-style pillars and pretty drapes grace the spacious and elegant foyer-lounge, which gives on to an attractive bar. Bedrooms are in the process of being upgraded. *Amenities* garden, solarium, keep-fit equipment, hairdressing, games room, snooker, in-house movies, fax, laundry service, coffee shop (10am–7.30pm), children's playroom.

Rooms 83	*Direct dial* Yes	*Confirm by* 6	*Parking* Limited
Ensuite bath/shower 83	*Room TV* Yes	*Last dinner* 9.30	*Room service* 24 hours

SCARBOROUGH   Holbeck Hall Hotel   66%   £D

H **Map 15 D6** North Yorkshire
Sea Cliff Road YO11 2XX
Scarborough (0723) 374374

Credit Access, Amex, Diners, Visa

Panoramic views of the harbour are an attraction of this mock-Tudor Victorian hotel in a cliff-top setting. Characterful public rooms include a panelled hall with a baronial fireplace and minstrels' gallery and an elegant lounge with some nice antiques. Individually decorated bedrooms with period furnishings have modern comforts including carpeted bathrooms.
Amenities garden, putting, secretarial services, laundry service.

Rooms 30	*Direct dial* Yes	*Confirm by* 6	*Parking* Ample
Ensuite bath/shower 30	*Room TV* Yes	*Last dinner* 9.30	*Room service* 24 hours

SCARBOROUGH   Palm Court Hotel   57%   £E

H **Map 15 D6** North Yorkshire
St Nicholas Cliff YO11 2ES
Scarborough (0723) 368161
Telex 527579

Credit Access, Amex, Diners, Visa

Conveniently located close to the town centre, this is a modest but friendly hotel. The foyer doubles as a lounge area: bank seating around the fireplace creates a welcoming impression. There's also a mirrored cocktail lounge. Basic bedrooms are attractively decorated; carpeted bathrooms have modern white suites. No dogs.
Amenities indoor swimming pool, sauna, keep-fit equipment, in-house movies, laundry service, coffee shop (9am–5pm Mon–Sat).

Rooms 50	*Direct dial* Yes	*Confirm by* arrang.	*Parking* Limited
Ensuite bath/shower 50	*Room TV* Yes	*Last dinner* 9	*Room service* 24 hours

★ For a *discount* on next year's guide, see **An Offer for Answers.** ★

SCARBOROUGH — Royal Hotel — 72% — £D

H **Map 15 D6** North Yorkshire
St Nicholas Street YO11 2HE
Scarborough (0723) 364333

Rooms 137
Ensuite bath/shower 137
Direct dial Yes
Room TV Yes
Confirm by arrang.
Last dinner 11.30
Parking Limited
Room service 24 hours

Credit Access, Amex, Diners, Visa

A fine example of Regency elegance, this handsome hotel overlooking the sea has preserved its ornate character. A double staircase sweeping up to classical pillared galleries makes a fine effect in the front hall, aided by glittering chandeliers and tasteful antiques. Spacious public rooms combine comfort and elegance, notably in the Prince Regent room, and there's a cosy cocktail bar. Good-size bedrooms, mostly in traditional style, are well maintained, with good modern bathrooms. No dogs. *Amenities* terrace, indoor swimming pool, sauna, solarium, whirlpool bath, keep-fit equipment, games room, snooker, in-house movies, secretarial services, laundry service, coffee shop (9am–5pm), children's play area (summer).

SEAHOUSES — Olde Ship Hotel — £E/F

I **Map 14 B2**
Northumberland NE68 7RD
Seahouses (0665) 720200

Closed Nov 1–Apr 1

Originally a farmhouse when built in 1745, this distinctive inn has been under the same family ownership for over 70 years. Its two bars are warm and friendly, one being crammed with nautical memorabilia, while upstairs the comfortable residents' lounge offers picturesque views over the harbour. The small snug bedrooms have such homely touches as books, magazines and tea-makers. No dogs. *Amenities* garden, whirlpool bath, putting, satellite TV, laundry service. ♿

Rooms 12	*Room phone* No	*Confirm by* arrang.	*Parking* Ample
Ensuite bath/shower 9	*Room TV* Yes	*Last dinner* 8	*Room service* None

SEALE — Hog's Back Hotel — 64% — £C/D

H **Map 5 E3** Surrey
Hog's Back, Nr Farnham
GU10 1EX
Runfold (025 18) 2345
Telex 859352

Credit Access, Amex, Diners, Visa

Named after the North Downs ridge on which it stands, this country hotel was completely renovated in the early 80s. Potted plants give appeal to reception, and there's an agreeable bar-lounge with cane furniture and stylised 20s decor. Bedrooms are modern, practical and comfortable. Uninspired management rubs off on some of the staff. Sub-standard breakfasts. *Amenities* garden, pool table, secretarial services, fax, laundry service. ♿

Rooms 50	*Direct dial* Yes	*Confirm by* 6	*Parking* Ample
Ensuite bath/shower 50	*Room TV* Yes	*Last dinner* 9.30	*Room service* 24 hours

SEAVIEW — Seaview Hotel — 61% — £E

H **Map 5 D4** Isle of Wight
High Street PO34 5EX
Isle of Wight (0983) 612711

Credit Access, Amex, Visa

Close to the harbour in a picturesque old sailing village, the Haywards' hotel provides peace and relaxation in the friendliest of surroundings. The public bar is very much the local, and there's a second bar, plus drawing rooms for smokers and non-smokers. Traditionally decorated bedrooms feature some nice period furniture and many thoughtful extras. Two newly built twins have their own patios. A popular family hotel. *Amenities* patio, laundry service.

Rooms 16	*Room phone* No	*Confirm by* arrang.	*Parking* Ample
Ensuite bath/shower 16	*Room TV* Yes	*Last dinner* 9.30	*Room service* All day

SEAVINGTON ST MARY — Pheasant Hotel — 60% — £D/E

H **Map 4 A4** Somerset
Nr Ilminster TA19 0QE
South Petherton (0460) 40502

Credit Access, Amex, Diners, Visa
Closed 26 Dec–8 Jan

A peaceful 17th-century farmhouse where the mellow public rooms, comprising a reception, a lounge and restaurant combined and a bar, boast beams and plenty of brass and copper. Two bedrooms in the main building are small and cottagy, while the remaining rooms, in converted outbuildings, are more spacious, with simple decor and carpeted bathrooms. Tea/coffee-makers and trouser presses are provided. Housekeeping is excellent. No dogs. *Amenities* garden.

Rooms 10	*Direct dial* Yes	*Confirm by* arrang.	*Parking* Ample
Ensuite bath/shower 10	*Room TV* Yes	*Last dinner* 9.30	*Room service* Limited

SEDLESCOMBE   Brickwall Hotel   57%   £E

H **Map 7 C6** East Sussex
Nr Battle TN33 0QA
Sedlescombe (042 487) 253

Credit Access, Amex, Diners, Visa

The village setting is delightful, the tranquillity a treat, the charm old-fashioned and the accommodation more than adequate. In the main building, dating back to 1597, are the well-furnished lounges and cosy bar, along with bedrooms of some period character. Other bedrooms in various extensions have a more contemporary appeal. A couple of rooms boast four-posters.
Amenities garden, outdoor swimming pool, putting.

Rooms 24	*Direct dial* Yes	*Confirm by* arrang.	*Parking* Ample
Ensuite bath/shower 22	*Room TV* Yes	*Last dinner* 8.45	*Room service* All day

SENNEN   Tregiffian Hotel   59%   £E

H **Map 2 A4** Cornwall
Nr Penzance TR19 7BE
Sennen (0736) 871408

Credit Access, Diners, Visa
Closed Nov–Feb

A converted farmhouse at the end of a long, narrow track, with a very peaceful setting and fine sea views. The former kitchen is now a tiny bar with an inglenook and photographs of local shipwrecks; there's also an invitingly furnished lounge and a TV room/conservatory. Seven neat, compact bedrooms are supplemented by four modern suites, which can be let self-catering. Most rooms have shower/WC only. *Amenities* garden, laundry service.

Rooms 11	*Room phone* No	*Confirm by* 6	*Parking* Ample
Ensuite bath/shower 11	*Room TV* Some	*Last dinner* 8.30	*Room service* Limited

SEVENOAKS   Royal Oak   56%   £E

HR **Map 7 B5** Kent
Upper High Street TN14 5PG
Sevenoaks (0732) 451109
Telex 95130

Credit Access, Diners, Visa
Closed 3 days Xmas

A popular hotel with a handsome Georgian frontage, right opposite the entrance to Knole House. A warm welcome awaits in the cosy, traditional reception-lounge. A small conservatory-lounge and a bar with stripped pine furniture provide two further pleasant public rooms. Individually decorated bedrooms range from compact, functional singles to spacious, bright doubles. All have contemporary fabrics, traditional freestanding furniture and modern bathrooms.

Rooms 21	*Direct dial* Yes	*Confirm by* 6	*Parking* Limited
Ensuite bath/shower 21	*Room TV* Yes	*Last dinner* 9.30	*Room service* None

Restaurant

Set L £10.75
Set D from £12.50
About £35 *for two*
Seats 40
Parties 26

A pleasant restaurant with unfussy decor and attractive table settings. Three fortnightly-changing fixed-price menus cater for most tastes and appetites and the cooking is skilful. Chicken in white wine and tomato sauce and pork with Calvados sauce are typical dishes. Short, selective wine list with some fine bottles; outstanding Muscadet Ch. La Touche '86 and the excellent Ch. Branaire Ducru '81 drinking well now. ♀ Well-chosen ☯

Lunch 12.30–2   *Dinner* 7.30–9.30
Closed L Sat & D Sun, 3 days Xmas

Changes in data sometimes occur in establishments
after the Guide goes to press.
Prices should be taken as indications rather than firm quotes.

SHAFTESBURY   Grosvenor Hotel   62%   £C/D

H **Map 4 B3** Dorset
The Commons SP7 8JA
Shaftesbury (0747) 2282

Credit Access, Amex, Diners, Visa

A former coaching inn built around a cobbled courtyard, which lends a true feel of the past. Old hunting prints and green velour chairs in the bar keep the traditional feel, while the first-floor residents' lounge is comfortingly chintzy, with ornately draped windows. Bedrooms have soft pastel colours, floral prints and quilted bedcovers; all have tea/coffee-makers. Bathrooms have shower facilities and toiletries.
Amenities laundry service.

Rooms 42	*Room phone* Yes	*Confirm by* 6	*Parking* Ample
Ensuite bath/shower 42	*Room TV* Yes	*Last dinner* 9.30	*Room service* All day

SHAFTESBURY Royal Chase Hotel 62% £D/E

H **Map 4 B3** Dorset
Royal Chase Roundabout
SP7 8DB
Shaftesbury (0747) 53355
Telex 418414

Credit Access, Amex, Diners, Visa

Pleasing improvements have been made here, including a new entrance and reception, enlarged conference facilities and a new library. Weekends are popular with families, who make the most of the good leisure facilities. Bedrooms are pleasantly decorated and well equipped. *Amenities* garden, indoor swimming pool, solarium, steam bath, games room, in-house movies, secretarial services, coffee shop (8am–8pm).

Rooms 30	Direct dial Yes	Confirm by 4	Parking Ample
Ensuite bath/shower 30	Room TV Yes	Last dinner 9.45	Room service Limited

We publish annually,
so make sure you use the current edition.
It's worth it!

SHALDON Ness House Hotel 59% *NEW ENTRY* £E

H **Map 3 D3** Devon
Marine Drive TQ14 0HP
Shaldon (0626) 873480

Credit Access, Visa

Built by Lord Clifford in 1810, Ness House enjoys an enviable position on a hill overlooking the Teign estuary. Traditionally furnished rooms make the most of the view, and a drink on the terrace is a summer treat. Simple yet comfortable bedrooms mostly afford pleasant vistas from private balconies. Furnished in practical style, they all have private bathrooms. No dogs.
Amenities garden, laundry service.

Rooms 7	Direct dial Yes	Confirm by arrang.	Parking Ample
Ensuite bath/shower 7	Room TV Yes	Last dinner 10	Room service All day

SHANKLIN Cliff Tops Hotel 63% £C/D

H **Map 5 D4** Isle of Wight
Park Road PO37 6BB
Isle of Wight (0983) 863262

Credit Access, Amex, Diners, Visa

There's an ambitious programme of refurbishment underway at this modern hotel overlooking the sea, with lots of plants, pretty lamps and drapes and stylishly coordinating fabrics. New bedrooms are comfortable and tastefully decorated. *Amenities* garden, indoor swimming pool, sauna, solarium, whirlpool bath, keep-fit equipment, beauty salon, hairdressing, games room, snooker, pool table, in-house movies, secretarial services, laundry service. ♿

Rooms 93	Direct dial Yes	Confirm by arrang.	Parking Ample
Ensuite bath/shower 93	Room TV Yes	Last dinner 10.15	Room service 24 hours

SHEDFIELD Meon Valley Hotel 58% £C/D

H **Map 5 D4** Hampshire
Sandy Lane SO3 2HQ
Wickham (0329) 833455
Telex 86272

Credit Access, Amex, Diners, Visa

A modern purpose-built hotel just off the A334. Bright and cheerful day rooms have pleasant views over the golf course, while bedrooms are neat, functional and well equipped. No dogs.
Amenities garden, indoor swimming pool, sauna, solarium, whirl-pool bath, steam room, gymnasium, tennis, squash, golf course, snooker, in-house movies, secretarial services, fax, laundry service, coffee shop (9am–11pm), 24-hour lounge service, children's play area.

Rooms 84	Direct dial Yes	Confirm by 6	Parking Ample
Ensuite bath/shower 84	Room TV Yes	Last dinner 9.45	Room service None

SHEFFIELD Charnwood Hotel 67% £D/E

H **Map 10 C2** South Yorkshire
Sharrow Lane S11 8AA
Sheffield (0742) 589411

Credit Access, Amex, Diners, Visa

A charming and friendly hotel in a residential area less than a mile from the city centre. Some original features of the restored Georgian mansion survive, notably splendid beams in the top-floor bedrooms. All rooms are of a good size, tastefully furnished and decorated, with smart bathrooms. A pleasant addition to the day rooms is a bright garden lounge. No dogs. *Amenities* secretarial services, laundry service, 24-hour lounge service.

Rooms 21	Direct dial Yes	Confirm by arrang.	Parking Ample
Ensuite bath/shower 21	Room TV Yes	Last dinner 10	Room service All day

SHEFFIELD   Grosvenor House Hotel   61%   £C

Map 10 C2 South Yorkshire
Charter Square S1 3EH
Sheffield (0742) 720041
Telex 54312

Credit Access, Amex, Diners, Visa

There's been some refurbishment at this modern multi-storey hotel and public areas have new, good quality sofas and chairs. Go for the Superior and Executive bedrooms, which have been given stylish matching bedcovers and curtains, solid Italian furniture, brass light fittings, smartly tiled bathrooms and lots of extras. All rooms have mini-bars, tea/coffee-makers and remote-control TVs.
Amenities fax, laundry service, coffee shop (10am–10pm). &

Rooms 103	Direct dial Yes	Confirm by 6	Parking Limited
Ensuite bath/shower 103	Room TV Yes	Last dinner 10	Room service 24 hours

SHEFFIELD   Hallam Tower Post House Hotel   65%   £C/D

Map 10 C2 South Yorkshire
Manchester Road S10 5DX
Sheffield (0742) 670067
Telex 547293

Credit Access, Amex, Diners, Visa

A modern high-rise hotel on the A57, with splendid views of city and countryside. The health and fitness club is a popular feature, and there's a roomy lounge and bar (note the life-size steel man in the latter). Bedroom accessories include mini-bars and remote-control TVs. *Amenities* garden, indoor swimming pool, sauna, solarium, whirlpool bath, keep-fit equipment, laundry service, coffee shop (10am–7pm)

Rooms 136	Direct dial Yes	Confirm by 6	Parking Ample
Ensuite bath/shower 136	Room TV Yes	Last dinner 10.15	Room service 24 hours

SHEFFIELD   Hotel St George   66%   £D

Map 10 C2 South Yorkshire
Kenwood Road S7 1NQ
Sheffield (0742) 583811
Telex 547030

Credit Access, Amex, Diners, Visa

Less than two miles from the city centre, this well-run modern hotel enjoys a peaceful and scenic setting in 11 acres of gardens and grounds complete with a lake (check directions). Public areas are light and roomy, and all the bedrooms are being brought up to the level of the refurbished rooms, which feature attractive contemporary fabrics and good lighting. Standard equipment includes irons and ironing boards, hairdryers and beverage facilities. Additional rooms are planned. Helpful management and staff.
Amenities garden, indoor swimming pool, sauna, solarium, steam room, whirlpool bath, keep-fit equipment, coarse fishing, secretarial services, fax, laundry service, coffee shop (10am–10pm).

Rooms 118	Direct dial Yes	Confirm by 6	Parking Ample
Ensuite bath/shower 118	Room TV Yes	Last dinner 10	Room service 24 hours

---

Any person using our name to obtain free hospitality is a fraud.
Proprietors, please inform the police and us.

SHEPPERTON   Shepperton Moat House   60%   £C/D

Map 5 E2 Middlesex
Felix Lane TW17 8NP
Walton-on-Thames
(0932) 241404
Telex 928170
Credit Access, Amex, Diners, Visa
Closed 5 days Xmas

A modern hotel with a quiet location on the Thames. The lobby-lounge is bright and roomy, and there's a bamboo-furnished bar with jazz on Thursdays and a pianist twice a week. Bedrooms have attractive built-in units, remote-control TVs and neat bathrooms; Club rooms are larger, with many extras. *Amenities* garden, sauna, solarium, keep-fit equipment, target golf, mooring, snooker, pool table, in-house movies, secretarial services, fax, laundry service, helipad.

Rooms 180	Direct dial Yes	Confirm by 6	Parking Ample
Ensuite bath/shower 180	Room TV Yes	Last dinner 10	Room service 24 hours

SHEPPERTON   Warren Lodge Hotel   £D/E

Map 5 E2 Middlesex
Church Square TW17 9JZ
Walton-on-Thames
(0932) 242972
Telex 923981

Credit Access, Amex, Diners, Visa

A pretty garden running down to a riverside terrace is a feature at this 18th-century inn. There's no lounge, but the attractively panelled lounge bar provides ample seating. Pleasant bedrooms, mostly in modern blocks, are plainly decorated and modestly furnished with simple laminate units; the majority have showers and all offer extras like radios, tea-makers and hairdryers. No dogs.
Amenities garden.

Rooms 49	Direct dial Yes	Confirm by arrang.	Parking Ample
Ensuite bath/shower 46	Room TV Yes	Last dinner 9.45	Room service None

SHEPTON MALLET Blostin's

R Map 4 B3 Somerset
29 Waterloo Road
Shepton Mallet (0749) 3648

Set L £7.95
Set D £10.95
About £36 for two
Seats 30 *Parties* 25
Parking Ample
Credit Access, Visa

Two blackboards announce the day's menu at this stylish yet intimate little bistro. The choice is well-balanced and the cooking agreeable throughout. Starters might include smoked salmon and spinach mousse or sweetbreads in puff pastry with Marsala and mushrooms, and there are main courses like honey-roasted breast of duck or fresh Cornish squid in white wine, shallots and tomatoes. To finish, a choice of home-made sorbets and ice creams. ☺

Lunch by arrang. only *Dinner* 7–10, Sat till 10.30
Closed Sun & Mon, Bank Hols exc. 25 Dec & 1st 2 wks Jan

SHEPTON MALLET Bowlish House Restaurant

RR Map 4 B3 Somerset
Wells Road
Shepton Mallet (0749) 2022

Set D £14
About £40 for two
Seats 26
Parties 36
Parking Ample

Brian Jordan, former racing driver, photographer, engineer and housebuilder, puts his culinary talents to good use in an attractive Georgian restaurant which he runs with his wife Julia. The menus change frequently, and sound cooking produces tasty, appetising dishes such as chicken liver and rabbit pâtés layered with slivers of pigeon breast, or medallions of veal fillet with vermouth, cream and rosemary. An exceptional wine list is presented informatively by style of wine rather than country of origin. No smoking. ➪ Outstanding ♟ Well-chosen ☺

Dinner only 7–9.30
Closed 4 days Xmas

BEDROOMS 4 £E/F
With bath/shower 4

Bedrooms are decorated and furnished in pleasing period style.

We welcome bona fide complaints and recommendations
on the tear-out pages at the back of the book for readers' comment.
They are followed up by our professional team.

SHERBORNE Eastbury Hotel 67% £D

H Map 4 B3 Dorset
Long Street DT9 3BY
Sherborne (0935) 813131
Telex 46644

Credit Access, Amex, Visa

A Georgian town house, refurbished throughout and with a pleasantly light and informal atmosphere. Day rooms include a comfortable lounge, a little bar and a library that overlooks the pretty walled garden. Bedrooms, even the four singles, are of a good size, and feature floral decor, decent-quality furniture, armchairs, magazines, hairdryers and trouser presses. There's one four-poster room. Modern bathrooms. No dogs. *Amenities* garden, laundry service.

Rooms 12	*Direct dial* Yes	*Confirm by* arrang.	*Parking* Ample
Ensuite bath/shower 12	*Room TV* Yes	*Last dinner* 9.30	*Room service* All day

SHERBORNE Post House Hotel 60% £C/D

H Map 4 B3 Dorset
Horsecastles Lane DT9 6BB
Sherborne (0935) 813191
Telex 46522

Credit Access, Amex, Diners, Visa

Sherborne's Post House is set back from the A30 in two acres of parkland just west of town. It carries its 20 years quite well, day rooms like the chalet-style restaurant and bar being particularly smart. Improvements in the plain and practical accommodation include mini-bars, direct-dial telephones and a shower in every bathroom. *Amenities* garden, putting, secretarial services, fax, laundry service, children's play area.

Rooms 60	*Direct dial* Yes	*Confirm by* 6	*Parking* Ample
Ensuite bath/shower 60	*Room TV* Yes	*Last dinner* 10	*Room service* 24 hours

---

 indicates a **well-chosen** house wine

SHIFNAL   Park House Hotel   75%   £C/D

H **Map 10 B4** Shropshire
Park Street, Nr Telford
TF11 9BA
Telford (0952) 460128
Telex 35438

Rooms 54
Ensuite bath/shower 54
Direct dial Yes
Room TV Yes
Confirm by 6
Last dinner 10.30
Parking Ample
Room service 24 hours

Credit Access, Amex, Diners, Visa

Two elegant period houses, one dating back to the 17th century, the other to the 18th, join with a modern bedroom block to form a hotel of considerable style and comfort. The lounges and bars in both buildings are beautifully appointed, with some luxurious fabrics, antiques and fine paintings taking the eye. Bedrooms, all of a good size, are decorated and furnished in handsome, traditional style and offer numerous extras, including trouser presses, hairdryers, fresh fruit and a decanter of sherry. Bathrooms, too, are very well equipped. Sixteen new bedrooms were added during 1988. Very good staff.
Amenities garden, indoor swimming pool, sauna, solarium, whirlpool bath, satellite TV, laundry service. ⑤

SHINFIELD   L'Ortolan ★★★   ♔ ♧

R **Map 5 D2** Berkshire
The Old Vicarage,
Church Lane
Reading (0734) 883783

French cooking

Lunch 12.15–2.15
Dinner 7.15–10.15, Sat 7–10.30
Set L from £18.50,
Sun from £26.50
Set D £28.50
About £85 *for two*
Seats 55
Parties 30
Parking Ample
Credit Access, Amex, Visa
Closed D Sun, all Mon, last 2 wks
Feb & last 2 wks Aug

All is stylish perfection at this elegant restaurant in a converted vicarage. John Burton-Race's lengthy menu descriptions make tempting reading yet they are invariably surpassed by results on the plate. Begin perhaps with a salad of meltingly tender langoustine tails flamed in Cognac, then settle for roast fillet of lamb topped with a sweetbread-spiked quenelle, wrapped in spinach and accompanied by a thyme-scented jus. End with a ravishing hot lime soufflé served with its own sorbet. Discreet service and a greatly improved cellar.
Specialities délice aux deux saumons crème de ciboulette, baron de lapereau au jus d'abricot et fumet de Bourgogne, assiette chocolatière.
▷ Outstanding   ♀ Well-chosen   ⊘   🍖

We welcome bona fide complaints and recommendations
on the tear-out pages at the back of the book for readers' comment.
They are followed up by our professional team.

SHIPDHAM   Shipdham Place

RR **Map 6 C2** Norfolk
Church Close
Nr Thetford IP25 7LX
Dereham (0362) 820303

Set D £18.50
About £50 *for two*
Seats 25
Parties 40
Parking Ample

BEDROOMS 8   **£D/E**
With bath/shower 5

The dining room at this 17th-century rectory is aglow with polished wood, silverware and glass. There's no choice on the five-course, daily-changing menu, although you may request alternatives if something is not to your taste. A typical meal might include salad of chicken livers, mushrooms and mange-tout, followed by monkfish tails in filo. Serious, good quality wine list: Ch. Larcis Ducasse St Emilion '70.
♀ Well-chosen   ⊘

Lunch by arrang.   *Dinner* 7.45–9.30
Closed 1 wk Xmas

The welcoming, cosy bedrooms, some with sloping ceilings, have Laura Ashley fabrics and paper and are furnished with modern pine and antiques.

SHIPTON-UNDER-WYCHWOOD   Lamb Inn   £E/F

Map 4 C1 Oxfordshire
High Street OX7 6DQ
Shipton-under-Wychwood
(0993) 830465

Credit Access, Amex, Diners, Visa
Closed 1 wk Xmas

The Wainwrights run their attractive Cotswold-stone inn with great care and pride and you can be sure of a warm welcome. Traditional ale is served in the beamed, countrified bar and there's a small, homely lounge for both residents and diners. Steep stairs lead to the spotlessly kept, charming bedrooms, which have floral fabrics, white period furniture and carpeted bathrooms. No under-14s. No dogs. *Amenities* garden.

| *Rooms* 5 | *Room phone* No | *Confirm by* 6 | *Parking* Ample |
| *Ensuite bath/shower* 5 | *Room TV* Yes | *Last dinner* 9 | *Room service* Limited |

SHORNE   Inn on the Lake   61%   £D/E

Map 7B5 Kent
Nr Gravesend DA12 3HB
Shorne (047 482) 3333
Telex 966356

Credit Access, Amex, Diners, Visa

Built in 1972, this well-kept hotel stands on the A2 by an attractive lake. Bedrooms are pleasant and practical, with good-sized bathrooms. Trouser presses are standard, and bowls of fresh fruit are a thoughtful touch. Conferences are big business here, so one of the two bars is sometimes unavailable to private guests, and there's no separate lounge. No dogs. *Amenities* garden, coarse fishing, in-house movies, secretarial services, laundry service.

| *Rooms* 78 | *Direct dial* Yes | *Confirm by* 6 | *Parking* Ample |
| *Ensuite bath/shower* 78 | *Room TV* Yes | *Last dinner* 10 | *Room service* 24 hours |

We publish annually,
so make sure you use the current edition.
It's worth it!

SHREWSBURY   Country Friends   ⌒

Map 10 A3 Shropshire
Dorrington
Dorrington (074 373) 707

Set L & D £12.50
About £40 for two
Seats 45 *Parties* 40
Parking Ample
Credit Amex, Diners, Visa

Potpourri and baskets of dried flowers on the antique furniture in the hall and dining room give the impression of a cherished private home, reinforced by the crackling log fire. The appealing menu makes choice difficult, but you can guarantee your selection being well cooked from high-quality ingredients. Typical dishes are mousseline of chicken with blue cheese sauce and rabbit in filo with peppercorn sauce. Scrumptious desserts. ⊘

Lunch 12–2   *Dinner* 7–9.30, Sat till 10
Closed Sun, Mon & 2 wks end Oct

SHREWSBURY   Lion Hotel   63%   £D/E

Map 10 A3 Shropshire
Wyle Cop SY1 1UY
Shrewsbury (0743) 53107

Credit Access, Amex, Diners, Visa

Once a coaching inn, the Lion is now a characterful hotel standing in Shrewsbury's main shopping street. The Tapestry Lounge is a lovely high-ceilinged room with beams, oil paintings and traditional furniture, and other attractive features are an Adam ballroom and a classic Georgian staircase. Comfortably appointed bedrooms include a quite delightful suite with a Dickensian theme. *Amenities* laundry service.

| *Rooms* 59 | *Room phone* Yes | *Confirm by* 6 | *Parking* Ample |
| *Ensuite bath/shower* 59 | *Room TV* Yes | *Last dinner* 10 | *Room service* 24 hours |

SHREWSBURY   Prince Rupert Hotel   60%   £D

Map 10 A3 Shropshire
Butcher Row SY1 1UG
Shrewsbury (0743) 236000
Telex 35100

Credit Access, Amex, Diners, Visa

Cobbled streets and quaint shops set the scene for a traditional hotel that keeps its friendly, unpretentious atmosphere. The foyer has a simple, traditional appeal enhanced by display cases of local wares and there's a homely lounge. Prettily decorated bedrooms, all with clean, compact bathrooms, include four Executive rooms with four-posters. Service is very helpful and welcoming. *Amenities* snooker, games room, in-house movies, secretarial services, laundry service.

| *Rooms* 70 | *Direct dial* Yes | *Confirm by* 6 | *Parking* Ample |
| *Ensuite bath/shower* 70 | *Room TV* Yes | *Last dinner* 10.15 | *Room service* 24 hours |

SIDMOUTH   **Belmont Hotel   63%**   £D/E

H Map 3 E2 Devon
The Esplanade EX10 8RX
Sidmouth (039 55) 2555

Credit Access, Amex, Diners, Visa
Closed 31 Dec–mid Feb

New owners have invested much money in this seaside hotel and
there's evidence of extensive refurbishment. Wonderful sea views are
available from the spacious cocktail lounge, and there's a further,
smaller, lounge and two bars. De luxe rooms are sea-facing, with
private balconies, and offer teletext, bathrobes and toiletries; all
rooms are light and airy in decor. No dogs. *Amenities* garden,
putting, in-house movies, laundry service.

| *Rooms* 50 | *Direct dial* Yes | *Confirm by* arrang. | *Parking* Ample |
| *Ensuite bath/shower* 50 | *Room TV* Yes | *Last dinner* 9 | *Room service* 24 hours |

SIDMOUTH   **Fortfield Hotel   59%**   £D/E

H Map 3 E2 Devon
Station Road EX10 8NU
Sidmouth (039 55) 2403

Credit Access, Amex, Visa

Overlooking the sea and cricket ground, this family-run hotel first
opened in the Edwardian era. Still comfortably traditional in character,
it offers a large sunny lounge with sea views and an interior bar with
no views at all. Homely bedrooms of varying sizes include four with
original late-Victorian furniture.
Amenities garden, indoor swimming pool, sauna, solarium, keep-fit
equipment, games room, in-house movies, laundry service.

| *Rooms* 52 | *Direct dial* Yes | *Confirm by* arrang. | *Parking* Ample |
| *Ensuite bath/shower* 43 | *Room TV* Yes | *Last dinner* 8.30 | *Room service* 24 hours |

SIDMOUTH   **Hotel Riviera   64%**   £C/D

H Map 3 E2 Devon
The Esplanade EX10 8AY
Sidmouth (039 55) 5201
Telex 42551

Credit Amex, Diners

Friendly staff are a strong point at this seafront Regency hotel. The
spacious sun terrace is a relaxing place for appreciating the view,
while the day rooms offer ample space and comfort. A recent
programme of bedroom refurbishment included pink-striped wallpaper and decent new furniture. Beds are turned down at night.
Amenities terrace, in-house movies, secretarial services, laundry
service. ♿

| *Rooms* 34 | *Direct dial* Yes | *Confirm by* arrang. | *Parking* Limited |
| *Ensuite bath/shower* 29 | *Room TV* Yes | *Last dinner* 9 | *Room service* 24 hours |

SIDMOUTH   **Victoria Hotel   67%**   £C

H Map 3 E2 Devon
Peak Hill EX10 8RY
Sidmouth (039 55) 2651
Telex 42551

Credit Access, Amex, Diners, Visa

An imposing turn-of-the-century building on a rise overlooking the
sea. It's a splendidly traditional hotel offering comfort, service, nice
views and good leisure facilities. Roomy public areas are bright and
welcoming, and some of the smartly furnished bedrooms have
balconies. Friendly management and staff. *Amenities* garden,
indoor and outdoor swimming pools, sauna, solarium, whirlpool bath,
keep-fit equipment, hairdressing, tennis, putting, snooker, in-house
movies, secretarial services, fax, laundry service.

| *Rooms* 65 | *Direct dial* Yes | *Confirm by* arrang. | *Parking* Ample |
| *Ensuite bath/shower* 65 | *Room TV* Yes | *Last dinner* 9 | *Room service* 24 hours |

Our inspectors *never* book in the name of Egon Ronay's Guides.
They disclose their identity only if they are considering an establishment
for inclusion in the next edition of the Guide.

SILCHESTER   **Romans Hotel   63%**   £D/E

H Map 5 D3 Hampshire
Little London Road
Nr Reading RG7 2PN
Silchester (0734) 700421
Telex 858122
Credit Access, Amex, Diners, Visa
Closed 10 days Xmas

Manicured lawns surround this splendid Lutyens house in the historic
village of Silchester. Original oak panelling, handsome polished floors,
leaded-glass windows and ornate mouldings are features of the public
rooms. Bedrooms have comfortable furniture and modern facilities
(direct-dial telephones, coffee-makers). Annexe rooms, recently refurbished, are more compact. *Amenities* garden, outdoor swimming
pool, tennis, putting, laundry service, 24-hour lounge service.

| *Rooms* 25 | *Direct dial* Yes | *Confirm by* arrang. | *Parking* Ample |
| *Ensuite bath/shower* 25 | *Room TV* Yes | *Last dinner* 9 | *Room service* Limited |

SILLOTH ON SOLWAY Skinburness Hotel 67% *NEW ENTRY* £E

H Map 13 C4 Cumbria
Nr Carlisle CA5 4QT
Silloth (069 73) 32332

Credit Access, Amex, Diners, Visa

Situated in a peaceful hamlet close to the Solway Firth, this elegant Victorian hotel has been impressively refurbished throughout. Attractive day rooms include a spacious, comfortable bar, cosy little writing room furnished in period style and a plant-filled conservatory lounge. Airy, prettily decorated bedrooms with cane seating all have smartly up-to-date bathrooms. *Amenities* garden, sauna, solarium, croquet, snooker, secretarial services, laundry service.

Rooms 25	Direct dial Yes	Confirm by arrang.	Parking Ample
Ensuite bath/shower 24	Room TV Yes	Last dinner 9.30	Room service All day

SIMONSBATH Simonsbath House Hotel 64% £E

H Map 3 D1 Somerset
Exmoor TA24 7SH
Exford (064 383) 259

Credit Access, Amex, Diners, Visa
Closed Jan

This 300-year-old house stands at the heart of Exmoor National Park and most rooms enjoy super views. Mike and Sue Burns welcome you like one of the family, and there is a warm, homely feeling and comfort aplenty in the panelled lounge and library bar. Bedrooms offer period furniture, pretty fabrics and thoughtful extras, plus compact modern bathrooms. No children under ten. No dogs.
Amenities garden.

Rooms 8	Direct dial Yes	Confirm by arrang.	Parking Ample
Ensuite bath/shower 8	Room TV Yes	Last dinner 8.30	Room service All day

SISSINGHURST Rankins ⑨

R Map 7 C5 Kent
The Street
Cranbrook (0580) 713964

Set L £8.50
Set D from £11.50
About £30 for two
Seats 28 Parties 23
Parking Ample
Credit Access, Visa

A cosy restaurant with simple, homely decor where Hugh Rankin cooks and wife Leonara provides friendly service. The menu is short but imaginative, and makes good use of local produce. Choices might include fillet of brill baked with fresh herbs, served with beurre blanc, or lamb noisettes accompanied by a port and juniper sauce. Lovely desserts and a concise list of decent wines. 🍷 Well-chosen

Lunch Sun only 12.30–1.30 *Dinner* 7.30–9
Closed D Sun, all Mon & Tues, Bank Hols & 2 wks Nov

SIX MILE BOTTOM Swynford Paddocks 76% £D

H Map 6 B3 Cambridgeshire
Nr Newmarket CB8 0UE
Six Mile Bottom (063 870) 234
Telex 817438

Rooms 15
Ensuite bath/shower 15
Direct dial Yes
Room TV Yes
Confirm by 6
Last dinner 9.30
Parking Ample
Room service All day

Credit Access, Amex, Diners, Visa

Set back from the A1304 in well-tended grounds, this white-painted gabled house was once the home of Byron's half-sister, Augusta Leigh. Byronic associations are kept firmly to the fore, with portraits in the oak-panelled hall and biographies in every bedroom. Fresh flowers and glowing log fires help to recreate the atmosphere of an English country house and there's a comfortably elegant feel  to the bar-lounge with its grand piano and French windows overlooking the garden. Individually appointed bedrooms are smartly traditional in style and have carpeted, fully-tiled bathrooms. Extras range from magazines and radio-alarms to mini-bars and hairdryers. *Amenities* garden, tennis, putting, croquet, fax, laundry service.

SLAIDBURN Hark To Bounty Inn £F

I Map 10 B1 Lancashire
Nr Clitheroe BB7 3AQ
Slaidburn (020 06) 246

Credit Access, Amex, Diners, Visa

An historic courtroom (in use until 1937) forms part of this 13th-century village inn. Guests enter a welcoming bar-lounge with open fireplace, gleaming brass ornaments and polished oak furniture. There's also a residents' TV lounge with comfy winged rockers. Centrally-heated bedrooms, including two with sitting areas, are cosy and full of character, with modern bathrooms (one with shower only).
Amenities garden, game fishing, laundry service.

Rooms 8	Room phone No	Confirm by arrang.	Parking Ample
Ensuite bath/shower 8	Room TV Yes	Last dinner 9	Room service All day

SLOUGH   Holiday Inn   76%   £B/C

H **Map 5 E2** Berkshire
Ditton Road, Langley SL3 8PT
Slough (0753) 44244
Telex 848646

Rooms 302
Ensuite bath/shower 302
Direct dial Yes
Room TV Yes
Confirm by 6
Last dinner 10.30
Parking Ample
Room service 24 hours

Credit Access, Amex, Diners, Visa

Just by junction 5 of the M4, this modern hotel has the usual Holiday Inn pluses of good-sized bedrooms and large beds. Solid lightwood furniture is employed, and bathrooms, though by no means large, have full-size baths, good showers above and decent toiletries. Rooms have benefited from a recent refurbishment programme. Public areas, where red-brick arches and columns are put to effective stylistic use, are attractive and inviting, especially the leisure centre with its ample poolside sitting area.
Amenities garden, indoor swimming pool, sauna, solarium, steam bath, gymnasium, tennis, hairdressing, in-house movies, coffee shop (7am–11pm), children's play area. ⅙

**Our inspectors are our full-time employees;
they are professionally trained by us.**

SOLIHULL   *George Hotel*   £D

H **Map 10 C4** West Midlands
The Square B91 3RF
021-711 2121

Credit Access, Amex, Diners, Visa

A major refurbishment and improvement programme is due to be completed in November 1988 at this modernised coaching inn. The work will include completely new public areas, upgrading existing bedrooms to Executive standard and the construction of 34 rooms. One of the hotel's more unusual features is a private bowling green. The George was graded at 57% in our 1988 Guide. *Amenities* patio, secretarial services, laundry service, coffee shop (7am–11pm).

Rooms 74	*Direct dial* Yes	*Confirm by* 6	*Parking* Ample
Ensuite bath/shower 74	*Room TV* Yes	*Last dinner* 9.45	*Room service* 24 hours

---

SOLIHULL   Liaison   ♈

R **Map 10 C4** West Midlands
761 Old Lode Lane
021-743 3993

Set D Tues only £17.50
About £50 for two
Seats 28
Parties 40
Parking Ample
Credit Access, Amex, Diners, Visa

Smart green and white decor provides an appropriately elegant setting for Patricia Plunkett's accomplished and imaginative cooking. Seasonally changing menus, devised around the finest fresh produce, offer attractively presented dishes like warm asparagus gâteau encircled by smoked salmon parcels, and breast of duck in a Calvados jus with a sprinkling of pink peppercorns. Liqueur-enhanced sauces are perhaps a shade too prevalent. Tempting sweets to follow. Ask for directions when booking. ☏

Dinner only 7–10 **Closed** Sun, Mon, Bank Hols, 2wks Xmas & all Aug

---

SOLIHULL   Regency Hotel   72%   £D

H **Map 10 C4** West Midlands
Stratford Road,
Shirley B90 4EB
021-745 6119
Telex 334400

Rooms 59
Ensuite bath/shower 59
Direct dial Yes
Room TV Yes
Confirm by 6
Last dinner 10
Parking Ample
Room service Limited

Credit Access, Amex, Visa

Standing in its own grounds alongside the A34 (not far from junction 4 of the M42), this attractive cream-painted hotel offers first-class accommodation. The leafy reception area is fresh and appealing and there's a spacious cocktail lounge with smart pastel decor and elegant drapes. The popular Victorian-style 'public' bar is separated from the hotel proper by a locked door. Attractively furnished bedrooms have light freestanding units and accessories like hairdryers, trouser presses, remote-control TVs and tea-makers. Tiled bathrooms are well equipped but compact. Eight suites provide additional comforts.
Amenities garden, secretarial services, laundry service, coffee shop (9–12am and 2.30–7pm), 24-hour lounge service.

SOLIHULL — St John's Swallow Hotel 63% £C/D

H **Map 10 C4** West Midlands
651 Warwick Road B91 1AT
021-711 3000
Telex 339352

Credit Access, Amex, Diners, Visa

A splendid new leisure complex and conference facilities for a thousand make this a popular and versatile hotel. Accommodation ranges from fairly simple older rooms to 14 smart former staff rooms and six very comfortable suites. Day rooms include a spacious lobby-lounge and a pleasant bar with plants and garden murals. ***Amenities*** garden, indoor swimming pool, sauna, solarium, whirlpool bath, steam room, gymnasium, in-house movies, fax, laundry service.

Rooms 206	*Direct dial* Yes	*Confirm by* 6	*Parking* Ample
Ensuite bath/shower 206	*Room TV* Yes	*Last dinner* 9.45	*Room service* 24 hours

SOMERTON — The Lynch Country House Hotel 69% £C/D

H **Map 4 A3** Somerset
Behind Berry TA11 7PD
Somerton (0458) 72316

Credit Access, Amex, Diners, Visa
Closed 2 days Xmas & 2 wks Jan

Roy Copeland runs this charming Georgian country house with friendliness and a refreshing lack of formality. Day rooms have a cosy period charm that extends to the bedrooms, each individually decorated and furnished. Accessories include remote-control TVs, sewing kits and magazines; bathrobes are supplied in the roomy carpeted bathrooms.
Amenities garden, outdoor swimming pool, croquet, laundry service.

Rooms 6	*Direct dial* Yes	*Confirm by* arrang.	*Parking* Ample
Ensuite bath/shower 5	*Room TV* Yes	*Last dinner* 9.30	*Room service* Limited

SOMERTON — Red Lion Hotel 60% £E/F

H **Map 4 A3** Somerset
Broad Street TA11 7NJ
Somerton (0458) 72339

Credit Access, Amex, Diners, Visa

In the centre of town, the Red Lion retains much period charm, and the atmosphere throughout is warm and cosy. The oak-panelled bar is a good place for a drink and a chat, and there's a quiet, modest lounge. The best bedrooms, designated superior, are also in period style, and some have four-posters; other rooms are rather plainer. Saturday night is disco night.
Amenities laundry service.

Rooms 15	*Direct dial* Yes	*Confirm by* arrang.	*Parking* Ample
Ensuite bath/shower 15	*Room TV* Yes	*Last dinner* 10	*Room service* 24 hours

SONNING-ON-THAMES — White Hart Hotel 64% £C/D

H **Map 5 D2** Berkshire
Nr Reading RG4 0UT
Reading (0734) 692277
Telex 849031

Credit Access, Amex, Diners, Visa

A major asset here is the splendid waterfront location, with lawns stretching from the terrace to half a mile of private river frontage. Period charm abounds, and owner Mrs Currie has made the place look stylish and pretty. Bedrooms, divided between the main building and two adjacent cottages, are well heated and nicely furnished; bathrooms – some quite large, with bidets – offer good shelf space and the usual extras. ***Amenities*** garden, mooring, laundry service.

Rooms 25	*Direct dial* Yes	*Confirm by* 6	*Parking* Ample
Ensuite bath/shower 25	*Room TV* Yes	*Last dinner* 10	*Room service* 24 hours

SOUTH GODSTONE — La Bonne Auberge ♛

R **Map 7 B5** Surrey
Tilburstow Hill
South Godstone (0342) 892318

French cooking

Set L from £14
Set D £24
About £60 *for two*
Seats 65
Parties 22
Parking Ample
Credit Access, Amex, Visa

Good food is a way of life at this civilised restaurant in a Victorian country mansion. The main dining room has the feel of Brittany, while there's a charming garden room for smaller parties. The chef, Olivier le Houezec, is a Breton, too – a man of imagination and talent who prizes the solid over the flashy. His fish soup is packed full of good things, and splendid main courses could include braised brill, pan-fried fillet steak and exemplary roast partridge served with a sauce of ale and caramelised orange. Puddings keep up the same high standard. The whole meal is enhanced by good wines and service is smooth and attentive. 🍷 Well-chosen

Lunch 12.15–2 *Dinner* 7–10
Closed D Sun, all Mon, Bank Hols

Any person using our name to obtain free hospitality is a fraud.
Proprietors, please inform the police and us.

SOUTH MARSTON   South Marston Hotel   55%   £C/D

H Map 4 C2 Wiltshire
Nr Swindon SN3 4SH
Swindon (0793) 827777
Telex 444634

Credit Access, Amex, Diners, Visa

Bedroom size, comfort and equipment are acceptable at this modern hotel, but public area space, apart from the leisure club, is limited, and both service and breakfast proved a disappointment on a recent visit. No dogs. *Amenities* garden, indoor & outdoor swimming pools, sauna, solarium, whirlpool bath, gymnasium, squash, badminton, games room, snooker, in-house movies, secretarial services, laundry service, coffee shop (9.30am–10.30pm), children's play area.

| Rooms 40 | Direct dial Yes | Confirm by arrang. | Parking Ample |
| Ensuite bath/shower 40 | Room TV Yes | Last dinner 9.45 | Room service Limited |

SOUTH MILFORD   Selby Fork Hotel   63%   £D

H Map 11 D1 North Yorkshire
Nr Leeds LS25 5LF
South Milford (0977) 682711
Telex 557074

Credit Access, Amex, Diners, Visa

A low, sprawling modern hotel, conveniently situated on the A1. Various improvements are planned or under way, including refurbishment of public areas and upgrading of some bedrooms. Rooms already improved are neat and pleasing to the eye, with good darkwood furniture, stylish curtains and excellent lighting. Singles have shower and WC only. *Amenities* garden, indoor swimming pool, sauna, tennis, pitch & putt, laundry service, helipad.

| Rooms 109 | Direct dial Yes | Confirm by arrang. | Parking Ample |
| Ensuite bath/shower 109 | Room TV Yes | Last dinner 10 | Room service 24 hours |

SOUTH MIMMS   Crest Hotel   60%   £C

H Map 5 E2 Hertfordshire
Bignells Corner,
Nr Potters Bar EN6 3NH
Potters Bar (0707) 43311
Telex 299162

Credit Access, Amex, Diners, Visa

A low-rise mid-60s hotel with practical overnight accommodation, a well-equipped leisure club and good facilities for functions and business meetings. Bedrooms, all with trouser presses, include non-smoking, Lady Crest and superior Executive rooms. *Amenities* garden, indoor swimming pool, sauna, solarium, whirlpool bath, keep-fit equipment, pool table, in-house movies, secretarial services, fax, laundry service, coffee shop (9.30am–6.30pm), children's playground.

| Rooms 120 | Direct dial Yes | Confirm by 6 | Parking Ample |
| Ensuite bath/shower 120 | Room TV Yes | Last dinner 10 | Room service Limited |

SOUTH MOLTON   Whitechapel Manor   75%   *NEW ENTRY*   £D

HR Map 3 D2 Devon
South Molton
(076 95) 3377

Rooms 10
Ensuite bath/shower 10
Direct dial Yes
Room TV Yes
Confirm by arrang.
Last dinner 9
Parking Ample
Room service All day

Credit Access, Amex, Diners, Visa

Unspoilt Devon countryside surrounds Whitechapel Manor, making it a haven of peace and beauty and an ideal bolthole from the bustle of the city. The present house was built about 1575 and is a Grade 1 listed building. Proud owners John and Patricia Shapland have sympathetically refurbished the whole place, and among many fine period features are a Jacobean carved oak screen and some splendid panelling.
Bedrooms, each named after a previous owner, have individual appeal; all are stylishly decorated and furnished, with remote-control TVs and well-lit bathrooms. Staff are willing and unobtrusive, and a super breakfast gets the day under way. *Amenities* garden, croquet, stabling, laundry service.

Restaurant   *NEW ENTRY*

Set L £15
Set D £20
About £50 for two
Seats 20
Parties 40

Thierry Leprêtre-Granet handles top-quality produce with great assurance, so a meal here is an occasion to savour. His short, imaginative menu tempts with delights like game consommé with vegetable julienne, Dover sole with crabmeat, noodles and sorrel sauce, or stuffed fillet of lamb with a beautifully constructed sauce of Madeira and rosemary. Leave room for a super sweet such as lime parfait with coconut ice cream.

Lunch 12–2
Dinner 7–9

SOUTH NORMANTON   Swallow Hotel   70%   £C/D

H **Map 11 D3** Derbyshire
Carter Lane East DE55 2EH
Ripley (0773) 812000
Telex 377264

Rooms 123
Ensuite bath/shower 123
Direct dial Yes
Room TV Yes
Confirm by 6
Last dinner 9.45
Parking Ample
Room service 24 hours

Credit Access, Amex, Diners, Visa

A modern, low-built, red-brick hotel that's popular both for its attractive little leisure centre and for its close proximity to junction 28 of the M1. Public areas include a spacious foyer with quarry-tiled floor and natural brick features, a softly lit bar and a coffee shop with lacework theme (a reference to nearby Nottingham's lacemaking industry). Frequent refurbishment keeps bedrooms bright and fresh; all

have comfortable seating and are equipped with hairdryers, tea-makers and mini-bars. Bathrooms offer showers over tubs and decent toiletries. *Amenities* garden, indoor swimming pool, sauna, solarium, whirlpool bath, keep-fit equipment, in-house movies, fax, laundry service, coffee shop (7am–10.30pm). &

SOUTH WALSHAM   South Walsham Hall Hotel   62%   £E

H **Map 6 D1** Norfolk
Nr Norwich NR13 6DQ
South Walsham (060 549) 378

Credit Access, Amex, Diners, Visa
Closed 1st 2 wks Jan

Thirty acres of well-tended grounds crossed by a winding stream provide a handsome setting for this fine red-brick country house much enlarged during Victorian and Edwardian times. The foyer is dominated by a splendid carved staircase, and public rooms are large and comfortable. Main-house bedrooms, individually furnished with both modern and antique pieces, vary in size and grandeur; one boasts a magnificent Hollywood-style bathroom. Rooms in the converted outhouses have a more modern, functional atmosphere.
Amenities garden, outdoor swimming pool, sauna, solarium, keep-fit equipment, tennis, squash, badminton, riding, coarse fishing, games room, pool table, laundry service.

| *Rooms* 19 | *Direct dial* Yes | *Confirm by* arrang. | *Parking* Ample |
| *Ensuite bath/shower* 16 | *Room TV* Yes | *Last dinner* 10 | *Room service* All day |

**Changes in data sometimes occur in establishments
after the Guide goes to press.
Prices should be taken as indications rather than firm quotes.**

SOUTHAMPTON   Dolphin Hotel   60%   £C/D

H **Map 5 D4** Hampshire
High Street SO9 2DS
Southampton (0703) 339955
Telex 477735

Credit Access, Amex, Diners, Visa

With its magnificent bow windows, said to be the largest in England, this important coaching hotel has been accommodating travellers for centuries. Public areas include five conference rooms, the nautically-themed Nelson Bar and a panelled lounge. Bedrooms vary in size and style, but there's an ongoing programme of refurbishment which has brought the best of them up-to-date in standards of furnishings and decor. *Amenities* garden, secretarial services, fax, laundry service.

| *Rooms* 74 | *Direct dial* Yes | *Confirm by* 6 | *Parking* Ample |
| *Ensuite bath/shower* 74 | *Room TV* Yes | *Last dinner* 9.45 | *Room service* 24 hours |

SOUTHAMPTON   Polygon Hotel   65%   £C/D

H **Map 5 D4** Hampshire
Cumberland Place SO9 4DG
Southampton (0703) 330055
Telex 47175

Credit Access, Amex, Diners, Visa

The original Polygon dates back to the 18th century, but extensive modernisation has taken place down the years. The lofty drawing room has kept a lot of period appeal and is a comfortable spot to relax; there's also a plush panelled bar. Best bedrooms are those which have been recently refurbished with attractive, matching bedspreads and curtains and much smarter bathrooms.
Amenities secretarial services, fax, laundry service.

| *Rooms* 119 | *Direct dial* Yes | *Confirm by* 6 | *Parking* Ample |
| *Ensuite bath/shower* 119 | *Room TV* Yes | *Last dinner* 10 | *Room service* 24 hours |

SOUTHAMPTON   Post House Hotel   59%   £C/D

H **Map 5 D4** Hampshire
Herbert Walker Avenue
SO1 0HJ
Southampton (0703) 330777
Telex 477368

Credit Access, Amex, Diners, Visa

A 10-storey hotel overlooking the QE2 berth and picking up the nautical theme in the Harbour Bar, with its fishing nets and marine paintings. 45 bedrooms have recently been completely refurbished, and all rooms have tea-makers and mini-bars. Executive suites also provide newspapers, chocolates, trouser presses and hairdryers. *Amenities* garden, indoor swimming pool, sauna, solarium, whirlpool bath, gymnasium, secretarial services, fax, laundry service, 24-hour lounge service. &

Rooms 133	*Direct dial* Yes	*Confirm by* 6	*Parking* Ample
Ensuite bath/shower 133	*Room TV* Yes	*Last dinner* 10	*Room service* All day

SOUTHAMPTON   Southampton Park Hotel   64%   £D/E

H **Map 5 D4** Hampshire
Cumberland Place SO9 4NY
Southampton (0703) 223467
Telex 47439

Credit Access, Amex, Diners, Visa

Behind a rather dull facade (the building has been likened to an apartment block) lies a modern and well-run hotel whose town-centre position and views of Watts Park make it a popular venue. The spacious foyer leads to a smart lounge and there's also a bar and basement bistro. Individually decorated bedrooms, some with balconies, are well equipped. Compact bathrooms are up-to-date.
Amenities in-house movies, secretarial services, fax, laundry service.

Rooms 75	*Direct dial* Yes	*Confirm by* 6	*Parking* Limited
Ensuite bath/shower 75	*Room TV* Yes	*Last dinner* 11	*Room service* 24 hours

★ For a *discount* on next year's guide, see **An Offer for Answers**. ★

SOUTHPORT   Bold Hotel   54%   £E

H **Map 10 A1** Merseyside
Lord Street PR9 0BE
Southport (0704) 32578

Credit Access, Amex, Diners, Visa

There has been complete refurbishment at this Victorian hotel since new owners took over. Public rooms include two bars, one a convivial haunt of the locals, the other a smarter cocktail bar, a first-floor reception and a large functions suite. Bedrooms are bright and new, and the pièce de résistance is the luxury room with king-sized bed and sunken bath. No dogs.
Amenities secretarial services, laundry service.

Rooms 25	*Direct dial* Yes	*Confirm by* 5	*Parking* Limited
Ensuite bath/shower 21	*Room TV* Yes	*Last dinner* 10	*Room service* 24 hours

SOUTHPORT   Prince of Wales Hotel   65%   £C/D

H **Map 10 A1** Merseyside
Lord Street PR8 1JS
Southport (0704) 36688
Telex 67415

Credit Access, Amex, Diners, Visa

A fine Victorian hotel set back from a handsome tree-lined street less than half a mile from the Royal Birkdale Golf Course. Public rooms include a grandly proportioned lounge with comfortable traditional appeal and a cosy cocktail bar sporting mirrors signed by golfing megastars. Most bedrooms have oak-effect units and pretty fabrics, and tiled bathrooms are well equipped. *Amenities* garden, in-house movies, secretarial services, laundry service.

Rooms 103	*Direct dial* Yes	*Confirm by* 6	*Parking* Ample
Ensuite bath/shower 103	*Room TV* Yes	*Last dinner* 10	*Room service* 24 hours

SOUTHSEA

See under PORTSMOUTH

SOUTHWELL   Saracen's Head Hotel   62%   £C/D

H **Map 11 D3** Nottinghamshire
Market Place NG25 0HE
Southwell (0636) 812701
Telex 377201

Credit Access, Amex, Diners, Visa

Like so many of its contemporaries, this smart 16th-century black and white building was formerly a coaching inn. The public areas – which are due for some necessary refurbishment – include a beamed reception area and two bars. Thanks to total refurbishment, bedrooms are uniformly good, with plenty of seating and space. Bathrooms are equally smart. One room with four-poster features a fine medieval wall painting. *Amenities* laundry service.

Rooms 27	*Direct dial* Yes	*Confirm by* 6	*Parking* Ample
Ensuite bath/shower 27	*Room TV* Yes	*Last dinner* 9.45	*Room service* 24 hours

SOUTHWOLD	Crown	£E/F

IR **Map 6 D2** Suffolk
High Street IP18 6DP
Southwold (0502) 722275
Telex 57223

Credit Access, Amex, Visa

The staff are a great strength at this old town-centre inn, offering cheerful and attentive concern for their guests' requirements. The main bar is furnished in solid country style, and there's a second bar and small parlour. Bedrooms are appealing, with fresh white walls and a variety of antiques; they are gradually being individually redecorated with pleasing matching fabrics. Three bathrooms are private but not en suite. *Amenities* patio.

Rooms 12	*Direct dial* Yes	*Confirm by* arrang.	*Parking* Ample
Ensuite bath/shower 9	*Room TV* Yes	*Last dinner* 9.45	*Room service* None

Restaurant

Set L from £11
Set D from £13
About £35 for two
Seats 26
Parties 50

Competent cooking and the general charm of the place, with friendly staff and most appealing surroundings, make this a pleasant spot for a meal. The shortish menu changes daily, and a typical day might feature smoked quail (served whole in a bowl with seasonal salads), sautéed fillet of brill, vegetable and lentil casserole with braised rice, and bread, butter and marmalade pudding. A masterly selection of great wines includes Ch. Latour '61 and '66, Barolo Riserva, Borgogno '61, and Pinot Noir Saintsbury '85. Exceptional wines are also available by the glass from the Cruover machine. There's a courtyard for summer eating. ➾ Outstanding ♇ Well-chosen ⊗

Lunch 12.30–1.45
Dinner 7.30–9.45

♇ indicates a **well-chosen** house wine

SPARK BRIDGE	Bridgefield House 58%	£E

HR **Map 13 C6** Cumbria
Nr Ulverston LA12 8DA
Lowick Bridge (022 985) 239

Credit Access

The Glisters are most friendly hosts and they have created a pleasing air of intimacy in their Lakeland stone house. A log fire warms the homely, chintzy lounge and the spacious bedrooms, though modest, are comfortable, with freestanding furniture and simple decor. Bathrooms are of a good size, with plenty of towels, hairdryers and excellent drying facilities for walkers caught in the Cumbrian rain. *Amenities* garden, laundry service.

Rooms 5	*Room phone* No	*Confirm by* arrang.	*Parking* Ample
Ensuite bath/shower 4	*Room TV* No	*Last dinner* 8	*Room service* All day

Restaurant ⊲

Set Sun L & D £17
About £45 for two
Seats 30
Parties 30

Rosemary Glister's daily-changing menus offer a choice of starters and sweets but a fixed main course, although vegetarians and those on special diets will be well catered for. A large range of seasonal produce is competently handled to produce unpretentious and flavoursome dishes such as lambs' sweetbreads, pan-fried steak with blackcurrants and green peppercorns and halibut poached in white wine with yoghurt, fennel and apple. Booking essential. Private lunch parties by arrangement. ⊗

Dinner only 7.30 for 8 **Closed** 25 Dec

SPEEN	Old Plow Inn	£D/E

IR **Map 5 E2**
Buckinghamshire
Flowers Bottom HP17 0PZ
Hampden Row (024 028) 300

Credit Access, Amex, Diners, Visa

A peaceful country setting is enjoyed by this well-run inn, where original 17th-century features include stone tiles and exposed beams. The bar is old-fashioned in a stylish way, with solid tables and chairs and cream walls; upstairs, there's a cosy residents' lounge. Bedrooms are a delight – matching fabrics, mineral water, fresh flowers and magazines give a feeling of peace and comfort. Bathrooms are neat and modern. *Amenities* garden.

Rooms 2	*Room phone* No	*Confirm by* arrang.	*Parking* Ample
Ensuite bath/shower 2	*Room TV* No	*Last dinner* 9.30	*Room service* Limited
			see over

Old Plow, Atkins Restaurant

Set L £12.50
About £50 for two
Seats 50

Oak beams, fresh flowers and waitresses in old-fashioned aprons give a period feel to the dining room, though the atmosphere on a recent visit was not very relaxing. Frances Atkins cooks with assurance and imagination through menus that tempt with such dishes as terrine of prawn and minted peas, honeyed saddle of lamb and a nice gooey treacle pud topped with cream. Fixed-price lunches, or excellent bar snacks.

Lunch 12.30–2   *Dinner* 7.30–9.30
Closed L Sat, D Sun, all Mon, Bank Hols, 1st 2 wks Feb & 1 wk Aug

SPELDHURST

George & Dragon, Oak Room

R **Map 7 B5** Kent
Nr Tunbridge Wells
Langton (089 286) 3125

Set L £7.50, Sun £11
Set D £16.75
About £55 for two
Seats 50 *Parking* Ample
Credit Access, Amex, Diners, Visa

Enjoyable food and exceptional wines in a restaurant topped by massive roof trusses and timbers. Cooking is honest and old-fashioned, with dishes like cream of vegetable soup, coquilles St. Jacques with a cheese sauce and sirloin steak stuffed with Stilton, accompanied by a robust Madeira sauce. Vegetables are good – fresh and nicely cooked. The great classic cellar boasts a superb collection of fine clarets: note five vintages of Ch. d'Yquem including '76 Bordeaux. ⌷ Outstanding ℗

Lunch 12–2   *Dinner* 7–10
Closed L Sat, D Sun & all Bank Hol Mons

STADDLE BRIDGE

McCoy's at the Tontine   70%   £C/D

HR **Map 15 C5**
North Yorkshire
Nr Northallerton DL6 3JB
East Harlsey (060 982) 671

Rooms 6
Ensuite bath/shower 6
Direct dial Yes
Room TV Yes
Confirm by arrang.
Last dinner 10
Parking Ample
Room service All day

Credit Access, Amex, Diners, Visa
Closed 24–26 Dec & 1 Jan

A programme of improvements over the last few years has transformed this establishment into a truly delightful hotel. Bold floral chintzes and enormous cushions beckon you to the seating in the lounge area and, in the bar, huge palms and elaborate wallpapers give a characterful '30s air. Apple green carpets in the bedrooms are complemented by stunning wallpaper by Givenchy; all rooms are air-conditioned and are equipped with sherry, glossy magazines, mineral water, fresh flowers and a tray of tea for afternoon arrivals – extras which typify the way the McCoy brothers look after their guests. Bathrooms are to a similarly high standard. Breakfasts are superb.
Amenities garden, coarse fishing, laundry service.

McCoy's Restaurant   ★★   ⚐

Lunch by arrang.
Dinner 7–10.30
About £72 for two
Seats 40
Parties 25

Closed Sun & Bank Hols (exc. Good Fri), 25 & 26 Dec & 1 Jan

Candlelight and William Morris-style wallpaper create a dark, romantic room in which to agonise over Tom McCoy's menus – so tempting that choice seems impossible. The best and freshest ingredients are used, skilfully cooked to result in dishes of sheer delight. Vegetables are delicious and the desserts sinful bliss. Some fine bottles – Puligny Montrachet Pucelles 1985 (Leflaive), Penfolds Grange Hermitage 1980 – but the list is not as exciting as the menu. *Specialities* foie gras de canard with black cherry sauce, roast loin of lamb with parsley and courgette dariole, fillet of sea bass with fresh truffle sauce, home-made cointreau ice cream with prunes soaked in Armagnac. ♀ Well-chosen ℗

STAFFORD   Tillington Hall Hotel   60%   £D/E

H **Map 10 B3** Staffordshire
Eccleshall Road ST16 1JJ
Stafford (0785) 53531
Telex 36566

Credit Access, Amex, Diners, Visa

Improvements are in hand at this relaxing hotel on the A5013 (close
to junction 14 of the M6). A new reception lounge and leisure complex
are due for completion as we publish, supplementing the existing
roomy lounge bar. 16 bedrooms, with smart modern freestanding
furniture, are in the main house, the rest, with pine fitted units, in a
purpose-built annexe; all are comfortable and well equipped.
Amenities garden, in-house movies, laundry service.

Rooms 90	*Direct dial* Yes	*Confirm by* 6	*Parking* Ample
Ensuite bath/shower 90	*Room TV* Yes	*Last dinner* 9.45	*Room service* 24 hours

**We welcome bona fide complaints and recommendations
on the tear-out pages at the back of the book for readers' comment.
They are followed up by our professional team.**

STAMFORD   Crown Hotel   £E/F

I **Map 11 E4** Lincolnshire
All Saints Place PE9 2AG
Stamford (0780) 63136

Credit Access, Amex, Diners, Visa
Closed 25 Dec

A comfortable family atmosphere pervades this lovely old inn. Public
rooms include a quiet, pretty stone-walled lounge and there is a cosy
bar area. Spacious bedrooms, many with armchairs, welcome
overnight guests. Fifteen of the 18 rooms have en-suite facilities; all
have radios, tea-makers and flowers. Ground floor accommodation
will suit those who have difficulty climbing stairs. Local fishing can
be arranged.

Rooms 18	*Room phone* Yes	*Confirm by* 7	*Parking* Ample
Ensuite bath/shower 15	*Room TV* Yes	*Last dinner* 9.30	*Room service* None

STAMFORD   George of Stamford   72%   £C/D

HR **Map 11 E4** Lincolnshire
71 St Martin's PE9 2LB
Stamford (0780) 55171
Telex 32578

Rooms 47
Ensuite bath/shower 47
Direct dial Yes
Room TV Yes
Confirm by arrang.
Last dinner 10
Parking Ample
Room service 24 hours

Credit Access, Amex, Diners, Visa

Period charm and modern comfort come in equal parts at this
delightful 18th-century coaching
inn where a gallows sign across
the road offers a warning to any
prospective highwaymen. Characterful public rooms include
two inviting lounges, one conservatory style with exotic
plants, a stylish cocktail bar and
a cosy little beamed snug. The
pretty walled garden is just the
place for sitting in summer. In-

dividually decorated bedrooms are stylish and luxurious, with fresh
fruit and flowers in every room and excellent well-stocked bathrooms.
Standards of housekeeping throughout are commendably high.
Amenities garden, fax, laundry service, coffee shop (9am–11pm).

Restaurant   ♛

About £47 for two
Seats 80
Parties 40

Christopher Pitman's daily roasts complement the strikingly traditional style, a handsome panelled dining room with an impressive
stone fireplace. But his interesting menu also has some imaginative
touches, partly inspired by his experience of Swiss and Italian kitchens.
We enjoyed a creamy Stilton terrine starter, and crab-filled fillet of
sole with a flavourful langoustine sauce. Excellent vegetables included
superb Byron potatoes. Tempting trolley sweets such as a rum and
raisin cheesecake. Service is helpful and attentive, with special dishes
willingly cooked to order. Wine list chosen with obvious flair includes
Cullen's Sauvignon Blanc Margaret River, '80 Santenay (Pousse D'Or),
and '76 Ch. Ausone. ➪ Outstanding 🍾 Well-chosen ℮

Lunch 12.30–2.30
Dinner 7–10

STANTON HARCOURT   Harcourt Arms   £E

IR **Map 5 D2** Oxfordshire
Nr Eynsham OX8 1RJ
Oxford (0865) 882192

Credit Access, Amex, Diners, Visa

An attractive old red-brick inn, partly creeper-clad, with a civilised, welcoming atmosphere. Most of the public space is occupied by the restaurant, but there's room for an agreeable bar. The ten bedrooms, all in a stone-built extension, are pleasantly cottagy, with assorted country furniture and pretty fabrics. Good modern bathrooms complete the picture. No children under ten. No dogs.
Amenities garden.

Rooms 10	*Direct dial* Yes	*Confirm by* arrang.	*Parking* Ample
Ensuite bath/shower 8	*Room TV* Yes	*Last dinner* 10	*Room service* None

Restaurant

Set Sun L £10.15
About £40 *for two*
Seats 100
Parties 45

Open log fires add to the cosy atmosphere, and when it's not too busy they're used for grilling the very popular 10oz fillet steaks. Among other favourites are grilled prawns, a splendid country terrine, duck with blackcurrant sauce, liver and bacon, and a port-rich steak and kidney pie. Good wholesome food, with decent raw materials and careful, uncomplicated cooking.

Lunch 12–2   *Dinner* 7–10
Closed 25 Dec

STEVENAGE   Roebuck Hotel   61%   £C/D

H **Map 6 B3** Hertfordshire
Old London Road,
Broadwater SG2 8DS
Stevenage (0438) 365444
Telex 825505

Credit Access, Amex, Diners, Visa

Standing alongside the B197 south of Stevenage, this one-time coaching inn retains considerable old-world character, notably in the cosy lounges and bars. Bedrooms are in a modern extension reached by a glass-sided walkway; they are decent sized, double glazed and simply decorated. Bathrooms have good-sized towels, heated towel rails and plentiful supplies of toiletries. Housekeeping is commendable.
Amenities garden.

Rooms 54	*Direct dial* Yes	*Confirm by* 6	*Parking* Ample
Ensuite bath/shower 54	*Room TV* Yes	*Last dinner* 10	*Room service* All day

Changes in data sometimes occur in establishments
after the Guide goes to press.
Prices should be taken as indications rather than firm quotes.

STEYNING   Springwells Hotel   58%   £E

H **Map 5 E4** West Sussex
9 High Street BN4 3GG
Steyning (0903) 812446

Credit Access, Amex, Diners, Visa

Built in 1772, this charming little creeper-clad hotel offers a warm welcome in homely surroundings. There's a comfortably traditional lounge in pink and green and a modest bar opening out onto the conservatory and neat garden. Best bedrooms are on the first floor and include two with four-posters; top-floor rooms are smaller and have characterful sloping ceilings.
Amenities garden, outdoor swimming pool, sauna, laundry service.

Rooms 11	*Direct dial* Yes	*Confirm by* arrang.	*Parking* Limited
Ensuite bath/shower 7	*Room TV* Yes	*Last dinner* None	*Room service* Limited

STOCKBRIDGE   Grosvenor Hotel   57%   £E

H **Map 4 C3** Hampshire
High Street SO20 6EU
Andover (0264) 810606
Telex 477677

Credit Access, Amex, Diners, Visa

A handsome colonnaded porch marks the entrance to this former coaching inn. Main public areas are warmly traditional, with wood panelling and racing pictures. Bedrooms, in both the original building and a converted stable block are equipped with radio-alarms, hairdryers, trouser presses and tea-makers. Good modern bathrooms have heated towel rails and bathtime extras. No dogs. *Amenities* garden, sauna, snooker, in-house movies.

Rooms 25	*Direct dial* Yes	*Confirm by* 8	*Parking* Ample
Ensuite bath/shower 25	*Room TV* Yes	*Last dinner* 10	*Room service* Limited

STOCKBRIDGE   Sheriff House   ★   ♕   ⚜

RR **Map 4 C3** Hampshire
High Street SO20 6EX
Andover (0264) 810677

Set L & D £30
About £68 for two
Seats 20
Parties 12
Parking Ample

Everything about Ernest and Joan Fisher's tiny, homely restaurant is charmingly traditional, from cottage decor and beautiful table settings to superbly prepared and totally unpretentious food. Only the very best ingredients are used – obtained, of course, from old-fashioned, traditional suppliers! Ernest's daily-changing menu might begin with freshly made duck liver pâté on toast, followed

by lemon sole in prawn, wine and cream sauce. Next, perhaps a châteaubriand béarnaise garnished with perfectly cooked vegetables and, after cheese and fruit, a mouthwatering rum baba. The cellar has some good clarets and Rhônes; fine Germans too. ***Specialities*** local lobster, corn-fed duck, roast beef with Yorkshire pudding, home-made ice-creams.   ♀ Well-chosen   ℮

Lunch by arrang. only   *Dinner* 7.30 for 8

BEDROOMS 6   £D
With bath/shower 3

Bedrooms are homely and comfortable, and a magnificent breakfast is guaranteed. No dogs.

STOCKPORT   Alma Lodge Hotel   61%   £D/E

H **Map 10 B2**
Greater Manchester
149 Buxton Road SK2 6EL
061-483 4431

Credit Access, Amex, Diners, Visa

South of town on the A6, this Victorian hotel retains attractive period features in its oak-panelled foyer, while other public areas include a smart cane-furnished bar and function suite. Main-house bedrooms are mostly slightly superior to those in the new wing, though all are decently furnished and have pleasant pastel decor. Five rooms in the main house have no bath and are more modest.
Amenities laundry service.

Rooms 57	*Direct dial* Yes	*Confirm by* 7	*Parking* Ample
Ensuite bath/shower 52	*Room TV* Yes	*Last dinner* 9.30	*Room service* 24 hours

STOKE FLEMING   Stoke Lodge Hotel   60%   *NEW ENTRY*   £E/F

H **Map 3 D3** Devon
Nr Dartmouth TQ6 0RA
Stoke Fleming (0803) 770523

In a village on the coastal road, Stoke Lodge is a family-run hotel with a friendly, welcoming air. Bedrooms are bright, cheerful and of a decent size, and day rooms include a little foyer with paintings of local scenes, a comfortable bar-lounge and a comfortable leisure centre.
Amenities garden, indoor & outdoor swimming pools, sauna, solarium, whirlpool bath, keep-fit equipment, putting, games room, laundry service.

Rooms 24	*Direct dial* Yes	*Confirm by* arrang.	*Parking* Ample
Ensuite bath/shower 23	*Room TV* Yes	*Last dinner* 9	*Room service* All day

STOCKTON-ON-TEES   Swallow Hotel   70%   £D

H **Map 15 C5** Cleveland
10 John Walker
Square TS18 1AQ
Stockton-on-Tees (0642) 679721
Telex 587895

Rooms 123
Ensuite bath/shower 123
Direct dial Yes
Room TV Yes
Confirm by arrang.
Last dinner 10
Parking Ample
Room service 24 hours

Credit Access, Amex, Diners, Visa

A modern hotel conveniently located in the centre of town, next to a multi-storey car park. There's plenty of comfortable seating in the bright and spacious foyer but if you want to relax with a drink in more peaceful surroundings you can head for the stylish bar-lounge at the top of the spiral staircase. Best bedrooms have light modern decor, nice coordinated fabrics and brass light fittings. Others are

rather more old-fashioned but still comfortable, and all offer remote-control TVs, hairdryers and tea-makers, plus well-equipped tiled bathrooms. Good conference facilities. ***Amenities*** in-house movies, secretarial services, fax, laundry service, coffee shop (7am–11pm).

STOKE MANDEVILLE   Belmore Hotel   59%   £D/E

H **Map 5 D2** Buckinghamshire
Risborough Road HP22 5UT
Stoke Mandeville (029 661) 2022

Credit Access, Amex, Diners, Visa
Closed 1 wk Xmas

Book well in advance to make sure of accommodation at the Bartmans' friendly little hotel on the A4010. Guests can help themselves to drinks in the cosy lounge, which has inviting settees. Most bedrooms are in a single-storey block overlooking the pool and are well equipped with useful extras and neat carpeted bathrooms. *Amenities* garden, outdoor swimming pool, sauna, solarium, keep-fit equipment, beauty salon, massage parlour. &

Rooms 16	Direct dial Yes	Confirm by arrang.	Parking Ample
Ensuite bath/shower 16	Room TV Yes	Last dinner 9.30	Room service All day

STOKE-ON-TRENT   North Stafford Hotel   63%   £C/D

H **Map 10 B3** Staffordshire
Station Road ST4 2AE
Stoke-on-Trent (0782) 744477
Telex 36287

Credit Access, Amex, Diners, Visa

A grand, red-brick, Tudor-style building standing across the road from the railway station. Guests arriving in the reception area can admire a display of lovely local chinaware before settling down in the lounge or enjoying a drink in one of the two bars. Decent-sized bedrooms, gradually being refurbished with smart modern furniture, are equipped with trouser presses, hairdryers and remote-control TVs. *Amenities* laundry service.

Rooms 70	Room phone Yes	Confirm by 6	Parking Ample
Ensuite bath/shower 70	Room TV Yes	Last dinner 10	Room service 24 hours

We publish annually,
so make sure you use the current edition.
It's worth it!

STOKESLEY   Chapters   ⑃

R **Map 15 C5** North Yorkshire
9 Bridge Road
Stokesley (0642) 711888

About £30 for two
Seats 24
Parties 26
Parking Ample
Credit Access, Amex, Diners, Visa

Alan Thompson's capable cooking continues to win approval at this friendly little bistro on the banks of the river Leven. Daily-changing blackboard menus reflect the best of the local markets. Start perhaps with mussels in wine and herbs, then choose monkfish and king prawns provençale or rack of lamb sauced with mustard. Tempting desserts range from fresh pineapple Alaska to coffee and brandy roulade. ⊖

Lunch Thurs only 12.30–2.30   *Dinner* 7.30–10
Closed Sun, Mon, Bank Hols, 25, 26 & 31 Dec & 1 Jan

STON EASTON   Ston Easton Park   88%   £B

HR **Map 4 B3** Somerset
Nr Bath BA3 4DF
Chewton Mendip (076 121) 631

Rooms 20
Ensuite bath/shower 20
Direct dial Yes
Room TV Yes
Confirm by arrang.
Last dinner 9.30
Parking Ample
Room service All day

Credit Access, Amex, Diners, Visa

No expense was spared in restoring this fine Palladian mansion to its former glory, and it is now one of England's top country house hotels. Expert advice on 18th-century interiors was sought when recreating the magnificent public rooms, and the salon in particular is a triumph of good taste with its lovely trompe l'oeil murals. Everywhere you look there are paintings, fine antiques, fresh flowers and deep comfy sofas – all contributing to the very real impression of gracious living. Grandly proportioned bedrooms feature handsome period furnishings and several four-posters. Best bathrooms are sumptuously marbled. No children under 12. Dogs in kennels only.   *Amenities* garden, croquet, billiards, secretarial services, fax, laundry service, helipad.

Restaurant ♕

Set L £17.50, Sun £18
Set D £27.50
About £67 *for two*
Seats 40
Parties 24

The quietly elegant setting is perfectly in tune with Mark Harrington's confident, sophisticated style of cooking. Top-quality seasonal produce enhances imaginative combinations like feather-light pike quenelles teamed with lobster sauce, and tender venison medallions accompanied by fresh cranberries and a good gamey sauce. Desserts include some lovely sorbets and there's a splendid classic wine list with a high-class selection from the New World.

▭ Outstanding ♟ Well-chosen ⊗ ⅊

Lunch 12.30–2   *Dinner* 7.30–9.30, Fri & Sat 7.30–10

STONE — Crown Hotel 55% £E

H Map 10 B3 Staffordshire
38 High Street ST15 8AS
Stone (0785) 813535

Credit Access, Amex, Visa
Closed 24 & 25 Dec

The Crown started life as a coaching inn 200 years ago, and today its character derives from the oak panelling and traditional furnishings in the day rooms. 13 bedrooms are in the main building – reached by a fine old oak staircase – while the rest are in a separate block next to the car park. All are furnished in simple modern style, with bathrooms for main-house rooms and showers for the others.

Rooms 29	*Room phone* Yes	*Confirm by* arrang.	*Parking* Ample
Ensuite bath/shower 29	*Room TV* Yes	*Last dinner* 9.30	*Room service* Limited

---

STONEHOUSE — Stonehouse Court Hotel 67% £D

H Map 4 B2 Gloucestershire
Bristol Road GL10 3RA
Stonehouse (045 382) 5155
Telex 437244

Credit Access, Amex, Diners, Visa

Built in the 17th century, this attractive hotel stands in its own grounds by the A419 west of Stroud. Period features abound in the cosy day rooms, and the seven main-house bedrooms are spacious and traditional. Other bedrooms, in light, modern style, are in a separate block that also contains the new conference centre. No dogs.
Amenities garden, keep-fit equipment, putting, croquet, coarse fishing, secretarial services, fax, laundry service.

Rooms 24	*Direct dial* Yes	*Confirm by* arrang.	*Parking* Ample
Ensuite bath/shower 24	*Room TV* Yes	*Last dinner* 9.30	*Room service* All day

---

**We welcome bona fide complaints and recommendations
on the tear-out pages at the back of the book for readers' comment.
They are followed up by our professional team.**

STONHAM — Mr Underhill's ★ ⚑

RR Map 6 C3 Suffolk
Stowmarket IP14 5DW
Stowmarket (0449) 711206

Lunch by arrang. only
Dinner 7.30–9
Set D £18.50
About £50 *for two*
Seats 28
Parties 28
Parking Ample
Credit Access, Amex, Visa
Closed D Sun, all Mon & most Bank Hols

Chris Bradley maintains a high standard of refined cooking in his warmly decorated, civilised restaurant. His dinner menu offers no choice, but you can discuss the meal with Judy Bradley when booking. Out most recent meal included asparagus beurre blanc, a memorable rib of veal with Madeira sauce, superb cheeses (wonderful triple crème Pavé d'Affinois), and delicious creole coffee parfait. The wine list is a model of balance and good taste: note the lovely Sauvignon and Chardonnay from Kumeu River, New Zealand. ***Specialities*** salad of tea-smoked duck, guinea-fowl with lime and ginger, rack of lamb with Chinese spices, passion-fruit pavlova. ♟ Well-chosen ⊗ ⅊

BEDROOMS 1 £E/F
With bath/shower 1

For overnight guests there's a comfortable double bedroom with private facilities and its own lounge. No dogs.

STONY STRATFORD   Stratfords   ♧

R **Map 5 D1** Buckinghamshire
7 St Paul's Court, High Street
Milton Keynes (0908) 566577

Set L from £9.50
Set D from £12.95
About £46 for two
Seats 70 *Parties* 70
Parking Ample
Credit Access, Amex, Diners, Visa

Dine in the nave at this attractive restaurant which was once the chapel of a public school. The fixed-price menus begin with a tureen of excellent soup with home-baked bread, followed perhaps by duck salad, salmon cocotte or chicken and apricot terrine. Main courses range from chicken breast stuffed with a ginger and spring onion mousse to salmon en croûte. Disappointing sweets, but good coffee.
🍷 Well-chosen ☺

Lunch 12–2   *Dinner* 7.30–10
Closed L Sat, all Sun & Mon, 2 wks Jan

---

  is our symbol for an **outstanding** wine list

STORRINGTON   Abingworth Hall   70%   £D

HR **Map 5 E3** West Sussex
Thakeham Road,
Pulborough RH20 3EF
West Chiltington (079 83) 3636
Telex 877835

Rooms 22
Ensuite bath/shower 22
Direct dial Yes
Room TV Yes
Confirm by arrang.
Last dinner 9
Parking Ample
Room service 24 hours

Credit Access, Amex, Diners, Visa
Closed 1st 2 wks Jan

The Bulmans offer a warm welcome to their Edwardian mansion, which occupies a beautiful
setting next to an ornamental
lake. Pauline's excellent taste is
evident throughout the hotel,
notably in the cocktail bar with
its pretty colour scheme and
elegant furnishings. The handsome lounge features panelling
and leaded windows, and there's
an attractive meeting room.
The tranquil bedrooms boast
thoughtful extras such as books, tissues, potpourri and sewing kits.
Those in a garden wing are less characterful, but still bright and well-
maintained. No children under ten. No dogs. *Amenities* garden,
outdoor swimming pool, tennis, 9-hole golf course, pitch & putt,
croquet, secretarial services, laundry service, helipad.

Restaurant   ♨

Set L Sun £11.50
Set D £21
About £50 for two
Seats 45
Parties 14

Sunny yellow and green decor coupled with white linen and shining
glassware make this an airy and elegant restaurant. On the menus are
a range of tempting dishes which are skilfully prepared from good
ingredients and beautifully presented. Typical dishes are smoked
bacon and Roquefort salad and poached salmon hollandaise. Finish
with the excellent cheese and luscious sweets such as profiteroles with
hot honey and chocolate sauce. 🍷 Well-chosen ☺

Lunch 12.30–2   *Dinner* 7.30–9
Closed 1st 2 wks Jan

STORRINGTON   Little Thakeham   78%   £B

HR **Map 5 E3** West Sussex
Merrywood Lane RH20 3HE
Storrington (090 66) 4416

Rooms 10
Ensuite bath/shower 10
Direct dial Yes
Room TV Yes
Confirm by arrang.
Last dinner 9.30
Parking Ample
Room service All day

Credit Access, Amex, Diners, Visa
Closed 2 wks Xmas

Delightful gardens designed by
Gertrude Jekyll surround this
handsome stone-built manor
house by Sir Edwin Lutyens,
which is tastefully furnished in
keeping with its period. It offers
today's guests the relaxing experience of a country house
smoothly run by the Rackcliffs
and their friendly staff. It's easy
to unwind in the splendid public
rooms, which include a lofty
lounge with mullioned windows

and a minstrel's gallery and a bar-lounge with inviting leather
armchairs and sofas. Spacious bedrooms are individually decorated
and stocked with thoughtful extras; bathrooms too are very well
equipped. Excellent breakfasts. No dogs. *Amenities* garden, outdoor
swimming pool, tennis, croquet, teletext, laundry service, helipad.

Restaurant ♛

Set L £15
Set D £19.50
About £60 *for two*
Seats 35
Parties 30

Quality materials are sympathetically handled by chef Frances Smith to create simple good food that is perfectly in keeping with the elegant country house setting. Typical of the short, fixed-price menu would be a game terrine with home-made chutney followed by roast lamb or duck with lime and juniper berries. Tempting sweets are displayed on a massive refectory table.

Lunch 12.30–2　*Dinner* 7.30–9.15
Closed D Sun & 2 wks Xmas

STORRINGTON　　Manleys ★ ♨

RR **Map 5 E3** West Sussex
Manleys Hill RH20 4BT
Storrington (090 66) 2331

Set L Sun only £17
Set D £26 (Fri only)
About £80 *for two*
Seats 48
Parties 22
Parking Ample

Credit Access, Amex, Diners, Visa

Austrian-born chef-patron Karl Löderer has built up an enviable reputation here in West Sussex, yet he cannot afford to rest on his laurels. Once renowned for the freshness of its ingredients, Manleys can now be faulted for the occasional lapse in quality. Cooking standards are becoming uneven, too, with dishes such as scallops with tomato sauce only adequately prepared. Main choices range from lamb fillet

roasted with herbs to lobster-garnished loin of veal. Desserts, with certain exceptions, continue to delight but service is patchy. *Specialities* caille rôtie et fumée et sa galette de pommes de terre, loup de mer braisé en croûte d'herbes, tranche de pommes en habit de filo. ♿

Lunch 12–1.45　*Dinner* 7–9.30, Fri & Sat 7–10.15
Closed D Sun, all Mon, 1st 2 wks Jan, last wk Aug & 1st wk Sept

BEDROOMS 1　£C
With bath/shower 1
Room TV Yes

One apartment (bedroom, sitting room and bath) is available for restaurant guests staying overnight. No children or dogs.

STOURBRIDGE　　Talbot Hotel　　£E

I **Map 10 B4** West Midlands
High Street DY8 1DW
Stourbridge (0384) 394350

Credit Access, Amex, Visa

A smart foyer welcomes guests to this fine old inn on the town's high street. The lounge bar, with its pale panelling and attractive lighting, is partnered by a lively public bar. Good-sized bedrooms are light, airy and well kept. Executive rooms add trouser presses to the standard accoutrements of tea-makers and hairdryers. Carpeted bathrooms are nicely decorated.
Amenities laundry service, coffee shop (9.30am–11pm).

Rooms 25	*Direct dial* Yes	*Confirm by* arrang.	*Parking* Limited
Ensuite bath/shower 25	*Room TV* Yes	*Last dinner* 9.45	*Room service* Limited

Our inspectors *never* book in the name of Egon Ronay's Guides.
They disclose their identity only if they are considering an establishment
for inclusion in the next edition of the Guide.

STOW-ON-THE-WOLD　　Fosse Manor Hotel　　59%　　£D/E

H **Map 4 C1** Gloucestershire
Fosse Way GL54 1JX
Cotswold (0451) 30354

Credit Access, Amex, Diners, Visa
Closed 1 wk Xmas

Set in pleasant grounds on the A429 about a mile south of Stow, this creeper-covered hotel is a comfortable base for a tour of the Cotswolds. Each homely bedroom is different and all but four have a private bath or shower room. The main day room is a large, relaxing lounge with flower arrangements and plenty of inviting armchairs. In the bar there's an interesting collection of headwear.
Amenities garden, children's playground.

Rooms 20	*Room phone* No	*Confirm by* arrang.	*Parking* Ample
Ensuite bath/shower 16	*Room TV* Yes	*Last dinner* 9.30	*Room service* Limited

STOW-ON-THE WOLD   Grapevine Hotel   66%   *NEW ENTRY*   £D/E

H Map 4 C1 Gloucestershire
Sheep Street GL54 1AU
Cotswold (0451) 30344
Telex 43423

Credit Access, Amex, Diners, Visa
Closed 24 Dec–10 Jan

A genial owner and friendly, helpful staff add to the enjoyment of a stay at this charming Cotswold hotel. Antiques, ornaments, prints and plants grace the comfortably furnished lounge, and there's a pleasant bar in rustic style. Exposed stone walls are a feature in many of the bedrooms, which have hairdryers and tea-makers, plus carpeted bath/shower rooms. The welcoming glass of sherry is a typical thoughtful touch. No dogs.

Rooms 17	Direct dial Yes	Confirm by 6	Parking Ample
Ensuite bath/shower 17	Room TV Yes	Last dinner 9.30	Room service All day

STOW-ON-THE-WOLD   Unicorn Crest Hotel   59%   £C/D

H Map 4 C1 Gloucestershire
Sheep Street GL54 1HQ
Cotswold (0451) 30257
Telex 437186

Credit Access, Amex, Diners, Visa

At the heart of the highest town in the Cotswolds, the Unicorn Crest is a small hotel with a steep tiled roof, dormer windows and many original beams. Bedrooms are quite well appointed – freestanding mahogany furniture, bright new carpets and bedcovers, trouser presses, remote-control TVs – and Executive rooms offer even more. There are two four-poster rooms. Day rooms are in pubby style. *Amenities* garden.

Rooms 20	Room phone Yes	Confirm by 6	Parking Ample
Ensuite bath/shower 20	Room TV Yes	Last dinner 9.30	Room service All day

STOW-ON-THE-WOLD   Wyck Hill House   75%   £C

HR Map 4 C1 Gloucestershire
Burford Road GL54 1HY
Cotswold (0451) 31936
Telex 43611

Rooms 16
Ensuite bath/shower 16
Direct dial Yes
Room TV Yes
Confirm by arrang.
Last dinner 9.30
Parking Ample
Room service 24 hours

Credit Access, Amex, Diners, Visa

There are marvellous views of the Windrush Valley from this sympathetically restored country house. Situated off the A424 south-east of Stow, the hotel welcomes guests with a large open fire in the comfortably furnished reception lounge. Antiques are much in evidence, as are colourful flower arrangements. The intimate bar has a clublike atmosphere and the cedar-panelled library provides the

perfect spot for a good read or game of backgammon. All bedrooms are individually decorated and have bathrobes and fresh fruit. Best rooms, including one with a four-poster, are spacious with seating areas. En suite bathrooms are equally impressive. No children under six. *Amenities* garden, croquet, laundry service, helipad.

Restaurant   ♨

Set L £13.75, Sun £15.50
Set D £21
About £60 *for two*
Seats 32
Parties 24

Chef Ian Smith's innovative menus are full of interest, though the standard of cooking occasionally disappoints. The setting is elegant, with superb views. Raw materials cannot be faulted in starters like spinach and Stilton soufflé and main courses like marinated venison or sautéed veal sweetbreads. Desserts include a pair of featherlight liqueur-flavoured mousses. Well-balanced wine list with some very fine clarets, including Châteaux Palmer '71 and Ducru Beaucaillou '61. ☕ &

Lunch 12.30–2.30   *Dinner* 7.30–9.30

STRATFIELD TURGIS   Wellington Arms Hotel   *NEW ENTRY*   £C/D

I Map 5 D3 Hampshire
Nr Basingstoke RG27 0AS
Basingstoke (0256) 882214
Telex 265871

Credit Access, Amex, Diners, Visa

A Georgian-fronted building set back from the A33. It's a comfortable, relaxing place, recently refurbished. Day rooms have a quiet, traditional elegance and bedrooms are decorated in the best of taste, with pretty wallpapers, prints and pine furnishings. Eight rooms are more individual, with something of a Continental air, and the four-poster suite boasts a whirlpool bath.
Amenities garden, game fishing, in-house movies, laundry service.

Rooms 15	Direct dial Yes	Confirm by arrang.	Parking Ample
Ensuite bath/shower 15	Room TV Yes	Last dinner 9.30	Room service Limited

STRATFORD-UPON-AVON   Alveston Manor   66%   £C

H **Town plan E2**
Warwickshire
Clopton Bridge CV37 7HP
Stratford-upon-Avon
(0789) 204581 Telex 31324
Credit Access, Amex, Diners, Visa

The first performance of *A Midsummer Night's Dream* was reputedly held in the gardens of this impressive hotel. The public areas are oak-panelled, with fine fireplaces and comfortable seating. Bedrooms in the main building have antiques and excellent fabrics; those in the modern extensions have either darkwood freestanding units and pretty coordinating fabrics or fitted units and rather dated schemes. *Amenities* garden, pitch & putt, valeting, laundry service.

Rooms 108	*Direct dial* Yes	*Confirm by* 6	*Parking* Ample
Ensuite bath/shower 108	*Room TV* Yes	*Last dinner* 9.30	*Room service* 24 hours

STRATFORD-UPON-AVON   Arden Hotel   61%   £D/E

H **Town plan D3**
Warwickshire
44 Waterside CV37 6BA
Stratford-upon-Avon
(0789) 294949 Telex 311726
Credit Access, Amex, Diners, Visa

A cheerful hotel with a long-serving general manager, obliging staff and a fine position right opposite the Royal Shakespeare Theatre. Prints of the bard adorn the modest little foyer, beyond which there is a bright carvery restaurant (popular with tourists) and a lounge with plenty of armchairs. Bedrooms are pleasantly functional, and many have recently been upgraded, along with their bathrooms. *Amenities* garden, laundry service.

Rooms 65	*Direct dial* Yes	*Confirm by* arrang.	*Parking* Ample
Ensuite bath/shower 65	*Room TV* Yes	*Last dinner* 9	*Room service* 24 hours

STRATFORD-UPON-AVON   Billesley Manor   77%   £C/D

HR **Town plan A1**
Warwickshire
Billesley, Nr Alcester B49 6NF
Stratford-upon-Avon
(0789) 400888
Telex 312599

Rooms 41
Ensuite bath/shower 41
Direct dial Yes
Room TV Yes
Confirm by arrang.
Last dinner 9.30
Parking Ample
Room service 24 hours

Credit Access, Amex, Diners, Visa

Refurbishment continues at this lovely old manor house three miles from Stratford. All the public rooms are smart, comfortable and spotlessly clean. Guests are greeted in a panelled foyer whose leather chesterfields provide a degree of comfort rivalled by the period-style sofas and armchairs in the spacious lounge and bar. Tasteful bedrooms have good-quality period furnishings. Those in the main house are particularly spacious. All have hairdryers, trouser presses and remote control TVs. Bathrooms are equally well equipped with thick towels and good toiletries. No dogs. *Amenities* garden, indoor swimming pool, sauna, tennis, croquet, secretarial services, fax, laundry service.

Restaurant   ♛

Set L £13
Set D £19
About £60 *for two*
Seats 48
Parties 80

Garden views provide a pleasing aspect from this elegant dining room, where quality fresh produce is skilfully transformed into tasty dishes in the modern French style. Starters like terrine of scallops and sole on watercress sauce are splendid, while main courses include succulent fillet with black and green peppercorns served with brandy cream sauce. Good wines, strongest in burgundy and Alsace: Chorey-les-Beaune (Arnoux) '76; Tokay Rangen (Zind Humbrecht) '84. ♟ Well-chosen ⊖ &

Lunch 12.30–2.30   *Dinner* 7.30–9.30, Fri & Sat till 10

STRATFORD-UPON-AVON   Bunbury's   ♗

R **Town plan B2**
Warwickshire
3 Greenhill Street
Stratford-upon-Avon
(0789) 293563

English cooking
Set L from £6.50 **Set D** £11.95
Seats 42 *Parties* 42
Parking Ample
Credit Access, Diners, Visa

Menus from the 16th and 17th centuries have been cleverly plundered to give visitors to this unusual restaurant a taste of the food Shakespeare would have eaten. Starters may include parsnip and apple fritters or prawn rissoles with, to follow, salmon pasties or Norfolk pottage. Authentic desserts to finish. Good wines: excellent Muscadet (Ch. La Touche) and Beaujolais (Chanut Frères). ♟ Well-chosen ⊖

Lunch 12–2.30, Sun 12–2   *Dinner* 5.45–11.30, Sun 7–11
About £32 *for two*
Closed D Sun in winter, all Mon (excp. L Bank Hols) & 1st Jan

STRATFORD-UPON-AVON

Map 4 C1
Town plan opposite

Population 21,675

A prosperous market-town on a lovely river site, with good Tudor and Jacobean architecture, would be a fair description of Stratford-upon-Avon–if it wasn't for the Bard. It took 200 years after Shakespeare's birth for proper tribute to be paid to him in a festival staged by David Garrick. The first Theatre was not built until 1879; it was burnt down in 1926 and succeeded by the present theatre in 1932, built with large overseas subscriptions, particularly from the U.S.

Annual Events
Map Fair *12th October*
Shakespeare's Birthday Celebration *22nd April*
Shakespeare Theatre Season *from April*
Stratford Festival *July*

Sights Outside Town
Coughton Court
Ragley Hall
Charlecote
Coventry Cathedral
Packwood House
Upton House
Warwick Castle

Information Centre
Judith Shakespeare's House
1 High Street
Telephone Stratford-upon-Avon 293127

1 Anne Hathaway's cottage *at Shottery* A3

2 Guild Chapel, Guildhall, Grammar School and Almshouses *exceptional medieval buildings* C3

3 Hall's Croft *fine Tudor house and walled garden, houses Hall's Croft Club* C3

4 Harvard House *1596 home of grandfather of Harvard's founder* C2

5 Holy Trinity Church *contains Shakespeare's tomb* C3

6 Information Centre C2

7 Mary Arden's house *at Wilmcote, 3 miles. Tudor farmhouse, home of Shakespeare's mother, farming museum* B1

8 New Place *Elizabethan garden on site of Shakespeare's last home* C3

9 Picture Gallery and Museum *pictures and relics of famous actors* D3

10 Railway Station A1

11 Royal Shakespeare Theatre D3

12 Shakespeare's birthplace *architectural interest and museum of rare Shakespeariana* C1

13 Swan Theatre D3

14 Town Hall C2

Fiat Dealer
G. M. Wyatt Garages
Western Road
Stratford-upon-Avon CV37 0AH
Tel. Stratford 67159

Stratford-upon-Avon

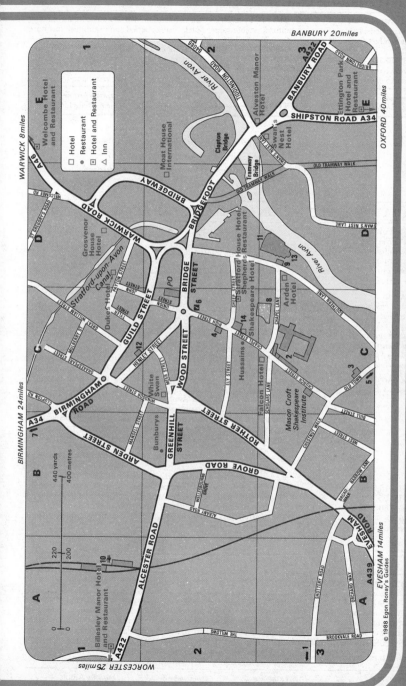

Legend:
- □ Hotel
- ● Restaurant
- ⊡ Hotel and Restaurant
- △ Inn

© 1988 Egon Ronay's Guides

STRATFORD-UPON-AVON   Dukes Hotel   68%   £D/E

H **Town plan D1**
Warwickshire
Payton Street CV37 6UA
Stratford-upon-Avon
(0789) 69300 Telex 31430
Credit Access, Amex, Diners, Visa
Closed 5 days Xmas

Alan and Brenda Power have turned this handsome Georgian building into a comfortable hotel, using period and antique furniture throughout. Ornaments add a homely touch to the spacious lounge, while prettily decorated bedrooms offer tea-makers and fully tiled bathrooms. Five of the bedrooms, including two suites, are very recent conversions. No children under ten. No dogs.
Amenities garden, games room, secretarial services, laundry service.

Rooms 22	*Direct dial* Yes	*Confirm by* arrang.	*Parking* Ample
Ensuite bath/shower 22	*Room TV* Yes	*Last dinner* 9.45	*Room service* Limited

Changes in data sometimes occur in establishments
after the Guide goes to press.
Prices should be taken as indications rather than firm quotes.

STRATFORD-UPON-AVON   Ettington Park Hotel   85%   £B

HR **Town plan E3**
Warwickshire
Alderminster CV37 8BS
Stratford-upon-Avon
(0789) 740740
Telex 311825

Rooms 48
Ensuite bath/shower 48
Direct dial Yes
Room TV Yes
Confirm by arrang.
Last dinner 9.30
Parking Ample
Room service 24 hours

Credit Access, Amex, Diners, Visa
Closed 3 days after New Year

Forty acres of beautiful grounds provide a fitting backdrop to this splendid Victorian Gothic mansion, parts of which date back to the Middle Ages. Public areas include a delightful conservatory with polychromatic tiled floor and a mellow, book-lined library-bar, but the real showpiece is the exquisite drawing room with its gilded ceiling, grand piano and elegant drapes. Spacious bedrooms are individually decorated in lavish but tasteful style and many have fine antiques and original paintings. Luxury bathrooms provide every cosseting extra. Excellent service throughout. *Amenities* garden, indoor swimming pool, sauna, solarium, whirlpool bath, tennis, croquet, riding, shooting, clay-pigeon shooting, game fishing, in-house movies, secretarial services, fax, laundry service, helipad.

Restaurant   ♛♛

Set L £15, Sun £14.75
Set D £25
About £60 *for two*
Seats 50
Parties 60

Don't be put off by the whimsical menu descriptions at this grandly elegant restaurant: Patrick McDonald has his feet planted firmly on the ground and uses plenty of sound judgement to temper his imaginative ideas. Top-quality ingredients, carefully harmonised and attractively presented, produce triumphs like clear crab soup with root ginger and scallops, and beef fillet with red wine, shallot and truffle sauce. Lovely puddings. ♟ Well-chosen ⌀ &

Lunch 12.30–2   *Dinner* 7–10

STRATFORD-UPON-AVON   Falcon Hotel   64%   £D

H **Town plan C3**
Warwickshire
Chapel Street CV37 6HA
Stratford-upon-Avon
(0789) 205777 Telex 312522
Credit Access, Amex, Diners, Visa

The Falcon has a fine timbered façade dating from about 1640, and today the 17th and 20th centuries blend harmoniously. A modern extension houses reception, a lounge and most of the bedrooms; these are spacious and well fitted, with slightly dated decor that is gradually being upgraded. A few compact, characterful rooms are in the old building. There are two delightful panelled bars. Pleasant efficient staff, so-so breakfast. *Amenities* garden, laundry service.

Rooms 73	*Direct dial* Yes	*Confirm by* 6	*Parking* Ample
Ensuite bath/shower 73	*Room TV* Yes	*Last dinner* 9	*Room service* 24 hours

STRATFORD-UPON-AVON   Grosvenor House Hotel   60%   £D/E

H Town plan D1
Warwickshire
12 Warwick Road CV37 6YT
Stratford-upon-Avon
(0789) 69213 Telex 311699
Credit Access, Amex, Diners, Visa
Closed 3 days Xmas

A friendly hotel which provides a comfortable base from which to explore Shakespeare country. The public areas, which include a bar, lounge, TV lounge and writing room, are enveloped by a warm, cosy feel. The bedrooms are all newly decorated and are equipped with tea/coffee makers; bath/shower rooms are adequate. No dogs.
Amenities garden, sauna, solarium, whirlpool bath, gymnasium, beauty salon, hairdressing, secretarial services, laundry service.

Rooms 57	*Direct dial* Yes	*Confirm by* arrang.	*Parking* Ample
Ensuite bath/shower 55	*Room TV* Yes	*Last dinner* 8.45	*Room service* 24 hours

STRATFORD-UPON-AVON   Hussain's

R Town plan C2
Warwickshire
6a Chapel Street
Stratford-upon-Avon
(0789) 67506

Indian cooking
Set L & D from £21.95 *for 2*
Seats 50 *Parking* Limited
Credit Access, Amex, Diners, Visa

Bang in the centre of town, this comfortable and attractive Indian restaurant is a useful place for a pre-theatre dinner. Service is pleasant and helpful, backing up a very good standard of cooking throughout the menu, from delicately spiced vegetable samosas and charcoal-cooked chicken shashlick to Gobhi peas, lamb sagwalla and tandoori prawn massala. Well-balanced set menus include a vegetarian thali. ♿

Lunch 12–2, Sun 12–2.30   *Dinner* 5.15–11.45, Fri & Sat 5–12, Sun 5.30–11.30   *About* £30 *for two*   **Closed** 25 Dec

★ For a *discount* on next year's guide, see **An Offer for Answers.** ★

STRATFORD-UPON-AVON   Moat House International   71%   £C/D

H Town plan D2
Warwickshire
Bridgefoot CV37 6YR
Stratford-upon-Avon
(0789) 414411
Telex 311127

Rooms 249
Ensuite bath/shower 249
Direct dial Yes
Room TV Yes
Confirm by arrang.
Last dinner 11
Parking Ample
Room service 24 hours

Credit Access, Amex, Diners, Visa

It's an easy walk to the town centre from this large modern hotel, which occupies five acres of gardens on the banks of the Avon. Public rooms are extensive and smartly contemporary, from the lobby with its large stone fireplace to the leafy lounge and the night club. There's also a tavern-style bar and restaurant and a long-hours grill room. Conference and banqueting facilities are excellent. Bedrooms,

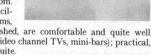

which are all being refurbished, are comfortable and quite well equipped (air-conditioning, video channel TVs, mini-bars); practical, well-fitted bathrooms, all en suite.
Amenities garden, hairdressing, in-house movies, secretarial services, fax, laundry service, coffee shop (7.30am–10.30pm). ♿

STRATFORD-UPON-AVON   Shakespeare Hotel   70%   £B/C

H Town plan C2
Warwickshire
Chapel Street CV37 6ER
Stratford-upon-Avon
(0789) 294771
Telex 311181

Rooms 70
Ensuite bath/shower 70
Direct dial Yes
Room TV Yes
Confirm by 6
Last dinner 10
Parking Limited
Room service 24 hours

Credit Access, Amex, Diners, Visa

An atmosphere of quiet dignity and elegant days gone by is immediately apparent on entering this well-run hotel in the heart of town. An open fire, beams, polished flagstone floor, period furniture and plump sofas in the lounge cannot fail to please, nor can the similarly characterful cocktail bar. In the Froth and Elbow public bar traditional beer is served. All the bedrooms are designed and decorated in

similar fashion, although the ones in the old building have more quaint charm, with freestanding period furniture, pretty floral fabrics and light, airy colour schemes. Modern bathrooms have bathrobes and good quality toiletries.
Amenities garden, fax, laundry service.

STRATFORD-UPON-AVON   Stratford House Hotel   64%   £D

HR Town plan C2
Warwickshire
18 Sheep Street CV37 6EF
Stratford-upon-Avon
(0789) 68288 Telex 311612
Credit Access, Amex, Diners, Visa
Closed 4 days Xmas

A Georgian house in the heart of Stratford lives on as a quiet, discreet little hotel. The whole place gleams with good housekeeping, and staff are friendly and attentive. Bedrooms feature pretty floral fabrics, neatly practical furniture and well-maintained modern bathrooms. The main day room is a homely yet stylish lounge with antique furniture, china and good pictures. Carefully cooked breakfasts. No children under three. No dogs. *Amenities* patio, laundry service.

Rooms 10	*Direct dial* Yes	*Confirm by* arrang.	*Parking* Difficult
Ensuite bath/shower 9	*Room TV* Yes	*Last dinner* 9.30	*Room service* Limited

Shepherds Restaurant   ♀

About £38 for two
Seats 40
Parties 30

In a colourful conservatory-style restaurant overlooking a delightful patio Nigel Lambert cooks with flair and skill. His food is attractive to look at and very good to eat, with pure, fresh flavours highlighting dishes like chicken livers served on crisp French leaves, guinea fowl with a lime and redcurrant sauce and a faultless crème brûlée with oranges and Grand Marnier. Good bottles from Australia and California figures on a carefully chosen wine list. ♀ Well-chosen ℮ &

Lunch 12–2   *Dinner* 6–9.30
Closed D Sun to non-residents & 4 days Xmas

STRATFORD-UPON-AVON   Swans Nest   61%   £C/D

H Town plan E3
Warwickshire
Bridgefoot CV37 7LT
Stratford-upon-Avon
(0789) 66761

Credit Access, Amex, Diners, Visa

The pruning of the privet hedge has opened up the views of river and theatre at this red-brick hotel, a popular base for tourists. The foyer-lounge is quite attractive, with pretty fabrics, and there's a pleasant panelled bar. Bedrooms are mainly fairly functional in looks, though 15 superior rooms in the old house are much more stylish. Staff smile, but not very warmly.
Amenities garden, secretarial services, laundry service.

Rooms 60	*Direct dial* Yes	*Confirm by* 6	*Parking* Ample
Ensuite bath/shower 60	*Room TV* Yes	*Last dinner* 9.30	*Room service* 24 hours

STRATFORD-UPON-AVON   Welcombe Hotel   75%   £B/C

HR Town plan E1
Warwickshire
Warwick Road CV37 0NR
Stratford-upon-Avon
(0789) 295252
Telex 31347

Rooms 78
Ensuite bath/shower 78
Direct dial Yes
Room TV Yes
Confirm by arrang.
Last dinner 9.45
Parking Ample
Room service 24 hours

Credit Access, Amex, Diners, Visa
Closed 29 Dec–2 Jan

An imposing Jacobean-style country mansion built in 1869 is now a discreetly luxurious hotel combining peace and period charm with modern-day comforts. The parkland grounds and golf course make a most agreeable setting, and the lounge and bar exude character and solid style. A handsome staircase leads to the spacious main-house bedrooms, most of which have been refurbished with top-quality fabrics; there are some marvellous antique-furnished suites. Rooms in the garden wing have an attractive contemporary look. Brian Miller is a very professional general manager, his staff keen and efficient. Good breakfasts. *Amenities* garden, golf course, putting, croquet, coarse fishing, snooker, secretarial services, fax, laundry service, helipad.

Restaurant   ♛

Set L £12.50, Sun £14.50
Set D £18.50
About £60 for two
Seats 60

Michael Carver's assured cooking has its home in an elegant bay-windowed restaurant overlooking the golf course. Dishes range widely from carpaccio and oyster-filled scallop mousse to smoked breast of chicken stuffed with Brie and chives, and lamb in strudel leaves with wild mushrooms and a mint and Drambuie sauce. Service is attentive under courteous manager Luigi Gregorio, also responsible for the meticulously chosen wine list. ♀ Well-chosen ℮ &

Lunch 12.15–3   *Dinner* 6–9.45, Sun 7–9.45   **Closed** 29 Dec–2 Jan

STRATFORD-UPON-AVON White Swan 62% £C

H Town plan C2
Warwickshire
Rother Street CV37 6NH
Stratford-upon-Avon
(0789) 297022

Credit Access, Amex, Diners, Visa

Public areas in this grand old hotel are full of period charm. The foyer, with its low ceilings and exposed beams, invites you in to the wood-panelled lounge, which features (behind protective glass) wall paintings which date back to 1550. The small beamed bar is popular with residents and locals alike. Refurbished bedrooms have dark freestanding units, pretty fabrics and modern, well-kept bathrooms. **Amenities** laundry service, 24-hour lounge service.

Rooms 35	*Direct dial* Yes	*Confirm by* 6	*Parking* Limited
Ensuite bath/shower 35	*Room TV* Yes	*Last dinner* 9	*Room service* Limited

STREATHAM Welcome Inn

See under LONDON RESTAURANTS under £30

STREATLEY-ON-THAMES Swan at Streatley 71% £C

H Map 5 D2 Berkshire
RG8 9HR
Goring-on-Thames
(0491) 873737
Telex 848259

Rooms 43
Ensuite bath/shower 43
Direct dial Yes
Room TV Yes
Confirm by arrang.
Last dinner 9.30
Parking Ample
Room service 24 hours

Credit Access, Amex, Diners, Visa

A hotel that has doubled in size in the last year, the Swan lies along a particularly attractive stretch of the Thames. In the new extension is a spacious foyer and the public Boathouse Bar. The cane-furnished cocktail bar is now for residents' and diners' use only. Both bars open on to riverside terraces, as does the lounge – which now extends into the old reception area. Spacious new bedrooms have soft colour schemes, good reproduction furniture and excellent bathrooms. Remaining accommodation varies in size and is currently being upgraded. **Amenities** garden, indoor swimming pool, sauna, solarium, keep-fit equipment, golf practice net, mooring, secretarial services, fax, laundry service. &

We welcome bona fide complaints and recommendations
on the tear-out pages at the back of the book for readers' comment.
They are followed up by our professional team.

STREET Bear Hotel 63% £E

H Map 4 A3 Somerset
53 High Street BA16 0EF
Street (0458) 42021

Credit Access, Amex, Diners, Visa

An attractive late-Victorian house in the middle of the town, providing pleasant overnight accommodation. Ten of the bedrooms are in the main house, quite spacious rooms with a light, contemporary feel. The remainder are in the adjoining cottage and have more of a country air, with pretty fabrics and pine furniture. There's a cosy lounge and a bright, airy bar. **Amenities** garden, patio, laundry service.

Rooms 15	*Direct dial* Yes	*Confirm by* arrang.	*Parking* Ample
Ensuite bath/shower 15	*Room TV* Yes	*Last dinner* 10	*Room service* Limited

STREET Wessex Hotel 60% £E

H Map 4 A3 Somerset
Nr Glastonbury BA16 0EF
Street (0458) 43383

Credit Access, Amex, Diners, Visa

Business visitors favour this modern main-street hotel, and are well catered for in bedrooms with plenty of work space, trouser presses, tea-makers and TVs. Public rooms include a relaxing foyer and spacious open-plan bar and restaurant area plus a lounge which may be used for meetings. Practical bathrooms have over-the-bath showers and separate en-suite WC's. **Amenities** secretarial services, laundry service. &

Rooms 50	*Room phone* Yes	*Confirm by* arrang.	*Parking* Ample
Ensuite bath/shower 50	*Room TV* Yes	*Last dinner* 9.30	*Room service* 24 hours

STRETTON — Ram Jam Inn — £E

Map 11 E3 Leicestershire
Great North Road,
Nr Oakham LE15 7QX
Castle Bytham (078 081) 776

Credit Access, Amex, Visa
Closed 25 Dec

A modern-day inn on the busy A1, offering excellent overnight accommodation and a stylish stone-tiled bar. Bedrooms (reached by a separate entrance) are located away from the road and are reasonably quiet. They're spacious and comfortable, with pine and wicker furniture, pleasant blue or red colour schemes and good modern bathrooms. Radios and tea-makers are standard. *Amenities* garden, coffee shop (7am–7pm).

| *Rooms* 8 | *Direct dial* Yes | *Confirm by* 6 | *Parking* Ample |
| *Ensuite bath/shower* 8 | *Room TV* Yes | *Last dinner* 11 | *Room service* All day |

STROUD — Bear of Rodborough — 64% — £D/E

Map 4 B2 Gloucestershire
Rodborough Common
GL5 5DE
Amberley (045 387) 3522
Telex 437130

Credit Access, Amex, Diners, Visa

Two stuffed bears greet visitors to this 17th-century Cotswold inn overlooking the Woodchester Valley. Public areas include a cosy panelled lounge, a bright and airy garden room and a characterful stone-walled bar. Upgrading of accommodation continues and most main-house bedrooms now have smart darkwood furniture and good bathrooms; annexe rooms are more modest. *Amenities* garden, croquet, secretarial services, laundry service, 24-hour lounge service.

| *Rooms* 47 | *Direct dial* Yes | *Confirm by* 6 | *Parking* Ample |
| *Ensuite bath/shower* 47 | *Room TV* Yes | *Last dinner* 9.30 | *Room service* All day |

STROUD — Oakes ★

Map 4 B2 Gloucestershire
169 Slad Road
Stroud (045 36) 79950

Lunch 12.30–2
Dinner 7.30–10
Set L £11.50, Sun £14.50
Set D from £19
About £56 *for two*
Seats 30
Parties 30
Parking Ample

Credit Access, Visa
Closed D Sun, all Mon & Jan

Chris Oakes' highly assured and accomplished style of cooking continues to win friends at this delightful restaurant overlooking the Slad valley. Using ingredients obtained from first-rate suppliers, Chris works in a refreshingly ungimmicky way that allows the quality of his materials to speak for itself. You might start with wonderfully light, pastry-encased pike quenelles on a mushroom and tarragon sauce,

then proceed to beef fillet sauced with bone marrow on a bed of garlicky spinach and, finally, hot cinnamon soufflé with Drambuie cream. Good short wine list. *Specialities* chicken and goose liver parfait, roast lamb cutlets with grain mustard noodles, chocolate marquise with coffee sauce. ♀ Well-chosen ⊖

**Any person using our name to obtain free hospitality is a fraud.
Proprietors, please inform the police and us.**

STUCKTON — The Three Lions ★

Map 4 C4 Hampshire
Stuckton Road,
Nr Fordingbridge SP6 2HF
Fordingbridge (0425) 52489

Lunch 12.15–1.30, Sun 12–1.30
Dinner 7.30–9, Sat till 9.30
About £50 *for two*
Seats 50
Parties 20
Parking Ample

Credit Access, Visa
Closed D Sun & all Mon

Pretty curtains, copper moulds and pewter plates lend an appealing rustic air to the dining areas of this red-brick pub where food takes precedence over ordinary drinking. June Wadsack supervises the service while her husband Karl exercises his considerable skills in the kitchen. The blackboard menu changes constantly, offering dishes such as spinach tortellini with tomatoes and mushrooms gratiné. Excellent fresh ingredients are accurately cooked, flavours are clear, and sauces expertly made. Good wines include Chablis 1er Cru Montée de Tonnerre (Pic) '86, Ch. Pavie '75. No children under 14. *Specialities* spinach and cheese strudels; steamed fillet of Avon salmon; Scotch fillet steak; parfait glacé val de russe. ♀ Well-chosen ⊖ ♿

STUDLAND BAY — Knoll House Hotel 62% £C/D

H **Map 4 C4** Dorset
Nr Swanage BH19 3AH
Studland (092 944) 251

Closed end Oct–end Mar

Close to the sea in this lovely part of Dorset, a family-run hotel that's finely tuned to the needs of the family holiday. Children of all ages will find plenty of amusements: for younger ones there's a large adventure playground; for older ones, the chance to use the hotel's excellent sports and leisure facilities. As you would expect in a family-style hotel, the atmosphere is friendly and relaxed. There are plenty of comfortable day rooms, two with TV. Modestly furnished bedrooms have simple, practical bathrooms.
Amenities garden, outdoor swimming pool, sauna, solarium, whirlpool bath, keep-fit equipment, tennis, 9-hole golf course, games room, kiosk, children's playground.

Rooms 79	*Direct dial* Yes	*Confirm by* arrang.	*Parking* Ample
Ensuite bath/shower 56	*Room TV* No	*Last dinner* 8.15	*Room service* None

STUDLEY — Peppers

R **Map 10 C4** Warwickshire
45 High Street
Studley (052 785) 3183

Indian cooking
Set L & D £18.50
About £28 *for two*
Seats 48 *Parties* 50
Parking Limited
Credit Access, Amex, Diners, Visa

Only the finest fresh ingredients are used at this popular restaurant specialising in southern Indian cuisine. Careful preparation and subtle spicing ensure mouthwatering results, and even the pickles are prepared on the premises. Start perhaps with a crisp, lightly fried onion pakora, then select a chef's recommendation like tandoori king prawns in a delicately spiced cream sauce. Perfect rice, lovely fresh vegetables, excellent breads and traditional Indian sweets. &

Lunch 12.30–2.15 *Dinner* 6.30–11.30
Closed L Sun & 25 & 26 Dec

STURMINSTER NEWTON — Plumber Manor Restaurant ♕ ♖

RR **Map 4 B4** Dorset
Hazelbury Bryan Road
DT10 2AF
Sturminster Newton
(0258) 72507

Set D from £17.50
About £46 *for two*
Seats 60 *Parties* 40
Parking Ample
Credit Access, Visa

Book for dinner in this elegant dining room hung with family portraits. Brian Prideaux-Brune's very competent cooking is mostly classical in style, with modern touches. Dishes like pigeon breast with plum sauce or a lentil-based vegetarian version of beef Wellington are served with a splendid selection of nicely cooked vegetables and there are enjoyable sweets on a well-laden trolley. Good coffee and pleasant service. 🍷 Well-chosen 🏵 &

Lunch by arrang. only *Dinner* 7.30–9.30, Sun till 9
Closed 2 wks Feb

BEDROOMS 12 £D/E
With bath/shower 11

Bedrooms in the magnificent Jacobean manor or in the converted barn have tea/coffee-making facilities, biscuits, mineral water and colour TVs. Good bathrooms, more modern in the barn.

SUDBURY — Mill 59% £D/E

H **Map 6 C3** Suffolk
Walnut Tree Lane CO10 6BD
Sudbury (0787) 75544
Telex 987623

Credit Access, Amex, Diners, Visa

Enjoying a tranquil setting overlooking flat water meadows on the outskirts of town, this characterful hotel retains its own millstream and a huge old cast-iron wheel that stands behind glass in the spacious, picture-windowed bar. Redecoration is smartening up heavily beamed main-house bedrooms, while those in the extension have a simple, modern appeal. Private facilities are standard throughout.
Amenities terrace, coarse fishing, laundry service.

Rooms 53	*Direct dial* Yes	*Confirm by* arrang.	*Parking* Ample
Ensuite bath/shower 53	*Room TV* Yes	*Last dinner* 9.15	*Room service* Limited

SUNDERLAND — Seaburn Hotel 59% £D

H **Map 15 C4** Tyne & Wear
Queen's Parade SR6 8DB
Tyneside (091) 529 2041
Telex 53168

Credit Access, Amex, Diners, Visa

Built in the 1930s, the Seaburn stands on the seafront two miles north of Sunderland. Day rooms are bright and cheerful, and the cocktail bar looks out to sea. The recently redecorated reception area also serves as a lounge. Half the bedrooms are in the main house (these have the better bathrooms), the rest in a more modern extension. All are quite well equipped.
Amenities hairdressing, in-house movies, fax, laundry service. &

Rooms 82	*Direct dial* Yes	*Confirm by* 6	*Parking* Ample
Ensuite bath/shower 82	*Room TV* Yes	*Last dinner* 9.30	*Room service* 24 hours

SURBITON   Chez Max   ⑨

R **Map 5 E2** Surrey
85 Maple Road
01-399 2365

About £55 for two
Seats 32
Parties 32
Parking Ample

Credit Access, Amex, Diners, Visa

A comfortable little restaurant where high ambitions are somewhat
undermined by the disappointing quality of the ingredients. Max
Markarian's cooking is competent, the saucing being particularly
good, and there are some interesting dishes such as saddle of veal with
green and red pepper sauce and chicken quenelles with lime and raisin
sauce. Desserts are a high point. A serious, interesting wine list with
plenty of '82, '78, and '75 clarets. ⊖

Lunch 12.30–2   *Dinner* 7.30–10.30
Closed L Sat, all Sun & Mon, Good Fri, 2 wks Aug & 24 Dec–7 Jan

---

We publish annually,
so make sure you use the current edition.
It's worth it!

SUTTON   Partners 23   ⑨

R **Map 5 F3** Surrey
23 Stonecot Hill
01-644 7743

Set L from £13.25
Set D £19.95
About £50 for two
Seats 30
Parties 35
Parking Limited

Credit Access, Amex, Diners, Visa

A pleasant surprise found in a parade of shops is this very good little
restaurant. The room is small and inviting with elegant tables fairly
closely set. Tim McEntire's fixed-price menus are sensibly selective
and usually supplemented by interesting dishes of the day. Red
snapper and scallops served with a rosemary flavoured beurre
noisette, chicken with a leek mousse and pavé of beef with a rich port
sauce typify the choice. Vegetables are simply and elegantly presented.
There's an excellent cheeseboard and sweets include delights like
gratin of mandarin and fig. Excellent house wines (try the Saumur
Blanc) vie with scrupulously chosen crus. Service is friendly and well
informed. ⊖

Lunch 12.30–2   *Dinner* 7.30–9.30
Closed L Sat, all Sun, Mon & 1 wk Aug

SUTTON BENGER   Bell House Hotel   64%   £D/E

H **Map 4 B2** Wiltshire
Nr Chippenham SN15 4RH
Seagry (0249) 720401

Credit Access, Amex, Diners, Visa

A hotel which started life as a private house in the 15th century and
has since been much extended and modernised. The intimate, plushly
furnished Carriage Bar takes its name from the splendid 18th-century
coach in the forecourt, and there's a popular modern conference suite.
Bedrooms are in smart reproduction Regency style (one has a four-
poster) and all have up-to-date bathrooms.
Amenities garden, laundry service.

Rooms 14	*Direct dial* Yes	*Confirm by* 8.30	*Parking* Ample
Ensuite bath/shower 14	*Room TV* Yes	*Last dinner* 10.30	*Room service* Limited

---

SUTTON COLDFIELD   Moor Hall Hotel   62%   £D/E

H **Map 10 C4** West Midlands
Moor Hall Drive,
Four Oaks B75 6LN
021-308 3751
Telex 335127
Credit Access, Amex, Diners, Visa

Overlooking a golf course, and close to the A453, Moor Hall is an
imposing building. The spacious foyer, with its antiques and
aspidistras, exudes the atmosphere of the past, as does the panelled
lounge. A modern winer/diner seems anachronistic but is very popular.
Housekeeping is exemplary in bedrooms that combine modern
facilities with period charm. *Amenities* garden, sauna, solarium,
steam room, gymnasium, secretarial services, fax, laundry service.

Rooms 48	*Direct dial* Yes	*Confirm by* arrang.	*Parking* Ample
Ensuite bath/shower 48	*Room TV* Yes	*Last dinner* 10.30	*Room service* 24 hours

---

Our inspectors are our full-time employees;
they are professionally trained by us.

SUTTON COLDFIELD   New Hall   *NEW ENTRY*   76%   £B

HR **Map 10 C4** West Midlands
Walmley Road B75 7UU
021–378 2442

Rooms 65
Ensuite bath/shower 65
Direct dial Yes
Room TV Yes
Confirm by 6
Last dinner 10
Parking Ample
Room service 24 hours

Credit Access, Amex, Diners, Visa

Reputedly the oldest moated manor house in England, New Hall with its towers, cupolas, battlements and 26 acres of wooded grounds is today a romantic hotel. Leaded windows, coats of arms, tapestries and ornate ceilings lend their charm to the public rooms, which include an impressive first-floor chamber lit by antique chandeliers. Most of the bedrooms are in a tasteful modern extension and individually furnished with charming chintz or designer fabrics. All have welcoming decanters of sherry and many other thoughtful extras, but attention to detail could be improved. No children under seven.
Amenities garden, golf practice net, putting, croquet, coarse fishing, secretarial services, laundry service.

Restaurant   *NEW ENTRY*

Set L from £12.50, Sun £18
Set D £20
About £70 for two
Seats 65
Parties 50

The oak-panelled dining room and well-appointed tables provide a stylish setting for Allen Garth's commendable cooking. He conjures quality ingredients into some imaginative dishes such as succulent lambs' brains on a chiffonade of lettuce and tender veal in a morel mushroom sauce, with flashes of brilliance such as an outstanding chicken liver parfait. Service enthusiastic but inexperienced. Classic cellar has some splendid burgundies: Batard Montrachet (Latour) '78.

Lunch 12.30–2, Sun till 2.15   *Dinner* 7–10, Sun till 9.30

**Our inspectors *never* book in the name of Egon Ronay's Guides.
They disclose their identity only if they are considering an establishment
for inclusion in the next edition of the Guide.**

SUTTON COLDFIELD Penns Hall Hotel   66%   £C

HR **Map 10 C4** West Midlands
Penns Lane,
Walmley B76 8LH
021-351 3111 Telex 335789

Credit Access, Amex, Diners, Visa
Closed 1 Jan

Top marks at this extended 17th-century house go to the staff, who perform with a will and a smile under long-serving General Manager Colin Campbell. Bedrooms are comfortable and well equipped, the best being the stylish Connaught wing rooms. The foyer and lounge are plush and inviting, and there are two pleasant bars. A leisure centre heads the plans for 1989.
Amenities garden, coarse fishing, laundry service.

Rooms 115	*Direct dial* Yes	*Confirm by* arrang.	*Parking* Ample
Ensuite bath/shower 115	*Room TV* Yes	*Last dinner* 10	*Room service* 24 hours

Restaurant

Set L from £13
Set D from £13
About £43 for two
Seats 120

An old-fashioned dining room with panelling, leaded windows and high-backed chairs. Sergio Grassi's cooking is very enjoyable, with pasta a strong suit. Typical main courses run from baked salmon en papillote to chicken basquaise, calf's liver with cassis and roast loin of venison with pears and cranberries. Good clarets feature on a sound wine list. Service by a charming Italian team is orchestrated by the ebullient Pepe Massari. ♋

Lunch 12.30–2, Sun 12.30–2   *Dinner* 7–10
Closed L Sat, 1 Jan

SWINDON   Blunsdon House Hotel   70%   £C/D

H **Map 4 C2** Wiltshire
Blunsdon SN2 4AD
Swindon (0793) 721701
Telex 444491

Rooms 89
Ensuite bath/shower 89
Direct dial Yes
Room TV Yes
Confirm by 6
Last dinner 10.30
Parking Ample
Room service 24 hours

Credit Access, Amex, Diners, Visa

The Clifford family opened a guest house 28 years ago; now it has become a popular conference venue with a Scandinavian-designed leisure club boasting over a thousand members. The public areas, which include a mahogany panelled bar, have recently been smartly refurbished. Standard rooms in the main house and Concorde wing are large and comfortable, with well-fitted bathrooms; Prestige rooms boast

mini-bars, barometers, fitted ironing boards, radio alarms, wall safes, teletext and spa baths. No dogs. *Amenities* garden, indoor swimming pool, sauna, solarium, whirlpool bath, steam bath, gymnasium, beauty salon, hairdressing, tennis, squash, putting, games room, snooker, secretarial services, fax, laundry service, creche. &

**If we recommend meals in a Hotel or Inn,
a separate entry is made for its restaurant.**

SWINDON   Crest Hotel   61%   £C/D

H **Map 4 C2** Wiltshire
Oxford Road,
Stratton St Margaret SN3 4TL
Swindon (0793) 822921
Telex 444456

Credit Access, Amex, Diners, Visa

Accommodation at this modern low-rise hotel ranges from pleasant standard rooms to Lady Crest (with feminine decor and extras), Executive (larger and smarter with accessories like mini-bars) and Executive Study rooms (with desks and everything from paper clips to dictionaries). The foyer doubles as a lounge and there is a split-level bar. *Amenities* pool table, in-house movies, secretarial services, fax, laundry service, children's play area (weekends). &

Rooms 94	*Direct dial* Yes	*Confirm by* 6	*Parking* Ample
Ensuite bath/shower 94	*Room TV* Yes	*Last dinner* 9.45	*Room service* Limited

---

SWINDON   The Pear Tree at Purton   71% *NEW ENTRY*   £D

HR **Map 4 C2** Wiltshire
Church End,
Purton SN5 9ED
Swindon (0793) 772100

Rooms 4
Ensuite bath/shower 4
Direct dial Yes
Room TV Yes
Confirm by arrang.
Last dinner 9.30
Parking Ample
Room service All day

Credit Access, Amex, Diners, Visa

High standards of comfort, food and service in the tranquil surroundings of a converted vicarage. The decor is outstanding throughout, with everything carefully chosen to please – from the fresh flowers, plants and greenery to the glass-topped antique coffee tables. The four luxurious bedrooms are each decorated in an individual style, and the Hyde Suite (named after Anne Hyde, a resident of Purton

and the mother of Queen Mary and Queen Anne) features a four-poster bed, a massive oak trunk and an antique cheval-glass. All the proper services are provided, including turning down the beds and changing towels.
Amenities garden, in-house movies, laundry service.

Restaurant   ♛ ♀

English cooking

Set L from £9.50
Set D £14.50
About £40 for two
Seats 36
Parties 10

Closed L Sat

The style is decidedly and appropriately English in the elegant Conservatory restaurant. Janet Pichel-Juan's repertoire includes pillow of puff pastry filled with prawns and snow peas, sweetbreads with a spicy tomato sauce and noisettes of pork in a rich sauce of marjoram and Marsala. West Country farmhouse cheeses are an alternative to a sweet course. There's a good, informative wine list: note the superb Savigny Les Beaune '85 from Michel Maurice.
♀ Well-chosen ☺

Lunch 12.30–2.30   *Dinner* 7.30–9.30, Fri & Sat 7.30–10.30

SWINDON | Post House Hotel 62% | £C

H **Map 4 C2** Wiltshire
Marlborough Road SN3 6AQ
Swindon (0793) 24601
Telex 444464

Credit Access, Amex, Diners, Visa

Swindon's Post House is a 1970s brick-built complex halfway between the town centre and the M4 (junction 15). Bedrooms, in two-storey wings, provide ample space and up-to-date comfort, and more are being upgraded to Executive standard. Bathrooms throughout are well equipped. *Amenities* garden, indoor swimming pool, sauna, solarium, whirlpool bath, gymnasium, secretarial services, fax, laundry service, coffee shop (10am–9pm, Sun till 7), children's play area.

| Rooms 104 | Direct dial Yes | Confirm by 6 | Parking Ample |
| Ensuite bath/shower 104 | Room TV Yes | Last dinner 10 | Room service Limited |

SWINDON | Wiltshire Hotel | £C/D

H **Map 4 C2** Wiltshire
Fleming Way SN1 1TN
Swindon (0793) 28282
Telex 444250

Credit Access, Amex, Diners, Visa

1988 was a year of improvements at the Wiltshire, a modern purpose-built hotel in the town centre. Existing bedrooms were to be upgraded to Executive standard, and seven extra rooms were to be created from a small wing of staff rooms. Changes in the day rooms included turning the Old Vic Bar into an all-hours coffee shop. The hotel was graded at 63% in our 1988 Guide. *Amenities* secretarial services, laundry service.

| Rooms 92 | Direct dial Yes | Confirm by 6 | Parking Ample |
| Ensuite bath/shower 92 | Room TV Yes | Last dinner 10.30 | Room service 24 hours |

**We publish annually,
so make sure you use the current edition.
It's worth it!**

TAPLOW | Cliveden 89% | £A

HR **Map 5 E2** Berkshire
Nr Maidenhead SL6 0JF
Burnham (062 86) 68561
Telex 846562

Rooms 25
Ensuite bath/shower 25
Direct dial Yes
Room TV Yes
Confirm by arrang.
Last dinner 9.30
Parking Ample
Room service 24 hours

Credit Access, Amex, Diners, Visa

Magnificent grounds, one of England's great stately homes and outstanding quality of service are all one could dream of in a hotel. The public rooms are quite stunning, with oak panelling, fine oil paintings, tapestries and suits of armour. The spacious bedrooms, named by former resident Nancy Astor after people associated with Cliveden, are individually decorated, many with antique furniture, and have pure linen sheets on the beds, open fireplaces and wonderful views. Bathrooms are equipped with Victorian-style tubs and luxurious towels and bathrobes. *Amenities* garden, outdoor swimming pool, sauna, gymnasium, tennis, squash, croquet, riding, coarse fishing, boating, hotel boat, games room, snooker, teletext, secretarial services, fax, valeting, laundry service.

Cliveden Dining Room

Set L £26.80
Set D £37.80
About £95 *for two*
Seats 60
Parties 30

Wonderful views of the Parterre provide a sumptuous backdrop against which to sample new head chef Ronald Maxfield's competent cooking. The set price, limited-choice menu changes daily, offering imaginative modern dishes, and there is also an à la carte. Smart staff provide friendly, polite service. At first glance, an impressive classic cellar but some average wines among the gems prevent it being classed as outstanding.

Lunch 12.30–2.30   *Dinner* 7.30–9.30

TARRANT MONKTON Langton Arms   £F

IR **Map 4 B4** Dorset
Blandford Forum DT11 8RX
Tarrant Hinton (025 889) 225

Credit Access, Amex, Diners, Visa

A pretty, 17th-century thatched inn, with modern bedroom accommodation built around a paved courtyard. Pretty fabrics, duvets and pine furniture give the rooms homely touches; all have bay windows overlooking gardens and fields. Accessories include tea-makers and individual heating controls; bathrooms are roomy and well equipped. Breakfast is served in the rooms or in the conservatory, and there are two cosy bars and a skittles alley. *Amenities* garden. ൴

Rooms 6	*Direct dial* Yes	*Confirm by* arrang.	*Parking* Ample
Ensuite bath/shower 6	*Room TV* Yes	*Last dinner* 9.30	*Room service* Limited

Langtons

Set L Sun £7
About £34 for two
Seats 60
Parties 60

Converted stables extended by a summery conservatory make up this informal, cottagey restaurant. The basic menu is short and fairly conservative and is largely overshadowed by Barbara Garnsworthy's much more adventurous blackboard specials. These might include a crisp-edged salmon and dill pancake, followed perhaps by tender lambs' kidneys in a Dijon mustard, cider and cream sauce, and then, to finish, a deliciously tangy ginger syllabub. Careful, competent cooking. 🍷 Well-chosen ⊕ ൴

Lunch Sun only 12–2   *Dinner* 7–9.30   **Closed** 25 Dec

---

 indicates a **well-chosen** house wine

TAUNTON Castle Hotel 79%   £B/C

HR **Map 3 E2** Somerset
Castle Green TA1 1NF
Taunton (0823) 272671
Telex 46488

Rooms 35
Ensuite bath/shower 35
Direct dial Yes
Room TV Yes
Confirm by arrang.
Last dinner 9
Parking Ample
Room service 24 hours

Credit Access, Amex, Diners, Visa

Judge Jeffreys conducted his notorious assizes in this fine wisteria-clad building, originally part of a Norman fortress, but history takes a backseat to comfort at this elegant, superbly run hotel. Splendid tapestries, quality furnishings and plenty of inviting sofas create an atmosphere of unhurried luxury in the sophisticated day rooms, which include the panelled Oak room. There are also two stylish conference/function rooms with an extensive range of equipment. Bedrooms are equally tasteful, with individual colour schemes, thick carpets, and remote-control TVs. The garden suites with their self-contained dressing rooms and well-equipped bathrooms are particularly luxurious. *Amenities* garden, secretarial services, laundry service.

Restaurant ★   ♛

Lunch 12.30–2
Dinner 7.30–9, Fri & Sat 7.30–9.30
Set L from £9.50
Set D £19.90
About £65 for two
Seats 65
Parties 80

Gary Rhodes continues to enhance his reputation for handling quality ingredients with flair and respect, and the handsome dining room makes an elegant setting for his interesting and varied menus. His superb seasonal dishes may include a perfect rabbit Pithiviers and venison with celeriac, apples and game sauce. The splendid wine list includes such prizes as Ch. d'Yquem '76 and Ch. Trotanoy

'75. *Specialities* Loch Fyne oysters with a champagne sauce, salmon filled with a sea bass mousse layered between puff pastry and spinach with a champagne butter sauce, best end of lamb with a mint and peppercorn crust on a lamb sauce with poached currants, hot passion fruit soufflé. ➪ Outstanding 🍷 Well-chosen ⊕

TAUNTON County Hotel 61% £C/D

H **Map 3 E2** Somerset
East Street TA1 3LT
Taunton (0823) 337651
Telex 46484

Credit Access, Amex, Diners, Visa

Taunton's oldest recorded pub is now a pleasant, comfortable hotel. Its focal point is the Wyvern Bar, a popular local meeting place themed on past and present Somerset cricketers; there's also a quiet cocktail lounge. Most bedrooms are in plainish, practical style, but some have been upgraded with pretty fabrics and superior furnishings. *Amenities* laundry service, coffee shop (9.30am–5.30pm), 24-hour lounge service.

| *Rooms* 67 | *Direct dial* Yes | *Confirm by* 6 | *Parking* Ample |
| *Ensuite bath/shower* 67 | *Room TV* Yes | *Last dinner* 9.30 | *Room service* All day |

TAUNTON Crest Hotel 67% *NEW ENTRY* £D

H **Map 3 E2** Somerset
Deane Gate Avenue TA1 2UA
Taunton (0823) 332222
Telex 46703

Credit Access, Amex, Diners, Visa

A new hotel at exit 25 of the M5. Lounge bar, coffee shop, cocktail bar and restaurant are beyond the ample reception area, and there are various conference rooms and suites. Decent-sized bedrooms have double and single beds, hairdryers and tiled bathrooms. The hotel has its own petrol station. *Amenities* garden, sauna, keep-fit equipment, in-house movies, fax, laundry service, coffee shop (10am–10pm).

| *Rooms* 101 | *Direct dial* Yes | *Confirm by* 6 | *Parking* Ample |
| *Ensuite bath/shower* 101 | *Room TV* Yes | *Last dinner* 10 | *Room service* 24 hours |

⮕ is our symbol for an **outstanding** wine list

TEBAY Tebay Mountain Lodge 59% £E/F

H **Map 13 D5** Cumbria
Orton, Nr Penrith CA10 3SB
Orton (058 74) 351

Credit Access, Amex, Diners, Visa

Simple, up-to-date comforts are the stock in trade of the Tebay Mountain Lodge, which lies beyond the Tebay Service Area slip road a mile north of junction 38 of the M6 (northbound carriageway). The setting is peaceful, and there are fine views of the Cumbrian hills from the bright, bamboo-furnished bar-lounge and from the generously sized bedrooms. Friendly, helpful staff are another plus.

| *Rooms* 30 | *Direct dial* Yes | *Confirm by* arrang. | *Parking* Ample |
| *Ensuite bath/shower* 30 | *Room TV* Yes | *Last dinner* 9.30 | *Room service* 24 hours |

TEIGNMOUTH Venn Farm Country House Hotel 59% £E/F

H **Map 3 E3** Devon
Higher Exeter Road TQ14 9PB
Teignmouth (062 67) 2196
Telex 42513

Credit Access, Amex, Diners, Visa

Overlooking the moorland and the sea, this Victorian farmhouse between Exeter and Torbay has a friendly home-from-home atmosphere. Relax in the peaceful lounge, with its ample armchairs and small bar, or step downstairs to the pub. Bedrooms have fitted units, tea-makers and sensible writing space. Carpeted bathrooms are spotless. Bedrooms are heated by means of electric wall fires. No dogs. *Amenities* garden, in-house movies.

| *Rooms* 10 | *Direct dial* Yes | *Confirm by* arrang. | *Parking* Ample |
| *Ensuite bath/shower* 10 | *Room TV* Yes | *Last dinner* 9 | *Room service* None |

TELFORD Telford Hotel, Golf & Country Club 64% £D

H **Map 10 B3** Shropshire
Great Hay, Sutton Hill
TF7 4DT
Telford (0952) 585642
Telex 35481

Credit Access, Amex, Diners, Visa

Friendly staff make guests feel very welcome in this modern hotel standing in huge grounds off the A442 above Ironbridge Gorge. Sporty types will find plenty of things to do, while the less active will find the spacious, well-laid-out day rooms just right for relaxing. Most bedrooms have quite simple, contemporary decor and furnishings, but ten rooms in the handsome 200-year-old Darby House are in country house style. A very agreeable hotel, competently run by an enthusiastic team. *Amenities* garden, indoor swimming pool, sauna, squash, golf course, putting, clay-pigeon shooting, snooker, coffee shop (9am–10pm), secretarial services, laundry service, children's play area.

| *Rooms* 58 | *Direct dial* Yes | *Confirm by* 6 | *Parking* Ample |
| *Ensuite bath/shower* 58 | *Room TV* Yes | *Last dinner* 10 | *Room service* 24 hours |

TELFORD   Telford Moat House   67%   £D/E

H **Map 10 B3** Shropshire
Forgegate, Telford Centre
TF3 4NA
Telford (0952) 291291
Telex 35588

Credit Access, Amex, Diners, Visa
Closed 26–30 Dec

A major building programme has added 50 new bedrooms to this modern hotel close to junction 5 on the M54. The spacious foyer now leads to a smart atrium lounge with access to the leisure area. All bedrooms have light ash furniture and ample extras.
Amenities garden, indoor swimming pool, sauna, solarium, keep-fit equipment, games room, in-house movies, secretarial services, fax, laundry service, 24-hour lounge service. &

Rooms 148	Direct dial Yes	Confirm by arrang.	Parking Ample
Ensuite bath/shower 148	Room TV Yes	Last dinner 9.30	Room service Limited

★ For a *discount* on next year's guide, see **An Offer for Answers.** ★

TETBURY   Calcot Manor   75%   £C

HR **Map 4 B2** Gloucestershire
Nr Beverston GL8 8YJ
Leighterton (066 689) 355

Rooms 12
Ensuite bath/shower 12
Direct dial Yes
Room TV Yes
Confirm by arrang.
Last dinner 9.30
Parking Ample
Room service All day

Credit Access, Amex, Diners, Visa
Closed 1st full wk Jan

A supremely comfortable country house hotel run in a highly professional fashion by the charming Bell family. A log fire welcomes you to the bar-lounge area, while deep sofas and nice antiques make for a delightful drawing room. The individually decorated bedrooms have great appeal: most have lovely views over the surrounding countryside and all have delightful decor.

One has a splendid four-poster and one, in a separate outbuilding, has its own lounge. Many thoughtful extras exemplify the high standards espoused by the Bells. Bathrooms are particularly stylish, with smart fittings and good toiletries. No children under 12. No dogs. *Amenities* garden, outdoor swimming pool, croquet, laundry service. &

Restaurant   ♛

Set L £14.50
Set D £17.50
About £60 *for two*
Seats 40
Parties 50

There's plenty to delight the diner here – Ramon Farthing's highly imaginative cooking produces some truly delicious dishes and his desserts are hard to beat. You might start with a tartlet of goose liver with oyster mushrooms, then move on to fillet of sea bass with artichoke and cream sauce before finishing triumphantly with hot rhubarb soufflé and vanilla sauce. Some good wines, especially burgundies: Volnay from Lafarge, Savigny from Bize. &

Lunch 12.30–2 *Dinner* 7.30–9.30
Closed D Sun to non-residents & 1st wk Jan

TETBURY   Close Hotel   71%   £C

HR **Map 4 B2**
Gloucestershire
8 Long Street GL8 8AQ
Tetbury (0666) 52272

Rooms 10
Ensuite bath/shower 10
Direct dial Yes
Room TV Yes
Confirm by 6
Last dinner 9.45
Parking Ample
Room service All day

Credit Access, Amex, Diners, Visa

An ongoing programme of ambitious refurbishment is transforming this fine old house into a hotel of a very high standard. The elegant entrance hall sets the tone with its polished wood floor, period furniture and delightful drapes, while the spacious drawing room has attractive flower displays, a pale yellow and blue decor and comfortable seating. Bedrooms have been individually decorated in excellent taste,

using top quality fabrics, delightful coordinating colour schemes and period furnishings; four have four-posters. All are equipped with sherry, fruit, mineral water and sweets. Bath and shower rooms are similarly impressive. No children under ten. No dogs.
Amenities garden, croquet, secretarial services, fax, laundry service.

Restaurant

Set L £10.95, Sun £12.95
Set D £22
About £56 for two
Seats 55
Parties 25
Parking Ample

Chris Amor has been provided with an elegantly refurbished restaurant in which to present his considerable culinary skills. His weekly-changing menus feature interesting and imaginative modern dishes, created from good fresh ingredients. Starter might be seafood in filo pastry, with loin of lamb with fresh figs served on port wine glaze to follow. Appealing sweets include fruit pavlova with an apricot sauce. Young waiters are immaculately dressed, efficient and helpful.

Lunch 12.30–2   *Dinner* 7.30–9.45

TETBURY Snooty Fox Hotel 70% £C/D

H **Map 4 B2** Gloucestershire
Market Place GL8 8DD
Tetbury (0666) 52436

Rooms 12
Ensuite bath/shower 12
Direct dial Yes
Room TV Yes
Confirm by 6
Last dinner 10
Parking Difficult
Room service All day

Credit Access, Amex, Diners, Visa

Originally a 16th-century coaching inn, the Snooty Fox stands in the centre of town opposite the old market hall. Now it's a delightfully civilised and comfortable hotel with friendly staff led by enthusiastic manageress Julie Stuart. Open fires warm the well-furnished day rooms, where exposed stone is an attractive feature. Bedrooms, each individual in size and style, are filled with extras large and small, and the  five de luxe rooms boast top-quality fabrics, original paintings and fine antique or reproduction furniture. The lounge, bar, corridors and bedrooms have recently been refurbished. No dogs.
Amenities patio, in-house movies, secretarial services, laundry service.

TEWKESBURY Bell Hotel 61% £D/E

H **Map 4 B1** Gloucestershire
Church Street GL20 5SA
Tewkesbury (0684) 293293
Telex 43535

Credit Access, Amex, Diners, Visa

Standing in the town centre, beside the abbey and river, this fine half-timbered building dates back to medieval times. Public areas with low ceilings and exposed beams include a cosily panelled bar and comfortably appointed lounge. Best bedrooms have pretty floral fabrics and attractive freestanding furniture (including two four-posters); all rooms are well-equipped. *Amenities* garden, secretarial services, laundry service, 24-hour lounge service.

Rooms 25	*Direct dial* Yes	*Confirm by* 6	*Parking* Ample
Ensuite bath/shower 25	*Room TV* Yes	*Last dinner* 9.15	*Room service* All day

TEWKESBURY Bredon Manor 67% £C/D

H **Map 4 B1** Gloucestershire
Bredon GL20 7EG
Tewkesbury (0684) 72293

Credit Access, Amex, Diners, Visa

Run by friendly owners almost like a private house, this centuries-old mansion enjoys a lovely garden setting by the river Avon. Fresh flowers and plenty of ornaments add a homely touch to the inviting day rooms while comfortably traditional bedrooms are spacious and well equipped. No children under 12. No dogs.
Amenities garden, outdoor swimming pool, tennis, putting, croquet, coarse fishing, games room, secretarial services, laundry service.

Rooms 4	*Direct dial* Yes	*Confirm by* arrang.	*Parking* Ample
Ensuite bath/shower 4	*Room TV* Yes	*Last dinner* 8	*Room service* Limited

TEWKESBURY Royal Hop Pole Hotel 66% *NEW ENTRY* £C/D

H **Map 4 B1** Gloucestershire
Church Street GL20 5RT
Tewkesbury (0684) 293236
Telex 437176

Credit Access, Amex, Diners, Visa

Extensive, sympathetic refurbishment has transformed this riverside hotel into a most comfortable establishment. A welcoming reception area gives on to an elegant, airy drawing room and there's a lively bar. The bedrooms, some with exposed beams, have pretty contemporary fabrics, antique or modern furniture and small, up-to-date bathrooms. Management and staff are enthusiastic and friendly.
Amenities garden, mooring, secretarial services, fax, laundry service.

Rooms 29	*Direct dial* Yes	*Confirm by* 6	*Parking* Ample
Ensuite bath/shower 29	*Room TV* Yes	*Last dinner* 10	*Room service* 24 hours

TEWKESBURY   Tewkesbury Park Hotel   62%   £C/D

H **Map 4 B1** Gloucestershire
Lincoln Green Lane GL20 7DN
Tewkesbury (0684) 295405
Telex 43563

Credit Access, Amex, Diners, Visa

A well-run, smartly kept hotel and country club with its own golf course and many other sporting facilities. Foyer, lounge and main bar are airy and leafy, and there are other bars and a bright coffee shop. Bedrooms are modern, with soft colour schemes, solid lightwood furniture and well-equipped bathrooms. Staff are notably friendly and helpful, the self-service breakfast better than average. No dogs.
Amenities garden, indoor swimming pool, sauna, solarium, whirlpool bath, steam room, gymnasium, tennis, squash, golf course, games room, snooker, in-house movies, secretarial services, fax, laundry service, coffee shop (10am–10.30pm), children's play area.

| *Rooms* 78 | *Direct dial* Yes | *Confirm by* 6 | *Parking* Ample |
| *Ensuite bath/shower* 78 | *Room TV* Yes | *Last dinner* 9.45 | *Room service* 24 hours |

TEYNHAM   Old School Club

R **Map 7 C5** Kent
Teynham, Nr Sittingbourne
Sittingbourne (0795) 522421

Set L £7.50
Set D £12
About £40 for two
Seats 30 *Parties* 36
Parking Ample
Credit Access, Visa

Two cuisines merge in the friendly public restaurant of a squash and fitness club. Bernard Giroth is the Indonesian chef, and dishes from his homeland make up most of the menu. Spicy sweetcorn fritters, fish curry Mandonese-style, chicken with coconut and peanut sauce and strips of beef with mixed vegetables typify the choice. The rest of the menu is given over to grills and familiar Continental fare.
🍷 Well-chosen   ⊖ &

Lunch 12–2.30   *Dinner* 7–9.30
Closed D Sun & Mon, 25 & 26 Dec & 1 Jan

THAME   Thatchers

RR **Map 5 D2** Oxfordshire
29 Lower High Street
OX9 2AA
Thame (084 421) 2146

Set L & D £13.50
About £40 for two
Seats 30
Parking Ample

Credit Access, Visa

There's a friendly, relaxed atmosphere in this mellow, beamed restaurant, where the food is imaginative and enjoyable. Choose the set menu for simple dishes like garlic mussels, coriander chicken or rabbit basquaise, or go à la carte for pastry-covered scallops with whisky and a julienne of vegetables, or succulent venison with delicious sauce of honey and cumin and splendid vegetables. Excellent coffee and wines chosen with discernment (Beaujolais from Janodet, Alsace from Ostertag). 🍷 Well-chosen   ⊖

Lunch 12–2   *Dinner* 7–10
Closed Sun & 25 & 26 Dec

BEDROOMS 10   £E
With bath/shower 10

Traditionally furnished bedrooms – four newly added – include some with four-posters. One boasts a whirlpool bath.

THEBERTON   Theberton Grange   64%   NEW ENTRY   £E

H **Map 6 D2** Suffolk
Nr Leiston IP16 4RR
Leiston (0728) 830625

Credit Access, Visa
Closed all Jan

The facade is Victorian, but the house dates from Tudor times. It's a peaceful, relaxing little hotel, set in attractive gardens and charmingly run by Roger and Annette James. The main day room is a splendidly comfortable lounge with inviting sofas, an open fire, magazines and flowers. An eye-catching pine staircase leads to bright, pretty bedrooms with pine furnishings. No children under five. No dogs.
Amenities garden.

| *Rooms* 6 | *Room phone* No | *Confirm by* arrang. | *Parking* Ample |
| *Ensuite bath/shower* 3 | *Room TV* Yes | *Last dinner* 9 | *Room service* Limited |

THETFORD   The Bell   62%   £C/D

H **Map 6 C2** Norfolk
King Street IP24 2AZ
Thetford (0842) 4455
Telex 818868

Credit Access, Amex, Diners, Visa

A former coaching inn of considerable character. Public rooms comprise two atmospheric bars with beams and paisley-patterned sofas and an attractive lounge furnished with antiques. Bedrooms in the main house are extremely quaint, seven having four-posters and one boasting a medieval wall painting and a ghost. Those in a newer wing are neat and contemporary. *Amenities* garden, secretarial services, fax, laundry service, coffee shop (10am–10pm).

| *Rooms* 43 | *Direct dial* Yes | *Confirm by* 6 | *Parking* Ample |
| *Ensuite bath/shower* 43 | *Room TV* Yes | *Last dinner* 9.45 | *Room service* 24 hours |

THORNABY-ON-TEES Post House Hotel 59% £C/D

H Map 15 C5 Cleveland
Low Lane, By Stainton
Village TS17 9LW
Middlesbrough (0642) 591213
Telex 58428

Credit Access, Amex, Diners, Visa

The accommodation at this older style Post House is very serviceable: all bedrooms have mini-bars and remote-control TVs, with trouser presses and hairdryers in rooms designated Superior. The foyer-lounge is comfortable enough, if a little in need of redecoration, and there's a bar and coffee shop. **Amenities** garden, sauna, solarium, secretarial services, fax, laundry service, coffee shop (7am–10pm), 24-hour lounge service, children's play area.

Rooms 135	*Direct dial* Yes	*Confirm by* 6	*Parking* Ample
Ensuite bath/shower 135	*Room TV* Yes	*Last dinner* 10.30	*Room service* Limited

**Changes in data sometimes occur in establishments
after the Guide goes to press.
Prices should be taken as indications rather than firm quotes.**

THORNBURY Thornbury Castle Hotel 82% £B

HR Map 4 B2 Avon
Nr Bristol BS12 1HH
Thornbury (0454) 418511
Telex 449986

Rooms 18
Ensuite bath/shower 18
Direct dial Yes
Room TV Yes
Confirm by 6
Last dinner 9.30
Parking Ample
Room service All day

Credit Access, Amex, Diners, Visa
Closed 6 days Xmas

Walled gardens and a vineyard surround this fairytale castle built by the ill-fated third Duke of Buckingham and subsequently seized by his implacable master, Henry VIII. Nearly five centuries on, it's owned and run by Maurice Taylor, who stayed here as a guest, fell in love with the place and bought it. Grandly proportioned public rooms with stone fireplaces, mullioned windows and deep sofas feature antiques, tapestries and oil paintings. Equally luxurious bedrooms (five in a recently converted wing) range from compact singles to palatial suites; typically pampering touches include embroidered linen, tins of shortbread, potpourri and huge bathsheets. No children under 12. No dogs. **Amenities** garden, croquet, laundry service, helipad.

Restaurant ♕

Set L £15.50
Set D from £19
About £60 *for two*
Seats 50
Parties 24

Two handsomely panelled dining rooms create a mellow yet dignified setting for Colin Hingston's accomplished yet blissfully unpretentious cooking. Savoury delights range from scallops poached in sweet white wine and basil to tender-pink lamb noisettes topped with pesto, while desserts might include a delicious hot butterscotch pudding. There's an excellent cheeseboard, and the wine list is a collector's dream – gently priced, too, for the gems offered. No smoking. ➪ Outstanding ♀ Well-chosen ⊗

Lunch 12–2 *Dinner* 7–9.30, Sun 7–9 **Closed** 6 days Xmas

THORNTON HEATH Mamma Adele ♟

R Map 7 B5 Surrey
23 Brigstock Road
01-683 2233

Italian cooking
About £40 *for two*
Seats 36
Parties 40
Parking Limited
Credit Access, Amex, Diners, Visa

Adele and Kam Memon provide a warm welcome at their simple, unpretentious restaurant. Kam attends to the customers with great solicitude while Adele works away in the kitchen, turning out good honest dishes like veal in pizzaiola sauce. There are the usual Italian starters like antipasto misto, and plenty of fresh pasta favourites generously served. Trifle and other sweets from the trolley. Not a bad wine list: Amarone Reciato della Valpolicella (Bolla) '80. ⊗ ♿

Lunch 12–3 *Dinner* 7–11 (Fri & Sat 7–11.30) **Closed** L Mon & Sat, all Sun (except by arrang.) D Bank Hols & all Aug

THORNTON-LE-FYLDE   River House   £D/E

IR **Map 10 A1** Lancashire
Skippool Creek,
Nr Blackpool FY5 5LF
Poulton-le-Fylde (0253) 883497

Credit Access, Amex, Visa

Carole and Bill Scott have created an air of warmth and individuality at their hotel, which overlooks the Wyre estuary and is surrounded by unspoilt countryside. There's a homely TV lounge with deep-cushioned seating and a very cosy bar on the ground floor, while upstairs four characterful bedrooms offer antique furniture and plenty of extras such as books, electric blankets, pot pourri and sherry. *Amenities* garden, laundry service.

Rooms 4	*Direct dial* Yes	*Confirm by* arrang.	*Parking* Ample
Ensuite bath/shower 1	*Room TV* Yes	*Last dinner* 9	*Room service* All day

Restaurant   ⊰

About £46 for two
Seats 40
Parties 40

Bottle green walls, deep red drapes and polished mahogany tables give a warm, period feel to this most attractive restaurant, while adjacent to it is a new Victorian-style conservatory in which to take pre-dinner drinks. The extensive menu offers imaginative and well thought-out dishes, drawing inspiration worldwide, with helpful descriptions for each to further tempt the appetite. Paul Scott is an enthusiastic cook of great talent, and he uses the best quality ingredients to produce food that is truly delicious. He turns his hand to Japanese delicacies, French cuisine and English roasts with equal ease and in a five-course meal every mouthful is a delight. ☐

Lunch Mon–Sat by arrang.   *Dinner* 7–9
Closed Sun, 26 Dec & 1 Jan

THRESHFIELD   Wilson Arms Hotel   63%   £D/E

H **Map 15 B6** North Yorkshire
Grassington BD23 5EL
Skipton (0756) 752666

Credit Access, Amex, Diners, Visa

An unpretentious roadside inn in the very heart of the Yorkshire Dales surrounded by beautiful countryside. Public rooms comprise a variety of informal lounges with homely couches and armchairs, a cosy cocktail bar and an up-to-date public bar. Bedrooms have pleasant floral wallcoverings, matching fabrics, practical fitted units, fruit and tea/coffee-makers. Bathrooms are neat and functional. *Amenities* garden, in-house movies, laundry service.

Rooms 28	*Direct dial* Yes	*Confirm by* arrang.	*Parking* Ample
Ensuite bath/shower 28	*Room TV* Yes	*Last dinner* 9.45	*Room service* Limited

THURLESTONE   Thurlestone Hotel   69%   £C

H **Map 3 D3** Devon
Nr Kingsbridge TQ7 3NN
Kingsbridge (0548) 560382

Credit Access, Amex, Diners, Visa
Closed 3–10 Jan

Originally a popular boarding house, the Thurlestone outgrew its former home (now a pub) and developed into a full-scale resort hotel. It's set in attractive, well-tended grounds overlooking the sea. Day rooms range from a spacious, airy lounge – tastefully furnished in traditional English drawing room style – to a wood-panelled cocktail bar. Bedrooms in restful peach or green feature locally-made ashwood furniture and offer well-appointed bathrooms. *Amenities* garden, indoor & outdoor swimming pools, sauna, solarium, whirlpool bath, keep-fit equipment, beauty salon, hairdressing, tennis, squash, badminton, 9-hole golf course, putting, games room, snooker, secretarial services, fax, valeting, laundry service, laundry room.

Rooms 68	*Direct dial* Yes	*Confirm by* arrang.	*Parking* Ample
Ensuite bath/shower 68	*Room TV* Yes	*Last dinner* 9	*Room service* 24 hours

TICKTON   Tickton Grange Hotel   62%   £D/E

H **Map 11 E1** Humberside
Nr Beverley HU17 9SH
Hornsea (0964) 543666
Telex 527254

Credit Access, Amex, Diners, Visa

Family owned and run, this attractive Georgian hotel stands in well-kept gardens just off the A1035, east of Beverley. Public rooms are comfortably traditional in style, with a friendly, welcoming atmosphere. Apples, shortbread and home-made truffles are among the nice little extras to be found in the bedrooms, which have freestanding furniture and carpeted bath or shower rooms. *Amenities* garden, secretarial services, laundry service.

Rooms 17	*Direct dial* Yes	*Confirm by* arrang.	*Parking* Ample
Ensuite bath/shower 17	*Room TV* Yes	*Last dinner* 9.30	*Room service* All day

TONBRIDGE — Rose & Crown Hotel 59% £C/D

H **Map 7 B5** Kent
125 High Street TN9 1DD
Tonbridge (0732) 357966

Credit Access, Amex, Diners, Visa

A popular old coaching inn with an impressive Georgian frontage, and old black beams and Jacobean panelling. Inside pretty coordinating fabrics and lacy white tablecloths make for an attractive lounge and the bedrooms which have been recently refurbished have decent oak furniture and stylish fabrics. The remaining rooms are more basic but are clean and adequate.
Amenities garden, laundry service, 24-hour lounge service.

Rooms 51	*Direct dial* Yes	*Confirm by* 6	*Parking* Limited
Ensuite bath/shower 51	*Room TV* Yes	*Last dinner* 10	*Room service* None

**Our inspectors *never* book in the name of Egon Ronay's Guides.
They disclose their identity only if they are considering an establishment
for inclusion in the next edition of the Guide.**

TORQUAY — Grand Hotel 69% £C

H **Map 3 D3** Devon
Seafront TQ2 6NT
Torquay (0803) 296677
Telex 42891

Credit Access, Amex, Diners, Visa

The setting, in pleasant gardens overlooking the bay, is one of this elegant Edwardian hotel's many assets. Excellent management and steady investment keep standards high, and the whole place is very well looked after. Day rooms are comfortable and relaxing, and the hotel offers excellent leisure facilities, including a most attractive indoor swimming pool. Good-sized bedrooms, many with sea views, are light, airy and well appointed, the suites being particularly desirable.
Amenities garden, indoor & outdoor swimming pools, solarium, whirlpool bath, keep-fit equipment, hairdressing, tennis, games room, snooker, in-house movies, secretarial services, fax, laundry service.

Rooms 112	*Direct dial* Yes	*Confirm by* arrang.	*Parking* Ample
Ensuite bath/shower 112	*Room TV* Yes	*Last dinner* 9.30	*Room service* 24 hours

TORQUAY — Homers Hotel 63% £E

H **Map 3 D3** Devon
Warren Road TQ2 5TN
Torquay (0803) 213456

Credit Access, Amex, Diners, Visa
Closed All Jan

A position high on the cliffs affords spectacular sea views at this family-run hotel. An ornate ceiling, rich colours and gilt mirrors give grandeur to the comfortable lounge, which is warmed by a log fire. Bedrooms are smartly decorated and have good quality furniture and fabrics, neat carpeted bathrooms, hairdryers and mini-bars. No children under seven. *Amenities* garden, in-house movies, secretarial services, laundry service. ♿

Rooms 15	*Direct dial* Yes	*Confirm by* arrang.	*Parking* Limited
Ensuite bath/shower 15	*Room TV* Yes	*Last dinner* 9	*Room service* All day

TORQUAY — Imperial Hotel 84% £A

H **Map 3 D3** Devon
Parkhill Road TQ1 2DG
Torquay (0803) 24301

Rooms 167
Ensuite bath/shower 167
Direct dial Yes
Room TV Yes
Confirm by 6
Last dinner 9.30
Parking Ample
Room service 24 hours

Credit Access, Amex, Diners, Visa

Lush gardens sweep up from the sea to frame this imposing Torquay landmark. The pillared foyer is splendid, with marble floors reflecting the pale pink colour scheme. The vast lounge, hung with chandeliers, is equally splendid. Bedrooms, particularly those whose balconies overlook the sea, are stylishly decorated, but it is the spacious suites that really impress. These offer individually decorated and beauti-fully furnished bedrooms with generous bathrooms and luxury accessories including dressing gowns. *Amenities* garden, indoor & outdoor swimming pools, sauna, solarium, whirlpool bath, gymnasium, hairdressing, tennis, squash, games room, snooker, in-house movies, secretarial services, fax, laundry service. ♿

TORQUAY   Kistor Hotel   58%   £E

H **Map 3 D3** Devon
Belgrave Road TQ2 5HF
Torquay (0803) 212632

Credit Access, Amex, Diners, Visa

A friendly welcome awaits at this seaside hotel where guests can relax in bright, homely day rooms or make use of the good keep-fit and leisure facilities. Bedrooms are quite modest, but comfortable enough and well kept, with functional tiled bathrooms. Seven bedrooms have just been added.
Amenities garden, indoor swimming pool, sauna, solarium, whirlpool bath, keep-fit equipment, putting, croquet, laundry service.

Rooms 59	Direct dial Yes	Confirm by arrang.	Parking Ample
Ensuite bath/shower 59	Room TV Yes	Last dinner 8.30	Room service Limited

TORQUAY   Livermead Cliff Hotel   60%   £C/D

H **Map 3 D3** Devon
Sea Front TQ2 6QJ
Torquay (0803) 22881
Telex 42918

Credit Access, Amex, Visa

Long-serving manager Jeffrey Poat leads a friendly and unfailingly helpful team at this agreeable hotel right by the water's edge. Day rooms make up in sea views for what they lack in decorative charm, and bedrooms are also in quite simple, modern style, most are of a good size. The facilities of the Livermead House Hotel across the road are available to guests. *Amenities* garden, outdoor swimming pool, fax, laundry service, laundry room.

Rooms 64	Direct dial Yes	Confirm by arrang.	Parking Ample
Ensuite bath/shower 64	Room TV Yes	Last dinner 8.30	Room service 24 hours

TORQUAY   Livermead House Hotel   64%   £E

H **Map 3 D3** Devon
Sea Front TQ2 6QJ
Torquay (0803) 24361
Telex 42918

Credit Access, Amex, Diners, Visa

Most rooms at this well-run seaside hotel enjoy splendid sea views. The lounge and bar are comfortably if plainly furnished, while simple, neat bedrooms are equipped with lightwood fitted furniture, tea-makers, radios and hairdryers. Some back rooms overlook a branch railway line. *Amenities* garden, outdoor swimming pool, sauna, solarium, keep-fit equipment, hairdressing, tennis, squash, putting, sea fishing, games room, snooker, secretarial services, fax, laundry room.

Rooms 69	Direct dial Yes	Confirm by arrang.	Parking Ample
Ensuite bath/shower 69	Room TV Yes	Last dinner 8.30	Room service 24 hours

TORQUAY   Osborne Hotel   69%   £B

H **Map 3 D3** Devon
Hesketh Crescent
Meadfoot Beach TQ1 2LL
Torquay (0803) 213311

Credit Access, Amex, Diners, Visa

In a splendid Regency crescent overlooking the bay, the Osborne offers comfort, hospitality and good leisure facilities. Bedrooms, with names instead of numbers, are individually decorated and furnished to a high standard and in a style sympathetic to the hotel's origins. They're not lacking in modern amenities, and all have seating areas; many enjoy lovely sea views. Among the day rooms are an elegant lounge bar and a panelled library. Smart, professional staff and management are another plus, and a good breakfast starts the day. No dogs. *Amenities* garden, outdoor swimming pool, sauna, solarium, whirlpool bath, keep-fit equipment, putting, snooker, secretarial services, fax, laundry service.

Rooms 23	Direct dial Yes	Confirm by arrang.	Parking Ample
Ensuite bath/shower 23	Room TV Yes	Last dinner 9.30	Room service 24 hours

TORQUAY   Palace Hotel   68%   £C

H **Map 3 D3** Devon
Babbacombe Road
TQ1 3TG
Torquay (0803) 22271
Telex 42606

Credit Access, Amex, Diners, Visa

Everything at this large Victorian hotel seems to be on the grand scale: 25 acres of landscaped gardens and woodlands; extensive sporting facilities; vast public rooms with high moulded ceilings supported by elegant columns. There are three bars and several large lounges and writing rooms. Bedrooms are also generously proportioned with TVs, direct-dial telephones and plenty of writing space. The individually decorated suites, have splendid views, freestanding furniture of good quality, mini-bars and trouser presses. *Amenities* garden, indoor & outdoor swimming pools, sauna, hairdressing, tennis, squash, 9-hole golf course, croquet, games room, billiards, in-house movies, secretarial services, fax, laundry service, nanny.

Rooms 141	Direct dial Yes	Confirm by arrang.	Parking Ample
Ensuite bath/shower 141	Room TV Yes	Last dinner 9.15	Room service 24 hours

TORQUAY   Remy's   ♨

R **Map 3 D3** Devon
3 Croft Road
Torquay (0803) 22359

French cooking
Set D from £10.85
About £34 for two
Seats 28 *Parties* 25
Parking Ample
Credit Access, Amex, Visa

Frenchman Remy Bopp does the cooking in this quiet, civilised restaurant, while service is in the hands of his wife Dolene and a French waiter. Good fresh produce is prepared with no undue fuss in a repertoire that runs from sole terrine with a prawn sauce to chicken with Riesling and saddle of venison with cranberry sauce. Note Alsatian desserts and wines. The three-course dinner menus are on three price levels. 🍷 Well-chosen 🄮

Dinner only 7.30–9.30
Closed Sun, Mon, all Bank Hols exc Good Fri & 2 wks early Aug

TORQUAY   Toorak Hotel   57%   £D/E

H **Map 3 D3** Devon
Chestnut Avenue TQ2 5JS
Torquay (0803) 211866

Credit Access, Amex, Visa

A well-established holiday hotel standing opposite Torquay's conference centre, just a short stroll from the sea. A block of 20 new bedrooms is a welcome addition, as some of the older rooms are looking a bit faded. Beyond the sunny foyer, public rooms, including several small lounges with sea views, are comfortably traditional. *Amenities* garden, outdoor swimming pool, hairdressing, tennis, snooker, secretarial services, laundry service.

| *Rooms* 60 | *Direct dial* Yes | *Confirm by* arrang. | *Parking* Ample |
| *Ensuite bath/shower* 60 | *Room TV* Yes | *Last dinner* 8.30 | *Room service* 24 hours |

TREBARWITH STRAND   Old Millfloor   ♛ ♨

RR **Map 2 B2** Cornwall
Nr Tintagel
Camelford (0840) 770234

English cooking

Set D from £9.50
About £28 for two
Seats 14
Parties 14
Parking Ample

A steep path leads down to this delightfully secluded, part 16th-century guest house beside a millstream. Here, a charmingly cottage dining room with leaded windows, open fireplace, country fabrics and fresh flowers is the perfect setting for Janice Waddon-Martyn's good home cooking. Hearty soups and simple, wholesome starters like country pâté and garlicky prawns are a prelude to satisfying main courses like pan-fried steak with mushrooms and red wine. Puds include excellent home bakes such as chocolate almond flan. Discuss any special orders when you book, and bring your own wine. 🄮

Dinner only 7.30–9.30
Closed Sun & 2 days Xmas

BEDROOMS 3   £F
With bath/shower 0

Chintzy bedrooms have washbasins and TVs, and share a single bathroom. Traditional English breakfast.

TRESCO   Island Hotel   67%   £B

HR **Map 2 A2** Isles of Scilly
(Cornwall) TR24 0PU
Scillonia (0720) 22883

Credit Access, Visa
Closed mid Oct–mid Mar

An excellent, marvellously relaxing hotel set in outstandingly beautiful scenery, with no dogs or cars allowed on the island to disturb the tranquillity. The picture windows in the lounge give stupendous sea views, and there are also plenty of books and board games to hand. There's a very stylish suite and five large rooms with sitting areas, tastefully decorated and equipped with attractive modern bathrooms. Smaller rooms are comfortably furnished and all are provided with clock radios, tea-makers and toiletries. Exceptional management ensures the return of guests year after year. Half-board terms only. *Amenities* garden, outdoor swimming pool, bowling green, croquet, sea fishing, sailing, boating, games room.

| *Rooms* 30 | *Direct dial* Yes | *Confirm by* arrang. | *Parking* No cars |
| *Ensuite bath/shower* 30 | *Room TV* Yes | *Last dinner* 8.30 | *Room service* Limited |

Restaurant

Set L Sun £9.50
Set D £18.50, Sun £20
About £48 for two
Seats 60

Wonderful sea views are to be had from the light and airy restaurant where you can enjoy Robert Coombe's highly competent cooking. Fish straight from the sea features strongly on the menu, simply cooked to preserve the fresh natural flavour, and there are plenty of meat choices too. Excellent cheeses and a tempting sweet buffet round off a delicious meal. Good local produce and generous portions are the hallmark here. Good wines, notably burgundies – Nuits St Georges (Robert Dubois) '80. 🄮

Lunch 12.30–1.30   *Dinner* 7.15–8.30   **Closed** mid Oct–mid Mar

TROUTBECK — Mortal Man Hotel £E

Map 13 D5 Cumbria
Nr Windermere LA23 1PL
Ambleside (053 94) 33193

Closed mid Nov–mid Feb

Built in 1689 on a hillside above the Troutbeck Valley, this lovely old inn offers tranquillity in relaxing surroundings. The public rooms have a friendly well-cared-for atmosphere with gleaming brass-topped tables, comfortable seating and fresh flowers. Outside the small TV lounge is another homely touch – a table stacked with books and magazines. Neatly maintained bedrooms have compact bathrooms. No children under five. *Amenities* garden.

Rooms 12	Room phone No	Confirm by arrang.	Parking Ample
Ensuite bath/shower 12	Room TV Most	Last dinner 8	Room service Limited

TRURO — Alverton Manor 75% NEW ENTRY £C

HR Map 2 B3 Cornwall
Tregolls Road TR1 1XQ
Truro (0872) 76633

Rooms 15
Ensuite bath/shower 15
Direct dial Yes
Room TV Yes
Confirm by 6
Last dinner 9.45
Parking Ample
Room service 24 hours

Credit Access, Amex, Diners, Visa

Painstaking restoration and renovation by new owners the Costellos has transformed this former convent into a hotel of charm and quality. Standing on a hillside alongside the A39, it makes a handsome sight with its sandstone walls, mullioned windows and Delabole slate roof. The interior impresses, too, from the lofty entrance hall and plushly comfortable bar-lounge filled with plants and fresh flowers to  the individually decorated bedrooms of varying shapes and sizes. Reproduction French furniture combines with modern chintzy fabrics to stylish effect and all the rooms boast up-to-date accessories like hairdryers, trouser presses and teletext TVs. Excellent private bathrooms. Cheerful young staff provide polite, friendly service. No dogs. *Amenities* garden, laundry service.

Terrace Restaurant ★ NEW ENTRY ♛

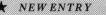

Set L £5.95, Sun £9.95
Set D £19.95
About £55 for two
Seats 50
Parties 40
Parking Ample

Talented chef Alan Vickops offers a short selection of skilfully prepared and stunningly presented dishes at this opulent restaurant. Natural flavours shine through such inventive combinations as Cornish red mullet served in a buttery shortcrust tartlet with a flavoursome tomato and basil sauce, veal and beef fillets topped by a herb mousse crust, or pot-pourri of local seafish accompanied by a  coriander and orange-scented butter sauce. Delicious desserts and fine British farmhouse cheeses. *Specialities* chicken and rabbit soup, Cornish sea trout with a seafish mousse and hazelnut noodles, white peach with Fleuris wine crystals and tuile biscuit. Wine is taken seriously: the list is balanced, discerning and informative. ♀ Well-chosen ⊖

Lunch 12.15–1.45 Dinner 7.15–9.45

TUNBRIDGE WELLS — Cheevers ⬦

R Map 7 B5 Kent
56 High Street
Tunbridge Wells (0892) 45524

Set D £15.95
About £40 for two
Seats 32
Parties 32
Parking Limited

Credit Access Visa

Bright fresh decor and excellent cooking are combined at this enterprising bistro-style restaurant. A brasserie operates at lunchtime, when you can simply have soup or a three-course meal from the daily-changing blackboard menu. Evenings bring a set dinner with a good choice of refined modern dishes and some fine desserts. We enjoyed a delicate mousse of crab wrapped in spinach and an excellent parfait of two chocolates. ♀ Well-chosen ⊖

Lunch 12–2.30 Dinner 7–10.30
Closed Sun, Mon, Bank Hols, 1 wk Easter & 2 wks Sept

TUNBRIDGE WELLS Royal Wells Inn 62% £D/E

HR Map 7 B5 Kent
Mount Ephraim TN4 8BE
Tunbridge Wells (0892) 511188

Credit Access, Amex, Diners, Visa
Closed 25 & 26 Dec

A visit by Queen Victoria when a Princess is commemorated in the double coat of arms that tops the handsome facade of this late 18th-century hotel. Refurbishment has smartened the public rooms and added a stylish reception lounge as well as nine new bedrooms with brass beds, pretty fabrics and good bathrooms. Other rooms in pleasant traditional style include two with four-posters.

Rooms 25	*Direct dial* Yes	*Confirm by* arrang.	*Parking* Limited
Ensuite bath/shower 25	*Room TV* Yes	*Last dinner* 9.45	*Room service* All day

Restaurant

Set L from £10.50
Set D from £12.50
About £50 for two
Seats 45
Parties 80

Relocated in the handsome first-floor conservatory, the new dining room provides a plushy setting in which to enjoy Robert Sloan's skilled cooking. His repertoire ranges from traditional dishes such as steak, kidney and oyster pie and tender lamb cutlets Reform to the more adventurous matelote of eels in Armagnac and red wine, while tempting sweets include a delicious chocolate roulade.

Lunch 12.30–2.30 *Dinner* 7.30–9.45, Sat till 10.30, Sun till 9.15
Closed Bank Hol Mons & 25 & 26 Dec

**We welcome bona fide complaints and recommendations
on the tear-out pages at the back of the book for readers' comment.
They are followed up by our professional team.**

TUNBRIDGE WELLS Spa Hotel 72% £C

HR Map 7 B5 Kent
Mount Ephraim TN4 8XJ
Tunbridge Wells (0892) 20331
Telex 957188

Rooms 75
Ensuite bath/shower 75
Direct dial Yes
Room TV Yes
Confirm by arrang.
Last dinner 9.30
Parking Ample
Room service 24 hours

Credit Access, Amex, Diners, Visa

An elegant 18th-century building which has been a fine hotel for over a hundred years. Handsome, period public rooms and high standards of courtesy and efficiency from the staff have lingered from more gracious days and every attention is paid to the guests' comfort. All the bedrooms have hairdryers, remote control TVs and convenient bedside controls; most have been refurbished with attractive matching bed-

spreads and curtains and a few have sitting areas. Bathrooms have smart vinyl floors, panelled surrounds and efficient showers; many have bidets. No dogs. *Amenities* garden, indoor swimming pool, sauna, solarium, whirlpool bath, beauty salon, hairdressing, tennis, secretarial services, fax, laundry service, children's play area.

Regency Restaurant

Set L £13.50
Set D £15
About £47 for two
Seats 80
Parties 10

Splendid chandeliers and nice garden views make for pleasant surroundings in which to sample James Donaldson's sound, enjoyable cooking (the lunch menu is particularly good value). There's an excellent hors d'oeuvre trolley and main courses might be tournedos aux champignons or chicken breast stuffed with Brie. The sweet trolley is attractive and freshly prepared. Good clarets and burgundies: Ch. de Camensac '79, Mercurey Clos des Myglands (Faiveley) '83.

Lunch 12.30–2, Sun 1–2.30
Dinner 7–9.30

**If we recommend meals in a Hotel or Inn,
a separate entry is made for its restaurant.**

TUNBRIDGE WELLS Thackeray's House ★ ♛ ♗

R **Map 7 B5** Kent
85 London Road
Tunbridge Wells (0892) 37558

Lunch 12.30–2.30
Dinner 7.15–10
Set L from £9.95
Set D from £19.85
About £55 for two
Seats 40
Parties 20
Parking Difficult

Credit Access, Visa
Closed Sun, Mon, Bank Hols & 1
wk Xmas

Yes, Thackeray did live here and the period charm is preserved intact. At street level is the more informal bistro (next entry), while upstairs is a very fine restaurant. Service is friendly yet discreet and cooking first-rate. Bruce Wass puts a lot of thought and care into his imaginative menus; even the biscuits and bread that accompany the excellent British cheeses come from his kitchen. Good wines include

the delicious '87 Rosemount Chardonnay (Hunter Valley) and a mature '78 Chinon from Couilly Dutheil. *Specialities* marinated salmon and duck liver salad; baron of farmed rabbit with roast garlic cloves; lamb fillet with kidneys and sweet breads; chocolate Armagnac loaf with a coffee and walnut liqueur sauce. ♟ Well-chosen ☙

TUNBRIDGE WELLS Downstairs at Thackeray's *NEW ENTRY*

R **Map 7 B5** Kent
85 London Road
Tunbridge Wells (0892) 37559

Set L £6.90
About £33 for two
Seats 30
Parties 30
Parking Difficult
Credit Access, Visa

Close-set tables, fresh flowers and good pictures set the scene at this small and intimate restaurant. Service is just right, professional but friendly and the menus offer a wide choice of skilfully prepared dishes running from poached eggs in a pastry case with duxelle and hollandaise to halibut baked with vermouth and herbs and breast of chicken cooked in yoghurt and spices. Burnt orange cream is a delicious sweet. ☙

Lunch 12.30–2.30 *Dinner* 7–11
Closed All Sun & Mon, Bank Hols & 1 wk Xmas

**Our inspectors are our full-time employees;
they are professionally trained by us.**

TURNERS HILL Alexander House 80% *NEW ENTRY* £A

HR **Map 7 B5** West Sussex
Fen Place
Copthorne (0342) 714914
Telex 849169

Rooms 12
Ensuite bath/shower 12
Direct dial Yes
Room TV Yes
Confirm by arrang.
Last dinner 9.30
Parking Ample
Room service 24 hours

Credit Access, Amex, Diners, Visa

A sturdy late Victorian house set in mature grounds some 15 minutes' drive from Gatwick Airport. Quality, taste and quiet luxury are evident, notably in the panelled hall, the magnificent drawing room hung with Chinese silk, and in the huge, comfortable library-bar with carved wooden fireplace and discreet butler service. Bedrooms follow the pattern, with good reproduction furniture, discreet lighting, handsome

fabrics and cosseting extras. Similar thought and care continues in the bathrooms, where you'll find big towels, first-class toiletries and even softened water. Good breakfast, excellent staff. Courtesy transport. No children under seven. No dogs. *Amenities* garden, hairdressing, tennis, croquet, secretarial services, fax, laundry service, helipad.

Alexander's ♛

Set L from £23.50
Set D £28.50
About £60 for two
Seats 44
Parties 44

Good cooking and informed, polished service in stylish surroundings. The à la carte menu provides straightforward dishes using quality ingredients while a small, fixed-price menu offers a difficult choice with temptations like home-made noodles in lobster sauce and lamb fillet with wild mushrooms and Madeira sauce. Some very good wines: Muscadet Ch. La Touche '86, Corton Clos du Roi (Dubreuil Fontaine) '82. No smoking. ♟ Well-chosen ☙ ♿

Lunch 12.30–2
Dinner 7–9.30, Sun 7–9

TUTBURY — Ye Olde Dog & Partridge Hotel £D/E

Map 10 C3 Staffordshire
High Street DE13 9LS
Tutbury (0283) 813030
Telex 347220

Credit Access, Amex, Diners, Visa

A charming old coaching inn (oldest part 15th century), where everything, including the prize-winning garden, is kept in apple-pie order. There are two bars – one a popular local rendezvous – and a quiet lounge. Three quaint beamed bedrooms are in the main part, the rest, including a couple of four-poster rooms, in a Georgian annexe. Good modern bathrooms. Very pleasant staff. No children under ten.
Amenities garden, in-house movies, laundry service.

Rooms 17	*Direct dial* Yes	*Confirm by* arrang.	*Parking* Ample
Ensuite bath/shower 17	*Room TV* Yes	*Last dinner* 9.45	*Room service* Limited

TWICKENHAM — Cézanne *NEW ENTRY* ♀

Map 7 A5 Middlesex
68 Richmond Road
01-892 3526

About £38 for two
Seats 40
Parking Limited

Credit Access, Amex, Visa

Cézanne prints provide an attractive backdrop at this informal restaurant, where Tim Jefferson has created a short but imaginative menu offering something for everyone. Creamy, delicate broccoli soup or goose breast and bacon salad might precede pink juicy venison with a rich port and beetroot sauce, vegetarian pasta with pine kernels and pesto, or a simple steak béarnaise. Good vegetables and tempting sweets like chocolate and praline marquise. ♀ Well-chosen ⌨ &

Lunch 12.30–2.30   *Dinner* 7–10.30
Closed L Sat, all Sun, Bank Hol Mon only, 3 days Xmas

TWICKENHAM — McClements ♀

Map 7 A5 Middlesex
12 The Green
01-755 0176

Set L £12
Set D from £17.50
About £65 for two
Seats 28 *Parties* 25
Parking Difficult
Credit Access, Amex, Diners, Visa

John McClements continues to work miracles in the tiny kitchen of his delightfully elegant little restaurant. The menu is short but highly imaginative, with each beautifully prepared dish a near-masterpiece of teasing yet subtly balanced flavours. Start with a delicate bouillabaisse of fresh Cornish lobster and scallops, go on to guinea fowl roasted with garlic, served with pistachio stuffing, and end with the magnificent sweet platter: Book. ♀ Well-chosen ⌨ 🍷

Lunch 12–2.30   *Dinner* 7–10.30
Closed L Sat, all Sun, Bank Hols & Feb

UCKFIELD — Horsted Place 80% £B/C

Map 7 B6 East Sussex
Little Horsted TN22 5TS
Isfield (082 575) 581
Telex 95548

Rooms 17
Ensuite bath/shower 17
Direct dial Yes
Room TV Yes
Confirm by arrang.
Last dinner 10
Parking Ample
Room service All day

Credit Access, Amex, Diners, Visa
Closed 2 wks Jan

Set back from the A26 just south of Uckfield, this immaculately kept country house hotel is run by Guy Rigby and a young, friendly team united in their aim of pleasing their guests. The red-brick Victorian house has some eye-catching features, including the tapestry-hung Grand Gallery and a splendid carved oak stair-case by Pugin. Sumptuously dec-orated bedrooms, some of almost palatial proportions, are supplied

with a host of extras, from mineral water and fresh fruit to books, magazines and modern teletext TVs. Outstanding breakfasts. No children under seven. No dogs.
Amenities garden, indoor swimming pool, tennis, croquet, fax, valeting, laundry service.

Dining Room

Set L £12.50, Sun £17.50
Set D £27.50
Seats 40
Parties 24

Chef Keith Mitchell applies skill and artistry to top-notch produce, and the result is some really delightful dishes: lovely light crab mousse, salmon medallions with a delicate lemon and vanilla dressing, fillet of lamb with aubergine and mushrooms, chicken suprême with crayfish tails. Scrupulously chosen wines come from the best producers: Fleurie (Gobet) 1985, Chassagne Montrachet les Caillerets (A. Morey) 1984, Ch. Potensac 1982. ♀ Well-chosen ⌨ &

Lunch 12–2.30, Sun 12–2   *Dinner* 7.30–10
About £70 for two

UCKFIELD — Sussex Barn Restaurant *NEW ENTRY*

R **Map 7 B6** East Sussex
Ringles Cross
Uckfield (0825) 3827

Set L £9.50
Set D £15
About £40 for two
Seats 21 *Parties* 30
Parking Ample
Credit Access, Amex, Diners, Visa

North of Uckfield on the A22, this is a charming cottage-style restaurant. Barrie Larvin does a fine job front of house, matched by Brian Harries in the kitchen. Typical dishes run from apple and cheese flan to poached salmon hollandaise, sautéed beef with peppers and a lovely chocolate mouse. Excellent bottles on a skilfully compiled wine list include Chiroubles (George Passot) '86, Jordan Cabernet Sauvignon '79. Well-chosen

Lunch 12–2, Sun 11.30–2.30 *Dinner* 7–10
Closed D Sun & all Mon

ULLSWATER — Leeming House Hotel 75% £C/D

HR **Map 13 D5** Cumbria
Watermillock CA11 0JJ
Pooley Bridge (085 36) 622
Telex 64111

Rooms 25
Ensuite bath/shower 23
Direct dial Yes
Room TV Yes
Confirm by 6
Last dinner 8.45
Parking Ample
Room service All day
Credit Access, Amex, Diners, Visa

A friendly country house atmosphere and stunning views of the lake and fells guarantee a pleasurable stay at this Georgian-style building set in landscaped grounds. Two large lounges, one opulent in style, the other more simple, offer civilised comfort and warmth in winter from log fires and there's a small and intimate panelled bar. The bedrooms, some of which are balconied, are spacious and well-appointed, with colour TV, direct-dial phones, flowers and fruit; the bathrooms are carpeted and semi-tiled, the two that are not en suite being adjacent and private to the bedrooms. Staff are smart and efficient.
Amenities gardens, coarse fishing, fax, laundry service.

Restaurant

Set L Sun only £12.50
Set D £25
About £60 for two
Seats 60
Parties 20

The emphasis is on home-made fare at this elegant restaurant – chutneys, jams, biscuits and bread all derive from Jon Reed's kitchen – and the cooking is solid and reliable. Start with fricassée of chicken and prawns; main course might be escalope of salmon with sole mousse or noisettes of venison with wild mushrooms and peppercorn sauce. Good cheese trolley and a lush display of sweets. Well-chosen

Lunch 12.30–1.45 *Dinner* 7.30–8.45

ULLSWATER — Old Church Hotel 67% £B/C

HR **Map 13 D5** Cumbria
Watermillock,
Nr Penrith CA11 0JN
Pooley Bridge (085 36) 204

Closed mid Nov–mid Mar

A wonderful setting on the shore of Ullswater brings peace, relaxation and stunning views. The Whitemores are friendly hosts, and Maureen's talent for interior design makes the rooms delightful. Three lounges in muted colours offer comfortable armchairs and plenty of reading material, while the lovingly designed bedrooms have half-testers or canopies, pine dressing tables and plenty of extras. Super staff. No dogs. ***Amenities*** garden, coarse and game fishing, boating.

Rooms 10
Ensuite bath/shower 10
Room phone No
Room TV No
Confirm by arrang.
Last dinner 9
Parking Ample
Room service All day

Restaurant

English cooking
Set D £17.50
About £50 for two
Seats 25

Gentle green decor, old wooden tables and fresh flowers create a pleasing ambience in which to enjoy wholesome and unpretentious food, carefully cooked. The short four-course menu changes daily, and a typical meal would be hot smoked salmon on a bed of noodles, chicken soup flavoured with walnuts and pine kernels, and roast breast of duck for a main course. Desserts are a high point. Non-residents must book.

Dinner only 7.30–9
Closed mid Nov–mid Mar

ULLSWATER — Rampsbeck Hotel 60% £E

HR Map 13 D5 Cumbria
Watermillock, Nr Penrith
CA11 0LP
Pooley Bridge (085 36) 442

Credit Access, Visa
Closed early Jan–end Feb

A garden filled with rhododendrons and a position overlooking the lake make this a delightful hotel to visit. The friendly informality of the Gibbs creates a homely atmosphere, which makes the place popular with families, who also enjoy the spacious public areas. Bedrooms, though modest, boast duvets, stylish furniture, tiled, carpeted bathrooms (nine of them new) and, of course, wonderful views.
Amenities garden, coarse fishing.

Rooms 18	Room *phone* No	*Confirm by* arrang.	*Parking* Ample
Ensuite bath/shower 18	Room *TV* Yes	*Last dinner* 9	Room service Limited

Restaurant

Set L £9.75
Set D £16
About £45 *for two*
Seats 60
Parties 20

Eamon Webster's cooking is modern and self-assured, using good fresh ingredients. The fixed-price menu offers tempting dishes such as monkfish terrine with cashew nuts served with a lemon beurre blanc for a starter and poached Scottish salmon with elderflower wine sauce as a main course. Vegetables are fresh, colourful and crisp and saucing is the high point. Traditional Sunday lunch; non-residents must book for weekday lunches. ⊝ &

Lunch 12–2 *Dinner* 7–9
Closed early Jan–end Feb

ULLSWATER — Sharrow Bay Hotel 81% £A

HR Map 13 D5 Cumbria
Lake Ullswater,
Nr Penrith CA10 2LZ
Pooley Bridge (085 36) 301

Rooms 30
Ensuite bath/shower 26
Direct dial Yes
Room TV Yes
Confirm by arrang.
Last dinner 8.45
Parking Ample
Room service All day

Closed 5 Dec–3 Mar

A country house hotel par excellence, the Sharrow Bay stands in a beautiful wooded setting at the edge of Ullswater. Latest improvement is a stylish conservatory added to the lounge, where a bewildering array of antiques, objets d'art, mirrors and plants create a cluttered but utterly charming effect. Highly individual bedrooms feature elegant drapes and likewise are comfortably crowded with fine furniture,

ornaments and flowers. Main-house rooms are generally small but enjoy stunning views; larger rooms in the outhouses. Bathrooms are compact but well equipped. Superb breakfast and excellent service from a highly professional team. Half-board terms only. No children under 13. No dogs. *Amenities* garden, laundry service.

Restaurant ★ ♕

Lunch 1–1.45
Dinner 8–8.45
Set L from £14
Set D £29.50
About £80 *for two*
Seats 65
Parties 10

Closed 5 Dec–3 Mar

Johnnie Martin heads a talented team at this delightful restaurant, producing some of the most memorable food in the area. Any meal here is nothing less than a gastronomic event – an experience only enhanced by the stylish surroundings and discreet, attentive service. Chicken breast stuffed with fresh fruits and nuts, served with pilaff and cream sauce, is a typically imaginative treat, but there are traditional

favourites too, like roast beef and Yorkshire pudding. Desserts are sheer perfection. No smoking. Good conventional wine list, strong on burgundies. *Specialities* roast duck breast with pink peppercorn sauce and duck ravioli, pâté foie gras and truffle parfait bouchée, chocolate and praline terrine with vanilla sauce. ⊝ ♣

★ For a *discount* on next year's guide, see **An Offer for Answers**. ★

ULVERSTON — Bay Horse Inn & Bistro *NEW ENTRY*

R **Map 13 C6** Cumbria
Canal Foot
Ulverston (0229) 53972

About £35 for two
Seats 26
Parties 26
Parking Ample

Credit Access

Pigeon and rabbit terrine with plum and brandy chutney, guinea fowl with sage and onion stuffing, salmon in a lovely cream chive sauce – such are the delights proposed by Bobby Lyons and his capable team at this attractive seafront inn. Fresh-baked bread, imaginative vegetabes and super sweets add to the pleasure, along with the marvellous views. Try Orlando Jacob's Creek Australian red from the short, interesting wine list. Well-chosen

Lunch 12–2 *Dinner* 7–9
Closed D Sun, all Mon, 26 Dec & 1 Jan

UMBERLEIGH — Rising Sun Hotel £E/F

I **Map 3 D2** Devón
EX37 9DU
High Bickington (0769) 60447
Credit Access, Amex, Diners, Visa

Fishing rights on the river Taw are a major attraction at this characterful 17th-century inn. Angling photographs decorate the smart little lounge bar, and there's also a flagstoned public bar and stylishly comfortable residents' lounge. Bedrooms (two in a cottage annexe) are all named after pools in the river and have good-quality pine furniture and attractive salmon-pink decor. Modern tiled bathrooms. No children. No dogs. ***Amenities*** game fishing.

Rooms 8	*Direct dial* Yes	*Confirm by* arrang.	*Parking* Ample
Ensuite bath/shower 6	*Room TV* Yes	*Last dinner* 9	*Room service* None

UNDERBARROW — Greenriggs Country House £E

I **Map 13 D5** Cumbria
Nr Kendal LA8 8HF
Crosthwaite (044 88) 387

Closed Mon–Thurs Nov–early Mar & all Jan & Feb

There's a special home-from-home atmosphere at this splendidly located hotel, conferred by its small size and the friendly informality of the Smithsons. Interconnecting chintzy lounges provide cosy relaxation and there's a TV room with access to the garden. Bedrooms, distributed between the main house and modern extensions, are modest but pleasing and each one has a fine view. No dogs.
Amenities garden, croquet, laundry service.

Rooms 13	*Room phone* No	*Confirm by* 6	*Parking* Ample
Ensuite bath/shower 10	*Room TV* No	*Last dinner* 8	*Room service* Limited

UPPER SLAUGHTER — Lords of the Manor Hotel 71% £C/D

HR **Map 4 C1** Gloucestershire
Nr Bourton-on-the-Water
GL54 2JD
Cotswold (0451) 20243
Telex 83147

Rooms 15
Ensuite bath/shower 15
Direct dial Yes
Room TV Yes
Confirm by arrang.
Last dinner 9.30
Parking Ample
Room service All day

Credit Access, Amex, Diners, Visa

This attractive 17th-century manor house enjoys a peaceful, rural setting, standing in seven acres of gardens. An open fireplace has been installed to give a warm and welcoming touch to the foyer, and the newly refurbished reception retains the character of the rest of the house. The other public areas comprise a smart, comfortably furnished bar, a traditional lounge and a bright and cheerful garden room. Bedrooms are individually decorated in light and airy style, with pale colour schemes, good quality floral fabrics and nice pieces of period furniture. The neat, tidy bathrooms have showers and luxurious toiletries. Housekeeping is excellent. ***Amenities*** garden, croquet, coarse fishing, secretarial services, fax, laundry service.

Restaurant

Set L £11.25
Set D Sun £26.50
About £60 for two
Seats 50

A smart restaurant where Richard Mundy offers an interesting à la carte menu, supplemented by seasonal specialities. Starters include roast quail in a pastry parcel with woodland mushrooms; main dish may be breast of guinea fowl with a timbale of wild rice or honey-roasted breast of duck with leeks and truffle. Good wines, fine burgundies; Chassagne Montrachet (Olivier Leflaive) '85, Savigny les Beaune (Bruno Clair) '83. Well-chosen

Lunch 12.30–1.45 *Dinner* 7.30–9.30

UPPINGHAM — Falcon Hotel 62% — £D/E

H Map 11 E4 Leicestershire
High Street East LE15 9PY
Uppingham (0572) 823535

Credit Access, Amex, Diners, Visa

A friendly former coaching inn, the Falcon overlooks the market place. Public rooms, include a spacious and comfortable foyer lounge. The two bars are full of character, but it's the bedrooms that are the establishment's strongest suit. All are individually decorated, with white period-style furniture, attractive soft furnishings and well-equipped, ensuite bathrooms.
Amenities garden, laundry service.

Rooms 26	*Direct dial* Yes	*Confirm by* 6	*Parking* Ample
Ensuite bath/shower 26	*Room TV* Yes	*Last dinner* 9.45	*Room service* 24 hours

UPPINGHAM — Lake Isle

RR Map 11 E4 Leicestershire
16 High Street East
Uppingham (0572) 822951

Set L *from* £9
Set D £13.50
About £38 for two
Seats 35
Parking Limited

Credit Access, Amex, Diners, Visa

The sort of restaurant that every country town should have, offering fine food, excellent service and comfort aplenty for an overnight stay. In the rustic restaurant, panelled with Victorian pine, David Whitfield presents interesting, daily-changing set menus using the freshest produce complemented by nice light sauces. Dishes may include deeply-flavoured wild mushroom soup, hot parfait of chicken livers and lamb's sweetbreads, rendezvous of seafood and a splendid chocolate rum torte. Super wines include a great choice of half-bottles.
Well-chosen

Lunch 12.30–1.45, Sun 12.30–2 *Dinner* 7.30–9.30, Sat 7–10
Closed L Mon, D Sun & all Bank Hols

BEDROOMS 8 £E/F
With bath/shower 8

Bedrooms, decorated in pretty, pale colours, are full of extras ranging from fruit and magazines to trouser presses.

UTTOXETER — White Hart Hotel — £E

I Map 10 C3 Staffordshire
Carter Street ST14 8EU
Uttoxeter (0889) 562437

Credit Access, Amex, Diners, Visa

One of the best features of this 16th-century former coaching inn is a banqueting room with some fine carved oak panelling. The main informal place to meet is the bar-lounge, an open-plan area with lots of cosy corners and a Victorian feel. Decor in the bedrooms varies from traditional to more modern; eight rooms in the annexe share a ground-floor shower room.
Amenities laundry service.

Rooms 26	*Direct dial* Yes	*Confirm by* arrang.	*Parking* Ample
Ensuite bath/shower 15	*Room TV* Yes	*Last dinner* 9.45	*Room service* Limited

**If we recommend meals in a Hotel or Inn,
a separate entry is made for its restaurant.**

VENTNOR — Royal Hotel 61% — £D

H Map 5 D4 Isle of Wight
Belgrave Road PO38 1JJ
Isle of Wight (0983) 852186

Credit Access, Amex, Diners, Visa

Peaceful lawns and a long verandah front this mellow sandstone hotel. Inside is an attractive cane-furnished lounge area, a cosy beamed bar and another, rather worn lounge area – mainly used for children's videos, for this is very much a place for family holidays. Decent-sized bedrooms mostly offer basic fittings and the usual accessories.
Amenities garden, outdoor swimming pool, solarium, croquet, bicycles, games room, snooker, laundry service, children's play area.

Rooms 54	*Room phone* Yes	*Confirm by* arrang.	*Parking* Ample
Ensuite bath/shower 54	*Room TV* Yes	*Last dinner* 9	*Room service* All day

VERYAN — Nare Hotel 62% — £D/E

H Map 2 B3 Cornwall
Carn Beach TR2 5PF
Truro (0872) 501279

Credit Access, Amex, Diners, Visa

A clifftop setting overlooking a mile of sandy beach ensures splendid views from many of the spotless bedrooms of this pleasant hotel. Six have balconies and there are two with patios. All have solid, old-fashioned appeal, with decent furniture and immaculate bathrooms. Public rooms comprise two comfortable lounges and a cheerful bar. No dogs. *Amenities* garden, outdoor swimming pool, sauna, solarium, gymnasium, tennis, games room, snooker, laundry service.

Rooms 40	*Room phone* No	*Confirm by* arrang.	*Parking* Ample
Ensuite bath/shower 35	*Room TV* Some	*Last dinner* 9.15	*Room service* Limited

WADHURST   Spindlewood Country House Hotel   61%   £D/E

HR **Map 7 B6** East Sussex
Wallcrouch TN5 7JG
Ticehurst (0580) 200430

Credit Access, Amex, Diners, Visa
Closed 4 days Xmas

Five acres of gardens, ponds and woodland provide a lovely setting
for the friendly Fitzsimmonses' late-Victorian hotel off the B2099.
Public rooms offer solid, old-fashioned comfort, with a panelled lounge
that doubles as a function room. Bedrooms – some with garden views
– are fresh and homely, with floral wallpaper, simple comforts and
well-kept bathrooms. No dogs.
Amenities garden, tennis, laundry service.

Rooms 9	*Direct dial* Yes	*Confirm by* arrang.	*Parking* Ample
Ensuite bath/shower 9	*Room TV* Yes	*Last dinner* 9	*Room service* All day

Restaurant

Set L Sun £10.85
Set D £15.90
About £47 *for two*
Seats 40
Parties 60

An interesting menu and pleasant service make for a most enjoyable
meal in this spacious restaurant with the peaceful charm of a French
provincial dining room. Chef Paul Clayton has a talent for sauces,
from his salmon and sole mousse with a chive cream sauce to duck
with redcurrant and lime and venison with juniper berries and sherry.
There are delicious puds too, and a choice of savoury endings.
♟ Well-chosen ⓔ

Lunch 12.15–1.30   *Dinner* 7.15–9, Sun till 8.30
Closed 4 days Xmas

Changes in data sometimes occur in establishments
after the Guide goes to press.
Prices should be taken as indications rather than firm quotes.

WAKEFIELD   Cedar Court Hotel   58%   £C/D

H **Map 10 C1** West Yorkshire
Denby Dale Road,
Calder Grove WF4 3QZ
Wakefield (0924) 276310
Telex 557647

Credit Access, Amex, Diners, Visa

A touch of classical styling gives character to this modern hotel next
to junction 39 of the M1. Open-plan public rooms, including a spacious
bar, are pleasantly smart but informal. Good-sized bedrooms with
well-designed furniture and ample writing space have tea-makers and
remote-control TVs. Compact bathrooms offer shower facilities,
complimentary toiletries and decent towels. **Amenities** garden,
secretarial services, laundry service, coffee shop (7am–10.30pm).

Rooms 100	*Direct dial* Yes	*Confirm by* arrang.	*Parking* Ample
Ensuite bath/shower 100	*Room TV* Yes	*Last dinner* 10	*Room service* 24 hours

WAKEFIELD   Post House Hotel   64%   £C/D

H **Map 10 C1** West Yorkshire
Queen's Drive, Ossett WF5 9BE
Wakefield (0924) 276388
Telex 55407

Credit Access, Amex, Diners, Visa

Pleasant public rooms in this modern, low-rise hotel include a
welcoming foyer-lounge, a cheerful pine-furnished coffee shop and a
softly-lit cocktail bar. Spacious bedrooms are equipped with tea-
makers, mini-bar with fresh milk, and bathrooms with showers.
Executive rooms have double beds and seating. Book early as it's a
popular business venue.
Amenities garden, laundry service, coffee shop (7am–11pm). &

Rooms 96	*Direct dial* Yes	*Confirm by* 6	*Parking* Ample
Ensuite bath/shower 96	*Room TV* Yes	*Last dinner* 10.15	*Room service* 24 hours

WAKEFIELD   Swallow Hotel   58%   £D

H **Map 10 C1** West Yorkshire
Queen Street WF1 1JU
Wakefield (0924) 372111
Telex 557464

Credit Access, Amex, Diners, Visa

A tall modern hotel which offers splendid views from the upper floors.
The public areas, which are on the first and second floors, comprise
two bars which serve as simple lounge areas. Bedrooms have modern
fitted units and most have coordinating fabrics. Tea/coffee-makers
and bedside controls for TV, radio and lights are standard. Bathrooms
have hairdryers and good soap. **Amenities** secretarial services,
laundry service, 24-hour lounge service.

Rooms 64	*Direct dial* Yes	*Confirm by* 6	*Parking* Ample
Ensuite bath/shower 64	*Room TV* Yes	*Last dinner* 9.15	*Room service* Limited

WALBERTON   Avisford Park Hotel   66%   £C/D

H **Map 5 E4** West Sussex
Nr Arundel BN18 0LS
Yapton (0243) 551215
Telex 86137

Credit Access, Amex, Visa

This practical yet comfortable hotel has an attractive conservatory-style lounge for non-smokers, a bar-lounge and extensive conference facilities. Well-equipped bedrooms are decorated in pastel colours and have fully tiled bathrooms. *Amenities* garden, indoor swimming pool, sauna, solarium, keep-fit equipment, tennis, squash, 9-hole golf course, croquet, snooker, games room, secretarial services, fax, laundry service, 24-hour lounge service, helipad.

Rooms 98	*Direct dial* Yes	*Confirm by* arrang.	*Parking* Ample
Ensuite bath/shower 98	*Room TV* Yes	*Last dinner* 9.30	*Room service* Limited

WALL   Hadrian Hotel   £E/F

I **Map 15 B4** Northumberland
Nr Hexham NE46 4EE
Humshaugh (043 481) 232

Credit Access

A peaceful, friendly roadside inn close to Hadrian's Wall has been allowed to retain its warmth and character in the stone fireplaces, traditionally upholstered banquettes and polished wooden tables. Bedrooms are simple and pleasingly traditional – two have half-testers and all have tea/coffee-makers and fruit. The bathrooms are modern and functional. No children under 12. *Amenities* garden.

Rooms 9	*Room phone* No	*Confirm by* arrang.	*Parking* Ample
Ensuite bath/shower 3	*Room TV* Some	*Last dinner* 9.30	*Room service* None

WALLINGFORD   George Hotel   66%   £C/D

H **Map 5 D2** Oxfordshire
High Street OX10 0BS
Wallingford (0491) 36665
Telex 847468

Credit Access, Amex, Diners, Visa

The exterior of this coaching inn is solidly traditional; inside old and new blend in a stylish fashion that retains many original features such as the inglenook in the pubby bar. Cottage-style bedrooms in the original building are well appointed with plenty of thoughtful extras; Executive rooms in a new wing are even more luxurious. *Amenities* patio, in-house movies, secretarial services, laundry service.

Rooms 39	*Direct dial* Yes	*Confirm by* arrang.	*Parking* Ample
Ensuite bath/shower 39	*Room TV* Yes	*Last dinner* 10.30	*Room service* 24 hours

WALLINGFORD   Shillingford Bridge Hotel   58%   £D/E

H **Map 5 D2** Oxfordshire
Ferry Road, Shillingford
OX10 8LZ
Warborough (086 732) 8567
Telex 837763
Credit Access, Amex, Diners, Visa
Closed 3 days Xmas

With a quarter-mile stretch of very pretty river frontage, this collection of white-painted buildings is a pleasant place to stay. Inside, all is spick-and-span, both in the roomy bars and lounge and in the bedrooms, five of which are in an annexe and five in a bungalow. *Amenities* garden, outdoor swimming pool, squash, coarse fishing, laundry service, laundry room.

Rooms 37	*Direct dial* Yes	*Confirm by* arrang.	*Parking* Ample
Ensuite bath/shower 37	*Room TV* Yes	*Last dinner* 10	*Room service* Limited

WALSALL   Barons Court Hotel   63%   £E

H **Map 10 C4** West Midlands
Lichfield Road,
Walsall Wood WS9 9AH
Brownhills (0543) 452020
Telex 333061
Credit Access, Amex, Diners, Visa

Cheerful staff enhance a stay at this modern Tudor-style hotel on the A461. Bedrooms are well equipped; many have four-posters, and a dozen boast whirlpool baths. The bar area – seven separate serving points – has a medieval theme. *Amenities* patio, indoor swimming pool, sauna, solarium, whirlpool bath, steam room, keep-fit equipment, beauty salon, satellite TV, fax, laundry service.

Rooms 100	*Direct dial* Yes	*Confirm by* arrang.	*Parking* Ample
Ensuite bath/shower 100	*Room TV* Yes	*Last dinner* 9.45	*Room service* 24 hours

WALSALL   Crest Hotel   61%   £C/D

H **Map 10 C4** West Midlands
Birmingham Road WS5 3AB
Walsall (0922) 33555
Telex 335479

Credit Access, Amex, Diners, Visa

A modern brick building standing alongside the A34 about a mile from junction 7 of the M6. Standard pine-furnished bedrooms are supplied with trouser presses and tea-making facilities, and all have neat little bathrooms. Executive and Lady Crest rooms offer superior decor and a larger range of accessories. There are three bars, one with regular jazz sessions. *Amenities* pool tables, secretarial services, fax, laundry service.

Rooms 101	*Direct dial* Yes	*Confirm by* 6	*Parking* Ample
Ensuite bath/shower 101	*Room TV* Yes	*Last dinner* 9.45	*Room service* 24 hours

WALTHAM ABBEY   Blunk's

R **Map 7 B4** Essex
20 Market Square
Lea Valley (0992) 712352

Set L & D £16
About £55 for two
Seats 40
Parties 40
Parking Ample

Credit Access, Amex, Diners, Visa

Parisian Pierre Mauroux is a chef of the old school, applying considerable skills and a wealth of experience to a wide range of dishes including seafood specialities – lobster cocktail, a faultless crab bisque, classic treatment of sole and turbot. Pepper steak, veal escalope chasseur and duck with cherries are among the meaty delights, and sweets include a number of ice cream creations à la Blunk. This is a really charming restaurant, with polished tiled floor, polished wooden tables and polished service from pleasant, attentive staff. Open every day of the year, lunchtime and evening. You'll find it on the market square.   ♀ Well-chosen

Lunch 12.30–2.30
Dinner 7.30–10.30, Sat 7.30–11.30

WANSFORD-IN-ENGLAND   Haycock Hotel   69%   £C/D

HR **Map 6 A2**
Cambridgeshire
Nr Peterborough PE8 6JA
Stamford (0780) 782223
Telex 32710

Credit Access, Diners, Visa

A 17th-century coaching inn set in a delightfully unspoilt village of stone-built cottages. Modest day rooms include two comfortably traditional lounges and a cheerful bar. Bedrooms are much smarter – some contemporary, some period in style (the latter featuring antiques and several four-posters). All have Italian-tiled bathrooms.
Amenities garden, pétanque, coarse fishing, mooring, secretarial services, laundry service.

Rooms 25	*Direct dial* Yes	*Confirm by* 6	*Parking* Ample
Ensuite bath/shower 25	*Room TV* Yes	*Last dinner* 10.15	*Room service* 24 hours

Restaurant   *NEW ENTRY*

About £45 for two
Seats 40
Parties 40
Parking ample

The dining room is traditional and so is much of the menu: farmhouse soup, rack of lamb, steak and kidney pie, roast beef. Hitting a more contemporary note are stir-fry of prawns and mange-tout, fish kebabs and deep-fried breast of chicken stuffed with banana in a mild curry sauce. Chocolate gâteau is a scrumptious sweet. Good cooking (also excellent bar snacks); attentive service.   ♀ Well-chosen ☕

Lunch 12–2
Dinner 7–10.15

WANTAGE   Bear Hotel   58%   £D/E

H **Map 5 D2** Oxfordshire
Market Square OX12 8AB
Wantage (023 57) 66366

Credit Access, Amex, Diners, Visa

The cobbled courtyard conjures up coaching days at this centuries-old hostelry on the market square. The best bedrooms, in the older part, are quite attractive, with pretty wallpapers and fabrics, brass bedsteads, traditional furniture and an easy chair. Remaining rooms are rather more functional, but all are clean and presentable. There are two bars, one of them popular with the locals.
Amenities laundry service.

Rooms 33	*Direct dial* Yes	*Confirm by* arrang.	*Parking* Limited
Ensuite bath/shower 33	*Room TV* Yes	*Last dinner* 9.45	*Room service* Limited

WARE   Briggens House Hotel   69%   £C

H **Map 7 B4** Hertfordshire
Stanstead Road
Nr Stanstead Abbots SG12 8LD
Roydon (027 979) 2416
Telex 817906

Credit Access, Amex, Diners, Visa

Travelling along the A414 from Ware to Harlow you'll find this sturdy Georgian mansion just past the turning to Stanstead Abbots. It's been a hotel only in the 80s, and it's a very popular place for conferences. Refurbishment has taken place in the well-proportioned day rooms, among which are a roomy entrance hall (quite tastefully decorated) and a lounge and adjoining bar (rather less so). Bedrooms have also been given a facelift; standard rooms are decently sized, with sturdy furnishings, good lighting and ample desk/dressing table space. Executive rooms have more accessories. No dogs.
Amenities garden, outdoor swimming pool, tennis, 9-hole golf course, croquet, coarse fishing, in-house movies, fax, laundry service.

Rooms 58	*Direct dial* Yes	*Confirm by* 6	*Parking* Ample
Ensuite bath/shower 58	*Room TV* Yes	*Last dinner* 9.45	*Room service* 24 hours

WAREHAM | Priory Hotel 73% | £D/E

HR **Map 4 B4** Dorset
Church Green BH20 4ND
Wareham (092 95) 51666
Telex 41143

Rooms 19
Ensuite bath/shower 19
Direct dial Yes
Room TV Yes
Confirm by arrang.
Last dinner 10
Parking Ample
Room service All day

Credit Access, Amex, Diners, Visa

Four acres of lovingly tended gardens run down to the river Frome, and the hotel – dating from 1535 – stands opposite the Church of St Mary. Two elegant lounges, with antiques and inviting easy chairs, open on to the patio. In the larger lounge, polished oak flooring and a grand piano are features. Considerable attention to detail is evident in the bedrooms, epitomised by well-chosen antiques, luxurious bathrobes and a complimentary newspaper that arrives with morning tea. The two waterside suites and adjacent Kingfisher and Mallard rooms each have individually designed beds and whirlpool baths. No dogs. *Amenities* garden, croquet, coarse & game fishing, valeting, laundry service.

Restaurant ♛

Set L from £10, Sun £10.95
Set D £15
About £56 for two
Seats 44
Parties 44

In the cellars of the old priory, this is a comfortable, well-appointed restaurant, with an intimate atmosphere and professional, unobtrusive service. Cooking is modern, with an English accent, and local fresh produce features prominently. Seafood and vegetable terrine, asparagus soup with pine kernels and grilled lamb with kidneys, sweetbreads and a port wine sauce are typical fare, with British regional cheeses and good ices and sweets to finish. ♟ Well-chosen ☙

Lunch 12.30–2 *Dinner* 7.30–10

WAREHAM | Springfield Country Hotel 57% | £D

H **Map 4 B4** Dorset
Grange Road, Stoborough
BH20 5AL
Wareham (092 95) 2177

Credit Access, Amex, Visa

Mr. Alford expanded his private house into a hotel in 1971, and he now has four members of his family to help. Other families are frequent visitors, as both accommodation and facilities are very suitable. Bedrooms are bright and well kept, with ample storage space and tiled bathrooms. The bar and lounges provide easy relaxation but no great style, and there are pleasant terraces for sipping alfresco. A new leisure complex is planned for a spring 1989 opening, with more bedrooms to follow. No children under two. *Amenities* garden, outdoor swimming pool, gymnasium, tennis, riding, snooker, pool table, laundry service.

Rooms 32	*Direct dial* Yes	*Confirm by* arrang.	*Parking* Ample
Ensuite bath/shower 32	*Room TV* Yes	*Last dinner* 9	*Room service* All day

WARMINSTER | Bishopstrow House 87% | £B

HR **Map 4 B3** Wiltshire
BA12 9HH
Warminster (0985) 212312
Telex 444829

Rooms 26
Ensuite bath/shower 26
Direct dial Yes
Room TV Yes
Confirm by 6
Last dinner 9.30
Parking Ample
Room service 24 hours

Credit Access, Amex, Diners, Visa

Standards remain as high as ever at the Schillers' lovingly converted Georgian mansion. Indoor pleasures include relaxing in the sunny morning room, leafing through a magazine in the elegant lounge, or lunch in the delightful conservatory. Bedrooms offer the ultimate luxury experience, with smart furnishings, many thoughtful extras, and immaculate housekeeping. Many of the bathrooms have whirlpool baths. No children under three. *Amenities* garden, indoor & outdoor swimming pools, sauna, solarium, whirlpool bath, tennis, coarse fishing, secretarial services, valeting, laundry service, helipad. *see over*

Bishopstrow House Restaurant ♛

Set L £16.50
Set D from £23
About £65 for two
Seats 65
Parties 65

Everything is stylish here, from the elegant setting and professional service to Nigel Davis' artistic handling of first-class produce. His fixed-price set menus offer a varied choice of such appealing dishes as Cornish crab sausage with herb butter or a smooth duck liver parfait, followed by confit of duck, roulade of wild rabbit, or noisettes of spring lamb. Tempting sweets. There's a trolley of English cheeses in prime condition. Good wines include some very fine clarets.
♟ Well-chosen ℮

Lunch 12.30–2   *Dinner* 7.30–9.30

WARREN ROW   The Warrener *NEW ENTRY*   ⚘

R **Map 5 D2** Berkshire
Nr Wargrave
Littlewick Green (062 882) 2803

About £60 for two
Seats 60
Parties 85
Parking Ample

Credit Access, Amex, Diners, Visa

An excellent French restaurant where very high standards of cooking guarantee an exciting meal. Start with a finely flavoured saddle of rabbit then move on to fresh and smoked salmon in Chablis and dill sauce; follow with a perfect veal cutlet in a wild mushroom and calvados sauce. Serious wine list chosen with care: some fine burgundies from good growers (W Fèvre, Bruno Clair, Chandon de Brialles). ♟ Well-chosen ℮ &

Lunch 12–2   *Dinner* 7–9.30
Closed L Sat, D Sun, 1st wk Jan, last 2 wks Aug

WARRINGTON   Lord Daresbury Hotel   67%   £C

H **Map 10 B2** Cheshire
Daresbury WA4 4BB
Warrington (0925) 67331
Telex 629330

Credit Access, Amex, Diners, Visa

Close to the M56, this popular modern hotel boasts excellent business and leisure facilities. Public areas are smart in pine and pastels, while spacious bedrooms (including top-floor Executive rooms with extra accessories) all offer good desk space and neat bathrooms.
Amenities indoor swimming pool, sauna, solarium, whirlpool bath, gymnasium, beauty salon, squash, snooker, in-house movies, laundry service, kiosk, children's play area, helipad.

Rooms 141	*Direct dial* Yes	*Confirm by* 6	*Parking* Ample
Ensuite bath/shower 141	*Room TV* Yes	*Last dinner* 10	*Room service* 24 hours

WARSOP   Goff's *NEW ENTRY*

R **Map 11 D2** Nottinghamshire
4a Burns Lane
Mansfield (0623) 844137

About £40 for two
Seats 50
Parties 50
Parking Ample

Credit Access, Amex, Diners, Visa

The Goffs own the butchers shop a few doors down, so the meat's very good at their restaurant with beams, soft lighting and fresh flowers. Rex Hewell's bold, assertive methods also work well with the excellent fresh fish that arrives on a day-to-day basis. His sauces are well judged – just the right amount of cream – and tempting sweets include honey ice cream and a delicious sticky toffee pudding.

Lunch 12–2   *Dinner* 7–9.45
Closed L Sat, D Sun, all Mon & Bank Hols

WARWICK   Hilton Inn   70%   £C

H **Map 10 C4** Warwickshire
Stratford Road CV34 6RE
Warwick (0926) 499555
Telex 312468

Rooms 150
Ensuite bath/shower 150
Direct dial Yes
Room TV Yes
Confirm by 6
Last dinner 9.45
Parking Ample
Room service 24 hours

Credit Access, Amex, Diners, Visa

Formerly the Ladbroke, this well-run modern hotel is conveniently sited at a roundabout on the outskirts of Warwick, close to the A46 and the proposed M40. Open-plan public areas are stylishly contemporary, and there are versatile facilities for functions and conferences. Bedrooms, all of a good size, are a big strength; the majority are standard rooms with lightwood furniture, nicely coordinated fabrics

and excellent bathrooms with tubs and top-quality showers. Gold Star rooms (about 35) are of a superior specification, with bigger beds, trouser presses, hairdryers, bathrobes and miniatures of whisky. Staff are smart and friendly. *Amenities* garden, indoor swimming pool, in-house movies, fax, laundry service. &

WARWICK | Randolphs ♀

R **Map 10 C4** Warwickshire
19 Coten End
Warwick (0926) 491292

About £50 for two
Seats 30
Parties 30
Parking Limited

Credit Access, Visa

Iris Gordon is a talented and imaginative chef who uses best quality raw materials to produce some really excellent, unique dishes: roast quail with poached pears and a light pink peppercorn sauce, veal fillet with a sauce of chocolate, cherries and wine, banana steamed pudding with dark rum sauce and custard. Note Brunello di Montalcino (Tenuta di Sesta) '79 on a quality wine list. ♀ Well-chosen ⊖

Dinner only 7.45–9.30
Closed Sun, Bank Hols & 1 wk Xmas

---

 indicates a **well-chosen** house wine

WASHINGTON | George Washington Hotel   69%   £D

H **Map 15 C4** Tyne & Wear
Stone Cellar Road,
District 12 NE37 1PH
Washington (091) 417 2626
Telex 537143

Credit Access, Amex, Diners, Visa

A low-built modern hotel with superb leisure facilities and smart public areas. It's considerably grown in size with an extra 36 new bedrooms – some with whirlpool baths, all with stylish cane furniture. *Amenities* garden, indoor swimming pool, sauna, solarium, whirlpool bath, keep fit equipment, beautician, hairdressing, squash, golf course, pitch & putt, games room, snooker, in-house movies, secretarial services, fax, laundry service, coffee shop (7am–7pm).

| *Rooms* 106 | *Direct dial* Yes | *Confirm by* 6 | *Parking* Ample |
| *Ensuite bath/shower* 106 | *Room TV* Yes | *Last dinner* 9 | *Room service* 24 hours |

WASHINGTON | Post House Hotel   59%   £C/D

H **Map 15 C4** Tyne & Wear
Emerson, District 5 NE37 1LB
Tyneside (091) 416 2264
Telex 537574

Credit Access, Amex, Diners, Visa

Six floors of bedrooms provide practical overnight comforts for guests at this modern hotel just off the A1(M) and close to the A195. Decor is quite pleasant and fresh, and a number of Executive Club rooms with superior furnishings and appointments are available. The marble-floored foyer is presentable, and refurbishment will improve the tired-looking bar-lounge. *Amenities* garden, fax, laundry service, coffee shop (7am–10.30pm), children's playground.

| *Rooms* 138 | *Direct dial* Yes | *Confirm by* 6 | *Parking* Ample |
| *Ensuite bath/shower* 138 | *Room TV* Yes | *Last dinner* 10 | *Room service* 24 hours |

WATERHOUSES | Old Beams   ♨ ♀

RR **Map 10 C3** Staffordshire
ST10 3HW
Waterhouses (053 86) 254

Set L £9.50
About £50 for two
Seats 50
Parties 14
Parking Ample

Credit Access, Amex, Diners, Visa

A marvellous restaurant in an attractive old stone house. It is full of magnificent floral displays that combine elegantly with beams, wheelback chairs and candlelight. Nigel Wallis cooks with a delicate, artistic touch; start with steamed scallops with a julienne of vegetables and truffles, and follow with grilled breast of duck with strawberries or venison in a port wine sauce. Puds may include bread and butter pudding or apricot pie. Among wines chosen with exceptional flair are Tokay Rangen '84 (Zind Humbrecht), Ch. Laville Haut-Brion (Blanc) '81, La Tache '70. ⊃ Outstanding ♀ Well-chosen ⊖ &

Lunch 12–2   *Dinner* 7–10
Closed Sun, Mon, 1st 2 wks Jan & 1 wk Oct

BEDROOMS 2 £D/E
With bath/shower 2

The two beautiful bedrooms have handmade limed oak furniture, top-quality linen and carpeted bathrooms with gold-plated fittings.

WATERINGBURY | Wateringbury Hotel   57%   £D/E

H **Map 7 B5** Kent
Tonbridge Road,
Nr Maidstone ME18 5NS
Maidstone (0622) 812632
Telex 96265
Credit Access, Amex, Diners, Visa

A tile-hung roadside inn with a matching bedroom extension, linked by an attractive little conservatory with cane furniture and lots of plants. There's a pleasant residents' lounge and patio, but the King's Head pub is now a conference area. Bedrooms are neat and bright, with the usual up-to-date accessories and tiled, carpeted bathrooms. No dogs. *Amenities* garden, sauna, in-house movies, secretarial services, laundry service.

| *Rooms* 28 | *Direct dial* Yes | *Confirm by* 6 | *Parking* Ample |
| *Ensuite bath/shower* 28 | *Room TV* Yes | *Last dinner* 10 | *Room service* 24 hours |

WATFORD   Hilton National Hotel   64%   £C

H Map 5 E2 Hertfordshire
Elton Way WD2 8HA
Watford (0923) 35881
Telex 923422

Credit Access, Amex, Diners, Visa

A modern concrete-and-glass hotel standing on the A41, just south of junction 5 of the M1. Automatic doors open into a smart lobby-lounge with marble floor, soft lighting, comfortable armchairs and tasteful artwork on the walls. Overnight accommodation is well designed and reasonably roomy, Gold Star rooms offering the most in terms of style and accessories. Affable staff do their jobs well.
Amenities in-house movies, fax, laundry service.

Rooms 172	*Direct dial* Yes	*Confirm by* 6	*Parking* Ample
Ensuite bath/shower 172	*Room TV* Yes	*Last dinner* 10	*Room service* 24 hours

WATH-IN-NIDDERDALE   Sportsman's Arms   ♕   ⌇

R Map 15 B6 North Yorkshire
Nr Pateley Bridge
Harrogate (0423) 711306

Set L Sun £7.50
Set D £12.90
About £39 for two
Seats 50 *Parties* 55
Parking Ample
Credit Access, Amex, Diners, Visa

A delightful inn with a very happy atmosphere. Relax and give your order over a pre-dinner drink in the cosy lounge before moving into the attractive dining room. Ray Carter's menus offer imaginative dishes which are expertly prepared from prime ingredients such as Nidderdale trout and fresh Rothesay scallops. Fairly good wine list with *some* interesting bottles: Chablis Mont de Milleu (Bacheroy Josselin) '86, Ch. de Beaucastel '80. ⊜

Lunch Sun only 12–2.30   *Dinner* 7–9.30
Closed D Sun

🖝 is our symbol for an **outstanding** wine list

WEEDON   Crossroads Hotel   66%   £D/E

H Map 5 D1 Northamptonshire
High Street NW7 4PX
Weedon (0327) 40354
Telex 312311

Credit Access, Amex, Diners, Visa
Closed 25 Dec

Resident proprietors have made this former toll house a relaxing and attractive hotel with bags of character. Public rooms include a spacious foyer and cosy beamed bar. The restaurant reveals the owner's passion for clocks and includes the visible workings of the clock whose tower is a feature of the hotel. Individually-furnished bedrooms – most in modern centrally heated and double-glazed garden blocks – have freestanding furniture and tasteful fabrics. All have TVs, tea-makers, trouser presses and hairdryers, plus pretty ensuite bathrooms. No dogs.
Amenities garden, tennis, in-house movies, secretarial services, fax, laundry service, coffee shop (7am–6pm).   &

Rooms 50	*Direct dial* Yes	*Confirm by* 6	*Parking* Ample
Ensuite bath/shower 48	*Room TV* Yes	*Last dinner* 10.15	*Room service* Limited

WELWYN   Heath Lodge Hotel   £C/D

HR Map 7 A4 Hertfordshire
Danesbury Park Road
AL6 9SL
Welwyn (043 871) 7064
Telex 827618

Credit Access, Amex, Diners, Visa

A four million pound scheme of alterations and improvements was well under way as we went to press, November 1988 being the due date for completion. 16 suites and six studio suites are included among the rooms, which will feature classic furniture, specially woven carpets and all-new decor. The hotel stands in ample grounds near the A1 (M). Graded at 60% in our 1988 guide. No children under 10.
Amenities garden, fax.

Rooms 47	*Direct dial* Yes	*Confirm by* arrang.	*Parking* Ample
Ensuite bath/shower 47	*Room TV* Yes	*Last dinner* 9.30	*Room service* 24 hours

Restaurant

French cooking

Set L from £13.95
Sun from £10.95
Set D from £21.95
About £50 for two
Seats 50
Parties 150

A new and elegant setting for Clive Jackson's very talented cooking. His ambitious menus change regularly, and the day's market brings extra choices. We much enjoyed parfait of chicken livers and foie gras with Sauternes jelly, turbot with champagne and a lovely chocolate mousse with orange sauce. Sauces are a particular strength, and presentation gets a lot of attention. Very good wines strong in Rhône, Beaujolais and Burgundy (Guigal, Gobet, Ampeau). ⊜

Lunch 12.30–2   *Dinner* 7–9.30, Sun till 9
Closed L Sat

The tea consumed
was the very best, the coffee the very blackest,
the cream the very thickest; there was dry toast and
buttered toast, muffins and crumpets; hot bread and cold
bread, white bread and brown bread, home-made bread
and bakers' bread, wheaten bread and oaten bread...
there were eggs in napkins, and crispy bits of bacon under
silver covers; there were little fishes in a little box, and
devilled kidneys frizzling on a hot-water dish...
Over and above this, on a snow white napkin, spread upon
the side-board, was a huge ham and a huge sirloin; the latter
having laden the dinner table on the previous evening.
Such was the ordinary fare at Plumstead Episcopi.

ANTHONY TROLLOPE 1815-82
THE WARDEN

In the eighteenth century,
one could only eat at special cookshops or inns.
But in 1765...Boulanger, a soup-seller, called his soups
by the special name of *restaurant* - restorative.
Their sale was so successful he wanted to enlarge his menu,
but since he was not a member of the *traiteurs* corporation -
eating-house keepers - he was not permitted to serve ragouts.
Instead he offered his customers sheeps' feet in
white sauce... not a ragout. Boulanger's sheeps' feet in
white sauce became famous all over Paris.
From 1786 onwards the great cuisiniers opened restaurants,
nearly all of which were famous for a particular speciality.

PHILIPPA PULLAR
CONSUMING PASSIONS (1970)

WELWYN GARDEN CITY   Crest Hotel   59%   £C/D

H **Map 7 B4** Hertfordshire
Homestead Lane AL7 4LX
Welwyn Garden (070 73) 24336
Telex 261523

Credit Access, Amex, Diners, Visa

It's sensible to check directions when booking at this modest modern hotel in a quiet position on the outskirts of town. Popular with business visitors, it offers decent overnight accommodation in reasonably-sized bedrooms that provide storage/writing space, an easy chair and neat little bathrooms. The main day room is a combined lounge and bar with cane furniture and lots of plants.
Amenities garden, in-house movies, fax, laundry service.

| *Rooms* 58 | *Direct dial* Yes | *Confirm by* 6 | *Parking* Ample |
| *Ensuite bath/shower* 58 | *Room TV* Yes | *Last dinner* 10 | *Room service* Limited |

WEM   Hawkstone Park Hotel   60%   £D/E

H **Map 10 A3** Shropshire
Weston-under-Redcastle
SY4 5UY
Lee Brockhurst (093 924) 611
Telex 35793

Credit Access, Amex, Diners, Visa

This sturdy 18th-century building set in 300 acres of grounds is nothing short of a golfer's paradise. Comfortable and convivial public areas resound to tales of the day's play. Bedrooms have simple furniture, light colour schemes and traditional fabrics.
Amenities garden, outdoor swimming pool, sauna, solarium, keep-fit equipment, tennis, golf courses; putting, croquet, games room, snooker, secretarial services, laundry service, coffee shop (12am–9.30pm), 24-hour lounge service.

| *Rooms* 59 | *Direct dial* Yes | *Confirm by* arrang. | *Parking* Ample |
| *Ensuite bath/shower* 59 | *Room TV* Yes | *Last dinner* 9.30 | *Room service* Limited |

WEMBLEY   Hilton National Wembley   63%   £B

H **Map 5 E2** Middlesex
Empire Way HA9 8DS
01-902 8839
Telex 24837

Credit Access, Amex, Diners, Visa

A high-rise hotel adjacent to the Wembley complex. Best of the public areas is Fultons bar, which has movie stills covering the walls and bentwood chairs. Bedrooms have functional laminate units, stylish fabrics, radios, hairdryers, trouser presses and tea/coffee-makers; Gold Star rooms have more extras. Bathrooms are equipped with marble-effect vanity units and shower fitments. *Amenities* in-house movies, secretarial services, fax, laundry service, coffee shop (11am–11pm).

| *Rooms* 305 | *Direct dial* Yes | *Confirm by* 6 | *Parking* Ample |
| *Ensuite bath/shower* 305 | *Room TV* Yes | *Last dinner* 10 | *Room service* 24 hours |

WENTBRIDGE   Wentbridge House Hotel   63%   £E

H **Map 11 D1** West Yorkshire
Nr Pontefract WF8 3JJ
Pontefract (0977) 620444
Telex 946240

Credit Access, Amex, Diners, Visa
Closed 25 Dec

Standing in 15 acres of grounds close to the A1, Wentbridge House is a creeper-clad building dating back to 1700. Public areas retain a period charm, and the clubby bar is a particularly cosy spot in winter. Individually appointed bedrooms include the spacious Oak Room with panelling, antique furniture and a Thompson (Mouseman) four-poster. Friendly staff do their jobs well. No dogs.
Amenities garden, secretarial services, laundry service.

| *Rooms* 20 | *Direct dial* Yes | *Confirm by* arrang. | *Parking* Ample |
| *Ensuite bath/shower* 17 | *Room TV* Yes | *Last dinner* 9.30 | *Room service* Limited |

We publish annually,
so make sure you use the current edition.
It's worth it!

WEOBLEY   Red Lion Hotel   59%   £E/F

H **Map 4 A1**
Hereford & Worcester
Broad Street HR4 8SE
Weobley (0544) 318220

Credit Access, Amex, Visa

A handsome building in a handsome village, the Red Lion is a fine example of 'Hereford Black and White' timbered architecture. Day rooms include a splendid beamed bar, a carvery and a quiet upstairs lounge. Bedrooms are simple but cosy, with plenty of writing space and excellent housekeeping. Keen young manager Tim Foster leads by example in terms of courtesy and efficiency. Decent breakfast.
Amenities garden.

| *Rooms* 7 | *Room phone* Yes | *Confirm by* arrang. | *Parking* Ample |
| *Ensuite bath/shower* 7 | *Room TV* Yes | *Last dinner* 9.30 | *Room service* All day |

WEST BEXINGTON   Manor Hotel   57%   £E

H **Map 4 A4** Dorset
Nr Dorchester DT2 9DF
Burton Bradstock (0308) 897785

Credit Access, Amex, Visa

A family-run hotel with a lovely setting in large open gardens above
Chesil Bank. The main building is a splendid stone manor house with
an ancestry going back to the Domesday Book. A chintzy lounge
overlooks the gardens, and there's a lively cellar bar. Bedrooms, all
with sea views, sport new wallpaper and paintwork. Fabrics are
bright and cheerful, and there are colourful dried flower displays.
Amenities garden, sea fishing, children's playground.

Rooms 10	*Room phone* No	*Confirm by* arrang.	*Parking* Ample
Ensuite bath/shower 10	*Room TV* Yes	*Last dinner* 9.30	*Room service* Limited

WEST BROMWICH   West Bromwich Moat House   59%   £D

H **Map 10 C4** West Midlands
Birmingham Road B70 6RS
021-553 6111
Telex 336232

Credit Access, Amex, Diners, Visa

Follow the signs carefully to this modern red-brick hotel just off
junction 1 of the M5. Bedrooms are of a good size and well equipped,
and there's ample space for writing. Day rooms are in the throes of
being reorganised and ample car parking, good conference facilities
and pleasant staff are major pluses.
Amenities garden, in-house movies, fax, laundry service, coffee shop
(8am–8pm).

Rooms 180	*Direct dial* Yes	*Confirm by* 6	*Parking* Ample
Ensuite bath/shower 180	*Room TV* Yes	*Last dinner* 9.45	*Room service* 24 hours

WEST CHILTINGTON   Roundabout Hotel   57%   £D/E

H **Map 5 E3** West Sussex
Monkmead Lane,
Nr Pulborough RH20 2PF
West Chiltington (079 83) 3838

Credit Access, Amex, Diners, Visa

A 1930s period piece, with a high-pitched roof and leaded windows
and a real Old English country garden to match. Flowery fabrics give
a homely appeal to the spacious lounge and cheeerful cocktail bar,
while solid oak furniture characterizes the comfortably traditional
bedrooms. Radio-alarms and remote-control TVs are standard,
superior rooms also have trouser presses and hairdryers, and there are
two cottage suites. *Amenities* garden.

Rooms 21	*Direct dial* Yes	*Confirm by* arrang.	*Parking* Ample
Ensuite bath/shower 21	*Room TV* Yes	*Last dinner* 9	*Room service* Limited

WEST CLANDON   Onslow Arms   ♕

R **Map 5 E3** Surrey
The Street
Guildford (0483) 222447

Set L £9.95, Sun £11.95
Set D £11.95
About £60 *for two*
Seats 80 *Parties* 30
Parking Ample
Credit Access, Amex, Diners, Visa

A classic, comfortable pub restaurant with highly enjoyable cooking
by Ewart Morgan. Traditional and modern ideas combine on his
menus, which run from vegetable terrine and seafood pasta to chicken
with mangoes, calf's liver dijonnaise and a very good steak bordelaise.
Also grills and several ways with sole; lamb duckling is a winter
speciality. Good clarets on a sound wine list. Service is professional
and attentive. ❷

Lunch 12.30–2 *Dinner* 7.30–10
Closed D Sun, all Mon & Bank Hols

★ For a *discount* on next year's guide, see **An Offer for Answers.** ★

WEST RUNTON   Links Country Park Hotel   62%   £C

H **Map 6 C1** Norfolk
Nr Cromer NR27 9QH
West Runton (026 375) 691

Credit Access, Visa

A popular, well-run hotel and golf club standing in 35 acres of grounds
not far from the sea. The atmosphere throughout is very peaceful and
friendly, and warm, personal attention is offered to every guest. The
lounge is a relaxing place to take tea, play cards or read, and there's a
choice of bars. Bedrooms, including some suitable for family
occupation, are well maintained and decently furnished (some
antiques); all have their own bright bathrooms. Rooms in the separate
Garden Room block, built in 1987, are particularly quiet and secluded.
Amenities garden, indoor swimming pool, sauna, solarium, tennis,
9-hole golf course, games room, pool table, in-house movies. ♿

Rooms 32	*Direct dial* Yes	*Confirm by* arrang.	*Parking* Ample
Ensuite bath/shower 32	*Room TV* Yes	*Last dinner* 9.30	*Room service* 24 hours

WEST RUNTON — Mirabelle Restaurant ♫

R **Map 6 C1** Norfolk
7 Station Approach,
Nr Cromer
West Runton (026 375) 396

Set L £8.75, Sun £11.50
Set D from £11.50
About £35 for two
Seats 45 *Parking* Ample
Credit Access, Amex, Diners, Visa

Austrian-born Manfred Hollwoger has worked hard here for 15 years, and his reward is a loyal band of regulars who are happy to spread the word. The word is cosy, cottage surroundings, friendly staff and enjoyable dishes such as asparagus with melted butter, salmon with lobster sauce, wienerschnitzel and roast Norfolk duckling. The long, interesting wine list is strong in clarets: Chx. Branaire Ducru '76, Léoville Las Cases '70, Lynch Bages '61. ☺

Lunch 12.30–2   *Dinner* 7–9.30
Closed D Sun Nov–end May, all Mon & 1st 2 wks Nov

WEST STOUGHTON — Burnt House Farm 65% NEW ENTRY £D/E

H **Map 4 A3** Somerset
Nr Wedmore BS28 4PW
Wedmore (0934) 713214

Credit Access, Amex, Diners, Visa

Get directions when booking at this peaceful converted farmhouse. Owners John and Elaine Snow have retained much of its original charm, and the feeling throughout is one of a friendly, well-ordered private house. The lounges (one a converted barn) are exceedingly relaxing, so too are the bedrooms, which feature beams, pine furniture and shower rooms. No dogs. *Amenities* garden, indoor swimming pool, sauna, snooker, laundry service.

Rooms 4	*Direct dial* Yes	*Confirm by* arrang.	*Parking* Ample
Ensuite bath/shower 4	*Room TV* Yes	*Last dinner* 9	*Room service* None

Our inspectors *never* book in the name of Egon Ronay's Guides.
They disclose their identity only if they are considering an establishment
for inclusion in the next edition of the Guide.

WESTON-ON-THE-GREEN — Weston Manor Hotel 66% £C

H **Map 5 D1** Oxfordshire
Nr Oxford OX6 8QL
Bletchington (0869) 50621
Telex 83409

Credit Access, Amex, Diners, Visa

A colourful 900-year-long history attaches to this attractive manor house and former monastery on the A43. The past comes alive as you enter the lofty baronial hall, and there's an oak-panelled dining room with minstrel's gallery. Individually decorated bedrooms are full of character. No dogs. *Amenities* garden, outdoor swimming pool, tennis, squash, putting, croquet, clay-pigeon shooting, coarse & game fishing, secretarial services, fax, laundry service.

Rooms 39	*Direct dial* Yes	*Confirm by* arrang.	*Parking* Ample
Ensuite bath/shower 39	*Room TV* Yes	*Last dinner* 9.30	*Room service* All day

WESTON-SUPER-MARE — Grand Atlantic Hotel 63% £C/D

H **Map 4 A3** Avon
Beach Road BS23 1BA
Weston-super-Mare (0934) 26543

Credit Access, Amex, Diners, Visa

The seafront setting makes this a popular holiday hotel, and its large garden and good leisure facilities are added attractions. Day rooms in cosy, traditional style include a nautically-themed bar and two sun lounges that look out to sea. Most of the bedrooms have been improved and now boast smart Italian furniture and brass light fittings. *Amenities* garden, outdoor swimming pool, tennis, games room, laundry service.

Rooms 76	*Room phone* Yes	*Confirm by* 6	*Parking* Ample
Ensuite bath/shower 76	*Room TV* Yes	*Last dinner* 9.30	*Room service* 24 hours

WESTONBIRT — Hare & Hounds Hotel 60% £E

H **Map 4 B2** Gloucestershire
Nr Tetbury GL8 8QL
Westonbirt (066 688) 233

Credit Access, Amex, Visa

An attractive Cotswold-stone house standing back from the A433 close to the famous Westonbirt Arboretum. Bedrooms, including five in an adjoining cottage, are warm and comfortable, and all have modern carpeted bathrooms. There are two lounges, one cosy and homely, the other larger and airier. The resident proprietors of many years run the hotel on friendly, informal lines. *Amenities* garden, tennis, squash, putting, croquet, snooker, laundry service.

Rooms 26	*Direct dial* Yes	*Confirm by* arrang.	*Parking* Ample
Ensuite bath/shower 26	*Room TV* Yes	*Last dinner* 9 (10 Sat)	*Room service* Limited

WETHERAL   Crown Hotel   70%   £D

H Map 13 D4 Cumbria
Nr Carlisle CA4 8ES
Carlisle (0228) 61888
Telex 64175

Rooms 50
Ensuite bath/shower 50
Direct dial Yes
Room TV Yes
Confirm by arrang.
Last dinner 9.30
Parking Ample
Room service 24 hours

Credit Access, Amex, Diners, Visa

Smart, friendly staff, fine leisure facilities and excellent all-round comfort in a peaceful setting near the river Eden (the hotel is signposted from the pretty village). Reception has been rebuilt with dark wood and parquet flooring, and the lounge is in tasteful country house style. Walton's Bar features fishing trophies in display cabinets. Mini-bars, trouser presses and hairdryers head the list of extras in the good-sized bedrooms; well-kept bathrooms have tubs and showers, decent toiletries and heated towel rails. *Amenities* garden, indoor swimming pool, sauna, solarium, whirlpool bath, keep-fit equipment, squash, snooker, pool table, in-house movies, secretarial services, fax, laundry service. &

WETHERAL   Fantails   *NEW ENTRY*

R Map 13 D4 Cumbria
The Green, Nr Carlisle
Wetheral (0228) 60239

About £30 for two
Seats 50
Parking Limited

Credit Access, Amex, Diners, Visa

Step back into the past at this delightful 18th-century cottage opposite the village green, where the robust, no-nonsense cooking recalls the simple fare of yesteryear. Scallops mornay could be followed by pan-fried veal or fresh salmon with watercress hollandaise, rounded off with a marvellous orange and Cointreau trifle. Wine list includes Condrieu Côte du Columbier '85 and Torres Gran Corronas at bargain prices.

Lunch 12–2   *Dinner* 6–9.30
Closed Sun, Mon, Bank Hols & Feb

WETHERBY   Penguin Hotel   65%   £C

H Map 11 D1 West Yorkshire
Leeds Road LS22 5HE
Wetherby (0937) 63881
Telex 556428

Credit Access, Amex, Diners, Visa

New owners have taken over the former Ladbroke Hotel, located at the junction of the A1 and A58. Public areas are bright and fresh, with central hooded fires a feature of both foyer-lounge and bar. Gold Star bedrooms sport deep-toned colour schemes and masses of extras; cheerfully decorated standard rooms offer tea-makers and remote-control TVs. *Amenities* garden, in-house movies, secretarial services, laundry service, 24-hour lounge service.

Rooms 72	*Direct dial* Yes	*Confirm by* 6	*Parking* Ample
Ensuite bath/shower 72	*Room TV* Yes	*Last dinner* 10	*Room service* Limited

We publish annually,
so make sure you use the current edition.
It's worth it!

WEYBOURNE   Maltings Hotel   57%   £E

H Map 6 C1 Norfolk
The Street NR25 6SY
Weybourne (026 370) 731

Credit Access, Amex, Diners, Visa

A 16th-century house of Norfolk flint forms the core of this family-run hotel. Public rooms are old-fashioned and unfussy, and the snug is popular with the locals. Bedrooms in the main house offer functional modest fittings; two rooms in the original malters' mash house have incongruously glitzy bathrooms; and others in a cottage annexe sport attractive country-style decor and some fine antiques. *Amenities* garden, secretarial services.

Rooms 21	*Direct dial* Yes	*Confirm by* 6	*Parking* Ample
Ensuite bath/shower 17	*Room TV* Yes	*Last dinner* 9	*Room service* Limited

ENGLAND

WEYBOURNE — The Swiss Restaurant

R Map 6 C1 Norfolk
The Street
Weybourne (026 370) 220

Set L from £4.95, Sun £9.75
Set D from £12.15
About £45 for two
Seats 65
Parking Ample

Credit Access, Amex, Diners, Visa

The building – originally three cottages – is very pretty, flagstoned and thatched, with a homely, rustic dining room. Nigel Massingham, in the kitchen for more than 30 years, cooks consistently well through a range of largely familiar dishes, from garlic mushrooms and game pâté to trout with almonds, chicken chasseur and emincé de veau à la Suisse (if you're lucky and they're not too busy, they'll make some excellent rösti potatoes). Portions are huge, so arrive hungry or greedy if you intend to clear your plate! Only the dedicated trencherman will guarantee space for peach pancakes with brandy sauce. Staff are nice and chatty, making a real effort to look after you. ☯

Lunch 12–2 *Dinner* 7–9
Closed D Sun, all Mon & Bank Hols

WEYBRIDGE — Oatlands Park Hotel 62% £D/E

H Map 5 E3 Surrey
146 Oatlands Drive KT13 9HB
Weybridge (0932) 847242
Telex 915123

Credit Access, Amex, Diners, Visa

Major investment is transforming Oatland Park, a much-extended Victorian mansion set in 20 tranquil acres. Public areas are being restyled, and the glass dome in the grandly proportioned main lounge will be restored. 16 of the largest bedrooms have been upgraded with deep-pile carpets, decent darkwood furnishings and attractive fabrics, their bathrooms acquiring high-quality ceramic bathware and no-expense-spared fittings. Bedrooms in the wing are smaller, with a simpler sixties style; these, too, are included in the improvement plans. Now management and staff must get their act together.
Amenities garden, tennis, squash, 9-hole golf course, in-house movies, secretarial services, fax, laundry service. ♿

Rooms 140	*Direct dial* Yes	*Confirm by* 6	*Parking* Ample
Ensuite bath/shower 140	*Room TV* Yes	*Last dinner* 9.30	*Room service* 24 hours

WEYBRIDGE — Ship Thistle Hotel 65% £B/C

H Map 5 E3 Surrey
Monument Green KT13 8BQ
Weybridge (0932) 48364
Telex 894271

Credit Access, Amex, Diners, Visa

A characterful town-centre hotel that's kept in ship-shape condition. The foyer-lounge is particularly charming, with its pretty furniture and soft blue and yellow decor, and there's also a stylish Art Deco bar. Well-equipped bedrooms, all in a rear extension, have attractive floral fabrics and decent darkwood units. Bathrooms are all now smartly retiled, some in marble. *Amenities* patio, in-house movies, secretarial services, fax, laundry service.

Rooms 39	*Direct dial* Yes	*Confirm by* 6	*Parking* Ample
Ensuite bath/shower 39	*Room TV* Yes	*Last dinner* 10.30	*Room service* 24 hours

Any person using our name to obtain free hospitality is a fraud.
Proprietors, please inform the police and us.

WHIMPLE — Woodhayes 74% £C/D

HR Map 3 E2 Devon
Nr Exeter EX5 2TD
Whimple (0404) 822237

Rooms 7
Ensuite bath/shower 7
Direct dial Yes
Room TV Yes
Confirm by 6
Last dinner 8
Parking Ample
Room service All day

Credit Access, Amex, Diners, Visa
Closed Jan

John and Alison Allan run their small, attractive Georgian hotel in the most charming fashion and guests are made to feel very much at home. There's no bar but drinks are served in two comfortable lounges, where oil paintings, antiques and pleasing soft furnishings give an air of elegance. The spacious, traditional bedrooms are a delight; all have individual decor and offer a high degree of comfort. Well-kept Victorian and Edwardian furniture, soft lights, desks, armchairs, remote control TV, radios, mineral water and magazines make for a feeling of luxury yet homeliness. Sumptuous carpeted bathrooms have many thoughtful extras.
Amenities garden, tennis, croquet, laundry service.   *see over*

Woodhayes Restaurant ♔

Set L £16
Set D £17.50
About £45 for two
Seats 20
Parties 20

Flickering reflections from the log fire and the candles light up the dark, polished woodwork to provide a romantic atmosphere in which to sample Paul Mason's enjoyable meals. The small, seasonal menu offers such dishes as smoked salmon en papillote as a starter with fillet of beef in a provençale sauce to follow. Admirable range of house wines including a delicious Mosel and a fine Vacqueyras. ♀ Well-chosen ⊖

Lunch by arrang. *Dinner* 7.30 for 8
Closed Jan

WHITEWELL Inn at Whitewell £E

Map 10 B1 Lancashire
Forest of Bowland,
Nr Clitheroe BB7 3AT
Dunsop Bridge (020 08) 222

Credit Access, Amex, Diners, Visa

On a hillside overlooking the River Hoddle, this ancient inn offers friendly, comfortable accommodation. The pleasant Tap room, with open fireplace and oak furniture, doubles as the village 'local' with extra seating in the hall. The residents' lounge has books and paintings (it's part of an art gallery). Traditional bedrooms. TVs and telephones on request. *Amenities* garden, clay-pigeon shooting, game fishing, pool table, secretarial services, laundry service.

Rooms 10	*Room phone* Yes	*Confirm by* arrang.	*Parking* Ample
Ensuite bath/shower 6	*Room TV* Yes	*Last dinner* 9.30	*Room service* All day

WHITWELL-ON-THE-HILL

Whitwell Hall Country House Hotel 67% £D/E

Map 15 C6 North Yorkshire
Nr York YO6 7JJ
Whitwell-on-the-Hill
(065 381) 551

Credit Access, Amex, Visa

Built in 1834 in Neo-Gothic style, this ivy-clad hotel has a lot of character and offers some of the most impressive views over the Vale of York. The main hall is splendidly baronial, and off this there's a comfortable drawing room. The orangery, a light, bright room with plants and garden furniture, overlooks the pool. Bedrooms are individually decorated and all include some nice solid pieces of furniture; rooms in the coach house are more modern. Bath/shower rooms are fairly modest. No children. Dogs in coach house only. *Amenities* garden, indoor swimming pool, sauna, tennis, putting, croquet, bicycles, games room, laundry service.

Rooms 20	*Direct dial* Yes	*Confirm by* arrang.	*Parking* Ample
Ensuite bath/shower 20	*Room TV* Yes	*Last dinner* 8.30	*Room service* All day

Our inspectors are our full-time employees;
they are professionally trained by us.

WICKHAM Old House Hotel 66% £C/D

HR **Map 5 D4** Hampshire
The Square PO17 5JG
Wickham (0329) 833049

Credit Access, Amex, Diners, Visa
Closed 10 days Xmas, 2 wks
Easter & 2 wks Aug–Sept

French-born Annie Skipwith has imbued a delightful Gallic feel to the interior of this quintessentially Georgian house dating from about 1715. Fresh flowers and period furniture grace the ground and first floor rooms. The charming bedrooms have either period or antique furniture, excellent writing areas, well-equipped bathrooms and many thoughtful extras such as hairdryers, trouser presses, portable radios, books and magazines. No dogs. *Amenities* garden, laundry service.

Rooms 10	*Room phone* Yes	*Confirm by* arrang.	*Parking* Ample
Ensuite bath/shower 8	*Room TV* Yes	*Last dinner* 9.30	*Room service* All day

Restaurant

French cooking

About £50 for two
Seats 45
Parties 14

Annie Skipwith plays a large part in the planning of the menus at her beamed restaurant and French regional cooking is the hallmark here. The menus are short – four starters and four main courses – but well-balanced and you might start with carrot and orange soup or ox tongue in cream and walnut sauce with roast quail or supreme of turbot to follow. Finish with a gratin of fresh fruit. ⊖

Lunch 12.30–1.45 *Dinner* 7–9.30
Closed L Sat & Mon, all Sun, Bank Hols, 10 days Xmas, 2 wks Easter & 2 wks Aug–Sept

WIGAN | Brocket Arms Hotel 55% | £E/F

H **Map 10 B2**
Greater Manchester
Mesnes Road WN1 2DD
Wigan (0942) 46283

Credit Access, Amex, Diners, Visa
Closed 25 Dec

Check directions to this sprawling red-brick hotel in a residential area north of town. The lounge bar is the place for a quiet drink, or you can meet the locals in the cheerful Brocket Pub. Simply furnished bedrooms, with good-sized, spotless bathrooms, are equipped with tea-makers, fresh fruit, and bedside radio alarms. There are good conference and banquet facilities. No dogs.
Amenities pool table, secretarial services, laundry service.

Rooms 27	*Direct dial* Yes	*Confirm by* arrang.	*Parking* Ample
Ensuite bath/shower 27	*Room TV* Yes	*Last dinner* 9.30	*Room service* Limited

---

**Changes in data sometimes occur in establishments
after the Guide goes to press.
Prices should be taken as indications rather than firm quotes.**

WILLERBY | Grange Park Hotel 68% *NEW ENTRY* | £D

HR **Map 11 E1** Humberside
Main Street, Nr Hull
HU10 6EA
Hull (0482) 656488
Telex 592773

Credit Access, Amex, Diners, Visa

A well-run hotel by the A164, with comfortable accommodation and extensive meeting and leisure facilities. Bedrooms feature pale pine units, modern designer fabrics and the usual up-to-date accessories, and their carpeted bathrooms are warm and very well equipped. Good breakfasts. Friendly staff.
Amenities garden, indoor swimming pool, sauna, solarium, whirl-pool bath, keep-fit equipment, satellite TV, in-house movies, secretarial services, fax, laundry service, coffee shop (10am–11pm).

Rooms 50	*Direct dial* Yes	*Confirm by* arrang.	*Parking* Ample
Ensuite bath/shower 50	*Room TV* Yes	*Last dinner* 9.30	*Room service* 24 hours

L'Eau Vive Restaurant *NEW ENTRY*

French cooking
Set L from £8.50
Set D £15.75
About £50 *for two*
Seats 70
Parties 20
Parking Ample

Smartly set tables, soft lighting and pleasant, professional service complement the culinary skills of Frenchman Jean Gysemans. His menus run from classic to modern, the lunchtime roast and grilled Dover sole to warm pigeon salad on a bed of autumn leaves and medallions of Scotch fillet in a goat's cheese sauce. Excellent little nibbles in the bar and petits fours with splendid coffee. 🍴 ♿

Lunch 12–1.30 *Dinner* 7–9.30
Closed L Sat, all Sun

WILLERBY | Willerby Manor Hotel 61% | £D/E

HR **Map 11 E1** Humberside
Well Lane HU10 6ER
Hull (0482) 652616

Credit Access, Amex, Visa

Standing in its own grounds in a quiet suburban setting, this converted Victorian house has seen recent major improvements. The restaurant is the first of the day rooms to be attractively refurbished, and the bedrooms are decorated and furnished in pleasant contemporary style, with smart tiled bathrooms. Four rooms in the main house are more traditional. Check directions. No dogs.
Amenities garden, secretarial services, laundry service, 24-hour lounge service.

Rooms 42	*Direct dial* Yes	*Confirm by* 6	*Parking* Ample
Ensuite bath/shower 42	*Room TV* Yes	*Last dinner* 9.30	*Room service* Limited

Restaurant Lafite

French cooking
Set L £7.50
Set D £9
About £42 *for two*
Seats 80
Parties 500

Elegant surroundings for excellent eating provided by head chef Valentine Rodriguez and his capable team. The principal menu is modern French, and dishes like halibut, salmon and monkfish with sauces of sorrel, white wine and lobster, or noisettes of venison with a rich game sauce, pink peppercorns and a pastry basket of chesnut purée are as delicious as they sound. Simpler menu also available. ♿

Lunch 12.30–2 *Dinner* 7.45–9.30, Sat 7.45–10
Closed L Sat, D Sun & Bank Hol Mons

WILMINGTON · Home Farm Hotel · 58% · £D/E

H Map 3 E2 Devon
Nr Honiton EX14 9JR
Wilmington (040 483) 278

Credit Access, Amex, Diners, Visa
Closed Jan & Feb

Old-fashioned comfort and rural charm are the order of the day at the Robsons' former farmhouse, which stands by the A35 just outside Honiton. The lounge, well supplied with books, games and inviting armchairs, has a homely, lived-in feel, and a stone-walled bar overlooks the gardens. Bedrooms, including some in the old stable block, are unfussy but comfortable; all are centrally heated.
Amenities garden.

Rooms 10	*Room phone* No	*Confirm by* arrang.	*Parking* Ample
Ensuite bath/shower 8	*Room TV* Yes	*Last dinner* 9	*Room service* Limited

WILMSLOW · Stanneylands Hotel · 70% · £D/E

HR Map 10 B2 Cheshire
Stanneylands Road SK9 4EY
Wilmslow (0625) 525225

Rooms 33
Ensuite bath/shower 33
Direct dial Yes
Room TV Yes
Confirm by 6
Last dinner 10
Parking Ample
Room service 24 hours

Credit Access, Amex, Diners, Visa
Closed 1 Jan, Good Fri & 26 Dec

Once the home of a wealthy stockbroker, this large red-brick Edwardian house stands in handsome gardens to the north of Wilmslow, just off the A34. It's now an outstandingly well-kept, well-run hotel, with the Beech family ensuring friendly efficient service and a pleasant, relaxing environment. Day rooms include a comfortable panelled lounge and a cosy bar-lounge with open fire. Among the main-house bedrooms, one offers a four-poster and an enormous period bathtub; another, a private sun terrace. Rooms in the purpose-built extension are large, with freestanding units. Bathrooms throughout are modern and well equipped. No dogs.

Amenities garden, secretarial services, fax, laundry service. &

Restaurant ★ ♛

Lunch 12.30–2
Dinner 7–10
Set L from £8.50
Set D £18
About £48 *for two*
Seats 80
Parties 100

Closed D Sun, 1 Jan, Good Fri & 26 Dec

Don't be put off by the flowery menu descriptions, for Iain Donald is a highly talented chef, whose only fault is a slight tendency towards over-fussy presentation and novelty for its own sake. Top-quality raw materials star in an exciting repertoire that ranges from salmon gâteau baked with wild mushrooms to boned quail stuffed with a foie gras and spinach mousse. Lovely desserts, and very good wines from impeccable sources: for quality and value try the Côtes du Rhône (Guigal).
Specialities spiced marinated beef fillet with celeriac mousseline, baked lamb rosettes on a sweet pepper fondue, mousse of sugared carrots on a potpourri of exotic fruits. ♥ Well-chosen ⊗ &

WILMSLOW · Valley Lodge Hotel · 59% · £D/E

H Map 10 B2 Cheshire
Altrincham Road SK9 4LR
Wilmslow (0625) 529201
Telex 666401

Credit Access, Amex, Diners, Visa

Built in the style of a Tyrolean chalet, this popular hotel near to the airport provides a haven for weary travellers. Public areas are bright and modern; bedrooms are all of good standard and are equipped with tea/coffee makers, hairdryers, trouser presses and fully-tiled bathrooms. *Amenities* garden, indoor swimming pool, sauna, solarium, whirlpool bath, keep-fit equipment, squash, snooker, secretarial services, fax, laundry service, 24-hour lounge service.

Rooms 105	*Direct dial* Yes	*Confirm by* 6	*Parking* Ample
Ensuite bath/shower 105	*Room TV* Yes	*Last dinner* 10.30	*Room service* Limited

WIMBLEDON   Cannizaro House & San Lorenzo Fuoriporta

See under LONDON

WIMBORNE MINSTER   The King's Head   57%   £D

H **Map 4 C4** Dorset
The Square BH21 1JA
Wimborne (0202) 880101

Credit Access, Amex, Diners, Visa

Overlooking the square in the centre of town, the King's Head is a Georgian inn rebuilt in the 19th century. Refurbishment has been completed in most of the bedrooms, where soft furnishings in bold reds and green blend well with dark polished furniture. Good en suite bathrooms throughout. The lounge has also been given a facelift, but not the rather dull bar.
Amenities secretarial services, laundry service.

Rooms 27	*Direct dial* Yes	*Confirm by* 6	*Parking* Limited
Ensuite bath/shower 27	*Room TV* Yes	*Last dinner* 9	*Room service* Limited

WINCANTON   Holbrook House Hotel   56%   £E

H **Map 4 B3** Somerset
Holbrook BA9 8BS
Wincanton (0963) 32377

Credit Access, Amex, Visa
Closed eve 31 Dec

There's been a house here since the 14th century, but the present one (alongside the A371 north of Wincanton) was built in the 1800s. It's a quiet, old-fashioned country hotel with a friendly atmosphere and homely comforts. Decent-sized bedrooms are simply appointed, with period or modern furnishings. Bath/shower rooms are fairly basic. TV available on request.
Amenities garden, outdoor swimming pool, tennis, squash, croquet.

Rooms 20	*Room phone* No	*Confirm by* arrang.	*Parking* Ample
Ensuite bath/shower 14	*Room TV* No	*Last dinner* 8.30	*Room service* None

WINCHESTER   Lainston House   80%   £B/C

H **Map 5 D3** Hampshire
Sparsholt SO21 2LT
Winchester (0962) 63588
Telex 477375

Rooms 32
Ensuite bath/shower 32
Direct dial Yes
Room TV Yes
Confirm by 6
Last dinner 10
Parking Ample
Room service 24 hours

Credit Access, Amex, Diners, Visa

This fine old William and Mary house set in rolling parkland is now a comfortable and elegant hotel. The lounge is light and spacious, with handsome drapes and deep sofas in matching fabric, while the club-like bar (formerly the library) is panelled with home-grown cedar wood (a tree felled by a storm in 1930 was used for the purpose). Good-sized bedrooms both in the main house and annexe are tastefully

furnished in a variety of styles; all have mini-bars and most have wall safes. Attractively tiled bathrooms (some in marble) offer bidets and bathtime luxuries.
Amenities garden, tennis, croquet, secretarial services, fax, laundry service, helipad. ⟨&⟩

WINCHESTER   Royal Hotel   67%   £D

H **Map 5 D3** Hampshire
St Peter Street SO23 8BS
Winchester (0962) 840840
Telex 477071

Credit Access, Amex, Diners, Visa

Standards continue to rise at this charming former convent in a narrow street off the city centre. All the bedrooms in the old building have recently been upgraded and now vie with the spacious, well-designed bedrooms in the new wing. Executive and Country House rooms have generous extras. Public rooms, radiating from the entrance hall, are attractive, with traditional furnishings. *Amenities* garden, in-house movies, secretarial services, fax, laundry service.

Rooms 59	*Direct dial* Yes	*Confirm by* 6	*Parking* Ample
Ensuite bath/shower 59	*Room TV* Yes	*Last dinner* 9.30	*Room service* 24 hours

WINCHESTER   The Wessex   69%   £B/C

H **Map 5 D3** Hampshire
Paternoster Row SO23 9LQ
Winchester (0962) 61611
Telex 47419

Credit Access, Amex, Diners, Visa

Located in the city centre, with splendid views of Winchester Cathedral, this relatively modern hotel has cheerful public rooms including a spacious well-lit foyer and cheerful lounge. The cocktail lounge has comfortable easy chairs and chesterfields. Bedrooms, including 20 for non-smokers, have smart Italian furniture and neat bathrooms. Executive rooms have generous extras.
Amenities laundry service, coffee shop (7am–10pm).

Rooms 94	*Direct dial* Yes	*Confirm by* 6	*Parking* Ample
Ensuite bath/shower 94	*Room TV* Yes	*Last dinner* 10	*Room service* 24 hours

WINDERMERE — Langdale Chase Hotel — 60% — £D/E

H Map 13 D5 Cumbria
LA23 1LW
Ambleside (0966) 32201

Credit Access, Amex, Diners, Visa

Well-tended grounds and magnificent views across Lake Windermere from this splendid building cannot fail to please the eye. Inside, there's a baronial oak-panelled hall with friezes, a minstrels' gallery and an impressive staircase. Best bedrooms are the individually decorated ones at the front and the secluded rooms in a new bungalow. Interiors and staff need improving. *Amenities* garden, tennis, putting, croquet, boating, laundry service, 24-hour lounge service.

Rooms 35	*Direct dial* Yes	*Confirm by* 6	*Parking* Ample
Ensuite bath/shower 33	*Room TV* Yes	*Last dinner* 8.30	*Room service* Limited

WINDERMERE — Miller Howe Hotel — 73% — £B

HR Map 13 D5 Cumbria
Rayrigg Road LA23 1EY
Windermere (096 62) 2536

Rooms 13
Ensuite bath/shower 12
Room phone No
Room TV No
Confirm by arrang.
Last dinner 8.30
Parking Ample
Room service Limited

Credit Access, Amex, Diners, Visa
Closed early Dec–mid Mar

With charming staff, beautiful grounds and panoramic views of the lakes and fells this hotel is a delight to visit. In the absence of a bar drinks are served in any of the three relaxing lounges, which are decorated in dark, strong colours and have plenty of leather chesterfields, antique furniture, objets d'art and glassware. A pretty sun lounge with wicker furniture is a popular spot in summer. Bedrooms at the front have balconies overlooking the lake as a bonus, but all are delightfully appointed and have myriad extras including books, games, hi-fi systems and classical cassettes. Bathrooms are modern, with further thoughtful touches. No children under twelve. *Amenities* garden.

Restaurant — ♔ ⌐

Set D £22
About £62 *for two*
Seats 70
Parties 36

Pre-dinner drinks are served in the lounges before guests are called to the modern dining room overlooking the floodlit garden, where the no-choice menu is served, course by course, to all at the same time. The cooking is of a very high standard and the menu so well-balanced that one arrives undaunted at the fifth and final course. We enjoyed the light, delightfully flavoured smoked salmon quiche and the excellent orange steamed pudding with home-made custard. ☺

Dinner only 8 for 8.30, Sat 7 & 9.30 **Closed** early Dec–mid Mar

WINDERMERE — Roger's — ⌐

R Map 13 D5 Cumbria
4 High Street
Windermere (096 62) 4954

Set D £16.50
About £40 *for two*
Seats 42
Parties 30
Parking Limited
Credit Access, Amex, Diners, Visa

Roger Pergl-Wilson has been pleasing the diners at his cosy, sophisticated restaurant for seven years now. His short menu offers some interesting combinations which are competently prepared and served in simple, unpretentious fashion. Starter might be noodles with langoustines; for the main course, perhaps Windermere char with sorrel sauce or excellent hare with green peppercorn sauce. Finish with an impressive selection of cheeses or an outstanding white chocolate marquise. ♀ Well-chosen ☺

Lunch by arrang. only *Dinner* 7–9.30
Closed Sun, 3 days Xmas & 2 wks Jan/Feb

WINDSOR — Castle Hotel — 66% — £B/C

H Map 5 E2 Berkshire
High Street SL4 1LJ
Windsor (0753) 851011
Telex 849220

Credit Access, Amex, Diners, Visa

A fine Georgian facade distinguishes this former posting house opposite the Guildhall. Charming period rooms include an elegant foyer-lounge decorated with stylish settees, old paintings and fresh flowers. Best main-house bedrooms have antique furniture and superior extras. Standard and annexe rooms are more modest, but all have tea-makers, colour TVs, and direct-dial telephones. Housekeeping needs attention. *Amenities* in-house movies, secretarial services, fax, laundry service, coffee shop (7am–10.30pm).

Rooms 85	*Direct dial* Yes	*Confirm by* 6	*Parking* Ample
Ensuite bath/shower 85	*Room TV* Yes	*Last dinner* 10	*Room service* 24 hours

WINDSOR

Oakley Court Hotel   82%   £B/C

HR **Map 5 E2** Berkshire
Windsor Road SL4 5UR
Maidenhead (0628) 74141
Telex 849958

Rooms 91
Ensuite bath/shower 91
Direct dial Yes
Room TV Yes
Confirm by 6
Last dinner 10
Parking Ample
Room service 24 hours

Credit Access, Amex, Diners, Visa

Mature gardens sloping down to the Thames provide a most attractive setting for this Victorian Gothic hotel with lots of nice architectural features. Public rooms include several comfortable lounges with ornate ceilings and original glass-fronted cabinets. There are also seven rather splendid period bedrooms, though the majority are in two modern wings. Most are a good size, with traditional furnishings, and remote-control TVs. Executive rooms have other extras, such as fruit, sherry and bathrobes, as well as nicer views. Neat, carpeted bathrooms are well stocked with toiletries. No dogs.
Amenities garden, pitch & putt, croquet, coarse fishing, billiards, secretarial services, fax, valeting, laundry service, helipad.

Oak Leaf Room   ♨

Set L £15.50, Sun £16
Set D £22
About £75 for two
Seats 120
Parties 30

Fresh produce and home-grown herbs are well handled by Murdo MacSween at this elegant dining room, somewhat let down by slow service. Set menus include a roast joint and perhaps lamb cutlets topped with a Stilton mousse or trout with a ginger and herb sauce. Starters could be a duck terrine, or the exotic fig and paw paw cocktail. Disappointing cheeseboard and unimpressive sweets.

Lunch 12.30–2   *Dinner* 7.30–10

WINKLEIGH

King's Arms   ♀

R **Map 3 D2** Devon
The Square
Winkleigh (083 783) 384

Set D £16.50
About £42 for two
Seats 16
Parking Ample

Credit Access, Amex, Visa

The dining room at this traditional 16th-century village pub is tiny, so booking is essential. The six-course dinner is served at 8.15pm (although the menu is no-choice, alternatives can be discussed over the 'phone). The cooking is light and confident, with accurately judged portions to keep one sailing through to the sweet. Typical dishes are stilton and celery soup, stuffed fillet of sole and medallions of pork. ♨

Dinner only 8.15
Closed Sun

WINKTON

Fisherman's Haunt Hotel   £E/F

Map 4 C4 Dorset
Salisbury Road, Christchurch
BH23 7AS
Christchurch (0202) 477283

Closed 25 Dec

With the river Avon just across the road, it's easy to see how this friendly inn acquired its name. The building dates back to the 17th century and its two beamed bars are full of character. An airy conservatory leads on to the garden and there's a cosy TV lounge upstairs. Bedrooms, mostly in nearby outbuildings, are bright and comfortable; tea-makers are provided.
Amenities garden, laundry service. ♿

Rooms 19	*Direct dial* Yes	*Confirm by* arrang.	*Parking* Ample
Ensuite bath/shower 19	*Room TV* Yes	*Last dinner* 10	*Room service* Limited

WINSFORD

Royal Oak Inn   £C

Map 3 D2 Somerset
Nr Minehead TA24 7JE
Winsford (064 385) 455
Telex 46529

Credit Access, Amex, Diners, Visa

The sound of cameras clicking is all that disturbs the peace at this picturesque 12th-century inn. Perfect for exploring Exmoor (there's a guidebook in each of the cottage-style or modern bedrooms), the establishment has three stylish lounges and two rustic bars with log fires warming winter visitors. Home-baked wholemeal bread for breakfast. *Amenities* garden, coarse fishing, secretarial services, laundry service.

Rooms 14	*Direct dial* Yes	*Confirm by* arrang.	*Parking* Ample
Ensuite bath/shower 14	*Room TV* Yes	*Last dinner* 9.30	*Room service* Limited

WINTERBOURNE   Grange Hotel at Northwoods   68%   £C/D

H Map 4 B2 Avon
Old Gloucester Road,
Northwoods BS17 1RP
Winterbourne (0454) 777333
Telex 449205
Credit Access, Amex, Diners, Visa
Closed 4 days Xmas

Just off the B4427 and handy for the motorway network (check directions), this sturdily built hotel stands in spacious grounds that include a magnificent cedar. Day rooms are bright and attractive, so too the decent-sized bedrooms, which all have neat little bathrooms. A leisure centre and further bedrooms are planned for 1989. *Amenities* garden, secretarial services, fax, laundry service, 24-hour lounge service.

Rooms 32	*Direct dial* Yes	*Confirm by* 6	*Parking* Ample
Ensuite bath/shower 32	*Room TV* Yes	*Last dinner* 10	*Room service* All day

WISBECH   Rose & Crown Hotel,   *NEW ENTRY* ♛   ♗
                 Marais Restaurant

R Map 6 B1 Cambridgeshire
Market Place
Wisbech (0945) 583187

Set D £12
About £35 *for two*
Seats 60 *Parties* 80
Parking Limited
Credit Access, Amex, Diners, Visa

A stylish first-floor restaurant with elegant drapes, jet black chairs and quality table settings. The cooking is serious and sophisticated, with some notable successes like tomatoes filled with baby fruits de mer or warm pigeon salad with raspberry vinegar among starters, plus such tempting main courses as smoked chicken sausage with onion marmalade or steamed salmon with samphire. Attractively presented sweets and good French cheeses to finish. ♟ Well-chosen ⊖

Lunch 12.30–2   *Dinner* 7.30–9.30, Fri & Sat till 10.30
Closed Sun

WISHAW   Belfry Hotel   73%   £C

H Map 10 C4 Warwickshire
Lichfield Road B76 9PR
Curdworth (0675) 70301
Telex 338848

Rooms 168
Ensuite bath/shower 168
Direct dial Yes
Room TV Yes
Confirm by arrang.
Last dinner 10.30
Parking Ample
Room service 24 hours

Credit Access, Amex, Diners, Visa

Set in 370 acres of parkland, the Belfry offers outstanding sports and leisure facilities. The main building, an ivy-clad house topped by a little clock tower, has plenty of character, and day rooms include two panelled bars and a smart cane-furnished coffee shop. Bedrooms range from traditional in the old house, with beams and four-posters, to more modern in the two wings. Staff are friendly and efficient, but the buffet breakfast could certainly be better. No dogs.
Amenities garden, indoor swimming pool, sauna, solarium, whirlpool bath, keep-fit equipment, tennis, squash, golf courses, snooker, in-house movies, secretarial services, fax, laundry service, coffee shop (7am–10.30pm), children's playground, helipad. ❧

WITHERSLACK   Old Vicarage Country House Hotel   65%   £D

HR Map 13 D6 Cumbria
Nr Grange-over-Sands
LA11 6RS
Witherslack (044 852) 381
Credit Access, Amex, Diners, Visa
Closed 1 wk Xmas

Two couples run this lovely Georgian house. Delightful bedrooms successfully combine antiques with contemporary furniture. Fresh flowers, books, magazines and mineral water are typical of many thoughtful touches and en suite bathrooms (four with shower only) are immaculate. Downstairs, there are two cosy sitting rooms. Don't miss the Cumberland breakfast, with free-range eggs and home-cured bacon. *Amenities* garden, croquet, laundry service.

Rooms 8	*Direct dial* Yes	*Confirm by* arrang.	*Parking* Ample
Ensuite bath/shower 8	*Room TV* Yes	*Last dinner* 7.30 for 8	*Room service* All day

Restaurant   ♗

Set D £17.50
About £48 *for two*
Seats 38
Parties 20

Dinner at this mellow hotel restaurant is an excellent five-course set meal, using carefully chosen ingredients. A typical starter might be mousseline of artichoke with tomato sauce, followed by roast veal, or local partridge. Hot and cold sweets precede an impressive cheese list and coffee is served with Kendal mint cake. A fine wine list that would be outstanding were it not for too many '84 red Burgundies. ♟ Well-chosen ⊖

Dinner only 7.30 for 8   **Closed** 1 wk Xmas

WIVELISCOMBE | Langley House Hotel 64% | £D/E

HR Map 3 E2 Somerset
Langley Marsh TA4 2UF
Wiveliscombe (0984) 23318
Telex 46648

Credit Access, Amex

A delightfully intimate 16th-century hotel set amidst an attractive garden and cobbled courtyard. Public areas include a boldly decorated drawing room with polished parquet floor, scatter rugs and fresh flower displays. The compact bedrooms boast lacy bedspreads and canopies and pretty colour schemes. All have sherry, flowers and hairdryers. Excellent breakfast. Children under seven by arrangement. *Amenities* garden, croquet, bicycles, laundry service.

Rooms 9	Direct dial Yes	Confirm by 6	Parking Ample
Ensuite bath/shower 8	Room TV Yes	Last dinner 8.30	Room service All day

Restaurant ♏

Set D £16.25, Fri & Sat £18.75
About £45 for two
Seats 20
Parties 20

Candlelight, crystal, fresh flowers and smart silver create a delightful ambience in this small restaurant. Peter Wilson's careful cooking, using home-grown herbs and vegetables, provides some very pleasing dishes such as dessert pear marinated in hazelnut oil and served with a herb savoury for a starter, with Quantock veal fillet in sherry and mustard sauce as a main dish. Finish with a well-prepared dessert. Non-residents must book. ⊖ &

Dinner only 7.30–8.30 Fri & Sat at 8.30

We welcome bona fide complaints and recommendations on the tear-out pages at the back of the book for readers' comment. They are followed up by our professional team.

WOBURN | Bedford Arms Hotel 68% | £C/D

H Map 5 E1 Bedfordshire
George Street,
Nr Milton Keynes MK17 9PX
Woburn (0525) 290441
Telex 825205

Credit Access, Amex, Diners, Visa

New ownership has brought about some welcome changes behind the Georgian facade of this characterful hotel. The foyer and cocktail bar are now refurbished in comfortable traditional style, and work proceeds apace on the older bedrooms. Ten rooms are designated non-smoking and nine ground-floor rooms are equipped for the disabled. Compact modern bathrooms throughout. No dogs. *Amenities* patio, in-house movies, secretarial services, laundry service. &

Rooms 55	Direct dial Yes	Confirm by arrang.	Parking Ample
Ensuite bath/shower 55	Room TV Yes	Last dinner 10.30	Room service 24 hours

WOBURN | Paris House | ♛ ♏

R Map 5 E1 Bedfordshire
Woburn Park
Woburn (0525) 290692

Set L £13.50
Set D £19.50
About £60 for two
Seats 56 *Parties* 40
Parking Ample
Credit Access, Amex, Diners, Visa

Through park gates on the A4012 and along a sweeping drive to this handsome half-timbered house, originally on show at the Great Exhibition of Paris in 1878. Peter Chandler explains his set menus before retiring to the kitchen, whence come delights like feuilleté of wild mushrooms, navarin of scallops, rack of lamb with tarragon and an array of gorgeous, not-to-be-missed sweets. Excellent coffee and petits fours to finish. ⊖

Lunch 12.30–2, Sun 12–2 *Dinner* 7–10
Closed D Sun, all Mon, & all Feb

WOLVERHAMPTON | Goldthorn Hotel 61% *NEW ENTRY* | £D/E

H Map 10 B4 West Midlands
Penn Road WV3 0ER
Wolverhampton (0902) 714801
Telex 339516

Credit Access, Amex, Diners, Visa
Closed 25 & 26 Dec

Ornate plasterwork, fine panelling, paintings and statues in the bars and lounges add a flamboyant touch to this popular 19th-century hotel on the A449 about a mile out of town. The best bedrooms – with four-posters – are cosy and characterful, the rest smaller and simpler. Rooms in the separate conference centre are spacious and modern. *Amenities* garden, satellite TV, laundry service, coffee shop (9.30am–11pm).

Rooms 97	Direct dial Yes	Confirm by 7	Parking Ample
Ensuite bath/shower 94	Room TV Yes	Last dinner 9.30	Room service 24 hours

WOLVERHAMPTON   Mount Hotel   60%   *NEW ENTRY*   £C/D

H **Map 10 B4** West Midlands
Mount Road, Tettenhall
Wood WV6 8HL
Wolverhampton (0902) 752055
Telex 333546

Credit Access, Amex, Diners, Visa

Surrounded by woodland and formal gardens, the former private home of Sir Charles Mander makes an attractive, efficiently run country hotel. A wealth of oak panelling distinguishes the entrance hall, bar and splendid ballroom complete with minstrels' gallery. Best bedrooms are in the spacious new wing and enjoy fine garden views from picture windows. Good accessories and neat, tiled bathrooms.
Amenities garden, secretarial services, laundry service.

Rooms 58	*Direct dial* Yes	*Confirm by* 6	*Parking* Ample
Ensuite bath/shower 58	*Room TV* Yes	*Last dinner* 9.30	*Room service* 24 hours

WOODBRIDGE   Seckford Hall Hotel   71%   £D/E

H **Map 6 D3** Suffolk
IP13 6NU
Woodbridge (0394) 385678
Telex 987446

Rooms 24
Ensuite bath/shower 23
Direct dial Yes
Room TV Yes
Confirm by arrang.
Last dinner 9.30
Parking Ample
Room service All day

Credit Access, Amex, Diners, Visa

Clearly signposted on the A12 to Lowestoft (avoid the Woodbridge turning), Seckford Hall is a splendid ivy-clad Tudor mansion set in mature parkland. The heavy original oak door opens on to a wealth of fine features, including many fine examples of linenfold panelling. There are three lounges, the main one impressive and very Tudor, and a most agreeable beamed bar. Decent-sized bedrooms, pretty in shades of pink, cream and green, are individually styled, with a solid, comfortable look. The Seckford Room is one of two very large Tudor rooms with four-poster, oak furniture and exposed beams. Modern bathrooms offer specially softened water.
Amenities garden, coarse fishing, laundry service.

WOODFORD BRIDGE   Prince Regent Hotel   57%   £D/E

H **Map 7 B4** Essex
Manor Road IG8 8AE
01-504 7635

Credit Access, Amex, Diners, Visa

A Georgian building with a classical entrance hall and a fine sweeping staircase, the Prince Regent is a pleasant and comfortable hotel. Regency-style chairs, and polished wood tables furnish an attractive bar-lounge and, upstairs, the neat bedrooms have cream laminate units and pretty floral fabrics. Bathrooms (some with showers only) are tiled and carpeted. No dogs.
Amenities garden, laundry service.

Rooms 10	*Direct dial* Yes	*Confirm by* arrang.	*Parking* Ample
Ensuite bath/shower 10	*Room TV* Yes	*Last dinner* 10.30	*Room service* 24 hours

WOODHALL SPA   Dower House Hotel   62%   £E

H **Map 11 E2** Lincolnshire
Manor Estate LN10 6PY
Woodhall Spa (0526) 52588

Credit Access, Amex, Visa

With a championship golf course on its doorstep and a warm welcome within its walls, this is a delightfully peaceful hotel. Public rooms are solidly handsome. The entrance hall leads to a darkwood lounge and bar with brass-topped tables and garden views. Traditional bedrooms are spacious and comfortable, with antique furnishings and well-kept private bathrooms.
Amenities garden, laundry service.

Rooms 7	*Room phone* No	*Confirm by* arrang.	*Parking* Ample
Ensuite bath/shower 6	*Room TV* Yes	*Last dinner* 9.30	*Room service* All day

WOODHALL SPA   Golf Hotel   57%   £D/E

H **Map 11 E2** Lincolnshire
The Broadway LN10 6SG
Woodhall Spa (0526) 53535
Telex 56448

Credit Access, Amex, Diners, Visa

The mock-Tudor facade is quite impressive and the setting, in seven acres of lawns and gardens by Woodhall Spa golf course, very pleasant. Day rooms are fairly simple and modern, the wicker-furnished bar being perhaps the most attractive. Bedrooms are modest but cheerful, with lovely views. The hotel, which is under new management, could do with a general spring clean.
Amenities garden, croquet, secretarial services, fax, laundry service.

Rooms 51	*Room phone* Yes	*Confirm by* arrang.	*Parking* Ample
Ensuite bath/shower 51	*Room TV* Yes	*Last dinner* 9.30	*Room service* 24 hours

WOODSTOCK — Bear Hotel 73% £B

H Map 5 D1 Oxfordshire
Park Street OX7 1SZ
Woodstock (0993) 811511
Telex 56448

Rooms 45
Ensuite bath/shower 45
Direct dial Yes
Room TV Yes
Confirm by 6
Last dinner 10.30
Parking Limited
Room service 24 hours

Credit Access, Amex, Diners, Visa

The new owners plan no major upheavals for this splendid 12th-century coaching inn. A cosy cocktail bar and rustic beamed public bar lead off the flagstoned entrance hall, while upstairs there's an elegant, antique-furnished sitting room. Good-sized bedrooms (some in a separate stable block) feature smart period-style furnishings and extras ranging from tea-makers and mini-bars to remote-control TVs and radio-alarms. Four rooms have four-posters and there are three characterful attic rooms with sloping ceilings. Excellent bathrooms provide hairdryers, bath robes and good-quality toiletries. Pleasant, efficient staff.
Amenities garden, fishing, in-house movies, fax, laundry service.

WOODSTOCK — Feathers Hotel 73% £C/D

HR Map 5 D1 Oxfordshire
Market Street OX7 1SX
Woodstock (0993) 812291

Rooms 16
Ensuite bath/shower 14
Direct dial Yes
Room TV Yes
Confirm by arrang.
Last dinner 9.45
Parking Difficult
Room service All day

Credit Access, Amex, Diners, Visa

Colourful flower baskets and window boxes festoon the facade of this 17th-century hotel, and there are some eye-catching flower displays within. It's a rambling place (originally three private houses), with characterful public rooms furnished with antiques. Bedrooms of various sizes are individually appointed in traditional style, and for the most part are amply furnished, though in our double room there was only one chair and no writing surface; it was also rather dimly lit. All rooms have remote-control TVs and thoughtfully equipped bathrooms, three with shower only, two other private though not en suite. Staff are friendly and breakfast quite good.
Amenities garden.

Restaurant ♨

Set L £10.50
Set D £16.50
About £55 for two
Seats 40
Parties 40

A most appealing restaurant with yellow-painted panelled walls, comfortably upholstered high-backed chairs, crisp white linen and fresh flowers in abundance. The food is good, too, with Sonya Kidney applying a sure hand to dishes such as cheese and creamed wild mushroom soufflé; loin of veal with tarragon sauce and a tartlet of veal sweetbreads; and hot gâteau Pithiviers with custard sauce. Smart, attentive service completes the picture. ♀ Well-chosen ⊖

Lunch 12.30–2.15   Dinner 7.30–9.45

**If we recommend meals in a Hotel or Inn,
a separate entry is made for its restaurant.**

WOODY BAY — Woody Bay Hotel 59% £E

H Map 3 D1 Devon
Nr Parracombe EX31 4QX
Parracombe (059 83) 264

Credit Access, Visa
Closed Jan–mid Feb

The Scotts offer the warmest of welcomes at their delightfully old-fashioned hotel in a spectacular position overlooking the bay. A log fire and other traditional comforts make the lounge an easy place in which to relax, and the simply furnished floral bedrooms (all but one with en suite bathrooms) enjoy lovely views. Friendly, helpful staff. No children under eleven.
Amenities patio.

Rooms 15	*Room phone* No	*Confirm by* arrang.	*Parking* Ample
Ensuite bath/shower 14	*Room TV* No	*Last dinner* 8.30	*Room service* None

WOOLACOMBE Woolacombe Bay Hotel 65% *NEW ENTRY* £C

H Map 2 C1 Devon
South Street EX34 7BN
Woolacombe (0271) 870388

Credit Access, Visa
Closed 3 wks Jan

An imposing Edwardian seaside hotel with extensive lawns leading to the beach. The sporting and leisure facilities are outstanding, and there's ample room to unwind in the well-furnished lounges and bars. Bedrooms are of a decent size, with remote-control TVs, hairdryers and mostly modern furnishings. There are quite a few suites and family rooms, and several rooms have balconies. Half-board terms only. No dogs. *Amenities* garden, indoor & outdoor swimming pools, sauna, solarium, whirlpool bath, keep-fit equipment, hairdressing, tennis, squash, pitch & putt, games room, snooker, satellite TV, in-house movies, laundry service, laundry room, coffee shop (10–10, till 6 in winter).

Rooms 48	*Room phone* Yes	*Confirm by* arrang.	*Parking* Ample
Ensuite bath/shower 48	*Room TV* Yes	*Last dinner* 9.45	*Room service* 24 hours

WOOLER Ryecroft Hotel 55% £F

HR Map 14 B2
Northumberland
NE71 6AB
Wooler (0668) 81459
Credit Access, Visa
Closed 1st 2 wks Nov & 1 wk
Xmas

A really delightful little red-brick hotel close to the A697. Pat and David McKechnie are charming owners and most conscientious housekeepers. The whole place gleams, from the octagonal hall-lounge with its roaring log fire and the comfortable bar to the bedrooms, where well-sprung mattresses and impeccably laundered sheets provide very restful nights. A good, freshly-prepared breakfast starts the day. *Amenities* garden.

Rooms 11	*Room phone* No	*Confirm by* arrang.	*Parking* Ample
Ensuite bath/shower 0	*Room TV* No	*Last dinner* 8.30	*Room service* Limited

Restaurant ♀

Set L £6
Set D £12
About £30 *for two*
Seats 30
Parties 20

In a spotlessly kept, homely room, guests sit down to enjoy Pat's set dinners. Good flavours abound in dishes such as prawn and smoked salmon roulade, cream of artichoke soup, trout in oatmeal with hollandaise sauce or leg of lamb with butter, garlic and herbs. Delicious sweets include syllabubs and ice creams. Good wines at unbeatable prices: note Gewurtzraminer (Heim) '86 and the splendid Dalwood Shiraz Cabernet (Penfolds) '84. ⊜ ⅋

Lunch Sun only 12.30–1.30 *Dinner* Tues–Sat 7–8.30
Closed L Mon–Sat, D Sun & Mon, 2 wks Nov & 1 wk Xmas

WOOLER Tankerville Arms Hotel £F

I Map 14 B2 Northumberland
Cottage Road NE71 6AD
Wooler (0668) 81581

Credit Access, Diners, Visa

Friendly owners and staff provide a warm welcome at this 300-year-old stone-built inn on the A697. Besides the public bar there's a popular lounge bar with gleaming copper-topped tables and a coal fire in winter; a third bar is furnished as a dining area. There's also a residents' TV lounge. Simply furnished bedrooms, some with pleasant views, offer modest comforts.
Amenities garden.

Rooms 15	*Room phone* No	*Confirm by* arrang.	*Parking* Ample
Ensuite bath/shower 8	*Room TV* Most	*Last dinner* 9.30	*Room service* Limited

WOOTTON COMMON Lugleys Restaurant ♀

RR Map 5 D4 Isle of Wight
Staplers Road PO33 4RW
Isle of Wight (0983) 882202

Set L Sun £8.95
About £34 *for two*
Seats 20
Parties 16
Parking Ample

Polished floorboards, pine furniture, nostalgic pictures and lush drapes make for a charmingly intimate and relaxed atmosphere, reinforced by the informal friendliness of Angela Hewitt and her staff. The very best produce is used, including traditionally reared meat free of antibiotics. Careful attention is paid to every aspect of the meal and we enjoyed an excellent sauté of chicken livers with a marvellous rich cream and green peppercorn sauce and a superb main course of nuggets of local lobster.

Lunch Sun only at 1 *Dinner* 7–9.30
Closed D Sun, 2 wks Feb & 2 Wks Nov

BEDROOMS 3 £F
With bath/shower 0

Bedrooms are delightfully furnished with antiques and fine fabrics. All have beverage facilities, TVs and telephones. The bathroom is spotlessly clean. No children or dogs.

WORCESTER — Brown's Restaurant   ♕ ♊

R Map 4 B1
Hereford & Worcester
24 Quay Street
Worcester (0905) 26263

Set L £17.50, Sun £13.20
Set D £23
About £54 for two
Seats 75 *Parking* Ample
Credit Access, Amex, Visa

In a former corn mill overlooking the river Severn guests make their choice from a well thought-out modern menu of dishes. Cheese beignets with mustard sauce and monkfish en brochette typify the starters, while main courses could include quails with celery and walnuts, saddle of venison or chicken breast stuffed with vegetable mousseline. Home-made ices, excellent cheeses, sound wines (note some fine burgundies). ♟ Well-chosen ⊖ ⅍

Lunch 12.30–1.45   *Dinner* 7.30–9.30
Closed L Sat, D Sun, Bank Hols & 1 wk Xmas

WORCESTER — Fownes Hotel 70% *NEW ENTRY*   £C/D

H Map 4 B1
Hereford & Worcester
City Walls Road WR1 2AP
Worcester (0905) 613151
Telex 335021

Rooms 61
Ensuite bath/shower 61
Direct dial Yes
Room TV Yes
Confirm by 6
Last dinner 10
Parking Ample
Room service 24 hours

Credit Access, Amex, Diners, Visa

Originally a Victorian glove factory, this imposing building has been tailored into a roomy and restful modern hotel. It's set alongside an attractive canalside walk, just a short stroll from the Cathedral and the city centre. Bedrooms are very comfortable and of a good size, with soft colour schemes, well-lit work space and excellent bathrooms with generous towels. Three handsome suites have whirlpool

baths. Among the day rooms are a smart, well-furnished foyer-lounge, a stylishly contemporary cocktail bar, a small library and a long-hours brasserie. Staff are friendly, though of varying efficiency. No dogs. *Amenities* sauna, keep-fit equipment, in-house movies, secretarial services, fax, laundry service, brasserie (10.30am–11.30pm). ⅍

WORCESTER — Giffard Hotel 64%   £C

H Map 4 B1
Hereford & Worcester
High Street WR1 2QR
Worcester (0905) 726262
Telex 338869

Credit Access, Amex, Diners, Visa

Situated opposite Worcester Cathedral, this modern purpose-built hotel has a first-floor lounge and cocktail bar above the reception area and coffee shop. Compact bedrooms have practical fitted furniture with writing space, TVs and tea-makers. Executive rooms, furnished in dark wood, have extras such as hairdryers. Functional bathrooms are well equipped and include complimentary toiletries. *Amenities* snooker, laundry service, coffee shop (10am–9pm).

Rooms 104	*Direct dial* Yes	*Confirm by* arrang.	*Parking* Ample
Ensuite bath/shower 104	*Room TV* Yes	*Last dinner* 9.45	*Room service* 24 hours

WORFIELD — Old Vicarage Hotel 68%   £D/E

HR Map 10 B4 Shropshire
Bridgnorth WV15 5JZ
Worfield (074 64) 497
Telex 35438

Credit Access, Amex, Diners, Visa

A turn-of-the-century village parsonage, now a comfortable and relaxing hotel. Day rooms have a delightful country-house atmosphere but the real strength of the place is the bedrooms – all individually appointed with lovely fabrics and fine Victorian and Edwardian furniture (reproduction pieces in the smaller rooms). Thoughtful extras range from radio-alarms to electric blankets, and bathrooms are well equipped. *Amenities* garden, croquet, laundry service.

Rooms 10	*Direct dial* Yes	*Confirm by* arrang.	*Parking* Ample
Ensuite bath/shower 10	*Room TV* Yes	*Last dinner* 9	*Room service* Limited

Restaurant

Set L £12.50
Set D £19.50
About £46 for two
Seats 36
Parties 50

The new conservatory is a welcome addition to this unpretentious restaurant, where regularly-changing menus always offer a decent choice of good, honest dishes – prepared from fresh local produce wherever possible. Start perhaps with home-made vegetable soup accompanied by warm sage and onion bread; then try roast loin of venison served with spiced pears and redcurrant sauce; and end with a well-flavoured raspberry soufflé. ♟ Well-chosen ⊖

Lunch 12–1.30
Dinner 7–9

| **WORTHING** | **Beach Hotel 64%** | **£D/E** |

H **Map 5 E4** West Sussex
Marine Parade BN11 3QJ
Worthing (0903) 34001

Credit Access, Amex, Diners, Visa

Long-serving staff provide splendid service at this 1930s seafront hotel. Good housekeeping is evident in the spacious bedrooms, which have modern bathrooms. First-floor front rooms enjoy the bonus of private balconies; back rooms are more modest and can be hot, being above the kitchens. There's a comfortable lounge and smart cocktail bar. Good breakfast. No children under eight. No dogs.
Amenities laundry service.

| *Rooms* 90 | *Direct dial* Yes | *Confirm by* arrang. | *Parking* Ample |
| *Ensuite bath/shower* 81 | *Room TV* Yes | *Last dinner* 8.45 | *Room service* 24 hours |

| **WORTHING** | **Chatsworth Hotel 59%** | **£D/E** |

H **Map 5 E4** West Sussex
Steyne BN11 3DU
Worthing (0903) 36103
Telex 877046

Credit Access, Amex, Visa

Part of a Georgian terrace overlooking Steyne Gardens and the sea, Chatsworth is a comfortable hotel where the fabric is consistently maintained by an ongoing programme of refurbishment. Public rooms are furnished in simple, traditional style. Bedrooms, though modest, all now have en suite facilities, thanks to the conversion of some single rooms to bathrooms. *Amenities* games room, snooker, pool table, in-house movies, secretarial services, laundry service.

| *Rooms* 105 | *Direct dial* Yes | *Confirm by* 6.30 | *Parking* Difficult |
| *Ensuite bath/shower* 105 | *Room TV* Yes | *Last dinner* 8.30 | *Room service* 24 hours |

| **WORTHING** | **River Kwai Restaurant** *NEW ENTRY* |

R **Map 5 E4** West Sussex
16 Ambrose Place
Worthing (0903) 211901

Thai cooking
About £30 for two
Seats 44
Parking Ample

Credit Access, Amex, Diners, Visa

You can find good fresh food and stylish surroundings at this friendly Thai restaurant. Bamboo chairs, traditionally costumed waitresses and appropriate background music provide a pleasingly authentic feel and excellent ingredients are capably handled to produce some truly mouthwatering dishes. Try the excellent hot and sour soup with prawns and the pud Thai – fried rice noodles with chicken, crab meat, bean sprouts, ground peanuts, egg and chopped salted turnip.

Lunch 12–2.30   *Dinner* 6–11.30
Closed Sun & 3 days Xmas

| **WROTHAM HEATH** | **Ming** *NEW ENTRY* |

R **Map 7 B5** Kent
London Road
Borough Green (0732) 883427

Chinese cooking
Set L and D from £11
About £42 for two
Seats 85 *Parties* 85
Parking Limited
Credit Access, Amex, Diners, Visa

Spotlights and soft classical music create a sophisticated setting for enjoying a Chinese meal. The menu has a fairly familiar ring, running from soups, deep-fried seaweed and succulent steamed scallops to chicken or duck in ginger sauce, crispy beef in a potato nest and a few sizzling dishes. Cooking is sound, presentation simple and artistic, service swift and helpful.

Lunch 12–2.30   *Dinner* 6–11.30
Closed 2 days Xmas

| **WROTHAM HEATH** | **Post House Hotel 74%** | **£C** |

H **Map 7 B5** Kent
London Road,
Nr Sevenoaks TN15 7RS
Borough Green (0732) 883311
Telex 957309

Rooms 119
Ensuite bath/shower 119
Direct dial Yes
Room TV Yes
Confirm by 6
Last dinner 10.30
Parking Ample
Room service 24 hours

Credit Access, Amex, Diners, Visa

A low-rise hotel by junction 2a of the M26, this particular Post House won design awards when built a few years ago, and some black-painted weatherboard features are appropriate for Kent. Stylish public areas provide ample space to unwind, and the conservatory, looking out over a pond and rock garden, is a particularly pleasant spot. Good-sized bedrooms all have mini-bars and remote-control TVs, while extras

in Executive rooms include trouser presses, hairdryers, coffee tables and easy chairs. Excellent bathrooms.
Amenities garden, indoor swimming pool, sauna, solarium, whirlpool bath, gymnasium, snooker, secretarial services, fax, laundry service, children's play area. ♿

WROXTON ST MARY   Wroxton House Hotel   £C/D

H **Map 3 D1** Oxfordshire
Nr Banbury OX15 6QB
Wroxton St Mary (029 573) 482
Telex 83409

Credit Access, Amex, Diners, Visa

Enthusiastic new owners have masterminded a massive improvement programme due for completion soon after we publish. 20 new bedrooms and a conference suite will be added in a corner of the car park, and day rooms are being reorganised to include a new reception area and residents' lounge. Existing bedrooms are unfussy and well-equipped. Graded at 62% in our 1988 Guide. No dogs.
Amenities garden, secretarial services, fax, laundry service.

Rooms 35	*Direct dial* Yes	*Confirm by* 6	*Parking* Ample
Ensuite bath/shower 35	*Room TV* Yes	*Last dinner* 9.30	*Room service* All day

---

Our inspectors *never* book in the name of Egon Ronay's Guides.
They disclose their identity only if they are considering an establishment
for inclusion in the next edition of the Guide.

WYE   Wife of Bath

R **Map 7 C5** Kent
4 Upper Bridge Street
Wye (0233) 812540

Set L & D £14.90
About £40 *for two*
Seats 50
Parties 18
Parking Ample
Credit Access

Reliability rather than novelty has been the key to success at this homely and long-established restaurant. Chef and part-owner Bob Johnson offers good, French country-style dishes prepared from fresh ingredients: scallop chowder, monkfish bonne femme, spiced lamb brochette, roast duck with fresh apricots and brandy sauce. Simple, enjoyable sweets and a short list of decent wines. ♀ Well-chosen ℮

Lunch 12–2   *Dinner* 7–10
Closed Sun, Mon & 1 wk Xmas

WYMONDHAM   Adlard's ★

R **Map 6 C2** Norfolk
16 Damgate Street
Wymondham (0953) 603533

Dinner only 7.30–9
Set D £19.50
About £50 *for two*
Seats 25
Parties 20
Parking Difficult

Closed Sun, Mon, all Bank Hols
& 1 wk Xmas

Originally a butcher's shop, Adlard's is a very pretty little restaurant with an old-fashioned country town feel. David Adlard, a highly accomplished chef, cooks in the modern style and his dishes are notable for subtle but distinct flavours and superb sauces. Recent delights like scallop mousse with watercress sauce, duck flavoured with soya and honey and a lovely iced chocolate marquise showed him

in peak form, and the fine wines, coffee and petits fours kept the pleasure level high. Smoking discouraged. *Specialities* salmon and mushroom duxelle tart with fennel hollandaise; loin of Norfolk venison with game sauce, pasta and bacon; peaches with red wine, raspberry purée and a peach brandy sabayon. ♀ Well-chosen ℮

STOP PRESS: MOVING TO NORWICH

YATTENDON   Royal Oak Hotel   £D

IR **Map 5 D2** Berkshire
Nr Newbury RG16 0UF
Hermitage (0635) 201325

Credit Access, Amex, Visa

An air of warm hospitality and delightfully homely rooms make this creeper-clad hotel a joy to visit. Deep sofas, a log fire and magazines make the sitting room a haven of relaxation, and for those in a lively mood there's a convivial bar. Bedrooms are tastefully furnished with good chintzy fabrics, embroidered sheets and antique furniture; bathrooms have big fluffy towels and plenty of toiletries.
Amenities garden, laundry service.

Rooms 5	*Direct dial* Yes	*Confirm by* arrang.	*Parking* Ample
Ensuite bath/shower 3	*Room TV* Yes	*Last dinner* 10	*Room service* 24 hours

see over

Royal Oak Restaurant ★   👑 ⬤

Lunch 12.30–2
Dinner 7.30–10
About £60 for two
Seats 30
Parties 8

Closed D Sun & 3 wks mid Jan–
early Feb

Fresh flowers grace the tables in the elegant restaurant, where the most noticeable feature is the attention to detail throughout. Richard Smith handles top quality ingredients with great aplomb, and his menus offer some stylish and imaginative dishes for both starters and main courses. Sweets are shamefully rich and quite irresistible. Shrewdly chosen wines: Savigny Les Beaune (Bize) '83, Ch. Pichon

Lalande Pauillac '76 are both delicious now. *Specialities* grilled scallops with noodles, asparagus tips and lemon sauce; grilled calf's kidneys and black pudding with green herb mustard sauce; grilled fillet of turbot with asparagus tips and tarragon sauce; almond parfait with a chocolate and roasted almond sauce. 🍷 Well-chosen 🈂 🍴

YELVERTON   Moorland Links Hotel   64%   £D/E

H **Map 2 C3** Devon
Nr Plymouth PL20 6DA
Yelverton (0822) 852245
Telex 45616

Credit Access, Amex, Diners, Visa
Closed 25 Dec–1 Jan

Peace and quiet are in good supply at this long, low, white-painted building pleasantly situated on the edge of Dartmoor. Comfortable, stylishly-decorated bedrooms have traditional furnishings and attractive ensuite bathrooms; desk space is provided plus hairdryers, trouser presses, radio-alarms and tea-makers. Five are reserved for non-smokers. Day rooms include a split-level bar.
Amenities garden, tennis, in-house movies, laundry service, helipad.

Rooms 30	*Direct dial* Yes	*Confirm by* arrang.	*Parking* Ample
Ensuite bath/shower 30	*Room TV* Yes	*Last dinner* 10	*Room service* 24 hours

We publish annually,
so make sure you use the current edition.
It's worth it!

YEOVIL   Little Barwick House   ⬤

RR **Map 4 B3** Somerset
Barwick BA22 9TD
Yeovil (0935) 23902

Set D £15.60
About £38 for two
Seats 32
Parties 14
Parking Ample

Credit Access, Amex, Diners, Visa

Turn off the A37 opposite the Red House pub to find the tiny village of Barwick where Christopher and Veronica Colley have turned their lovely Georgian dower house into a restaurant with rooms. A softly lit dining room with rich-red decor is the setting for Veronica's careful and enthusiastic cookery, her constantly changing menus featuring straightforward dishes like fish soup with garlicky mayonnaise and roast pheasant with chestnut stuffing. Tempting puddings and a short list of high-quality wines: among clarets, note the Ch. Thieuley '85. 🍷 Well-chosen 🈂

Dinner only 7–9
Closed 25 & 26 Dec

BEDROOMS 6   £D/E
With bath/shower 6

Six homely rooms offer tea-makers and TV. Guests also have use of the sitting room and garden.

YEOVIL   Manor Crest Hotel   63%   £C/D

H **Map 4 B3** Somerset
Hendford BA20 1TG
Yeovil (0935) 23116
Telex 46580

Credit Access, Amex, Diners, Visa

The original manor house was built in 1735, and it's here that the smartly refurbished lounge and bar are located. Here too are half the bedrooms, larger and more traditional than those in the extension. All rooms are equipped with tea-makers and trouser presses, and some have hairdryers; nine rooms are designated non-smoking.
Amenities garden, secretarial services, fax, laundry service.

Rooms 41	*Direct dial* Yes	*Confirm by* 6	*Parking* Ample
Ensuite bath/shower 41	*Room TV* Yes	*Last dinner* 9.45	*Room service* 24 hours

YORK · Abbey Park Hotel 59% · £C

H Town plan A3
North Yorkshire
The Mount YO2 2BN
York (0904) 658301
Telex 57993

Credit Access, Amex, Diners, Visa

You can find pleasant overnight accommodation at this modern hotel just outside the city walls. Polished brass tables and smart lightwood furniture make for an attractive lounge bar, and there's also a bright cocktail bar. Bedrooms have well-coordinated decor, darkwood units and carpeted bathrooms with shower facilities; Gold Star rooms boast plenty of extras such as fruit, flowers and mineral water.
Amenities in-house movies, secretarial services, laundry service.

Rooms 85	Direct dial Yes	Confirm by 6	Parking Limited
Ensuite bath/shower 84	Room TV Yes	Last dinner 9.30	Room service Limited

YORK · Abbots Mews Hotel 56% · £D/E

H Town plan B1
North Yorkshire
Marygate Lane YO3 7DE
York (0904) 34866
Telex 57777

Credit Access, Amex, Diners, Visa

Quietly situated near the historic city centre, a modern conversion of a coachman's cottage, coach house and stables dating from early Victorian times. Period charm has largely been lost, and most of the accommodation is in neat, bright motel style. Several rooms are suitable for family occupation. There's a pleasant lounge with plants and garden furniture, and a traditionally appointed bar. No dogs.
Amenities garden, laundry service.

Rooms 43	Direct dial Yes	Confirm by 6	Parking Ample
Ensuite bath/shower 43	Room TV Yes	Last dinner 9.30	Room service All day

**Our inspectors *never* book in the name of Egon Ronay's Guides.
They disclose their identity only if they are considering an establishment
for inclusion in the next edition of the Guide.**

YORK · Crest Hotel 69% *NEW ENTRY* · £C

H Town plan C2
North Yorkshire
Clifford's Tower, Tower Street
YO1 1SB
York (0904) 648111
Telex 57566

Credit Access, Amex, Diners, Visa

Its position in the very heart of York is a scoring point for this modern hotel. Public rooms include a delightful little lounge with a period feel and a stylish panelled bar with a Roman theme. Bedrooms have matching fabrics, brass light fittings, beverage facilities, trouser presses, hairdryers and tiled bathrooms; Executive rooms have more extras.
Amenities in-house movies, secretarial services, fax, laundry service.

Rooms 128	Direct dial Yes	Confirm by 6	Parking Limited
Ensuite bath/shower 128	Room TV Yes	Last dinner 10.30	Room service 24 hours

YORK · Dean Court Hotel 59% · £C/D

H Town plan C1
North Yorkshire
Duncombe Place YO1 2EF
York (0904) 625082
Telex 57584

Credit Access, Amex, Diners, Visa

A charming, characterful hotel opposite the minster. Green velour chairs and panelling in the foyer set the tone for the cosy, traditional lounges and there are two bars, one smart, the other a typical 'local'. Bedrooms are simple yet comfortable, with modern units and bright colour schemes. Eight superior rooms have Laura Ashley fabrics and wallcoverings. No dogs. *Amenities* in-house movies, laundry service, coffee shop (10am–8pm).

Rooms 36	Direct dial Yes	Confirm by 6	Parking Ample
Ensuite bath/shower 36	Room TV Yes	Last dinner 10	Room service 24 hours

YORK · Hill Hotel 59% · £E

H Town plan A3
North Yorkshire
60 York Road, Acomb YO2 5LW
York (0904) 790777
Telex 57567
Credit Access, Amex, Diners, Visa
Closed 15 Dec–15 Jan

Located some two miles from the centre of York along the B1224, this well-proportioned hotel looks like a beautifully maintained private house, an impression that is fostered by the home-from-home atmosphere. The split-level lounge is comfy and welcoming. Spotless bedrooms have tea-makers, magazines and radios; carpeted bathrooms are thoughtfully equipped with hairdryers, shampoo and bathfoam. No dogs. *Amenities* garden, laundry service, children's playground.

Rooms 10	Direct dial Yes	Confirm by 3	Parking Ample
Ensuite bath/shower 10	Room TV Yes	Last dinner 8	Room service All day

YORK

Map 15 C6
Town plan opposite

Population 99,910

A northern bastion and trading town from Roman times, in the 8th century York became a religious and learning centre, although the present university is twenty-four years old. York's medieval wealth came from wool and monasteries, its modern prosperity from the advent of the railway, chocolate factories and tourists. Architectural gems blend the Middle Ages, pre-Reformation churches and the 18th century.

Annual Events
York Races *10th–12th May, 10th & 11th June, 8th & 9th July, 16th–18th & 31st August, 1st September, 5th, 6th & 8th October*
York Early Music Festival *July*
Historic Vehicle Rally, *Knavesmine, 11th September*

Sights Outside City
Castle Howard, Fountains Abbey, Ripley Castle, Harewood House, Knaresborough, Newby Hall (Boroughbridge), Kirkham Priory

Information Centre
De Grey Rooms, Exhibition Square, York YO1 2HB
Telephone York 621756

Fiat Dealer
Piccadilly Auto Centre Ltd
84 Piccadilly, York YO1 1NX
Tel. York 34321
Map reference C3

1 Art Gallery *English and European* B1
2 Castle Folk Museum *unique reconstruction of period street and interiors* C3
3 Clifford's Tower *13th-c keep* C2/3
4 Fairfax House *former Georgian Gentlemans Residence* C2
5 Guildhall and Mansion House C2
6 Impressions Gallery of Photography C2
7 Jorvik Viking Centre C2
8 King's Manor *home of monks and kings* B1
9 Merchant's Adventurers' Hall *timbered medieval Guild Hall* C2
10 Merchant's Taylor's Hall *14th-c tailors' livery* C1
11 Minister *chief glory of York* C1
12 National Railway Museum *Britain's chief collection* A1/2
13 Racecourse A3
14 Railriders World *model railway exhibition* B2
15 Regimental Museum C2
16 St Mary's Abbey *ruins* B1
17 Shambles *derived from 'Fleshammels' meaning 'street butchers'* C2
18 Station A/B2
19 Theatre Royal B/C1
20 Tourist Information Centre C1
21 Treasurer's House *mainly 17th-c valuable furniture and pictures* C1
22 University *modern architectural interest* E3
23 Waxwork Museum C2
24 York Story *exhibition of York's history and architecture* C2
25 Yorkshire Museum *archaeology, natural history* B1

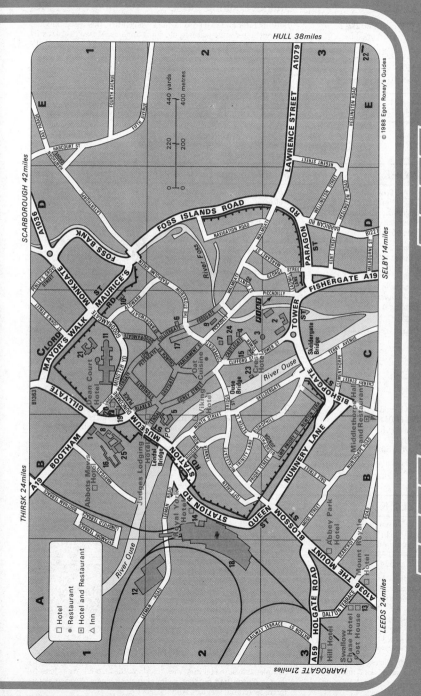

York F I A T

SCARBOROUGH 42miles
THIRSK 24miles
HULL 38miles
SELBY 14miles
FISHERGATE A19
LEEDS 24miles
HARROGATE 21miles

© 1988 Egon Ronay's Guides

440 yards
400 metres

Hotel
Restaurant
Hotel and Restaurant
Inn

YORK   Judges Lodging   67%   £C

H **Town plan B2**
North Yorkshire
9 Lendal YO1 2AQ
York (0904) 38733
Telex 57577

Credit Amex, Diners, Visa

Built in 1704 and extended in the 19th century, this listed building has some interesting features, including an unusual oval cantilevered staircase. The entrance hall, with its lofty ceiling and Corinthian half-pillars, doubles as a lounge of some style and splendour. Bedrooms are individually decorated and furnished, and various little extras add a homely touch. Standards of housekeeping and maintenance could be improved. *Amenities* laundry service.

Rooms 13	*Room phone* Yes	*Confirm by* arrang.	*Parking* Ample
Ensuite bath/shower 13	*Room TV* Yes	*Last dinner* 10.30	*Room service* 24 hours

 indicates a **well-chosen** house wine

YORK   Middlethorpe Hall   78%   £B

HR **Town plan B3**
North Yorkshire
Bishopthorpe Road YO12 1QP
York (0904) 641241
Telex 57802

Rooms 31
Ensuite bath/shower 31
Direct dial Yes
Room TV Yes
Confirm by arrang.
Last dinner 9.45
Parking Ample
Room service 24 hours

Credit Access, Amex, Diners, Visa

An atmosphere of comfort and wellbeing pervades this elegant 17th-century country house, which has been skilfully converted to a sumptuous hotel. Furnishings and fine paintings are totally consistent with the period. The beautiful flower arrangements add a personal touch while deep-cushioned sofas in the drawing room provide unparalleled comfort. Drinks are served here as there is no formal bar.

Bedrooms, some of which are in a courtyard block, have period-style furniture flattered by fine fabrics in coordinated colours. Again, personal touches like porcelain ornaments, books and hairdryers indicate a concern for guests' comfort equally apparent in the magnificently appointed bathrooms. No children under eight. No dogs. *Amenities* garden, secretarial services, laundry service.

Restaurant   ♕

Set L from £13.90
Set D £24.50
About £58 for two
Seats 60
Parties 50

The mantle of Aidan McCormack, former head chef, has fallen on Kevin Francksen. Kevin trained at this elegant establishment, so maintains high standards while giving his own interpretation to starters like fish mousse with cream and pistachio sauce and main courses such as veal sweetbreads glazed with Madeira. Good wines, best in the classics, with clarets back to Ch. Petrus '64. For value, try the Pernand-Vergelesses Blanc from Rapet. ♟ Well-chosen ✆

Lunch 12.30–2   *Dinner* 7.30–9.45

YORK   Mount Royale Hotel   70%   £D

H **Town plan A3**
North Yorkshire
The Mount YO2 2DA
York (0904) 628856
Telex 57414

Rooms 21
Ensuite bath/shower 21
Direct dial Yes
Room TV Yes
Confirm by 6
Last dinner 9.45
Parking Limited
Room service All day

Credit Access, Amex, Diners, Visa
Closed 3 wks Xmas

Two handsome William IV houses make up this delightful hotel. Inside, owners Richard and Christine Oxtoby have created a very individual atmosphere, using antiques, fine period furniture, ornaments and beautifully framed pictures to suggest a much-loved private home. The panelled bar is particularly cosy, and there are two comfortable lounges. Traditionally furnished bedrooms are well equipped and

have easy chairs and homely touches like potted plants and potpourri. Four new bedrooms are more modern in style and, with the recently completed leisure facilities, they overlook the attractive gardens. No dogs. *Amenities* outdoor swimming pool, sauna, keep-fit equipment, secretarial services, laundry service.

YORK — Oat Cuisine

Town plan C2
North Yorkshire
13a High Ousegate
York (0904) 627929

Set L £7.25
About £30 for two
Seats 56
Parking Difficult
Credit Access, Amex, Visa

Striking black and white decor gives a smart image to this modern vegetarian restaurant in the heart of town. The appetising menu is both varied and interesting, from starters like courgette roulade with mushroom filling and guacamole to ratatouille, spinach cannelloni, aubergine with coconut, and cashew nut and mushroom strudel, plus a selection of Mexican specialities. Lovely fresh ingredients are handled with care and obvious knowledge, and sweets are superb. ℮

Lunch 12–3 *Dinner* 7–11
Closed Sun, 25 & 26 Dec & 1st wk Jan

YORK — Post House Hotel 63% £C

H **Town plan A3**
North Yorkshire
Tadcaster Road YO2 2QF
York (0904) 707921
Telex 57798
Credit Access, Amex, Diners, Visa
LVs

A magnificent old cedar on the central lawn makes a focal point for this modern hotel on the A1036. Open-plan public rooms are light and airy; a flagstone-floored foyer leads into a comfortable, cheery lounge where there's an all-day snack service. Pleasant, good-sized bedrooms have well-coordinated decor; all provide tea-making facilities, with fresh milk in the mini-bars.
Amenities garden, putting, laundry service.

| *Rooms* 147 | *Direct dial* Yes | *Confirm by* 6 | *Parking* Ample |
| *Ensuite bath/shower* 147 | *Room TV* Yes | *Last dinner* 10 | *Room service* All day |

YORK — Royal York Hotel 67% £D

H **Town plan B2**
North Yorkshire
Station Road YO2 2AA
York (0904) 653681
Telex 579512

Credit Access, Amex, Diners, Visa

Next to the railway station, the Royal York is a rambling hotel with three entrances and signposts to reception. There's an elegant feel to the day rooms, particularly the main lounge/bar with its potted palms, splendid Corinthian pillars and galleried stairwell. Bedrooms range from fairly basic standard to stylish, well-furnished superior and Executive rooms with excellent bathrooms. *Amenities* garden, putting, men's hairdressing, laundry service, coffee shop (10am–9pm).

| *Rooms* 140 | *Direct dial* Yes | *Confirm by* arrang. | *Parking* Ample |
| *Ensuite bath/shower* 133 | *Room TV* Yes | *Last dinner* 9.45 | *Room service* 24 hours |

YORK — Swallow Chase Hotel £C/D

H **Town plan A3**
North Yorkshire
Tadcaster Road, Dringhouses
YO2 2QQ
York (0904) 701000
Telex 57582
Credit Access, Amex, Diners, Visa

Major building work and refurbishment are transforming this white-painted hotel graded at 59% in our 1988 Guide. A bedroom block and leisure centre are new and many of the bedrooms have been upgraded with smart contemporary furniture and colour schemes. *Amenities* garden, indoor swimming pool, sauna, solarium, whirlpool bath, keep-fit equipment, tennis, putting, secretarial services, fax, laundry service, coffee shop (10am–10pm), 24-hour lounge service.

| *Rooms* 120 | *Direct dial* Yes | *Confirm by* 6 | *Parking* Ample |
| *Ensuite bath/shower* 120 | *Room TV* Yes | *Last dinner* 10 | *Room service* All day |

YORK — Viking Hotel 70% £C

H **Town plan C2**
North Yorkshire
North Street YO1 1JF
York (0904) 659822
Telex 57937

Rooms 188
Ensuite bath/shower 188
Direct dial Yes
Room TV Yes
Confirm by 6
Last dinner 10
Parking Ample
Room service 24 hours

Credit Access, Amex, Diners, Visa

A tall, modern and outwardly not very distinguished building standing in a convenient central location on the banks of the river Ouse. Inside, a stylish impression is at once created in the reception area, with its solid lightwood desks and natural brick walls; upstairs, the lounge and bar provide abundant space and comfort, plus river views. Bedrooms are well lit and amply furnished, with colour schemes that range from soft shades of blue to burgundy with peach. All rooms have tea-makers, trouser presses and hairdryers, along with neat, compact bathrooms.

Amenities garden, sauna, solarium, whirlpool bath, gymnasium, in-house movies, secretarial services, fax, laundry service.

YOXFORD

Satis House   63%   £E

HR Map 6 D2 Suffolk
Saxmundham 1P17 3EX
Yoxford (072 877) 418

Credit Access, Amex, Visa

Run with care and pride by Chris and Chiu Blackmore, Satis House is
a converted Georgian house set in three acres of parkland in unspoilt
Suffolk. The lounge is a graceful, restful room with antiques, paintings
and Oriental ornaments harmonising well. Spacious, characterful
bedrooms are mainly in period style; some have amazingly comfortable Victorian half-tester beds and Edwardian bathroom fittings,
while others mix traditional pieces with more modern pine. All
bathrooms are supplied with generously sized towels, bathrobes and
toiletries. Decent breakfasts. No children under 14. No dogs.
Amenities garden, sauna, solarium, whirlpool bath, keep-fit equipment, laundry service.

Rooms 7	*Direct dial* Yes	*Confirm by* arrang.	*Parking* Ample
Ensuite bath/shower 7	*Room TV* Yes	*Last dinner* 9.30	*Room service* All day

Restaurant   *NEW ENTRY*   ᛩ

Malaysian cooking

Set L £11.25
Set D £15.75
About £38 for two
Seats 26
Parties 16

The Malaysian specialities are the dishes to go for at this elegant hotel
restaurant, though there are also English and French dishes on the
menu. The Kenduri feast (normally for two or more) includes satay,
Balinese pork, delicious spicy coconut beef, crisp stir-fried vegetables,
and super garlicky prawns. An exotic fruit salad makes the perfect
ending. Vegetarian dishes can be provided with advance warning.

Lunch 12–2   *Dinner* 7–9.30
Closed D Sun

HOTELS
RESTAURANTS
AND INNS

SCOTLAND

ABERDEEN	Ardoe House Hotel　63%	£E

H **Map 17 D4** Grampian
South Deeside Road AB1 5YP
Aberdeen (0224) 867355

Credit Access, Amex, Diners, Visa

Turreted and crenellated in the Scottish Baronial style, this sturdy granite mansion enjoys a peaceful parkland setting. Public areas include a lobby-lounge with fine wooden mantel, stained-glass window and magnificently carved staircase. Eight small bedrooms are simply furnished and decorated; remaining rooms feature bold wallpapers and coordinated fabrics. Tea-makers, radio-alarms and trouser presses are standard. *Amenities* garden, laundry service.

Rooms 13	*Room phone* Yes	*Confirm by* arrang.	*Parking* Ample
Ensuite bath/shower 13	*Room TV* Yes	*Last dinner* 9.30	*Room service* All day

ABERDEEN	Atlantis	

R **Map 17 D4** Grampian
16 Bon Accord Crescent
Aberdeen (0224) 591 403

Seafood
Set L £3.95
About £40 for two
Seats 45 *Parties* 45
Parking Limited
Credit Access, Amex, Diners, Visa

Good news all round for fish-lovers: David Edwards' seafood restaurant has proved so popular that the whole operation has had to move into larger premises – and has even reduced its prices! Smart cream and burgundy decor is the new setting for enjoyable fish cookery ranging from seafood terrine and lobster bisque to dartoise of salmon – all prepared by award-winning chef Ian Wilson.

Lunch 12–2　*Dinner* 6–10
Closed L Sat & all Sun, 25 & 26 Dec & 1 & 2 Jan

Changes in data sometimes occur in establishments
after the Guide goes to press.
Prices should be taken as indications rather than firm quotes.

ABERDEEN	Bucksburn Moat House　71%	£C

H **Map 17 D4** Grampian
Oldmeldrum Road,
Bucksburn AB2 9LN
Aberdeen (0224) 713911
Telex 73108

Rooms 98
Ensuite bath/shower 98
Direct dial Yes
Room TV Yes
Confirm by arrang.
Last dinner 10.30
Parking Ample
Room service 24 hours

Credit Access, Amex, Diners, Visa

The austere exterior of this largely modern hotel, designed round a 17th-century grain mill, belies the neat though slightly dated interior. You can overlook the swimming pool from the comfort of a leather chesterfield in the compact foyer-lounge, while the lounge bar has geometric soft furnishings. The Laird's Bar, with its open stone walls and art deco theme, is a popular venue for the locals. Bedrooms have two double beds, functional laminate furniture, hairdryers, mini-bars, trouser presses, tea/coffee-makers and individual thermostatic controls for heating and air-conditioning. Courtesy coach.
Amenities indoor swimming pool, keep-fit equipment, in-house movies, secretarial services, fax, laundry service.

ABERDEEN	Caledonian Thistle Hotel　67%	£C

H **Map 17 D4** Grampian
Union Terrace AB9 1HE
Aberdeen (0224) 640233
Telex 73758

Credit Access, Amex, Diners, Visa

A bright, new, all-day restaurant has added to the amenities of this well-run city-centre hotel; other more formal public rooms include an elegant Regency-style bar-lounge. All bedrooms have double glazing and hairdryers, trouser presses and tea-makers; back rooms are less spacious. Stylish suites and executive rooms have extras like bathroom telephones. *Amenities* sauna, solarium, in-house movies, secretarial services, fax, laundry service, coffee shop (11am–midnight).

Rooms 80	*Direct dial* Yes	*Confirm by* 6	*Parking* Limited
Ensuite bath/shower 80	*Room TV* Yes	*Last dinner* 10	*Room service* 24 hours

ABERDEEN Copthorne Hotel 71% £C

H **Map 17 D4** Grampian
122 Huntly Street AB1 1SU
Aberdeen (0224) 630404
Telex 739707

Rooms 67
Ensuite bath/shower 67
Direct dial Yes
Room TV Yes
Confirm by arrang.
Last dinner 10
Parking Limited
Room service 24 hours

Credit Access, Amex, Diners, Visa

The ground floor of this well-converted old warehouse near the city centre has been completely refurbished and all is smart and new. Warm pastel colours and a gleaming tiled floor make for an elegant reception, while marble pillars grace the elegant bar. Upstairs, the bedrooms are of a decent size and are equipped with good, solid darkwood furniture, pleasing light fittings, quilted bedspreads on large beds and attractive wallcoverings and curtains. All have remote-control TVs, radio alarms, direct-dial phones and tea/coffeemakers. The spacious, tiled bathrooms have showers over the tubs and a range of toiletries.
Amenities secretarial services, fax, laundry service.

ABERDEEN Holiday Inn 74% £B/C

H **Map 17 D4** Grampian
Riverview Drive AB2 0AZ
Aberdeen (0224) 770011
Telex 739651

Rooms 154
Ensuite bath/shower 154
Direct dial Yes
Room TV Yes
Confirm by 6
Last dinner 10.30
Parking Ample
Room service 24 hours

Credit Access, Amex, Diners, Visa

Travellers will appreciate this hotel's close proximity to the airport. Well thought-out public areas include a restful lounge with comfortable armchairs and flourishing plants and an elegant cocktail bar decorated in burnt orange with wooden trellis dividers separating it from the large swimming pool. Standard bedrooms are spacious, with tan and beige decor, tables and chairs and king-size beds; Club Europe rooms are similar in decor, with higher quality towels and toiletries. Non-smoking rooms available. Disappointing breakfast.
Amenities indoor swimming pool, sauna, solarium, whirlpool bath, gymnasium, satellite TV, in-house movies, secretarial services, fax, laundry service, coffee shop (11am–11pm). &

ABERDEEN Stakis Tree Tops Hotel 62% £B/C

H **Map 17 D4** Grampian
161 Springfield Road AB9 2QH
Aberdeen (0224) 313377
Telex 73794

Credit Access, Amex, Diners, Visa

Landscaped gardens surround this busy hotel on the outskirts of the city. The verdant look continues in the spacious reception-lounge, where lush plants complement a relaxing peach and darkwood colour scheme. The club-style bar has green leather armchairs and there's a residents' lounge with giant TV screen. Twenty rooms, let first, are set aside for non-smokers and there are five pretty and well-equipped rooms for women. Luxury rooms have plenty of storage and seating, good facilities and modern bathrooms. *Amenities* garden, indoor swimming pool, sauna, solarium, whirlpool bath, keep-fit equipment, tennis, in-house movies, secretarial services, fax, laundry service, coffee shop (11am–11pm), children's playground.

Rooms 114	*Direct dial* Yes	*Confirm by* 6	*Parking* Ample
Ensuite bath/shower 114	*Room TV* Yes	*Last dinner* 10.30	*Room service* 24 hours

ABERDEEN Swallow Imperial Hotel 58% £D/E

H **Map 17 D4** Grampian
Stirling Street AB9 2JY
Aberdeen (0224) 589101
Telex 73365

Credit Access, Amex, Diners, Visa

The stern granite exterior of this town centre hotel belies the stylish decor within. Comfortable armchairs abound in the up-to-date foyer and the appealing Pillars Bar has a pink and grey colour scheme. East wing bedrooms have been totally refurbished with coordinating soft furnishings in designer fabrics and modern bathrooms; west wing rooms are to follow suit.
Amenities in-house movies, secretarial services, fax, laundry service

Rooms 108	*Direct dial* Yes	*Confirm by* 6	*Parking* Limited
Ensuite bath/shower 105	*Room TV* Yes	*Last dinner* 9.30	*Room service* 24 hours

ABERDEEN AIRPORT   Skean Dhu Hotel   65%   £C/D
Aberdeen Airport

H **Map 17 D4** Grampian
Argyll Road, Dyce AB2 0DU
Aberdeen (0224) 725252
Telex 739239

Credit Access, Amex, Diners, Visa

On entering this low-rise airport hotel, it is an unexpected pleasure to find a spacious and luxuriously appointed foyer-lounge with splendid chandeliers, marble pillars and deep sofas. Bedrooms are spacious and well maintained. Trouser presses and hairdryers are standard and all rooms have modern tiled bathrooms. *Amenities* garden, outdoor swimming pool, in-house movies, secretarial services, fax, laundry service, coffee shop (6am–11pm, Sat 7am, Sun 8am).

Rooms 148	*Direct dial* Yes	*Confirm by* 6	*Parking* Ample
Ensuite bath/shower 148	*Room TV* Yes	*Last dinner* 9.45	*Room service* 24 hours

ABERDEEN AIRPORT   Skean Dhu Hotel Dyce   61%   £D/E

H **Map 17 D4** Grampian
Farburn Terrace AB2 0DW
Aberdeen (0224) 723101
Telex 73473

Credit Access, Amex, Diners, Visa

The nondescript exterior of this modern hotel off the A947 belies the pleasant interior. A comfortable seating area forms part of the reception and there's a tasteful lounge/cocktail bar. Studio rooms have twin single beds, one convertible to a sofa; de luxe rooms boast two double beds and a sitting area. Courtesy coach to the airport. *Amenities* sauna, solarium, gymnasium, squash, in-house movies, secretarial services, coffee shop (11am–11pm), helipad.

Rooms 220	*Direct dial* Yes	*Confirm by* 6	*Parking* Ample
Ensuite bath/shower 220	*Room TV* Yes	*Last dinner* 10	*Room service* 24 hours

ACHILTIBUIE   Summer Isles Hotel   62%   £D/E

HR **Map 16 B2** Highland
By Ullapool IV26 2YG
Achiltibuie (085 482) 282

Closed mid Oct–Easter

Birdwatching, fishing and walking are popular pursuits at this beautifully situated hotel overlooking the Summer Isles and the Hebrides. Choose from a bright and cheerful bedroom or sleep Scandinavian-style in a log cabin room. Public areas include a cosy lounge, a TV lounge with writing desk and bookshelves and a snug bar. No children under eight. *Amenities* garden, game fishing, hotel boats, coffee shop (10.30am–8.30pm), 24-hour lounge service.

Rooms 13	*Room phone* No	*Confirm by* arrang.	*Parking* Ample
Ensuite bath/shower 12	*Room TV* No	*Last dinner* 8	*Room service* None

Restaurant

Set D £20
About £50 *for two*
Seats 25

The restaurant has recently been refurbished by enthusiastic owner-managers, Mark and Geraldine Irvine. Dinner is a no-choice set meal served at 8 and might consist of vegetable soup, baked fish, roast beef (with simply served vegetables from the hotel's own gardens) and desserts from the trolley. Cheeses are accompanied by very good oatcakes – the last-mentioned example of the standard the hotel should strive to match elsewhere on the menu. ☙

Dinner only at 8   **Closed** mid Oct–Easter

ADVIE   Tulchan Lodge   82%   £A

H **Map 16 C3** Highland
Nr Grantown-on-Spey
PH26 3PW
Advie (080 75) 200
Telex 75405

Rooms 11
Ensuite bath/shower 11
Direct dial Yes
Room TV No
Confirm by arrang.
Last dinner by arrang.
Parking Ample
Room service All day

Closed Feb–mid Apr

A sporting hotel par excellence, this Edwardian hunting lodge provides a wide range of shooting plus eight miles of fishing on the salmon-rich Spey. But the vast estate, with its glorious scenery, also has plenty to offer the non-sporting guest. The atmosphere here is more that of a country house than a hotel, with antique furniture and fine paintings contributing to the immensely civilized feel of the place. Spacious bedrooms are truly luxurious, and lovely bathrooms are designed to pamper with huge bath sheets and top-quality toiletries. Breakfasts are magnificent. Dogs in kennels only. *Amenities* garden, tennis, shooting, game fishing, snooker, fax, valeting, laundry service.

AIRTH — Airth Castle Hotel 68% £D

H Map 17 C5 Central
Nr Falkirk FK2 8JF
Airth (0324 83) 411
Telex 777975

Credit Access, Amex, Diners, Visa

A sense of history pervades the elegant public rooms of this 14th century castle, with conference centre and leisure facilities. Bedrooms, whether ancient or modern, are comfortable and attractively furnished with generous desk space, good bathrooms and plenty of extras. No dogs. **Amenities** garden, indoor swimming pool, sauna, solarium, whirlpool bath, keep-fit equipment, snooker, satellite TV, in-house movies, fax, laundry service. &

Rooms 47	*Direct dial* Yes	*Confirm by* arrang.	*Parking* Ample
Ensuite bath/shower 47	*Room TV* Yes	*Last dinner* 9.30	*Room service* 24 hours

ALLOWAY — Burns Byre Restaurant

R Map 12 B3 Strathclyde
Mount Oliphant Farm
Alloway (0292) 43644

About £35 for two
Seats 40
Parking Ample

Credit Access, Amex, Diners, Visa

Robert Burns once lived at this small Scottish farm where the cow byre has been excellently converted into a charming restaurant. The food is simply cooked from the very best local raw materials which, since this is still a working farm, is mainly from Duncan Baird's own land. Typical dishes are smoked River Doon salmon paupiette, rack of lamb with redcurrant orange sauce and fillet steak with green peppercorn sauce. &

Lunch noon–2.30 *Dinner* 7–9.30
Closed all Tues (exc. Summer) & 1 Jan

 is our symbol for an **outstanding** wine list

ALTNAHARRA — Altnaharra Hotel 57% £E

H Map 16 B2 Highland
By Lairg IV27 4UE
Altnaharra (054 981) 222

Credit Access, Visa
Closed Nov–Mar

A renowned fishing hotel standing alone in rugged countryside. Other outdoor sports are available, and there's splendid walking and climbing. The owners have made many improvements, both in the day rooms, adorned with fishing trophies and tackle, and in the well-kept bedrooms, which have modern fitted furniture and neat bathrooms. Two rooms in a cottage are usually let as a family suite. **Amenities** garden, golf practice net, game fishing, laundry service.

Rooms 21	*Room phone* No	*Confirm by* arrang.	*Parking* Ample
Ensuite bath/shower 21	*Room TV* No	*Last dinner* 8.30	*Room service* None

ALYTH — Lands of Loyal Hotel 61% £E/F

H Map 17 C4 Tayside
By Blairgowrie PH11 8JQ
Alyth (082 83) 3151

Credit Access, Amex, Visa

Six acres of gardens surround this attractive Victorian mansion, from which fine views of the countryside are to be had. There's an impressive central hall with a glass ceiling, red marble fireplace (with real fire) and carved oak panelling and staircase, while a cosy bar and lounge offer relaxation and ease. Five bedrooms boast antique furniture; the remainder have functional white laminate units. **Amenities** garden, putting, laundry service.

Rooms 11	*Direct dial* Yes	*Confirm by* arrang.	*Parking* Ample
Ensuite bath/shower 11	*Room TV* Some	*Last dinner* 10	*Room service* All day

ANNAN — Warmanbie Hotel 60% *NEW ENTRY* £F

H Map 13 C4
Dumfries & Galloway
DG12 5LL
Annan (046 12) 4015

Credit Access, Amex, Visa

For many years the home of the Duncan family, this handsome Georgian house is a popular fishing hotel with a stretch of salmon water on the river Annan at the foot of the garden. The airy drawing room provides pleasing garden views, and there's a cosy, convivial bar. Family furniture features in the bedrooms, largest of which are at the front. All rooms are equipped with tea-making facilities, radio-alarms and thoughtful touches like flasks of iced water. Two of the bathrooms boast splendid Victorian tubs. Resident manager Rod Duncan works hard for the comfort of his guests. **Amenities** garden, game fishing.

Rooms 6	*Room phone* Yes	*Confirm by* arrang.	*Parking* Ample
Ensuite bath/shower 6	*Room TV* Yes	*Last dinner* 9.30	*Room service* All day

ANSTRUTHER	Cellar Restaurant	♨

R Map 17 D5 Fife
24 East Green
Anstruther (0333) 310378

Seafood
Set D £10.95 (winter)
About £45 for two
Seats 30 *Parties* 26
Parking Ample
Credit Access, Amex, Visa

Such is the popularity of Peter Jukes' predominantly seafood menu that booking is heartily recommended. A simple lunchtime menu gives way at dusk to dishes ranging from a fluffy smoked haddock omelette to fresh West Coast langoustines or grilled halibut supreme. The quality of the fish is outstanding. Good simple vegetables. Some very good wines including Riesling Schoenenburg V.T. (Dopff au Moulin) '83 and Beaujolais Juliénas (Aujas) '83. ♀ Well-chosen

Lunch 12.30–1.30   *Dinner* 7–9.30
Closed L Mon, all Sun, Bank Hols & 10 days Xmas & New Year

ANSTRUTHER	Craw's Nest Hotel 59%	£E

H Map 17 D5 Fife
Bankwell Road KY10 3DA
Anstruther (0333) 310691
Telex 727049

Credit Access, Amex, Diners, Visa

A converted and much-extended manse makes up this unpretentious family-run hotel, where public rooms include a bright and spacious bar overlooking the garden. Best bedrooms, in a modern wing, are smartly appointed with good-quality furniture (including two four-posters); but all rooms are well kept and have tea-makers, radio-alarms and en suite bath or shower. No dogs. *Amenities* garden, solarium, games room, pool table, laundry service. ♿

Rooms 50	*Direct dial* Yes	*Confirm by* arrang.	*Parking* Ample
Ensuite bath/shower 50	*Room TV* Yes	*Last dinner* 8.45	*Room service* All day

**Changes in data sometimes occur in establishments
after the Guide goes to press.
Prices should be taken as indications rather than firm quotes.**

ARDENTINNY	Ardentinny Hotel 59%	£D/E

H Map 17 B5 Strathclyde
Loch Long PA23 8TR
Ardentinny (036 981) 209
Telex 777205

Credit Access, Amex, Diners, Visa
Closed end Oct–mid Mar

Friendly owners and staff provide a pleasant welcome, and the setting on the banks of Loch Long offers some really lovely views. Bedrooms are neat, light and quite spacious, and all have their own bath or shower room en suite. There's a choice of cosy lounges and bars, one with pictures of local hero Sir Harry Lauder.
Amenities garden, game & sea fishing, mooring, hotel boat, pool table, secretarial services.

Rooms 11	*Room phone* No	*Confirm by* 6	*Parking* Ample
Ensuite bath/shower 11	*Room TV* Some	*Last dinner* 9	*Room service* All day

ARDNADAM	Firpark Hotel 60%	£F

H Map 17 B5 Strathclyde
Sandbank, By Dunoon
PA23 8QG
Dunoon (0369) 6506

Credit Visa

A cheerful, double-fronted Victorian house run with care and friendliness by Pat Lamont. For socialising, there's a bright and contemporary bar and a fine lounge with a minstrels' gallery, panelling and green leather chesterfields to maintain the Victorian feel. Good-sized bedrooms have a mixture of freestanding units – white, period or modern lightwood – and simple colour schemes and fabrics. Bathrooms are modern, neat and tidy. *Amenities* garden.

Rooms 6	*Room phone* No	*Confirm by* arrang.	*Parking* Ample
Ensuite bath/shower 2	*Room TV* Yes	*Last dinner* 9	*Room service* All day

ARDUAINE	Loch Melfort Hotel 62%	£D

HR Map 17 B5 Strathclyde
Nr Oban PA34 4XG
Kilmelford (085 22) 233

Credit Access
Closed mid Oct–Thur before Easter

A hotel boasting a magnificent position overlooking the sea and the islands of Jura and Scarba. Public areas include the Chart Bar, the nautical theme of which appeals to the many yachting guests, and a cosy TV lounge. Best bedroom in the main house is huge, with panoramic views and traditional furnishings. In the new wing, many rooms have been pleasantly refurbished.
Amenities garden, mooring, laundry service, kiosk.

Rooms 23	*Room phone* No	*Confirm by* arrang.	*Parking* Ample
Ensuite bath/shower 23	*Room TV* No	*Last dinner* 8.30	*Room service* Limited

Restaurant

Set D Sun from £16
About £38 for two
Seats 50

Book a window table to revel in the splendid view while you sample the tasty food. The à la carte and fixed price menus offer dishes such as smoked Tobermory mussels as a starter, with charcoal-grilled steaks or salmon hollandaise for a main course. Sunday evenings bring only a cold buffet, but a magnificent one at that – beautifully cooked and presented cold meats and fish and imaginative salads. Well-chosen

Dinner only 7.15–8.30
Closed mid Oct–Thur before Easter

ARISAIG

Arisaig House 75% £A/B

HR **Map 17 A4** Highland
Beasdale PH39 4NR
Arisaig (068 75) 622
Telex 777279

Rooms 14
Ensuite bath/shower 13
Direct dial Yes
Room TV Yes
Confirm by 6
Last dinner 8.30
Parking Ample
Room service All day

Credit Access, Visa
Closed Nov–1 wk before Easter

Caring owners and friendly, obliging staff add to the pleasure of the surroundings at this handsome stone-built mansion. The setting, in gardens and woodlands reaching down to the loch, is quite delightful, and a feeling of great peace and calm is all around. Fresh flowers from the garden abound, both in the comfortable day rooms and in the bedrooms. The latter are of a good size, particularly the five master rooms, fairly simple in decor, very tidily kept and well stocked with thoughtful extras. Furniture ranges from antique and reproduction to pine, cane and wicker. Well-kept bathrooms, all private but one not en suite. No children under ten. No dogs. ***Amenities*** garden, croquet, billiards, secretarial services, laundry service.

Restaurant

Set L from £8
Set D £23
About £54 for two
Seats 30

A 30s-style dining room that is especially attractive when candlelit in the evening. Daily-changing dinner menus offer a suggested five courses with a few alternatives. Cooking is skilled and quite refined, from salmon mousse with leek sauce to courgette and almond soup, saddle of lamb stuffed with watercress and a simple sweet like plum tart or pineapple sorbet. Many of the vegetables and herbs are home grown. Good selection of cheeses.

Lunch 12.30–2 *Dinner* 7.30–8.30
Closed Nov–1 wk before Easter

★ For a *discount* on next year's guide, see **An Offer for Answers.** ★

AUCHTERARDER

Auchterarder House 74% £C

HR **Map 17 C5** Tayside
PH3 1DZ
Auchterarder (0764) 63646

Rooms 11
Ensuite bath/shower 11
Direct dial Yes
Room TV Yes
Confirm by arrang.
Last dinner 10.30
Parking Ample
Room service 24 hours
Credit Access, Amex, Diners, Visa

Character, charm and individuality are the hallmarks of this splendid Victorian country house in 17 acres of lovely mature gardens. A ring at the bell alerts the friendly, efficient staff, who make guests feel very welcome. Handsome public rooms range from the marble-floored entrance hall to the winter garden conservatory and vaulted billiards room, which doubles as a bar. Spacious, well-proportioned bedrooms – some with fine antique wardrobes – have recently been upgraded to de luxe standard, while good bathrooms include one with impressive original fittings. Good breakfasts. No children under ten. ***Amenities*** garden, golf driving range, putting, croquet, secretarial services, laundry service.

Auchterarder House Restaurant   ♛ ⚹

Set L £15.50
Set D £20
About £66 for two
Seats 23
Parties 50

The elegant dining room is well matched by Paul Brown's enjoyable cooking, which makes excellent use of local produce. Typical dishes include venison Balmoral, breast of grouse with a red wine and port sauce, and fresh salmon poached in white wine and lime, with tasty soups or perhaps a French snail casserole first. Well-kept cheeses and nice sweets. Fine classic wines include a Pommard 1er cru (Machard de Gramont) '81. ⊜ ᴋ

Lunch 12–3   *Dinner* 7–10.30

AUCHTERARDER   Gleneagles Hotel 88%   £A

H **Map 17 C5** Tayside
PH3 1NF
Auchterarder (076 46) 2231
Telex 76105

Rooms 249
Ensuite bath/shower 249
Direct dial Yes
Room TV Yes
Confirm by arrang.
Last dinner 11
Parking Ample
Room service 24 hours

Credit Access, Amex, Diners, Visa

No less than four championship golf courses are included in the grounds of this famous hotel built on the grand scale in 1924. Latest addition to the unrivalled leisure facilities is the Mark Phillips Equestrian Centre. Elegant public areas include a classically pillared drawing room, a glittering ballroom, and a delightful balconied library. Spacious bedrooms have handsome furnishings and luxurious bathrooms. *Amenities* garden, indoor swimming pool, sauna, solarium, whirlpool bath, gymnasium, hairdressing, tennis, squash, golf courses, pitch & putt, bowling green, croquet, riding, clay-pigeon shooting, game fishing, snooker, in-house movies, secretarial services, fax, valeting, laundry service, shopping arcade. ᴋ

**We welcome bona fide complaints and recommendations
on the tear-out pages at the back of the book for readers' comment.
They are followed up by our professional team.**

AUCHTERHOUSE   Old Mansion House Hotel 68%   £C/D

HR **Map 17 C5** Tayside
Nr Dundee DD3 0QN
Auchterhouse (082 626) 366

Credit Access, Amex, Diners, Visa
Closed 24 Dec–2 Jan

Nigel and Eva Bell have skilfully converted a distinguished Jacobean manor house into a small, comfortable hotel with plenty of period charm. Civilised public rooms include two delightful bars, one offering book-filled shelves, the other a pretty patio. Spacious, nicely furnished bedrooms have excellent bathrooms.
Amenities outdoor swimming pool, tennis, squash, croquet, in-house movies, secretarial services, laundry service.

Rooms 6	*Direct dial* Yes	*Confirm by* arrang.	*Parking* Ample
Ensuite bath/shower 6	*Room TV* Yes	*Last dinner* 9.30	*Room service* All day

Restaurant   ♛

Set L £19.50
About £55 for two
Seats 45
Parties 20

Quality materials handled sympathetically and good basic standards of cooking are the hallmarks of this handsome restaurant with a fine moulded ceiling and the friendly, cheerful staff add to the enjoyment. Classically inspired dishes such as paupiettes de sole and lobster thermidor are teamed up with Scottish specialities such as Arbroath smokie, Tay salmon and collops in the pan, while fruity desserts include a delicious brandy basket. Table d'hôte lunch.

Lunch 12–2   *Dinner* 7–9.30, Sun till 9
Closed 24 Dec–2 Jan

AVIEMORE — Post House Hotel — 62% — £D/E

H **Map 17 C4** Highland
Aviemore Centre PH22 1PJ
Aviemore (0479) 810771
Telex 75597

Credit Access, Amex, Diners, Visa

Public areas are fairly extensive, a useful feature in a resort hotel. This Post House is in the heart of the Aviemore Centre and offers a decent standard of up-to-date comfort and practicality, including remote-control TVs in the bedrooms and showers over all the tubs.
Amenities garden, solarium, games room, secretarial services, fax, laundry service, coffee shop (10am–10pm), 24-hour lounge service.

Rooms 103	Direct dial Yes	Confirm by 6	Parking Ample
Ensuite bath/shower 103	Room TV Yes	Last dinner 9.30	Room service None

---

AVIEMORE — Stakis Badenoch Hotel — 59% — £E

H **Map 17 C4** Highland
Aviemore Centre PH22 1PF
Aviemore (0479) 810261
Telex 75601

Credit Access, Amex, Diners, Visa

A modest but comfortable base for an active holiday in the Aviemore complex. Standard bedrooms have been given a facelift with brighter colour schemes and a reconditioning of the solid fitted furniture. 18 rooms, usually let to children in the skiing season, are more basic, with shared bathroom facilities. There's a lounge, a small disco and a pleasant bar with tweedy furnishings.
Amenities in-house movies, secretarial services, fax, laundry service.

Rooms 80	Direct dial Yes	Confirm by 6	Parking Ample
Ensuite bath/shower 62	Room TV Most	Last dinner 9.15	Room service 24 hours

---

We publish annually,
so make sure you use the current edition.
It's worth it!

AVIEMORE — Stakis Coylumbridge Resort Hotel — 61% — £C/D

H **Map 17 C4** Highland
PH22 1QN
Aviemore (0479) 810661
Telex 75272

Credit Access, Amex, Diners, Visa

This lively, unpretentious hotel is totally geared up to active family holidays, and besides the impressive leisure facilities there are 63 acres of gardens and grounds. The tiled reception is at the hub of the open-plan day rooms, which also include a comfortable lounge and bar, a coffee shop and a huge restaurant. Bedrooms, done out in simple, bold colours, include many family units. Bathrooms are straightforward, tiled and clean. *Amenities* garden, indoor swimming pools, sauna, solarium, whirlpool bath, keep-fit equipment, hairdressing, tennis, badminton, putting, clay-pigeon shooting, games room, in-house movies, secretarial services, fax, laundry service, coffee shop (7am–11pm), children's playground.

Rooms 175	Direct dial Yes	Confirm by arrang.	Parking Ample
Ensuite bath/shower 175	Room TV Yes	Last dinner 9.30	Room service 24 hours

---

AVIEMORE — Stakis Four Seasons Hotel — 71% — £C/D

H **Map 17 C4** Highland
Aviemore Centre PH22 1PF
Aviemore (0479) 810681
Telex 75213

Rooms 89
Ensuite bath/shower 89
Direct dial Yes
Room TV Yes
Confirm by 6
Last dinner 9.30
Parking Ample
Room service 24 hours

Credit Access, Amex, Diners, Visa

A good modern hotel in the middle of the Aviemore complex. Beyond the very inconspicuous main entrance there's quite a lot of style in day rooms like the midnight-blue lobby-lounge and bar, the coffee shop and the excellent leisure centre (note the brand new pool). Good-quality darkwood furniture is fitted in the well-kept bedrooms, and fabrics, modern but with old-fashioned floral designs, are in subtle  shades. Hairdryers, tea-makers and remote-control TVs are standard equipment, and all rooms have smart tiled bathrooms en suite.
Amenities garden, indoor swimming pool, sauna, solarium, whirlpool bath, steam room, keep-fit equipment, in-house movies, secretarial services, fax, laundry service, coffee shop (10am–6pm).

AYR — Balgarth Hotel 56% — £F

H Map 12 B2 Strathclyde
8 Dunure Road,
Doonfoot KA7 4HR
Alloway (0292) 42441

Credit Access, Amex, Diners, Visa

Not far from Burns' cottage, this late Victorian sandstone building, now a pleasant if modest hotel, makes a convenient base for exploring Burns country. There's a fine collection of golfing photographs in the comfortable red plush bar, warmed by a log fire, and there are also two little lounges. Compact, well-kept bedrooms offer simple comforts. *Amenities* garden, secretarial services, laundry service, children's play area.

Rooms 15	*Room phone* Yes	*Confirm by* arrang.	*Parking* Ample
Ensuite bath/shower 11	*Room TV* Yes	*Last dinner* 10	*Room service* All day

AYR — Caledonian Hotel £64% — £C/D

H Map 12 B2 Strathclyde
Dalblair Road KA7 1UG
Ayr (0292) 269331
Telex 776611

Credit Access, Amex, Diners, Visa

There's been a complete transformation of this high-rise town-centre hotel. The remodelled public rooms include a spacious reception with comfortable sofas and a smart cocktail bar. Pastel colour schemes and lightwood furniture make the bedrooms pleasant, and all have tea/coffee-makers and hairdryers; Executive rooms also boast teletext and bathrobes. *Amenities* indoor swimming pool, sauna, solarium, whirlpool bath, gymnasium, snooker, laundry service.

Rooms 114	*Direct dial* Yes	*Confirm by* 6	*Parking* Limited
Ensuite bath/shower 114	*Room TV* Yes	*Last dinner* 9.45	*Room service* 24 hours

AYR — Pickwick Hotel 59% — £D/E

H Map 12 B2 Strathclyde
19 Racecourse Road KA7 2TD
Ayr (0292) 260111

Credit Access, Visa

Now under new ownership, this Victorian hotel stands on the A719 in a leafy suburb south of the town centre. Day rooms include a simply-furnished lounge and a half-panelled bar with stone-mullioned windows. Bedrooms of varying sizes have contemporary decor and modern units and are equipped with remote-control TV, trouser presses, tea-makers and drinks dispensers. Ensuite bathrooms throughout (four with shower only). No dogs. *Amenities* garden.

Rooms 15	*Room phone* Yes	*Confirm by* arrang.	*Parking* Ample
Ensuite bath/shower 15	*Room TV* Yes	*Last dinner* 9	*Room service* All day

BALLACHULISH — Ballachulish Hotel 60% — £E

H Map 17 B4 Highland
Argyll PA39 4JY
Ballachulish (085 52) 606
Telex 94013696

Credit Access, Amex, Diners, Visa

Views of glorious sunsets through the arched Gothic windows are a notable feature of this comfortable, friendly hotel. Public areas include an airy lounge with chesterfield-style seating, a cocktail bar and an unpretentious, lively public bar with folk music. The spotlessly clean bedrooms have attractive, solid pine furniture, floral fabrics and simple, tiled bathrooms. *Amenities* garden, sea fishing, snooker, secretarial services, fax, laundry service, coffee shop (10am–10pm).

Rooms 30	*Direct dial* Yes	*Confirm by* 6	*Parking* Ample
Ensuite bath/shower 30	*Room TV* Yes	*Last dinner* 10	*Room service* 24 hours

BALLATER — Craigendarroch Hotel & Country Club 74% *NEW ENTRY* — £C/D

HR Map 17 C4 Grampian
Braemar Road AB3 5AX
Ballater (0338) 55858
Telex 739952

Rooms 29
Ensuite bath/shower 29
Direct dial Yes
Room TV Yes
Confirm by 6
Last dinner 10
Parking Ample
Room service 24 hours

Credit Access, Amex, Diners, Visa

Guests staying at the Scottish baronial hotel can use the splendid leisure club and the many outdoor facilities, which include an adventure playground and a dry ski slope. More cerebral pursuits are also at hand, including a good range of reading in the comfortable study bar. Fair-sized bedrooms have all sorts of extras, from a useful little trinket box to drinks fridges and teletext TVs. First-class management and

friendly staff. No dogs. *Amenities* garden, indoor swimming pool, sauna, solarium, whirlpool bath, gymnasium, beauty salon, hairdressing, squash, games room, snooker, in-house movies, secretarial services, fax, laundry service, coffee shop (7.30am–10pm), creche.

Oaks Restaurant

Set L from £9.50
Set D from £18.75
About £55 for two
Seats 42
Parties 12
Parking Ample

Bill Gibb brings modern touches to first-rate cooking skills, and the result is a meal to remember in smart comfortable surroundings. The menus tempt at every turn with original dishes like roe deer consommé with game dumplings, brill enclosing scampi in a cucumber and champagne sauce or breast of duck filled with an apricot and pistachio forcemeat and set on a crème de cassis sauce. Order plain if you prefer. Good wines from excellent growers. ℮

Lunch 12.30–2
Dinner 7.30–10

BALLATER   Tullich Lodge   70%   £B

HR Map 17 C4 Grampian
AB3 5SB
Ballater (0338) 55406

Rooms 10
Ensuite bath/shower 10
Direct dial Yes
Room TV No
Confirm by arrang.
Last dinner 8.30
Parking Ample
Room service Limited

Credit Access, Amex
Closed Dec–Mar

A solidly built Victorian mansion in a lovely wooded setting overlooking the Dee valley, not far from a golf course. Constructed out of pink granite, it's prettier than most Scottish Baronial residences – though sporting the usual turret and crenellations. The drawing room is a delightfully civilised spot, with handsome antique sofas and fine open views across Strathdee and towards Lochnagar. There's also a

cosy little sitting room, well stocked with books and magazines, and an oak-panelled bar where guests are encouraged to forgather for a pre-prandial drink. Individually decorated bedrooms of varying sizes feature good antiques and decent bathrooms (two with shower only). *Amenities* garden, laundry service.

Tullich Lodge Dining Room   ♨ ♌

Set D £16
About £42 for two
Seats 25
Parties 10

Gleaming wood panelling, crisp table cloths and fresh posies of wild flowers all suggest the care and attention that are lavished on this well-ordered dining room. Neil Bannister's no-choice set dinner might begin with game terrine and go on to gratin of mussels and then roast leg of lamb with garlic and anchovy sauce. End with Scottish cheeses or a well-made fruit flan. Book. No smoking. ℮

Lunch by arrang. only   *Dinner* 7.30–8.30
Closed Dec–Mar

★ For a *discount* on next year's guide, see **An Offer for Answers.** ★

BANCHORY   Invery House   79%   *NEW ENTRY*   £B

HR Map 17 D4 Grampian
Bridge of Feugh AB3 3NJ
Banchory (033 02) 4782
Telex 73737

Rooms 14
Ensuite bath/shower 14
Direct dial Yes
Room TV Yes
Confirm by arrang.
Last dinner 9.45
Parking Ample
Room service 24 hours

Credit Access, Amex, Diners, Visa
Closed 1st 2 wks Jan

Owners Stewart and Sheila Spence masterminded the conversion of a Georgian mansion into a really superb hotel. The setting is among the most beautiful and tranquil, and the whole place invites relaxation. Handsome antiques grace the public rooms, and there are some fine oil paintings. Inviting armchairs and settees abound, and there's an ample supply of reading material. Good-sized bedrooms are

also beautifully appointed – antiques again, stylish fabrics, homely ornaments, extras from fresh fruit and sherry to teletext TVs. In the bathrooms, tubs and separate showers, thick, fluffy towels, top-quality toiletries. Super breakfasts, super staff. No children under eight. Dogs in kennels.
Amenities garden, putting, croquet, game fishing, snooker, secretarial services, laundry service, helipad.   *see over*

Invery House Restaurant   *NEW ENTRY*   ♛

Set Sun L only £13.50
Set D £21.50
About £60 *for two*
Seats 32
Parties 26

Daily-changing menus make fine use of fresh, mostly local, produce. Everything is tasty and appetising, from a light-textured salmon mousse flavoured with dill to grilled sole, beef in a rich red wine sauce and an omelette filled with lobster, Stilton, port and mushrooms. Iced pistachio soufflé with strawberry sauce is a luscious sweet. The wine list is long and interesting, but could do with some pruning of poorer years. No smoking in the dining room. ⊖ &

Lunch 12.15–2.15   *Dinner* 7.15–9.45   **Closed** 1st 2 wks Jan

---

BANCHORY   Raemoir House Hotel   71%   £C/D

H **Map 17 D4** Grampian
AB3 4ED
Banchory (033 02) 4884
Telex 73315

Rooms 22
Ensuite bath/shower 22
Direct dial Yes
Room TV Yes
Confirm by arrang.
Last dinner 9
Parking Ample
Room service All day

Credit Access, Amex, Diners, Visa

Run by the inimitable Mrs Kit Sabin and her staunch staff, this highly individual hotel offers an indefinable feeling of luxury that money alone cannot provide. Huge sash windows in all the public rooms give views over the 3500-acre estate, and the bar features a counter made from a heavily carved Tudor four-poster. Bedrooms are spacious and full of well-worn antiques; five are in the 16th-century Ha' Hoose, once visited by Mary Queen of Scots. The main house dates from 1750.

Amenities garden, sauna, solarium, keep-fit equipment, tennis, 9-hole mini-golf course, shooting, game fishing, secretarial services, helipad. &

BANCHORY   Tor-na-Coille Hotel   64%   £E

H **Map 17 D4** Grampian
Inchmarlo Road AB3 4AB
Banchory (033 02) 2242

Credit Access, Amex, Diners, Visa

Attractive grounds surround this solid Victorian mansion on the A93, affording pretty views from the huge sash windows of the spacious lounge bar. Good-sized bedrooms are individually decorated with coordinating soft furnishings and large antique pieces; gargantuan old tubs are to be found in some of the bathrooms, while others are more compact and modern. *Amenities* garden, hairdressing, health clinic, squash, indoor bowling, snooker, laundry service.

Rooms 22	*Direct dial* Yes	*Confirm by* arrang.	*Parking* Ample
Ensuite bath/shower 22	*Room TV* Yes	*Last dinner* 10	*Room service* Limited

---

BARRHILL   Kildonan Hotel   *NEW ENTRY*   68%   £D

HR **Map 12 A3** Strathclyde
Ayrshire KA26 0PU
Barrhill (0465 82) 360

Credit Access, Amex, Diners, Visa

A Lutyens mansion attractively situated in an 83-acre estate off the A714. Public areas include a spacious, tall-windowed lounge and a cosy cocktail bar. Bedrooms vary from decent-sized to very spacious, and are furnished with antique pieces. No supplement for single guests. *Amenities* garden, indoor swimming pool, sauna, solarium, keep-fit equipment, squash, shooting, clay-pigeon shooting, sea, coarse and game fishing, games room, fax, laundry service. &

Rooms 35	*Direct dial* Yes	*Confirm by* arrang.	*Parking* Ample
Ensuite bath/shower 35	*Room TV* Yes	*Last dinner* 9	*Room service* 24 hours

---

Restaurant   *NEW ENTRY*

Set L £12.50
Set D £14.95
About £40 *for two*
Seats 70
Parties 65

Excellent raw materials, competent cooking and delightful presentation combine to make a meal here highly enjoyable. Starters include smoked breast of duck with orange and red peppercorn dressing and rosettes of chicken liver and brandy served on a whisky and Seville orange sauce; medallions of veal served with a morel sauce is a delicious main course. Don't miss the hot sticky toffee pudding, which is truly a triumph.

Lunch 12–2   *Dinner* 7.30–9

BEATTOCK — Auchen Castle Hotel 65% £E

H Map 12 C3
Dumfries & Galloway
Nr Moffat DG10 9SH
Beattock (068 33) 407
Telex 777205

Credit Access, Amex, Diners, Visa
Closed 21 Dec–8 Jan

High on a hillside above the A74, and about a mile north of Beattock village stands this fine Victorian mansion house. Chintzy armchairs and sofas grace the traditional lounge, while the bar has some lovely handmade Thai rosewood furniture. The best of the bedrooms are in the main house. Large rooms have antiques; others have attractive lightwood fitted units made by a local cabinetmaker. Fabrics and furnishings suggest a designer with a good sense of colour. Ten rooms in the Cedar Lodge are rather more functional, but have very fine views. The 50-acre grounds are beautifully laid out and include a trout loch.
Amenities garden, shooting, game fishing, fax.

Rooms 25	Direct dial Yes	Confirm by arrang.	Parking Ample
Ensuite bath/shower 25	Room TV Yes	Last dinner 9	Room service Limited

**Any person using our name to obtain free hospitality is a fraud.
Proprietors, please inform the police and us.**

BONNYRIGG — Dalhousie Castle Hotel 72% £B/C

H Map 12 C1 Lothian
Nr Edinburgh EH19 3JB
Gorebridge (0875) 20153
Telex 72380

Rooms 24
Ensuite bath/shower 24
Direct dial Yes
Room TV Yes
Confirm by arrang.
Last dinner 10
Parking Ample
Room service 24 hours

Credit Access, Amex, Diners, Visa

Guarding a history dating back more than 800 years, this turreted sandstone castle on the river Esk is the former seat of the Ramsay family. The present building dates from around 1450 and retains fascinating features like the ancient barrel-vaulted dungeons. There's a handsomely panelled library with a fine moulded ceiling and an attractive mezzanine lounge with a mural depicting the castle's past.

Bedrooms are mostly spacious and furnished with solid oak; five have just been updated with new carpets and curtains. For honeymoon couples, there's a magnificent circular suite in the tower wing, complete with four-poster. Neat modern bathrooms throughout.
Amenities garden, games room, secretarial services, laundry service.

BRAE — Busta House Hotel 67% *NEW ENTRY* £E

HR Map 16 D2 Shetland
ZE2 9QN
Brae (080 622) 506
Telex 9312100218

Credit Access, Amex, Diners, Visa

A house rich in history, with a lovely lochside setting, a little private harbour and a tree-filled walled garden. The main feature in the gracious Long Room is a group of portraits in oil of the 18th-century owners; there's a delightful bar with a superb collection of malt whiskies, a garden bar and a quiet library. Bedrooms vary from characterful small-scale in the oldest part to more modern and spacious in the garden wing; all offer a good degree of comfort, and there are lots of extras in the bathrooms. Staff are friendly and obliging, and the day starts with a decent breakfast.
Amenities garden, game fishing, laundry service.

Rooms 21	Direct dial Yes	Confirm by arrang.	Parking Ample
Ensuite bath/shower 21	Room TV Yes	Last dinner 9.30	Room service Limited

Restaurant

Set D £14.95
About £38 for two
Seats 60
Parties 60

Sound cooking and cheerful service in mellow, comfortable surroundings. Chef and joint-owner Gordon Stark produces few surprises but lots of good flavours in dishes like chicken liver pâté, seafood risotto, roast duckling bigarade and tournedos with Madeira sauce. Excellent vegetables, simple sweets, a couple of well-kept cheeses and a wine list strong in fine burgundies and clarets. No smoking in the dining room.

Dinner only 7–9.30

BRIDGE OF ALLAN   Kipling's   ⧣

R Map 17 C5 Central
Mine Road
Stirling (0786) 833617

Set L £6.60
About £40 for two
Seats 68 Parties 65
Parking Ample

Credit Access, Amex, Visa

Peter Bannister raids the Glasgow markets first thing every morning
and constructs his evening menus according to his haul. Game features
heavily on the menu in season and all the food is prepared so as to
preserve the excellent natural flavours. Typical starters are artichoke
salsa verde and cream of crayfish soup, with venison haggis with
Drambuie to follow. Simple sweets to finish. Short wine list with
couple of good clarets; excellent Wynn's Cabernet. 🍷 &

Lunch 12.30–2   *Dinner* 7–9   **Closed** Sun, Mon, Bank Hols (exc.
Good Fri), 2 wks Xmas & 1st 2 wks Aug

BRIDGE OF ALLAN   Royal Hotel   59%   £D/E

H Map 17 C5 Central
Henderson Street FK9 4HG
Stirling (0786) 832284

Credit Access, Amex, Diners, Visa

Pleasant accommodation is to be found at this white-painted hotel on
the main street. Public areas comprise three lounges, one pleasantly
panelled and equipped with easy chairs, the other two also doubling
as function rooms, and a deep blue bar with plush banquettes.
Bedrooms are all greatly improved, with smart bathrooms, trouser
presses and satellite TVs. Excellent housekeeping.
Amenities garden, laundry service.

Rooms 32	*Direct dial* Yes	*Confirm by* arrang.	*Parking* Ample
Ensuite bath/shower 32	*Room TV* Yes	*Last dinner* 9.30	*Room service* All day

BRIDGE OF CALLY   Bridge of Cally Hotel   56%   £F

HR Map 17 C4 Tayside
By Blairgowrie PH10 7JJ
Bridge of Cally (025 086) 231

Credit Access, Diners, Visa
Closed Nov & 25 & 26 Dec

The river Ardle flows peacefully past this friendly, homely hotel in a
village six miles north of Blairgowrie in the beautiful Perthshire
countryside. Downstairs, there's a warm and relaxing cocktail bar
and a TV lounge well stocked with comfortable chairs. The nine
bedrooms are simply furnished but clean and bright; all have
washbasins and six have a private bath or shower.
Amenities garden, game fishing.

Rooms 9	*Room phone* No	*Confirm by* arrang.	*Parking* Ample
Ensuite bath/shower 6	*Room TV* No	*Last dinner* 8.30	*Room service* Limited

Restaurant   ⧣

Set D £10.50
About £35 for two
Seats 32
Parties 35

A simple, neat establishment with white walls and posies of wild
flowers on the tablecloths. The short menu changes daily, offering
straightforward dishes that are capably prepared. Starter might be a
good port and Stilton pâté with excellent home-made wholemeal
bread or seafood cocktail; for a main course, perhaps pork escalopes
with orange and ginger. Delicious puds include fresh fruit pavlova
and apple strudel.

Lunch 12–2, Sun 12.30–1.45   *Dinner* 7–8.30
Closed Nov & 25 & 26 Dec

CALLANDER   Roman Camp Hotel   72%   £D

HR Map 17 C5 Central
Main Street FK17 8BG
Callander (0877) 30003

Rooms 14
Ensuite bath/shower 14
Direct dial Yes
Room TV Yes
Confirm by 5
Last dinner 9
Parking Ample
Room service Limited

Closed mid Nov–mid Mar

The surrounding countryside is
rich in Roman ruins, which explains the name of this civilised
little hotel standing in lovely
gardens on the banks of the river
Teith. The style is that of a
miniature French château and
the day rooms, including lounge,
sun lounge and panelled library,
combine formal, traditional
looks with a restful, relaxing
atmosphere. Many of the com-
fortable, well-equipped bed-
rooms feature attractive hand-painted furniture; there are three
stylish suites, and three rooms on the ground floor have French
windows that give on to the gardens. Bathrooms, too, are individually
decorated and finished to a high standard.
Amenities garden, game fishing, laundry service. &

Restaurant

Set L £11.50, Sun £12
Set D £18
About £43 *for two*
Seats 46

Pre-prandial drinks are taken in a pleasant bar, after which guests repair to the bright, spacious restaurant to enjoy Swiss-born Sami Denzler's tasty food. Various European cuisines are featured on his fixed-price menus, with dishes such as gazpacho Andaluz, schnitzel, venison with spätzli, robust pot au feu ... Note the excellent Dézaley Blanc Premier Cru from Switzerland on a good wine list. ⚑ Well-chosen ⓔ

Lunch 12.15–1.30, Sun 12.30–2   *Dinner* 7–8.30
Closed mid Nov–mid Mar

CANONBIE — Riverside Inn

RR **Map 12 D3**
Dumfries & Galloway
DG14 0UX
Canonbie (054 15) 512

Set D £15
About £45 *for two*
Seats 30 *Parties* 28
Parking Ample
Credit Access, Visa

The A7 bypass has provided this pretty pub on the Esk with a quiet and peaceful setting. At lunchtimes there's a pub lunch menu only, except by prior arrangement, but evenings bring excellent local trout, salmon, beef and game, straightforwardly and carefully cooked. Good cheeses include Ribblesdale and Allendale goats' milk, Blue Shropshire and Cumbrian farmhouse; for a sweet, try the delicious hot apple and lemon brown Betty. ⓔ

Lunch by arrang. only   *Dinner* 7.30–8.30, Sat 7.30–9
Closed Sun, 25 & 26 Dec, 1 & 2 Jan & last 2 wks Feb

BEDROOMS 6   £E
With bath/shower 6

The six delightfully light and airy bedrooms have good en suite shower or bathrooms, electric blankets, tea trays, fresh fruit and colour TVs.

CLEISH — Nivingston House   68%   £D

HR **Map 17 C5** Tayside
Nr Kinross KY13 7LS
Cleish Hills (057 75) 216

Credit Access, Amex, Diners, Visa
Closed 24 & 25 Dec & 2 wks Jan

A pleasant stone-built hotel in a delightfully rural setting only two miles from Junction 5 of the M90. Public rooms include two lounges and a plush red bar. The pretty bedrooms have coordinating fabrics, modern freestanding units, tea/coffee-makers and smart bathrooms, five with shower only; all have good toiletries, mineral water, decent towels and hairdryers. *Amenities* garden, golf practice net, putting, croquet, secretarial services, laundry service.

Rooms 17	*Direct dial* Yes	*Confirm by* arrang.	*Parking* Ample
Ensuite bath/shower 17	*Room TV* Yes	*Last dinner* 9	*Room service* Limited

Restaurant

Set L £12.50
Set D £19
About £49 *for two*
Seats 50
Parties 30

In the elegant, comfortable restaurant with its handsome table settings and pretty floral curtains you can enjoy Michael Thompson's sound, reliable cooking. The menus contain a cheerful hotchpotch of ideas, skilfully executed. Starters might include venison pâté with wholegrain mustard sauce and grilled scallops wrapped in bacon; main course could be breast of chicken stuffed with smoked goose, topped with Cointreau cream sauce. Finish with an excellent Scotch trifle. ⓔ

Lunch 12–2
Dinner 7–9

COLBOST — Three Chimneys

R **Map 16 A3** Highland
Nr Dunvegan, Isle of Skye
Glendale (047 081) 258

About £38 *for two*
Seats 30
Parties 35
Parking Ample

Credit Access, Visa

An old stone crofter's cottage is home to this charming lochside restaurant opposite Dunvegan. Shirley Spear is an inventive cook whose food is full of flavour. She makes the most of marvellous local seafood (including peat-smoked salmon from North Uist), game and organically grown vegetables. A typical dinner might begin with fresh scallops with bacon, proceed to peppercorn steak with hot onion relish and conclude with rhubarb oatie nut crumble. Lunch is a simpler affair; perhaps a slice of crab and salmon quiche with coleslaw or simply home-made vegetable soup with freshly baked bread. Absorbing wine list includes Tokay Pinot Gris Altenbourg (Blanck) '83 and Ch. Pichon Baron '79. ⚑ Well-chosen ⓔ

Lunch 12.30–2   *Dinner* 7–9
Closed Sun except June–Sept, Nov–March

CONTIN | Craigdarroch Lodge Hotel   55% | £E/F

H Map 16 B3 Highland
Strathpeffer IV14 9EH
Strathpeffer (0997) 21265

Credit Visa
Closed 25 Dec

The peace is undisturbed at this modest little fishing and walking hotel, which stands at the end of a tree-lined drive off the A835. The comfortable lounge has been brightened up, and there's a cosy lounge-bar that opens on to a pretty garden. Bedrooms, too, have been given a facelift; extras are few, but the basic comforts are there.
Amenities garden, tennis, croquet, game fishing, snooker, laundry service. ♿

Rooms 13	*Room phone* No	*Confirm by* arrang.	*Parking* Ample
Ensuite bath/shower 10	*Room TV* No	*Last dinner* 8.30	*Room service* All day

**Our inspectors are our full-time employees;
they are professionally trained by us.**

CRAIGNURE | Isle of Mull Hotel   56% | £D/E

H Map 17 A5 Strathclyde
Isle of Mull PA65 6BB
Craignure (068 02) 351

Credit Access, Amex, Diners, Visa
Closed end Oct–Easter

Clever design has ensured that all the bedrooms and recreation rooms in this modern hotel have splendid views across the Sound of Mull. Public areas include a spacious foyer-lounge and a further lounge leading on to a patio. Bedrooms have practical laminate fitted units and pretty duvet covers; bathrooms are fitted with over-the-tub showers. *Amenities* garden, games room, pool table, in-house movies, laundry service.

Rooms 60	*Room phone* No	*Confirm by* 7	*Parking* Ample
Ensuite bath/shower 60	*Room TV* Yes	*Last dinner* 8.30	*Room service* Limited

CRINAN | Crinan Hotel   70% | £D

HR Map 17 B5 Strathclyde
By Lochgilphead PA31 8SR
Crinan (054 683) 261

Rooms 22
Ensuite bath/shower 22
Direct dial Yes
Room TV No
Confirm by 6
Last dinner 9
Parking Ample
Room service All day

Credit Access, Visa
Closed end Oct–wk before Easter

A spectacularly situated hotel with, to one side, a view across the sea to the outlying islands and to the other a picturesque loch where the local fishing fleet drops anchor. Public rooms include a number of cosy lounges with a mixture of sturdy, comfortable seating and two pleasing bars, one for residents and the other popular with the local fishermen. The well-kept bedrooms, some with balconies, all

have a magnificent outlook and are decorated in pretty matching fabrics and solidly attractive Italian pine furniture. There are two compact singles. All have pristine modern bathrooms. ♿
Amenities garden, sea fishing, hotel boat, laundry service, coffee shop (9am–5pm).

Lock 16 Restaurant ★

Seafood

Lunch 12.30–2
Dinner at 8
Set D £26.50
About £64 for two
Seats 24
Parties 24

Closed L Tues, all Mon & end Oct–wk before Easter

A rooftop restaurant which operates on a winning formula of simple decor and cooking, the richesse coming from the freshness of the seafood which is landed only 50 yards from the hotel and the breathtaking location – at certain times of the year the sunsets are quite magical. The five-course set menu changes little and all is perfectly cooked to retain natural flavours. Excellent Pouilly Fumé (Dagueneau) on a good wine list. Booking is essential for non-residents.
Specialities Loch Craignish mussels, galia melon with fresh lime, jumbo prawns Corryvreckan, strawberry vacherin. 🍷 Well-chosen ♿

Telford Room

Set D £22.50
About £55 for two
Seats 50
Parties 12

Friendly service and confident cooking of good fresh local produce guarantee an enjoyable meal. The fixed-price five-course menu offers a choice of two main dishes, one meat and one fish. A typical meal might be cream of spinach soup, Loch Crinan jumbo prawn platter and lemon sorbet, with wild river Tay salmon hollandaise as a main course and chocolate profiteroles to finish. 🍷 Well-chosen ⊖

Dinner only 7–9
Closed end Oct–wk before Easter

CROMARTY Le Chardon *NEW ENTRY*

R **Map 16 C3** Highland
Church Street
Cromarty (038 17) 471

Set L Sun £9
Set D £15.50
About £40 for two
Seats 26 *Parties* 32
Parking Ample
Credit Access, Amex, Visa

An agreeable little restaurant with 30s decor and music. Chef-patron Robyn Aitchison allies sound technique to imagination, and good fresh produce goes into tasty dishes like marinated herring, roast chicken breast with rosemary, veal with chanterelles and rabbit braised in Marsala. A vegetarian main course is always available. There's a serious wine list: note Côte-Rôtie Brune et Blonde 1979 (Guigal). No smoking in the dining room. 🍷 Well-chosen ⊖ ♿

Lunch Sun 12.30–2, Mon–Sat by arrang. *Dinner* 7.30–9.30
Closed D Sun, all Mon, 25 Dec & 1 Jan

CULLEN Seafield Arms Hotel 60% £F

H **Map 16 D3** Grampian
Seafield Street AB5 2SG
Cullen (0542) 40791

Credit Access, Amex, Diners, Visa

A friendly, white-painted hotel in the centre of the village. A carved Adam fireplace features in the pleasant lounge bar, which has inviting sofas and a view on to the courtyard. Brass or cane beds lend character to the bedrooms, all of which have desk space and smart modern bathrooms; attic rooms sport pretty cottage decor and front rooms are double-glazed.
Amenities patio, snooker, secretarial services, laundry service.

Rooms 22	Direct dial Yes	Confirm by 6	Parking Ample
Ensuite bath/shower 22	Room TV Yes	Last dinner 9.30	Room service Limited

CUPAR Ostlers Close Restaurant

R **Map 17 C5** Fife
Bonnygate KY15 4BU
Cupar (0334) 55574

About £39 for two
Seats 28
Parties 20
Parking Limited

Credit Access, Visa

At the Grahams' attractively traditional restaurant Amanda exudes charm and efficiency at the front while James cooks backstage with a sure technique and a good deal of imagination. Ingredients are as fresh as could be and the short, frequently changing menu is full of interest; chicken and partridge liver pâté and breast of pigeon in gin and juniper berry sauce are typical dishes. Sweets are luscious.
🍷 Well-chosen ⊖

Lunch 12.15–2 *Dinner* 7–9.30, Sat 7–10
Closed All Sun & Mon & 2 wks winter

Our inspectors *never* book in the name of Egon Ronay's Guides.
They disclose their identity only if they are considering an establishment
for inclusion in the next edition of the Guide.

DIRLETON Open Arms Hotel 67% £C/D

H **Map 12 D1** Lothian
EH39 5EG
Dirleton (062 085) 241
Telex 727887

Credit Access, Amex, Diners, Visa
Closed 1 wk Jan

Two old houses have been converted into this welcoming hotel overlooking the romantic ruins of Dirleton Castle. The main lounge is a homely room with comfortable pastel-toned armchairs and sofas, log fire and magazines and newspapers; and there's also a tiny bar. Bedrooms have bright floral curtains, fresh flowers, fruit and easy chairs. Bathrooms are carpeted and fitted with well-lit mirrors and hairdryers. *Amenities* garden, secretarial services.

Rooms 7	Direct dial Yes	Confirm by arrang.	Parking Ample
Ensuite bath/shower 7	Room TV Yes	Last dinner 10	Room service All day

DRUMNADROCHIT   Polmaily House Hotel   63%   £D/E

HR **Map 16 B3** Highland
IV3 6XT
Drumnadrochit (045 62) 343

Credit Access, Visa
Closed mid Oct–Easter

A charming hotel with 18 acres of grounds set in lovely walking country. Nicholas and Alison Parsons emphasize peace, informality and comfort rather than show or style, and the formula works admirably. The lounge, with its open fire, fresh flowers and chintzy armchairs, is an ideal spot for a chat or a read, and there's a room for TV or board games and a neat little bar. There are just nine bedrooms, all individually furnished, the two singles sharing a smart bathroom, the rest with warm, carpeted en suite facilities. The best room features a four-poster bed. Delightful staff make guests feel instantly at home. No dogs. *Amenities* garden, outdoor swimming pool, tennis, croquet, laundry service.

Rooms 9	*Room phone* No	*Confirm by* arrang.	*Parking* Ample
Ensuite bath/shower 7	*Room TV* No	*Last dinner* 9.30	*Room service* All day

Restaurant   ⌂

About £40 for two
Seats 35
Parties 30

Ancestral portraits look down from the walls, and a collection of deep-blue porcelain graces a large sideboard. An inventive menu offers delights such as feuilleté of Paris mushrooms and home-grown asparagus, or wild salmon in filo pastry with honey, ginger and raisins. To finish, perhaps peach ice cream or a lovely hazelnut and passion fruit roulade. Wines include good burgundies: Sauvignon de St. Bris (Sorin) '86, Fixin (Mongeard Mugneret) '84. No smoking. ⊘

Dinner only 7.30–9.30
Closed mid Oct–Easter

 indicates a **well-chosen** house wine

DRYBRIDGE   Old Monastery Restaurant   *NEW ENTRY*   ⌂

R **Map 16 C3** Grampian
Nr Buckie
Buckie (0542) 32660

About £42 for two
Seats 45
Parties 45
Parking Ample

Credit Access, Amex, Diners, Visa

An atmospheric restaurant in what was once the chapel of a holiday house for Benedictine novices. The menu is straightforward, with local seafood and Aberdeen Angus beef playing their part. Other typical choices are French onion soup and oatmeal-coated breast of chicken with a mild mustard sauce. Excellent, keenly priced wines: Sauvignon de St. Bris (Brocard) 1986, Rhônes from Guigal and Brunier.   Well-chosen ⊘

Lunch 12–2   *Dinner* 7–9.30
Closed Sun, Mon, all Bank Hols, 2 wks Nov & 3 wks Jan

DRYBURGH   Dryburgh Abbey Hotel   61%   £D

H **Map 12 D2** Borders
St Boswells TD6 0RQ
St Boswells (0835) 22261
Telex 727201

Credit Access, Amex, Diners, Visa

Period features and modern comforts blend happily in this imposing Victorian country house. Attractive gardens lead down to the river Tweed and the famous abbey ruins. Day rooms include two comfortably traditional first-floor lounges; bedrooms (one with a four-poster) have old-fashioned furniture and candlewick bedspreads. Most have simple, well-kept bathrooms.
Amenities garden, putting, croquet, games room, laundry service.

Rooms 28	*Direct dial* Yes	*Confirm by* arrang.	*Parking* Ample
Ensuite bath/shower 23	*Room TV* Yes	*Last dinner* 8.30	*Room service* Limited

DRYMEN   Buchanan Arms Hotel   62%   £D

H **Map 17 B5** Central
Main Street G63 0BQ
Drymen (0360) 60588

Credit Access, Amex, Diners, Visa

A white-painted hotel in attractive gardens which boast glorious rhododendrons. There's a very Scottish feel to the tartan-carpeted public rooms, the nicest of which is •the spacious lounge with conservatory-style extension. Bedrooms have been recently refurbished and are bright and pleasant. *Amenities* garden, tennis, 9-hole golf course, bowling green, pool table, in-house movies, secretarial services, laundry service, 24-hour lounge service.

Rooms 35	*Direct dial* Yes	*Confirm by* 6	*Parking* Ample
Ensuite bath/shower 35	*Room TV* Yes	*Last dinner* 9.30	*Room service* All day

DULNAIN BRIDGE   Muckrach Lodge Hotel   58%   £E

H Map 16 C3 Highland
Nr Grantown-on-Spey
PH26 3LY
Dulnain Bridge (047 985) 257

Credit Access, Amex, Diners, Visa

Captain Roy Watson, his wife Pat and their cheerful, friendly staff run a comfortable, relaxing and homely little hotel. A log fire warms the lounge, and there's a bright bar serving good lunchtime snacks. Prettily decorated bedrooms are mainly of a good size, with modern furniture and the odd older piece here and there. All have en suite bathrooms offering fluffy towels and a good range of toiletries. No dogs. *Amenities* garden, laundry service.

Rooms 10	*Direct dial* Yes	*Confirm by* arrang.	*Parking* Ample
Ensuite bath/shower 10	*Room TV* Yes	*Last dinner* 8.45	*Room service* All day

**If we recommend meals in a Hotel or Inn,
a separate entry is made for its restaurant.**

DUNBLANE   Cromlix House   83%   £B

HR Map 17 C5 Central
Kin Buck FK15 9JT
Dunblane (0786) 822125
Telex 779959

Rooms 14
Ensuite bath/shower 14
Direct dial Yes
Room TV Yes
Confirm by arrang.
Last dinner 9.30
Parking Ample
Room service 24 hours

Credit Access, Amex, Diners, Visa
Closed 1st 2 wks Feb

Five thousand acres of beautiful land surrounds this solid, late Victorian house, which still retains many of its original features such as old bell pushes and massive bathroom fittings. The Eden family have owned the estate for 450 years and their fine paintings, porcelain and glassware are to be found throughout the hotel. Public rooms include an imposing hall with panelled walls and antique pieces, an elegant lounge and a delightful new conservatory-lounge extension. Bedrooms are a strength, particularly the eight large suites: bathrooms are palatial. *Amenities* garden, tennis, croquet, riding, clay-pigeon shooting, coarse & game fishing, secretarial services, laundry service.

Restaurant ★   ♛♛

Lunch 12.30–2.30
Dinner 7–9.30
Set L £18
Set D £29
About £80 *for two*
Seats 28
Parties 28

Closed 1st 2 wks Feb

Mark Salter has introduced some choice into his imaginatively conceived five course menus at this grandly elegant restaurant. His cooking is subtle and refined, his presentation artistic but unfussy. You might start with sautéed sweetbread and wild mushroom sauce followed by fillet of wild salmon with a Riesling sauce, and roedeer pastries filled with braised lentils and baby glazed vegetables.

Sweets are a great strength. Service is professional and discreet, the cellar as fine as ever with an expanded choice from Burgundy, California and Australia. *Specialities* salad of smoked duck and guinea fowl with glazed sautéed apples, gratinated fillet of wild salmon with a Riesling sorrel sauce, gratin of fresh fruits with white wine sabayon. ➪ Outstanding ♟ Well-chosen ☺ ♿

DUNBLANE   Stakis Dunblane Hydro   61%   £D

H Map 17 C5 Central
Perth Road FK15 0HG
Dunblane (0786) 822551
Telex 776284

Credit Access, Amex, Diners, Visa

An imposing late-Victorian hotel where the lone guest may be overwhelmed by coachloads of golfers and conference delegates. Best of the public rooms is the attractive cocktail bar, which is decorated in soft pastel colours. Executive bedrooms have desk space and armchairs. *Amenities* garden, indoor swimming pool, sauna, solarium, whirlpool bath, keep-fit equipment, tennis, putting, games room, secretarial services, laundry service, coffee shop (9–5.30). ♿

Rooms 224	*Direct dial* Yes	*Confirm by* 6	*Parking* Ample
Ensuite bath/shower 224	*Room TV* Yes	*Last dinner* 9.30	*Room service* 24 hours

DUNDEE   Angus Thistle Hotel   69%   £C/D

H Map 17 C5 Tayside
Marketgait DD1 1QN
Dundee (0382) 26874
Telex 76456

Credit Access, Amex, Diners, Visa

French-style furniture and expensive fabrics give a luxurious feel to public rooms at this low-rise city-centre hotel. Bedrooms are attractive, too, with coordinated colour schemes, smart darkwood units and brass light fittings. All are equipped with tea-makers, hairdryers and trouser presses, and compact, well-fitted bathrooms. Several suites with whirlpool baths.   *Amenities* in-house movies, secretarial services, fax, laundry service, 24-hour lounge service.

Rooms 58	*Direct dial* Yes	*Confirm by* 6	*Parking* Difficult
Ensuite bath/shower 58	*Room TV* Yes	*Last dinner* 10.30	*Room service* All day

DUNDEE   Invercarse Hotel   60%   £D

H Map 17 C5 Tayside
371 Perth Road DD2 1PG
Dundee (0382) 69231
Telex 76608

Credit Access, Amex, Diners, Visa

An old but much extended house to the west of the city centre. Public rooms comprise a smart, comfortable lounge bar, a cocktail bar and a reception with easy chairs. Newest bedrooms are the best, with nice lightwood units and matching fabrics; singles are very basic, with functional shower rooms, while the larger old rooms have darkwood units and baths or showers.
Amenities garden, in-house movies, laundry service.

Rooms 40	*Direct dial* Yes	*Confirm by* 6	*Parking* Ample
Ensuite bath/shower 40	*Room TV* Yes	*Last dinner* 9.45	*Room service* 24 hours

Changes in data sometimes occur in establishments
after the Guide goes to press.
Prices should be taken as indications rather than firm quotes.

DUNFERMLINE   King Malcolm Thistle Hotel   65%   £D

H Map 17 C5 Fife
Queensferry Road KY11 5DS
Dunfermline (0383) 722611
Telex 727721

Credit Access, Amex, Diners, Visa
Closed 25 Dec–1 Jan

A smart modern hotel on the outskirts of town, near junction 2 of the M90. Soft pastel tones are used to stylish effect in public areas, including the elegant foyer-lounge and chic cocktail bar with conservatory extension. Bedrooms with bare-brick and wood-effect decor are comfortable and well equipped. Executive rooms offer queen-size beds and teletext.
Amenities in-house movies, secretarial services, fax, laundry service.

Rooms 48	*Direct dial* Yes	*Confirm by* 6	*Parking* Ample
Ensuite bath/shower 48	*Room TV* Yes	*Last dinner* 9.30	*Room service* 24 hours

DUNKELD   Hillhead of Dunkeld   64%   *NEW ENTRY*   £C/D

H Map 17 C5 Tayside
Brae Street PH8 0BA
Dunkeld (035 02) 8851

Credit Visa

This solidly-built hotel enjoys a splendid situation overlooking the ancient cathedral city, with views of surrounding countryside and river Tay. A warm welcome is assured in the little reception area, and a waiter serves drinks in the gracious lounge. Bedrooms are roomy and homely, with period furniture, pretty fabrics and neat tiled bathrooms.   *Amenities* garden, tennis, croquet, secretarial services, laundry service.

Rooms 5	*Room phone* No	*Confirm by* arrang.	*Parking* Ample
Ensuite bath/shower 5	*Room TV* Yes	*Last dinner* 8.30	*Room service* All day

DUROR   Stewart Hotel   58%   £E

H Map 17 B4 Highland
Glen Duror, Appin PA38 4BW
Duror (063 174) 268
Telex 94014994
Credit Access, Amex, Diners, Visa
Closed 6 Nov–22 Dec & 3 Jan–
25 Mar

A little bridge over a stream brings you to this granite house perched high above Loch Linnhe. An attractive, comfortable lounge takes full advantage of the spectacular view, and the cosy bar is a convivial place to end the day. A purpose-built block houses the bedrooms; although some are quite small, all are bright and neat, with ingeniously fitted, well-kept little bathrooms.   *Amenities* garden, sauna, solarium, sailing.

Rooms 26	*Direct dial* Yes	*Confirm by* 6	*Parking* Ample
Ensuite bath/shower 26	*Room TV* Yes	*Last dinner* 9.30	*Room service* Limited

EAST KILBRIDE Bruce Hotel 59% £E

H Map 12 B2 Strathclyde
Cornwall Street G74 1AF
East Kilbride (035 52) 29771
Telex 778428

Credit Access, Amex, Diners, Visa

Brilliant colour schemes assault the eye in the public areas of this purpose-built hotel in the centre of town. The receptionists are dressed to match the turquoise of the foyer, and the cocktail bar is a striking geranium red, while the discotheque bar has a purple ceiling. Refurbished bedrooms, however, have soft, pale colours. Some bathrooms need attention. **Amenities** secretarial services, fax, laundry service.

Rooms 80	*Direct dial* Yes	*Confirm by* 6	*Parking* Limited
Ensuite bath/shower 80	*Room TV* Yes	*Last dinner* 10	*Room service* 24 hours

EAST KILBRIDE Stuart Hotel 62% £E

H Map 12 B2 Strathclyde
Cornwall Way G74 1JR
East Kilbride (035 52) 21161
Telex 778504

Credit Access, Amex, Diners, Visa

The refurbished Lindsey function suite with its striking brass ceiling is the latest improvement to this pleasant modern hotel. Locals throng the popular Archies Bar, and there's a cocktail bar for a quieter drink. Best of the compact, functional bedrooms are the Executive rooms, which are more comfortable and have superior en suite bathrooms. **Amenities** secretarial services, laundry service.

Rooms 39	*Direct dial* Yes	*Confirm by* arrang.	*Parking* Limited
Ensuite bath/shower 39	*Room TV* Yes	*Last dinner* 9.15	*Room service* 24 hours

**We welcome bona fide complaints and recommendations
on the tear-out pages at the back of the book for readers' comment.
They are followed up by our professional team.**

EDINBURGH Albany Hotel 58% £D/E

H Town plan D1 Lothian
39 Albany Street EH1 3QY
031-556 0397
Telex 727079

Credit Access, Amex, Diners, Visa
Closed 25 & 26 Dec, 1 & 2 Jan

On the eastern fringe of the city centre this modest but comfortable hotel is a conversion of three Georgian terraced houses, retaining fine original features such as a glass cupola and elegant spiral staircase. Day rooms include a quiet lounge and cosy basement bar, while bedrooms offer practical furnishings, radio-alarms, tea-makers and good modern bathrooms (five with shower only). Decent Scottish breakfast. **Amenities** garden, laundry service.

Rooms 20	*Direct dial* Yes	*Confirm by* 4	*Parking* Limited
Ensuite bath/shower 20	*Room TV* Yes	*Last dinner* 9.30	*Room service* Limited

EDINBURGH Alp Horn ♞

R Town plan B2 Lothian
167 Rose Street
031-225 4787

Swiss cooking
About £35 for two
Seats 65
Parking Difficult

Credit Access, Visa

Appropriately a huge alp horn complements the extensive menu of down-to-earth, authentic Swiss dishes offered by Miggi Meier in her simple, popular restaurant. Specialities include air-dried beef, veal with rösti potatoes, and venison in piquant sauce with home-made spätzli (noodles served crisped and brown). Don't miss the apfelstrudel which comes (like all the sweets) with lashings of cream. Some French and Spanish dishes too. Booking advisable. ☺

Lunch 12–2 *Dinner* 6.30–10
Closed Sun, Mon, Bank Hols, 3 wks July & 2 wks Xmas

EDINBURGH L'Auberge ♛

R Town plan E3 Lothian
56 St Mary's Street
031-556 5888

French cooking
Set L from £6.95
Set D £26
About £58 for two
Seats 48 *Parking* Difficult
Credit Access, Amex, Diners, Visa

An elegant, sophisticated restaurant with accomplished cooking by Jacques Labat and polished, formal service. Seafood is a strong feature of the monthly-changing menus – perhaps deliciously light lobster mousse or Scottish salmon with watercress – while robust meat dishes might include fillet of beef with a rich bordelaise sauce. Wonderfully indulgent sweets. All-French wine list with exceptional Muscadet (Dom des Dorices) and Côte de Brouilly (Thivin). 🍷 Well-chosen ☺

Lunch 12.15–2 *Dinner* 6.45–9.30, Fri & Sat 6.45–10.15
Closed 26 Dec & 1 & 2 Jan

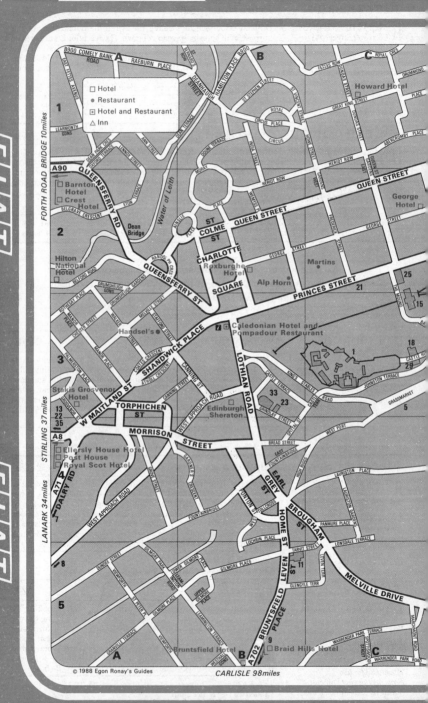

F/I/A/T Edinburgh

□ Hotel
● Restaurant
⊡ Hotel and Restaurant
△ Inn

© 1988 Egon Ronay's Guides

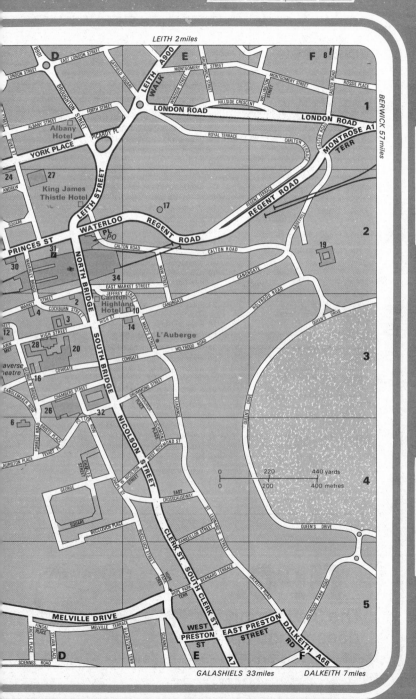

EDINBURGH

Map 12 C1
Town plan on preceding page

Population 444,741

Edinburgh was founded about a thousand years ago on the Rock which dominates the city. The narrow Old Town, with its one main street (the Royal Mile stretching from the Castle to Holyroodhouse) is the city of John Knox and Mary Queen of Scots. Its Royal Charter was granted by Robert the Bruce in 1329. The gracious New Town is a magnificient example of 18th-century town planning. Today Edinburgh is a centre of festival and pageantry, culture and conferences.

Annual Events
Edinburgh Festival *13th August–2nd September*
Festival Fringe *13th August–2nd September*
Military Tattoo *11th August–2nd September*
Royal Highland Show *18th–21st June*

Sights Outside City
Cramond Village, Duddingston Village, Forth Bridge, Lauriston Castle, Craigmillar Castle

Tourist Information Centre
Waverley Market
3 Princes Street EH2 2QP
Telephone 031-557 2727

Fiat Dealers
Hamilton Bros. (Edinburgh) Ltd
162 St Johns Road
Corstorphine
Edinburgh EH12 8AZ
Tel. 031-334 6248

Croall & Croall
Glenogle Road
Edinburgh EH3 5HW
Telephone 031-556 6404

1 Castle **C3**
2 City Art Centre **D3**
3 City Chambers **D3**
4 Festival Booking Office **D3**
5 Grassmarket *picturesque old buildings and antique shops* **C3**
6 Greyfriars Kirk *and Greyfriars Bobby statue* **D4**
7 Heart of Midlothian F.C. **A4**
8 Hibernian F.C. *Easter Road Park* **F1**
9 Hillend *dry ski centre open all year* **B5**
10 John Knox's House *1490, timber galleries* **D/E3**
11 King's Theatre **B5**
12 Lady Stair's House *1692, literary museum* **D3**
13 Murrayfield Rugby Ground **A4**
14 Museum of Childhood **E3**
15 National Gallery *try 'Sound Guide'* **C3**
16 National Library **D3**
17 Nelson's Monument *viewpoint* **E2**
18 Outlook Tower *Camera obscura and Scottish life exhibition* **C3**
19 Palace of Holyroodhouse and Arthur's Seat and the Park **F2**
20 Parliament House and Law Courts **D3**
21 Princes Street *shopping and gardens, bandstand, floral clock, war memorials* **B3/C2/D2**
22 Royal Highland Showground **A3**
23 Royal Lyceum Theatre **B3**
24 Royal Museum of Scotland **D2**
25 Royal Scottish Academy **C2**
26 Royal Scottish Museum *largest museum of science and art in U.K.* **D3**
27 St Andrew Square Bus Station **D2**
28 St Giles' Cathedral **D3**
29 Scotch Whisky Heritage Centre **C3**
30 Scott Monument *viewpoint* **D2**
31 Tourist Information Centre **D2**
32 University of Edinburgh **D3**
33 Usher Hall **B3**
34 Waverley Station **D2**
35 Zoo **A3**

EDINBURGH | Barnton Thistle Hotel 63% | £C/D

H **Town plan A2** Lothian
Queensferry Road EH4 6AS
Edinburgh (031) 339 1144
Telex 727928

Credit Access, Amex, Diners, Visa

A conveniently located hotel situated on the A90, midway between the city and airport. Relaxing public areas include a quiet lounge and two bars. Bedrooms are functional and modern, with chintzy fabrics, darkwood furniture, well-lit writing areas and easy chairs – plus trouser presses, hairdryers, tea-makers and radio-alarms. Bathrooms are small, with marble-effect tiles. *Amenities* sauna, solarium, in-house movies, secretarial services, fax, coffee shop (noon–10pm).

| *Rooms* 50 | *Direct dial* Yes | *Confirm by* 6 | *Parking* Ample |
| *Ensuite bath/shower* 50 | *Room TV* Yes | *Last dinner* 10 | *Room service* 24 hours |

EDINBURGH | Braid Hills Hotel 60% | £D

H **Town plan B5** Lothian
134 Braid Road EH10 6JD
031-447 8888
Telex 72311

Credit Access, Amex, Diners, Visa

The distinctive turrets and gables of this sturdy stone hotel, built in 1886 to accommodate golfers visiting the nearby course, are clearly visible from the A702. The comfortable foyer-lounge and inviting bar have a Victorian feel, while modern comforts such as tea-makers, hairdryers and trouser presses blend happily with the old-world charm of the bright bedrooms. Disappointing breakfast.
Amenities garden, laundry service.

| *Rooms* 68 | *Direct dial* Yes | *Confirm by* 6 | *Parking* Ample |
| *Ensuite bath/shower* 68 | *Room TV* Yes | *Last dinner* 9 | *Room service* 24 hours |

EDINBURGH | Bruntsfield Hotel 65% | £C/D

H **Town plan B5** Lothian
69 Bruntsfield Place EH10 4HH
031-229 1393
Telex 727897

Credit Access, Amex, Diners, Visa

Business people and tourists are well catered for at this imposing gabled hotel overlooking a park not far from the city centre. Day rooms include an elegant bar lounge and a conservatory-style café bar overlooking the patio. Attractive bedrooms, in modern and traditional styles, have excellent bathrooms and thoughtful extras. Pleasant, helpful staff. *Amenities* patio, secretarial services, fax, laundry service, coffee shop (7.30am–11pm).

| *Rooms* 52 | *Direct dial* Yes | *Confirm by* 6 | *Parking* Ample |
| *Ensuite bath/shower* 52 | *Room TV* Yes | *Last dinner* 11 | *Room service* 24 hours |

EDINBURGH | Caledonian Hotel 80% | £A/B

HR **Town plan B3** Lothian
Princes Street EH1 2AB
031-225 2433
Telex 72179

Rooms 238
Ensuite bath/shower 238
Direct dial Yes
Room TV Yes
Confirm by 6
Last dinner 10.30
Parking Ample
Room service 24 hours

Credit Access, Amex, Diners, Visa

A large cash investment and an ambitious development project look like revolutionising this sturdy Edwardian hotel at the western end of Princes Street. Already the elegant foyer has sumptuous drapes and new chandeliers, while the Pullman Lounge, with its classical pillars and festoon blinds, retains its old-world grandeur. Bedrooms combine grandeur with comfort, offering tasteful furnishings, luxurious bathrooms, and many thoughtful extras from fresh flowers to mini-bars. Service is, appropriately, of the old school, with courteous staff going out of their way to be helpful. No dogs.
Amenities garden, hairdressing, in-house movies, secretarial services, fax, valeting, laundry service, kiosk. &

Pompadour Restaurant

Set L £12.50
Set D £27.50
About £72 for two
Seats 65

Louis Quinze decor provides a sophisticated setting in which to enjoy Scottish produce at its best. The lunchtime selection, entitled 'Legends of the Scottish Table', offers venison, beef, salmon and excellent vegetables, while the evening menu concentrates on modern French dishes. There's an impressive trolley of home-baked bread, well-kept cheeses, and tempting sweets. Good short wine list includes a Crozes Hermitage '86 and a Ch. d'Angludet Margaux '83. ☺ &

Lunch 12.30–2   *Dinner* 7.30–10.30
Closed L Sat & Sun, 26 Dec & 2 Jan

EDINBURGH

Carlton Highland Hotel   71%   £B/C

H **Town plan D3** Lothian
North Bridge EH1 1SD
031-556 7277
Telex 727001

Rooms 207
Ensuite bath/shower 207
Direct dial Yes
Room TV Yes
Confirm by 6
Last dinner 10
Parking Ample
Room service 24 hours

Credit Access, Amex, Diners, Visa

A stately granite hotel on the grand scale which offers comfortable, civilised accommodation. An attractive staircase leads from the reception up to the public rooms, which include a cheerful cocktail bar with a large lounge area and a pianist in the evenings. The bedrooms vary in size but all have smart wood units, floor-to-ceiling drapes and coordinating bedcovers, a luxurious effect somewhat marred by the noisy central heating. Smart bathrooms have good towels and toiletries. *Amenities* indoor swimming pool, sauna, solarium, whirlpool bath, steam bath, gymnasium, squash, games room, snooker, pool table, in-house movies, fax, laundry service, coffee shop (10am–6pm Mon–Sat). &

EDINBURGH

Crest Hotel, Edinburgh   65%   £C

H **Town plan A2** Lothian
Queensferry Road EH4 3HL
031-332 2442
Telex 72541

Credit Access, Amex, Diners, Visa

Rising above the A90 about a mile from the city centre, this modern eight-storey hotel has a bright and busy cocktail bar, a lounge in '30s style and a smart conference room. Well-appointed bedrooms include Executive, ladies and non-smoking versions, all with compact bathrooms. Maintenance needs attention.
Amenities garden, in-house movies, secretarial services, fax, laundry service, children's play area.

Rooms 119	*Direct dial* Yes	*Confirm by* 6	*Parking* Ample
Ensuite bath/shower 119	*Room TV* Yes	*Last dinner* 9.45	*Room service* 24 hours

**If we recommend meals in a Hotel or Inn,
a separate entry is made for its restaurant.**

EDINBURGH

Edinburgh Sheraton   78%   £B

H **Town plan B3** Lothian
1 Festival Square EH3 9SR
031-229 9131
Telex 72398

Rooms 263
Ensuite bath/shower 263
Direct dial Yes
Room TV Yes
Confirm by 4
Last dinner 10.30
Parking Ample
Room service 24 hours

Credit Access, Amex, Diners, Visa

The clean-lined exterior of this hotel hints at the pristine accommodation found within. Though perhaps a little lacking in character, there's a deliciously affluent feel about the whole place. Spacious air-conditioned bedrooms all have king or queen-size beds, fitted bleached-wood units, smart brass lamps and sophisticated bedside controls; best rooms overlook the castle. Good-sized bathrooms are equally well-equipped. Downstairs there's a popular galleried cocktail bar and a relaxing lounge area filled with tropical plants. Excellent conference facilities and good breakfasts. No dogs. *Amenities* patio, indoor swimming pool, sauna, solarium, whirlpool bath, gymnasium, in-house movies, teletext, fax, valeting, laundry service, kiosk. &

EDINBURGH

Ellersly House Hotel   60%   £C/D

H **Town plan A4** Lothian
Ellersly Road EH12 6HZ
031-337 6888
Telex 727860

Credit Access, Amex, Diners, Visa

A cheerful reception awaits guests at this pleasant, extended Edwardian house situated in a quiet residential area near Murrayfield rugby ground. Refurbished day rooms include an inviting cocktail bar and comfortably furnished lounge overlooking the garden. Traditional style, spacious main-house bedrooms and annexe rooms, which are more modern, are now due for a necessary facelift. No dogs. *Amenities* garden, croquet.

Rooms 55	*Direct dial* Yes	*Confirm by* 6	*Parking* Ample
Ensuite bath/shower 55	*Room TV* Yes	*Last dinner* 9	*Room service* 24 hours

EDINBURGH   George Hotel   78%   £B

H **Town plan C2** Lothian
George Street EH2 2PB
031-225 1251
Telex 72570

Rooms 195
Ensuite bath/shower 195
Direct dial Yes
Room TV Yes
Confirm by 6
Last dinner 10
Parking Limited
Room service 24 hours

Credit Access, Amex, Diners, Visa

A very grand hotel which successfully manages to combine modern facilities with traditional decor and service. The foyer sets the tone with its marble floor and elegant pillars while the lounge area boasts comfortable plush sofas and stylish drapes. Leather chesterfields, hunting trophies and clan mementoes give a clubby atmosphere to the large bar. The luxurious bedrooms have coordinating fabrics, traditional furniture and remote control TVs concealed in mahogany cabinets; all have trouser presses, hairdryers and tea/coffee-makers. Some suites have mini-bars and kingsize beds, and one has a spa bath. Bathrooms have modern shower fittings, generously sized baths and quality toiletries. *Amenities* teletext, fax, laundry service. &

We publish annually,
so make sure you use the current edition.
It's worth it!

EDINBURGH   Handsel's   ★   ♛

R **Town plan A3** Lothian
22 Stafford Street
031-225 5521

Lunch 12.30–2
Dinner 7.30–9
Set D £25
About £65 for two
Seats 30
Parties 30
Parking Limited

Credit Access, Amex, Diners, Visa
Closed L Sat, all Sun & Bank Hols, 25 & 26 Dec, 1st wk Jan

Self-taught young chef Andrew Radford is now well into his stride at this sumptuously elegant restaurant on the first floor of a Georgian house. The short fixed-price menus offer some beautifully balanced dishes with lovely true flavours. Vegetables are cooked to perfection, and there are French cheeses, tempting desserts, and excellent coffee with petit fours. Outstanding wine list includes Ch. Branaire '70, Ch. Latour '62, Shiraz (Taltarni) '82. *Specialities* fillet of John Dory with asparagus and oyster butter sauce; breast of wood pigeon with truffles, wild mushrooms and juniper sauce; veal fillets with sweetbreads and lime and tarragon sauce; poached pear with bitter chocolate mousse. ➪ Outstanding ♀ Well-chosen ☻ ❦

EDINBURGH   Hilton National   74%   £B

H **Town plan A2** Lothian
Bells Mills, Belford Road
EH4 3DG
031-332 2545
Telex 727979

Rooms 146
Ensuite bath/shower 146
Direct dial Yes
Room TV Yes
Confirm by arrang.
Last dinner 10
Parking Ample
Room service 24 hours

Credit Access, Amex, Diners, Visa

Formerly the Ladbroke Dragonara, this modern hotel enjoys a tranquil setting beside the Water of Leith, only minutes from the city centre. Part of it was once an old grain mill and this is reflected by the atmospheric Granary Bar with its natural stone walls and simple rustic furniture. Other public areas, including the lounge and cocktail bar, are currently being redesigned. Decent-sized bedrooms have well-coordinated colour schemes and extras like trouser presses, hairdryers, tea-makers and radio-alarms (with bathroom speakers). Gold Star rooms provide bath robes, luxury toiletries, miniature whisky and mineral water. *Amenities* in-house movies, secretarial services, fax, laundry service. &

EDINBURGH | Howard Hotel   64% | £C/D

H **Town plan C1** Lothian
32 Great King Street EH3 6QH
031-557 3500
Telex 727887

Credit Access, Amex, Diners, Visa
Closed 25 & 26 Dec, 1 & 2 Jan

An elegant Georgian house which has plenty of period features to delight the eye, including a pastoral mural by the 19th-century painter David Roberts and a domed stairwell ceiling with a glass cupola. Public areas include a gracefully furnished lounge, a cocktail bar and the Claret Jug bar, a popular student venue. Bedrooms are comfortable and stylish; all have en suite bathrooms (singles with showers only). *Amenities* garden, fax, laundry service. &

Rooms 25	*Direct dial* Yes	*Confirm by* arrang.	*Parking* Limited
Ensuite bath/shower 25	*Room TV* Yes	*Last dinner* 9.30	*Room service* 24 hours

EDINBURGH | King James Thistle Hotel   70% | £C

H **Town plan D2** Lothian
St James Centre,
Leith Street EH1 3SW
031-556 0111
Telex 727200

Rooms 147
Ensuite bath/shower 147
Direct dial Yes
Room TV Yes
Confirm by 6
Last dinner 10.25
Parking Limited
Room service 24 hours

Credit Access, Amex, Diners, Visa
Closed 25 & 26 Dec

Behind a rather austere frontage there's a good deal of style and luxury at this modern city-centre hotel. New sofas and wall coverings enhance the already elegant lobby-lounge with its panelling and marble floor, and up on the third floor there's an American-themed bar, a brasserie and a smart cocktail bar. Double-glazed bedrooms are most attractive: plush coordinated fabrics, rich darkwood furniture, many up-to-date accessories, good bathrooms. Lack of attention to detail sometimes spoils things here – witness an inadequate supply of hot water on a recent visit. There's some scope for improvement in management and communications.
Amenities in-house movies, fax, laundry service.

EDINBURGH | Martins

R **Town plan C2** Lothian
70 Rose Street, North Lane
031-225 3106

Set L £6.75
About £45 for two
Seats 28
Parties 28
Parking Difficult
Credit Access, Amex, Diners, Visa

Martin and Gay Irons have consistently provided good cuisine at their intimate, tucked-away restaurant and latest chef David Macrae has become noted for his inventive, daily-changing menus. Starter might be crayfish nage with a wonderfully fresh poached escalope of salmon to follow. Excellent cheese and delectable sweets. Good wines with exceptional Alsace from Rolly Gassmann; try his superb Auxerrois 'Moenchreben' '83. 🍷 Well-chosen ⊖

Lunch 12–2   *Dinner* 7–10, Fri & Sat till 10.30
Closed L Sat, all Sun & Mon & 2 wks Xmas

EDINBURGH | Post House Hotel   63% | £C

H **Town plan A4** Lothian
Corstorphine Road EH12 6UA
031-334 0390
Telex 727103

Credit Access, Amex, Diners, Visa

Rugby and zoo fans (it's near Murrayfield and the zoological gardens) will find this modern hotel on the A8 convenient. Pleasant staff welcome you in the spacious reception lounge, and the popular Cross Bar boasts an appropriate rugby theme. Spacious bedrooms, many family size, include some Superior rooms with trouser presses, hairdryers and extra toiletries. *Amenities* in-house movies, fax, coffee shop (10.30am–10.30pm), kiosk. &

Rooms 208	*Direct dial* Yes	*Confirm by* 6	*Parking* Ample
Ensuite bath/shower 208	*Room TV* Yes	*Last dinner* 9.45	*Room service* Limited

EDINBURGH | Roxburghe Hotel   65% | £B/C

H **Town plan B2** Lothian
Charlotte Square EH2 4HG
031-225 3921
Telex 727054

Credit Access, Amex, Diners, Visa

A fine Adam facade and handsome Adam fireplace lend a touch of distinction to this comfortably traditional hotel. Elegant public rooms could be smarter, and the good-size bedrooms (singles are on the small side) could also do with a facelift. Comforts include tea-makers, radio-alarms and trouser presses.
Amenities fax, laundry service, coffee shop (7.30am–6pm), 24-hour lounge service. &

Rooms 76	*Direct dial* Yes	*Confirm by* 6	*Parking* Difficult
Ensuite bath/shower 76	*Room TV* Yes	*Last dinner* 10	*Room service* Limited

EDINBURGH Royal Scot Hotel 65% £C

H Town plan A4 Lothian
111 Glasgow Road EH12 8NF
031-334 9191
Telex 727197

Credit Access, Amex, Diners, Visa

Good conference and leisure facilities make this modern hotel four miles from the city centre popular with business people and families. The plush bar-lounge overlooks the pool, and double-glazed bedrooms are very comfortable. *Amenities* garden, indoor swimming pool, sauna, solarium, whirlpool bath, keep-fit equipment, hairdressing, pitch & putt, in-house movies, secretarial services, fax, laundry service, coffee shop (7.30am–11pm).

Rooms 252	*Direct dial* Yes	*Confirm by* 6	*Parking* Ample
Ensuite bath/shower 252	*Room TV* Yes	*Last dinner* 10	*Room service* 24 hours

EDINBURGH Stakis Grosvenor Hotel 60% £B/C

H Town plan A3 Lothian
Grosvenor Street EH12 5EA
031-226 6001
Telex 72445

Credit Access, Amex, Diners, Visa

Business people and holidaymakers alike head for this popular hotel, which was created from a row of Victorian terraced houses. Public areas include a large open-plan lounge with chesterfield seating and an intimate cocktail bar. Bedrooms in the main been recently refurbished with stencilled paintwork and coordinating fabrics; all have trouser presses, hairdryers and fruit. Bathrooms are neat and modern. *Amenities* secretarial services, laundry service. &

Rooms 128	*Direct dial* Yes	*Confirm by* 6	*Parking* Limited
Ensuite bath/shower 128	*Room TV* Yes	*Last dinner* 10	*Room service* 24 hours

**We welcome bona fide complaints and recommendations
on the tear-out pages at the back of the book for readers' comment.
They are followed up by our professional team.**

ELGIN Mansion House Hotel 65% *NEW ENTRY* £D/E

H Map 6 C3 Grampian
The Haugh Moray IV30 1AN
Elgin (0343) 48811

Credit Access, Amex, Visa

Standing by the river Lossie, this is a fine Victorian mansion in Scottish Baronial style. Pleasant day rooms include a roomy hall/reception area with original panelling, a comfortable bar-lounge and a public bar. Most of the bedrooms have attractive bird-print wallpapers with matching curtains. Furniture is mainly French style, and all rooms have modern teletext TVs, plus mini-bars, hairdryers and various thoughtful little extras like notepads and a welcoming glass of sherry. There are two four-poster suites. Smart, up-to-date bathrooms. Housekeeping is good, service friendly and attentive. No dogs.
Amenities garden, in-house movies, laundry service.

Rooms 12	*Direct dial* Yes	*Confirm by* arrang.	*Parking* Ample
Ensuite bath/shower 12	*Room TV* Yes	*Last dinner* 9	*Room service* 24 hours

ELLON Mercury Hotel 60% £E

H Map 16 D3 Grampian
AB4 9NP
Ellon (0358) 20666
Telex 739200

Credit Access, Amex, Diners, Visa
Closed 24–29 Dec

A modern hotel, popular with business visitors for its practical accommodation. Best of the public areas is the cocktail bar, with its pine-covered bar and beige decor. Bedrooms have natural wood fitted furniture, a soft russet and cream scheme and excellent storage and desk space; Lady Executive and Gold Star rooms have dressing gowns and toiletries. Bathrooms are fully tiled and modern.
Amenities snooker, laundry service.

Rooms 40	*Room phone* Yes	*Confirm by* arrang.	*Parking* Ample
Ensuite bath/shower 40	*Room TV* Yes	*Last dinner* 9.30	*Room service* 24 hours

**Any person using our name to obtain free hospitality is a fraud.
Proprietors, please inform the police and us.**

ERISKA

Isle of Eriska   73%   £A

HR **Map 17 B5** Strathclyde
Ledaig, by Oban PA37 1SD
Ledaig (063 172) 371
Telex 777040

Rooms 17
Ensuite bath/shower 17
Direct dial Yes
Room TV Yes
Confirm by 10am
Last dinner 8.30
Parking Ample
Room service 24 hours

Credit Access, Amex, Diners
Closed Nov–early Mar

A small bridge provides the
entrance to the island world of
Robin and Sheena Buchanan-
Smith, who give guests the
warmest of welcomes to their
splendid 19th-century baronial
home. Log fires, fine panelling,
handsome ceilings, plus plenty of
inviting settees and armchairs,
make the day rooms havens of
taste and comfort. Spacious bedrooms, individually furnished
with stylish fabrics and some fine

antiques, are enhanced by fresh flowers and superb housekeeping.
There are many extras, and the bright, carpeted bathrooms are also
thoughtfully equipped. Half-board terms only.
Amenities garden, tennis, croquet, riding, sea & coarse fishing,
secretarial services, laundry service. &

Restaurant   ♛ ⚘

Set L from £6.33
Set D £26.45
About £56 for two
Seats 40
Parking Ample

Elegance is the keynote of a very civilised restaurant where the chairs
are set round polished antique tables. Chef Simon Burns prepares a
six-course dinner that centres round a roast or fish and includes a
starter, soup, a savoury and cheese; nice sweets by the hand of Sheena
Buchanan-Smith. Competent use is made of local produce, and there
are lighter lunches with a roast on Sundays. ⊖ &

Lunch 12.45–1.45, Sun 1–1.45   *Dinner* 7.30–8.30
Closed Nov–early Mar

ERSKINE

Crest Hotel   60%   £C

H **Map 12 B1** Strathclyde
By Erskine Bridge PA8 6AN
041-812 0123
Telex 777713

Credit Access, Amex, Diners, Visa

Refurbishment continues at this modern hotel, and both public rooms
and accommodation now do justice to an excellent position overlooking the Clyde on the south side of Erskine Bridge. The management
are now turning their attention to the leisure area. Public rooms
include a cleverly lit and comfortable foyer, and a bar with side
lounge. *Amenities* garden, solarium, keep-fit equipment, pitch &
putt, pool table, secretarial services, fax, kiosk. &

Rooms 186	*Direct dial* Yes	*Confirm by* arrang.	*Parking* Ample
Ensuite bath/shower 186	*Room TV* Yes	*Last dinner* 10	*Room service* 24 hours

ETTRICKBRIDGE

Ettrickshaws Hotel   62%   £D/E

H **Map 12 D2** Borders
Nr Selkirk TD7 5HW
Ettrickbridge (0750) 52229
Telex 94013112

Credit Access, Amex, Diners, Visa
Closed mid Dec–mid Feb

Fine walking country surrounds this substantial Victorian hotel
beside the river Ettrick. The half-panelled hall lounge has been
recently refurbished and there's a new reception area; the main lounge
is reserved for non-smokers. The bedrooms are comfortable and
traditional – most have pretty tiled fireplaces and all have good
modern bathrooms. No under-nines.
Amenities garden, croquet, clay-pigeon shooting, game fishing, in-
house movies, laundry service.

Rooms 6	*Direct dial* Yes	*Confirm by* 6	*Parking* Ample
Ensuite bath/shower 6	*Room TV* Yes	*Last dinner* 9	*Room service* All day

FALKIRK

Hotel Cladhan   60%   £E

H **Map 12 C1** Central
Kemper Avenue FK1 1VF
Falkirk (0324) 27421

Credit Access, Amex, Diners, Visa

A friendly well-run establishment not far from the town centre.
Behind the stark early '70s exterior are functional public areas
including a spacious open-plan lounge with a bar at each end. All
bedrooms are smartly appointed with good fitted furniture. All are
double-glazed and have well-equipped bathrooms.
Amenities in-house movies, teletext, secretarial services, laundry
service, coffee shop (7am–9.20pm). &

Rooms 37	*Direct dial* Yes	*Confirm by* 6	*Parking* Ample
Ensuite bath/shower 37	*Room TV* Yes	*Last dinner* 9.30	*Room service* None

...**A** little tavern in the Rue Vavin,

Chez Clémence, who makes only one dish,

but a stupendous one: *le cassoulet de Castelnaudry*...

Clémence's cassoulet has been cooking for twenty years.

She replenishes the pot...but it is always the same cassoulet.

The basis remains, and this ancient and precious substance

gives it a taste which one finds in the paintings of old

Venetian masters, in the amber flesh-tints of their women.

ANATOLE FRANCE 1844-1924
HISTOIRE COMIQUE

We may live

without poetry, music and art;

We may live without conscience and live without heart;

We may live without friends, we may live without books,

But civilised man cannot live without cooks.

OWEN MEREDITH 1831-91
LUCILE

FALKIRK   Pierre's   ⑨

R **Map 12 C1** Central
140 Graham's Road
Falkirk (0324) 35843

French cooking
Set D £9.75
About £45 for two
Seats 38 *Parties* 40
Parking Ample
Credit Access, Amex, Diners, Visa

Pierre Renjard's son Anthony has taken over in the kitchen, carrying on a tradition of enjoyable bourgeois cooking in their jolly little French restaurant. The market provides good fresh produce for a menu that runs from country pâté, grilled sardines and moules marinière to chicken provençale and boeuf bourguignon. Simple sweets, and a good short wine list featuring the very drinkable La Vieille Ferme wines. Well-chosen ℮

Lunch 12–2.15   *Dinner* 7–9.30
Closed L Sat, all Sun & Mon, 25, 26 Dec & 1, 2 Jan

FORFAR   Royal Hotel   57%   £E

H **Map 17 C4** Tayside
Castle Street DD8 3AE
Forfar (0307) 62691

Credit Amex, Diners, Visa

The Bonnymans continue to improve their former coaching inn and the pleasing style is set by the leather chesterfields and smiling staff in reception. Bedrooms range from compact singles with shower only and mahogany-style freestanding furniture to an Executive suite with a modern four-poster. No dogs. *Amenities* garden, indoor swimming pool, sauna, solarium, whirlpool bath, keep-fit equipment, hairdressing, laundry service, coffee shop (10am–11pm).

Rooms 19	*Direct dial* Yes	*Confirm by* 6	*Parking* Ample
Ensuite bath/shower 19	*Room TV* Yes	*Last dinner* 9	*Room service* All day

 indicates a **well-chosen** house wine

FORT WILLIAM   The Factor's House

RR **Map 17 B4** Highland
Torlundy PH33 6SN
Fort William (0397) 5767

Set D £15.50
About £40 for two
Seats 30
Parking Ample

Credit Access, Amex, Diners, Visa

You can expect a pleasant, unpretentious meal at this informal little restaurant. Quality local ingredients are prepared and presented in a straightforward manner and portions are generous. Start with an excellent prawn salad before moving on to a tasty chicken supreme in filo pastry with good accompanying vegetables. Finish with hot rum and currant flan. Delightful kilted service is provided by Peter Hobbs and manager Ronald Duff. No children under six. ℮

Dinner only 7.30–9.30
Closed Mon & mid Dec–mid March

BEDROOMS 7 £D
With bath/shower 7

The seven stylish, comfortable bedrooms all have modern private facilities and there are two charming lounges with hi-fi for music-loving guests. No dogs.

FORT WILLIAM   Inverlochy Castle   91%   £A

HR **Map 17 B4** Highland
Torlundy PH33 6SN
Fort William (0397) 2177

Rooms 16
Ensuite bath/shower 16
Direct dial Yes
Room TV Yes
Confirm by arrang.
Last dinner 9.15
Parking Ample
Room service 24 hours

Credit Access, Amex, Visa
Closed mid Nov–mid Mar

Built in 1863 in a spectacular setting among the foothills of Ben Nevis, this magnificent castle was much admired by Queen Victoria, who recorded in her diary: 'I never saw a lovelier or more romantic spot.' The interior is equally breathtaking: crystal chandeliers and a lovely frescoed ceiling in the great hall; handsome antiques and paintings, elegant drapes and fresh flowers throughout the public rooms. Spacious bedrooms are immaculately appointed with the finest fabrics and furniture and bathrooms are equally luxurious. Such splendid surroundings could prove intimidating, but friendly staff soon put guests at their ease. No dogs. *Amenities* garden, tennis, game fishing, billiards, snooker, secretarial services, valeting, fax, laundry service.

Restaurant ♛♛♛

Set L from £18.40
Set D £35
About £90 for two
Seats 40
Parties 12

Sumptuously carved oak furniture and a marvellous view set the scene for Graham Newbould's memorable cooking. After a light and refreshing warm minted cucumber soup, you could try deliciously plump and tender scallops in a fragrant vermouth sauce – accompanied by seven exquisitely presented vegetables – then a wonderful passion fruit mousse. Discreet, impeccable service and a splendid classic cellar. No smoking. ⌢ Outstanding ♟ Well-chosen ☙

Lunch 12.30–2 *Dinner* 7.30–9.15
Closed mid Nov–mid Mar

FORT WILLIAM Mercury Hotel 59% £C/D

H **Map 17 B4** Highland
Achintore Road PH33 6RW
Fort William (0397) 3117
Telex 778454

Credit Access, Amex, Diners, Visa

Splendid views are to be had from the spacious bar-lounge and many of the bedrooms of this modern hotel. Lightwood fitted units and coordinating fabrics in autumnal colours make for pleasing bedrooms and they are all equipped with remote control TV/radios and tea/coffee-makers. Bathrooms are smartly tiled and have over-the-tub showers and good shelf space.
Amenities sauna, pool table, secretarial services, laundry service.

Rooms 86	*Direct dial* Yes	*Confirm by* 6	*Parking* Ample
Ensuite bath/shower 86	*Room TV* Yes	*Last dinner* 9.30	*Room service* None

---

Our inspectors *never* book in the name of Egon Ronay's Guides.
They disclose their identity only if they are considering an establishment
for inclusion in the next edition of the Guide.

GARVE Inchbae Lodge Hotel 57% £F

H **Map 16 B3** Highland
Inchbae IV23 2PH
Garve (099 75) 269

Closed 25 & 26 Dec

Five miles from Garve on the A835, Inchbae Lodge is a peaceful base for touring the Highlands. The lounge and dining rooms enjoy river and mountain views, and there's a little panelled bar for snacks and a drink. Six bedrooms, tastefully furnished in pine, are in the lodge itself, the rest in a red cedar chalet. All rooms are bright, cheerful and well looked after. Pleasant, informal service.
Amenities garden, clay-pigeon shooting, game fishing.

Rooms 12	*Room phone* No	*Confirm by* arrang.	*Parking* Ample
Ensuite bath/shower 9	*Room TV* No	*Last dinner* 8.30	*Room service* Limited

---

GATEHOUSE OF FLEET Cally Palace Hotel 67% £C/D

H **Map 13 B4**
Dumfries & Galloway
DG7 2DL
Gatehouse (055 74) 341

Credit Visa
Closed Jan & Feb

Families cannot fail to enjoy a stay at this splendid hotel where facilities for children are plentiful and public rooms on a grand scale please their parents. Bedrooms vary considerably in size and style of furnishings, but most are family rooms with balconies. All have plenty of extras and decent bathrooms. *Amenities* garden, outdoor swimming pool, sauna, solarium, tennis, putting, croquet, games room, secretarial services, laundry service, children's play area.

Rooms 65	*Direct dial* Yes	*Confirm by* arrang.	*Parking* Ample
Ensuite bath/shower 65	*Room TV* Yes	*Last dinner* 9.30	*Room service* 24 hours

---

GATEHOUSE OF FLEET Murray Arms £E

I **Map 13 B4**
Dumfries & Galloway
Anne Street DG7 2HY
Gatehouse (055 74) 207

Credit Access, Amex, Diners, Visa

Numerous little parlours, a pair of cosy cocktail bars and an old stone arch in reception give plenty of character to this old posting inn. Bedrooms are simple but pleasant, with a variety of traditional furniture and modest but clean bathrooms. Across the pretty garden is a chalet with a smart suite.
Amenities garden, tennis, 9-hole golf course, croquet, game fishing, coffee shop (noon–9.30pm), 24-hour lounge service.

Rooms 13	*Direct dial* Yes	*Confirm by* 6	*Parking* Ample
Ensuite bath/shower 13	*Room TV* Yes	*Last dinner* 8.45	*Room service* Limited

GIFFNOCK   Macdonald Thistle Hotel   65%   £C/D

H **Map 12 B2** Strathclyde
Eastwood Toll G46 6RA
041-638 2225
Telex 779138

Credit Access, Amex, Diners, Visa

A well-run modern hotel on the A77 just south of Glasgow. There's a
stylish foyer-lounge, with lightwood panelling and upholstered wicker
chairs, and a colonial-style bar with white rattan furniture. Well-
equipped bedrooms are pleasantly furnished, with coordinated fabrics,
decent darkwood units and easy chairs. The four suites are particularly
attractive.   *Amenities* sauna, solarium, keep-fit equipment, pool
table, in-house movies, secretarial services, fax, laundry service.

Rooms 58	*Direct dial* Yes	*Confirm by* 6	*Parking* Ample
Ensuite bath/shower 58	*Room TV* Yes	*Last dinner* 9.45	*Room service* 24 hours

GLASGOW   Albany   75%   £B/C

H **Town plan B3** Strathclyde
Bothwell Street G2 7EN
041-248 2656
Telex 77440

Rooms 254
Ensuite bath/shower 254
Direct dial Yes
Room TV Yes
Confirm by 6
Last dinner 11
Parking Limited
Room service 24 hours

Credit Access, Amex, Diners, Visa

The extensive conference facilities make this large city-centre
hotel a popular spot for business
people, while all guests will enjoy
the elegant, comfortable surroundings. A fine marble floor
graces the impressive foyer-
lounge area, where large leather
chesterfields and walls liberally
hung with prints give a feeling
of luxury. Other public areas
include the light and airy Albany
Bar and a pine-panelled pubby

bar in the basement. Bedrooms are attractive and spacious, with white
units, pine furniture and coordinating floral fabrics; all have mini-
bars, tea/coffee-makers and fully tiled bathrooms with hairdryers,
bath foam and shampoo.
Amenities secretarial services, laundry service.

GLASGOW   Amber

R **Town plan A1** Strathclyde
130 Byres Road
041-339 6121

Chinese cooking
Set L fr £3.50 **Set D** fr £9.50
About £35 for two
Seats 80 *Parking* Limited

Credit Access, Amex, Diners, Visa

A menu of Cantonese favourites pulls in the customers at this large,
well-run Chinese restaurant with friendly, welcoming staff. The choice
ranges from soup and satay to sweet and sour, chop suey, foo yung,
chow mein dishes and curries, and there are also steaks, omelettes and
salads. Portions are generous, but if you do have room, the freshly
prepared toffee apples are excellent.

Lunch 12–2   *Dinner* 5–11.30, Fri till midnight, Meals Sat 12–12
Closed L Sun

GLASGOW   Buttery   ♨

R **Town plan A3** Strathclyde
652 Argyle Street
041-221 8188

Set L £11.50
About £52 for two
Seats 50
Parties 8
Parking Ample
Credit Access, Amex, Diners, Visa

It's well worth seeking out this converted Victorian pub because the
rewards include sophisticated food served by smart long-aproned
waitresses in a stylishly old-world, plushy atmosphere. Likely dishes
– the menu changes every six weeks – include a tasty terrine of
Perthshire game, halibut in a watercress and orange sauce, excellent
medallions of veal, and the house speciality: saddle of venison with
blackcurrants and Kirsch.   ☻ Well-chosen   ⊞ &

Lunch 12–2.30   *Dinner* 7–10
Closed L Sat, all Sun & Bank Hols

GLASGOW   Central Hotel   61%   £D

H **Town plan C3** Strathclyde
Gordon Street G1 3SF
041-221 9680
Telex 777771

Credit Access, Amex, Diners, Visa

There has been much refurbishment at this huge Victorian station
hotel and there is more yet to come. Public areas include an attractive
reception with brass chandeliers and plenty of greenery and a smart
red bar. Go for the newly-done Premier rooms, which have darkwood
units, soft colour schemes, brass light fittings, tea/coffee-makers, mini
bars, hairdryers and retiled bathrooms.
Amenities in-house movies, secretarial services, fax, laundry service.

Rooms 229	*Direct dial* Yes	*Confirm by* 6	*Parking* Difficult
Ensuite bath/shower 170	*Room TV* Yes	*Last dinner* 9.30	*Room service* 24 hours

GLASGOW — The Colonial Restaurant 🝓

R Town plan E4 Strathclyde
25 High Street
041-552 1923

Set L from £5.45
Set D from £16.60
About £50 for two
Seats 40
Parking Ample

Credit Access, Amex, Diners, Visa

Rising talents like Peter Jackson are making sure that Glasgow's renaissance extends to the culinary as well as the visual arts. Some three years ago he took over what was then a humble Italian eatery and swiftly turned it into a serious restaurant of the modern Scottish school. Decor remains unsophisticated, but food has long ago outstripped its surroundings. Monthly-changing menus using ingredients culled from Scottish and French sources offer delights like terrine of crab and sole with herb yoghurt sauce, poached oysters with raspberry vinaigrette and roast guinea fowl with beetroot coulis. If it's hard to choose, try Peter's 'menu surprise'. Wines range from the modest to the superb. 🍷 Well-chosen ♺

Lunch 12–2.30 *Dinner* 6–10.30 **Closed** L Sat, D Mon, all Sun, Bank Hols, 4 days Xmas & 4 days New Year

GLASGOW — Copthorne 63% £C/D

H Town plan D3 Strathclyde
George Square G2 1DS
041-332 6711
Telex 778147

Credit Access, Amex, Diners, Visa

George Square provides a pleasant outlook for this massive hotel by the station. Luxurious public areas include a marble-floored reception and a lively split-level bar boasting a mahogany gazebo with stained-glass roof. Bedrooms in the new wing have fitted units, matching fabrics and compact bathrooms; those in the old wing are larger and have freestanding furniture and better bathrooms.
Amenities in-house movies, secretarial services, fax, laundry service.

Rooms 140	Direct dial Yes	Confirm by 6	Parking Difficult
Ensuite bath/shower 140	Room TV Yes	Last dinner 10	Room service 24 hours

GLASGOW — Crest Hotel, Glasgow City 65% £C

H Town plan B4 Strathclyde
Argyle Street G2 8LL
041-248 2355
Telex 779652

Credit Access, Amex, Diners, Visa

A modern city-centre hotel offering comfortable accommodation. The smart foyer-lounge features stained natural wood to blend in with its pastel colour scheme and other public rooms are equally tasteful. Standard bedrooms have lightwood units and prettily tiled bathrooms; Executive rooms have darkwood units, mineral water and fruit juice, as do feminine Lady Crest rooms. *Amenities* in-house movies, secretarial services, fax, laundry service, 24-hour lounge service.

Rooms 121	Direct dial Yes	Confirm by 6	Parking Difficult
Ensuite bath/shower 121	Room TV Yes	Last dinner 9.45	Room service Limited

Changes in data sometimes occur in establishments
after the Guide goes to press.
Prices should be taken as indications rather than firm quotes.

GLASGOW — Holiday Inn 78% £B/C

H Town plan A4 Strathclyde
Argyle Street, Anderston
G3 8RR
041-226 5577
Telex 776355

Rooms 298
Ensuite bath/shower 298
Direct dial Yes
Room TV Yes
Confirm by 6
Last dinner 11
Parking Ample
Room service 24 hours

Credit Access, Amex, Diners, Visa

Take the Anderston exit off the M8 to find this high-rise city-centre hotel. Open-plan public areas include a sunken lounge with circular hooded fire and, overlooking the pool complex, a pleasant cocktail bar. Decent-sized bedrooms offer large beds, nice units and attractive fabrics; all are equipped with air conditioning, trouser presses, hair-dryers and sophisticated bedside controls (there's even a switch to

operate a 'do not disturb' light in the corridor). Luxuriously fitted bathrooms have radio extensions and usual toiletries. *Amenities* indoor swimming pool, sauna, solarium, whirlpool bath, gymnasium, hairdressing, squash, in-house movies, secretarial services, laundry service, coffee shop (11am–11pm), kiosk. ♿

F I A T Glasgow

DUMBARTON 14 miles   ABERFOYLE 27 miles

A Stakis
Grosvenor Hotel
Stakis Pond Hotel
Amber
White House
One Devonshire
Gardens Hotel and
Restaurant

B NEW CITY ROAD

C

DOBBIES LOAN

WEST GRAHAM STREET

COWCADDENS ROAD

WOODSIDE

RENFREW STREET

SAUCHIEHALL STREET

Kelvin Park
Lorne Hotel

BERKELEY STREET

KENT ROAD

Charing
Cross
Station

BATH STREET

Hospitality Inn

SAUCHIEHALL STREET

WEST REGENT STREET

WEST GEORGE STREET

ST VINCENT STREET

Buttery
Restaurant

Albany Hotel

BOTHWELL STREET

WATERLOO STREET

ST VINCENT STREET

Holiday
Inn

Bus Station

Crest Hotel
Glasgow

ARGYLE STREET

ARGYLE STREET

Central Hotel

JAMES WATT STREET

YORK STREET

BROOMIELAW

Kingston
Bridge

River   Clyde

George V
Bridge

Glasgow
Bridge

SPRINGFIELD QUAY

WINDMILLCROFT QUAY

CLYDE PLACE

CLYDE STREET

Bellahouston
Hotel

A8 PAISLEY RD

Swallow
Hotel

A

PAISLEY ROAD

MORRISON STREET

NELSON STREET

KINGSTON ST

B

COMMERCE ST

BRIDGE ST

Tinto Firs
Thistle Hotel

C

GREENOCK 23 miles
© 1988 Egon Ronay's Guides

KILMARNOCK 21 miles

CLYDEBANK 5 miles

RENFREW 7 miles

GLASGOW

Map 12 B1
Town plan on preceding page

Population 755,429

Prime factors in Glasgow's history were the River Clyde and the Industrial Revolution (helped by the Lowland genius for shipbuilding and engineering). Glasgow is the home of Scottish Opera, Scottish Ballet and the Scottish National Orchestra. The city has a fine collection of museums, most notably that at Kelvingrove and the Burrell Gallery. Famous for learning (two universities), sport (soccer), shops, and art galleries, the city boasts over seventy parks and the Scottish Exhibition and Conference Centre.

Annual Events
Mayfest, Paisley Festival *May*
Horse Show and Country Fair *July*
Jazz Festival *June/July*

Sights Outside City
Paisley Abbey, Forth and Clyde Canal at Kirkintilloch, Clyde Muirshiel Park at Lochwinnoch, Weavers Cottage (Kilbarchan)

Tourist Information Offices
35/39 St Vincent Place, Glasgow G1 2ER. Open June–Sept Mon–Sat 9am–9pm Sun 10am–6pm. Open Oct–May Mon–Sat 9am–6pm Sun Closed
Telephone 041–227 4880.
Telex 779504
Town Hall, Abbey Close, Paisley PA1 1JS. Open June–Sept Mon–Fri 9am–6pm, Sat 9am–5pm, Oct–May Mon–Fri 9am–5pm
Telephone 041–889 0711

Fiat Dealers
Peat Road Motors (Jordanhill) Ltd
120 Whittingehame Drive
Jordanhill, Glasgow GL12 0YJ
Tel. 041–357 1939

Ritchie's
393 Shields Road, Glasgow G41 1 NZ
Tel. 041–429 5611

Currie of Shettleston
85–89 Amulree Street
Glasgow G32 7UN
Tel. 041–778 1295

1 Airport **A5**
2 Art Gallery and Museum *paintings, ceramics, silver, costumes, etc.* **A2**
3 The Barrows *weekend street market* **F5**
4 Botanic Gardens **A1**
5 Briggait **D5**
6 Burrell Gallery *paintings, stained glass, tapestries, ceramics* **C5**
7 Central Station **C4**
8 Citizens' Theatre **D5**
9 City Chambers *fine loggia* **D3**
10 City Hall **E4**
11 Clyde Tunnel **A4**
12 Glasgow Cathedral *impressive Gothic* **F3**
13 Glasgow Cross *1626 Tolbooth Steeple* **E5**
14 Glasgow Green *city's oldest riverside park* **F5**
15 Glasgow Zoo **F5**
16 Haggs Castle—*ideal for children* **C5**
17 Hunterian Museum & Art Gallery (Glasgow University) *early books, archaeology* **A2**
18 King's Theatre **A2**
19 Mitchell Library and Theatre **A2**
20 Museum of Transport *comprehensive collection. Also engineering, shipbuilding* **A2**
21 People's Palace *local history* **F5**
22 Pollok House *Spanish paintings, English furniture, rare silver, in Adam building amid parkland* **C5**
23 Queen Street Station **D3**
24 Scottish Exhibition and Conference Centre **A4**
25 Tenement House **B1**
26 Theatre Royal **C2**
27 Tourist Information Centre **C3**

GLASGOW | Hospitality Inn 70% | £D/E

H **Town plan C2** Strathclyde
Cambridge Street G3 7DS
041-332 3311
Telex 777334

Rooms 313
Ensuite bath/shower 313
Direct dial Yes
Room TV Yes
Confirm by 6
Last dinner 11.30
Parking Ample
Room service 24 hours

Credit Access, Amex, Diners, Visa

Spacious bedrooms are a feature at this large, modern, city-centre hotel. Standard rooms are very generous while de luxe rooms are simply enormous. Decor is unexciting but perfectly adequate, and accessories include hairdryers, tea-makers and trouser presses; de luxe rooms offer bathroom lobbies with twin washbasins. The four suites are rather more stylish. A waterfall strikes a soothing note in the busy foyer, but your best bet for a quiet spot is the peaceful cocktail bar. Another, livelier bar sports a cheerful seafaring theme.
Amenities hairdressing, in-house movies, fax, laundry service, coffee shop (7am–11.30pm), kiosk. &

GLASGOW | Kelvin Park Lorne Hotel 61% | £E

H **Town plan A2** Strathclyde
923 Sauchiehall Street G3 7TE
041-334 4891
Telex 778935

Credit Access, Amex, Diners, Visa

A modern hotel with an attractive, well-designed interior. Leather armchairs and a green colour scheme make for an inviting foyer and the lounge, with its black and white theme, has a light, airy feel. The cocktail bar is 1900s in flavour, based on the style of Charles Rennie Mackintosh. Bedrooms are bright and stylish, with darkwood units, coordinating fabrics and fully tiled bathrooms. *Amenities* in-house movies, secretarial serivices, fax, laundry service.

| *Rooms* 80 | *Direct dial* Yes | *Confirm by* 6.30 | *Parking* Ample |
| *Ensuite bath/shower* 80 | *Room TV* Yes | *Last dinner* 10.45 | *Room service* 24 hours |

**Our inspectors are our full-time employees;
they are professionally trained by us.**

GLASGOW | One Devonshire Gardens 76% | £B

HR **Town plan A1**
Strathclyde
1 Devonshire Gardens G12 0UX
041-339 2001

Rooms 8
Ensuite bath/shower 8
Direct dial Yes
Room TV Yes
Confirm by arrang.
Last dinner 10
Parking Ample
Room service 24 hours

Credit Access, Amex, Diners, Visa

The stylish decor of this Victorian town house is perhaps what you might expect from an owner who also runs an interior design business. All is delightfully sophisticated, from the elegant drawing room with its fashionable drapes and artificial tree to the equally sumptuous bedrooms with their striking single-tone colour schemes, rich drapes and high-quality traditional furniture (including three four-posters). Luxurious bathrooms boast large tubs, drag-painted woodwork, classy toiletries and huge towels. (One room has shower only.) Staff smartly attired in Victorian-style uniforms include a butler who greets you when you ring the bell. (There is no reception desk.)
Amenities secretarial services, laundry service.

Restaurant

Set L £13.75
Set D £23.65
About £54 *for two*
Seats 35
Parties 16

Stylish blue decor sets the tone of this elegant restaurant, where James Kerr devises a new and interesting menu for every meal, inspired by the best raw ingredients available. Skilful preparation combines with attractive presentation to produce winning dishes like feuilleté of chicken livers with almonds, and suprême of salmon with orange and ginger sauce. Notable wines include St Aubin 1er Cru '85 and Ch. Grand Puy Ducasse '81. ♀ Well-chosen ⓔ

Lunch 12.30–2.30 *Dinner* 7–10
Closed L Sat

GLASGOW | Rogano | ♛

Town plan C4 Strathclyde
11 Exchange Place
041-248 4055

About £60 for two
Seats 55
Parking Difficult

Credit Access, Amex, Diners, Visa

There's a strong emphasis on fish at this '20s-style restaurant, which features a lively diner downstairs for the younger crowd, a main restaurant on the ground floor and an oyster bar near the entrance. The seafood is deliciously fresh and accurately cooked and there is also a meat section on the menu offering such dishes as venison liver pâté and mignons of beef; vegetarians are catered for too. ♟ Well-chosen ℗

Lunch 12–2.30   *Dinner* 7–10, Sat till 10.30
Closed Sun & Bank Hols   *Meals* (in diner) noon–midnight

GLASGOW | Stakis Grosvenor Hotel   72% | £C

Town plan A1 Strathclyde
Grosvenor Terrace G12 0TA
041-339 8811
Telex 776247

Rooms 94
Ensuite bath/shower 94
Direct dial Yes
Room TV Yes
Confirm by arrang.
Last dinner 10.30
Parking Ample
Room service 24 hours

Credit Access, Amex, Diners, Visa

Behind the floodlit classical facade lies a smart modern hotel
with high standards of decor in
the public rooms – the elegant
split-level foyer-bar has panelled
walls, leather settees and modern
chandeliers, while the luxurious
and spacious main bar boasts red
crushed velvet effect walls, dado
panelling, red plush and black
leather seating and massed
greenery. Standard bedrooms
have decent darkwood units,

coordinating fabrics, easy chairs and plenty of extras; top floor rooms are similarly furnished but larger, with two double beds. Bathrooms have decent tiling, shower fitments and good towels and toiletries; top floor rooms have bidets too.
Amenities in-house movies, secretarial services, fax, laundry service.

GLASGOW | Stakis Pond Hotel   59% | £C

Town plan A1
Strathclyde
2 Shelly Road,
Great Western Road G12 0XP
041-334 8161 Telex 776573

Credit Access, Amex, Diners, Visa

Pleasant, practical accommodation is on offer at this modern five-storey hotel. Public areas include a comfortable public bar and the bright Galley Bar, which has rattan furniture and a view of the pool. Compact bedrooms have attractive soft furnishings, simple darkwood units, radio-alarms, tea/coffee-makers, trouser presses and hairdryers. *Amenities* indoor swimming pool, sauna, solarium, whirlpool bath, keep-fit equipment, secretarial services, laundry service.

Rooms 137	*Direct dial* Yes	*Confirm by* 6	*Parking* Ample
Ensuite bath/shower 137	*Room TV* Yes	*Last dinner* 10	*Room service* 24 hours

GLASGOW | Swallow Hotel   61% | £D

Town plan A5 Strathclyde
517 Paisley Road West
G51 1RW
041-427 3146
Telex 778795

Credit Access, Amex, Diners, Visa

A mile west of the city centre, this is a modern three-storey hotel. Pleasant public rooms include a cocktail bar which groups wicker chairs around marble-topped coffee tables. The best bedrooms are decorated in soft pastels, with attractive blue-grey furniture. Some rooms are rather on the small side. *Amenities* indoor swimming pool, sauna, solarium, whirlpool bath, keep-fit equipment, in-house movies, secretarial services, fax, laundry service. ♿

Rooms 122	*Direct dial* Yes	*Confirm by* 6	*Parking* Ample
Ensuite bath/shower 122	*Room TV* Yes	*Last dinner* 9.30	*Room service* 24 hours

GLASGOW | Tinto Firs Thistle Hotel   64% | £C/D

Town plan C5 Strathclyde
470 Kilmarnock Road G43 2BB
041-637 2353
Telex 778329

Credit Access, Amex, Diners, Visa

You'll find pleasant accommodation at this modern hotel south of Glasgow. The smart foyer-lounge/cocktail bar features darkwood panelling and rattan chairs, while in the dark blue Traders Bar nicely framed old photographs catch the eye. Bedrooms have laminate furniture, watered silk effect wallcoverings and matching fabrics; bathrooms boast good tiling and thermostatic showers. *Amenities* garden, in-house movies, secretarial services, fax, laundry service.

Rooms 27	*Direct dial* Yes	*Confirm by* 6	*Parking* Ample
Ensuite bath/shower 27	*Room TV* Yes	*Last dinner* 9.45	*Room service* 24 hours

GLASGOW — White House — 65% — £C/D

P H **Town plan A1**
Strathclyde
12 Clevedon Crescent G12 0PA
041-339 9375
Telex 777582

Credit Access, Amex, Diners, Visa

Three adjoining houses in a quiet Georgian crescent make up this unusual establishment, which falls somewhere between a hotel and a serviced apartment building. There are no public rooms, only self-contained suites complete with bath and kitchen. These vary enormously in style and number of rooms, the best being quite luxurious. A conference suite is also available. No dogs. *Amenities* garden, in-house movies, secretarial services, fax, laundry service.

Rooms 32	Direct dial Yes	Confirm by 6	Parking Limited
Ensuite bath/shower 32	Room TV Yes		Room service 24 hours

GLASGOW AIRPORT — Excelsior — 68% — £B/C

H **Map 12 B1** Strathclyde
Abbotsinch
Nr Paisley PA3 2TR
041-887 1212
Telex 777733

Credit Access, Amex, Diners, Visa

Just 60 yards from the terminal of Glasgow Airport, this large modern hotel could not be more convenient for the traveller. A marble tiled floor, leather seating and much greenery make for an attractive foyer and there's a smart contemporary bar. The pleasant bedrooms have modern fitted units, bright curtains and bedspreads, compact, fully tiled bathrooms and plenty of extras. Courtesy car to airport. *Amenities* hairdressing, secretarial services, fax, laundry service.

Rooms 290	Direct dial Yes	Confirm by 6	Parking Ample
Ensuite bath/shower 290	Room TV Yes	Last dinner 10.30	Room service 24 hours

GLASGOW AIRPORT — Stakis Normandy Hotel — 61% — £C/D

H **Map 12 B1** Strathclyde
Inchinnan Road, Renfrew
PA4 5EJ
041-886 4100
Telex 778897

Credit Access, Amex, Diners, Visa

You can find practical accommodation at this '60s hotel on the A8. Public areas include a comfortable cocktail bar in shades of turquoise and pink. Bedrooms have mostly been updated with attractive curtains and matching quilted bedspreads; all have trouser presses, hairdryers, tea/coffee-makers, fresh fruit, shortbread and functional bathrooms. Coach to the airport. *Amenities* garden, golf driving range, in-house movies, secretarial services, fax, laundry service.

Rooms 142	Direct dial Yes	Confirm by 6	Parking Ample
Ensuite bath/shower 142	Room TV Yes	Last dinner 10	Room service 24 hours

GLENBORRODALE — Glenborrodale Castle — 72% — *NEW ENTRY* £A

HR **Map 17 A4** Strathclyde
Ardnamurchan
Peninsula PH36 4JP
Glenborrodale (09724) 266
Telex 778815

Rooms 15
Ensuite bath/shower 15
Direct dial Yes
Room TV Yes
Confirm by arrang.
Last dinner 9
Parking Ample
Room service None

Credit Access, Amex, Visa
Closed Nov–Easter

An imposing turn-of-the-century mansion in a stunning setting of acres of rhododendrons and an outlook over Loch Sunart and the Isle of Mull. Take the panelled staircase from the reception up to the dado-panelled hall with vaulted ceilings and open fire, off which are the informal relaxing bar and lounge, the latter boasting magnificent views. A spiral stone staircase leads you on to the bedrooms, which are graced

by antique furniture and stylish fabrics. Bathrooms have good towelling and generous old-fashioned basins. Dogs in kennels only. *Amenities* garden, sauna, solarium, gymnasium, beauty salon, tennis, putting, croquet, riding, clay-pigeon shooting, mooring, hotel boat, fax, laundry service.

Restaurant *NEW ENTRY*

Set D£25
About £60 for two
Seats 28
Parties 12

A beamed ceiling and dado panelling make this an attractive dining room, further enhanced by fine quality tableware and unusual brass candle-holders. The short, fixed-price menu offers some interesting and tasty items such as lettuce and mint soup, avocado and smoked salmon roulade, beef with mustard and green olives, all well prepared, with vegetables and herbs coming from the hotel's own garden. Service is friendly but haphazard. Booking is essential. ℮

Dinner only 7–9
Closed Nov–Easter

GLENLIVET   Blairfindy Lodge Hotel 61%   £D/E

H **Map 16 C3** Grampian
Ballindalloch AB3 9DJ
Glenlivet (080 73) 376

Credit Access, Amex, Visa

Comfort, tranquillity and a friendly welcome are assured at this
granite hotel perched on the side of a hill and commanding panoramic
views of the surrounding peaks. Public rooms include a cosy bar-
lounge with log fire and a chintzy lounge. Bedrooms are being
refurbished with antique and period-style furniture; duvets and tea/
coffee-makers are standard. Simple and functional bathrooms.
Amenities garden, game fishing, laundry service.

Rooms 12	*Room phone* No	*Confirm by* arrang.	*Parking* Ample
Ensuite bath/shower 9	*Room TV* No	*Last dinner* 9.30	*Room service* All day

GLENROTHES   Balgeddie House Hotel 65%   £D/E

H **Map 17 C5** Fife
Balgeddie Way KY6 3ET
Glenrothes (0592) 742511

Credit Access, Amex, Visa
Closed 2 wks from 25 Dec

A solid stone house, set in peaceful grounds, where the Crombie family
firmly adhere to the tenets of old-fashioned hotelkeeping. Impeccable
housekeeping, careful maintenance and efficient, friendly service are
the hallmarks of their excellent establishment. A deep-carpeted
entrance hall leads to a stylish lounge with French-style chairs and to
a panelled cocktail bar well-stocked with malt whiskies. Two other
lively bars are located in the annexe. Bedrooms range from spacious
first-floor rooms with fresh flowers, pretty fabrics and sturdy furniture
to charming little attics, all spotlessly kept. Bathrooms have excellent
shower units and soft, generous towels.
Amenities garden, croquet, snooker, pool table, laundry service.

Rooms 18	*Direct dial* Yes	*Confirm by* arrang.	*Parking* Ample
Ensuite bath/shower 18	*Room TV* Yes	*Last dinner* 9.30	*Room service* All day

**We welcome bona fide complaints and recommendations
on the tear-out pages at the back of the book for readers' comment.
They are followed up by our professional team.**

GULLANE   Greywalls 77%   £C

HR **Map 12 D1** Lothian
Muirfield EH31 2EG
Gullane (0620) 842144
Telex 72294

Rooms 23
Ensuite bath/shower 23
Direct dial Yes
Room TV Yes
Confirm by arrang.
Last dinner 9.30
Parking Ample
Room service 24 hours

Credit Access, Amex, Visa
Closed Nov–mid Apr

A small holiday home designed
by Sir Edwin Lutyens has grown
by means of tasteful extensions
into an elegant hotel that's especially popular with golfers – there
are several courses nearby. The
large, panelled library with deep,
comfortable sofas and welcoming fire is a favourite spot, and
there's also a lovely light sitting
room, a cane-furnished sun room
and a cosy little bar. Bedrooms
are individually decorated to a

high standard and contain some fine antique pieces; standard lamps,
sofas, armchairs, books, fruit and flowers contribute to the feeling of
luxurious ease. Ultra-modern bathrooms offer bathrobes and good
toiletries. *Amenities* garden, tennis, putting, croquet, secretarial
services, laundry service.

Restaurant   ♔

Set L Sun from £8.50
Set D from £19.50
About £57 for two
Seats 60
Parties 20

Imaginative cooking by Andrew Mitchell, combined with excellent
service, makes for delightful eating. Unusual combinations such as
calf's liver teamed with apricot sauce are confidently executed from
good fresh produce. A typical meal might consist of chilled duck and
lobster terrine, followed by delicately poached halibut in a creamy
truffle sauce and, to finish, a delicious chilled passion fruit cake.
Splendid classic wine list. ➪ Outstanding ♟ Well-chosen ☻

Lunch 12.30–2 *Dinner* 7.30–9.30
Closed Nov–mid Apr

GULLANE La Potinière ★

R Map 12 D1 Lothian
Main Street
Gullane (0620) 843214

Lunch at 1
Dinner Sat only at 8
Set L £11.50, Sun £12.75
Set D £17.50
About £45 *for two*
Seats 32
Parties 30
Parking Ample

Closed L Sat & Wed, 1 & 2 Jan,
25 & 26 Dec, 1 wk June & all Oct

The waiting list is just about the lengthiest, such is the esteem in which this high-street temple of gastronomy is held. Hilary Brown's cooking shows delicacy of touch and scrupulous attention to detail in delightful dishes such as turkey liver gâteau with a sweet pepper sauce, tarragon chicken and lemon tart. For quality, depth, flair in selection and value for money, David Brown's is unquestionably the

finest French wine list in the kingdom. There are also some lovely things from Italy and Australia tucked away in the cellar. ***Specialities*** tomato and mint soup, pastry tricorns of smoked salmon with fresh basil and spinach sauce, Barbary duck breast à la japonaise, praline soufflé glacé. ⇨ Outstanding 🍷 Well-chosen 🏵

We publish annually,
so make sure you use the current edition.
It's worth it!

HARRAY LOCH Merkister Hotel 57% *NEW ENTRY* £E/F

H Map 16 C1 Orkney
Dounby KW17 2LF
Loch Harray (085 677) 366

Credit Access, Amex, Visa
Closed Oct–Apr

A renowned fishing hotel on the loch shore. Owner Angus MacDonald is a keen fisherman, always on hand with advice, while his wife Elma runs the hotel with warmth and efficiency. The hotel's heart is the main bar, full of fishermen and fishy tales, and there's a cosy lounge. Bedrooms, though modest, are comfortable enough and very clean; six have private showers.
Amenities garden, game fishing, hotel boat, laundry service.

Rooms 18	*Room phone* No	*Confirm by* arrang.	*Parking* Ample
Ensuite bath/shower 6	*Room TV* No	*Last dinner* 9	*Room service* All day

HAWICK Kirklands Hotel 60% £E

H Map 12 D3 Borders
West Stewart Place TD9 8BH
Hawick (0450) 72263

Closed 25 & 26 Dec & 1 Jan

Two new annexes, providing recreation rooms and extra accommodation, have nudged this comfortably old-fashioned Victorian hotel just slightly towards the modern era! Main-house public rooms still make few concessions to contemporary taste but the bar is bright and sunny and enjoys pleasant views of the distant hills. Original bedrooms are spacious and equally traditional in style; all have washbasins or en suite bathrooms. *Amenities* garden, games room, snooker.

Rooms 14	*Direct dial* Yes	*Confirm by* 6	*Parking* Ample
Ensuite bath/shower 5	*Room TV* Yes	*Last dinner* 8.30	*Room service* All day

HELMSDALE Navidale House Hotel 57% *NEW ENTRY* £E

H Map 16 C2 Highland
KW8 6JS
Helmsdale (043 12) 258

Credit Access, Visa
Closed Dec & Jan

A former shooting lodge set in five acres of gardens and woodland just north of Helmsdale off the A9. The views over the Moray Firth are breathtaking, and the hotel offers marvellous salmon and trout fishing, as well as other sporting pursuits. There's a cosy little bar and two lounges, solidly old-fashioned but bright as a new pin. Assiduous housework is also evident in the bedrooms, furnished with a variety of traditional or more modern pieces. Annexe rooms have a cottage feel. Delightfully warm-hearted girls give a real Highland welcome, and a decent breakfast starts the day.
Amenities garden, shooting, clay-pigeon shooting, game fishing, laundry service.

Rooms 21	*Room phone* No	*Confirm by* arrang.	*Parking* Ample
Ensuite bath/shower 10	*Room TV* Yes	*Last dinner* 8.30	*Room service* All day

HUMBIE   Johnstounburn House Hotel   72%   £C

H **Map 17 C6** Lothian
EH36 5PL
Humbie (087 553) 696
Telex 557934

Rooms 20
Ensuite bath/shower 19
Direct dial Yes
Room TV Yes
Confirm by 6
Last dinner 9
Parking Ample
Room service All day

Credit Access, Amex, Diners, Visa

Old-fashioned walled gardens, a splendid cedar on the lawn and an historic listed dovecote, provide the setting for this handsome 17th-century country house on the edge of the Lammermuir Hills. The interior is equally gracious, with moulded ceilings, lustrous panelling and wall-paintings by the 18th-century artist Robert Norrie complemented by cosy log fires and fine antiques. Main-house bedrooms

– some with spectacular views – are furnished in a comfortable, traditional style. Rooms in the converted coach-house are larger and more luxurious, with extra facilities such as mini-bars and trouser presses. Management, staff and breakfasts, alas, are disappointing. **Amenities** garden, clay-pigeon shooting, laundry service.

Our inspectors *never* book in the name of Egon Ronay's Guides.
They disclose their identity only if they are considering an establishment
for inclusion in the next edition of the Guide.

INGLISTON   Norton House Hotel   68%   £D

H **Map 12 C1** Lothian
Edinburgh EH28 8LX
031-333 1275
Telex 727232

Credit Access, Amex, Diners, Visa

Fifty-five acres of grounds surround this splendid Victorian mansion, guaranteeing beautiful views from every room. The magnificent entrance hall is graced by marble pillars and an oak fireplace and staircase, which are echoed by the panelling in the comfortable lounge bar. Bedrooms have excellent quality modern darkwood furniture and soft colour themes; all have plenty of extras and smart modern bathrooms. **Amenities** garden, putting, secretarial services, fax.

Rooms 19	*Direct dial* Yes	*Confirm by* arrang.	*Parking* Ample
Ensuite bath/shower 19	*Room TV* Yes	*Last dinner* 9.30	*Room service* 24 hours

INVERNESS   Bunchrew House Hotel   69%   £D

H **Map 16 C3** Highland
Bunchrew IV3 6TA
Inverness (0463) 234917

Credit Access, Amex, Visa

Personal service is a strong point at this handsome Scottish mansion, which stands in beautiful woodland and landscaped gardens on the shores of Beauly Firth. Wood panelling features strongly in the peaceful, elegant day rooms, and family portraits hang in the lounge bar. Bedrooms are furnished mainly with antiques, and one boasts a massive four-poster; another has a half-tester (and a whirlpool bath). All the bathrooms are supplied with huge, fluffy towels. Fresh fruit and magazines are among thoughtful extras, and room service is excellent; a super breakfast is served with a flourish under silver. **Amenities** garden, clay-pigeon shooting, sea fishing, laundry service.

Rooms 6	*Direct dial* Yes	*Confirm by* arrang.	*Parking* Ample
Ensuite bath/shower 6	*Room TV* Yes	*Last dinner* 9	*Room service* All day

INVERNESS   Caledonian Hotel   67%   *NEW ENTRY*   £D

H **Map 16 C3** Highland
33 Church Street IV1 1DX
Inverness (0463) 235181
Telex 75232

Credit Access, Amex, Diners, Visa

A modern hotel, reopened in summer 1987 after refurbishment. Among the day rooms are a spacious lobby-lounge, a clubby bar and a coffee shop; there's also a well-appointed leisure centre. Decently equipped bedrooms have pleasant bleached-wood furniture and neat, practical bathrooms. **Amenities** indoor swimming pool, sauna, solarium, whirlpool bath, keep-fit equipment, snooker, secretarial services, laundry service, coffee shop (10–4.30).

Rooms 100	*Direct dial* Yes	*Confirm by* 6	*Parking* Ample
Ensuite bath/shower 100	*Room TV* Yes	*Last dinner* 9	*Room service* 24 hours

INVERNESS   Culloden House   76%   £B

HR Map 16 C3 Highland
Nr Culloden IV1 2NZ
Inverness (0463) 790461
Telex 75402

Rooms 20
Ensuite bath/shower 20
Direct dial Yes
Room TV Yes
Confirm by arrang.
Last dinner 9
Parking Ample
Room service All day

Credit Access, Amex, Diners, Visa

The battlefield of Culloden is just moments away, and Bonnie Prince Charlie is one of many distinguished visitors to this handsome country mansion. Forty acres of lawns and parkland make a lovely, peaceful setting, and inside all is dignified elegance, with fine antiques, magnificent mouldings and splendidly comfortable sofas. Bedrooms, all of a good size and some really vast, are individually styled, and Marjory McKenzie is constantly adding to or upgrading the antiques and fine paintings. Decor is stylish and luxurious; extras abound, and all rooms have superbly appointed bathrooms (one with whirlpool bath). No children under ten. No dogs. *Amenities* garden, sauna, solarium, tennis, snooker, fax, laundry service.

Restaurant   ♛

Set D £21.50
About £55 *for two*
Seats 40
Parties 22

À la carte lunches and table d'hôte dinners provide enjoyable eating, and the Adam-style room, with its decorative mouldings, is an elegant setting. Smoked venison sausage salad, chicken liver terrine, poached salmon hollandaise and medallions of pork with melted Brie on a sherry sauce are typical dishes, and the sweet trolley offers a tempting selection that includes some traditional Scottish favourites. Good wines: Sancerre (Millerioux) '86, Ch. Branaire '76. ♟ Well-chosen
℗

Lunch 12.30–2   *Dinner* 7–9

INVERNESS   Dunain Park Hotel   68%   £C

HR Map 16 C3 Highland
IV3 6JN
Inverness (0463) 230512

Credit Access, Amex, Diners, Visa
Closed 1 wk Feb and 1 wk Nov

Six secluded acres provide a quiet setting for a former hunting lodge just off the A82. The Nicolls take good care of their guests, and standards of housekeeping and repair are high. Antiques, a log fire, books and magazines make the lounge a cosy, homely spot, and the bedrooms are individually appointed in a pleasing, traditional style. Two suites are in the nearby coach house.
Amenities garden, badminton, croquet, laundry service.

Rooms 8	*Direct dial* Yes	*Confirm by* arrang.	*Parking* Ample
Ensuite bath/shower 6	*Room TV* Yes	*Last dinner* 9	*Room service* All day

Restaurant   ♙

Set L £12.50
Set D £19.50
About £40 *for two*
Seats 30
Parties 30

A four-course menu features imaginative dishes using top-quality local ingredients. Salmon, lobster, grouse, pheasant, venison and beef all appear regularly, and vegetables come fresh from the garden. The help-yourself sweet buffet is liable to provoke a show of shameless indulgence. Smoking is not allowed in the restaurant, but the drawing room is available with coffee (or between courses for the really desperate!) Good wines: Chasse Spleen '66, Coulée de Serrant '80. ℗

Lunch 12–2   *Dinner* 7–9
Closed 1 wk Feb & 1 wk Nov

INVERNESS   Kingsmills Hotel   66%   £D

H Map 16 C3 Highland
Culcabock Road IV2 3LP
Inverness (0463) 237166
Telex 75566

Credit Access, Amex, Diners, Visa

An attractive 18th-century mansion in a semi-rural position. The two lounges are comfortable and tastefully decorated. Standard bedrooms have fitted units, executive ones lightwood freestanding furniture. Twelve rooms in the garden wing are quite spacious, with smart bathrooms.
Amenities garden, indoor swimming pool, sauna, keep-fit equipment, squash, pitch & putt, secretarial services, fax, laundry service.

Rooms 64	*Direct dial* Yes	*Confirm by* 6	*Parking* Ample
Ensuite bath/shower 64	*Room TV* Yes	*Last dinner* 9.45, Sun 9.30	*Room service* 24 hours

INVERNESS   Mercury Hotel   62%   £C

H **Map 16 C3** Highland
Millburn Road IV2 3TR
Inverness (0463) 239666
Telex 75377

Credit Access, Amex, Diners, Visa

New owners are planning a major revamp of public areas at this
modern six-storey building, formerly the Ladbroke Hotel, standing at
the junction of the A9 and A82. Basic bedrooms sport bright floral
fabrics, smart fitted units and neat functional bathrooms. Executive
rooms offer more stylish decor, attractive bathrooms and many extras.
Ten rooms are non-smoking. *Amenities* patio, in-house movies,
secretarial services, laundry service, coffee shop (7am–11pm).

Rooms 118	*Direct dial* Yes	*Confirm by* 6	*Parking* Ample
Ensuite bath/shower 118	*Room TV* Yes	*Last dinner* 9.30	*Room service* 24 hours

INVERNESS   Station Hotel   65%   £C/D

H **Map 16 C3** Highland
Academy Street IV1 1LG
Inverness (0463) 231926
Telex 75275

Credit Access, Amex, Diners, Visa
Closed 10 days Xmas

Many of the staff at this solid Victorian hotel are long-established and
their friendly and professional care cannot fail to please. A pillared
foyer-lounge has a fine wrought iron staircase leading to two
comfortable bars. Bedrooms have a mélange of furniture but they are
well-maintained and pleasantly decorated, as are the bathrooms. All
have trouser presses, hairdryers and tea/coffee makers.
Amenities secretarial services, laundry service. &

Rooms 65	*Direct dial* Yes	*Confirm by* 6	*Parking* Difficult
Ensuite bath/shower 53	*Room TV* Yes	*Last dinner* 9.15	*Room service* 24 hours

**Changes in data sometimes occur in establishments
after the Guide goes to press.
Prices should be taken as indications rather than firm quotes.**

IRVINE   Hospitality Inn   69%   £D/E

H **Map 12 B2** Strathclyde
Roseholm, Annick Water
KA11 4LD
Irvine (0294) 74272
Telex 777097

Credit Access, Amex, Diners, Visa

A modern red-brick hotel boasting distinctive public areas. The open-
plan bar, lounge and foyer have a Moorish flavour, with arches
between octagonal pillars and decorative tiling, and there's a
spectacular Hawaiian lagoon with mature palms. Well-equipped
bedrooms have matching fabrics and darkwood furniture.
Amenities indoor swimming pool, whirlpool bath, hairdressing, in-
house movies, laundry service, coffee shop (7am–11pm), kiosk. &

Rooms 128	*Direct dial* Yes	*Confirm by* 6	*Parking* Ample
Ensuite bath/shower 128	*Room TV* Yes	*Last dinner* 10	*Room service* 24 hours

ISLE OF GIGHA   Gigha Hotel   60%   £E

HR **Map 17 A6** Strathclyde
PA41 7AD
Gigha (058 35) 254

Credit Access, Visa

The only hotel on the island, and very much a place for enjoying
peace, solitude and the rugged, unspoilt beauty of the surroundings.
No TVs, radios or telephones spoil the calm in the spick-and-span
bedrooms, though there is a TV in a little lounge off the dining room.
There's another homely lounge and a small pine bar.
Amenities garden, game fishing, laundry service.

Rooms 9	*Room phone* No	*Confirm by* arrang.	*Parking* Ample
Ensuite bath/shower 3	*Room TV* No	*Last dinner* 8	*Room service* Limited

Restaurant

Set L from £5
Set D £13
About £35 for two
Seats 40

The quality of the produce is the thing here, and local scallops or
prawns usually appear on the four-course dinner menu. Steak or a
roast is generally available as a main-course alternative, and among
the sweets you might find an excellent chocolate mousse, crème
caramel or raspberry sponge. Cooking is straightforward and
enjoyable, service willing. The delightful dining room features rough
stone walls and solid refectory-style tables. Buffet lunch. ☢

Lunch Noon–2
Dinner 7–8

ISLE OF RAASAY — Isle of Raasay Hotel — 57% — £E/F

H Map 16 A3 Highland
By Kyle of Lochalsh IV40 8PB
Raasay (047 862) 222

Closed Oct–Easter

The only hotel on the island, just 15 minutes by ferry from Skye. The original Victorian stone house has been sympathetically extended, the gothic arched windows being reproduced in the new lounge and dining areas, which boast views to Skye. The bedrooms have plain white walls, tweedy bedspreads and matching curtains, traditional wooden furniture and carpeted bathrooms. Transport is provided to the ferry. *Amenities* garden, game fishing, laundry room. &

Rooms 12	Room phone No	Confirm by arrang.	Parking Ample
Ensuite bath/shower 12	Room TV Yes	Last dinner 7.30	Room service None

We welcome bona fide complaints and recommendations on the tear-out pages at the back of the book for readers' comment. They are followed up by our professional team.

KELSO — Ednam House Hotel — 61% — £E

H Map 12 D2 Borders
Bridge Street TD5 7HT
Kelso (0573) 24168

Credit Visa
Closed 2 wks Xmas

A hotel which owes much of its popularity to its proximity to the Tweed. Ninety-five per cent of the guests are return visitors and the waders and waterproofs in the hall, the open fire, sporting paintings and cosy armchairs give a homely feel. There's a selection of compact single rooms for lone fishermen and all bedrooms continue the traditional feel.
Amenities garden, croquet, coarse & game fishing, laundry service.

Rooms 32	Direct dial Yes	Confirm by 6	Parking Ample
Ensuite bath/shower 31	Room TV Yes	Last dinner 9	Room service All day

KELSO — Sunlaws House Hotel — 74% — £D/E

H Map 12 D2 Borders
Heiton TD5 8JZ
Roxburgh (057 35) 331
Telex 728147

Rooms 21
Ensuite bath/shower 21
Direct dial Yes
Room TV Yes
Confirm by arrang.
Last dinner 9.30
Parking Ample
Room service 24 hours

Credit Access, Amex, Diners, Visa

Guests who delight in combining country sports with comfortable accommodation are well catered for in this fine late Victorian house, the property of the Duke and Duchess of Roxburghe. Shooting, fishing and horse-riding are all on offer, with tuition for the inexperienced. Public rooms include a cheerful entrance hall (where winter is banished by a roaring fire), an elegant drawing room with conservatory and a

handsome library bar. Spacious bedrooms in the main house are solidly comfortable; those in a converted stable block are pretty and modern. The standard of service is high. Bathrooms reflect the excellent housekeeping. *Amenities* garden, tennis, croquet, riding, shooting, game fishing, secretarial services, laundry service, helipad. &

KENMORE — Kenmore Hotel — 62% — £D/E

H Map 17 C5 Tayside
By Aberfeldy PH15 2NU
Kenmore (088 73) 205

Credit Access, Amex, Visa
Closed Mon & Tues mid Nov–mid Feb

A delightful 16th-century hotel in a beautiful position beside the river Tay. Inside, there is an enchantingly rustic bar-lounge, a simple public bar and two relaxing lounges, one with TV, the other with high beamed ceiling, open fire and Scottish pastoral scenes on the walls. Comfortable bedrooms range from spacious and traditional in the main house (three with superior fittings, several with lovely river views) to compact and more modern in the annexe across the pretty village square. All the bathrooms are of a high standard and have bidets. Dogs in annexe only.
Amenities garden, golf courses, game fishing, boating, fax, laundry service, helipad.

Rooms 38	Direct dial Yes	Confirm by arrang.	Parking Ample
Ensuite bath/shower 38	Room TV Yes	Last dinner 9	Room service All day

KENTALLEN OF APPIN   Ardsheal House   67%   £B

HR **Map 17 B4** Highland
Argyll PA38 4BX
Duror (063 174) 227

Credit Access, Amex, Visa
Closed Nov–Easter

Even for the Highlands, the setting is outstandingly beautiful, and the
Taylors run their hotel in the style of friends giving a house party;
their staff, too, are very amiable and efficient. Antiques take the eye
in the entrance hall and cosy drawing rooms, and there are Victorian
pictures and modern cartoons in the tiny bar (once the butler's pantry).
The billiard room has board games and a TV. Bedrooms, each having
individual charm and character, are pleasingly decorated in traditional
style, with some notable antiques and spotless bathrooms. Very good
breakfast with home-baking and free-range eggs. Half-board terms
only.
Amenities garden, tennis, snooker, laundry service.

Rooms 13	Room phone No	Confirm by 5	Parking Ample
Ensuite bath/shower 13	Room TV No	Last dinner 8.30	Room service Limited

Restaurant

Set L from £6
About £55 for two
Seats 35
Parties 35

Pretty garden views accompany the delicious food, and in the evening
candlelight adds to the charm. Fresh seafood and other local produce
is available in abundance and many of the vegetables and herbs are
home-grown. Colin John Bussey cooks with a light, sure touch, and
typical of the beautifully presented dishes on his short-choice menus
are Colonsay oysters marinated with pink grapefruit and herbs, John
Dory lightly sauced with chive and ginger and candied apricot
pancakes with a caramel sauce. Some very good bottles are kept in
the cellar, particularly Chardonnays: Hawk Crest (Stag's Leap),
Puligny from Leflaive. Young staff are enthusiastic and attentive.
🍷 Well-chosen ☺

Lunch 12–2   *Dinner* at 8.30
Closed Nov–Easter

We publish annually,
so make sure you use the current edition.
It's worth it!

KENTALLEN OF APPIN   Holly Tree Hotel   64%   *NEW ENTRY*   £D/E

HR **Map 17 B4** Highland
Argyll PA38 4BY
Duror (063 174) 292

Credit Access, Visa

Prior to the fall of Dr Beeching's axe this was a railway station, and
part of the old platform can still be seen. The hotel stands on the edge
of Loch Linnhe in a setting of great beauty, and all but two of the
bedrooms enjoy spectacular views. Rooms are bright and attractive,
with very comfortable beds and smart modern bathrooms (the two
rooms without the views are converted from the original waiting
rooms and are popular with railway buffs). There's a sunny lounge
and a nice little bar. Owners Alasdair and Jane Robertson are friendly
and welcoming. Good breakfasts.
Amenities garden, laundry service. ♿

Rooms 12	Direct dial Yes	Confirm by arrang.	Parking Ample
Ensuite bath/shower 12	Room TV Yes	Last dinner 9.30	Room service All day

Restaurant   *NEW ENTRY*   ♊

Set L Sun £8.25
Set D £12.50
About £33 for two
Seats 50
Parties 75

A bright, comfortable dining room with marvellous views across the
loch to the mountains of Ardgour. Alasdair Robertson produces an
interesting dinner menu that changes daily and makes good use of
local produce. Typical main courses are Lochy trout baked with
almonds, rabbit casserole and roast loin of lamb with redcurrants and
capers. The luncheon menu includes lighter items like ploughman's,
salads and omelettes. Set Sunday lunch. Book in winter. ☺ ♿

Lunch 12.30–2   *Dinner* 7.30–9.30

KILCHRENAN Ardanaiseig 78% £A

HR Map 17 B5 Strathclyde
By Taynuilt PA35 1HE
Kilchrenan (086 63) 333

Rooms 14
Ensuite bath/shower 14
Direct dial Yes
Room TV Yes
Confirm by arrang.
Last dinner 9
Parking Ample
Room service Limited

Credit Access, Amex, Diners, Visa
Closed end Oct–mid Apr

Visitors come to admire the magnificent gardens of this 19th-century stone house which enjoys breathtaking views over Loch Awe. A grand piano and clusters of chintz suit the splendidly proportioned drawing room and the library with its carved wooden fireplace is a welcoming place for a pre-dinner drink. Bedrooms vary in size, but all have pretty matching fabrics and good period furniture; bathrooms are well maintained. Service is a strong point here, and Jane and Jonathan Brown, the charming new resident directors, go out of their way to make guests comfortable. No children under eight.
Amenities garden, tennis, croquet, clay-pigeon shooting, game fishing, hotel boat, games room, snooker, secretarial services, laundry service.

Restaurant ★ ♛

Lunch 12–2
Dinner 7.30–9
Set D from £25
About £60 for two
Seats 36
Parties 36

Closed end Oct–mid Apr

A view of the loch and pretty decor add to the pleasure of dining in this thoroughly civilised restaurant. Chef Lindsay Little shows a remarkable degree of skill and flair for his tender years and takes great care to match his five-course set menus to local and seasonal produce. A typical dinner might consist of beautifully presented tartare of wild salmon with sprigs of dill and a flavoursome tomato coulis, followed by scallops in filo pastry with a splendid beurre blanc, or roast spring lamb and fresh vegetables among a range of main courses. Iced pear soufflé or chocolate truffle cake to finish.
Specialities fillet of beef, breast of duckling, best end of lamb, wild salmon.

♟ indicates a **well-chosen** house wine

KILCHRENAN Taychreggan Hotel 67% £C/D

HR Map 17 B5 Strathclyde
By Taynuilt PA35 1HQ
Kilchrenan (086 63) 211

Credit Access, Amex, Diners, Visa
Closed 29 Oct–Mon before Easter

On the shores of Loch Awe nestles this whitewashed hotel which has undergone sympathetic conversion from a simple drovers' inn. Peace, tranquillity and dramatic scenery are the attractions here, and their well-maintained establishment is the Taylors' pride and joy. There are a number of pleasant lounge areas, while the bedrooms are quiet and very pretty. *Amenities* garden, croquet, coarse & game fishing, boating, board sailing, secretarial services, laundry service.

| *Rooms* 16 | *Direct dial* Yes | *Confirm by* 6 | *Parking* Ample |
| *Ensuite bath/shower* 16 | *Room TV* No | *Last dinner* 9 | *Room service* All day |

Restaurant

Set L £11
Set D £17.50
About £40 for two
Seats 40
Parties 40

A comfortable, pretty restaurant where the hallmark is excellent local produce, sympathetically handled. Gail Struthers' well-balanced five-course menus offer good wholesome fare without fuss and frills; you might start with Loch Etive prawns with herb mayonnaise, then move on to grilled fillet of halibut with fresh crayfish sauce or grilled escalope of salmon with mustard and tarragon sauce. Simple sweets to finish. ♟ Well-chosen ♟ ♿

Lunch 12–2.15 *Dinner* 7.30–9
Closed 29 Oct–Mon before Easter

KILDRUMMY　　　Kildrummy Castle Hotel　71%　　£D

HR Map 17 C4 Grampian
By Alford AB3 8RA
Kildrummy (033 65) 288
Telex 94012529

Rooms 16
Ensuite bath/shower 16
Direct dial Yes
Room TV Yes
Confirm by arrang.
Last dinner 9
Parking Ample
Room service All day

Credit Access, Amex, Diners, Visa
Closed 4 Jan–14 Mar

Romance seems part of the fabric of this castellated country house. There's a ruined castle in the grounds, a grand panelled hall complete with hunting trophies and a dramatic staircase inviting inspection of the comfortable bedrooms. Excellent heating coupled with thoughtful touches like electric blankets, tea-makers, fruit and flowers help to create the atmosphere of a country house without constraints to comfort. Public rooms include a splendidly solid bar, hung with tapestries. By contrast, the drawing room is light and airy, with garden views echoed in floral fabrics on comfortable chairs and sofas. There's also a peaceful library overlooking the ruins. *Amenities* garden, game fishing, billiards, secretarial services, laundry service.

Our inspectors *never* book in the name of Egon Ronay's Guides.
They disclose their identity only if they are considering an establishment
for inclusion in the next edition of the Guide.

KILFINAN　　　Kilfinan Hotel　*NEW ENTRY*　　£E

IR Map 17 B5 Strathclyde
Nr Tighnabruaich PA21 2AP
Kilfinan (070 082) 201

Credit Access, Amex, Diners, Visa

Next to the ancient church of St. Finan, this former coaching inn offers up-to-date comforts and old-fashioned hospitality. Some bedrooms are larger and more attractively furnished than others, but all have modern carpeted bathrooms and lots of thoughtful little extras. There are two bars, one a popular local rendezvous. Good freshly prepared breakfasts.
Amenities garden, game & sea fishing, clay-pigeon shooting, pool table, laundry service.

Rooms 11	*Direct dial* Yes	*Confirm by* arrang.	*Parking* Ample
Ensuite bath/shower 11	*Room TV* Yes	*Last dinner* 9.30	*Room service* 24 hours

Restaurant　*NEW ENTRY*

Set D *from* £15
About £40 *for two*
Seats 22
Parties 50

Top-quality produce goes into David Kinnear's dishes, including game from surrounding estates. Seafood terrine with tomato coulis is a nice starter, and both the carte and the set menu provide a trio of main courses such as salmon with saffron sauce, Brie-stuffed chicken with mushroom sauce and grilled lamb cutlets. The room has an Edwardian feel, linen-clad tables and a crackling log fire.

Lunch by arrang.　*Dinner* 7.30–9.30

KILLIECRANKIE　　　Killiecrankie Hotel　60%　　£E

H Map 17 C4 Tayside
By Pitlochry PH16 5LG
Pitlochry (0796) 3220

Closed 12 Oct–Easter

Loyal guests return year after year to this friendly, family-run hotel – a former dower house set in attractive grounds near the A9. In winter the bar with its cheerful open fire is a cosy place to be, while in summer the sun lounge is a favoured retreat. Prettily decorated, pine-furnished bedrooms are full of thoughtful extras like magazines. Compact bath/shower rooms.
Amenities garden, putting, croquet.

Rooms 12	*Room phone* No	*Confirm by* 6	*Parking* Ample
Ensuite bath/shower 10	*Room TV* No	*Last dinner* 8.30	*Room service* All day

KILMORE Glenfeochan House 70% *NEW ENTRY* £D/E

HR **Map 17 B5** Strathclyde
Nr Oban PA34 4QR
Kilmore (063 177) 273

Rooms 3
Ensuite bath/shower 3
Room phone No
Room TV Yes
Confirm by arrang.
Last dinner 8
Parking Ample
Room service All day

Closed Dec–Mar

A long drive through woodland brings the visitor to a greystone turreted house set among six acres of glorious gardens and grounds. The building dates from 1875 and has been lovingly restored by sociable owners David and Patricia Babor. Guests meet for a drink and a chat in a splendid drawing room replete with antiques, fine fabrics and fresh flowers gathered from the garden. The three bedrooms also boast antiques, plus thick carpets and pretty floral curtains. Tea-makers and digital clock radios are provided, along with plenty of fresh fruit. Excellent breakfasts with home-made marmalade and home-baked bread. No children under ten.
Amenities garden, game fishing, croquet.

Restaurant 🍴

Set D £15
About £40 *for two*
Seats 6
Parking Ample

Residents meet in the drawing room at 8, and non-residents will be catered for if prior arrangements are made. Everyone will enjoy the delightful food prepared in straightforward style by Patricia Babor on her daily-changing no-choice dinner menu. Freshness is paramount, and most of the raw materials come from the estate, including salmon and trout, game and a wealth of fruit, vegetables and salads. 🍵 &

Lunch by arrang. *Dinner* 8 for 8.30
Closed Dec–Mar

We publish annually,
so make sure you use the current edition.
It's worth it!

KILWINNING Montgreenan Mansion House 74% £D/E

H **Map 12 A2** Strathclyde
Montgreenan Street KA13 7QZ
Kilwinning (0294) 57733
Telex 778525

Rooms 11
Ensuite bath/shower 11
Direct dial Yes
Room TV Yes
Confirm by arrang.
Last dinner 9.30
Parking Ample
Room service All day

Credit Access, Amex, Diners, Visa

Built in 1817 and set amid 45 acres of splendid grounds, this fine Regency mansion stands at the end of a long wooded drive off the A736. Day rooms enjoy splendid garden views and include a handsome high-ceilinged bar with green leather chesterfields; a lovely, light, elegantly furnished drawing room with polished wood floor and fine rugs; and a smaller, book-lined lounge (formerly the library). Bedrooms feature attractive period furnishings and mini-bars; first-floor rooms are slightly larger than those above. Bathrooms – two with luxury spa baths – are mostly spacious, light and airy. No dogs.
Amenities garden, tennis, croquet, billiards, secretarial services, laundry service.

★ For a *discount* on next year's guide, see **An Offer for Answers**. ★

KINCLAVEN BY STANLEY   Ballathie House   73%   £C/D

H Map 17 C5 Tayside
Perth PH1 4QN
Meikleour (025 083) 268

Rooms 22
Ensuite bath/shower 22
Direct dial Yes
Room TV Yes
Confirm by arrang.
Last dinner 8.30
Parking Ample
Room service All day

Credit Access, Amex, Diners, Visa
Closed Feb

This Scottish baronial-style hotel in lovely grounds overlooking the river Tay offers most attractive accommodation in smartly refurbished bedrooms. Each is individually furnished with co-ordinating fabrics, and thoughtfully equipped with many extras from baskets of fruit to hair-dryers and radio alarms. The most palatial enjoy fine river and garden views. Stylish bathrooms – four with Victorian fittings –

are well stocked with towels and toiletries. Elegant public areas range from a comfortable drawing room with relaxing garden views and an appealing cocktail bar, to a quiet morning room with a very restful atmosphere. *Amenities* garden, tennis, putting, croquet, clay-pigeon shooting, game fishing, laundry service.

---

 is our symbol for an **outstanding** wine list

KINGUSSIE   The Cross

RR Map 17 C4 Highland
High Street PH21 1HX
Kingussie (054 02) 762

Set D £13.50, Sat £17.50
About £36 *for two*
Seats 20
Parties 18
Parking Ample

An intimate restaurant where a log fire burns in the cosy bar-lounge and flowers and candles grace the small dining room. The enthusiasm for food and wine is immediately apparent and Ruth Hadley's meals cannot fail to please. The short à la carte menu draws on local produce where possible; Saturday nights offer a limited choice, fixed-price gastronomic menu only. The cheeseboard features unusual French and English cheeses. ⊖

Dinner only 6.30–9.30
Closed Mon (& Sun in winter), 1st 2 wks June & 3 wks Dec

BEDROOMS 3   £F
With bath/shower 3

Three bedrooms with coordinating fabrics, nice freestanding furniture, books, flowers and smart modern bathrooms (two with shower only). No under-tens. No dogs. No smoking.

KINGUSSIE   Osprey Hotel Restaurant   *NEW ENTRY*

R Map 17 C4 Highland
Inverness-shire
Kingussie (054 02) 510

Set D £14
About £36 *for two*
Seats 23
Parking Ample

Credit Access, Amex, Diners, Visa

Sharing a table is part of the fun at this unpretentious and popular little hotel restaurant. Duncan Reeves serves drinks in the lounge, while Pauline does sterling work in the kitchen, using naturally produced local ingredients in delightful dishes such as wild mushrooms with herbs, cold pheasant soufflé and fillets of sole stuffed with the marvellous peat-smoked salmon from North Uist. Pauline's Pudding is a delicious concoction of grapes, cream and crunchy caramel. There's also a small but well-chosen selection of cheese. To accompany all this fine fare there's a shrewdly compiled list of excellent wines: Chasse Spleen '82 (halves), Bourgneuf-Vayron '78, three Pulignys from Leflaive. ♀ Well-chosen ⊖

D only at 7.30
Closed Nov–Dec

KINLOCH RANNOCH Loch Rannoch Hotel   59%   £D/E

H Map 17 C4 Tayside
By Pitlochry PH16 5PS
Kinloch Rannoch (088 22) 201

Credit Access, Amex, Diners, Visa

Beautifully situated overlooking Loch Rannoch, this late-Victorian hotel is the perfect choice for an activity holiday. Public areas are bright and appealing; bedrooms simple, modern and well kept. Sports and leisure facilities also used by adjacent time-share apartments. *Amenities* garden, indoor swimming pool, sauna, solarium, whirl-pool bath, gymnasium, tennis, squash, coarse fishing, games room, snooker, in-house movies, fax, coffee shop (8am–10pm).

Rooms 13	*Direct dial* Yes	*Confirm by* 6	*Parking* Ample
Ensuite bath/shower 13	*Room TV* Yes	*Last dinner* 10	*Room service* All day

KINLOCHBERVIE — Kinlochbervie Hotel 66% £D

HR Map 16 B2 Highland
By Lairg IV27 4RP
Kinlochbervie (097 182) 275

Credit Access, Amex, Diners, Visa
Restricted service 15 Nov–1 Mar

The hotel stands on a hill overlooking the sea in rugged Highland setting. Picture windows in the lounge are perfect for watching the sea's changing moods, while the convivial lounge bar is the place for enjoying morning coffee, afternoon tea or a wee sampling of malt whiskies. Bedrooms are modern, cosy and thoughtfully equipped, attractively furnished and very comfortable. David and Geraldine Gregory are kind, thoughtful hosts. **Amenities** fax, laundry service.

Rooms 14	*Direct dial* Yes	*Confirm by* 6	*Parking* Ample
Ensuite bath/shower 14	*Room TV* Yes	*Last dinner* 8.30	*Room service* All day

Restaurant ⌇

Set D £21.50
About £50 for two
Seats 40

Nicely varied menus take advantage of local produce and Geraldine's cooking brings out all the freshness and flavour. David has charge of the smokery, and his salmon makes an excellent starter. We followed with a very good cauliflower soup, then came a fine dish of brill, cod and prawns in a delicious sauce with a citrus tang. Sweets from the sideboard, coffee in the lounge. Good wines: Pouilly Fumé (Pabiot) '86, Ch. Fombrauge St. Emilion '82. ☺

Lunch by arrang. only   *Dinner* 7.30–8.30
Restricted service 15 Nov–1 Mar

Any person using our name to obtain free hospitality is a fraud.
Proprietors, please inform the police and us.

KINROSS — Windlestrae Hotel 61% £E

H Map 12 C1 Tayside
The Muirs KY13 7AS
Kinross (0577) 63217

Credit Access, Amex, Diners, Visa

The former swimming pool makes an interesting two-level bar at this cheerful family-run hotel, and the contemporary-style foyer-lounge is smart and appealing. A modern extension houses most of the accommodation – bright, neat rooms with darkwood furniture, trouser presses, hairdryers, radio-alarms and well-stocked bathrooms. Main-house rooms are similarly equipped but homelier in character. **Amenities** garden, sauna, in-house movies, laundry service. ♿

Rooms 18	*Direct dial* Yes	*Confirm by* 6	*Parking* Ample
Ensuite bath/shower 18	*Room TV* Yes	*Last dinner* 9.30	*Room service* Limited

KIRKMICHAEL — Log Cabin Hotel 59% £F

H Map 17 C4 Tayside
PH10 7NB
Strathardle (025 081) 288

Credit Access, Diners, Visa
Closed mid Nov–mid Dec

Set 900 feet above sea level in wooded hills, this modern hotel lives up to its name in its structure of Norwegian logs. It's an ideal location for outdoor types while, for the more sedentary, the pleasant lounge and bar are well-equipped with books, games and magazines. Bedrooms are basically furnished and bathrooms simply equipped. Attention to maintenance necessary. **Amenities** garden, shooting, clay-pigeon shooting, game fishing, games room, laundry service. ♿

Rooms 13	*Room phone* No	*Confirm by* arrang.	*Parking* Ample
Ensuite bath/shower 13	*Room TV* Some	*Last dinner* 9	*Room service* Limited

KNIPOCH — Knipoch Hotel

See under OBAN

KYLE OF LOCHALSH — Lochalsh Hotel 65% £C/D

H Map 16 A3 Highland
IV40 8AF
Kyle of Lochalsh (0599) 4202
Telex 75318

Credit Access, Amex, Diners, Visa
Closed 2 wks Xmas

A squat white building next to the Skye ferry terminal. The setting is very pleasant, and bright day rooms, smartly carpeted in contemporary style, make the most of it. Bedrooms, which share the views, are tastefully decorated and well equipped (teletext TVs, hairdryers, tea-makers, mineral water, desks, often easy chairs). Spotless, fully-tiled bathrooms include some with Victorian-style baths and fittings. **Amenities** garden, hotel boat, 24-hour lounge service.

Rooms 40	*Direct dial* Yes	*Confirm by* arrang.	*Parking* Ample
Ensuite bath/shower 38	*Room TV* Yes	*Last dinner* 9	*Room service* All day

LANARK   Cartland Bridge Hotel   55%   £E

H **Map 12 C2** Strathclyde
ML11 9UF
Lanark (0555) 4426

Credit Access, Amex, Diners, Visa

A tree-lined drive leads from the A73 just north of Lanark to this imposing Scottish baronial residence. There's a welcoming log fire in the panelled reception area, an inviting lounge with smart, soft blue decor, and a choice of two bars. Spacious, traditionally appointed bedrooms offer radio-alarms but no TV. Bathrooms (none en suite) range from basic to quite attractive.
Amenities garden, coarse fishing, laundry service.

Rooms 15	*Room phone* Yes	*Confirm by* arrang.	*Parking* Ample
Ensuite bath/shower 0	*Room TV* No	*Last dinner* 9.30	*Room service* Limited

LANGBANK   Gleddoch House Hotel   70%   £C

HR **Map 12 B1** Strathclyde
PA14 6YE
Langbank (047 554) 711
Telex 779801

Rooms 33
Ensuite bath/shower 33
Direct dial Yes
Room TV Yes
Confirm by arrang.
Last dinner 9.30
Parking Ample
Room service 24 hours

Credit Access, Amex, Diners, Visa

There is a fine view of the River Clyde from this attractive, white-painted hotel, built in the 1920s by the shipbuilding magnate Sir James Lithgow. Pleasantly traditional public rooms include the fine high-ceilinged foyer with its pillars, paintings and panelling, the clubby bar with its inviting leather chesterfields and fine weather terrace, and the chintzy first-floor lounge. Bedrooms are pretty and spacious, with floral decor and either period furnishings in the main house or modern style in the annexe. All are equipped with tea-makers, fresh fruit, trouser presses, hairdryers, and good carpeted bathrooms.
Amenities garden, sauna, squash, golf course, riding, snooker, pool table, secretarial services, laundry service.

Restaurant   ♕

Set L £9.75
Set D £22
About £60 for two
Seats 80
Parties 120

Charles Price's respectful and imaginative treatment of lovely fresh produce is complemented by a quietly elegant setting. There's a four-course house menu, or such tempting choices as a terrine of smoked trout, mackerel and prawns, whisky-flavoured crab broth, or a sole and lobster mousse, followed by venison with a juniper and port sauce, casseroled veal kidney and sweetbread in a basil and lime sauce, or brill with lobster. ♟ Well-chosen ⊖

Lunch 12.30–2   *Dinner* 7.30–9.30
Closed L Sat, 1 & 2 Jan & 26 & 27 Dec

LERWICK   Shetland Hotel   61%   *NEW ENTRY*   £D/E

H **Map 16 D2** Shetland
Holmsgarth Road ZE1 0PW
Lerwick (0595) 5515
Telex 75432

Credit Access, Amex, Diners, Visa

Built into a hillside overlooking the harbour, this cleverly designed hotel dates from 1984. With bright, pleasant day rooms and an impressive conference facility, it's popular with business people and the tourists who pour off the boats in summer. Bedrooms are of a decent size, with good lighting and practical fitted furniture.
Amenities indoor swimming pool, sauna, solarium, secretarial services, fax, coffee shop (10am–11pm).

Rooms 64	*Direct dial* Yes	*Confirm by* 6	*Parking* Ample
Ensuite bath/shower 64	*Room TV* Yes	*Last dinner* 9.30	*Room service* 24 hours

LETHAM   Fernie Castle Hotel   60%   £D/E

H **Map 17 C5** Fife
Nr Cupar KY7 7RU
Letham (033 781) 381

Credit Access, Amex, Diners, Visa

Set alongside the A914, this historic castle provides a warm and friendly welcome. The Keep Bar has a cellar-like atmosphere and there's a spacious elegant drawing room on the first floor. Bedrooms are well equipped and have simple bathrooms. Housekeeping needs attention and breakfast was a disappointment.
Amenities garden, putting, clay-pigeon shooting, coarse fishing, satellite TV, secretarial services, fax, laundry service.

Rooms 16	*Direct dial* Yes	*Confirm by* 6	*Parking* Ample
Ensuite bath/shower 16	*Room TV* Yes	*Last dinner* 9.30	*Room service* All day

LINLITHGOW — Champany Inn, Chop & Ale House

R Map 12 C1 Lothian
Champany
Philipstoun (050 683) 4352

About £30 for two
Seats 32
Parking Ample

Credit Access, Amex, Diners, Visa

A simpler version of the starred restaurant sharing this lovingly restored 16th-century building, the Chop & Ale House uses the same prime ingredients with as much care as its more upmarket cousin. Starter might be brandy-enriched oatcakes; for main course don't miss the beef, which is the speciality. Straightforward, succulent sweets to finish. Concise, well chosen wine list with around eight own-label imports. ♀ Well-chosen ℮

Lunch 12–2, Sat till 2.15   *Dinner* 6.30–10, Sat 6–10
Closed 3 wks Xmas

LINLITHGOW — Champany Inn Restaurant ★ ♛ ᖆ

R Map 12 C1 Lothian
Champany EH49 7LU
Philipstoun (050 683) 4532

Lunch 12.30–2
Dinner 7.30–10
About £58 for two
Seats 50
Parties 50
Parking Ample

Credit Access, Amex, Diners, Visa
Closed L Sat, all Sun, 1 wk Nov
& 3 wks Xmas

The Davidsons' tireless pursuit of excellence continues at their splendid hexagonal restaurant. Clive – a former butcher – uses his training to produce the finest beef, rearing the animals himself and supervising every stage right to the table, where steaks arrive chargrilled to perfection. Another speciality is his salmon starters, available in seven versions from grilled to gravalax. Shellfish comes fresh from a tank

in the bar, vegetables are steamed to order, and desserts include home-made ice cream. Superb burgundies (lovely Clos St Denis Dujac '80) as well as fine Californian, Australian and South African wines. ***Specialities*** charcoal grilled salmon, steak tartare, châteaubriand, home-made ice cream. ➥ Outstanding ♀ Well-chosen ℮

LOCHGAIR — Lochgair Hotel 54% £F

H Map 17 B5 Strathclyde
By Lochgilphead PA31 8SA
Minard (0546) 86333

Credit Access, Visa

Craig Whale extends a warm welcome to guests at his modest hotel on the A83, in a tiny village on the shores of Loch Fyne. Inviting areas in which to relax include a roomy foyer with a variety of easy chairs, a pleasant lounge with comfortable settees and two bars. Good-size bedrooms offer simple, neat accommodation, and half have their own bathrooms.
Amenities garden, pool table.

Rooms 16	*Room phone* No	*Confirm by* arrang.	*Parking* Ample
Ensuite bath/shower 9	*Room TV* No	*Last dinner* 9.30	*Room service* Limited

LUNDIN LINKS — Old Manor Hotel 62% £E

HR Map 17 C5 Fife
Leven Road KY8 6AJ
Lundin Links (0333) 320368
Telex 727606

Credit Access, Amex, Visa
Closed 26 Dec, 1 & 2 Jan

A 19th-century manor standing atop a hill overlooking a golf course and the Firth of Forth. The spacious cocktail bar has splendid views (although attention is distracted by the choice of over 100 malt whiskies) and there is a comfortable foyer-lounge. Bedrooms in a new extension are attractive and well-equipped, while those in the main house are older in style. No dogs.
Amenities garden, laundry service.

Rooms 19	*Direct dial* Yes	*Confirm by* arrang.	*Parking* Ample
Ensuite bath/shower 19	*Room TV* Yes	*Last dinner* 9.30	*Room service* 24 hours

Restaurant

Set L £8.25
Set D £14.50
About £42 for two
Seats 50
Parties 100

Enjoy the view of the sea while you tuck into fresh local fish at this traditional, comfortable restaurant. Piscine dishes include Largo Bay crab mayonnaise, poached fillet of haddock and scallops and prawns in white wine, Noilly Prat and cream sauce, while meat eaters might go for haunch of venison with green peppercorns or fillet of beef in armagnac and raisin sauce. Home-made sweets are a high point. ℮

Lunch 12.30–2   *Dinner* 7–9, Sat 7–9.30
Closed Xmas night, 1 & 2 Jan

MILNGAVIE — Black Bull Thistle Hotel — 61% — £D

H Map 12 B1 Strathclyde
Main Street G62 6BH
041-956 2291
Telex 778323

Credit Access, Amex, Diners, Visa

Located in the centre of Milngavie, six miles from Glasgow, this is a popular hotel. The first-floor lounge is warm and welcoming and there's a choice of four bars, from the simple to the stylish. Smart bedrooms have darkwood units and are well equipped, with tea-makers, trouser presses and hairdryers as standard extras. Bathrooms are equally impressive. *Amenities* in-house movies, secretarial services, fax, laundry service, coffee shop (10am–5pm).

Rooms 27	Direct dial Yes	Confirm by arrang.	Parking Ample
Ensuite bath/shower 27	Room TV Yes	Last dinner 9.30	Room service 24 hours

MOFFAT — Beechwood Country House Hotel — 60% — *NEW ENTRY* — £E

H Map 12 C3
Dumfries & Galloway
DG10 9RS
Moffat (0683) 20210

Credit Access, Amex, Diners, Visa

The Cheynes are friendly hosts and there's a welcoming atmosphere at their sturdy Victorian hotel. The cosy lounges are furnished in traditional style, with plenty of plants, books and games to create a homely feel. Bedrooms are bright and airy, and the best have been redecorated with pretty wallcoverings and matching fabrics: the others are in line for the same treatment. Clean, tidy bathrooms have good toiletries. *Amenities* garden.

Rooms 7	Direct dial Yes	Confirm by arrang.	Parking Ample
Ensuite bath/shower 7	Room TV Yes	Last dinner 9	Room service Limited

MOFFAT — Mercury Hotel — 52% — £D

H Map 12 C3
Dumfries & Galloway
Ladyknowe DG10 9EL
Moffat (0683) 20464
Telex 64183

Credit Access, Amex, Diners, Visa

A basic hotel, popular with coach operators, where some much-needed refurbishment is planned. Public rooms include a large bar with a lounge alcove and a pine-clad restaurant. Bedrooms have melamine chests of drawers and dressing tables, open wardrobes, painted chipboard paper or wallpaper on the walls, comfortable beds, some with new bedspreads, and tea/coffee-makers. All bathrooms have shower fitments. *Amenities* pool table, secretarial services, laundry service.

Rooms 51	Room phone Some	Confirm by arrang.	Parking Ample
Ensuite bath/shower 48	Room TV Yes	Last dinner 9	Room service 24 hours

MUIR OF ORD — Ord Arms Hotel — £F

I Map 16 B3 Highland
Great North Road IV6 7XR
Inverness (0463) 870286

Credit Access

A mellow, stone-built hotel which provides pleasant accommodation. A stag's head and a highly polished antique sideboard establish a traditional feel to the foyer-reception, while the cocktail bar has pastel colours and upholstered wicker chairs. Bedrooms mostly have white melamine or louvred fitted furniture and Laura Ashley-style wallpaper and fabrics. All have tea/coffee-makers. *Amenities* garden, secretarial services, laundry service, coffee shop (9am–10pm).

Rooms 15	Room phone Yes	Confirm by arrang.	Parking Ample
Ensuite bath/shower 8	Room TV Yes	Last dinner 10	Room service All day

NAIRN — Clifton Hotel — 70% — £D

HR Map 16 C3 Highlands
Viewfield Street IV12 4HW
Nairn (0667) 53119

Rooms 16
Ensuite bath/shower 16
Room phone No
Room TV No
Confirm by arrang.
Last dinner 9.30
Parking Ample
Room service All day

Credit Access, Amex, Diners, Visa
Closed 1 Nov–1 Mar

Overlooking the Moray Firth to the rear, this creeper-clad Victorian house crammed full of antique furniture, objets d'art and paintings is splendidly characterful. The drawing room in particular is a real showpiece of the collector's art, while other public areas include a TV room and a bar that is being converted into a sitting room (drinks are served by a waiter). Bedrooms reflect the style of the day rooms

in their period furniture, artefacts and books; modern amenities like radio, TV and telephone are conspicuously absent. Housekeeping is sometimes less than perfect but the eccentric charm of the place makes up for any minor shortcomings.
Amenities garden, valeting, laundry service.

Restaurant & Green Room ♛

About £40 for two
Seats 60
Parties 14

Guests are invited to eat in the main dining room or in the smaller, delightfully elegant Green Room. Daily-changing menus with a strong French accent offer straightforward dishes like eggs en cocotte, potage parmentier, fresh salmon beurre rouge, veal blanquette and beef fillet marchand de vin. Ingredients are first-class, cooking is careful and presentation most attractive. Excellent clarets: Ch. Branaire '81, Ch. Gloria '70. Booking essential. 🍷 Well-chosen ⊘

Lunch 12.30–1.30 *Dinner* 7–9.30
Closed 1 Nov–1 Mar

NAIRN Golf View Hotel 59% £C/D

H **Map 16 C3** Highland
Seabank Road IV12 4HD
Nairn (0667) 52301
Telex 75134

Credit Access, Amex, Diners, Visa

This solid Victorian hotel is a firm favourite with golfers. Pleasantly situated on the shores of the Moray Firth, it offers comfortably traditional public rooms and practical, decent accommodation. Best bedrooms, at the front, have sea views and freestanding furniture. *Amenities* garden, outdoor swimming pool, sauna, hairdressing, tennis, putting, games room, in-house movies, secretarial services, laundry service, creche (Easter, summer & Christmas).

Rooms 55	*Direct dial* Yes	*Confirm by* 6	*Parking* Ample
Ensuite bath/shower 54	*Room TV* Yes	*Last dinner* 9.15	*Room service* 24 hours

NAIRN Newton Hotel 65% £D/E

H **Map 16 C3** Highland
Inverness Road IV12 4RX
Nairn (0667) 53144
Telex 739248

Credit Access, Amex, Diners, Visa

Access is by a winding, tree-lined road, and the austere, imposing hall stands in extensive grounds overlooking the Moray Firth. Antiques and pine panelling grace the handsomely proportioned day rooms, and decor in the lofty bedrooms gives the feel of a well-cared-for private home. 14 contemporary rooms are in converted outbuildings set peacefully round a garden courtyard. *Amenities* garden, sauna, tennis, croquet, putting, pool table, laundry service.

Rooms 44	*Direct dial* Yes	*Confirm by* arrang.	*Parking* Ample
Ensuite bath/shower 44	*Room TV* Yes	*Last dinner* 9.15	*Room service* 24 hours

**We welcome bona fide complaints and recommendations
on the tear-out pages at the back of the book for readers' comment.
They are followed up by our professional team.**

NEWBURGH Udny Arms Hotel 60% £E/F

H **Map 16 D3** Grampian
Main Street AB4 0BL
Newburgh (035 86) 444
Telex 265871

Credit Access, Amex, Visa

A charming Victorian hotel with high standards of comfort. Period furniture and prints give a reassuringly traditional feel to the chintzy lounge, and there's a homely cocktail bar with fishing and bird mementos. Characterful bedrooms are individually decorated and furnished, and equipped with tea-makers and radios. Carpeted bathrooms have tubs with showers. *Amenities* garden, secretarial services, laundry service, coffee shop (11am–11pm, limited in winter).

Rooms 26	*Direct dial* Yes	*Confirm by* arrang.	*Parking* Ample
Ensuite bath/shower 26	*Room TV* Yes	*Last dinner* 9.30	*Room service* 24 hours

NEWTON STEWART Bruce Hotel 60% £E

H **Map 13 B4**
Dumfries & Galloway
88 Queen Street DG8 6JL
Newton Stewart (0671) 2294
Credit Access, Amex, Diners, Visa
Closed 2nd week Dec–2nd week
Feb

A family-run hotel offering a warm welcome. A boldly striped carpet, orange seating and a copper fire surround make for a vivid lounge, while the bar is divided in two, one side a cosy burgundy colour, the other brighter and more modern. Bedrooms are simply furnished with white units and floral curtains; bathrooms have orange floral wallcoverings. *Amenities* solarium, keep-fit equipment, in-house movies, secretarial services, laundry service, children's playroom.

Rooms 18	*Direct dial* Yes	*Confirm by* arrang.	*Parking* Ample
Ensuite bath/shower 18	*Room TV* Yes	*Last dinner* 9	*Room service* All day

NEWTON STEWART   Creebridge House Hotel   57%   £E

H Map 13 B4
Dumfries & Galloway
DG8 6NP
Newton Stewart (0671) 2121

Credit Access, Visa

Local staff are friendly and hospitable at this former shooting lodge, and the bar is a popular meeting place. Overnight accommodation is fairly modest, but certainly adequate, the best and biggest rooms being six that overlook the garden; those in the rear block are more basic. The lounge, with a grand piano and smart new carpeting, is a lovely spot to relax and enjoy the view.
Amenities garden, croquet, laundry service.

Rooms 17	Direct dial Yes	Confirm by arrang.	Parking Ample
Ensuite bath/shower 17	Room TV Yes	Last dinner 8.30	Room service All day

NEWTON STEWART   Kirroughtree Hotel   75%   £B

HR Map 13 B4
Dumfries & Galloway
DG8 6AN
Newton Stewart (0671) 2141

Rooms 23
Ensuite bath/shower 23
Direct dial Yes
Room TV Yes
Confirm by arrang.
Last dinner 9.30
Parking Ample
Room service All day

Closed 4 Jan–2 Mar

Owner, manager and staff work as a happy team to ensure a pleasant stay for guests at this handsome Georgian mansion. The setting, in eight acres of landscaped gardens, is both picturesque and peaceful, and there are some splendid walks. Public rooms, which show some French and Spanish influences, are quite opulent but also homely, particularly the lounge with its velour-clad settees and onyx-topped coffee tables. Luxurious bedrooms are furnished in French style. They vary in size – one is a suite with a separate lounge. Bathrooms are smartly tiled and carpeted. Half-board terms only. No children under ten.
Amenities garden, tennis, badminton, putting, bowling green, laundry service.

Restaurant   ♨

Set D £23
About £55 for two
Seats 48
Parties 30
Parking Ample

Two talented chefs – Adi Schmidt and Ian Bennett – and two plush dining rooms, one decorated in red, the other, for non-smokers, in blue. Four-course dinner menus and the lunchtime à la carte provide a short but tempting choice, from terrine of leeks and creamy celery soup to sole with salmon mousseline, herby loin of lamb and breast of duck accompanied by a subtle blackcurrant flavoured sauce. Splendid vegetables, home-baked bread and sweets that definitely should not be resisted. In the cellar, some fine classic wines: Cornas '84 Alain Voge; Eichberg Gewürztraminer '83 Dopff au Moulin. Service is polite and professional. ♟ Well-chosen ⊖

Lunch 12.30–1.30   *Dinner* 7–9.30
Closed 4 Jan–2 Mar

We publish annually,
so make sure you use the current edition.
It's worth it!

NORTH BERWICK   Marine Hotel   63%   £C/D

H Map 12 D1 Lothian
Cromwell Road EH39 4LZ
North Berwick (0620) 2406
Telex 72550

Credit Access, Amex, Diners, Visa

Despite major improvements to this gabled and turreted Victorian mansion overlooking a golf course, standards of cleanliness and housekeeping still need to be raised. Refurbished areas include an attractive reception lounge and cosy bar and all the bedrooms, which are well equipped and have neat bathrooms. *Amenities* garden, outdoor swimming pool, sauna, solarium, tennis, squash, putting, games room, snooker, laundry service.

Rooms 84	Direct dial Yes	Confirm by 6	Parking Ample
Ensuite bath/shower 84	Room TV Yes	Last dinner 9.30	Room service 24 hours

NORTH MIDDLETON Borthwick Castle   67%   £C

H Map 12 D2 Lothian
By Gorebridge EH23 4QY
Gorebridge (0875) 20514
Telex 72422

Credit Amex, Diners, Visa

Historians and romantics will enjoy a stay at this impressive baronial keep. Dating from 1430, its 14-foot thick walls once harboured Mary Queen of Scots and the Earl of Bothwell during the Queen's last days of freedom. The structure is protected by conservation orders so some bathrooms are only big enough for showers. Bedrooms, reached by narrow winding stone staircases, are grand, with tiny windows and solid old-fashioned furniture; the rooms used by the Queen and Bothwell have four-posters. The magnificent Great Hall has a 20-foot high canopied fireplace and a minstrel's gallery and the splendid lounge still contains Mary's private chapel. No dogs.
Amenities garden.

Rooms 10	*Direct dial* Yes	*Confirm by* 7	*Parking* Ample
Ensuite bath/shower 10	*Room TV* No	*Last dinner* 9	*Room service* None

Our inspectors *never* book in the name of Egon Ronay's Guides.
They disclose their identity only if they are considering an establishment
for inclusion in the next edition of the Guide.

OBAN   Alexandra Hotel   57%   £D/E

H Map 17 B5 Strathclyde
Corran Esplanade PA34 5AA
Oban (0631) 62381
Telex 778215

Credit Access, Amex, Diners, Visa
Closed end Oct–early Apr

A Victorian seafront hotel whose day rooms, including two modest lounges and a smart cocktail bar, look out over the harbour to the hills of the outlying islands. Some of the bedrooms have been perked up with cheerful modern fabrics and up-to-date tiled bathrooms, but still have no telephones. Leisure facilities are planned for 1989.
Amenities garden, games room, in-house movies, secretarial services, laundry service, children's playroom.

Rooms 56	*Room phone* No	*Confirm by* 6	*Parking* Ample
Ensuite bath/shower 49	*Room TV* Yes	*Last dinner* 9	*Room service* 24 hours

OBAN   Columba Hotel   61%   £E

H Map 17 B5 Strathclyde
North Pier,
Corran Esplanade PA34 5PP
Oban (0631) 62183
Telex 728256

Credit Access, Amex, Diners, Visa

Situated between the quayside and the town, this hotel offers stylish day rooms including two bars, one with a cheerful nautical theme. Most bedrooms have decent darkwood furniture, attractive coordinated fabrics and smart bathrooms; a few older-style rooms have showers only. All are equipped with remote-control TVs, hairdryers, trouser presses and tea-makers. *Amenities* in-house movies, secretarial services, fax, laundry service, coffee shop (10am–6pm).

Rooms 49	*Direct dial* Yes	*Confirm by* 6	*Parking* Limited
Ensuite bath/shower 49	*Room TV* Yes	*Last dinner* 10	*Room service* 24 hours

OBAN   Knipoch Hotel   72%   £C

HR Map 17 B5 Strathclyde
Knipoch PA34 4QT
Kilninver (085 26) 251

Rooms 21
Ensuite bath/shower 21
Direct dial Yes
Room TV Yes
Confirm by arrang.
Last dinner 9
Parking Ample
Room service All day

Credit Access, Amex, Diners, Visa
Closed Jan–mid Feb

Set back from the A816, overlooking Loch Feochan, this modernised and much extended Georgian country house is owned and run by the dedicated Craig family. Public areas are comfortably welcoming, sporting leather armchairs and chesterfields, fine rugs, fresh flower arrangements and open fires; there's a lovely stoned-tiled floor in the entrance hall, and individually lit gilt-framed oil paintings adorn the

green panelling in the lounge. Spacious bedrooms are pleasantly if simply furnished, using plain colours throughout except in the curtains and lampshades; bathrooms are fully tiled and offer shower attachments and usual toiletries. Some attention to maintenance is needed. No dogs. *Amenities* garden, laundry service.   *see over*

Knipoch Restaurant ♕ ♫

Set L £12.50
Set D £23
About £60 for two
Seats 44
Parties 24

First-class raw materials, expertly prepared, are the Craig family's key to success. Jenny Craig and her son Colin are justifiably proud of their smoked salmon and scallops (they use their own smokers) and everything on the daily-changing menus, from flavoursome cock-a-leekie to herb-stuffed saddle of lamb, is of really excellent quality. The Scottish tendency to over-salting is a minor grumble. Very good cellar, strong in fine Bordeaux. ♀ Well-chosen ☺

Lunch 12.30–1.30   *Dinner* 7.30–9
Closed Jan–mid Feb

OLD MELDRUM   Meldrum House Hotel   74%   £D/E

HR Map 16 D3 Grampian
AB5 0AE
Old Meldrum (065 12) 2294

Rooms 11
Ensuite bath/shower 10
Direct dial Yes
Room TV Yes
Confirm by arrang.
Last dinner 9.30
Parking Ample
Room service All day

Credit Amex, Diners
Closed mid Dec–beginning Mar

In many ways this lovely grey-stone turreted mansion is run more like a country house than a hotel. Day rooms with log fires, assorted period furniture and antiques, family portraits and photographs, fresh flowers and magazines give the impression of a much-loved family home. All are spacious except the tiny cocktail bar – an ancient stone-walled closet leading off the hall. Characterful bedrooms convey

their own individual style, again suggesting a comfortable private house, with plants, books, pictures and porcelain contributing to this homely feel. Two rooms have four-posters and most have chaises longues. Carpeted bathrooms throughout (one not en suite, three shower rooms). *Amenities* garden, 9-hole golf course.

Restaurant ♕

Set D £19
About £52 for two
Seats 60
Parties 60

Prime local produce is the star attraction at this quietly elegant restaurant, with fish and game making frequent appearances in interesting and unusual guises. Daily-changing menus might feature herring marinated in champagne, haddock and salmon in shrimp sauce, roast wild duck with spiced apple stuffing, and venison in puff pastry. Portions are generous, but leave some room for a tempting dessert from the trolley. ☺ ⛎

Lunch 12–1.30 (Sun residents only)   *Dinner* 7–9.30, Sun 7–8
Closed mid Dec–beginning Mar

ONICH   The Lodge on the Loch   62%   *NEW ENTRY*   £D/E

H Map 17 B4 Highland
Nr Fort William PH33 6RY
Onich (085 53) 238
Telex 94013696

Credit Access, Amex, Diners, Visa
Closed Nov–end Mar

Calm and tranquillity reign at the Young family's friendly hotel, which stands in pretty gardens looking across Onich Bay to the mountains. Soothing colour schemes assist the restful mood in the day rooms, and bedrooms, too, are decorated in gentle shades. Chieftain rooms are the biggest and best, but Laird and Clansman rooms are also very comfortable. Bathrooms are compact, neat and functional. *Amenities* mooring, garden, fax, laundry service.

Rooms 18	*Direct dial* Yes	*Confirm by* arrang.	*Parking* Ample
Ensuite bath/shower 17	*Room TV* Yes	*Last dinner* 9.30	*Room service* All day

ONICH   Onich Hotel   60%   £D/E

H Map 17 B4 Highland
PH33 6RY
Onich (085 53) 214

Credit Access, Amex, Diners, Visa

On the shores of Loch Linnhe, the Onich Hotel welcomes families, and the same owners (two brothers) have run it for 25 years. Neat, smart bedrooms, cheered up by new carpets and bedspreads, all enjoy super views; bathrooms are particularly nice, attractively tiled, bright and spotlessly clean. There are two bars, one for residents only, and a sun lounge. *Amenities* garden, solarium, whirlpool bath, snooker, sea fishing, in-house movies.

Rooms 27	*Direct dial* Yes	*Confirm by* 6	*Parking* Ample
Ensuite bath/shower 27	*Room TV* Yes	*Last dinner* 8.30	*Room service* Limited

PEAT INN | The Peat Inn ★★ ♛ ⌕

RR **Map 17 D5** Fife
Nr Cupar
Peat Inn (033 484) 206

Set L £12.50
Set D £28
About £55 for two
Seats 48
Parties 24
Parking Ample

Credit Access, Amex, Diners, Visa

This intimate, stylish restaurant provides perhaps the best eating in Scotland. David Wilson sees that nothing but the best produce gets into his kitchen, and what comes out is a succession of dishes notable for pure, unsullied flavours. The cellar is magnificent with wonderful burgundies and superb Cabernet Sauvignons from California and Australia (Stag's Leap, Jordan, Balgownie). *Specialities* flan of Arbroath Smokie with lemon sauce; whole lobster in a lightly spiced sauce with Barsac; breast of pigeon with wild mushrooms; caramelised apple pastry with caramel sauce. ▭ Outstanding ⊕ ♣ ら

Lunch at 1   *Dinner* 7–9.30
Closed Sun, Mon, Bank Hols & 1st 2 wks Jan

BEDROOMS 8 **£B/C**
With bath/shower 8

Eight suites provide overnight accommodation of a very high quality: magnificent French reproduction furniture, chintz, sumptuous marble bathrooms and an abundance of cosseting comforts. No dogs.

Our inspectors *never* book in the name of Egon Ronay's Guides.
They disclose their identity only if they are considering an establishment
for inclusion in the next edition of the Guide.

PEEBLES | Cringletie House Hotel 63% | £D/E

H **Map 12 C2** Borders
Eddleston EH45 8PL
Eddleston (072 13) 233

Credit Access, Visa
Closed 27 Dec–mid March

Take a private bridge off the A703 about 2 miles north of Peebles to reach this fine 19th-century mansion set in 28 acres of beautiful grounds. Best of the public rooms is the first floor lounge, which has handsome panelling, a trompe l'oeil ceiling and a carved fireplace. Bedrooms are prettily decorated in homely style and have many thoughtful touches. Bathrooms are spotlessly clean.
Amenities garden, tennis, putting, croquet.

| *Rooms* 16 | *Direct dial* Yes | *Confirm by* 5 | *Parking* Ample |
| *Ensuite bath/shower* 9 | *Room TV* Yes | *Last dinner* 8.30 | *Room service* All day |

PEEBLES | Park Hotel 64% | £D/E

H **Map 12 C2** Borders
Innerleithen Road EH45 8BA
Peebles (0721) 20451
Telex 53168

Credit Access, Amex, Diners, Visa

An elegant whitewashed hotel standing by the A72, with views of pretty gardens, the river Tweed and the Cademuir Hills. Bedrooms, spacious and stylishly traditional in the main part, more modern but equally smart in the extension, have well-kept tiled bathrooms. The bar-lounge has been redesigned with a raised platform area and plush banquette seating. Staff are generally friendly and willing to please.
Amenities garden, putting, secretarial services. ら

| *Rooms* 26 | *Room phone* Yes | *Confirm by* 6 | *Parking* Ample |
| *Ensuite bath/shower* 26 | *Room TV* Yes | *Last dinner* 10 | *Room service* 24 hours |

★ For a *discount* on next year's guide, see **An Offer for Answers.** ★

PEEBLES   Peebles Hotel Hydro   71%   £D

H **Map 12 C2** Borders
Innerleithen Road EH45 8LX
Peebles (0721) 20602
Telex 72568

Rooms 137
Ensuite bath/shower 137
Direct dial Yes
Room TV Yes
Confirm by arrang.
Last dinner 9
Parking Ample
Room service 24 hours

Credit Access, Amex, Diners, Visa

The charming and courteous Pieter van Dijk manages this former hydropathic hotel high above the Tweed valley with great flair and expertise. He heads a loyal, hard-working team whose efforts, and the hotel's comfort and facilities, ensure a high occupancy rate. Bedrooms and bathrooms are well looked after, and many enjoy fine views. Day areas include a roomy, relaxing lounge, a sun lounge and a cosy bar well stocked with malts. No dogs. *Amenities* garden, indoor swimming pool, sauna, steam room, whirlpool bath, gymnasium, hairdressing, tennis, squash, badminton, pitch & putt, putting, croquet, riding, games room, snooker, fax, laundry service, coffee shop (10am–11pm), kiosk, children's play area, helipad.

PEEBLES   Tontine Hotel   59%   £D

H **Map 12 C2** Borders
High Street EH45 8AJ
Peebles (0721) 20892

Credit Access, Amex, Diners, Visa

Built by subscription in the early 19th century, this handsome hotel stands on the high street behind a cobbled, fountained courtyard. Bedrooms, in both the main building and the extension, are of a good size, comfortably furnished and with ample hanging and writing space; several large family rooms are always popular. Day rooms are cosy and convivial, and there's now a little conference room. Cheerful, relaxed staff. *Amenities* secretarial services.

Rooms 37	*Direct dial* Yes	*Confirm by* 6	*Parking* Ample
Ensuite bath/shower 37	*Room TV* Yes	*Last dinner* 9	*Room service* Limited

PERTH   Royal George Hotel   60%   £C/D

H **Map 17 C5** Tayside
Tay Street PH1 5LD
Perth (0738) 24455

Credit Access, Amex, Diners, Visa

An elegant building with a splendid position in the centre of town. Public rooms include a spacious, comfortable lounge with views of the Tay from the picture windows and a relaxing wood-panelled bar. The best bedrooms are large, light and airy and overlook the Tay; those to the rear of the hotel are darker but comfortable nevertheless. All have practical, well-fitted bathrooms. *Amenities* terrace, laundry service.

Rooms 43	*Direct dial* Yes	*Confirm by* 6	*Parking* Ample
Ensuite bath/shower 43	*Room TV* Yes	*Last dinner* 9.30	*Room service* All day

PERTH   Stakis City Mills Hotel   59%   £C/D

H **Map 17 C5** Tayside
West Mill Street PH1 5QP
Perth (0738) 28281

Credit Access, Amex, Diners, Visa

You can see the water flowing beneath the bar floor in this attractive old water mill. There's a smart and comfortable foyer-lounge to relax in, and a second bar is given character by its beamed ceiling. Bedrooms, in two modern Extensions, have pretty quilts, thick carpets, brass lamps, pleasing darkwood furniture and good accessories; bathrooms are compact and modern. *Amenities* garden, secretarial services, laundry service.

Rooms 76	*Direct dial* Yes	*Confirm by* 6	*Parking* Ample
Ensuite bath/shower 76	*Room TV* Yes	*Last dinner* 10	*Room service* Limited

PERTH   Station Hotel   60%   £E

H **Map 17 C5** Tayside
Leonard Street PH2 8HE
Perth (0738) 24141
Telex 76481

Credit Access, Amex, Diners, Visa

New ownership continues to revitalise this grand old Victorian hotel. Public areas now include a smart foyer-lounge and a stylish bar overlooking the garden. Bedrooms are mostly spacious and well equipped, the executive class offering hairdryers and mini-bars. Top-floor rooms are smaller and more modern. Extensive conference facilities and keen, efficient staff. *Amenities* garden, keep-fit equipment, in-house movies, secretarial services, laundry service. &

Rooms 71	*Direct dial* Yes	*Confirm by* 6	*Parking* Ample
Ensuite bath/shower 51	*Room TV* Yes	*Last dinner* 9	*Room service* 24 hours

PETERHEAD — Waterside Inn 67% NEW ENTRY £E

H Map 16 D3 Grampian
Fraserburgh Road AB4 7BN
Peterhead (0779) 71121
Telex 739413

Credit Access, Amex, Diners, Visa

Just outside Peterhead on the Fraserburgh road, this is a modern purpose-built hotel with a distinctive black-tiled roof. There are two smart bars – one with a couple of full-size snooker tables – and a cheerful coffee shop, plus a leisure club and three conference rooms. Bedrooms in the main block are amply proportioned, with sitting areas and extra sofa beds, while 40 in a separate block are more compact but still well equipped, with good writing surfaces and lighting. *Amenities* indoor swimming pool, sauna, solarium, whirlpool bath, keep-fit equipment, snooker, in-house movies, secretarial services, laundry service, coffee shop (7am–10pm).

| Rooms 110 | Direct dial Yes | Confirm by arrang. | Parking Ample |
| Ensuite bath/shower 110 | Room TV Yes | Last dinner 10 | Room service 24 Hours |

Our inspectors are our full-time employees; they are professionally trained by us.

PITCAPLE — Pittodrie House Hotel 65% £E

H Map 16 D3 Grampian
Nr Inverurie AB5 9HS
Pitcaple (046 76) 444
Telex 739935

Credit Access, Amex, Diners, Visa
Closed 2 days Xmas

A fine old creeper-covered mansion dating mainly from the 17th century but with substantial Victorian additions. The estate on which it stands is very extensive, providing a delightfully serene setting, lovely views, and interesting walks. Antiques are a feature both in the day rooms and in the bedrooms, all of which have private bathrooms (four not en suite). *Amenities* garden, tennis, squash, croquet, clay-pigeon shooting, snooker, laundry service.

| Rooms 12 | Direct dial Yes | Confirm by arrang. | Parking Ample |
| Ensuite bath/shower 8 | Room TV Yes | Last dinner 8.45 | Room service All day |

PITLOCHRY — Atholl Palace Hotel 59% £C/D

H Map 17 C4 Tayside
PH16 5LY
Pitlochry (0796) 2400
Telex 76406

Credit Access, Amex, Diners, Visa

A turreted Victorian hotel in a commanding position high above Pitlochry. Grandly proportioned public rooms include a panelled bar decorated with stags' heads. Bedrooms vary in size and are plainly furnished with a mixture of fitted units and freestanding pieces. Tea-makers are provided. *Amenities* garden, outdoor swimming pool, sauna, solarium, keep-fit equipment, tennis, pitch & putt, games room, snooker, secretarial services, fax, children's playroom, helipad.

| Rooms 84 | Direct dial Yes | Confirm by 6 | Parking Ample |
| Ensuite bath/shower 84 | Room TV Yes | Last dinner 9 | Room service 24 hours |

We welcome bona fide complaints and recommendations on the tear-out pages at the back of the book for readers' comment. They are followed up by our professional team.

PITLOCHRY — Green Park Hotel 57% £E

H Map 17 C4 Tayside
PH16 5JY
Pitlochry (0796) 3248

Credit Access
Closed 1 Nov–end Mar

Just north-west of Pitlochry, in an enchantingly beautiful setting beside Loch Faskally, is this white-painted Victorian country house with modern extension. Comfortable, well-maintained public areas include a panelled hall, pleasant sun lounge and cheerful bar. Simply-furnished bedrooms, most with lovely views of the loch, have private bath en suite. Friendly, obliging staff. No dogs. *Amenities* garden, putting, game fishing, games room.

| Rooms 37 | Direct dial Yes | Confirm by 6 | Parking Ample |
| Ensuite bath/shower 37 | Room TV Yes | Last dinner 8.30 | Room service Limited |

PITLOCHRY   Pitlochry Hydro Hotel   63%   £D/E

H **Map 17 C4** Tayside
Knockard Road PH16 5JH
Pitlochry (0796) 2666

Credit Access, Amex, Diners, Visa
Closed Nov–March

Set in ample grounds high above Pitlochry, this large, late-Victorian hotel is popular with the coach trade. Soft, contemporary colour schemes, smart fabrics and stylish seating make for a pleasant atmosphere in the open-plan lounges. The good-sized bedrooms continue to be upgraded and have attractive lightwood furniture, coordinating bedspreads and curtains and handsomely tiled bathrooms. *Amenities* garden, tennis, putting, croquet, in-house movies. ♿

Rooms 64	*Direct dial* Yes	*Confirm by* arrang.	*Parking* Ample
Ensuite bath/shower 64	*Room TV* Yes	*Last dinner* 8.30	*Room service* Limited

**If we recommend meals in a Hotel or Inn,
a separate entry is made for its restaurant.**

PORT APPIN   Airds Hotel   73%   £C/D

HR **Map 17 B5** Strathclyde
Appin PA38 4DF
Appin (063 173) 236

Rooms 14
Ensuite bath/shower 14
Direct dial Yes
Room TV Yes
Confirm by 4
Last dinner 8.30
Parking Ample
Room service All day

Credit Access, Amex, Diners, Visa
Closed mid Nov–mid Mar

Refurbishment has given a smart, stylish image to this lovely old ferry inn on the shores of Loch Linnhe without detracting from its delightful character. Inviting armchairs and sofas, books, plants and flowers, grandfather clocks and tasteful ornaments give the public rooms a homely charm, and guests can take their drinks from the small bar to the sun lounge with its ever-changing view of the moun-

tains of Morven. Bedrooms have been attractively redecorated and equipped with every possible extra. TVs are now available, and all rooms have direct-dial telephones and excellent bathrooms. The caring Allens and their courteous staff are ultra-efficient. No children under five. *Amenities* garden, laundry service.

Restaurant ★

Lunch 12.30–1.30
Dinner 8–8.30
Set D £25
About £55 *for two*
Seats 36
Parties 8

Closed mid Nov–mid Mar

Betty Allen's cooking is as excellent as ever, with top quality ingredients benefiting from her culinary skill, precision and flair. Her four-course dinner menus offer such delights as tasty chicken liver pâté, excellent pea and mint soup, beautifully cooked turbot in a tarragon cream sauce, and one of Betty's marvellous sweets, such as a superb chocolate roulade. The consistently splendid cellar in-

cludes Ch. Figeac '78, Ch. Fuissé '78, and Ch. d'Yquem '67.
Specialities mousseline of scallops, terrine of sole and salmon with a tomato and basil coulis, breast of wood pigeon with a wine and juniper sauce, caramel ice cream with toasted almonds. ⊂ Outstanding

PORT WILLIAM   Corsemalzie House Hotel   62%   £D/E

H **Map 13 B4**
Dumfries & Galloway
By Newton Stewart DG8 9RL
Mochrum (098 886) 254

Credit Access, Amex, Diners, Visa
Closed 25 & 26 Dec & mid Jan–mid Mar

Extensive woodland surrounds this sturdy 19th-century mansion six miles west of Wigtown on the B7005. Rather spartan public areas include a quarry-tiled bar with bench seating and an autumnally decorated lounge. Bedrooms are better, with attractive duvets and lovely views; bathrooms are compact, six having showers only. General repair and cleanliness are only average. *Amenities* garden, putting, croquet, shooting, game fishing, laundry service.

Rooms 15	*Direct dial* Yes	*Confirm by* arrang.	*Parking* Ample
Ensuite bath/shower 15	*Room TV* Yes	*Last dinner* 9.15	*Room service* All day

All human history attests
That happiness for man - the hungry sinner,
Since Eve ate apples, much depends on dinner!

LORD BYRON 1788-1824
DON JUAN

I know
a little restaurant
Behind a brownstone stoop
Where *pottage du jour* is French
For a can of onion soup.

OGDEN NASH 1902-71
*TRY IT SUNS. AND HOLS:
IT'S CLOSED THEN*

A master cook!

why he's the man of men

For a professor; he designs, he draws,

He paints, he carves, he builds, he fortifies,

Makes citadels of curious fowl and fish.

Some he dry-ditches, some moats around with broths,

Mounts marrow bones, cuts fifty-angled custards,

Rears bulwark pies; and for his outer works,

He raiseth ramparts of immortal crust,

And teacheth all the tactics at one dinner -

What ranks, what files to put his dishes in,

The whole art military! Then he knows

The influence of the stars upon his meats,

And all their seasons, tempers and qualities;

And so to fit his relishes and sauces,

He has nature in a pot, 'bove all the chemists

Or airy brethren of the rosy cross.

He is an architect, an engineer,

A soldier, a physician, a philosopher,

A general mathematician.

BEN JONSON 1572-1637

Cited in
THE GENTLE ART OF COOKERY

PORTPATRICK

Knockinaam Lodge Hotel 72% £B

HR **Map 13 A4**
Dumfries & Galloway
Nr Stranraer DG9 9AD
Portpatrick (077 681) 471

Rooms 10
Ensuite bath/shower 10
Direct dial Yes
Room TV Yes
Confirm by arrang.
Last dinner 9
Parking Ample
Room service All day

Credit Access, Amex, Diners, Visa
Closed 4 Jan–2 wks before Easter

Winston Churchill once picked this secluded greystone house as the venue for a secret meeting with Eisenhower. Today it's a delightful country house hotel which the Frichots are constantly improving and restoring. Guests enter through a conservatory-style porch leading to a parquet-floored hall with a handsome staircase. In the newly revamped lounge, the homely atmosphere has been preserved with comfortable chairs, books, magazines and a log fire in winter. Bedrooms are individually and tastefully decorated to preserve their character and have plenty of extras, as do the excellent bathrooms. Half-board terms only. *Amenities* garden, croquet, sea fishing, mooring, laundry service, helipad.

Restaurant ♛

French cooking

Set D £23
About £60 *for two*
Seats 30
Parties 20

Pleasing decor, a large marble fireplace and display cabinets of china provide an elegant setting, well-suited to Daniel Galmiche's refined cooking. The short lunchtime menu and four course dinner menu (choice for main course only) offer modern dishes with a sound base in classical French cooking and the top-notch ingredients are mostly local or imported from Paris. Service is efficient and friendly.
♟ Well-chosen ⊖ &

Lunch 12–2 by arrang. *Dinner* 7.30–9
Closed 4 Jan–2 wks before Easter

PORTREE

Rosedale Hotel 52% £E

H **Map 16 A3** Highland
Beaumont Crescent,
Isle of Skye IV51 9DB
Portree (0478) 2531

Closed Oct–mid May

Three harbourside fishermen's cottages form the basis of a modest, pleasant little hotel. A sympathetic conversion has left a characterful warren of passages and stairways linking two simple lounges and two bars. Bedrooms vary in size, some of the singles being very compact, but all have colourful curtains and practical white furniture. Four are in a separate cottage. Seven of the neat bedrooms have shower only. *Amenities* garden.

Rooms 22	*Room phone* No	*Confirm by* arrang.	*Parking* Limited
Ensuite bath/shower 22	*Room TV* No	*Last dinner* 8	*Room service* None

PRESTWICK

Carlton Hotel 61% £E

H **Map 12 B2** Strathclyde
Ayr Road KA9 1TP
Prestwick (0292) 76811

Credit Access, Amex, Diners, Visa

A modern hotel on the A79 with high standards of decoration and repair throughout. A new lounge bar is traditional in feel and there's also a new pre-food bar/drawing room. Bedrooms have pretty duvet covers, lightwood and laminate units, radio alarms, tea/coffee makers and remote control TVs. Smartly tiled bathrooms have showers over the tubs. *Amenities* garden, in-house movies, secretarial services, coffee shop (11am–11pm).

Rooms 36	*Direct dial* Yes	*Confirm by* 6	*Parking* Ample
Ensuite bath/shower 36	*Room TV* Yes	*Last dinner* 10	*Room service* 24 hours

ROCKCLIFFE

Baron's Craig Hotel 65% £D

H **Map 13 C4**
Dumfries & Galloway
By Dalbeattie DG5 4QF
Rockcliffe (055 663) 225

Credit Access, Visa
Closed mid Oct–Easter

Twelve acres of wooded grounds and a view of the Solway Firth are just two of the attractions of this sturdy Victorian hotel. Inside, the charming foyer boasts antique furniture and the spacious lounge is full of cosy seating. Bedrooms in the extension are simply furnished in modern style, while those in the main house are more traditional. *Amenities* garden, golf practice net, putting, sailing, windsurfing, in-house movies, laundry service. &

Rooms 27	*Direct dial* Yes	*Confirm by* 6	*Parking* Ample
Ensuite bath/shower 22	*Room TV* Yes	*Last dinner* 9	*Room service* All day

ROTHES — Rothes Glen Hotel   64%   £C/D

Map 16 C3 Grampian
Nr Elgin IV33 7AH
Rothes (034 03) 254

Credit Access, Amex, Diners, Visa
Closed Jan

About two miles north of Rothes on the A941 you'll find this baronial turreted mansion, flag flying from a crenellated tower. Ornately carved Chinese furniture graces the appealing hall, while the elegant lounge boasts a ribbed ceiling, a white marble fireplace and comfortable chairs. Bedrooms have antique pieces, coordinating fabrics, radios, trouser presses, mini-bars and most have good-sized, carpeted bathrooms with good accessories. *Amenities* garden, putting.

Rooms 16	*Direct dial* Yes	*Confirm by* arrang.	*Parking* Ample
Ensuite bath/shower 13	*Room TV* Yes	*Last dinner* 9	*Room service* Limited

**If we recommend meals in a Hotel or Inn,
a separate entry is made for its restaurant.**

ST ANDREWS — Old Course Golf & Country Club   76%   £A/B

Map 17 D5
Fife KY16 9SP
St Andrews (0334) 74371
Telex 76280

Rooms 142
Ensuite bath/shower 142
Direct dial Yes
Room TV Yes
Confirm by 6
Last dinner 10.30
Parking Ample
Room service 24 hours

Credit Access, Amex, Diners, Visa
Closed 26–28 Dec

Occupying a marvellous position by the Old Course, this golfers' paradise of a hotel has everything from traditional locker rooms to an indoor golf school – and splendid views at every turn. Inside the austerely modern building, deep carpets, polished wood and potted plants set the tone in comfortable day rooms like the foyer, cocktail bar and top-floor lounge and bar. Balconied bedrooms with raised sitting areas have quality fabrics and elegant furnishings; bathrooms are fully-tiled and comprehensively equipped.
Amenities garden, indoor swimming pool, sauna, solarium, whirlpool bath, gymnasium, beauty salon, hairdressing, fax, valeting, laundry service, helipad.

ST ANDREWS — Rufflets Hotel   65%   £D

Map 17 D5 Fife
Strathkinness Low Road
KY16 9TX
St Andrews (0334) 72594

Credit Access, Amex, Diners, Visa
Closed Jan–mid Feb

The landscaped grounds (complete with a stream and topiary), are an attractive feature of this extended Edwardian hotel on the B939. A comfortable bow-windowed lounge overlooks the gardens, and there's an agreeable little bar and a card room. Bedrooms in the main house are furnished in solidly traditional style, while five in an extension have modern units. Three rooms are in a separate cottage. No dogs.
Amenities garden, putting, laundry service, 24-hour lounge service.

Rooms 21	*Direct dial* Yes	*Confirm by* 6	*Parking* Ample
Ensuite bath/shower 21	*Room TV* Yes	*Last dinner* 9.15	*Room service* Limited

ST ANDREWS — The Rusack's   77%   £B

Map 17 D5 Fife
Pilmour Links KY16 9JQ
St Andrews (0334) 74321

Rooms 50
Ensuite bath/shower 50
Direct dial Yes
Room TV Yes
Confirm by arrang.
Last dinner 10
Parking Ample
Room service 24 hours

Credit Access, Amex, Diners, Visa

This handsome Victorian hotel – which notched up its century in 1987 – enjoys the perfect golfing location alongside the 18th fairway of the Old Course. Public areas make a dramatic impression with their trompe-l'oeil marble columns, chandeliers, vivid red colour scheme and book-lined 'library' decor. Golfers can observe the course from the roomy sun lounge, or drown their sorrows beneath the gaze of the golfing stars whose photographs adorn the basement Champions Bar. Bedrooms, some with spectacular views over West Sands, are most attractive, with quality furnishings and many thoughtful extras. There are two spacious suites. All have stylish bathrooms.
Amenities laundry service.

ST FILLANS — Four Seasons Hotel 60% £E

HR Map 17 C5 Tayside
Nr Crieff PH6 2NF
St Fillans (076 485) 333

Credit Access, Amex, Visa
Closed Jan & Feb

The idyllic setting, with views across Loch Earn to distant peaks, is a splendid bonus in most of the rooms here. Bars and lounges provide space to unwind, and in summer the terrace is a popular spot. Bedrooms are appointed in plain, practical style, and all have their own neat bathrooms. Six rooms are chalets perched in steep grounds behind the hotel. *Amenities* mooring, laundry service, coffee shop (10am–6pm in season). ☇

Rooms 18	Room phone Yes	Confirm by arrang.	Parking Ample
Ensuite bath/shower 18	Room TV Yes	Last dinner 9.45	Room service All day

Restaurant ☺

Set Sun L £8.50
Set D £14.75
About £40 for two
Seats 44
Parties 80

Andrew Scott, son of the new owners, changes his menu daily, offering diners a tempting choice of dishes such as duck liver pâté with walnuts, cabby doos (mussels), Stilton-stuffed veal escalope and collops of venison with whisky and herbs. Sweets from the trolley, coffee in the lounge. Lunch is by arrangement only except for Sunday. Get a window table for the best views. ☻ ☇

Lunch Sun 12.30–2, Mon–Sat by arrang. *Dinner* 7–9.45, Sat & Sun till 9.30 **Closed** Jan & Feb

Changes in data sometimes occur in establishments
after the Guide goes to press.
Prices should be taken as indications rather than firm quotes.

SCARISTA — Scarista House 67% £D/E

HR Map 16 A2 Highland
Isle of Harris PA85 3HX
Scarista (085 985) 238

Closed end Sept–Easter

The Johnsons rescued this former Church of Scotland manse from dereliction a decade ago and turned it into a civilised, comfortable hotel. On arrival, tea and home-made scones are offered in the library where a roaring fire burns in the old cast iron fireplace. Bedrooms have attractive fabrics, period furniture and electric blankets; bathrooms are smart and modern. Superb breakfasts. No under eights. *Amenities* garden.

Rooms 7	Direct dial Yes	Confirm by arrang.	Parking Ample
Ensuite bath/shower 7	Room TV No	Last dinner 8	Room service None

Restaurant ♛ ☺

Set D £16
About £42 for two
Seats 20

The delightful dining rooms have polished wood tables set with candles, wild flowers and attractive china. Alison Johnson's menus use local produce and all eggs and meat are from free-range animals. The no-choice four course menu is inventive – starter might be tomato granita with sweet pepper fritters, and perhaps pheasant with apple and rosemary to follow. Finish with an outstanding chocolate mousse gâteau. ☙ Well-chosen ☻

Dinner only at 8
Closed Sat, Sun & end Sept–Easter

SCOURIE — Eddrachilles Hotel 60% £E

H Map 16 B2 Highland
Badcall Bay IV27 4TH
Scourie (0971) 2080

Closed 1 Nov–1 Mar

A commanding position above Badcall Bay with its myriad islands, seals and dolphins makes this an ideal place for nature-lovers. There's a comfortable bar-lounge with tweedy seating and a sun lounge with stunning views. Modestly furnished but well-maintained bedrooms offer extras like electric blankets and radio-alarms; TVs available on request. Eight bathrooms have showers only. No children under three. *Amenities* garden, sea & game fishing, boating.

Rooms 11	Room phone No	Confirm by arrang.	Parking Ample
Ensuite bath/shower 11	Room TV No	Last dinner 8.30	Room service Limited

SCOURIE — Scourie Hotel   60%   £E

H **Map 16 B2** Highland
By Lairg, Sutherland IV27 4SX
Scourie (0971) 2396

Credit Access, Diners, Visa
Closed 3rd wk Oct–mid Mar

A modest hotel with a far from modest 25,000 acres of hills and lochs for the guests to disport themselves in. Cheery public rooms include two tartan-carpeted lounges and a small cocktail bar. Bedrooms are modern and well-kept, with an ongoing programme of refurbishment. Most have contemporary fitted units and simply patterned fabrics. Bathrooms are good-sized, carpeted and prettily tiled. Friendly, relaxed staff. *Amenities* game fishing.

| Rooms 20 | Direct dial Yes | Confirm by 6 | Parking Ample |
| Ensuite bath/shower 18 | Room TV No | Last dinner 8.30 | Room service None |

SELKIRK — Philipburn House Hotel   60%   £D/E

HR **Map 12 D2** Borders
Linglie Road TD7 5LS
Selkirk (0750) 20747

Credit Access, Amex, Diners, Visa

A very friendly hotel near the junction of the A708 and A707 just outside Selkirk. The interior, particularly the lively bar, features much natural pine. Bedrooms in the main house are traditional in feel, while those in the annexe are more modern; all have tea/coffee-makers and baby listeners. There's also a Scandinavian-style log cabin. *Amenities* garden, outdoor swimming pool, solarium, games room, snooker, fax, laundry service, children's playground.

| Rooms 16 | Direct dial Yes | Confirm by 4 | Parking Ample |
| Ensuite bath/shower 16 | Room TV Yes | Last dinner 9.30 | Room service Limited |

Restaurant   ⑨

Set L from £4.50, Sun £9.50
Set D £15
About £45 for two
Seats 70
Parties 80

Brian Hogg provides a thoughtful selection of menus catering for vegetarians and for those who are health-conscious. The main menu features European dishes such as boudin noir with apple, bacon and wholegrain mustard; main course might be a hearty steak or breast of local duckling with strawberries. Enticing sweets and a good selection of Scottish cheeses to finish. A wide-ranging wine list with entertaining notes and anecdotes. ♥ Well-chosen ⊖ ♿

Lunch 12–2.30
Dinner 7.30–9.30

We welcome bona fide complaints and recommendations
on the tear-out pages at the back of the book for readers' comment.
They are followed up by our professional team.

SKEABOST BRIDGE — Skeabost House Hotel   59%   £E

H **Map 16 A3** Highland
By Portree, Isle of Skye
IV51 9NP
Skeabost Bridge (047 032) 202

Closed 22 Oct–Easter

Lovely views over Loch Snizort and delightful interiors make this a most enjoyable hotel to visit. The public rooms are mainly panelled and grandly proportioned but homely, with tasteful decor and comfortable seating. Bedrooms are old-fashioned yet pretty; the cheery bathrooms have parquet floors and painted wooded walls. Five rooms are in a modern extension. *Amenities* garden, 9-hole golf course, putting, bowling green, sea & game fishing, snooker.

| Rooms 27 | Room phone No | Confirm by arrang. | Parking Ample |
| Ensuite bath/shower 17 | Room TV No | Last dinner 8.30 | Room service 24 hours |

SKELMORLIE — Manor Park Hotel   60%   £C/D

H **Map 12 A1** Strathclyde
PA17 5HE
Wemyss Bay (0475) 520832

Built in 1840, Manor Park stands on a hill above the coast road between Largs and Wemyss Bay. Day rooms are homely and traditional, with views over beautiful gardens to the Clyde, mountains and sea lochs. Good-sized bedrooms are bright and simple, their furniture mainly period – though rooms in the former stable block have more modern pieces. Tea-makers and hairdryers are standard accessories. No dogs. *Amenities* garden, laundry service.

| Rooms 23 | Direct dial Yes | Confirm by arrang. | Parking Ample |
| Ensuite bath/shower 22 | Room TV Yes | Last dinner 9 | Room service All day |

SLEAT · Kinloch Lodge · 67% · £B

HR **Map 17 A4** Highland
Isle of Skye IV43 8QY
Isle Ornsay (047 13) 214

Credit Access, Visa
Closed 1–28 Dec & 8 Jan–mid Mar

Lord and Lady Macdonald have created a very warm and relaxing hotel, where guests can follow various outdoor pursuits or just sit back and enjoy the marvellous views. Ancestral portraits are found throughout the day rooms, along with some fine antiquities. Small but comfortable bedrooms are individually and charmingly decorated and thoughtfully equipped. No children under ten.
Amenities garden, shooting, coarse & game fishing.

Rooms 10	*Room phone* No	*Confirm by* 4	*Parking* Ample
Ensuite bath/shower 8	*Room TV* No	*Last dinner* 8	*Room service* Limited

Dining Room ♛ ♀

Set D £20
About £50 *for two*
Seats 28

Fine silver and elegant etched glassware are married with short, tempting menus that emphasise freshness and unsullied flavours. Carrot, lime and coriander soup is a lovely delicate starter which we followed with tarragon chicken accompanied by superb vegetables. Very good Stilton, then a terrific hazelnut meringue with raspberries and cream. Coffee is served in the drawing room with home-made fudge. Excellent Rhônes on a good wine list. ♀ Well-chosen ℮

Dinner at 8
Closed L to non-residents, 1–26 Dec & 8 Jan–end Feb

We publish annually,
so make sure you use the current edition.
It's worth it!

SOUTH QUEENSFERRY · Forth Bridges Moat House · 61% · £C/D

H **Map 12 C1** Lothian
EH30 9SF
031-331 1199
Telex 727430

Credit Access, Amex, Diners, Visa

There are spectacular views of both Forth bridges from the public areas and nearly all the bedrooms of this '60s hotel, which is currently benefiting from a major programme of stylish refurbishment.
Amenities garden, indoor swimming pool, sauna, solarium, whirlpool bath, gymnasium, beauty salon, hairdressing, squash, snooker, pool table, in-house movies, laundry service, coffee shop (9am–5pm).

Rooms 108	*Direct dial* Yes	*Confirm by* 6	*Parking* Ample
Ensuite bath/shower 108	*Room TV* Yes	*Last dinner* 9.45	*Room service* 24 hours

SPEAN BRIDGE · Letterfinlay Lodge Hotel · 55% · £E/F

H **Map 17 B4** Highland
PH34 4DZ
Spean Bridge (039 781) 622

Credit Access, Amex, Diners, Visa
Closed Nov–beg. Mar

The Forsyth family have an informal and unpretentious approach that makes guests feel instantly at ease. The setting, on the banks of Loch Lochy, is one of restful, rugged beauty, and the hotel has extensive private grounds. Public areas comprise a cosy bar, a picture-windowed sun lounge and a homely little TV room with overstuffed old chairs and sofas. Bedrooms, each decorated in a different colour, are modest but not without character; older rooms are large, with painted panelled walls. Five newer rooms have en suite facilities, the rest share big, old-fashioned bathrooms with an amazing Victorian shower system. *Amenities* garden, game fishing, mooring, boating, games room, snooker, laundry service.

Rooms 15	*Room phone* No	*Confirm by* arrang.	*Parking* Ample
Ensuite bath/shower 5	*Room TV* No	*Last dinner* 8.30	*Room service* All day

★ For a *discount* on next year's guide, see **An Offer for Answers.** ★

STEWARTON   Chapeltoun House   74%   £B/C

H **Map 17 B6** Strathclyde
KA3 3ED
Stewarton (0560) 82696

Rooms 6
Ensuite bath/shower 6
Direct dial Yes
Room TV Yes
Confirm by arrang.
Last dinner 9.30
Parking Ample
Room service All day

Credit Access, Amex, Visa

Twenty acres of grounds surround this turn-of-the-century
mansion. A feeling of timeless-
ness pervades the oak-panelled
hall, where the slow tick of a
clock mingles with the crackle of
a log fire. Below the ribbed ceiling
is a plaster frieze, its thistle and
rose emblems commemorating
the first Scottish owner and his
English bride. A comfortable
drawing room upholstered in
shades of green has fine views

over the countryside. Bedrooms are mostly spacious, with antique
furniture and tastefully coordinated decor; a host of extras includes
trouser presses, hairdryers and sherry. Smart, carpeted bathrooms
have good toiletries.
Amenities garden, secretarial services, fax, laundry service.

STONEHAVEN   Commodore Hotel   58%   £E

H **Map 17 D4** Grampian
Cowie Park AB3 2PZ
Stonehaven (0569) 62936
Telex 739111

Credit Access, Amex, Diners, Visa

New owners plan improvements to this pleasant modern hotel on the
A92. It has good conference facilities, and the two bars, one with
mellow panelling, are cosy and inviting. Bedrooms – all with simple
bathrooms – tend to be functional, but some have been refurbished
and equipped with attractive quilted bedcovers, trouser presses and
hairdryers.
Amenities fax, laundry service.

Rooms 40	*Room phone* Yes	*Confirm by* arrang.	*Parking* Ample
Ensuite bath/shower 40	*Room TV* Yes	*Last dinner* 9.30	*Room service* 24 hours

STORNOWAY   Caberfeidh Hotel   62%   £D/E

H **Map 16 A2** Highland
Isle of Lewis PA87 2EU
Stornoway (0851) 2604
Telex 75509

Credit Access, Amex, Diners, Visa

An early '70s hotel located on the edge of town. Gaelic is the common
language in the public bar, while Old Norse might be more appropriate
in the Viking Bar, which is built on the theme of a Viking longship.
There's also a snug cocktail bar. Decent-sized, well-equipped bedrooms
have good-quality lightwood fitted units, attractive coordinated
fabrics and nicely tiled bathrooms.
Amenities garden, fax, laundry service.

Rooms 40	*Direct dial* Yes	*Confirm by* arrang.	*Parking* Ample
Ensuite bath/shower 40	*Room TV* Yes	*Last dinner* 9.30	*Room service* 24 hours

STRACHUR   Creggans Inn   61%   £D

H **Map 17 B5** Strathclyde
PA27 8BX
Strachur (036 986) 279
Telex 778425

Credit Access, Amex, Diners, Visa

Laura Huggins and her friendly, helpful staff run a really charming
hotel in a picturesque setting by Loch Fyne. Linked bars provide a
convivial spot for enjoying a drink and admiring the views, and there
are two lounges (one with TV) and a new conservatory. Bedrooms,
whose furnishings range from antique to modern, are individually
and prettily decorated. *Amenities* garden, coarse & game fishing,
games room, secretarial services, laundry service. ⅃

Rooms 22	*Direct dial* Yes	*Confirm by* arrang.	*Parking* Ample
Ensuite bath/shower 17	*Room TV* No	*Last dinner* 9.30	*Room service* All day

STRANRAER   North West Castle Hotel   67%   £E

H **Map 13 A4**
Dumfries & Galloway
Cairnryan Road DG9 8EH
Stranraer (0776) 4413
Telex 777088

A Georgian building, now much extended, which is well run by the
owners and their long-established staff. The extensive public rooms
are luxurious and the Alpine lounge and bar overlooks an impressive
curling rink. Attractive, comfortable bedrooms have good facilities.
Amenities garden, indoor swimming pool, sauna, solarium, games
room, snooker, pool table, in-house movies, secretarial services,
laundry service, coffee shop (noon–9.30pm Oct–May), kiosk.

Rooms 77	*Direct dial* Yes	*Confirm by* arrang.	*Parking* Ample
Ensuite bath/shower 77	*Room TV* Yes	*Last dinner* 9.30	*Room service* 24 hours

STRATHBLANE — Kirkhouse Inn — £E

Map 12 B1 Central
Glasgow Road G63 9AA
Blanefield (0360) 70621

Credit Access, Amex, Diners, Visa

Beautiful hilly countryside surrounds this efficiently run white-painted inn on the A81. Public areas have been recarpeted throughout; they include a bustling public bar and a quieter lounge bar. The bedrooms are spotlessly kept and boast well-coordinated pastel wallcovering and fabrics and neat private bathrooms. There's a honeymoon suite with four-poster and sunken bath. *Amenities* garden, games room, snooker, laundry service, 24-hour lounge service.

| Rooms 15 | Room *phone* Yes | *Confirm by* arrang. | *Parking* Ample |
| Ensuite bath/shower 15 | Room *TV* Yes | *Last dinner* 10 | *Room service* Limited |

STRATHTUMMEL — Port-an-Eilean Hotel — 65% — £E/F

Map 17 C4 Tayside
By Pitlochry PH16 5RU
Tummel Bridge (088 24) 233

Closed mid Oct–late Apr

Built as a sporting lodge in 1865 for the 6th Duke of Atholl, this is a handsome lochside hotel. The most impressive public room is the lofty and spacious main lounge, with its ornate ceilings. Next door, in the sun lounge, it is the lovely views of the loch that enchant. Individually decorated bedrooms are neat and clean with welcoming touches like tea-makers and magazines. Simple bathrooms with good-sized tubs. *Amenities* garden, coarse & game fishing.

| Rooms 9 | Room *phone* No | *Confirm by* arrang. | *Parking* Ample |
| Ensuite bath/shower 9 | Room *TV* No | *Last dinner* 8.45 | *Room service* None |

STROMNESS — Hamnavoe Restaurant — *NEW ENTRY*

Map 16 C1 Orkney
35 Graham Place
Stromness (0856) 850606

About £35 for two
Seats 30
Parties 30
Parking Ample

Credit Access, Visa

Bearing the old Norse name for Stromness, this delightful little restaurant is to be found down a side street off the picturesque high street. It's a cosy place with much homely character and features a collection of books about Orkney or by Orkney authors. Denis Moylan is an accomplished, professional chef who seeks out fresh produce throughout the year as the basis of his imaginative and highly enjoyable dishes. His repertoire ranges from smoked scallops and oysters with curry mayonnaise to chicken breast stuffed with scampi and creamed leeks, lamb with tarragon sauce and commendable apple vol-au-vents. Short, well-chosen wine list: note Hardy's Chardonnay 1985 from Australia. ☘ Well-chosen ⊖ ♿

Dinner 7–10
Closed Tues, also Mon Oct–Mar

TALLADALE — Loch Maree Hotel — £E

Map 16 B3 Highland
Achnasheen IV2 2HN
Kinlochewe (044 584) 288

Closed beg Oct–Easter

The great outdoors beckons at this fishing hotel, which faces spectacularly beautiful Loch Maree. The views seem initially to put the hotel itself in the shade, but in fact it's quite a cosy place, with a Victorian feel in the day rooms and the basics for a decent night's sleep in the modestly appointed bedrooms. Public facilities include some huge Victorian tubs. *Amenities* garden, game fishing.

| Rooms 14 | Room *phone* No | *Confirm by* 6 | *Parking* Ample |
| Ensuite bath/shower 0 | Room *TV* No | *Last dinner* 8.30 | *Room service* None |

TARBERT — Stonefield Castle Hotel — 63% — £C

Map 12 A1 Strathclyde
Loch Fyne PA29 6YJ
Tarbert (088 02) 836
Telex 776321

Credit Access, Amex, Diners, Visa

Perched above Loch Fyne and surrounded by glorious rhododendron woods, this Scottish Baronial mansion was built in 1837 by the Campbell family. Public rooms have a nice authentic feel about them, thanks to period furnishings and a number of family portraits, and there are splendid floral displays throughout. Best bedrooms, in the original house, have freestanding darkwood furniture and attractive decor; those in an extension are more simply appointed. Three bathrooms have shower only. *Amenities* garden, outdoor swimming pool, sauna, solarium, whirlpool bath, keep-fit equipment, tennis, squash, 9-hole golf course, putting, riding, mooring, boating, snooker, pool table, satellite TV, laundry service, children's play area.

| Rooms 33 | *Direct dial* Yes | *Confirm by* arrang. | *Parking* Ample |
| Ensuite bath/shower 33 | Room *TV* Yes | *Last dinner* 9.45 | *Room service* 24 hours |

THORNHILL   Barjarg Tower   69%   *NEW ENTRY*   £D/E

H Map 12 C3
Dumfries & Galloway
Auldgirth
Thornhill (0848) 31545

Credit Access, Amex, Diners, Visa
Closed 25 Dec

Ask for directions to the Donaldsons' converted peel tower, originally dating from the 16th century. There's a friendly and personal atmosphere and the public rooms combine interesting architectural details with smart but homely decor and furnishings. Bedrooms are attractively and individually decorated, with elaborate drapes and decent solid furniture; bathrooms have excellent towels and bathrobes. No dogs. *Amenities* garden, game fishing, secretarial services, fax.

Rooms 10	*Direct dial* Yes	*Confirm by* arrang.	*Parking* Ample
Ensuite bath/shower 7	*Room TV* Yes	*Last dinner* 8	*Room service* Limited

TIRORAN   Tiroran House   70%   £C/D

HR Map 17 A5 Strathclyde
Isle of Mull PA69 6ES
Tiroran (068 15) 232

Rooms 9
Ensuite bath/shower 8
Room phone No
Room TV No
Confirm by arrang.
Last dinner 7.45
Parking Ample
Room service All day

Closed early Oct–late May

A drive through some of the most dramatic scenery on the Isle of Mull takes you to Sue and Robin Blockey's peaceful country house with its wooded gardens and stream running down to the edge of Loch Scridain. Tasteful decor in the two lounges, including chintzy armchairs and a splendid Chinese carpet, helps to make you feel like a privileged private guest. Bedrooms, in a mixture of styles, are equally attractive, and

have good up-to-date bathrooms. There are tea-making facilities and radios in the rooms, as well as a supply of books and magazines, but no TVs. No children under ten.
Amenities garden, croquet, game fishing, games room, laundry service.

Restaurant   ♔   ⌐

Set D £19.50
About £50 for two
Seats 20

Two charming dining rooms – one furnished with antiques, the other a vine-covered conservatory – are the scene for Sue Blockey's splendidly enjoyable meals. Daily changing menus revolve around prime local and home-grown produce, and are accompanied by home-baked bread. Typical dishes might be Loch Scridain prawns with herb and garlic mayonnaise, pork fillet with kumquats or excellent steak and kidney pie. Lovely puddings and Scottish cheeses. ⊖ &

Dinner only 7.45
Closed early Oct–late May

TOBERMORY   The Tobermory Hotel   57%   £E/F

H Map 17 A4 Strathclyde
53 Main Street, Isle of Mull
PA75 6NT
Tobermory (0688) 2091

Closed 1 week Xmas & mid Jan–mid Feb

Impeccable housekeeping and a delightful position among a row of brightly coloured buildings overlooking the bay are attractions of the Ratcliffes' charming little hotel. Clever use is made of limited space, from the tiny reception and two cosy lounges to the cheerful compact bedrooms and spotless bathrooms. The hotel's yacht *Sea Topaz* offers cruises and nights afloat.
Amenities sea fishing.

Rooms 15	*Room phone* No	*Confirm by* arrang.	*Parking* Ample
Ensuite bath/shower 5	*Room TV* No	*Last dinner* 7.45	*Room service* Limited

TROON   Marine Highland Hotel   66%   £C

H Map 12 B2 Strathclyde
Crosbie Road KA10 6HE
Troon (0292) 314444
Telex 777595

Credit Access, Amex, Diners, Visa

A new leisure centre, brasserie and conference and banqueting centre are the latest additions to this ever-improving Edwardian hotel on the Royal Troon golf course. Bedrooms have good quality furniture, brass light fittings, and pretty colour schemes; bright, pleasing bathrooms are mosaic-tiled. *Amenities* garden, indoor swimming pool, sauna, solarium, gymnasium, beauty salon, squash, putting, games room, billiards, secretarial services, fax, laundry service, helipad.

Rooms 72	*Direct dial* Yes	*Confirm by* 6	*Parking* Ample
Ensuite bath/shower 72	*Room TV* Yes	*Last dinner* 10	*Room service* 24 hours

TROON — Piersland House Hotel 64% £D/E

H Map 12 B2 Strathclyde
Craigend Road KA10 6HD
Troon (0292) 314747

Credit Access, Amex, Diners, Visa

An attractive sandstone and timbered house built by the grandson of Johnnie Walker of whisky fame. The main hall opens on to a pleasant bar-lounge area and boasts many features of architectural interest. Bedrooms have attractive coordinating fabrics and darkwood furniture; four superior rooms are more stylish and there are two new suites. All have plenty of extras. *Amenities* garden, putting, croquet, secretarial services, laundry service.

Rooms 17	*Direct dial* Yes	*Confirm by* arrang.	*Parking* Ample
Ensuite bath/shower 17	*Room TV* Yes	*Last dinner* 9.30	*Room service* All day

TROON — Sun Court Hotel 58% £D

H Map 12 B2 Strathclyde
19 Crosbie Road KA10 6HF
Troon (0292) 312727
Telex 779830

Credit Access, Amex, Diners, Visa
Closed 25 Dec

The real tennis court is a rare amenity at this converted Edwardian house which also offers all-weather lawn tennis and four squash courts. Traditional day rooms include two comfortable lounges and a spacious cocktail bar overlooking Royal Troon golf course. Variously furnished bedrooms sport cheerful colour schemes and well-kept bathrooms. Enthusiastic owner Alastair Breckenridge leads a friendly team. *Amenities* garden, tennis, real tennis, squash, laundry service.

Rooms 20	*Direct dial* Yes	*Confirm by* arrang.	*Parking* Ample
Ensuite bath/shower 18	*Room TV* Yes	*Last dinner* 9.30	*Room service* All day

TURNBERRY — Turnberry Hotel 81% £B

H Map 12 A3 Strathclyde
KA26 9LT
Turnberry (0655) 31000
Telex 777779

Rooms 130
Ensuite bath/shower 130
Direct dial Yes
Room TV Yes
Confirm by arrang.
Last dinner 9.30
Parking Ample
Room service 24 hours

Credit Access, Amex, Diners, Visa
Closed end Nov–end Feb

Two championship golf courses and superb leisure facilities have made this luxurious hotel world-famous. The tone is set by the elegant foyer-reception, with its high ceilings and panelled walls, and the combined lounges and bar are truly sumptuous, with beautiful decor, fine paintings and comfortable seating. Most bedrooms are smartly decorated and have traditional furnishings and pretty fabrics. Bathrooms

have marble tiled floors and good toiletries. Six suites offer even greater luxury. *Amenities* garden, indoor swimming pool, sauna, solarium, keep-fit equipment, hairdressing, tennis, golf courses, putting, pitch & putt, croquet, riding, snooker, teletext, secretarial services, fax, valeting, laundry service, restaurant (8am–8pm), helipad.

TWEEDSMUIR — Crook Inn £E

I Map 12 C2 Borders
Nr Biggar ML12 6QN
Tweedsmuir (089 97) 272

Credit Amex, Diners
Closed 4 Jan–mid Mar

Border scenery provides a rugged setting for this historic inn on the A701. Inviting areas include the entrance hall – warmed by an open fire – and a flagstoned bar, formerly an old kitchen where Burns wrote one of his famous poems. Simple comforts are provided by the immaculate bedrooms, modestly furnished with sturdy old pieces. No dogs. *Amenities* garden, shooting, games room, pool table, laundry service, children's play area.

Rooms 8	*Room phone* No	*Confirm by* arrang.	*Parking* Ample
Ensuite bath/shower 6	*Room TV* No	*Last dinner* 9.15	*Room service* Limited

UIG — Uig Hotel 59% £E

H Map 16 A3 Highland
Isle of Skye IV51 9YE
Uig (047 042) 205

Credit Access, Amex, Diners, Visa
Closed 1st wk Oct–Easter

In the same mother-and-son ownership for 40 years, Uig Hotel has an attractive location that's handy for the summer ferries to the Outer Hebrides. Fresh, bright bedrooms, some in an annexe, enjoy views of either the bay or the hills and fields, and nice views also enhance the homely day rooms. Skye is reached by air (Glasgow) or ferry (Mallaig or Kyle of Lochalsh). No children under 12.
Amenities garden, riding, laundry service. &

Rooms 20	*Room phone* No	*Confirm by* 6	*Parking* Ample
Ensuite bath/shower 20	*Room TV* No	*Last dinner* 8.15	*Room service* All day

ULLAPOOL   Altnaharrie Inn ★   ♕ ⚑

RR Map 16 B2 Highland
IV26 2SS
Dundonnell (085 483) 230

Set D £33
About £70 for two
Seats 14
Parties 14
Parking Ample

Phone for the private launch from Ullapool and prepare for the delights of Gunn Erikson's original and exciting cooking in a lovely setting on the shores of Loch Broom. She doesn't offer a choice, but you can always discuss special needs in advance. Soup comes first, perhaps haw-thorn and cucumber or delicate elderflower; next maybe little scallops with a sauce of bitter cress and white burgundy; and a

main course such as saddle of lamb or medallions of roe deer with a sauce of leeks, grapes, juniper and dill. Wild raspberry ice cream is a nice sweet, and there's a selection of cheeses. Lunch for residents only. Excellent wines. 🍷 Well-chosen 🅮

Lunch residents only   *Dinner* at 7.45
Closed L to non-residents and late Oct–late Mar

BEDROOMS 5   £C/D
With bath/shower 4

The bedrooms, with attractive views over the bay, are kept in spotless order. No children under 10. Half-board.

ULLAPOOL   Ceilidh Place   £D/E

Map 16 B2 Highland
West Argyle Street,
Wester Ross IV26 2TY
Ullapool (0854) 2103

Credit Access, Amex, Diners, Visa

Ceilidh (pronounced Kay-Lee) means a sort of spontaneous and joyous meeting, and Ceilidh Place is just the spot for it. It developed from a coffee shop in an old boathouse into a splendid little hotel, professionally run but with a delightfully informal and folksy feel. Music and entertainment find a congenial home here, and conversation fairly buzzes around the bar. Beamed bedrooms (no phones, no TV, but home comfort a-plenty) are furnished mainly with nice old pine pieces, and antique tiles make a pretty sight in most of the bathrooms. The bedrooms without en suite facilities share two bright, clean bathrooms.
Amenities garden, coffee shop (10am–10pm), laundry service.

Rooms 15	*Room phone* No	*Confirm by* arrang.	*Parking* Ample
Ensuite bath/shower 8	*Room TV* No	*Last dinner* 9	*Room service* None

Our inspectors *never* book in the name of Egon Ronay's Guides.
They disclose their identity only if they are considering an establishment
for inclusion in the next edition of the Guide.

UPHALL   Houstoun House   69%   £C/D

H Map 12 C1 Lothian
EH52 6JS
Broxburn (0506) 853831
Telex 727148

Credit Access, Amex, Diners, Visa
Closed 1–3 Jan

Just north of the M8 between Edinburgh and Glasgow, Houstoun House stands in 20 acres of woodland and garden, the latter dominated by a magnificent cedar of Lebanon. Best of the public areas are the refurbished vaulted bar with its huge log fire and the reception-lounge, which looks on to the tree-lined drive. Bedrooms are either contemporary in style or traditional, some with comfortable four-posters. Trouser presses and hairdryers are standard, and there are good-quality toiletries in the bathrooms. Standards of service and housekeeping disappointed on our last visit, and the cooking is not what it once was (the hotel used to provide one of best breakfasts in the land). *Amenities* garden, laundry service.

Rooms 30	*Direct dial* Yes	*Confirm by* arrang.	*Parking* Ample
Ensuite bath/shower 30	*Room TV* Yes	*Last dinner* 9.30	*Room service* 24 hours

WALLS | Burrastow House   62%   *NEW ENTRY*   £E

HR   **Map 16 D2** Shetland
ZE2 9PD
Walls (0595) 71307

Closed Oct–Feb

A single-track road runs west from Walls past Linga Island and Vaila Sound, ending abruptly at the Tuckeys' delightful little shoreside hotel. The setting is one of incomparable, rugged beauty, and relaxation comes easily in the cosy lounge or summery garden room. Bedrooms are spacious, airy and comfortable, with superb views. Each has its own bathroom with good soft towels.
Amenities garden, pitch & putt, sea fishing.

Rooms 3	*Room phone* No	*Confirm by* arrang.	*Parking* Ample
Ensuite bath/shower 3	*Room TV* Yes	*Last dinner* 9	*Room service* Limited

Restaurant   ♘

About £35 for two
Seats 10

Book 24 hours ahead and discuss your main-course choice, which could be anything from baked monkfish to jugged hare and succulent leg of heather-grazed Shetland lamb with apricot stuffing. Stella Tuckey is a very good home cook who obviously cares about food. Granary bread is baked daily, vegetables are crisp and plentiful, and there's a separate vegetarian menu. Simple puddings, well-kept local cheese, good concise wine list.   ♀ Well-chosen ⊘

Dinner 7.30–9
Closed Some Thurs, all Sun & Oct–Feb

WHITEBRIDGE | Knockie Lodge Hotel   65%   £D

H   **Map 17 B4**
Highland IV1 2UP
Gorthleck (045 63) 276

Credit Access, Amex, Visa
Closed end Oct–end Apr

Peace and quiet are the greatest asset of this charming former hunting lodge with enviable views of fields and mountains. Books, magazines and a bar set into the shelves make the lounge particularly relaxing. Varying sized bedrooms without phones, TVs or radios feature antiques, attractive matching fabrics, and electric blankets for chilly nights. Bathrooms, often roomy, are equally pretty. No children under ten. *Amenities* garden, game fishing.

Rooms 10	*Room phone* No	*Confirm by* arrang.	*Parking* Ample
Ensuite bath/shower 10	*Room TV* No	*Last dinner* 8	*Room service* Limited

WICK | Mercury Hotel   57%   £D

H   **Map 16 C2** Highland
Riverside KW1 4NL
Wick (0955) 3344

Credit Access, Amex, Diners, Visa
Closed 10 days Xmas

Modest but comfortable accommodation in a modern purpose-built hotel handily placed in the centre of town. Bedrooms – a different colour scheme for each floor – are neat and quite attractive, with practical fitted units, tea-makers and compact bathrooms. The residents' lounge, though simple, is spacious and relaxing, and there's a very smart bar with alcove bench seating.
Amenities garden, laundry service, 24 hour lounge service.

Rooms 48	*Direct dial* Yes	*Confirm by* 6	*Parking* Ample
Ensuite bath/shower 48	*Room TV* Yes	*Last dinner* 8.45	*Room service* Limited

My father was a blacksmith ...

the tender bouquets of vegetables he brought were so full

of flavour and aroma that all that was needed was the

addition of a few of the big rosy strips of pork fat which

sizzled in the big cast-iron pot.

This was the 'cuisine heureuse', which consisted of marrying

natural products with one another, of finding simple

harmonies and enhancing the flavour of each ingredient by

contact with another complementary flavour...

It is the antithesis of cooking to impress.

ROGER VERGE
CUISINE OF THE SUN
Trans. Caroline Conran (1979)

HOTELS
RESTAURANTS
AND INNS

WALES

ABERDOVEY — Hotel Plas Penhelig 62% £D/E

H **Map 8 B3** Gwynedd
LL35 0NA
Aberdovey (065 472) 676

Credit Access, Amex, Diners, Visa
Closed 2 wks Nov & all Jan & Feb

An Edwardian house set in well-tended grounds on a hillside above the village. The splendid oak-panelled hall-cum-lounge features leaded and stained-glass windows, comfortable chintzy chairs and fresh flower arrangements. A second, smaller lounge is equally homely in style, and there's a cosy bar opening on to an attractive terrace. Bedrooms have decent modern furnishings and carpeted bathrooms. No dogs. ***Amenities*** garden, tennis, putting, croquet.

Rooms 11
Ensuite bath/shower 11
Direct dial Yes
Room TV Yes
Confirm by arrang.
Last dinner 8.45
Parking Ample
Room service All day

ABERDOVEY — Trefeddian Hotel 58% £D

H **Map 8 B3** Gwynedd
LL35 0SB
Aberdovey (065 472) 213

Credit Access
Closed 3 Jan–17 Mar

Enjoying splendid wide-open views over golf links and the sea, this popular family-run hotel is located just one mile north of Aberdovey on the A493. Day rooms are reassuringly traditional in character while compact bedrooms – 11 with balconies – have simple white laminate units and carpeted bath/shower rooms. Half-board only. ***Amenities*** garden, indoor swimming pool, solarium, tennis, badminton, putting, games room, laundry service, children's play area. ♿

Rooms 46
Ensuite bath/shower 46
Direct dial Yes
Room TV Yes
Confirm by 6
Last dinner 8.45
Parking Ample
Room service All day

★ For a *discount* on next year's guide, see **An Offer for Answers.** ★

ABERGAVENNY — Walnut Tree Inn ★

R **Map 9 D5** Gwent
Llandewi Skirrid
Abergavenny (0873) 2797

Lunch 12–2.30
Dinner 7–10.30
About £46 for two
Seats 40
Parties 20
Parking Ample

Closed Sun, Mon, 24–26 Dec & 2 wks late Feb

In the early sixties Franco and Ann Taruschio arrived here, and their charm and enthusiasm remain undiminished, their staff as wonderful as ever. Their restaurant is warm and homely, an unassuming backdrop for some remarkable eating. Marvellous flavours and textures are the hallmark of dishes whether elaborate or forcefully robust: there are many unmissable delights, including crispy crab pancakes, trenette with truffles, roast suckling pig, seafood platter, Sicilian cheesecake ... and the wine list is superb, with helpful and witty comments by Bill Baker – note Ch. Camensac '71, Ch. Coutet '67. ***Specialities*** bresaola, Thai pork appetiser, grilled lobster with vin santo, gâteau Ambassadeur. Outstanding Well-chosen

ABERGWESYN — Llwynderw Hotel 70% £A

HR **Map 9 C4** Powys
Nr Llanwrtyd Wells
LD5 4TW
Llanwrtyd Wells (059 13) 238

Rooms 12
Ensuite bath/shower 12
Room phone No
Room TV No
Confirm by arrang.
Last dinner 8
Parking Ample
Room service Limited

Credit Access, Amex
Closed Jan & Feb

Elegance, tranquillity and comfort are the hallmarks of this 18th-century house situated on a wooded hillside and overlooking an uninhabited valley. To either side of the handsome entrance hall are the well-stocked library and the attractive drawing room, both offering deep-cushioned sofas, large armchairs, fresh flowers and the fine original artwork that is to be found throughout the hotel. The bedrooms are of a good size and are furnished with fine antiques and simple, old-fashioned pieces; lace bedcovers and heavy floral drapes create a feeling of luxury continued by the extra-thick towels in the carpeted bathrooms. No children under ten.
Amenities garden, laundry service.

Restaurant

Set D from £21
About £55 for two
Seats 24
Parties 12

The informal dining room with sturdy beech tables and a log fire provides a pleasing setting for the very enjoyable meals. The four-course menu (no choice except for cheese and desserts) changes daily, offering mainly traditional French and English dishes, and the combination of high standards of cooking and top quality ingredients produces excellent results. Desserts are truly wonderful. Short, skilfully chosen wine list. ♥ Well-chosen ⊖

Lunch by arrang. only   *Dinner* at 8
Closed Jan & Feb

ABERSOCH   Porth Tocyn Hotel   69%   £D/E

HR **Map 8 B2** Gwynedd
Bwlch Tocyn LL53 7BU
Abersoch (075 881) 2966

Credit Access
Closed Nov–Easter exc.
10 days Xmas

There's little evidence left of the miners' cottages which formed the basis of this well-cared-for and homely country house hotel, save for the progression of small lounges. The abundance of dried flowers, pomanders and lace mats provides a delightful atmosphere and the Fletcher-Brewers are most charming hosts. Bedrooms are furnished to the highest standard and have lovely sea views.
Amenities garden, outdoor swimming pool, tennis, laundry service.

Rooms 17	*Direct dial* Yes	*Confirm by* arrang.	*Parking* Ample
Ensuite bath/shower 17	*Room TV* Yes	*Last dinner* 9.30	*Room service* Limited

Restaurant   ⚐

Set L Sun only £8.50
Set D from £11.25
About £44 for two
Seats 55
Parties 55

A polished parquet floor and candles and fresh flowers on the tables make a delightful setting. Dinner is a serious affair, while lunches are more informal. A typical evening meal might be wild mushrooms stuffed with walnuts and Madeira, celery and chive soup, roast loin of veal with apricot and prune stuffing and chocolate puddle pudding. Leave room for the superb cheeseboard. ♥ Well-chosen ⊖ &

Lunch 12.30–2   *Dinner* 7.30–9.30
Closed Nov–Easter exc. 10 days Xmas

ABERSOCH   Riverside Hotel   58%   £D/E

H **Map 8 B2** Gwynedd
LL53 7HW
Abersoch (075 881) 2419

Credit Access, Visa
Closed 1 Nov–Feb

A friendly holiday hotel overlooking both the harbour just across the busy road in front and the quiet river Soch to the rear. Day rooms, though smallish, are prettily furnished. Best bedrooms are in the main house and are bright and airy, with good fitted furniture and easy chairs; those in a newer wing are more compact. No dogs.
Amenities garden, indoor swimming pool, laundry service.

Rooms 14	*Direct dial* Yes	*Confirm by* arrang.	*Parking* Ample
Ensuite bath/shower 14	*Room TV* Yes	*Last dinner* 9	*Room service* All day

---

We publish annually,
so make sure you use the current edition.
It's worth it!

ABERYSTWYTH   Conrah Country Hotel   62%   £C/D

H **Map 9 B4** Dyfed
Chancery SY23 4DF
Aberystwyth (0970) 617941
Telex 35892

Credit Access, Amex, Diners, Visa
Closed 22–31 Dec

The mansion house is splendid, with well-proportioned public rooms and spacious bedrooms, many with valley views. Downstairs there's a charming writing room off the main lounge and a comfortable lounge bar. A short walk (umbrellas provided for rainy nights) brings you to the adjoining motel complex, where rooms are compact, with tiny shower rooms. No children under three. No dogs. *Amenities* garden, indoor swimming pool, sauna, croquet, secretarial services.

Rooms 22	*Direct dial* Yes	*Confirm by* arrang.	*Parking* Ample
Ensuite bath/shower 20	*Room TV* Yes	*Last dinner* 9.30	*Room service* All day

BARRY   Mount Sorrel Hotel   59%   £E/F

H Map 9 C6 South Glamorgan
Porthkerry Road CF6 8AY
Barry (0446) 740069

Credit Access, Amex, Diners, Visa
Closed 25 Dec

On a hill towards the western end of the town centre, this pleasantly
relaxed hotel comprises two Victorian houses linked by a modern
building. Bamboo and potted plants lend a tropical touch to the
lounge, and there's a cosy, convivial bar. Bedrooms are decorated in
pale pinks and greys, with pine furniture and carpeted bath or shower
rooms. All is neat and well kept.
Amenities laundry service.

Rooms 37	Direct dial Yes	Confirm by 6	Parking Ample
Ensuite bath/shower 37	Room TV Yes	Last dinner 10	Room service 24 hours

BEAUMARIS   Bulkeley Arms Hotel   58%   £E

H Map 8 C1 Gwynedd
Castle Street LL58 8AW
Beaumaris (0248) 810415

Credit Access, Amex, Diners, Visa

Traditional comforts are offered by this handsome Victorian hotel in
a fine position looking across the Menai Straits. Public rooms are lofty
and spacious, especially the relaxing residents' lounge, while the
comfortable bar is a popular watering hole of the locals. The best
bedrooms overlook the Straits; '30s enthusiasts will enjoy the old style
furniture and high beds. All rooms have tea-makers and most have
acceptable bathrooms. *Amenities* garden, snooker, laundry service.

Rooms 40	Direct dial Yes	Confirm by arrang.	Parking Ample
Ensuite bath/shower 37	· Room TV Yes	Last dinner 9	Room service All day

BEDDGELERT   Royal Goat Hotel   60%   £E

H Map 8 C2 Gwynedd
LL55 4YE
Beddgelert (076 686) 224

Credit Access, Amex, Diners, Visa

Set among stunning mountain scenery, the Royal Goat offers excellent
fishing, walking and climbing. The Roberts family keep the whole
place immaculate, and day rooms have a cosy inviting feel. Two
bedrooms are suites with four-posters, while the rest are in unfussy
modern style. Hairdryers, tea-makers and remote-control TVs are
standard, and pretty little ornaments add a homely touch. *Amenities* garden, game fishing, games room, satellite TV, in-house movies.

Rooms 34	Direct dial Yes	Confirm by arrang.	Parking Ample
Ensuite bath/shower 34	Room TV Yes	Last dinner 9	Room service All day

BETWS-Y-COED   Royal Oak Hotel   59%   *NEW ENTRY*   £D/E

H Map 8 C2 Gwynedd
Holyhead Road LL24 0AY
Betws-y-Coed (069 02) 219

Credit Access, Amex, Diners, Visa
Closed 25 & 26 Dec

Front bedrooms at this sturdy former coaching inn have good views
over the river Llugwy. Rooms are pleasantly decorated in soft shades
and most have simple modern units and a couple of easy chairs; six
rear rooms boast very glitzy beds with built-in stereo equipment.
There's a cheerful coffee shop, lounge and bar. Staff are friendly and
helpful. No dogs.
Amenities garden, coffee shop (7.30am–9.30pm).

Rooms 27	Direct dial Yes	Confirm by arrang.	Parking Ample
Ensuite bath/shower 27	Room TV Yes	Last dinner 8.45	Room service All day

Our inspectors *never* book in the name of Egon Ronay's Guides.
They disclose their identity only if they are considering an establishment
for inclusion in the next edition of the Guide.

BONTDDU   Bontddu Hall Hotel   58%   £E

H Map 8 C3 Gwynedd
Nr Dolgellau LL40 2SU
Dolgellau (0341) 49661

Credit Access, Amex, Diners, Visa
Closed Jan & Feb

Many original features remain at this Victorian Gothic mansion,
including the coloured tiles on the floor of the oak-panelled entrance
hall and the stained glass in the bar, once a billiards room. Two lounges
are restful and comfortable, one with traditional furnishings, while
the bedrooms, reached by a fine Victorian staircase, vary in style from
period to modern. No children under two.
Amenities garden, putting.

Rooms 20	Direct dial Yes	Confirm by 6	Parking Ample
Ensuite bath/shower 20	Room TV Yes	Last dinner 9.30	Room service All day

---

BRECHFA   Tŷ Mawr Country House Hotel   59%   £E

H **Map 9 B5** Dyfed
Nr Carmarthen SA32 7RA
Brechfa (026 789) 332

Credit Access, Visa
Closed 2 wks Feb & 2 wks Nov

A 16th-century house standing on the B4310 in the middle of the village. Day rooms, currently being reorganised, include two homely lounges, one with TV, the other with French windows opening on to the terrace and garden. Bedrooms are neat and simple, with cottagy decor and little extras like magazines, mineral water and sewing kits. Carpeted bathrooms all have tubs, showers and a range of toiletries. Enjoyable breakfasts. *Amenities* garden, laundry service.

Rooms 5	*Room phone* No	*Confirm by* arrang.	*Parking* Ample
Ensuite bath/shower 4	*Room TV* No	*Last dinner* 9	*Room service* Limited

---

CAERNARFON   Stables Hotel   58%   £E

H **Map 8 B2** Gwynedd
Llanwnda LL54 5SD
Llanwnda (0286) 830711

Credit Access, Amex, Visa

Set well back from the A499 Caernarfon to Pwllheli road, this hotel consists of a 12-room single storey accommodation block (with car-standing, motel-style). A covered walkway leads to a Victorian stable block, which houses the restaurant and Stirrup Bar, atmospheric areas retaining many of the original stall partitions. Bedrooms are decorated to a high, if simple standard. Carpeted bathrooms are well equipped. *Amenities* garden, outdoor swimming pool, laundry service.

Rooms 12	*Direct dial* Yes	*Confirm by* arrang.	*Parking* Ample
Ensuite bath/shower 12	*Room TV* Yes	*Last dinner* 9.45	*Room service* All day

---

Any person using our name to obtain free hospitality is a fraud.
Proprietors, please inform the police and us.

CARDIFF   Angel Hotel   65%   *NEW ENTRY*   £C

H **Town plan C2**
South Glamorgan
Castle Street CF1 2QZ
Cardiff (0222) 32633
Telex 498132

Credit Access, Amex, Diners, Visa

A massive crystal chandelier, marble pillars and a double central staircase make an impressive entrance to this interesting 19th-century hotel. The quiet lounge is stylish and comfortable while the basement Vaults Bar is an atmospheric spot; next to it is the smart new leisure area. Executive bedrooms and suites are strikingly decorated, with festoon blinds a feature; sofas, easy chairs and desks supplement a good array of accessories including trouser presses, tea-makers and concealed mini-bars. First-floor rooms are more dated and those facing inwards are noticeably short of light.
Amenities sauna, solariums, whirlpool bath, keep-fit equipment, in-house movies, secretarial services, laundry service.

Rooms 91	*Direct dial* Yes	*Confirm by* 6	*Parking* Ample
Ensuite bath/shower 91	*Room TV* Yes	*Last dinner* 10	*Room service* 24 hours

---

CARDIFF   Armless Dragon   *NEW ENTRY*   ⦄

R **Map Town plan D1**
South Glamorgan
97 Wyverne Road
Cardiff (0222) 382357

About £40 for two
Seats 45
Parking Ample

Credit Access, Amex, Diners, Visa

Booking is advisable in the evening, and first-time visitors should get clear directions to this very friendly little restaurant north of the city centre. The menu is varied and imaginative, with daily-changing blackboard specials adding to the choice. Crab soup is a tasty, satisfying starter, and main courses run from spicy Barbados-style garfish to roast suckling pig, guinea fowl with blackberries and fillet steak plain or sauced. ⊖

Lunch 12–2.15   *Dinner* 7.30–10.30, Sat till 11
Closed L Sat, all Sun, Bank Hols & 1 wk Xmas

CARDIFF   La Chaumière   ⦄

R **Map 9 D6** South Glamorgan
44 Cardiff Road, Llandaff
Cardiff (0222) 555319

French cooking
Set L Sun £6.95
Set D Sun by arrang. £11.95
Seats 40 *Parties* 40
Parking Ample
Credit Access, Amex, Diners

Booking is advisable for the Morgans' attractive French restaurant where everything is fresh, from the pastel decor to the quality ingredients Kay uses for her traditional French cooking. Start with puréed leeks en croûte or carrot and ginger soup, followed by crisp duckling, pigeon pie with quince jelly, or quail with port. Sweets include a delicious made-to-order syllabub.
♀ Well-chosen ⊖

Lunch 12–2, Sun till 2.30   *Dinner* 7–9.30, Sat till 10.30
Closed D Sun, all Mon & 1st 2 wks Jan   *About £35 for two*

CARDIFF

Map 9 D6
Town plan opposite

Population 284,400

Though it enshrines Welsh culture and history. Cardiff is both modern and cosmopolitan. Its population was less than 2,000 at the beginning of the 19th century, when its port developed with export of coal from the near-by mines. No British city is more compact in its many offerings to visitors, everything dominated by the comprehensive City Centre and the lovingly restored Castle. It is a matter of choice whether Welsh tradition, commerce or sport matter most to the visitor, though certainly the last attracts the most visitors *en masse*, especially to Cardiff Arms Park. Though Cardiff is an ideal base for touring South Wales, a short visit offers more than enough to remain within the city limits.

Annual Events
Cardiff Festival *July/August*
Festival of Music *November–December*
Horticultural Show *September*
Llandaff Festival *June*
Lord Mayor's Parade *August*
Military Tattoo *August* (every other year)

Information Office
Public Relations Officer
City Hall, Cardiff
Telephone Cardiff 822000

Wales Tourist Board
Brunel House
2 Fitzalan Road, Cardiff

Fiat Dealers
T. S. Grimshaw Ltd
Fiat House, 329 Cowbridge Road East
Cardiff CF5 1JD
Tel. Cardiff 395322
Map reference A2

Yapp's Garages Ltd
Fidlas Road
Llanishen
Cardiff CF4 5YW
Tel. Cardiff 751323

1 Bute Park **C1/2**
2 Cardiff Castle *fairy-tale magnificence bequeathed by the Bute family* **C2**
3 Civic Centre **C/D1/2**
4 General Station **C/D3**
5 Llandaff Cathedral **A1**
6 National Museum of Wales **D1**
7 National Sports Centre for Wales **B1**
8 New Theatre, Park Place **D2**
9 Queen Street Station **E2**
10 St David's Centre **D2**
11 St David's Hall **D3**
12 St John's Church, St John Square **D2**
13 Sherman Theatre **D1**
14 Tourist Information Office **D3**
15 Wales National Ice Rink **D3**
16 Welsh Industrial and Maritime Museum, Bute Street **D3**
17 Wood Street Bus Station **C3**

Cardiff FIAT

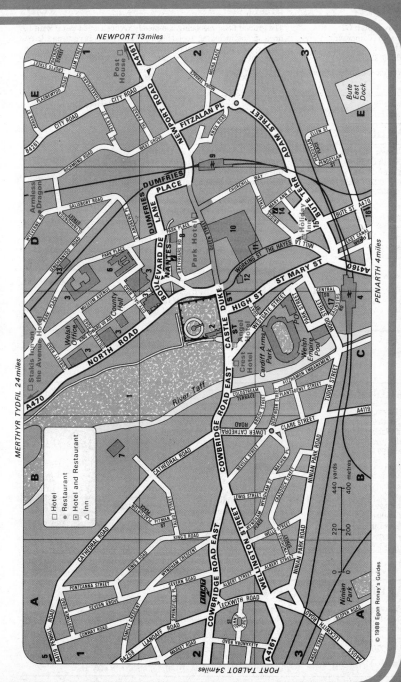

CARDIFF   Crest Hotel   £C/D

H Town plan C2
South Glamorgan
Westgate Street CF1 1JB
Cardiff (0222) 388681

Credit Access, Amex, Diners, Visa

The ground floor was being completely reconstructed as we went to press, plans including replacing the Gatehouse Tavern and Crest Pantry with a new bar and restaurant. Bedrooms had already been redecorated and the best are Executive rooms with superior fittings and accessories. Graded at 59% in our 1988 Guide, the Crest enjoys a central position overlooking the castle and river Taff. *Amenities* garden, in-house movies, secretarial services, fax, laundry service.

Rooms 159	*Direct dial* Yes	*Confirm by* 6	*Parking* Ample
Ensuite bath/shower 159	*Room TV* Yes	*Last dinner* 9.45	*Room service* 24 hours

CARDIFF   Holiday Inn   75%   £C

H Town plan D3
South Glamorgan
Mill Lane CF1 1EZ
Cardiff (0222) 399944
Telex 497365

Rooms 182
Ensuite bath/shower 182
Direct dial Yes
Room TV Yes
Confirm by 6
Last dinner 11
Parking Ample
Room service 24 hours

Credit Access, Amex, Diners, Visa

Dominating the skyline at the southern end of the city centre, this tall modern hotel offers luxurious accommodation and a fine range of leisure and business facilities. Marble columns and arches divide up the stylish public areas, which include a lounge, bar and coffee shop. Bedrooms are very comfortable and well planned, with pastel decor, deep carpets, smart lightwood furniture and splendidly fitted bathrooms. Air conditioning, remote-control TVs, trouser presses and hairdryers are standard. *Amenities* indoor swimming pool, sauna, solarium, whirlpool bath, steam bath, gymnasium, squash, satellite TV, in-house movies, secretarial services, fax, laundry service, coffee shop (7am–10.30pm), kiosk. &

**Our inspectors are our full-time employees;
they are professionally trained by us.**

CARDIFF   Park Hotel   71%   £C/D

H Town plan D2
South Glamorgan
Park Place CF1 3UD
Cardiff (0222) 383471
Telex 497195

Rooms 108
Ensuite bath/shower 108
Direct dial Yes
Room TV Yes
Confirm by 6
Last dinner 11
Parking Limited
Room service 24 hours

Credit Access, Amex, Diners, Visa
LVs

Right in the centre of the city, in the pedestrian zone, a Victorian hotel that's maintained and run with great efficiency and aplomb. (Access by car is now at the back, and drivers are advised to seek clear directions.) Much of the ground and first floors are given over to function and conference suites, but public areas include an elegant cocktail lounge and a period-style writing room with leather sofa and wing chairs. Top-grade bedrooms are simply enormous, with correspondingly huge, fully tiled bathrooms. Extras range from mineral water and tea-makers to hairdryers and bathtime luxuries. Housekeeping is excellent. *Amenities* in-house movies, secretarial services, laundry service.

CARDIFF   Post House Hotel   63%   £C/D

H Town plan E1
South Glamorgan
Pentwyn Road, Pentwyn CF2 7XA
Cardiff (0222) 731212
Telex 497633

Credit Access, Amex, Diners, Visa

Four miles from the centre, near junction 29 of the M4, this Post House has benefited from extensive refurbishment. Day rooms are bright and quite stylish, bedrooms practical and well equipped. Some rooms have been upgraded to Executive standard. The cold buffet breakfast is more appealing than the hot. *Amenities* garden, indoor swimming pool, sauna, solarium, whirlpool bath, gymnasium, laundry service, coffee shop (7am–10.30pm), children's play area.

Rooms 150	*Direct dial* Yes	*Confirm by* 6	*Parking* Ample
Ensuite bath/shower 150	*Room TV* Yes	*Last dinner* 9.30	*Room service* 24 hours

CARDIFF — Stakis Inn on the Avenue — 72% — £C/D

H **Town plan C1**
South Glamorgan
Circle Way East,
Llanedeyrn CF3 7XF
Cardiff (0222) 732520
Telex 497582

Rooms 144
Ensuite bath/shower 144
Direct dial Yes
Room TV Yes
Confirm by 6
Last dinner 10
Parking Ample
Room service 24 hours

Credit Access, Amex, Diners, Visa

Located a few miles east of the city, just off the A48(M), this modern hotel has benefited from a comprehensive programme of refurbishment. The roomy open-plan foyer and bar-lounge are decorated in smart contemporary style, with plants and Chinese lamps arranged among the chairs and settees. Light, bright bedrooms are furnished with white freestanding pieces, and all are equipped with tea-making facilities, trouser presses and hairdryers. Fresh fruit is provided, and the morning paper comes free. Bathrooms all have tubs and showers, plus a good range of toiletries.
Amenities garden, indoor swimming pool, sauna, solarium, whirlpool bath, keep-fit equipment, secretarial services, fax, laundry service.

CARMARTHEN — Ivy Bush Royal Hotel — 59% — £D

H **Map 9 B5** Dyfed
Spilman Street SA31 1LG
Carmarthen (0267) 235111
Telex 48520

Credit Access, Amex, Diners, Visa

Pleasant overnight accommodation in the centre of the town. Bedrooms are done out in comfortable, practical style, with built-in furniture and neat, modern bathrooms, and a few have been redecorated in restful soft shades. Dominating the lounge and bar is a splendid stained-glass window unveiled in 1974 and commemorating the formation of the first Gorsedd circle of bards, in the hotel's garden in 1819. *Amenities* garden, sauna, laundry service.

Rooms 80	*Direct dial* Yes	*Confirm by* 6	*Parking* Ample
Ensuite bath/shower 80	*Room TV* Yes	*Last dinner* 9	*Room service* 24 hours

Changes in data sometimes occur in establishments
after the Guide goes to press.
Prices should be taken as indications rather than firm quotes.

CHEPSTOW — Castle View Hotel — £E

I **Map 9 D6** Gwent
16 Bridge Street NP6 5EZ
Chepstow (029 12) 70349
Telex 498280

Credit Access, Amex, Diners, Visa

Built as a private residence 300 years ago, the Gilletts' charming inn stands across the road from the ruins of Chepstow Castle. Many original features survive, including massive stone walls (perhaps from the castle), timbers and a hand-turned oak staircase. Day rooms are cosy, bedrooms spotless and decently equipped, with mini-bars and hairdryers, plus shower facilities as well as baths in eight rooms.
Amenities garden, in-house movies.

Rooms 11	*Direct dial* Yes	*Confirm by* 6	*Parking* Ample
Ensuite bath/shower 11	*Room TV* Yes	*Last dinner* 9	*Room service* Limited

CHEPSTOW — St Pierre Hotel — 63% — £C/D

H **Map 9 D6** Gwent
St Pierre Park NP6 6YA
Chepstow (029 12) 5261
Telex 497562

Credit Access, Amex, Diners, Visa

With two championship golf courses and a league of other leisure activities, the St Pierre has great appeal for sports lovers. Its heart is a 14th-century mansion, which survives with its Norman church. The flagstoned lounge has echoes of the past, and there are three bars. Bedrooms in a separate courtyard block have well-coordinated decor and a catalogue of extras. Average buffet breakfast.
Amenities garden, indoor swimming pool, sauna, whirlpool bath, solarium, steam room, gymnasium, tennis, squash, badminton, golf courses, putting, croquet, bowling green, games room, snooker, fax, in-house movies, laundry service, coffee shop (9.30am–10pm), 24-hour lounge service, children's play area.

Rooms 108	*Direct dial* Yes	*Confirm by* arrang.	*Parking* Ample
Ensuite bath/shower 108	*Room TV* Yes	*Last dinner* 9.15	*Room service* All day

CHEPSTOW

Willow Tree   *NEW ENTRY*   ⌀

R **Map 9 D6** Gwent
Riverside, The Back
Chepstow (029 12) 6665

Set D from £11.95
About £36 for two
Seats 60
Parties 20
Parking Ample
Credit Access, Visa

Jeremy Hector's popular restaurant enjoys a most attractive setting
on the banks of the Wye. Decor is cosy and intimate, and dinner brings
the more formal choice on fixed-price menus: garlicky king prawns
or a tasty cheese-topped dish of noodles and vegetables to start, then
maybe succulent Wye salmon, coq au vin or succulent Greek-style
lamb chops with tzatziki. Consult the blackboard for lunchtime choice.
Traditional Sunday lunch. ⊖ ♿

Lunch 12.30–2.30   *Dinner* 7.30–9.30
Closed D Sun

We welcome bona fide complaints and recommendations
on the tear-out pages at the back of the book for readers' comment.
They are followed up by our professional team.

COLWYN BAY

Hotel Seventy Degrees   65%   **£D/E**

H **Map 8 C1** Clwyd
Penmaenhead,
Old Colwyn LL29 9LD
Colwyn Bay (0492) 516555
Telex 61362

Credit Access, Amex, Diners, Visa

The lounge, the restaurant and most of the bedrooms enjoy views of
the sea at this distinctive modern hotel, which occupies an elevated
position on the A547 hard by the A55 Expressway. The friendly and
enthusiastic new manager plans major updates both in the day rooms
and in the simply appointed bedrooms, all of which have well-kept,
carpeted bathrooms.   **Amenities** satellite TV, in-house movies,
secretarial services, fax, laundry service, helipad.

| *Rooms* 42 | *Direct dial* Yes | *Confirm by* 6 | *Parking* Ample |
| *Ensuite bath/shower* 42 | *Room TV* Yes | *Last dinner* 9.30 | *Room service* 24 hours |

CONWY

Sychnant Pass Hotel   62%   **£E/F**

HR **Map 8 C1** Gwynedd
Sychnant Pass Road
LL32 8BJ
Conwy (0492) 596868
Telex 61155
Credit Access, Amex, Diners, Visa
Closed Jan

Brian and Jean Jones are most delightful hosts at their remote and
homely hotel on the edge of Snowdonia National Park. The warm and
mellow decor gives a relaxing feel to the public areas, which comprise
two lounges and a cosy bar. Immaculately maintained bedrooms are
in soft autumnal colours with floral curtains, modern darkwood
furniture, carpeted bathrooms and plenty of extras.
Amenities garden, sauna, solarium, whirlpool bath, laundry service.

| *Rooms* 11 | *Direct dial* Yes | *Confirm by* arrang. | *Parking* Ample |
| *Ensuite bath/shower* 11 | *Room TV* Yes | *Last dinner* 9.30 | *Room service* All day |

Restaurant   ⌀

Set L £6.95
Set D £12.50
About £37 for two
Seats 30
Parties 10

The Jones family run their inviting little restaurant with care and
nothing is too much trouble when it comes to pleasing their guests.
The daily changing, fixed-price menu offers simple dishes, very well
prepared from excellent quality ingredients and beautifully presented.
Our inspector enthused over fresh tomato and orange soup, followed
by superb Welsh lamb cutlets, perfectly cooked and meltingly tender;
vegetables were crisp and full of flavour. ⊖

Lunch 12–2.30   *Dinner* 7–9.30
Closed Jan & L Oct–May

COYCHURCH

Coed-y-Mwstwr Hotel   69%   **£D**

HR **Map 9 C6** Mid Glamorgan
Nr Bridgend CF35 6AF
Bridgend (0656) 860621

Credit Access, Amex, Diners, Visa
Closed 26 Dec

Seventeen acres of woodland surround this late-Victorian mansion
reached via a long, winding lane. Chandeliers, heavy gold drapes and
velour upholstery grace the lounge, while the spacious bedrooms have
a mixture of antique and traditional furniture, well-coordinated
colour schemes and plenty of ornaments. All have radio alarms and
hairdryers. No children under seven. No dogs.   **Amenities** garden,
outdoor swimming pool, tennis, snooker, fax, laundry service. ♿

| *Rooms* 30 | *Direct dial* Yes | *Confirm by* arrang. | *Parking* Ample |
| *Ensuite bath/shower* 30 | *Room TV* Yes | *Last dinner* 10 | *Room service* 24 hours |

Restaurant

Set L from £7.25, Sun £10.95
Set D £15.95
About £50 for two
Seats 65
Parties 20

Expert cooking and an elegant oak-panelled dining room combine to guarantee an enjoyable meal. Michael Griffin offers a four-course fixed price menu plus an interesting à la carte and the food comes attractively presented. Start with a delicately flavoured mousseline of sole with a light chive sauce then move on to breast of Barbary duck with pineapple and brandy sauce. Sweets are delicious. 🍷 Well-chosen ℮

Lunch 12–2   *Dinner* 7–10
Closed 26 Dec

CRICCIETH   Bron Eifion Hotel   57%   £C/D

H **Map 8 B2** Gwynedd
LL52 0SA
Criccieth (0766) 522385

Credit Access, Visa

Modest furnishings contrast with the galleried splendour of the central hall of this Victorian country house built as the summer residence of a slate millionaire. Other public rooms include a pleasant lounge and a small bar. Prices seem rather high for the old-fashioned bedrooms, some of which are being refurbished. All have tea-makers and simple bathrooms.
Amenities garden, croquet, game fishing.

| *Rooms* 18 | *Direct dial* Yes | *Confirm by* arrang. | *Parking* Ample |
| *Ensuite bath/shower* 18 | *Room TV* No | *Last dinner* 8.45 | *Room service* Limited |

CRICKHOWELL   Bear Hotel   £E/F

| **Map 9 D5** Powys
Crickhowell (0873) 810408

Credit Access, Visa

In the centre of town, the Bear is an old coaching inn with a lot of character. Heavy black beams and farmhouse furniture set the tone in the bar, a roomy and popular meeting place for both locals and guests. Solid furnishings also appear in the warmly decorated bedrooms, one of which is a splendid honeymoon suite complete with four-poster and whirlpool bath. Very pleasant and helpful staff.
Amenities garden, fax, laundry service.

| *Rooms* 25 | *Direct dial* Yes | *Confirm by* arrang. | *Parking* Limited |
| *Ensuite bath/shower* 24 | *Room TV* Yes | *Last dinner* 9 | *Room service* All day |

CRICKHOWELL   Gliffaes Hotel   63%   £E/F

H **Map 9 D5** Powys
NP8 1RH
Bwlch (0874) 730371

Credit Access, Amex, Diners, Visa
Closed 31 Dec–mid Mar

West of Crickhowell off the A40, Gliffaes stands in extensive grounds that include mighty redwood trees and beautiful shrubs. The house was built in 1885 to a highly original design that incorporates an Italian-style bell tower. The lounge, with its open fire and groups of inviting settees, has a lovely traditional ambience, and there's a similar feel about the drawing room, whose French windows open on to a delightful sun room and terrace. Spacious bedrooms are attractively furnished and four look down on the river Usk far below. No TVs, but there's a set in a small lounge off the bar. Pleasant staff. Kennelling for dogs. ***Amenities*** garden, tennis, golf practice net, putting, croquet, game fishing, snooker, laundry service.

| *Rooms* 19 | *Direct dial* Yes | *Confirm by* arrang. | *Parking* Ample |
| *Ensuite bath/shower* 18 | *Room TV* No | *Last dinner* 9.30 | *Room service* All day |

If we recommend meals in a Hotel or Inn,

a separate entry is made for its restaurant.

EGLWYSFACH   Ynyshir Hall Hotel   61%   £E

H **Map 8 C3** Dyfed
Nr Machynlleth Powys
SY20 8TA
Glandyfi (065 474) 209
Credit Access, Amex, Diners, Visa
Closed mid Nov–Mar exc.
Xmas–New Year

Twelve acres of mature grounds enclosed by an RSPB bird sanctuary with mountain views beyond make this mellow 16th-century manor house a haven for the nature lover. Public areas include a nicely proportioned lounge and a bar. Bedrooms have pretty floral schemes and plenty of extras such as tissues and cotton wool. Three of the four rooms without bath have an en suite shower cabinet.
Amenities garden, laundry service.

| *Rooms* 10 | *Direct dial* Yes | *Confirm by* arrang. | *Parking* Ample |
| *Ensuite bath/shower* 8 | *Room TV* Yes | *Last dinner* 9 | *Room service* All day |

FELINGWM UCHAF   Plough Inn, Hickman's Restaurant   ♀

RR **Map 9 B5** Dyfed
Nantgaredig SA32 7PR
Nantgaredig (0267 88) 220

About £38 for two
Seats 40
Parties 40
Parking Ample

Credit Access, Amex, Diners, Visa

Talent and finesse are the hallmarks of chef patrons Leon and Eires
Hickman at this oak-beamed former coachhouse on the B4310 south
east of Carmarthen. Eires is famed for her lobster thermidor; Leon for
his duck en croûte. Main courses like pheasant with Beaujolais make
use of top quality raw materials. Delectable desserts including liqueur-
soaked gâteau precede fine cheeses. Reasonably-priced wine list: note
Corton Charlemagne '79 from Roland Rapet. ♀ Well-chosen ⊖

Lunch Mon–Sat by arrang., Sun 12–2   *Dinner* 7–9.30
Closed 25 & 26 Dec

BEDROOMS 5   £E
With bath/shower 2

Overnight guests are accommodated in a cottage across the road,
which offers two cheerful en suite doubles, one twin, one single and a
family room. No dogs.

FISHGUARD   Fishguard Bay Hotel   59%   £E

H **Map 9 A5** Dyfed
Quay Road, Goodwick
SA64 0BT
Fishguard (0348) 873571
Telex 48602

Credit Access, Amex, Diners, Visa

An imposing white-painted hotel set in woodland looking down on
the docks and ferry terminals. Fine old furnishings give a traditional
feel to some of the day rooms, which include three pleasant bars and a
couple of lounges. Bedrooms are practical and straightforward; some
are without TV, telephone and private facilities. Good old-fashioned
standards of service.
Amenities garden, outdoor swimming pool, snooker. ⅊

Rooms 62	*Direct dial* Some	*Confirm by* arrang.	*Parking* Ample
Ensuite bath/shower 26	*Room TV* Some	*Last dinner* 9.30	*Room service* 24 hours

Changes in data sometimes occur in establishments
after the Guide goes to press.
Prices should be taken as indications rather than firm quotes.

GLYN CEIRIOG   Golden Pheasant Hotel   62%   £E

H **Map 8 D2** Clwyd
Nr Chirk LL20 7BB
Glyn Ceiriog (069 172) 281
Telex 35664

Credit Access, Amex, Visa

Hidden on the slopes of a deep valley, the Golden Pheasant is a
charming combination of old-world local inn and stylish country
hotel. The atmosphere is informal, but the place is very well run.
Delightful public rooms include an elegant lounge with lovely
sweeping views, a cocktail bar decorated in Chinese-style and a public
bar with a slate floor, showcases of stuffed pheasants and swathes of
dried heather hanging from the ceiling. Prettily decorated bedrooms
range from inn-style in the main house to grander and strikingly
furnished themed rooms in the wing.
Amenities garden, riding, shooting, laundry service.

Rooms 18	*Direct dial* Yes	*Confirm by* arrang.	*Parking* Ample
Ensuite bath/shower 18	*Room TV* Yes	*Last dinner* 8.30	*Room service* All day

GWBERT-ON-SEA   Cliff Hotel   58%   £D

H **Map 9 B4** Dyfed
Cardigan SA43 1PP
Cardigan (0239) 613241
Telex 48440

Credit Access, Amex, Diners, Visa
Closed Jan

Standing on a headland looking out to sea, the Cliff offers three grades
of accommodation. The best and largest rooms have sea views and
some extra accessories; the next grade overlook the sea or estuary
while the third grade rooms have no sea views. There are two bars, a
roomy residents' lounge and a sun lounge.
Amenities garden, outdoor swimming pool, squash, 9-hole golf
course, putting, sea fishing, snooker, laundry service. ⅊

Rooms 75	*Direct dial* Yes	*Confirm by* arrang.	*Parking* Ample
Ensuite bath/shower 75	*Room TV* Yes	*Last dinner* 9	*Room service* 24 hours

HARLECH — The Cemlyn *NEW ENTRY* ♫

RR **Map 8 B2** Gwynedd
High Street LL46 2YA
Harlech (0766) 780425

Set D £13.50
About £40 for two
Seats 40
Parties 10
Parking Ample
Credit Amex, Diners

Modern paintings, fabric wall hangings and frogs in all shapes and sizes provide the decor for a charming, relaxed restaurant where diners feel instantly at ease. Amiable chef-patron Ken Goody cooks with care and enthusiasm, making excellent use of local seafood and Welsh lamb. Smoked chicken with onion marmalade, gravad lax and sirloin steak are other popular items, and Amaretto ice cream with butterscotch sauce makes an indulgent finale. ℮

Lunch by arrang.   *Dinner* 7–9 (till 10 in high season)
Closed end Oct–Easter

BEDROOMS 1   £F
With bath/shower 1

The homely bedroom (no children under eight, no dogs) has remote-control TV, easy chairs and lots of books, plus a large and luxurious bathroom.

 indicates a **well-chosen** house wine

LAKE VYRNWY — Lake Vyrnwy Hotel   64%   £E/F

H **Map 8 C3** Powys
Llanwddyn, via Oswestry,
Shropshire SY10 0LY
Llanwddyn (069 173) 692
Telex 35880

Credit Access, Amex, Diners, Visa

Standing high above the lake, this Victorian hotel enjoys spectacular views from its elegant, traditionally appointed day rooms. First-floor bedrooms are larger than those above; all are attractively decorated and furnished with a mixture of antique and period pieces. Good-sized carpeted bathrooms. The public bar is currently being redesigned and a conservatory created. *Amenities* garden, tennis, clay-pigeon shooting, game fishing, sailing, in-house movies, fax, laundry service.

Rooms 30	*Direct dial* Yes	*Confirm by* arrang.	*Parking* Ample
Ensuite bath/shower 30	*Room TV* Yes	*Last dinner* 9.30	*Room service* All day

LAMPHEY — Court Hotel   59%   £D/E

H **Map 9 A5** Dyfed
Nr Pembroke SA71 5NT
Lamphey (0646) 672273
Telex 48587

Credit Access, Amex, Diners, Visa

A fine example of Nash architecture dating back to the early 19th-century, the Court has been converted into a most successful country hotel. Public areas are smart and comfortable and a handsome Georgian staircase leads to boldly decorated bedrooms equipped with radio alarms, hairdryers, trouser presses and spacious carpeted and tiled bathrooms. *Amenities* garden, indoor swimming pool, sauna, solarium, keep-fit equipment, secretarial services, laundry service.

Rooms 27	*Direct dial* Yes	*Confirm by* arrang.	*Parking* Ample
Ensuite bath/shower 27	*Room TV* Yes	*Last dinner* 9.30	*Room service* All day

LLANARMON DYFFRYN CEIRIOG — Hand Hotel   £D/E

I **Map 8 D2** Clwyd
Nr Llangollen LL20 7LD
Llanarmon Dyffryn Ceiriog
(069 176) 666

Credit Access, Amex, Diners, Visa
Closed 1 Feb–mid Mar

The B4500 winds up the beautiful Ceiriog valley to bring guests to this tranquil hotel, where owners Tim and Carolyn Alexander offer a warm welcome. There's a beamed bar with an open fire and a smaller TV lounge. Bedrooms, some in the old stable block, are bright and attractively furnished, with spotless bathrooms. TVs on request. *Amenities* garden, tennis, game fishing, laundry service. ♿

Rooms 14	*Room phone* No	*Confirm by* arrang.	*Parking* Ample
Ensuite bath/shower 14	*Room TV* No	*Last dinner* 9	*Room service* All day

LLANBERIS — Y Bistro ♫

R **Map 8 B2** Gwynedd
43 High Street
Llanberis (0286) 871278

Set D £13.95
About £40 for two
Seats 50
Parties 40
Parking Difficult
Credit Access, Visa

Nerys Roberts is an enthusiastic and dedicated chef, husband Danny a charming host at their homely little restaurant. The bi-lingual menu offers a feast of good fresh flavours in dishes like vegetable soup, poached salmon with herb sauce and grilled riblets of lamb marinated in honey, mint and rosemary. Copious vegetables, splendid Welsh cheeses and the local speciality Snowdon suet pudding with lemon, raisins and white wine sauce. Smoking discouraged. ℮ ♿

Dinner only 7.30–9.30
Closed Sun (exc. Bank Hol Sun), 1wk Xmas & 3 wks Jan & Feb

LLANDDERFEL   Palé Hall   74%   £C

H Map 8 C2 Gwynedd
Nr Bala LL23 7PS
Llandderfel (067 83) 285

Rooms 17
Ensuite bath/shower 17
Direct dial Yes
Room TV Yes
Confirm by arrang.
Last dinner 9.30
Parking Ample
Room service All day

Credit Access, Amex, Diners, Visa

A long drive leads from the B4401 to this imposing stone-built mansion on the edge of Snowdonia National Park. The Victorian character of the building has been carefully retained, and fine original features include the oak panelling and galleried staircase in the hall and the lovely Italianate painted dome in the non-smoking lounge. Good-sized bedrooms (some with sitting areas) have well-coordinated traditional furnishings and are comfortably equipped – extras ranging from fresh fruit to hairdryers. Bathrooms offer bidets, shower facilities and a good range of toiletries. Dogs in kennels only.
Amenities garden, sauna, solarium, whirlpool bath, keep-fit equipment, clay-pigeon shooting, coarse & game fishing, laundry service.

**We welcome bona fide complaints and recommendations
on the tear-out pages at the back of the book for readers' comment.
They are followed up by our professional team.**

LLANDEILO   Cawdor Arms Hotel   64%   £E

H Map 9 C5 Dyfed
Rhosmaen Street SA19 6EN
Llandeilo (0558) 823500

Credit Access, Amex, Diners, Visa
Closed 24–26 Dec, 1 & 2 Jan

Traditional charm survives in good measure at the Cawdor Arms, a converted Georgian building in the town centre. Oil paintings adorn the walls of the comfortable lounge and the wide landings that lead to the bedrooms. Some rooms are furnished with antiques, and two boast four-posters; thoughtful little extras include chocolates and a glass of sherry. Staff are pleasant, but the decor is looking slightly faded.
Amenities laundry service.

Rooms 17	*Direct dial* Yes	*Confirm by* arrang.	*Parking* Limited
Ensuite bath/shower 17	*Room TV* Yes	*Last dinner* 9.30	*Room service* All day

LLANDRILLO   Tyddyn Llan   60%   *NEW ENTRY*   £E

HR Map 8 C2 Clwyd
Nr Corwen LL21 0ST
Llandrillo (049 084) 264

Credit Access, Visa
Closed Feb

Tyddyn Llan goes back some 250 years, but it's only in the last year or so that this stone-built house became a hotel. Peter and Bridget Kindred have done a very good job, both in the day rooms, with their antiques and fresh flowers, and in the pretty bedrooms, furnished with a mixture of antiques and period pieces.
Amenities garden, croquet, game fishing, laundry service.

Rooms 9	*Direct dial* Yes	*Confirm by* arrang.	*Parking* Ample
Ensuite bath/shower 8	*Room TV* No	*Last dinner* 9.30	*Room service* None

Restaurant   *NEW ENTRY*   ⚘

Set L Sun £9
Set D £12.50
About £35 for two
Seats 30

Fresh local produce is the key to Bridget's enjoyable cooking, and there's a tempting look to the short, fixed-price menus. Lettuce and hazelnut soup and stuffed oysters are typical starters, and main-course choice could include baked trout, Madeira-sauced tartlet of lamb's kidneys and Welsh beef braised in red wine with fresh vegetables and herbs. Farmhouse cheeses and a few sweets (apple and almond sponge).

Lunch Sun only 1–2   *Dinner* 7.30–9.30
Closed Feb

LLANDUDNO — Bodysgallen Hall 75% £B

HR Map 8 C1
Gwynedd LL30 1RS
Llandudno (0492) 84466
Telex 617163

Rooms 28
Ensuite bath/shower 28
Direct dial Yes
Room TV Yes
Confirm by arrang.
Last dinner 9.45
Parking Ample
Room service 24 hours

Credit Access, Amex, Diners, Visa

A lovely walled rose garden and ornamental box-hedge herb garden feature in the grounds of this imposing 17th-century mansion. Inside, the country-house atmosphere is ready-made in the stone-mullioned and stained-glass windows, ornately carved fireplaces and mellow oak panelling. Blissfully comfortable sofas with inviting, plumped-up feather cushions add a touch of luxury to the elegant lounges. Bedrooms too are very comfortable, with smart traditional furnishings and thoughtful extras like home-made ginger biscuits, fresh flowers, books and magazines. Edwardian-style bathrooms sport brass fittings. No children under eight. Dogs in cottage suites only. *Amenities* garden, tennis, croquet, secretarial services, laundry service. ♿

Restaurant ♔

Set L from £8.50, Sun £10.50
Set D £19.50
About £60 for two
Seats 55
Parties 40

Chandeliers and flowing drapes give a formal air to this grandly-proportioned dining room, where fresh local produce features prominently in the interesting menus. New ideas bend old traditions in dishes like breast of pheasant filled with chicken mousse on a herb mayonnaise, and tender-pink loin of Welsh lamb served with onion marmalade. Desserts are good and there's a splendid selection of Welsh cheeses. Pleasant, unobtrusive service. Serious wine list: Burgundies from Latour-Giraud, Beaujolais from Gobet. ☙ Well-chosen ☙ ♿

Lunch 12.30–2 *Dinner* 7.30–9.45

LLANDUDNO — Empire Hotel 69% £D/E

H Map 8 C1 Gwynedd
Church Walks LL30 2HE
Llandudno (0492) 860555
Telex 617161

Credit Access, Amex, Diners, Visa
Closed 2 wks Xmas

A splendid clifftop hotel run by friendly, caring family owners. Public rooms have individual interest and appeal: attractive prints in the stone-walled lounge, a bright coffee shop overlooking the indoor pool and a cosy cocktail bar. Bedrooms are extremely well equipped, with everything from wall safes to refrigerators. No. 72, next door, has been refurbished as a Victorian town house and serves as a stylish and luxurious annexe. Its eight rooms feature lovely antiques and splendid bathrooms with marble floors, spa baths and telephone extensions. *Amenities* indoor & outdoor swimming pools, sauna, solarium, whirlpool bath, games room, satellite TV, in-house movies, laundry service, coffee shop (11am–10.30pm Mon–Sat).

Rooms 64	*Direct dial* Yes	*Confirm by* arrang.	*Parking* Ample
Ensuite bath/shower 64	*Room TV* Yes	*Last dinner* 9.30	*Room service* All day

**We publish annually,
so make sure you use the current edition.
It's worth it!**

LLANDUDNO — Lanterns Restaurant ⚐

R Map 8 C1 Gwynedd
7 Church Walks
Llandudno (0492) 77924

Seafood
About £44 for two
Seats 28 *Parties* 12
Parking Limited

Credit Access, Amex, Diners, Visa

Chef Alan Hill describes himself as 'an ordinary chap' but displays considerable talent and flair at this elegant restaurant. His partner, Adrian Rice, supervises the service. Although there are some meat and poultry dishes, the accent is on seafood. Sample such specialities as Dover sole filled with poached oysters or lobster, coated in a cheese and wine sauce, or select something simple, like oven-baked sea bass with wine and herbs. ☙

Dinner only 7.30–9.30
Closed Sun & Mon

LLANDUDNO   St George's Hotel   60%   £E

H **Map 8 C1** Gwynedd
St George's Place LL30 2LG
Llandudno (0492) 77544
Telex 61520

Credit Access, Amex, Diners, Visa

An imposing Victorian seafront hotel. Lofty public rooms with comfortable, traditional furnishings have an air of sedately fading grandeur, while most of the bedrooms are in a more modern, practical style. On the front corners are the 'Grecian' and 'Roman' show bedrooms with balconies and spacious, up-to-date bathrooms. *Amenities* sauna, solarium, keep-fit equipment, beauty salon, hairdressing, secretarial services, laundry service, coffee shop (10am–5pm).

Rooms 90	*Room phone* Yes	*Confirm by* arrang.	*Parking* Limited
Ensuite bath/shower 90	*Room TV* Yes	*Last dinner* 8.45	*Room service* 24 hours

LLANDUDNO   St Tudno Hotel   69%   £D/E

HR **Map 8 C1** Gwynedd
North Parade,
The Promenade LL30 2LP
Llandudno (0492) 74411

Credit Access, Visa
Closed 18 Dec–20 Jan

Martin and Janette Bland, owner-managers of this stylish hotel for 16 years, strive tirelessly to raise already high standards. Refurbishment is carried out on a continuous basis here, and staff are friendly and courteous, public rooms are airy and charming, and spotlessly clean bathrooms have thoughtful extras like fresh flowers, pomanders, toiletries, hairdryers and shower caps. No dogs. *Amenities* patio, indoor swimming pool, satellite TV, laundry service.

Rooms 21	*Direct dial* Yes	*Confirm by* 5	*Parking* Limited
Ensuite bath/shower 21	*Room TV* Yes	*Last dinner* 9.30	*Room service* All day

Restaurant

Set D £15.95
About £45 *for two*
Seats 60

Dine in verdant surroundings with comfortable seating and quality table settings. The daily-changing set menu offers a wide selection, embracing Welsh specialities. Start with Conwy mussels, followed by roast leg of Welsh lamb with garlic and herbs, with blackberry mousse (or Welsh organic chesses) to finish. Fresh fish and vegetarian dishes are always on offer and there is an à la carte menu. Very good wine list: Chablis from Durup & Dauvissat, Gewurztraminer from Blanck.
🍷

Lunch 12.30–2   *Dinner* 6.45–9.30, Sun till 8.30
Closed 18 Dec–20 Jan

Our inspectors *never* book in the name of Egon Ronay's Guides.
They disclose their identity only if they are considering an establishment
for inclusion in the next edition of the Guide.

LLANELLI   Stradey Park Hotel   56%   £D

H **Map 9 B6** Dyfed
Furnace SA15 4HA
Llanelli (0554) 758171
Telex 48521

Credit Access, Amex, Diners, Visa

Follow the B4309 out of Llanelli to find this extended manor house standing on a hill overlooking the town. Behind the striking crenellated facade, public rooms are of very ample size, though the bar and lounge have no great character. Bedrooms are fitted with simple white units and all have compact bathrooms, tea-makers and bedside radios. *Amenities* garden, pool table, laundry service. ♿

Rooms 80	*Room phone* Yes	*Confirm by* 6	*Parking* Ample
Ensuite bath/shower 80	*Room TV* Yes	*Last dinner* 9.30	*Room service* 24 hours

LLANGOLLEN   Hand Hotel   55%   £D/E

H **Map 8 D2** Clwyd
Bridge Street LL20 8PL
Llangollen (0978) 860303
Telex 61160

Credit Access, Amex, Diners, Visa

Open fires glow a welcome in the foyer and lounge of this friendly hotel on the banks of the river Dee. The lounge is home to a few well-chosen antiques, and the bar is quite pubby, with studded furniture, burnished brass tables and a performing area for local musicians. Bedrooms are simply but prettily decorated, and all have a private bath or shower. *Amenities* garden, game fishing, laundry service.

Rooms 58	*Room phone* Yes	*Confirm by* 6	*Parking* Ample
Ensuite bath/shower 58	*Room TV* Yes	*Last dinner* 8.45	*Room service* 24 hours

LLANGOLLEN — Royal Hotel 59%   £C/D

Map 8 D2 Clwyd
Bridge Street·LL20 8PG
Llangollen (0978) 860202

Credit Access, Amex, Diners, Visa

The Royal stands on the banks of the Dee, overlooking a lovely 14th-century bridge. The river flows right below the lounge, a peaceful room with tapestry-covered chairs, vases of fresh flowers and a handsome grandfather clock. Bedrooms are neat and comfortable, with reproduction furniture in the few refurbished rooms and simple modern units in the rest. *Amenities* coarse fishing, pool table, secretarial services, laundry service.

Rooms 33	*Room phone* Yes	*Confirm by* 6	*Parking* Ample
Ensuite bath/shower 33	*Room TV* Yes	*Last dinner* 9.30	*Room service* All day

LLANGYBI — Cwrt Bleddyn Hotel 74%   £D

Map 9 D6 Gwent
Nr Usk NP5 1PG
Tredunnock (063 349) 521

Rooms 30
Ensuite bath/shower 30
Direct dial Yes
Room TV Yes
Confirm by arrang.
Last dinner 10
Parking Ample
Room service 24 hours

Credit Access, Amex, Diners, Visa

Parts of the hotel date back to the 17th century, but the whole place has been sympathetically modernised and a bedroom extension added. Tapestries, original panelling and a few antiques tone down the modern character in the day rooms, which include a splendid glass-roofed lounge. Apart from three with solid oak antiques the bedrooms are up to date, with cool cream and grey decor and bamboo furniture. Bathrooms are spacious, bright and modern, with efficient showers over the tubs. No dogs.
Amenities garden, indoor swimming pool, sauna, solarium, keep-fit equipment, putting, snooker, in-house movies, secretarial services, coffee shop (9am–11pm).

LLANNEFYDD — Hawk & Buckle Inn   £F

Map 8 C2 Clwyd
Nr Denbigh LL16 5ED
Llannefydd (074 579) 249

Credit Access, Visa

Careful planning and thoughtful design provide overnight guests with a degree of independence from pub patrons at this 17th-century inn. Residents have their own entrance and exclusive use of a lounge and bar. Modern extensions provide ten cosy bedrooms (one with a four-poster; all with ensuite facilities). Nine have views of the vale of Clwyd and distant Rhyl. No children under 8. No dogs.
Amenities patio, pool table.

Rooms 10	*Direct dial* Yes	*Confirm by* arrang.	*Parking* Ample
Ensuite bath/shower 10	*Room TV* Yes	*Last dinner* 9.30	*Room service* None

LLANRHAEADR — Llanrhaeadr Hall 63%   £D

Map 8 C2 Clwyd
Nr Denbigh LL16 4NP
Llanynys (074 578) 313
Telex 94012648

Credit Access, Amex, Visa

A long, straight drive runs from the A525 Ruthin–Denbigh road to this welcoming hotel, whose distinctive Georgian facade hides the original Tudor timbering. The large drawing room, with its elegant, comfortable furnishings, ornate plaster ceiling and splendid garden views, is the pick of the day rooms, while tops for atmosphere among the bedrooms are some family-sized attic rooms with Tudor beams taken from sailing ships. Most of the rooms are spacious, with fitted furniture that is neat and purposeful, if lacking somewhat in character. Bathrooms have splendid stocks of towels. No children under seven. No dogs.
Amenities garden, solarium, croquet, laundry service.

Rooms 12	*Direct dial* Yes	*Confirm by* arrang.	*Parking* Ample
Ensuite bath/shower 12	*Room TV* No	*Last dinner* 9	*Room service* All day

Changes in data sometimes occur in establishments
after the Guide goes to press.
Prices should be taken as indications rather than firm quotes.

LLANRWST   Meadowsweet Hotel   61%   £E/F

HR **Map 8 C2** Gwynedd
Station Road LL26 0DS
Llanrwst (0492) 640732

Credit Access, Amex, Visa

John and Joy Evans run their small hotel with pride and enthusiasm, which is reflected in the bright, cheerful rooms. For socialising there's a cosy sitting room and a traditional bar. Bedrooms are prettily decorated in feminine style, some having fine hand-painted furniture. All have mineral water, handcream, cotton wool balls and showers, while there are public bathrooms for those who prefer a tub. *Amenities* laundry service.

Rooms 10	Direct dial Yes	Confirm by arrang.	Parking Ample
Ensuite bath/shower 10	Room TV Yes	Last dinner 9.30	Room service All day

Restaurant   ⌐

Set D £15.50
About £57 for two
Seats 32
Parking Ample

A small, comfortable restaurant seating up to 32 diners, for whom John Evans gallantly cooks single-handed. His menus offer some interesting dishes, such as fillet of lamb served with a rosé wine and tomato sauce, and the vegetables are superb. A splendid classic cellar chosen with an admirable eye for value as well as quality: note the excellent Réserve du Général Margaux '83. ▭ Outstanding 🍷 Well-chosen ℮

Dinner only 6.30–9.30

LLANSANTFFRAID   Old Rectory   67%   *NEW ENTRY*   £C/D
GLAN CONWY

HR **Map 8 C1** Clwyd
Llanrwst Road LL28 5LF
Colwyn Bay (0492) 580611

Closed 20 Dec–1 Feb

A little jewel of a house, its classical Georgian facade hiding an earlier interior. Michael and Wendy Vaughan run it with great charm and personal involvement, and the whole place has a delightful relaxing feel. Pine panelling, elegant antiques, Victorian watercolours and fresh flowers make the drawing room a real joy, and the views over the estuary to distant Conwy Castle are breathtaking. Well-heated bedrooms show restrained good taste, with stylish fabrics, lots of pictures, furnishings of stripped pine or mahogany and various thoughtful touches. Modern bathrooms (one with shower/wc only) also have pictures, plus carpeting and attractive mirrors. There's a lovely two-acre garden. Half-board terms only. No children under 12. No dogs. *Amenities* garden.

Rooms 4	Room phone No	Confirm by arrang.	Parking Ample
Ensuite bath/shower 4	Room TV Yes	Last dinner 7.30	Room service Limited

Restaurant   ⌐

Set D £15
About £38 for two
Seats 14

Antiques, watercolours and stunning views make a perfect backdrop for Wendy Vaughan's talented cooking, which makes use of the best local produce and plenty of good ideas: poached pear stuffed with mushroom pâté served on a croûton with spinach and hollandaise sauce, boned quail filled with chicken mousseline, Conwy salmon with a mild mustard sauce. Excellent vegetables, Welsh cheeses, super sweets. Booking essential. Residents sit round a huge table. ℮

Dinner only 7.30   **Closed** 20 Dec–1 Feb

 is our symbol for an **outstanding** wine list

MACHYNLLETH   Wynnstay Arms   57%   £E

H **Map 8 C3** Powys
Maengwyn Street SY80 8AE
Machynlleth (0654) 2941

Credit Access, Amex, Diners, Visa

As you approach the handsome neo-Georgian facade that fronts this main-street hotel, keep an eye open for the signs indicating the narrow access to parking at the rear. Public areas including the bar and lounge are rather dated, while adequately furnished bedrooms have tea-makers, tiled bathrooms and complimentary toiletries. Hanging flower baskets, outdoor tables and colourful umbrellas make the rear patio attractive. *Amenities* patio.

Rooms 20	Direct dial Yes	Confirm by 6	Parking Ample
Ensuite bath/shower 20	Room TV Yes	Last dinner 9	Room service Limited

MERTHYR TYDFIL   Baverstocks Hotel   57%   *NEW ENTRY*   £E/F

H **Map 9 C5** Mid Glamorgan
Heads of the Valley Road
CF44 0LX
Merthyr Tydfil (0685) 6221

Credit Access, Amex, Diners, Visa

Day rooms have been reorganised at this family-run modern hotel, which stands above Merthyr on the A465. The lounge and bar are coolly contemporary if not all that stylish, and a leisure complex should come on stream as we publish. Bedrooms in two-storey blocks have practical built-in furniture, ample writing space and compact carpeted bathrooms. No dogs. *Amenities* garden, snooker, pool table, in-house movies, laundry service.

Rooms 43	Direct dial Yes	Confirm by arrang.	Parking Ample
Ensuite bath/shower 43	Room TV Yes	Last dinner 9.45	Room service 24 hours

MISKIN   Miskin Manor   71%   £C/D

H **Map 9 C6** Mid Glamorgan
Nr Llantrisant CF7 8ND
Llantrisant (0443) 224204

Rooms 32
Ensuite bath/shower 32
Direct dial Yes
Room TV Yes
Confirm by arrang.
Last dinner 9.45
Parking Ample
Room service 24 hours

Credit Access, Amex, Diners, Visa
Closed 24 Dec–1 Jan

On a site with a 900-year history, the present manor was rebuilt in 1858. A central staircase (now panelled) is a feature in the spacious entrance hall, off which lead two elegant lounges with leaded windows and deep-cushioned armchairs and settees. Good-sized bedrooms have a useful range of accessories large and small, from trouser presses and hairdryers to books, magazines, mineral water and sweets.

They're furnished in traditional style (even a few antiques) and all have well-fitted bathrooms. In the grounds is an extensive leisure complex. No dogs. *Amenities* garden, indoor swimming pool, sauna, solarium, whirlpool bath, gymnasium, beauty salon, clay-pigeon shooting, snooker, fax, laundry service, coffee shop (10am–11pm). &

We publish annually,
so make sure you use the current edition.
It's worth it!

MONMOUTH   King's Head Hotel   64%   £D/E

H **Map 9 D5** Gwent
Agincourt Square NP5 3DY
Monmouth (0600) 2177
Telex 497294

Credit Access, Amex, Diners, Visa

Manager Mr. Gough has instilled his own high standards in his staff, and friendly, caring service is a notable plus at this 17th-century coaching inn. Fresh flowers adorn the roomy entrance hall, and guests can enjoy a drink in either the oak-beamed bar or the cocktail lounge. Variously sized bedrooms, all with neat bathrooms, are equipped with hairdryers and trouser presses.
Amenities secretarial services, laundry service.

Rooms 26	Direct dial Yes	Confirm by 6	Parking Limited
Ensuite bath/shower 26	Room TV Yes	Last dinner 9.30	Room service 24 hours

MUMBLES   Langland Court Hotel   £E

I **Map 9 C6** West Glamorgan
31 Langland Court Road,
Langland Bay SA3 4TD
Swansea (0792) 361545
Telex 498037
Credit Access, Amex, Diners, Visa
Closed 25 Dec

Follow signs to Langland Bay from Mumbles to find this clifftop hotel. Off the impressive oak-panelled entrance hall are two bars, the Polly Garters pub and a tastefully-furnished cocktail bar. Most of the attractive bedrooms are in the main building and vary from four-postered rooms to family dormers. Rooms in the coach house across the road are smaller. All have well-equipped bathrooms.
Amenities garden, secretarial services, laundry service.

Rooms 21	Direct dial Yes	Confirm by 6	Parking Ample
Ensuite bath/shower 20	Room TV Yes	Last dinner 9.30	Room service Limited

MUMBLES   Norton House Hotel   69%   £E

H **Map 9 C6** West Glamorgan
Norton Road,
Swansea SA3 5TQ
Swansea (0792) 404891

Credit Access, Visa
Closed 2 wks Xmas

No one is more keenly appreciative of the Georgian charms of this fine white-painted house than owners Claude and Emma Rossi. They've lovingly restored the interior in a luxurious and very individual style, using chandeliers, huge velvet drapes and period furniture throughout. Four-poster rooms are especially opulent, with deep-pile carpets extending through to bathrooms, ample sofas, writing desks and free-standing full-length mirrors. Rooms in the new wing are less spacious, but all are well equipped. There's a comfortable, elegant lounge bar in the main house, and a separate lounge in the wing. No children under ten. No dogs.
Amenities garden, laundry service.

Rooms 16	*Direct dial* Yes	*Confirm by* arrang.	*Parking* Ample
Ensuite bath/shower 16	*Room TV* Yes	*Last dinner* 9.30	*Room service* All day

**We welcome bona fide complaints and recommendations
on the tear-out pages at the back of the book for readers' comment.
They are followed up by our professional team.**

NEWPORT   Celtic Manor Hotel   78%   £C

H **Map 9 D6** Gwent
Coldra Woods NP6 2YA
Newport (0633) 413000

Rooms 75
Ensuite bath/shower 75
Direct dial Yes
Room TV Yes
Confirm by 6
Last dinner 10.30
Parking Ample
Room service 24 hours

Credit Access, Amex, Diners, Visa

As we go to press (autumn '88) a new leisure centre and an additional 58 bedrooms are nearing completion and will much enlarge this hotel situated near junction 24 of the M4. Public rooms are in the original house and retain some fine 19th century decorative features such as the stucco mouldings in the cocktail bar and spacious lounge. Breakfast is served in the sunny conservatory coffee shop. Bedrooms in the main house are roomy and well appointed. No dogs.
Amenities garden, indoor swimming pool, solarium, whirlpool bath, keep-fit equipment, secretarial services, laundry service, coffee shop (7am–10.30pm), helipad. &

NEWPORT   Hilton National Hotel   61%   *NEW ENTRY*   £C/D

H **Map 9 D6** Gwent
The Coldra NP6 2YG
Newport (0633) 412777
Telex 497205

Credit Access, Amex, Diners, Visa

A low-rise modern hotel by a roundabout at junction 24 of the M4. It's an agreeable place for an overnight stay, and the bedrooms have all the usual up-to-date accessories of trouser presses, hairdryers and remote-control TVs (with teletext in the Gold Star rooms). Day rooms include a split-level bar where a pianist does evening duty. There's a new leisure complex. *Amenities* garden, in-house movies, secretarial services, fax, laundry service.

Rooms 119	*Direct dial* Yes	*Confirm by* 6	*Parking* Ample
Ensuite bath/shower 119	*Room TV* Yes	*Last dinner* 10	*Room service* 24 hours

NEWPORT   Kings Hotel   60%   £D/E

H **Map 9 D6** Gwent
High Street NP9 1QU
Newport (0633) 842020
Telex 497330

Credit Access, Amex, Diners, Visa

Overlooking the river Usk, the Kings Hotel stands opposite the station less than one mile from junction 26 of the M4. The interior was virtually rebuilt following a fire in 1983 but refurbishment continues; a smartly updated lounge bar is the latest improvement, complementing the elegantly furnished lounge. Bedrooms vary in size but are all well equipped.
Amenities satellite TV, in-house movies, laundry service.

Rooms 47	*Direct dial* Yes	*Confirm by* 6	*Parking* Limited
Ensuite bath/shower 47	*Room TV* Yes	*Last dinner* 9.30	*Room service* 24 hours

NORTHOP | Soughton Hall   78%   *NEW ENTRY*   £C

HR Map 8 D2 Clwyd
Nr Mold CH7 6AB
Northop (0352) 86207
Telex 61267

Rooms 12
Ensuite bath/shower 12
Direct dial Yes
Room TV Yes
Confirm by arrang.
Last dinner 9.30
Parking Ample
Room service 24 hours

Credit Access, Amex, Visa

A stately avenue of limes leads up to this distinctive Georgian manor set in peaceful parkland just off the A55. It has been beautifully restored by its new owners, John and Rosemary Rodenhurst. Among the elegant day rooms is the drawing room with its tapestries, Persian rugs and marble fireplaces, a charming library warmed by a log fire, and a snug little bar. A magnificent oak staircase leads to the pretty bedrooms whose assets include comfortable armchairs, bowls of fresh fruit, and splendid views. Bathrooms are superb and some have vast Victorian tubs. Staff are most attentive. No children under ten. No dogs. *Amenities* garden, shooting, games room, snooker, secretarial services, laundry service.

Restaurant   *NEW ENTRY*   ♨

Set L £10.50, Sun £9.50
Set D £19.95
About £50 *for two*
Seats 46
Parties 40

An elegant, high-ceilinged dining room forms the setting for young Malcolm Warham's thoughtful and imaginative dishes. Salmon, sole and mushroom terrine makes a subtle, refreshing starter, and there are main courses like tender noisette of lamb with Madeira sauce. Good sweets. Traditional roast on Sundays. Well balanced wine list strong in clarets (Ch. Palmer '71) and some good bottles from the New World (Shiraz Rothbury Estate). ♀ Well-chosen ℗

Lunch 12.30–2   *Dinner* 7.30–9.30, Sat 7.30–10
Closed L Sat except by arrang.

Our inspectors *never* book in the name of Egon Ronay's Guides.
They disclose their identity only if they are considering an establishment
for inclusion in the next edition of the Guide.

PANTMAWR | Glansevern Arms | £E/F

Map 9 C4 Powys
Nr Llangurig SY18 6SY
Llangurig (055 15) 240

Closed 2 wks Xmas

A very welcoming roadside inn, part of which dates back 300 years. Mr Edwards takes great pride in his establishment and homely touches abound throughout. There's a choice of two tiny and delightfully traditional bars in which to enjoy a drink and an attractive lived-in lounge area for residents. Bedrooms have tea/coffee-makers and modern carpeted bathrooms (one with shower only). *Amenities* game fishing.

Rooms 7	*Room phone* No	*Confirm by* arrang.	*Parking* Ample
Ensuite bath/shower 7	*Room TV* Yes	*Last dinner* 8	*Room service* None

PENMAENPOOL | George III Hotel | £F

Map 8 C3 Gwynedd
Nr Dolgellau LL40 1YD
Dolgellau (0341) 422525

Credit Access, Amex, Diners, Visa
Closed 2 wks Xmas

A most appealing inn overlooking an old wooden toll bridge and the Mawddach estuary. Polished wood tables and brasses give a warm and welcoming feel to the main bar, and there's also a cellar bar with beams and slate floor, and a cosy lounge for residents' use. Main-house bedrooms share a simple bathroom; remaining rooms, in a converted station house, have en suite private facilities. *Amenities* terrace, sea fishing.

Rooms 13	*Direct dial* Yes	*Confirm by* arrang.	*Parking* Ample
Ensuite bath/shower 8	*Room TV* Yes	*Last dinner* 9	*Room service* None

PORTMEIRION   Hotel Portmeirion   78%   *NEW ENTRY*   **£E**

H **Map 8 B2** Gwynedd
LL48 6ER
Porthmadog (0766) 770228
Telex 61540

Rooms 34
Ensuite bath/shower 34
Direct dial Yes
Room TV Yes
Confirm by arrang.
Last dinner 9.30
Parking Ample
Room service 24 hours

Credit Access, Amex, Diners, Visa

In the idyllic setting of Sir Clough Williams-Ellis' dream village, the hotel has now been gloriously restored. Public rooms are quite dazzling: the hall with its black-and-white marble floor and French limestone fireplace, the breathtakingly beautiful Mirror Room, the Indian-themed bar. Main-house bedrooms are very much in the luxury league, with deep, springy carpets, lovely co-ordinated fabrics, antiques and gold-plated bathroom fittings; remaining, simpler, rooms are in cottages scattered throughout the village (no room service in these). No dogs.
Amenities garden, outdoor swimming pool, tennis, 18-hole golf course, sea fishing, in-house movies, secretarial services, fax, laundry service, coffee shop (10am–5pm).

PRESTEIGNE   Radnorshire Arms Hotel   61%   **£C/D**

H **Map 9 D4** Powys
High Street LD8 2BE
Presteigne (0544) 267406

Credit Access, Amex, Diners, Visa

Originally the home of a favourite of Elizabeth I, it became a coaching house almost 200 years ago. Blackened beams and old oak furniture give much character to the bar, and there's a cosy panelled lounge that opens on to a lovely garden. Half the bedrooms are in the main building, the rest – spacious, modern and unfussily attractive – in a garden block reached by a covered walkway.
Amenities garden, laundry service.

Rooms 16	*Direct dial* Yes	*Confirm by* 6	*Parking* Ample
Ensuite bath/shower 16	*Room TV* Yes	*Last dinner* 9	*Room service* All day

PWLLHELI   Plas Bodegroes   *NEW ENTRY*   👑 🍴

RR **Map 8 B2** Gwynedd
Efailnewydd LL53 5TH
Pwllheli (0758) 612363

Set L Sun £7.50
Set D from £11.50
About £40 for two
Seats 45
Parties 16
Parking Ample

Credit Access, Visa

A manor house dating from the 14th century makes a delightful setting in which to enjoy the Chowns' hospitality. Christopher is an ambitious chef whose fixed-price menu (which changes fortnightly) shows talent and imagination. Start with a hot pot of local mussels or a chargrilled kebab of monkfish, followed by pan-fried salmon on a bed of leeks or plump guinea-fowl breast with a tasty stuffing. Tempting sweets include a delicious passion-fruit parfait. Booking is essential, and you should allow plenty of time, as service, though charming, is leisurely.   🍷 Well-chosen 🅮 ♿

Lunch Sun only 12–2   *Dinner* 7–9
Closed L Mon–Sat, all Jan & 1st 2 wks Feb

BEDROOMS 7   **£E**
With bath/shower 7

Upstairs are seven cosy bedrooms with antique pine furniture, thoughtful extras, and neat modern bathrooms.

Our inspectors *never* book in the name of Egon Ronay's Guides.
They disclose their identity only if they are considering an establishment
for inclusion in the next edition of the Guide.

REYNOLDSTON   Fairyhill   64%   *NEW ENTRY*   **£E**

H **Map 9 B6** West Glamorgan
Gower, Nr Swansea SA3 1BS
Gower (0792) 390139

Credit Access, Amex, Diners, Visa
Closed 1 wk Xmas

A delightful 18th-century mansion set in park and woodlands deep in the Gower peninsula. (Ask the helpful owners for directions when booking.) Public areas are full of character and include a homely bar with stone fireplace. Good-sized bedrooms, sporting darkwood furniture and fresh white walls, offer tea/coffee-makers and neat bathrooms. Cosy attic rooms are especially appealing.
Amenities garden, sauna, secretarial services.

Rooms 12	*Direct dial* Yes	*Confirm by* arrang.	*Parking* Ample
Ensuite bath/shower 12	*Room TV* Yes	*Last dinner* 9.30	*Room service* All day

My father was a blacksmith ...

the tender bouquets of vegetables he brought were so full

of flavour and aroma that all that was needed was the

addition of a few of the big rosy strips of pork fat which

sizzled in the big cast-iron pot.

This was the 'cuisine heureuse', which consisted of marrying

natural products with one another, of finding simple

harmonies and enhancing the flavour of each ingredient by

contact with another complementary flavour...

It is the antithesis of cooking to impress.

ROGER VERGE

CUISINE OF THE SUN
Trans. Caroline Conran (1979)

...**A** little tavern in the Rue Vavin,

Chez Clémence, who makes only one dish,

but a stupendous one: *le cassoulet de Castelnaudry*...

Clémence's cassoulet has been cooking for twenty years.

She replenishes the pot...but it is always the same cassoulet.

The basis remains, and this ancient and precious substance

gives it a taste which one finds in the paintings of old

Venetian masters, in the amber flesh-tints of their women.

ANATOLE FRANCE 1844-1924
HISTOIRE COMIQUE

We may live

without poetry, music and art;

We may live without conscience and live without heart;

We may live without friends, we may live without books,

But civilised man cannot live without cooks.

OWEN MEREDITH 1831-91
LUCILE

ROSSETT | Llyndir Hall 71% *NEW ENTRY* | £C

HR **Map 8 D2** Clywd
Llyndir Lane LL12 0AY
Chester (0244) 571648

Rooms 8
Ensuite bath/shower 8
Direct dial Yes
Room TV Yes
Confirm by arrang.
Last dinner 10
Parking Ample
Room service All day

Credit Access, Amex, Diners, Visa

A few miles out of Chester on the A483, this renovated Victorian country house is well situated for both business and pleasure stays. Antiques and fine furniture, objets d'art and fresh flowers abound, and the drawing room is an elegant marriage of pastel and chintz. The little bar, with its leafy *trompe-l'oeil*, is a charming spot for a drink. Bedrooms are individually and comfortably appointed: well-chosen, often

bold, colour schemes, handsome furniture much of it antique, trouser presses, hairdryers, tubs, showers and a comprehensive range of toiletries. Service is charming, and breakfast includes freshly squeezed orange juice.
Amenities garden, secretarial services, fax, laundry service.

Restaurant *NEW ENTRY*

Set L £9.95, Sun £12
Set D £19
About £45 *for two*
Seats 50
Parties 32

Fresh fish is the à la carte speciality here, and Patrick Allen combines sound cooking with some imaginative touches. Sauces are light and subtle, enhancing and never subduing the delicate flavours of the sea. Lobster soufflé, brochette of scallops and fricasse of turbot with spinach-wrapped salmon mousse are typical choices, and specials like fresh eels in saffron sauce cause an extra wriggle of interest. Steaks are always available, cooked on a lava-rock grill, plus other meat dishes on the table d'hôte menu. There's a good and varied list of sweets and well-priced, decent wines – note the beautiful Sancerre of Domaine Daulny. 🍷 Well-chosen ℮

Lunch 12–2 *Dinner* 7.30–10 (Sun residents only)
Closed Sat

Changes in data sometimes occur in establishments
after the Guide goes to press.
Prices should be taken as indications rather than firm quotes.

RUTHIN | Castle Hotel 54% | £E

H **Map 8 C2** Clwyd
St Peter's Square LL15 1AA
Ruthin (082 42) 2479
Telex 617074

Credit Access, Amex, Diners, Visa

A town-centre hotel offering pleasant, basic accommodation. Public areas comprise a smart bar with winged armchairs and chesterfields, a quaintly decorated coffee shop and a very simple first-floor lounge. Bedrooms are equipped with modern freestanding wooden furniture, two armchairs, attractive cream bedcovers and toning beige carpets. Bathrooms are functional and carpeted, two of them offering showers. **Amenities** patio, laundry service, coffee shop (10am–6pm).

Rooms 24	*Direct dial* Yes	*Confirm by* 6	*Parking* Ample
Ensuite bath/shower 24	*Room TV* Yes	*Last dinner* 9	*Room service* All day

RUTHIN | Ruthin Castle 64% | £E

H **Map 8 C2** Clwyd
Corwen Road LL15 2NU
Ruthin (082 42) 2664
Telex 61169

Credit Access, Amex, Diners, Visa

A medieval fortress set in parkland, Ruthin Castle has known attack, siege and virtual destruction, but today triumphs to offer a taste of gracious living in the vast lounge with its sweeping velvet drapes. There's also an oak-panelled bar, and two further lounges. Bedrooms – the finest are in the Moat and Castle Wings – have TVs and tea-makers in addition to well-equipped bathrooms. **Amenities** garden, game fishing, snooker, secretarial services, laundry service.

Rooms 60	*Direct dial* Yes	*Confirm by* 6	*Parking* Ample
Ensuite bath/shower 60	*Room TV* Yes	*Last dinner* 9.30	*Room service* All day

ST DAVID'S   St Non's Hotel   56%   £E

H Map 9 A5 Dyfed
Catherine Street SA62 6RJ
St David's (0437) 720239

Credit Access, Amex, Diners, Visa

A short drive south-west from the town centre will bring you to the simple, friendly surroundings of this pleasant little hotel. Staff are warm and hospitable, and relaxing is easy in the quiet lounges or more convivial bar. On summer evenings there are jolly barbecues on the terrace. Brightly decorated bedrooms, all with carpeted bathrooms, are furnished with plain modern units.
Amenities garden, 9-hole golf course, laundry service. &

| *Rooms* 20 | *Direct dial* Yes | *Confirm by* 9 | *Parking* Ample |
| *Ensuite bath/shower* 20 | *Room TV* Yes | *Last dinner* 9 | *Room service* Limited |

ST DAVID'S   Warpool Court Hotel   60%   £C/D

H Map 9 A5 Dyfed
SA62 6BN
St David's (0437) 720300

Credit Access, Amex, Diners, Visa

Built as a cathedral choir school in the 1860s, Warpool Court enjoys a splendid coastal setting. Bedrooms are fairly traditional (some antiques) and 15 have sea views. Among the day rooms are a cheerful bar and a roomy lounge with plenty of books. A feature throughout is a collection of lovely hand-painted tiles. Very pleasant staff.
Amenities garden, indoor swimming pool, sauna, keep-fit equipment, tennis, games room, in-house movies, laundry service.

| *Rooms* 25 | *Direct dial* Yes | *Confirm by* arrang. | *Parking* Ample |
| *Ensuite bath/shower* 25 | *Room TV* Yes | *Last dinner* 9.15 | *Room service* All day |

If we recommend **meals** in a Hotel or Inn,
a separate entry is made for its restaurant.

SWANBRIDGE   Sully House   ⌘

RR Map 9 D6
South Glamorgan
Nr Penarth
Cardiff (0222) 530448

Set L £7.95
Set D £15.25
Seats 60
Parties 50
Parking Ample

Credit Access, Visa

A really delightful and cosy restaurant with rooms overlooking Sully Island. Owner-chef Paul Westmacott's cooking is assured and very enjoyable, with honest, unsullied flavours and ample portions. Choose from such dishes as game terrine with Cumberland sauce, the day's fish dish, or the house speciality of veal fillets, chicken and ham with potatoes, tomatoes and mushrooms. Sweets are particularly good, and there are some excellent bargains on the wine list. Service is polite and professional. &

Lunch 12–2   *Dinner* 7–10   *About* £40 *for two*
Closed L Sat & all Sun, Bank Hols & 25 & 26 Dec

BEDROOMS 4   £E
With bath/shower 4

Overnight guests stay in bright, spacious bedrooms with simple carpeted bathrooms. No dogs.

SWANSEA   Dragon Hotel   67%   £D/E

H Map 9 C6 West Glamorgan
39 The Kingsway SA1 5LS
Swansea (0792) 51074
Telex 48309

Credit Access, Amex, Diners, Visa

Comfort and convenience abound at this smartly refurbished city-centre hotel. Warm coppery shades give a welcoming feel to the spacious public areas, while pastel tones and darkwood units strike an elegant note in the bedrooms. Tea/coffee-makers throughout, plus functional bathrooms. Executive rooms offer extras like potted plants, mini-bars, trouser presses and hairdryers. *Amenities* secretarial services, laundry service.

| *Rooms* 117 | *Direct dial* Yes | *Confirm by* 6 | *Parking* Limited |
| *Ensuite bath/shower* 117 | *Room TV* Yes | *Last dinner* 10 | *Room service* 24 hours |

SWANSEA   Hilton National   66%   £C

H Map 9 C6 West Glamorgan
Phoenix Way, Enterprise
Park, Llansamlet SA7 9EG
Swansea (0792) 310330
Telex 48589

Credit Access, Amex, Diners, Visa

Take exit 45 from the M4 to reach this two-storey hotel at the Swansea Enterprise Park. On the ground floor are open-plan public areas and four rooms fully equipped for the disabled. The remaining bedrooms have fitted furniture and, in the Gold Star rooms, plenty of extras. High standards of housekeeping. *Amenities* garden, indoor swimming pool, sauna, keep-fit equipment, pool table, in-house movies, secretarial services, fax, laundry service. &

| *Rooms* 114 | *Direct dial* Yes | *Confirm by* 6 | *Parking* Ample |
| *Ensuite bath/shower* 114 | *Room TV* Yes | *Last dinner* 9.45 | *Room service* 24 hours |

TALSARNAU — Maes-y-Neuadd Hotel 69% £D

HR Map 8 C2 Gwynedd
Nr Harlech LL47 6YA
Harlech (0766) 780200

Credit Access, Visa
Closed Jan

Two families have successfully converted this granite and slate country house into a delightfully homely hotel. The entrance hall, with its china ornaments and large bowls of potpourri, is most welcoming and there's a comfortable and relaxing lounge and mellow bar. Most of the bedrooms are traditional, with coordinated furnishings and plenty of extras to cosset the customer. No children under seven. *Amenities* garden, laundry service.

Rooms 15	*Direct dial* Yes	*Confirm by* arrang.	*Parking* Ample
Ensuite bath/shower 15	*Room TV* Yes	*Last dinner* 9.15	*Room service* All day

Restaurant

Set L £10.50, Sun £8.95
Set D £16.50
About £50 for two
Seats 32
Parties 12

Fresh ingredients form the basis of the short fixed-price menu in this comfortably appointed dining room. Starters could range from parfait of chicken livers to fresh crab croissant or artichokes stuffed with cheese and bacon. A carefully cooked soup introduces a main course that may be calf's sweetbreads with freshwater crayfish, maize-fed poussin or sole and salmon turban. Lamb features strongly, appearing on every menu in a wide variety of guises. ☺ ♿

Dinner 7.30–9.15
Closed Jan

TAL-Y-LLYN — Ty'n-y-Cornel Hotel 54% £D/E

H Map 8 C3 Gwynedd
Nr Tywyn LL36 9AJ
Abergynolwyn (065 477) 282

Credit Access, Amex, Diners, Visa
Closed Nov–Mar

With its own lake in front and the sweep of majestic mountains behind, this simple hotel is popular for climbing and water-sports. Unpretentious public rooms are cosy if a trifle cramped. There's a fine view from the lounge. Neat bedrooms have freestanding modern units with tea-making facilities. All but two have carpeted bathrooms. *Amenities* garden, outdoor swimming pool, sauna, solarium, game fishing, sailing, board sailing, secretarial services, laundry service.

Rooms 17	*Direct dial* Yes	*Confirm by* arrang.	*Parking* Ample
Ensuite bath/shower 14	*Room TV* Yes	*Last dinner* 9.30	*Room service* All day

We publish annually,
so make sure you use the current edition.
It's worth it!

THREE COCKS — Three Cocks Hotel 58% £E/F

H Map 9 D5 Powys
Nr Brecon LD3 0SL
Glasbury (049 74) 215

Credit Access, Visa
Closed Dec & Jan

Once a famous posting house, this ivy-clad 15th-century inn on the A938 has retained a good deal of its old-world character. The ancient beams, exposed stone walls and open fireplaces of the public rooms are set off by attractive rugs and comfortable, unfussy furniture. Bedrooms are similarly characterful, with carved oak furniture and pretty decor; all have simple, modern shower rooms. Excellent housekeeping. No dogs. *Amenities* garden.

Rooms 7	*Room phone* No	*Confirm by* arrang.	*Parking* Ample
Ensuite bath/shower 0	*Room TV* No	*Last dinner* 9	*Room service* Limited

TINTERN ABBEY — Beaufort Hotel 60% £D/E

H Map 9 D6 Gwent
Chepstow NP6 6SF
Tintern (029 18) 777

Credit Access, Amex, Diners, Visa

The Beaufort is just across the road from the ruins of Tintern Abbey, and about half the bedrooms take in the views. Entrance is into a roomy foyer-lounge with a pleasant, traditional character and groups of comfortable armchairs. Bedrooms are smart, bright and modern, with lightwood fitted units, tea-makers, hairdryers and trouser presses, plus neat bath/shower rooms. *Amenities* garden, game fishing, pool table, laundry service.

Rooms 24	*Direct dial* Yes	*Confirm by* 6	*Parking* Ample
Ensuite bath/shower 24	*Room TV* Yes	*Last dinner* 9	*Room service* All day

TINTERN ABBEY   Royal George Hotel   56%   £E

H Map 9 D6 Gwent
Nr Chepstow NP6 6SF
Tintern (029 18) 205

Credit Access, Amex, Diners, Visa

A feature here is the splendidly kept garden through which a stream
runs just before meeting the Wye across the road. Four of the bedrooms
are in the main building, the rest in garden chalets, with built-in units,
duvets and generally simple, unfussy appeal. The chief day room is a
comfortable, cosy bar-lounge. Staff are very pleasant and friendly.
Amenities garden, laundry service.

Rooms 19	Direct dial Yes	Confirm by 6	Parking Ample
Ensuite bath/shower 15	Room TV Yes	Last dinner 9.30	Room service All day

TRELLECK   Village Green   NEW ENTRY

RR Map 9 D5 Gwent
Nr Monmouth
Monmouth (0600) 860119

Set L £9.50
Set D £17.50
About £50 for two
Seats 50
Parties 24
Parking Ample

In a village south of Monmouth, Rob and Jane Evans have converted
a derelict inn into this smashing new restaurant. Both experienced
chefs in their own right, they give plenty of support to Colin Sparks
in the kitchen, and dishes are faultlessly prepared and refreshingly
different. You might try poached quail's eggs with three hollandaises
on a bed of spinach, pan-fried brill sauced with tarragon, feuilleté of
lamb's sweetbreads with tomato quenelles, and a magnificent assiette
gourmande of assorted desserts.   ♀ Well-chosen ⊖ ♣

Lunch 12–2   *Dinner* 7–9.30
Closed Sun, Mon, 25 Dec & last 2 wks Jan

BEDROOMS 3 £E
With bath/shower None

Accommodation consists of three double rooms with shared bathroom.
Two suites in an adjoining coach house are planned. No dogs.

WELSH HOOK   Stone Hall

RR Map 9 A5 Dyfed
Nr Wolf's Castle,
Haverfordwest
Letterston (0348) 840212

French cooking
Set D £10.20
About £35 for two
Seats 34
Parties 30
Parking Ample
Credit Access, Amex, Visa

The old manor house is very secluded, so check directions when
booking. Orders for dinner are taken in a cosy, convivial bar, and the
dining room has lots of character, with its slate floor, beamed ceiling
and great stone fireplace. Dishes are French, traditional and very
enjoyable: leek soup with delicious home-baked bread, salmon escalope
with sorrel sauce, confit de canard, sirloin steak with Roquefort sauce,
a superb Pithiviers au chocolat. Martine and Alan Watson are very
friendly hosts.   ♀ Well-chosen ⊖ ♿

Lunch by arrang.   *Dinner* 7.30–9.30
Closed Mon & 1 wk Nov

BEDROOMS 5 £E/F
With bath/shower 5

Bedrooms are simple and attractive, with modern furniture and
colour TVs; there's a lovely lounge. No dogs.

WOLF'S CASTLE   Wolfscastle Country Hotel   56%   £E/F

HR Map 9 A5 Dyfed
Nr Haverfordwest SA62 5LZ
Treffgarne (043 787) 225

Credit Access, Amex, Visa

A Georgian house forms the core of this cheerful hotel where the
squash club plays a major part, Andrew Stirling being a squash coach.
Public rooms include a recently added function room and a pubby
bar with a natural brick counter. The bedrooms have pretty duvets
and wallpaper, functional units and tea/coffee-makers; all have decent
private bathrooms.
Amenities garden, tennis, squash, laundry service.

Rooms 15	Direct dial Yes	Confirm by arrang.	Parking Ample
Ensuite bath/shower 15	Room TV Yes	Last dinner 9.15	Room service All day

Restaurant

About £35 for two
Seats 40
Parties 200

Elegant candle-lit tables and an appetising array of sweets arouse
pleasurable anticipation which is justified by the excellent food. Good
quality ingredients are simply and competently cooked and accompanied by perfect sauces and crisp vegetables. Starters include celery,
apple and Stilton soup, chicken liver pâté with Cognac and spiced
Mexican mushrooms; move on to grilled Dover sole or roast duck
with black cherry and red wine sauce. Good desserts. ⊖

Lunch Sun only 12–2   *Dinner* 7–9.15
Closed L Mon–Sat exc. by arrang.

HOTELS RESTAURANTS AND INNS
CHANNEL ISLANDS

ALDERNEY

ST ANNE   Inchalla Hotel   63%   £E

H **Map 3 F4** Alderney
The Val Alderney
(048 182) 3220

Credit Amex, Visa

At the edge of the pretty little town of St. Anne, Inchalla is an ideal base for touring Alderney. Charming owner Valerie Willis keeps everything relaxed and informal, and her staff work happily and efficiently. Spotless bedrooms have practical modern furniture, mini-bars and most have neat private bathrooms. Focus of the day rooms is a delightful cane-furnished lounge. No dogs.   *Amenities* garden, sauna, solarium, whirlpool bath, in-house movies, laundry service.

Rooms 11	*Direct dial* Yes	*Confirm by* arrang.	*Parking* Ample
Ensuite bath/shower 8	*Room TV* Yes	*Last dinner* 8.45	*Room service* All day

ST ANNE   Nellie Gray's

R **Map 3 F4** Alderney
Victoria Street
Alderney (048 182) 3333

About £45 for two
Seats 48
Parties 48
Parking Ample

Credit Access, Amex, Diners, Visa

A well-established and popular restaurant with a pleasant chintzy decor and a garden for summer eating. The menu offers good variety and hearty portions, and it's supplemented by interesting daily specials – usually featuring seafood. Your starter might be guacamole or fisherman's bisque, followed perhaps by steak or superbly fresh turbot accompanied by masses of carefully prepared choice vegetables. Finish with a selection of home-made sweets from the trolley.   ☙

Lunch 12–2 end May–end Sept only   *Dinner* 7.30–9.30, 7.15–10 end May–end Sept   **Closed** Sun (excl. D mid July–mid Sept), also Jan–Mar

★   For a *discount* on next year's guide, see **An Offer for Answers.**   ★

GUERNSEY

HERM ISLAND   White House Hotel   64%   £D

HR **Map 3 E4**
Herm (0481) 22159

Credit Access, Visa
Closed Oct–Easter

There are no cars on Herm, and the only hotel is the White House, where a warm welcome, good food, comfort and relaxation are provided. The lounges are well supplied with armchairs, and there are two pleasant bars. Bedrooms, some with balconies, are bright and well kept, cottage rooms being particularly appealing. Half-board only. No dogs.   *Amenities* garden, outdoor swimming pool, tennis, sea fishing, mooring, coffee shop (10am–4pm).

Rooms 32	*Room phone* No	*Confirm by* arrang.	*Parking* No cars
Ensuite bath/shower 32	*Room TV* No	*Last dinner* 9	*Room service* None

Restaurant

Set L £7.25
Set D £9.75
About £30 for two
Seats 90

Good-quality raw materials get skilled, straightforward treatment from Chris Walder, so it's a treat to have a meal here. Casserole of seafood with pasta shells and sweet tomatoes, cream of carrot soup, lamb with rosemary and a sweet from the trolley could be the choice, with coffee to follow in the lounge. Cold meats and salads are also available, and there's always a vegetarian dish. No smoking in dining room.   ♀ Well-chosen   ☙

Lunch 12.30–1.30   *Dinner* 7–9
Closed Oct–Easter

PLEINMONT   Imperial Hotel   £F

Map 3 E4 Guernsey
Torteval
Guernsey (0481) 64044

Credit Access, Visa
Closed 25 Dec

Fine views of Rocquaine Bay are to be had from this modest but friendly inn and very close by there are splendid sandy beaches and clifftop walks. Two comfortable bars with picture windows and a pretty outlook are reserved for residents, while the atmospheric Portelet Bar is popular with the locals. The cheerful bedrooms have melamine furniture, adequate, tiled bathrooms and tea/coffee-makers. *Amenities* garden.

Rooms 16	*Room phone* No	*Confirm by* arrang.	*Parking* Ample
Ensuite bath/shower 14	*Room TV* Yes	*Last dinner* 9.15	*Room service* None

**We welcome bona fide complaints and recommendations
on the tear-out pages at the back of the book for readers' comment.
They are followed up by our professional team.**

ST MARTIN'S   St Margaret's Lodge Hotel 63%   £E

Map 3 E4 Guernsey
Forest Road
Guernsey (0481) 35757
Telex 4191664

Credit Access, Amex, Diners, Visa

A welcoming white-painted hotel conveniently close to the airport. Public rooms include a cosy bar-lounge with panelling and an exposed stone fireplace. De luxe rooms and suites have smart fabrics, dark furniture setting off the light decor, hairdryers and trouser presses. Other rooms have well-matched light grey decor and fabrics. Well kept bathrooms with shower facilities. No dogs. *Amenities* garden, outdoor swimming pool, secretarial services, laundry service.

Rooms 48	*Direct dial* Yes	*Confirm by* arrang.	*Parking* Ample
Ensuite bath/shower 48	*Room TV* Yes	*Last dinner* 9.30	*Room service* 24 hours

ST MARTIN'S   La Trelade Hotel 59%   £D/E

Map 3 E4 Guernsey
Forest Road
Guernsey (0481) 35454

Credit Access, Visa

You can find pleasant accommodation at this friendly holiday hotel where three lounges and a spacious bar provide plenty of choice for socialising. 12 bedrooms have recently been refurbished with pretty wallcoverings and fabrics and simple fitted furniture; other rooms are more modest in decor. The bathrooms are clean and functional. Half-board terms only.
Amenities garden, outdoor swimming pool, putting, laundry service.

Rooms 45	*Direct dial* Yes	*Confirm by* arrang.	*Parking* Ample
Ensuite bath/shower 45	*Room TV* Yes	*Last dinner* 8.30	*Room service* 24 hours

ST PETER PORT   Duke of Richmond Hotel 65%   £D

Map 3 E4 Guernsey
Cambridge Park
Guernsey (0481) 26221
Telex 4191462

Credit Access, Amex, Diners, Visa

A purpose-built hotel in a hillside setting overlooking a park. There's a quietly relaxing lounge and two bars, one with a ship's cabin theme, the other chintzy and plush in Victorian style. The comfortable bedrooms are quite spacious, with solid furniture, direct-dial phones, hairdryers, trouser presses, tea/coffee-makers and smart modern bathrooms. Superior rooms have balconies and sea views.
Amenities outdoor swimming pool, fax, laundry service.

Rooms 75	*Direct dial* Yes	*Confirm by* arrang.	*Parking* Limited
Ensuite bath/shower 75	*Room TV* Yes	*Last dinner* 9.30	*Room service* 24 hours

ST PETER PORT   Flying Dutchman Hotel 57%   £E

Map 3 E4 Guernsey
Ruette Braye
Guernsey (0481) 23787

Credit Amex, Visa
Closed Feb

Ulla and Reinhard Deutschmann run their modest hotel, situated in a pretty valley a mile from St Peter Port, in warm-hearted, good-humoured fashion and the accommodation is basic yet comfortable. There's a jolly beer garden with old buses and carts to enchant the children, while a simple TV lounge provides for adults. Bedrooms have functional furniture, well-sprung mattresses and practical bathrooms. No dogs. *Amenities* garden, laundry service.

Rooms 21	*Room phone* No	*Confirm by* arrang.	*Parking* Ample
Ensuite bath/shower 16	*Room TV* Yes	*Last dinner* 10	*Room service* Limited

Restaurant ♙

Set D £6.50
About £32 for two
Seats 100
Parties 100

In her unpretentious, relaxing restaurant Swedish-born Ulla draws her culinary inspiration from many countries to produce a highly unusual menu. Starter might be raggmunkar (crispy potato pancakes with bacon and cranberry sauce) or gravad lax; for the main course, perhaps filet sauté Trinidad or pot roast pork with red cabbage. The cooking is truly excellent throughout, but the *pièce de résistance* is Reinhard Deutschmann's German pâtisserie. ℗

Lunch 12–2 *Dinner* 7.30–10
Closed Sun to non-residents & all Feb

ST PETER PORT La Frégate Hotel 65% £C/D

HR **Map 3 E4** Guernsey
Les Côtils
Guernsey (0481) 24624

Credit Access, Amex, Diners, Visa

The absence of radio and TV at this 18th-century manor house is a deliberate policy to provide peace and tranquillity. Staff are efficient yet unobtrusive and comfort is paramount in public rooms. A handsome bar-lounge with fine harbour views opens on to a sun terrace. Most of the spacious bedrooms have balconies and equally fine views. No children under 14. No dogs.
Amenities garden, laundry service.

Rooms 13	*Direct dial* Yes	*Confirm by* arrang.	*Parking* Ample
Ensuite bath/shower 13	*Room TV* No	*Last dinner* 9.30	*Room service* All day

Restaurant

French cooking

Set L £7.50
Set D £11.50
About £42 for two
Seats 65
Parties 14

There are magnificent views from this formal restaurant high above St Peter Port. The menu, French in essence, international in flavour, holds few surprises but cooking is competent in such dishes as veal escalopes with artichokes and mushrooms in Marsala sauce, and duck with apple and Calvados. Crisp vegetables from the hotel garden are well presented, as are the very good desserts including an excellent chocolate mousse.

Lunch 12.30–1.30
Dinner 7–9.30, Sun 7–9

ST PETER PORT Le Nautique

R **Map 3 E4** Guernsey
Quay Steps
Guernsey (0481) 21714

French cooking
About £46 for two
Seats 68
Parties 30
Parking Difficult
Credit Access, Amex, Diners, Visa

Booking is advisable if you want to make sure of a seat at Carlo Graziani's popular French restaurant, noted for its warm-hearted welcome and the delightful harbour views. Seafood is the order of the day – though there is plenty of choice for meat-eaters. Oysters, mussels, lobster, Dover sole, swordfish are all on the menu, and you can round off the meal with an enjoyable sweet. Service is amiable and efficient. ℗

Lunch 12–2 *Dinner* 7–10
Closed Sun & 3 wks Xmas

We publish annually,
so make sure you use the current edition.
It's worth it!

ST PETER PORT Old Government House Hotel 66% £C/D

H **Map 3 E4** Guernsey
Ann's Place
Guernsey (0481) 24921
Telex 4191144

Credit Access, Amex, Diners, Visa

Once the official residence of the Governors of Guernsey, and a hotel since 1858. The foyer and lounge keep the period feel, and there's a light, airy bar, a more intimate residents' bar and a popular basement disco. Bedrooms, generally of a good size, are furnished in the main with simple white units. Remote-control TVs and trouser presses are standard. *Amenities* garden, outdoor swimming pool, solarium, in-house movies, secretarial services, fax, laundry service.

Rooms 71	*Direct dial* Yes	*Confirm by* arrang.	*Parking* Limited
Ensuite bath/shower 71	*Room TV* Yes	*Last dinner* 9.15	*Room service* 24 hours

ST PETER PORT   St Pierre Park Hotel   74%   £B/C

H **Map 3 E4** Guernsey
Rohais
Guernsey (0481) 28282
Telex 4191662

Rooms 136
Ensuite bath/shower 136
Direct dial Yes
Room TV Yes
Confirm by arrang.
Last dinner 10
Parking Ample
Room service 24 hours

Credit Access, Amex, Diners, Visa

Forty acres of parkland studded with ornamental lakes make a fine setting for this modern hotel just outside St Peter Port. Period-style furnishings give an elegant feel to the spacious bar-lounge, while good-sized bedrooms sport darkwood units, easy chairs and well-appointed bathrooms. Housekeeping is good but maintenance could be improved and staff are a little casual at times. Airport coach. No dogs.

Amenities garden, indoor swimming pool, sauna, solarium, whirlpool bath, keep-fit equipment, massage, hairdressing, tennis, 9-hole golf course, golf driving range, putting, croquet, games room, in-house movies, secretarial services, fax, laundry service, coffee shop (10am–11pm), shopping arcade, children's playground. ♿

JERSEY

BOULEY BAY   Water's Edge Hotel   70%   £C/D

H **Map 3 F4** Jersey
The Slipway, Trinity
Jersey (0534) 62777
Telex 4192521

Rooms 56
Ensuite bath/shower 56
Direct dial Yes
Room TV Yes
Confirm by arrang.
Last dinner 9.45
Parking Limited
Room service 24 hours

Credit Access, Amex, Diners, Visa
Closed end Oct–end Mar

A well-run holiday hotel in a pretty position overlooking Bouley Bay with, on a clear day, a view of the Cherbourg peninsula. Pleasing places for relaxation include a handsomely panelled bar, comfortably furnished lounges with delightful views and a colourful and exotic garden graced with palm trees. The good-sized bedrooms mainly have white Regency-style furniture and pretty coordinated fab-

rics; the nicest rooms have balconies or sun terraces, but even those at the rear have a pleasing outlook over the garden. Bath and shower rooms are well-equipped and have generous towels.
Amenities garden, outdoor swimming pool, sauna, fax, laundry service, coffee shop (10am–5.30pm).

GOREY   Moorings Hotel   64%   £D/E

H **Map 3 F4** Jersey
Gorey Pier
Jersey (0534) 53633
Telex 4192085

Credit Access, Amex, Visa

A picturesque setting on Gorey Pier, nestling directly beneath Mont Orgueil Castle, is just one of the bonuses of this friendly, intimate hotel. A small panelled bar provides a cosy place for a drink, while the residents' lounge is spacious and pleasant. Bedrooms are a real strength – comfortable mattresses, deep-pile carpets and coordinated fabrics cannot fail to please. Bathrooms boast first-rate showers and luxurious towels. *Amenities* laundry service.

Rooms 17	*Direct dial* Yes	*Confirm by* arrang.	*Parking* Limited
Ensuite bath/shower 17	*Room TV* Yes	*Last dinner* 10.30	*Room service* 24 hours

GOREY   Old Court House Hotel   64%   £D

H **Map 3 F4** Jersey
Jersey (0534) 54444
Telex 4192032

Credit Access, Amex, Diners, Visa
Closed Nov–Easter

Just a short walk from the beach and the little port of Gorey, the Old Court House is a popular holiday hotel. Public areas are appointed in comfortable, traditional style, and the bar is the scene of a weekly summer cabaret. Well-kept bedrooms include ground-floor rooms with terraces and some with private balconies. No dogs.
Amenities garden, outdoor swimming pool, solarium, sauna, in-house movies, laundry service.

Rooms 58	*Direct dial* Yes	*Confirm by* arrang.	*Parking* Ample
Ensuite bath/shower 58	*Room TV* Yes	*Last dinner* 9	*Room service* 24 hours

HAVRE DES PAS	Hotel de la Plage 58%	£D/E

H Map 3 F4 Jersey
St Helier
Jersey (0534) 23474
Telex 4192328

Credit Access, Amex, Diners, Visa
Closed 1 Nov–Easter

Fine sea views, enhanced by picture windows, are a feature of this attractive modern hotel at the water's edge. Pleasant public areas include a smart foyer, spacious bar-lounge and delightful sun terrace. Refurbished bedrooms have pretty fabrics and lightwood furniture; older rooms are plainer, but all have remote-control TVs. No dogs. *Amenities* terrace, solarium, keep-fit equipment, games room, secretarial services, laundry service.

Rooms 78	*Direct dial* Yes	*Confirm by* arrang.	*Parking* Ample
Ensuite bath/shower 78	*Room TV* Yes	*Last dinner* 9	*Room service* 24 hours

HAVRE DES PAS	Ommaroo Hotel 58%	£E

H Map 3 F4 Jersey
St Helier
(0534) 23493
Telex 4192225

Credit Access, Amex, Diners, Visa
Closed end Oct–Apr

The attractive facade of this seafront hotel sports intricate ornamental ironwork and Victorian gables. Public areas, including several lounges, are sober by contrast but have a sleepy old-fashioned appeal. Unfussy bedrooms offer modest traditional furnishings and the best ones have sea-facing balconies. Most have up-to-date en suite facilities, and public bathrooms are in good order. *Amenities* garden, games room, secretarial services, laundry service. &

Rooms 85	*Direct dial* Yes	*Confirm by* arrang.	*Parking* Ample
Ensuite bath/shower 74	*Room TV* Yes	*Last dinner* 8.30	*Room service* 24 hours

Our inspectors *never* book in the name of Egon Ronay's Guides.
They disclose their identity only if they are considering an establishment
for inclusion in the next edition of the Guide.

PETIT PORT	Sea Crest Hotel 62%	£E

HR Map 3 F4 Jersey
Nr La Corbière
Jersey (0534) 46353

Credit Access, Amex, Visa
Closed end Oct–Easter

A fine coastal setting for an intimate little roadside hotel, whose public areas include a sun lounge and a patio that overlooks the pool. Spotless bedrooms, most of a decent size, with sea views, are light and airy, with modern white furnishings and well-equipped bathrooms, all but one en suite. Staff are friendly and convivial. No dogs. *Amenities* garden, outdoor swimming pool, laundry service.

Rooms 7	*Direct dial* Yes	*Confirm by* arrang.	*Parking* Ample
Ensuite bath/shower 6	*Room TV* Yes	*Last dinner* 10	*Room service* All day

	Restaurant

Set L £7.50
About £46 for two
Seats 55
Parties 65

Alfresco eating on the patio is a special summer treat at this friendly restaurant, where a straightforward menu relies on the best and freshest market produce. Tried and tested favourites include whitebait, onion soup and a variety of pasta dishes; crab and lobster; a medley of seafood poached in Noilly Prat, finished with cream and basil; roast duckling; veal and steaks; banoffi pie and zabaglione. There's a separate vegetarian menu. ♀ Well-chosen ☺

Lunch 12.30–2 *Dinner* 7.30–10
Closed end Oct–Easter

PORTELET BAY	Portelet Hotel 66%	£C/D

H Map 3 F4 Jersey
Nr St Brelade
Jersey (0534) 41204
Telex 4192039

Credit Access, Amex, Diners, Visa
Closed 9 Oct–29 Apr

A good holiday hotel with high standards of housekeeping and consistently courteous staff. Overlooking St Brelade's Bay, with splendid views, particularly from the restaurant, the modernised 1920s building has a well-planned foyer, cocktail bar and ballroom. Balconies on many of the spacious bedrooms make the most of the sunshine and there's also a comfortable sun lounge. No dogs. *Amenities* garden, outdoor swimming pool, games room.

Rooms 86	*Room phone* Yes	*Confirm by* arrang.	*Parking* Ample
Ensuite bath/shower 86	*Room TV* Yes	*Last dinner* 9	*Room service* 24 hours

ROZEL BAY

Château La Chaire   73%   *NEW ENTRY*   **£C/D**

HR **Map 3 F4** Jersey
Rozel Bay
Jersey (0534) 63354
Telex 437334

Rooms 13
Ensuite bath/shower 13
Direct dial Yes
Room TV Yes
Confirm by arrang.
Last dinner 10
Parking Ample
Room service All day

Credit Access, Amex, Diners, Visa

Seven acres of trees and shrubs surround this impressive hotel. A friendly welcome and a glass of sherry are to be found in the attractive entrance hall, setting the tone for the whole establishment. In the splendid rococo lounge, with its ornate ceiling and walls, you can relax in comfortable period seating, while the panelled bar provides an intimate spot for a drink. The luxurious bedrooms are individ-

ually designed with pastel shades, pretty, good quality fabrics and well-matched period furniture; extras include hairdryers, trouser presses, fruit, mineral water and flowers. Bathrooms are equally sumptuous. No dogs, no under-sevens. *Amenities* garden, in-house movies, laundry service, 24-hour lounge service.

La Chaire Restaurant

Set L £7.50
About £40 *for two*
Seats 80
Parties 25

Choose between the splendid setting of an elegant panelled room or an airy conservatory. Seafood features prominently on the menu in such dishes as casserole of mussels and mushrooms and turbot in a lime sauce with a timbale of crab. Also on offer is a range of meat dishes to please everyone. Sound wines: chablis from Remon, Pouilly Fumé from Saget. ♀ Well-chosen ℗

Lunch 12–2   *Dinner* 7–10

ST AUBIN

La Haule Manor   60%   **£D/E**

H **Map 3 F4** Jersey
La Haule
Jersey (0534) 41426

Credit Access, Amex, Diners, Visa

Splendid views of the bay are to be had from many of the rooms of this 18th-century manor and there's a broad sandy beach just across the road. Public rooms comprise a function room, two lounges (one with TV) and a warm and intimate cocktail bar. The lofty bedrooms have neat modern furnishings, candlewick bedspreads and hairdryers; bathrooms are modern and well-maintained.
Amenities garden, laundry service.

Rooms 20	*Room phone* No	*Confirm by* 6	*Parking* Ample
Ensuite bath/shower 14	*Room TV* Yes	*Last dinner* 8.15	*Room service* 24 hours

ST AUBIN

Hotel La Tour   63%   **£E**

H **Map 3 F4** Jersey
High Street
Jersey (0534) 43770

Credit Access, Amex, Visa
Closed Nov–end Feb

Its position high above the town at the top of High Street (ask for directions) gives this handsome Georgian hotel magnificent sea views. Public rooms comprise a spacious lounge in period style, a smart and atmospheric bar and an intimate TV lounge. The bedrooms are equipped with attractive freestanding furniture and most have neat bathrooms or shower rooms. Two boast four-posters. No dogs.
Amenities patio, secretarial services.

Rooms 21	*Room phone* No	*Confirm by* arrang.	*Parking* Limited
Ensuite bath/shower 18	*Room TV* Yes	*Last dinner* 9.30	*Room service* Limited

ST AUBIN'S HARBOUR   Old Court House Inn   *NEW ENTRY*   **£D/E**

IR **Map 3 F4** Jersey
The Bulwarks
Jersey (0534) 46433

Credit Access, Visa
Closed 25 & 26 Dec

Dating back in parts to the 15th century, the Old Court House offers period charm and a picturesque harbourside setting. The cellar bars are popular with tourists and locals alike, and there's a quieter bar (themed on a ship's cabin) and a nice little lounge. Bedrooms feature pretty contemporary fabrics and some handsome old pine furniture. Many enjoy harbour views, and the penthouse suite boasts a sun terrace. No children. *Amenities* patio, laundry service.

Rooms 9	*Direct dial* Yes	*Confirm by* arrang.	*Parking* Difficult
Ensuite bath/shower 9	*Room TV* Yes	*Last dinner* 11	*Room service* Limited

Restaurant

Seafood
Set L Sun only £7.95
About £40 for two
Seats 60
Parties 20

Seafood is the choice of many at this consistently popular restaurant on the quayside. A blackboard lists daily-changing specials, dependent on the day's catch. Fresh langoustines, perhaps, or local seabass are offered alongside Dover sole, chargrilled monkfish or halibut. Oysters, crab, mussels, even winkles and whelks have a place on a menu that also includes steaks and sausages and mash. There is a good selection of vegetables. Booking essential. ℮

Lunch 12.30–2.30 *Dinner* 7.30–11
Closed 25 & 26 Dec

ST BRELADE   Atlantic Hotel   73%   £C/D

H **Map 3 F4** Jersey
La Moye
Jersey (0534) 44101
Telex 4192405

Rooms 46
Ensuite bath/shower 46
Direct dial Yes
Room TV Yes
Confirm by arrang.
Last dinner 9.15
Parking Ample
Room service 24 hours

Credit Access, Amex, Diners, Visa
Closed Jan–16 Mar

Pleasantly situated between a golf course and the sea, this low-built modern hotel overlooks gardens running down to a long sandy beach. A tiled floor, bare stone walls and leather chairs give a cool contemporary feel to the spacious foyer-lounge, and there's an intimate, softly lit bar with equally stylish decor. Good-sized bedrooms feature balconies, simple fitted units, bedside controls and neat, compact bathrooms. The pool-side patio is a popular place for soaking up the sun, and a leisure centre is planned. Staff are smart and friendly, the manager impressively keen. No dogs.
Amenities garden, outdoor swimming pool, tennis, in-house movies, secretarial services, laundry service.

ST BRELADE   La Place Hotel   68%   £C/D

H **Map 3 F4** Jersey
Route Du Coin, La Haule
Jersey (0534) 44261
Telex 4192522

Credit Access, Amex, Diners, Visa

Originally a farmhouse, and at least 350 years old, La Place enjoys a quiet setting away from the bustle of the resorts. Low beams and open stone fireplaces create character in the comfortably furnished lounge, and there's a roomy bar that gives on to the pool. Bedrooms are bright and practical, with simple modern appointments and neatly kept bathrooms. *Amenities* terrace, outdoor swimming pool, sauna, secretarial services, fax, laundry service

Rooms 40	*Direct dial* Yes	*Confirm by* arrang.	*Parking* Ample
Ensuite bath/shower 40	*Room TV* Yes	*Last dinner* 9.45	*Room service* 24 hours

---

Changes in data sometimes occur in establishments
after the Guide goes to press.
Prices should be taken as indications rather than firm quotes.

ST BRELADE'S BAY   Hotel Château Valeuse   64%   £E

H **Map 3 F4** Jersey
Jersey (0534) 46281

Credit Access, Visa
Closed Jan–Mar

Château Valeuse stands peacefully in well-tended gardens back from the lovely bay. The surroundings are comfortable, and the atmosphere throughout is informal and relaxed. The lounge and sun terrace enjoy attractive views, and many of the light, airy bedrooms have their own balconies. Bathrooms are tiled and very neat, reflecting a high overall standard of housekeeping. No children under five. No dogs.
Amenities garden, outdoor swimming pool, laundry service.

Rooms 32	*Direct dial* Yes	*Confirm by* arrang.	*Parking* Ample
Ensuite bath/shower 32	*Room TV* Yes	*Last dinner* 9.15	*Room service* Limited

ST BRELADE'S BAY   Hotel l'Horizon   77%   £C

HR Map 3 F4 Jersey
St Brelade
Jersey (0534) 43101
Telex 4192281

Rooms 103
Ensuite bath/shower 103
Direct dial Yes
Room TV Yes
Confirm by arrang.
Last dinner 9.45
Parking Ample
Room service 24 hours

Credit Access, Amex, Diners, Visa

A super hotel in a wonderful setting alongside the beach. The elegant public rooms include a sumptuous and comfortable lounge with light pastel shades and contemporary seating, and a similarly smart bar overlooking the sea; in contrast, the drawing room is in period style with fine fabrics and furniture. Bedrooms have pretty decor, attractive floral fabrics, smart fitted furniture and good tiled bathrooms with TV speakers, decent showers and hairdryers. Rooms overlooking the sea have balconies; those in a centre wing are a little plainer but still comfortable. No dogs. *Amenities* terrace, indoor swimming pool, sauna, solarium, keep-fit equipment, beauty salon, hairdressing, in-house movies, secretarial services, fax, laundry service.

Star Grill   ♛

About £45 for two
Seats 45
Parties 40

A luxurious room overlooking the bay, where smart service, and superbly fresh fish on the menu cannot fail to please. There's a range of international dishes with a French emphasis and, beside the delicious seafood offerings such as fillet of sea bass garnished with prawn and lobster and served in a white wine sauce, there is a good selection of meat dishes. Finish with one of the attractive sweets. ⊖
&

Lunch 12.45–2.45   *Dinner* 7.45– 9.45
Closed Mon

ST BRELADE'S BAY   St Brelade's Bay Hotel   70%   £B/C

H Map 3 F4 Jersey
Jersey (0534) 46141
Telex 4192519

Rooms 82
Ensuite bath/shower 82
Direct dial Yes
Room TV Yes
Confirm by arrang.
Last dinner 9
Parking Ample
Room service 24 hours

Credit Access, Amex, Diners, Visa
Closed Nov–Apr

There are impressive views of the bay to be had from the terraced gardens of this fine hotel, which offers excellent leisure facilities for the family. Public areas succeed in being both elegant and warmly welcoming – Persian rugs on parquet floors and leather chesterfields grace the foyer-lounge and the chic cocktail bar has red-stained cane chairs. There's also a stylish sun lounge running half the length of the building. Best bedrooms are sea-facing, with smart bamboo furnishings and, in the bathrooms, marble vanity units. No dogs. *Amenities* garden, outdoor swimming pool, sauna, solarium, tennis, pitch & putt, croquet, games room, snooker, secretarial services, laundry service, children's play area.

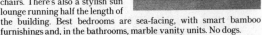

Any person using our name to obtain free hospitality is a fraud.
Proprietors, please inform the police and us.

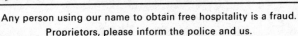

ST CLEMENT'S BAY   Hotel Ambassadeur   66%   £E

H Map 3 F4 Jersey
Jersey (0534) 24455
Telex 4192636

Credit Access, Amex, Diners, Visa

A well-designed, modern hotel with fine views over St Clement's Bay, which are capitalised on in the picture-windowed, chintzy lounge. In the bar-lounge, exposed brick walls and leather-look chairs make for pleasant surroundings. Half the bedrooms have sea views and all are bright and airy, with excellent, fully-tiled bathrooms with shower fitments and bidets. *Amenities* outdoor swimming pool, secretarial services, coffee shop (11am–6pm).

Rooms 39	*Room phone* Yes	*Confirm by* arrang.	*Parking* Ample
Ensuite bath/shower 39	*Room TV* Yes	*Last dinner* 9.45	*Room service* 24 hours

ST HELIER — Apollo Hotel — 65% — £D/E

H Map 3 F4 Jersey
9 St Saviour's Road
Jersey (0534) 25441
Telex 4192086

Credit Access, Amex, Diners, Visa

Popular with both the business and holiday markets, the Apollo has a roomy, contemporary feel. Public areas include a friendly public bar, and most of the bedrooms have been refurbished in light, modern style, with more accessories than before and neat tiled bathrooms. No dogs. *Amenities* indoor swimming pool, sauna, solarium, whirlpool bath, keep-fit equipment, games room, satellite TV, in-house movies, fax, coffee shop (11am–10pm).

Rooms 79	*Direct dial* Yes	*Confirm by* arrang.	*Parking* Ample
Ensuite bath/shower 79	*Room TV* Yes	*Last dinner* 8.45	*Room service* 24 hours

ST HELIER — Beaufort Hotel — 60% — £D/E

H Map 3 F4 Jersey
Green Street
Jersey (0534) 32471
Telex 4192160

Credit Access, Amex, Diners, Visa

A convenient position close to the town centre and the sea is one of the attractions of this modern hotel. Nicest of the public rooms is the lounge, decorated and furnished in contemporary style. 13 bedrooms have been refurbished with pretty fabrics, pastel decor and smart dark furniture; all rooms have tea/coffee-makers, trouser presses and hairdryers. No dogs. *Amenities* terrace, indoor swimming pool, satellite TV, teletext, laundry service.

Rooms 54	*Direct dial* Yes	*Confirm by* arrang.	*Parking* Ample
Ensuite bath/shower 54	*Room TV* Yes	*Last dinner* 8.45	*Room service* 24 hours

We welcome bona fide complaints and recommendations on the tear-out pages at the back of the book for readers' comment. They are followed up by our professional team.

ST HELIER — La Capannina

R Map 3 F4 Jersey
65 Halkett Place
Jersey (0534) 34602

Italian cooking
About £40 for two
Seats 80
Parties 20
Parking Difficult
Credit Access, Amex, Diners, Visa

Sound Italian cooking keeps things busy at this long-established and well-run restaurant in the middle of St. Helier. The menus change with the seasons, spanning a familiar range from Parma ham, salami and minestrone to lasagne and tagliatelle, veal in various guises, steaks and casseroled quail. Fish features strongly on the list of daily specials, and sweets include zabaglione, cassata and whatever's on the trolley. 🏠 ᴋ

Lunch 12–2   *Dinner* 7–10
Closed Sun, Bank Hols & 1 wk Xmas

ST HELIER — Grand Hotel — 68% — £B

HR Map 3 F4 Jersey
Esplanade
Jersey (0534) 22301
Telex 4192104

Credit Access, Amex, Diners, Visa

Debussy composed *La Mer* at this imposing late-Victorian hotel and he was only one of many notables to stay here. The public rooms have maintained their sombre period feel, while bedrooms have been refurbished in more contemporary style. A particularly well-managed establishment. *Amenities* terrace, indoor swimming pool, sauna, solarium, whirlpool bath, keep-fit equipment, beauty salon, massage parlour, hairdressing, snooker, in-house movies, teletext, secretarial services, fax, laundry service.

Rooms 115	*Direct dial* Yes	*Confirm by* arrang.	*Parking* Limited
Ensuite bath/shower 115	*Room TV* Yes	*Last dinner* 10.30	*Room service* 24 hours

Victoria's ♛

About £50 for two
Seats 150
Parties 160

A smart, elegant restaurant with an appropriately Victorian decor. The long menu offers mostly standard dishes, soundly prepared from top-quality ingredients. Typical starters are a beautifully moist salmon terrine, moules à la crème and huîtres à nôtre façon; main courses include medallions of lobster and Dover sole gougeons, breast of chicken en papillote and lamb cutlets in cream and tarragon sauce. Tempting sweet trolley to finish. 🍷 Well-chosen 🏠 ᴋ

Lunch 12.30–2.15   *Dinner* 7–10.15   **Closed** Sun

ST HELIER · Pomme D'or Hotel   65%   £D/E

H Map 3 F4 Jersey
The Esplanade
Jersey (0534) 78644
Telex 4192309

Credit Access, Amex, Diners, Visa

High standards of comfort ensure the continuing popularity of this large white-painted hotel opposite the harbour. Best bedrooms have soft colour schemes, remote-control TVs and trouser presses. All are kept spotlessly clean and have good modern bathrooms. Front rooms are double-glazed. Spacious public areas include a bierkeller-themed bar in the basement. No dogs. *Amenities* secretarial services, fax, laundry service, coffee shop (7am–10pm).

Rooms 151	*Direct dial* Yes	*Confirm by* 6	*Parking* Limited
Ensuite bath/shower 151	*Room TV* Yes	*Last dinner* 9	*Room service* 24 hours

**Our inspectors are our full-time employees;
they are professionally trained by us.**

ST LAWRENCE · Little Grove Hotel   73%   £B

H Map 3 F4 Jersey
Rue du Haut
Jersey (0534) 25321
Telex 4192567

Rooms 14
Ensuite bath/shower 14
Direct dial Yes
Room TV Yes
Confirm by arrang.
Last dinner 9.30
Parking Ample
Room service 24 hours

Credit Access, Amex, Diners, Visa

Peace, elegance and immaculate housekeeping are major pluses at this civilised pink-granite hotel, which enjoys a restful setting in three acres of attractive grounds. Staff greet guests with a smile, and relaxation comes easily in the light, comfortable lounges and bar (note the feature stone walls). Spacious bedrooms are stylishly appointed, with delightful fabrics, easy-on-the-eye colour schemes and furnishings that range from period to pine. Thoughtful extras abound, and there are good-quality toiletries in the bathrooms. Guests can arrange to be met by a hotel car, either a Rolls-Royce or a Renault Espace. No children under 12. No dogs.
Amenities garden, outdoor swimming pool, croquet, laundry service.

ST PETER · Mermaid Hotel   64%   £D

H Map 3 F4 Jersey
St Peter's Road
Jersey (0534) 41255
Telex 4192249

Credit Access, Amex, Diners, Visa

A new leisure centre with indoor pool has added to the amenities of this lakeside hotel close to the airport, while the adjoining inn dating back to 1710 provides plenty of atmosphere for a drink. Most bedrooms have balconies overlooking the gardens and all are well equipped. No dogs.
Amenities garden, indoor swimming pool, sauna, solarium, whirlpool bath, gymnasium, games room, satellite TV, fax, laundry service.

Rooms 68	*Direct dial* Yes	*Confirm by* arrang.	*Parking* Ample
Ensuite bath/shower 68	*Room TV* Yes	*Last dinner* 9.30	*Room service* 24 hours

ST SAVIOUR · Longueville Manor Hotel   81%   £B/C

HR Map 3 F4 Jersey
Jersey (0534) 25501
Telex 4192306

Rooms 34
Ensuite bath/shower 34
Direct dial Yes
Room TV Yes
Confirm by arrang.
Last dinner 9.30
Parking Ample
Room service 24 hours

Credit Access, Amex, Diners, Visa

Despite it being close to the road, wooded grounds with lawns and lakes ensure that peace reigns at this stone-built manor house. Cushioned armchairs, tasteful antiques and flowing drapes create a comfortable, relaxing atmosphere in the public rooms, and there are two bars, one opening on to the garden and one by the open-air pool. Tasteful, individually decorated bedrooms, many with small seating areas, have quality fabrics and period furniture including an 18th-century four-poster; remote-control TVs and direct-dial phones are standard. Bathrooms are equally luxurious. No children under seven.
Amenities garden, outdoor swimming pool, in-house movies, teletext, secretarial services, fax, valeting, laundry service.

Restaurant ♛

Set L from £13.75
Set D from £19.25
About £55 for two
Seats 65
Parties 15

Barry Forster's fixed price and à la carte menus can be enjoyed in an intimate, richly-panelled dining room or in a lighter, modern setting. Top-quality produce, skilfully handled, ensures a very satisfying meal. Main courses range from braised salmon with cabbage and caviar to medley of lamb with tagliatelle and creamed garlic. Unpasteurised farmhouse cheeses to follow. Classic wine list has notable burgundies and a careful selection from Italy. ♟ Well-chosen ☙

Lunch 12.30–2   *Dinner* 7.30–9.30

---

 is our symbol for an **outstanding** wine list

SARK

SARK	Aval du Creux Hotel 57%			£F

HR Map 3 E4 Sark
Sark (048 183) 2036

Credit Access, Visa
Closed 1 Oct–end April

A swimming pool and sun terrace are new attractions at this friendly former farmhouse. Convivial hosts Peter and Cheryl Tonks keep the welcome mat unfurled, and there's a delightfully informal and relaxed atmosphere in the lounges and bar. Six bedrooms in the main house are cosy, homely and quite roomy, while those in the annexe are smaller, but pleasantly light and airy.
Amenities garden, outdoor swimming pool.

Rooms 12	*Room phone* No	*Confirm by* arrang.	*Parking* No cars
Ensuite bath/shower 10	*Room TV* Yes	*Last dinner* 8.30	*Room service* Limited

Restaurant ⚐

Set L Sun £7.50
Set D £10.50
About £38 for two
Seats 35
Parties 40

Sound, reliable cooking is the keynote here, and the menus provide a good choice of familiar dishes. Seafood devotees can feast on fresh Sark crab, king-size prawns and the pick of the local catch, while carnivores could follow port-enriched chicken liver pâté with duckling bigarade, Cumberland lamb or a juicy sirloin steak. Surf 'n' turf is a good choice for amphibians. Cheryl cooks, Peter is an extrovert host. ☙

Lunch 12–1.30   *Dinner* 7–8.30
Closed 1 Oct–end April

SARK	Hotel Petit Champ 61%			£E

H Map 3 E4 Sark
Sark (048 183) 2046

Credit Access, Amex, Diners, Visa
Closed Oct–end Apr

The views are very special from the Petit Champ's lovely garden setting on Sark's west coast. The sun lounges are favourite spots for savouring the scenery, and there's a cosy little bar and TV room. Quiet, modest comfort characterizes the bedrooms, four of which have sea-facing balconies. The Scotts are friendly, welcoming owners. Half-board terms only. No children under eight. No dogs. *Amenities* garden, outdoor swimming pool, putting.

Rooms 16	*Room phone* No	*Confirm by* arrang.	*Parking* No cars
Ensuite bath/shower 15	*Room TV* No	*Last dinner* 8.15	*Room service* None

SARK	Stocks Hotel 61%			£E

HR Map 3 E4 Sark
Via Guernsey
Sark (0481 83) 2001

Credit Amex
Closed mid Oct–Easter

The friendly Armogie family do their utmost to give guests a peaceful stay at their attractive pink granite hotel standing in a sheltered wooded valley. Homely public rooms include a pleasant lounge, cosy bar and TV room, while the comfortable bedrooms with smart furniture and floral decor are blissfully quiet. Half-board terms only. No dogs. *Amenities* garden, outdoor swimming pool, laundry service, coffee shop (10am–10pm).

Rooms 24	*Room phone* No	*Confirm by* arrang.	*Parking* No cars
Ensuite bath/shower 14	*Room TV* No	*Last dinner* 8.30	*Room service* None

see over

Stocks Restaurant

Set D £12.50
About £32 for two
Seats 60
Parties 60

Fresh ingredients are given unfussy, very capable treatment at this pleasantly informal restaurant. Natural flavours speak for themselves in the distinctive celery soup, lightly cooked fruits de mer in a wine and cream sauce, and tender roast guinea fowl à l'américaine. The 4-course dinner menu changes daily, and the meal ends with cheese and a simple sweet. ℮

Dinner only 7–8.30
Closed mid Oct–Easter

HOTELS RESTAURANTS AND INNS
ISLE OF MAN

BALLASALLA   La Rosette   ⚑

R **Map 13 B6** Isle of Man
Main Street
Castletown (0624) 822940

French cooking
About £52 for two
Seats 40
Parties 16
Parking Ample
Credit Access, Visa

Be sure to book for the Phillips' quaint, justly popular little restaurant near Douglas. Charm and enthusiasm are married with a good choice of well-flavoured dishes. Baked snails, chef's pâté or coquilles St Jacques could be followed by roast quails, duck with orange sauce, or tender steak in a delicious port and mango sauce. Crisp vegetables and tempting desserts. Carefully chosen wine list: note Ch. Lanessan '82. ♀ Well-chosen ℮

Lunch 12–2.30   *Dinner* 7–10.30
Closed all Sun & Mon

DOUGLAS   Palace Hotel   58%   £D

H **Map 13 B6** Isle of Man
Central Promenade
Douglas (0624) 74521
Telex 627742

Credit Access, Amex, Diners, Visa

The casino and nightclub are popular attractions at this seafront hotel. Other public areas include the modern Round Bar and a functional residents' lounge. Bedrooms are comfortable and nine have been brought up-to-date with attractive freestanding units, pretty fabrics, trouser presses and hairdryers. All have mini-bars and tea/coffee-makers. No dogs. *Amenities* outdoor swimming pool, hairdressing, in-house movies, secretarial services, fax, laundry service.

Rooms 138	*Direct dial* Yes	*Confirm by* arrang.	*Parking* Ample
Ensuite bath/shower 138	*Room TV* Yes	*Last dinner* 11	*Room service* 24 hours

DOUGLAS   Sefton Hotel   62%   £E

H **Map 13 B6** Isle of Man
Harris Promenade
Douglas (0624) 26011
Telex 627519

Credit Access, Amex, Diners, Visa

A Victorian hotel which has recently been refurbished and equipped with new conference facilities. There's a welcoming public bar, a lounge with splendid sea views and an elegant cocktail bar that doubles as a coffee shop. Bedrooms sport pastel decor and coordinated fabrics. No dogs. *Amenities* indoor swimming pool, sauna, solarium, whirlpool bath, steam bath, keep-fit equipment, fax, laundry service, coffee shop (9.45am–1am), 24-hour lounge service. &

Rooms 80	*Direct dial* Yes	*Confirm by* arrang.	*Parking* Ample
Ensuite bath/shower 80	*Room TV* Yes	*Last dinner* 9.15	*Room service* Limited

**We welcome bona fide complaints and recommendations
on the tear-out pages at the back of the book for readers' comment.
They are followed up by our professional team.**

RAMSEY	Grand Island Hotel 62%	£C/D

H **Map 13 B5** Isle of 97Man
Bride Road
Ramsey (0624) 812455
Telex 629849

Credit Access, Amex, Diners, Visa

A friendly hotel in an elevated position with magnificent views across Ramsey Bay. Public areas are pleasing and comfortably furnished. Bedrooms have chintzy fabrics, white furniture and tiled bathrooms with shower facilities and decent toiletries. *Amenities* garden, indoor swimming pool, sauna, solarium, whirlpool bath, keep-fit equipment, beauty salon, hairdressing, putting, croquet, sea fishing, snooker, in-house movies, secretarial services, laundry service, helipad.

Rooms 57	*Direct dial* Yes	*Confirm by* arrang.	*Parking* Ample
Ensuite bath/shower 57	*Room TV* Yes	*Last dinner* 10.30	*Room service* 24 hours

RAMSEY	Harbour Bistro	ꝗ

R **Map 13 B5** Isle of Man
East Street
Ramsey (0624) 814182

About £28 for two
Seats 40
Parties 20
Parking Ample

Credit Access, Visa

The harbourside setting of Karl Meier's friendly, informal eating place ensures plentiful supplies of the fresh fish and seafood that dominate the menu. The famous Manx queenies are prepared in a variety of tempting ways, and other fishy treats include crab and cucumber soup, giant prawns, plaice and salmon baked in puff pastry. Also some meat dishes and nice simple sweets such as chocolate mousse or strawberry shortbread. &

Lunch 12–2.30   *Dinner* 6.30–10.30
Closed Sun, Good Fri, 24–26 Dec & Bank Hols

The tea consumed
was the very best, the coffee the very blackest,
the cream the very thickest; there was dry toast and
buttered toast, muffins and crumpets; hot bread and cold
bread, white bread and brown bread, home-made bread
and bakers' bread, wheaten bread and oaten bread...
there were eggs in napkins, and crispy bits of bacon under
silver covers; there were little fishes in a little box, and
devilled kidneys frizzling on a hot-water dish...
Over and above this, on a snow white napkin, spread upon
the side-board, was a huge ham and a huge sirloin; the latter
having laden the dinner table on the previous evening.
Such was the ordinary fare at Plumstead Episcopi.

ANTHONY TROLLOPE 1815-82
THE WARDEN

HOTELS
RESTAURANTS
AND INNS

NORTHERN
IRELAND

BELFAST

Map 18 D2
Town plan opposite

Population 360,000

Belfast, capital of Northern Ireland, gained city status as recently as 1888. The magnificent domed City Hall, lavish Opera House and decorated facades of many banks and shops as well as the ornamented interiors of Belfast's public houses typify its Victorian character. The area stretching from the pedestrianised shopping centre (plenty of car parking) to Queen's University is theatre and cinema land, popular for eating and drinking. There are few tall buildings and wherever you are you can see the green hills which ring the city. Riverside paths follow the Lagan's course for nine miles through rose gardens and parkland.

Annual Events
Belfast Civic Festival & Lord's Mayor's Show *May*
Belfast City Marathon *May Day*
International Arts Festival *November*
International Rose Trials *July–September*
Circuit of Ireland International motor rally *Easter*
Opera Northern Ireland Season *Autumn*
Royal Ulster Academy Art Exhibition *Autumn*
Royal Ulster Agricultural Show *May*
Twelfth Processions *12th July*

Sights Outside City
Belfast Zoo
Carrickfergus Castle
Rowallane Gardens, Saintfield
Strangford Lough
Ulster Folk and Transport Museum near Holywood

Tourist Information Centre
River House, 48 High Street
Telephone Belfast 246609
Telex 748087

1 Belfast Central Library A2
2 Belfast Central Rail Station C3
3 Belfast Civic Arts Theatre A4
4 Bord Failte Information Office A3
5 Botanic Gardens A/B5
6 Botanic Rail Station A4
7 Bus Station (Great Victoria Street) A3
8 Bus Station (Oxford Street) B3
9 City Hall A/B3
10 Grand Opera House A3
11 Law Courts B3
12 Linenhall Library *established 1788* A3
13 Lyric Theatre B5
14 Northern Ireland Tourist Board Information Centre B2
15 Ormeau Park C4/5
16 Queen's University A5
17 St Anne's Cathedral B2
18 Transport Museum C2
19 Ulster Museum *treasures from Spanish Armada* A5
20 Windsor Park football ground A4

Fiat Dealers
W. J. Bell & Son
40–50 Townsend Street
Belfast BT13 2ET
Tel. Belfast 241394
Map reference A2

B.A.S. (Motors) Ltd
45/47 Rosetta Road
Belfast BT6 9LP
Tel. Belfast 648049

Dick & Company (Belfast) Ltd
43 Mallusk Road
Newtownabbey BT36 8PH
Tel. Belfast 342511

Bairds Cars
7–9 Boucher Road
Belfast BT12 6HR
Tel. Belfast 247770

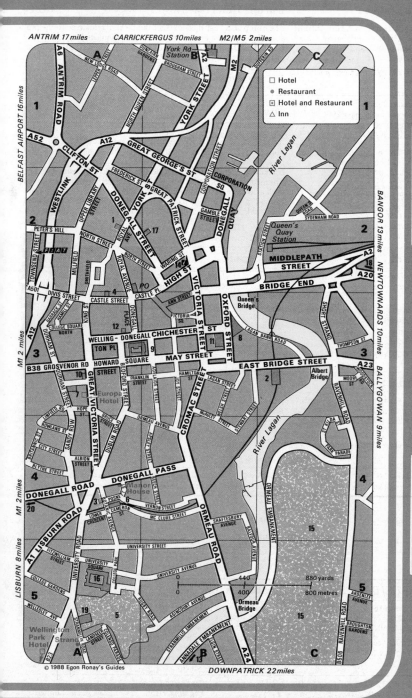

Belfast FIAT

BELFAST   Europa Hotel   69%   £B/C

H **Town plan A3** Co. Antrim
Great Victoria Street BT2 7AP
Belfast (0232) 327000
Telex 74491

Credit Access, Amex, Diners, Visa

The Europa is a busy modern hotel, but the staff remain polite, helpful
and efficient. A major, and welcome, refurbishment programme has
begun, and the smartly revamped restaurant is temporarily putting
other public areas in the shade. All bedrooms are of a very good size,
with coffee tables, armchairs and ample storage space. A number of
VIP rooms are being created. **Amenities** secretarial services, fax,
laundry service, coffee shop (7.30am–11.15pm), kiosk.

Rooms 200	*Direct dial* Yes	*Confirm by* 6	*Parking* Ample
Ensuite bath/shower 200	*Room TV* Yes	*Last dinner* 11.15	*Room service* 24 hours

---

BELFAST   Manor House   ⌘

R **Town plan A4** Co. Antrim
47 Donegall Pass
Belfast (0232) 238755

Chinese cooking
Set L & D from £10.50
About £30 for two
Seats 50 *Parties* 50
Parking Ample
Credit Access, Diners, Visa

Consistently well-prepared and enjoyable Chinese meals are on offer
here. Joe Wong, the amiable owner, rates good quality food and a
friendly atmosphere highly and this guarantees a pleasant evening.
The menu lists a wide choice of classical Cantonese fare from favourites
such as wun tun soup to more elaborate menus for the adventurous.
A good range of seafood includes eel, abalone, scallops, lobster, crab
and squid.

Meals 12–11.30
Closed 2 days Xmas

BELFAST   The Strand

R **Town plan A5** Co. Antrim
Stranmillis Road
Belfast (0232) 682266

About £27 for two
Seats 80
Parties 25
Parking Ample

Credit Access, Amex, Diners, Visa

An informal bistro-style restaurant in the heart of the University area.
Cooking is fairly basic and unsophisticated yet monthly-changing
menus always feature some interesting and imaginative combinations:
you might try egg and avocado bake, cod in spicy coconut and apple
sauce, or pork fillet roulades with celery, leek, walnut and cheese
stuffing. It's a popular and fashionable place, so booking is recommended.

Meals noon–11
Closed Sun, Easter Mon, 12 & 13 July & 25 & 26 Dec

BELFAST   Wellington Park Hotel   58%   £E

H **Town plan A5** Co. Antrim
21 Malone Road BT9 6RU
Belfast (0232) 381111
Telex 747052

Credit Access, Amex, Diners, Visa

Several bars and a night club make this a popular spot with Belfast
residents; it's also a thriving conference centre. Bedrooms, set well
away from the noise, are roomy and practical, with fitted wooden
furniture and modern tiled bathrooms (three with balcony sleeping
areas, a few with whirlpool baths). Staff are very friendly and helpful,
and there's a good, relaxed atmosphere. No dogs.
Amenities laundry service.

Rooms 50	*Direct dial* Yes	*Confirm by* 6	*Parking* Limited
Ensuite bath/shower 50	*Room TV* Yes	*Last dinner* 10	*Room service* 24 hours

We publish annually,
so make sure you use the current edition.
It's worth it!

BUSHMILLS   Bushmills Inn   *NEW ENTRY*   £E/F

I **Map 18 C1** Co Antrim
25 Main Street
Bushmills (026 57) 32339

Credit Access, Visa

Only a couple of miles from the spectacular coastal scenery of the
Giant's Causeway is this recently renovated inn dating from about
1830. Stripped pine and fashionable pastels set the tone for the stylish
and characterful day rooms; there's more pine in the individually-
decorated cottage-style bedrooms, two of which have platform beds
with ladders for children sharing with parents.
Amenities laundry service.

Rooms 12	*Direct dial* Yes	*Confirm by* arrang.	*Parking* Ample
Ensuite bath/shower 12	*Room TV* Yes	*Last dinner* 9.30	*Room service* Limited

COMBER — La Mon House Hotel — 59% — £E

Map 18 D2 Co. Down
The Mills, 41 Gransha Road
BT23 5RF
Castlereagh (0232) 448631

Credit Access, Amex, Diners, Visa

The leisure centre is a popular amenity at this modern hotel, which stands in manicured grounds near the village of Gransha (three miles from Comber). Scattered lounge areas provide plenty of seating space but no great character. The best of the bedrooms are some light, bright top-floor rooms with balconies. No dogs.
Amenities garden, indoor swimming pool, sauna, solarium, whirlpool bath, gymnasium, riding, fax, laundry service, kiosk.

Rooms 44	Direct dial Yes	Confirm by arrang.	Parking Ample
Ensuite bath/shower 38	Room TV Yes	Last dinner 10	Room service 24 hours

CRAWFORDSBURN — The Old Inn — £D/E

Map 18 D2 Co. Down
15 Main Street BT19 1JH
Helens Bay (0247) 853255

Credit Access, Amex, Diners, Visa
Closed 25 & 26 Dec

Established in 1614, it bills itself as Ireland's oldest hostelry. Fine linenfold panelling sets the tone in the solidly furnished reception area, and the parlour bar is also quietly traditional. The most striking day room, however, is the splendid main bar in extravagant Edwardian style. Individually decorated bedrooms – 15 more just added – are comfortable rather than stylish; two boast four-posters. No dogs. *Amenities* garden, laundry service.

Rooms 32	Direct dial Yes	Confirm by 7	Parking Ample
Ensuite bath/shower 32	Room TV Yes	Last dinner 10.30	Room service Limited

DUNADRY — Dunadry Inn — £D

Map 18 D2 Co. Antrim
BT41 2HA
Temple Patrick (084 94) 32474
Telex 747245

Credit Access, Amex, Diners, Visa
Closed 3 days Xmas

Although the exterior has a modern look, within there are many reminders of its linen mill origins. Old wooden pillars and a sweeping galleried staircase take the eye in reception, and there are some splendid old pieces of furniture. Quiet, comfortable bedrooms, many very spacious, include 12 that open on to the gardens or courtyard. No dogs.
Amenities garden, game fishing, laundry service.

Rooms 64	Direct dial Yes	Confirm by 6	Parking Ample
Ensuite bath/shower 64	Room TV Yes	Last dinner 9.45	Room service 24 hours

DUNMURRY — Conway Hotel — 68% — £D

Map 18 D2 Co. Antrim
300 Kingsway BT17 9ES
Belfast (0232) 612101
Telex 74281

Credit Access, Amex, Diners, Visa

Immaculate grounds surround this modern hotel. Friendly staff welcome guests in the open-plan reception, which leads to a smart, contemporary-style bar-lounge. Best bedrooms are spacious and attractively furnished; all are well equipped with extras ranging from fresh fruit and tea-makers to hairdryers and trouser presses. Good bathrooms throughout. *Amenities* garden, outdoor swimming pool, gymnasium, squash, snooker, in-house movies, laundry service.

Rooms 78	Direct dial Yes	Confirm by 6	Parking Ample
Ensuite bath/shower 78	Room TV Yes	Last dinner 9.30	Room service 24 hours

HOLYWOOD — Culloden Hotel — 72% — £B/C

Map 18 D2 Co. Down
Craigavad BT18 0EX
Holywood (023 17) 5223
Telex 74617

Rooms 93
Ensuite bath/shower 93
Direct dial Yes
Room TV Yes
Confirm by 6
Last dinner 9.30
Parking Ample
Room service 24 hours

Credit Access, Amex, Diners, Visa
Closed 24 & 25 Dec

A Scottish Baronial-style building standing in mature gardens on the A2. Reception leads into a spacious, well-furnished lounge, off which sweeps a huge staircase dominated by an impressive stained-glass window. The bar, in Gothic style, was formerly a chapel. Bedrooms in the original part have basic, white furniture but are large and lofty; rooms in the modern extension overlook neatly kept grounds. Hairdryers

and trouser presses are standard, and bathrooms are smart, modern and well-equipped. Housekeeping could be better, but general service is good and they serve a decent breakfast. *Amenities* garden, tennis, squash, keep-fit equipment, putting, croquet, games room, snooker, in-house movies, fax, laundry service, grill bar (11.30am–9.45pm).

HOLYWOOD   Iona   ⑨

R **Map 18 D2** Co. Down
27 Church Road
Holywood (023 17) 5655

French cooking
Set D £16.25
About £38 for two
Seats 30
Parties 30
Parking Ample

A small restaurant with a very fine chef in Bartjan Brave, whose French dishes display skill, flair and imagination in generous measures. His menus are particularly fresh and appealing, and recent delights were oysters with raspberry vinaigrette, peppers filled with cheese mousse, brill with a creamy parsley sauce and lamb cutlets with honey and thyme. Sweets keep up high standards, and the coffee's good, too. Excellent, personable staff. Unlicensed (take your own). ☺ 🍴

Dinner only 6.15–10.30
Closed Sun & Mon

HOLYWOOD   Schooner   ⑨

R **Map 18 D2** Co. Down
30 High Street
Belfast (0232) 428880

Set L Sun £7.50
About £30 for two
Seats 50
Parties 40
Parking Limited
Credit Access, Visa

Simple, well-cooked food – and plenty of it – is served throughout the day at the McClellands' recently refurbished wine bar-cum-restaurant. Minestrone, nutty Brie fingers and cabbage leaves stuffed with haggis figure among the starters, while main courses run from cod provençale and scampi kebabs to roast duckling, honey-glazed gammon and steaks. Vegetarian dishes are always available, and there are some very tempting sweets. ☺

Sunday Lunch 12.30–5 *Meals* noon–10
Closed D Sun, 1 Jan, 3 days Xmas, 2 wks July

Our inspectors *never* book in the name of Egon Ronay's Guides.
They disclose their identity only if they are considering an establishment
for inclusion in the next edition of the Guide.

KILLINCHY   Nick's   ⑨

R **Map 18 D2** Co. Down
18 Kilmood Church Road,
Newtownards
Killinchy (0238) 541472

About £37 for two
Seats 45
Parties 15
Parking Ample
Credit Access, Diners, Visa

Ask for directions when you book a table at this delightfully-run restaurant, situated in what was once the village courthouse. Nick Price's inventive and interesting menus cover a wide range from classics such as fresh asparagus to exotica like pork fillet with a chocolate and chilli sauce. Top quality raw materials are thoughtfully put together and attractively presented and service is friendly and informal. ♀ Well-chosen ☺

Dinner only 7.30–10 **Closed** Sun, Mon, Bank Hols, 1 wk New Year, last wk Sept & 1st wk Oct

LARNE   Magheramorne House Hotel   61%   £E

H **Map 18 D1** Co. Antrim
Magheramorne BT40 3HW
Larne (0574) 79444

Credit Access, Amex, Diners, Visa

Mature gardens and fine views of Lough Larne provide a delightful setting for this peaceful, traditional hotel, well-run by the charming Mrs Weir. Public rooms have huge sash windows, high, moulded ceilings, dado panelling and velour seating. Good-sized, neat bedrooms have darkwood furniture, pretty lampshades and modern, smart bathrooms.
Amenities garden, games room, laundry service. ฿

| *Rooms* 23 | *Direct dial* Yes | *Confirm by* arrang. | *Parking* Ample |
| *Ensuite bath/shower* 23 | *Room TV* Yes | *Last dinner* 9.30 | *Room service* 24 hours |

LONDONDERRY   Everglades Hotel   59%   £D

H **Map 18 C1** Co. Londonderry
Prehen Road BT47 2PA
Londonderry (0504) 44414
Telex 748005

Credit Access, Amex, Diners, Visa
Closed 24 & 25 Dec

South of Londonderry on the A5, this bustling 1970s hotel is a popular choice with business visitors. All the public areas have been redecorated and brightened, making them much pleasanter for a drink or a chat. Decent-sized bedrooms are furnished in functional style and all have up-to-date tiled bathrooms. No dogs.
Amenities garden, beauty salon, in-house movies, laundry service, coffee shop (11am–7pm, Sun 3pm–9.30pm).

| *Rooms* 39 | *Direct dial* Yes | *Confirm by* 6 | *Parking* Ample |
| *Ensuite bath/shower* 39 | *Room TV* Yes | *Last dinner* 9.45 | *Room service* 24 hours |

NEWTOWNARDS   Strangford Arms Hotel   58%   £D

H Map 18 D2 Co. Down
92 Church Street BT23 4AL
Newtownards (0247) 814141

Credit Access, Amex, Diners, Visa
Closed 2 days Easter & 25 Dec

Guests find comfortable, attractive accommodation at this pleasant
Victorian hotel with modern extensions. Public areas include an
elegant lounge bar with blue velour seating and panelled walls. Most
bedrooms have lightwood units, coordinating fabrics and smart
bathrooms with well-designed lighting; all have radio alarms, tea/
coffee-makers and mineral water. No dogs. *Amenities* patio, in-
house movies, fax, laundry service, 24-hour lounge service.

Rooms 36	*Direct dial* Yes	*Confirm by* arrang.	*Parking* Ample
Ensuite bath/shower 36	*Room TV* Yes	*Last dinner* 10	*Room service* All day

We publish annually,
so make sure you use the current edition.
It's worth it!

PORTBALLINTRAE   Bayview Hotel   60%   £E/F

H Map 18 C1 Co. Antrim
2 Bayhead Road,
Nr Bushmills BT57 8RZ
Bushmills (026 57) 31453

Credit Access, Visa

Within easy reach of the splendours of the Giant's Causeway, this is a
most agreeable base for relaxing, walking and enjoying the fresh air.
It's a friendly hotel, well run by its owner, and public rooms have a
homely, welcoming atmosphere. Simple bedrooms are quite pleasantly
furnished; one has a little sun-trap lounge. Modern, Victorian-style
bathrooms. No dogs. *Amenities* solarium, snooker, laundry service,
24-hour lounge service.

Rooms 16	*Direct dial* Yes	*Confirm by* arrang.	*Parking* Ample
Ensuite bath/shower 16	*Room TV* Yes	*Last dinner* 10	*Room service* All day

PORTAFERRY   Portaferry Hotel   £F

I Map 18 D2 Co. Down
10 The Strand BT22 1PE
Portaferry (024 72) 28231

Credit Access, Amex, Diners, Visa
Closed 25 Dec

The beautiful Lough Strangford makes a lovely setting for this honest
inn. Polished wood floors and oak furniture set the tone for the two
bars, one with splendid contemporary paintings by local artists;
upstairs there's a small residents' TV lounge. Simply furnished
bedrooms have floral prints, white fitted units and carpeted en suite
bathrooms. Breakfasts are commendable. No dogs.
Amenities mooring, laundry service.

Rooms 5	*Room phone* No	*Confirm by* arrang.	*Parking* Ample
Ensuite bath/shower 5	*Room TV* No	*Last dinner* 9	*Room service* All day

PORTRUSH   Ramore   ★   ⑨

R Map 18 C1 Co. Antrim
The Harbour
Portrush (0265) 824313

Dinner only 7–10
About £40 for two
Seats 55
Parties 55
Parking Ample

Closed Sun, Mon (except Easter
Mon), 25 Dec, last wk Jan & 1st
wk Feb

Huge picture windows overlook
the harbour, making a splendid
backdrop for an attractive, family-run restaurant. Joy Caithness
extends a warm welcome, and
service is absolutely charming.
Joy's son-in-law George McAlpin
holds the culinary reins, and well-
balanced flavours and classi-
cally-made sauces are his trade-
mark. His menus are full of
tempting things, posing delightful dilemmas for diners. With

Côtes du Rhône (Guigal) '83 on a short, select wine list.
Specialities scallops with Beluga caviar; roast lobster croissant with
lobster and champagne sauce; supreme of duck in filo pastry set on an
orange and chervil butter sauce; hot lemon and chocolate soufflés
with crème anglaise.

SAINTFIELD   The Barn   ⑨

R Map 18 D2 Co. Down
  120 Monlough Road
Saintfield (0238) 510396

Set D £14.95
About £38 for two
Seats 34
Parties 40
Parking Ample

Credit Access, Amex, Diners, Visa

Ask for directions when you book a table at this former barn which
has been converted into the most delightful restaurant you could hope
to find. Unobtrusive classical music, an open fire and charming service
from Jane Wright set the scene for Robbie Wright's excellent meals,
which are derived from carefully garnered local produce – fresh fish,
hedgerow berries, 40 varieties of homegrown herbs. Dishes range
from ambitious (and successful) ones such as layered terrine of smoked
fish to a simple watercress and asparagus soup. Main course could be
wild Fermanagh venison roasted in sloe gin and juniper berries. A
groaning sweet trolley holds mouthwatering delicacies to finish.
♀ Well-chosen ☺

Dinner only 7.30–10   **Closed** Sun, Mon, some Bank Hols, 3 days
Xmas, 2 wks Feb & 10 days July

WARINGSTOWN   The Grange   ⑨

R Map 18 D2 Co. Armagh
  Main Street
Waringstown (0762) 881989

About £48 for two
Seats 45
Parties 45
Parking Ample

Dining in this lovely old stone-built yeoman's cottage dating back to
1698 is a delight. There are a number of cosy lounges for a pre- or
post-prandial drink and the dining room boasts a timbered ceiling,
antique chairs and candlelit tables. The menu offers a combination of
classic dishes and more inventive items, carefully prepared and served
in generous portions. Service is thoughtful and friendly. Traditional
Sunday lunch. ♀ Well-chosen ☺

Lunch Sun only 12.30–2.30   *Dinner* 7.30–9.30
Closed Mon, 26 Dec & 1 wk July

HOTELS
RESTAURANTS
AND INNS

REPUBLIC
OF IRELAND

ADARE   Mustard Seed

R **Map 19 B5** Co. Limerick
Limerick (061) 86451

Irish cooking
Set D from £13
About £48 for two
Seats 40
Parties 45
Parking Ample
Credit Access, Diners, Visa

The welcome is warm at this appealing, yellow-washed cottage, where Irish dishes based on local seasonal produce are prepared with a light, modern touch. Try spiced beef with matured whiskey marrow chutney to start, followed by soup or salad then a tasty main course like beautifully tender lamb with port and rosemary gravy or salmon and black sole with leek and saffron. Tempting sweets such as white chocolate terrine to finish. ☻

Lunch by arrang.   *Dinner* 7–10, Sat 10.15
Closed Sun, Mon in winter, 25 & 26 Dec, 1 Jan & all Feb

AHAKISTA   Shiro ★   ⚑

R **Map 19 A6** Co. Cork
Nr Bantry
Bantry (027) 67030

Japanese cooking

Dinner only 7–10
Set D £22
About £55 for two
Seats 12
Parties 12
Parking Ample

Credit Access, Amex, Visa
Closed Jan

The home of Japanese artist Kei Pilz (who cooks) and her German husband Werner (who serves) is a remote country priest's house overlooking Dunmanus Bay. The whole place has immense charm, which together with Kei's exquisite Japanese cooking makes dinner here a rare and enchanting experience. Subtle flavours, interesting textures and the prettiest presentation are hallmarks throughout. There's a

separate menu for vegetarians. Booking is essential. ***Specialities*** sashimi (raw fish, vegetables, tenzuyu sauce); tempura (baked fish dipped in special sauce); teriyaki (beef with a ginger sauce); yakitori (spicy chicken cooked on the spit, served with a sweet sauce and fresh vegetables).

**Changes in data sometimes occur in establishments
after the Guide goes to press.
Prices should be taken as indications rather than firm quotes.**

BALLINA   Downhill Hotel   65%   £C/D

H **Map 18 B3** Co. Mayo
Downhill Road
Ballina (096) 21033
Telex 40796

Credit Access, Amex, Diners, Visa
Closed 4 days Xmas

Extensions hide the original house set in attractive gardens overlooking the Brosna River. Extensive leisure and conference facilities keep it busy, and the whole place has a friendly, well-run feel. The plush Piano Bar is the lively scene of nightly entertainment, and there's a comfortable reception-lounge and two traditionally appointed sitting rooms. Bedrooms, furnished mainly in quite functional style, offer satellite TV, hairdryers, flowers and fresh fruit. Ten Superior rooms have better-quality furnishings and fittings and smarter bathrooms. *Amenities* garden, indoor swimming pool, sauna, solarium, whirlpool bath, gymnasium, beauty salon, tennis, squash, snooker, in-house movies, laundry service, 24-hour lounge service, kiosk.

Rooms 54	*Direct dial* Yes	*Confirm by* 7	*Parking* Ample
Ensuite bath/shower 52	*Room TV* Yes	*Last dinner* 9.30	*Room service* All day

BALLINA   Mount Falcon Castle   59%   *NEW ENTRY*   £C/D

HR **Map 18 B3** Co Mayo
Ballina (096) 21172

Credit Access, Amex, Diners, Visa
Closed 5 days Xmas, all Feb & Mar

A no-frills hotel which is a fisherman's dream. Constance Aldridge has been making her guests feel thoroughly at home for 55 years now, and ghillies, fishing tackle and dogs abound in the comfortable, relaxing public rooms with their well-loved furniture. Decent, basic bedrooms are provided with candles against the erratic electricity supply. In all, an unusual and memorable establishment.
Amenities garden, tennis, game fishing, games room, laundry service.

Rooms 10	*Room phone* No	*Confirm by* arrang.	*Parking* Ample
Ensuite bath/shower 8	*Room TV* No	*Last dinner* 8	*Room service* All day

Restaurant NEW ENTRY ♃

Set D £15
About £45 for two
Seats 24

Dinner is served at 8pm in the candlelit dining room with Mrs Aldridge presiding at the head of a huge mahogany table. Most of the produce comes from the estate and is cooked to mouthwatering perfection; locally smoked salmon, exquisite soup, perfect roast lamb and delicious home-grown vegetables. Well-kept Irish cheeses and excellent, simple sweets follow before coffee is taken by the drawing room fire. Residents only. ☙

Dinner only at 8
Closed 5 days Xmas, all Feb & Mar

BALLYLICKEY — Ballylickey Manor House 67% £C

H Map 19 B6 Co. Cork
Bantry Bay
Bantry (027) 50071
Telex 75837

Credit Amex, Visa
Closed mid Oct–Easter

Four well-appointed suites with antiques and stylish fabrics are the pick of the bedrooms at a beautifully situated former shooting lodge. Also in the main house are two highly-civilised drawing rooms. The remaining accommodation is in pleasant garden chalets set around the pool. Smartly tiled bathrooms feature high-quality toiletries.
Amenities garden, outdoor swimming pool, game fishing, croquet, laundry service.

| Rooms 11 | Direct dial Yes | Confirm by 6 | Parking Ample |
| Ensuite bath/shower 11 | Room TV Yes | Last dinner 9.30 | Room service All day |

BALLYLICKEY — Sea View House Hotel 62% £E

HR Map 19 B6 Co. Cork
Nr Bantry
Bantry (027) 50462

Credit Access, Amex, Visa
Closed 1 Nov–1 Apr

A tall bay-windowed house standing in beautiful gardens. It's run with exemplary care and attention by Kathleen O'Sullivan and her band of enthusiastic young helpers, and guests definitely come first. Public rooms are attractively traditional (lots of antiques) and there's a quiet charm about the bedrooms, some of them in a cottage and lodge. Nice soft towels in the bathrooms. Good breakfasts.
Amenities garden, laundry service.

| Rooms 13 | Room phone Yes | Confirm by 6 | Parking Ample |
| Ensuite bath/shower 13 | Room TV No | Last dinner 9 | Room service All day |

Restaurant ♃

Set L £8.50
Set D £16.50
About £43 for two
Seats 35
Parties 40

Closed 1 Nov–1Apr

Kathleen O'Sullivan's fixed-price menu changes every night, and there's a special Sunday lunch. Good things abound: Bantry Bay mussels with garlic butter, chilled apple and apricot soup, rack of lamb with rosemary, a splendid banquet of salmon, monkfish and prawns in a cream dill sauce. Chocolate and hazelnut ice cream is home-made, and there's an Irish cheeseboard. Note Pinot Gris Réserve '85 and Marques de Murrieta Rioja '81 on a sound wine list. ♀ Well-chosen ☙

Lunch Sun at 1.30, Mon–Sat by arrang. only   Dinner 7.30–9

BALLYNAHINCH — Ballynahinch Castle 72% £C/D

H Map 18 A3 Co. Galway
Connemara
Clifden (095) 31006
Telex 50809

Rooms 28
Ensuite bath/shower 28
Direct dial Yes
Room TV No
Confirm by 6
Last dinner 9
Parking Ample
Room service All day

Credit Access, Amex, Diners, Visa

Fishermen flock to this 18th-century castle standing in 350 acres of land with two and a half miles of fishing rights. The relaxed style of the hotel echoes that of its guests and the welcoming entrance hall has a log fire, well-loved leather chairs and rugs on the terracotta floor. The catch is weighed in the simple fisherman's bar, while there's a smart cocktail bar for non-anglers and a comfortable drawing  room. The light, peaceful bedrooms are individually decorated, with solid traditional furniture and spotless, prettily tiled bathrooms with good toiletries. Eight have four-posters. No dogs.
Amenities garden, tennis, shooting, game fishing, bicycles, laundry service, 24-hour lounge service.

BALLYVAUGHAN | Gregans Castle Hotel 70% | £C/D

HR **Map 19 B4**
Co. Clare
Ennis (065) 77005
Telex 70130

Rooms 17
Ensuite bath/shower 14
Room phone No
Room TV No
Confirm by 5
Last dinner 8
Parking Ample
Room service All day

Credit Visa
Closed Nov–late Mar

A handsome country house surrounded by grey limestone mountains and overlooking Galway Bay. Peter and Moira Haden run their hotel with the greatest care and high standards of comfort and luxury prevail throughout. A delightful library boasts a large number of interesting books and plenty of comfortable sofas and armchairs in which to peruse them. There's also a pleasing lounge and an attractive bar.

Three sumptuous suites in the ground floor wing have beautifully designed bathrooms; the remaining bedrooms are individually furnished and have coordinating colour schemes. All are provided with plenty of extras and well-equipped bathrooms. No dogs.
Amenities garden.

Restaurant   ♔ ♖

Set D £18
About £50 *for two*
Seats 45

A luxurious restaurant decorated in excellent taste by Moira Haden and providing an elegant setting for husband Peter's highly enjoyable cooking. His menus take advantage of the best local produce, including the excellent Burren cheese. Starter might be stuffed courgettes, with grilled fresh salmon with a cassoulet of prawns or roast loin of spring Burren lamb to follow. Good wines – splendid Rhônes from Etienne Guigal, a true master. ♟ Well-chosen ⊖ ⑀

Dinner only 7–8
Closed Nov–late Mar

Prices quoted for the Republic of Ireland are in *Irish punts*.

BALTIMORE | Chez Youen | ♖

R **Map 19 B6** Co. Cork
The Pier
Skibbereen (028) 20136

Seafood
Set L £7.50 **Set D** £14.50
About £40 *for two*
Seats 45 *Parties* 60
Parking Ample
Credit Access, Amex, Diners, Visa

It's seafood nearly all the way at Youen Jacob's very civilised restaurant, and his straightforward cooking methods bring out all the natural flavours of prime local produce. The shellfish platter, with brown, spider and swimming crabs, prawns, shrimps and lobster or crawfish, is a dish of renown, and other delights could include scallops provençale, sea trout with fennel and wild salmon with basil sauce. Tarte tatin is a lovely sweet. ♟ Well-chosen ⊖

Lunch 12.30–2.30 *Dinner* 6.30–10, till midnight in summer
Closed L Mon–Sat Nov–1 Apr, also all 23–28 Dec, Feb & Oct

BEAUFORT | Hotel Dunloe Castle 72% | £D

H **Map 19 A5** Co. Kerry
Nr Killarney
Killarney (064) 44111
Telex 73833

Rooms 140
Ensuite bath/shower 140
Direct dial Yes
Room TV Yes
Confirm by arrang.
Last dinner 9.30
Parking Ample
Room service 24 hours

Credit Access, Amex, Diners, Visa
Closed Oct–mid Apr

A modern hotel in a quite splendid location, surrounded by beautiful parkland and offering fine views of lakes and mountains. Public rooms provide plenty of space and comfort (lots of new furniture this year) and more than a hint of the site's baronial heritage – the ruins of Dunloe Castle are in the grounds. Bedrooms are of a good size, with solid freestanding pine furniture and smart, spacious bathrooms.

The whole hotel is very well maintained, recent replacement of all the windows typifying the care taken.
Amenities garden, indoor swimming pool, sauna, tennis, golf driving range, putting, riding, coarse fishing, in-house movies, laundry service, coffee shop (12.30pm–6pm).

BLACKROCK — Colin O'Daly's Park Restaurant ★ ⌕

R Map 19 D4 Co. Dublin
26 Main Street
Dublin (01) 886177

French cooking

Lunch 12.30–2.30
Dinner 7–10
Set L £9.50
Set D £19.50
About £57 for two
Seats 56
Parties 50
Parking Ample

Credit Access, Amex, Diners, Visa
Closed L Sat, all Sun & Mon,
Bank Hols, 1 wk Easter & 3 days
Xmas

Booking is essential for Colin O'Daly's stylish restaurant, a taxi ride from the centre of Dublin. Attentive staff compliment skilful and imaginative five-course menus that range from a superb chicken and duck mousseline or baked avocado stuffed with ratatouille to venison with a chocolate and pine kernel sauce or baked trout sauced with peas and diced bacon. Delicious sweets include home-made honey ice cream with blackberry ripple in puff pastry.

Specialities panfried monkfish coated in coconut with a honey, date and almond sauce, duckling with a red wine and mussel sauce, cream of pigeon and wild mushroom soup, roseleaf parfait with a Sauternes sabayon. ♀ Well-chosen ⊘

BLESSINGTON — Downshire House Hotel 58% £E/F

H Map 19 D4 Co. Wicklow
Nass (045) 65199

Closed 2 wks Xmas

On the main street of town, this friendly little pebbledash Georgian hotel offers homely, unpretentious accommodation in neatly kept bedrooms. All have freshly painted white walls, older-style wooden furniture and candlewick bedspreads, while TVs, telephones and fully-tiled modern bathrooms are standard throughout. Downstairs, there are two residents' lounges (often used for business meetings) and a spacious bar with ample seating. **Amenities** garden, tennis, croquet.

| *Rooms* 25 | *Direct dial* Yes | *Confirm by* arrang. | *Parking* Ample |
| *Ensuite bath/shower* 25 | *Room TV* Yes | *Last dinner* 9.30 | *Room service* All day |

BRAY — Tree of Idleness

R Map 19 D4 Co. Wicklow
Seafront
Dublin (01) 863498

Greek-Cypriot cooking
Set D from £12.95
About £53 for two
Seats 56
Parking Ample
Credit Access, Diners, Visa

A Greek-Cypriot restaurant with a more elaborate menu than is normal. Starters include such dishes as lambs' tongues braised and served with a purée of aromatic vegetables as well as the ever-popular dolmades; for a main course, try baked quails on sweet peppers with grapes, figs, cashew nuts and pine kernels, served with fino. A great cellar with a powerful showing of château-bottled clarets. ➪ Outstanding ⊘

Dinner only 7.30–11, Sun till 10
Closed Mon, Good Fri, last wk Aug & 1st 2 wks Sept & 1 wk Xmas

BUNRATTY — Fitzpatrick's Shannon Shamrock Hotel 59% £B/C

H Map 19 B4 Co. Clare
Limerick (061) 361177
Telex 72114

Credit Access, Amex, Diners, Visa
Closed 25 Dec

Next door to Bunratty Castle, this low, rambling hotel makes effective use of mock-stonework throughout spacious public areas like the newly-carpeted reception and lounge. There's a plush, traditional bar, too, complete with pianist. Most bedrooms have stylish fabrics and good quality furniture; bathrooms are smartly tiled.
Amenities garden, indoor swimming pool, sauna, satellite TV, fax, laundry service, kiosk.

| *Rooms* 104 | *Direct dial* Yes | *Confirm by* 6 | *Parking* Ample |
| *Ensuite bath/shower* 104 | *Room TV* Yes | *Last dinner* 9.30 | *Room service* All day |

BUNRATTY — MacCloskey's ⌕

R Map 19 B4 Co. Clare
Bunratty House Mews
Limerick (061) 364082

Set D £23
About £55 for two
Seats 60
Parties 60
Parking Ample
Credit Access, Amex, Diners, Visa

An atmospheric restaurant in the restored cellars of 17th-century Bunratty House. The fixed-price dinner menu is nicely varied, with dishes ranging from crudités with dips and mussels in still champagne to brill with sorrel sauce, confit of duck and veal with green peppercorns. Crisp vegetables, lots of sweets and a wine list with good clarets back to Lafite '62. Skilled cooking by Gerrie MacCloskey, charming service from Marie. ⊘

Dinner only 7–9.30
Closed Sun, Mon, Bank Hols & 21 Dec–1 Feb

CARAGH LAKE   Ard-na-Sidhe   £D

H **Map 19 A5** Co. Kerry
Nr Killorglin
Tralee (066) 69105
Telex 73913

Credit Access, Amex, Diners, Visa
Closed end Sept–1 May

Built in 1880 and restored in 1915, Ard-na-Sidhe enjoys a beautiful
and serene setting on the edge of Caragh Lake. At the time of our visit
improvements were being carried out, notably renewing bathrooms,
building two extra suites and refurbishing two others with antiques.
Otherwise handsomely appointed bedrooms and day rooms remain as
before. Graded at 68% in our 1988 Guide.
Amenities garden, coarse & game fishing, laundry service.

Rooms 22	*Direct dial* Yes	*Confirm by* arrang.	*Parking* Ample
Ensuite bath/shower 22	*Room TV* No	*Last dinner* 8.30	*Room service* All day

---

CARAGH LAKE   Caragh Lodge   64%   £D/E

H **Map 19 A5** Co. Kerry
Nr Killorglin
Caragh Lake (066) 69115

Credit Access, Amex, Visa
Closed end Oct–mid Mar

Peace and quiet are major attractions at a friendly Victorian house set
in pleasant wooded countryside. Just three of the bedrooms, with a
mixture of modern and antique furniture, are in the main house, the
rest in annexes. All are of a decent size, with smart tiled bathrooms.
Homely day rooms have inviting armchairs and plenty of books for
browsing. No dogs.
Amenities garden, sauna, tennis, game fishing, rowing boats, bicycles.

Rooms 10	*Room phone* No	*Confirm by* arrang.	*Parking* Ample
Ensuite bath/shower 10	*Room TV* No	*Last dinner* 8.30	*Room service* Limited

---

CARRICKMACROSS   Nuremore Hotel   61%   £E

H **Map 18 C3** Co. Monaghan
Carrickmacross (042) 61438

Credit Access, Amex, Diners, Visa

South of town on the N2, this is a modern low-rise building set in
peaceful woods and parkland. There's a large bar, roomy reception-
lounge and little TV room. Simply furnished but well-heated bedrooms
all have pleasant views. No dogs. *Amenities* garden, indoor
swimming pool, sauna, whirlpool bath, tennis, squash, 9-hole golf
course, putting, coarse fishing, snooker, in-house movies, secretarial
services, fax, laundry service.

Rooms 50	*Direct dial* Yes	*Confirm by* 6	*Parking* Ample
Ensuite bath/shower 50	*Room TV* Yes	*Last dinner* 9.45	*Room service* 24 hours

---

CASHEL   Cashel House Hotel   73%   £C/D

HR **Map 18 A3**
Co. Galway
Cashel (095) 31001
Telex 50812

Rooms 32
Ensuite bath/shower 32
Direct dial Yes
Room TV Some
Confirm by arrang.
Last dinner 8.30
Parking Ample
Room service All day

Credit Access, Amex, Diners, Visa
Closed Dec–Feb inc

Charles de Gaulle once took a
holiday here, writing in the visitors' book *'excellent séjour'* and
the McEvillys, owners then and
now, have maintained their high
standards. Thirty-five acres of
award-winning gardens surround their 19th-century house
and the interiors reflect the same
aura of well cared-for tranquillity. The day rooms are comfortable and traditional, with
antiques, fine pictures and fresh

flower displays, and the library is particularly handsome. Many of the
bedrooms have recently been upgraded, and all are decorated with
flair; bathrooms are excellent. Four sumptuous suites looking on to
the garden have whirlpool baths. Superb staff. No children under 5.
Amenities garden, riding, fax, laundry service.

Restaurant   ♛

Set D £19.50
About £64 *for two*
Seats 50

An elegant and traditional dining room where you can feast off the
best seafood Connemara's waters have to offer. Fish dishes include
coulibiac of salmon in pastry hollandaise, home-made lobster bisque,
baked angler fish provençale and poached fillet of turbot; meat-eaters
might go for duck terrine, followed by roast quail or sirloin of beef
with béarnaise sauce. Pleasant sweets and an excellent selection of
Irish cheeses to finish.

Dinner only 7.30–8.30
Closed Dec–Feb inc

CASHEL — Zetland House Hotel 65% £D/E

H **Map 18 A3**
Co. Galway
Clifden (095) 31111
Telex 50853

Credit Access, Amex, Visa
Closed 15 Oct–Easter

A handsome mid-Victorian terrace with superb views across Cashel Bay. Complete refurbishment has resulted in pleasing, comfortable surroundings; the tranquil lounge has antiques, an Adam-style fireplace, magazines and flower arrangements, while the small bar is modern in style. The spacious bedrooms have fine period furniture and functional bathrooms and there are a number of suites. *Amenities* garden, shooting, game fishing, snooker, secretarial services.

Rooms 19	*Direct dial* Yes	*Confirm by* 6	*Parking* Ample
Ensuite bath/shower 19	*Room TV* No	*Last dinner* 8.30	*Room service* All day

CASHEL — Cashel Palace Hotel 75% £A/B

H **Map 19 C5** Co. Tipperary
Main Street
Cashel (062) 61411
Telex 26938

Rooms 20
Ensuite bath/shower 20
Direct dial Yes
Room TV Yes
Confirm by arrang.
Last dinner 9.30
Parking Ample
Room service 24 hours

Credit Access, Amex, Diners, Visa
Closed 25 & 26 Dec

A bishop's palace for over 200 years, this elegant Palladian mansion makes a splendid hotel enjoying a magnificent setting amid 20 acres of lovely gardens backing on to the Rock of Cashel. Nobly proportioned public rooms include a fine entrance hall panelled in red pine and a peaceful drawing room with large picture windows; down in the cellars there's a characterful vaulted bar and the Buttery

coffee shop. Stylish fabrics and handsome period furnishings distinguish the beautifully decorated bedrooms, which range from huge suites to smaller rooms on the top floor. Smart, comprehensively equipped bathrooms. No dogs. *Amenities* garden, game fishing, satellite TV, fax, laundry service, coffee shop (10am–10pm).

CASHEL — Chez Hans

R **Map 19 C5** Co. Tipperary
Rockside
Tipperary (062) 61177

About £48 for two
Seats 75
Parking Ample

Seafood dominates the menu at Hans Matthia's splendid restaurant in a converted Victorian gothic chapel. Everything is skilfully prepared and enjoyable, from simple starters like oak-smoked salmon or garlicky mussels to generously served entrées such as escalope of brill with splendidly plump prawns, sole meunière or sea bass with Pernod sauce. For dedicated carnivores there's lamb en croûte, steak, veal and chicken, while sweets include lovely home-made ices.

Dinner only 6–10
Closed Sun, Mon, St Patrick's Day & first 3 wks Jan

■ When calling a **Dublin** number from *outside* the Republic, dial **00** *before* the number we print, **e.g.** Berkely Court is **00**01 601711

■ For the rest of the Republic, dial **010-353** then the number we print *less* the initial zero, **e.g.** Park Hotel Kenmare is **010-353** 64 41200.

CAVAN — Hotel Kilmore 58% £E

H **Map 18 C3** Co. Cavan
Dublin Road
Cavan (049) 32288

Credit Access, Amex, Visa

A large, low-rise modern hotel just out of town on the Dublin road. A huge disco, large bar and function rooms are popular facilities, and the coffee shop is a busy lunchtime rendezvous. Most of the compact, practical bedrooms – some recently upgraded – are well away from the bustle of the day rooms. Housekeeping is not the hotel's strongest point. *Amenities* garden, in-house movies, coffee shop (10am–6pm).

Rooms 40	*Direct dial* Yes	*Confirm by* 6	*Parking* Ample
Ensuite bath/shower 40	*Room TV* Yes	*Last dinner* 9.30	*Room service* 24 hours

CLIFDEN	**Abbeyglen Castle Hotel 65%**	**£D**

HR Map 18 A3 Co. Galway
Sky Road
Clifden (095) 21201
Telex 28366

Credit Access, Amex, Diners, Visa
Closed 5 Jan–1 Feb

A modern hotel built in the style of a castle, with towers, turrets and battlements. Genial host Paul Hughes offers unlimited hospitality, urging the bar guests to sing along with traditional Irish tunes to accompany the resident pianist. While there is no lounge, the reception area contains several stylish and comfortable sofas. Bedrooms at the front have fine views across the bay and some are quite luxurious, with stylish drapes and antique pieces. Other rooms vary in style but all are good-sized and pleasant, with decent bathrooms. No children under seven.   *Amenities* garden, outdoor swimming pool, sauna, solarium, tennis, 9-hole golf course, snooker, in-house movies, laundry service, 24-hour lounge service.

Rooms 40	*Direct dial* Yes	*Confirm by* arrang.	*Parking* Ample
Ensuite bath/shower 40	*Room TV* Yes	*Last dinner* 9.30	*Room service* All day

Restaurant

Set D £16
About £40 for two
Seats 100

In this comfortable Gothic-style restaurant you can expect to find straightforward dishes, capably cooked from fresh local produce and served with friendliness and charm. There's an emphasis on super-fresh seafood and the menu may contain Connemara salmon, grilled crayfish with butter sauce and sea trout poached in white wine with a hollandaise sauce. There's an attractive sweet trolley which includes a good sherry trifle to finish with. ☮

Lunch 12.30–2.15 *Dinner* 7.30–9.30
Closed early Jan–early Feb

CLIFDEN	**Hotel Ardagh 62%**	**£E**

HR Map 18 A3 Co. Galway
Ballyconneely Road,
Ardbear Bay
Clifden (095) 21384

Credit Access, Amex, Visa
Closed Nov–Easter

There are spectacular views of Ardbear Bay from this modern well-maintained hotel. Henk and Ria Berings are perfect hosts, as much part of the scene in the lively bar after dark as they are actively involved by day. There's a comfortable lounge and sun room and spacious bedrooms (some recently upgraded) have en suite bathrooms. Top floor rooms have balconies. No dogs.
Amenities garden, solarium, sea fishing, games room, snooker.

Rooms 20	*Direct dial* Yes	*Confirm by* 6	*Parking* Ample
Ensuite bath/shower 20	*Room TV* No	*Last dinner* 9	*Room service* All day

Restaurant ♪

Set D from £15
About £40 for two
Seats 50
Parties 30

Seafood is the star attraction at this restaurant overlooking the sea, where Monique Berings, daughter of the hotel's owners, produces consistently popular offerings like baked ling with garlic butter and monkfish with fresh fennel sauce. Soups include a shimmering consommé with chervil, and delicious Dutch-style roast beef. Vegetables are full of flavour and sweets like fresh plum pie and Bailey's cheesecake divert attention briefly from the spectacular view. ☮

Dinner only 7.30–9, Sat & Sun till 9.30
Closed Nov–Easter

Prices quoted for the Republic of Ireland are in *Irish punts*.

CLIFDEN	**Rock Glen Hotel 61%**	**£D/E**

H Map 18 A3 Co. Galway
Roundstowe Road
Clifden (095) 21035
Telex 50915

Credit Access, Amex, Diners, Visa
Closed 1 Nov–15 Mar

Just south of Clifden, this delightful converted 18th-century shooting lodge enjoys splendid sea and moorland views. Owners John and Evangeline Roche run their hotel with typical west-coast warmth and charm, and housekeeping is immaculate. Large open-turf fires burn in the relaxing day rooms, while recently refurbished, individually styled bedrooms offer very comfortable beds and neat bathrooms. *Amenities* garden, tennis, snooker, secretarial services.

Rooms 30	*Direct dial* Yes	*Confirm by* 6	*Parking* Ample
Ensuite bath/shower 30	*Room TV* Yes	*Last dinner* 9	*Room service* All day

N*ovelty* ! It is the prevailing cry;

it is imperiously demanded by everyone ...

What feats of ingenuity have we not been forced

to perform ... to meet our customers' wishes? ...

I have ceased counting the nights spent in the attempt

to discover new combinations, when,

completely broken with fatigue of a heavy day,

my body ought to have been at rest.

G. A. ESCOFFIER 1847-1935
A GUIDE TO MODERN COOKERY (1907)

CLIFDEN | Shades Restaurant *NEW ENTRY*

R Map 18 A3 Co. Galway
The Square
Clifden (095) 21215

Set L £7
About £40 for two
Seats 36
Parties 35
Parking Ample
Credit Access, Amex, Diners, Visa

An attractive first-floor restaurant with well-spaced tables and a splendid turf fire; there's also a comfortable little bar for aperitifs and coffee. Young Brendan Elwood has quickly made an impact with his fine cooking, in which the freshest of ingredients proclaim their quality. Fish predominates – pan-fried turbot with creamed parsley, stuffed Connemara trout, an excellent chowder – but there are also dishes for meat-eaters, plus Irish cheeses and delicious sweets. ☺

Lunch 12.30–3   *Dinner* 6.30–10.30
Closed Mon (winter only), Jan & Feb

CLONMEL | Clonmel Arms Hotel 60% | £D/E

H Map 19 C5 Co. Tipperary
Sarsfield Street
Clonmel (052) 21233
Telex 80263

Credit Access, Amex, Diners, Visa
Closed 3 days Xmas

A bustling town-centre hotel with a modern interior behind a 19th-century facade. Regency-striped wallpaper and marble-topped tables create a period feel in the newly refurbished Paddock Bar, and there are two popular lounges. Darkwood units and pleasant floral fabrics feature in the well-kept bedrooms. TVs, tea-makers, telephones and hairdryers are standard throughout.
Amenities in-house movies, laundry service.

Rooms 35	*Direct dial* Yes	*Confirm by* 6	*Parking* Ample
Ensuite bath/shower 26	*Room TV* Yes	*Last dinner* 10.15	*Room service* 24 hours

We publish annually,
so make sure you use the current edition.
It's worth it!

CONG | Ashford Castle 87% | £A

HR Map 18 B3
Co. Mayo
Claremorris (092) 46003
Telex 53749

Rooms 83
Ensuite bath/shower 83
Direct dial Yes
Room TV Yes
Confirm by arrang.
Last dinner 10.30
Parking Ample
Room service 24 hours

Credit Access, Amex, Diners, Visa

American tourists are enthusiastic guests at this impressive castle – 13th century in parts – in a splendid setting overlooking Lough Corrib. Grandeur is the keynote of the vast public rooms, which include a baronial-style lounge and a cosy panelled bar. A harpist plays nightly in the flagstoned dungeon bar, which echoes to the sound of Irish airs. Characterful bedrooms range from de luxe suites patronised by the Reagans to standard rooms equipped with many comforts from dressing gowns to stylish bathrooms. Excellent service and good breakfasts. No dogs. *Amenities* garden, tennis, 9-hole golf course, shooting, coarse and game fishing, satellite TV, in-house movies, secretarial services, valeting, laundry service.

Restaurant ♔

Set D £27
About £85 for two
Seats 120
Parties 120

There are splendid views of the lake and grounds from this impressively large panelled restaurant with superb service. West coast salmon and the freshest of local produce feature strongly in the imaginative set menus, which offer such dishes as veal stuffed with prawns and oysters, noisettes of lamb en filo, and cream of spinach and coconut soup. The wine list is strong in Bordeaux and Jadot burgundies. 🍷 Well-chosen ☺ 🐖

Lunch 1–2.30   *Dinner* 7–9.30

Connaught Room ♕♕

Set L £16
Set D £35
About £95 for two
Seats 45
Parties 30

Prices are high and the setting appropriately luxurious in this intimate alternative to the main restaurant. The menu is supervised by the great French chef Alain Ducasse and executed by his protegés led by Laurent Chabert. Local produce, especially fish, is featured in classic French dishes with modern flourishes – our John Dory in basil-flavoured olive oil was delicious. Desserts are outstanding. ♀ Well-chosen ⊖ ♣

Lunch 1–2.30   *Dinner* 6.30–10.30

▭ is our symbol for an **outstanding** wine list

CORK	**Arbutus Lodge Hotel** 63%	£D

HR **Town plan E1** Co. Cork
Montenotte
Cork (021) 501237
Telex 75079

Credit Access, Amex, Diners, Visa
Closed 1 wk Xmas

Once the home of the Lord Mayor of Cork, Arbutus Lodge stands high above terraced gardens with fine views across the city. Best bedrooms are the refurbished 'superior' rooms with reproduction furniture, stylish fabrics and new marble bathrooms. Other rooms are more ordinary, but certainly comfortable enough. Note the award-winning gardens, with many rare trees, and a collection of contemporary Irish art. No dogs. *Amenities* garden, croquet, fax, laundry service.

Rooms 20	*Direct dial* Yes	*Confirm by* arrang.	*Parking* Ample
Ensuite bath/shower 20	*Room TV* Yes	*Last dinner* 9.30	*Room service* 24 hours

Restaurant ♗

Set L from £14.95
Set D from £17.95
About £65 for two
Seats 56
Parties 100

A comfortable period dining room is the setting for skilled and imaginative cooking by Michael and Declan Ryan. Hot oysters with cucumber and herbs is a speciality, and other delights include feuilleté of asparagus, fillet of sole with watercress sauce and an excellent dish of bacon and cabbage. Delicious sweets. A superb classic cellar features some wonderful clarets and burgundies: four vintages of Ch. Léoville Barton back to '29; Côte Rôtie La Landonne '80. ▭ Outstanding ♀ Well-chosen ⊖

Lunch 1–2   *Dinner* 7–9.30   **Closed** Sun & 1 wk Xmas

CORK	**Crawford Gallery Café**	♗

R **Town plan C2** Co. Cork
Emmet Place
Cork (021) 274415

About £42 for two
Seats 62
Parking Ample

A delightfully informal café/restaurant on the ground floor of the Crawford Art Gallery. Coffee and cakes are served in the morning and there's a light lunchtime menu offering a range of dishes from soup and pancakes to a choice of three hot main courses of the order of chicken pilaff, steak and Guinness pie and the fish dish of the day. Wednesday, Thursday and Friday evenings bring a more ambitious menu, when you may find timbale of smoked salmon with trout mousse and lettuce, cucumber and mint soup as starters, with roast duck or poached salmon with hollandaise sauce to follow. Short list of good wines. ♀ Well-chosen ⊖ ♿

Lunch 12.30–2.30   *Dinner* 6.30–9.30
Closed D Mon, Tues & Sat, all Sun & Bank Hols

CORK	**Fitzpatrick Silver Springs Hotel** 65%	£C/D

H **Town plan E1** Co. Cork
Tivoli
Cork (021) 507533
Telex 76111

Credit Access, Amex, Diners, Visa

A modern hotel on the Waterford road. New owners have made great strides with a major development plan, which includes a new bedroom block, a leisure centre and a night club. These are already on stream, and a 9-hole golf course is planned for May 1989. Existing bedrooms have new carpets and curtains, better beds and smart modern bathrooms. No dogs. *Amenities* garden, satellite TV, fax, laundry service, coffee shop (12.30pm–10pm).

Rooms 110	*Direct dial* Yes	*Confirm by* arrang.	*Parking* Ample
Ensuite bath/shower 110	*Room TV* Yes	*Last dinner* 10	*Room service* 24 hours

CORK

Map 19 B6
Town plan opposite

Population 136,000

Despite its 7th-century foundation as a place of scholarship by St Fin Barre, sustained today by University College, Cork's present tranquillity belies a turbulent history from 819 (the coming of the Danes) to 1921 (the end of the Troubles). It is a place of water–the River Lee that divides into channels to give the city centre four fascinating quays, and the sea with all its harbours and resorts. It is also a hill-surrounded valley; and despite its intense Irishness, has the physical aspect of an 18th-century town in France.

Annual Events
Cork Choral Festival *Late April*
Cork Jazz Festival *October*
Cork Summer Show *June*
Grand Opera Week *May*
International Film Festival *October*
St Patrick's Week *March*

Sights Outside City
Airport, Blackrock, Blarney, Cobh Harbour and Yacht Clubs, Crosshaven, Fermoy, Kinsale Forta Estate

Tourist Office
Grand Parade
Telephone Cork 273251

1 Bus Office **D2**
2 Christchurch **C3**
3 Church of St Francis *Byzantine with Italian mosaics* **B/C2**
4 Crawford School of Art and Gallery **C2**
5 Fitzgerald Park and Public Museum **A2**
6 G.A.A. Athletic Grounds **E2**
7 Mardyke Walk **A2**
8 Marina **E2**
9 Opera House **C2**
10 Railway Station **E1**
11 Red Abbey *oldest ruin* **C3**
12 St Ann's Church, Shandon **C1**
13 St Finbarr's Cathedral *Church of Ireland* **B3**
14 The Lough **B3**
15 Tourist Office **C2**
16 University College **A3**
17 University Sports Ground, Mardyke **A2**

Fiat Dealers
Grandon Car Sales Ltd
Glanmire
Cork
Tel. Cork 821874

Lee Garage (Cork) Ltd
11 South Terrace
Cork
Tel. Cork 507344
Map reference D3

Lee Garage Ltd
Model Farm Road
Cork
Tel. Cork 42933

Cork FIAT

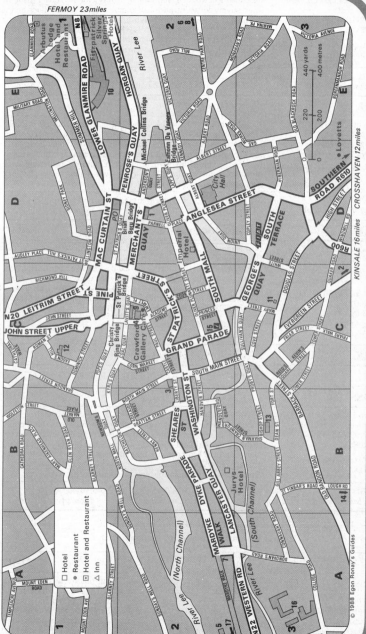

FERMOY 23 miles

MALLOW 22 miles

MACROOM 25 miles

KINSALE 16 miles   CROSSHAVEN 12 miles

© 1988 Egon Ronay's Guides

Legend:
- □ Hotel
- ● Restaurant
- ⊡ Hotel and Restaurant
- △ Inn

CORK | Imperial Hotel 69% | £B/C

H **Town plan D2** Co. Cork
South Mall
Cork (021) 274040
Telex 75126

Credit Access, Amex, Diners, Visa
Closed 1 wk Xmas

Centrally located, this substantial early-Victorian hotel boasts an impressively lofty entrance hall complete with marble floor and a splendid chandelier. Equally stylish are the new restaurant and bar (with pianist), the conservatory-style coffee lounge and handsome Captain's Bar. Impeccably kept bedrooms – all with bright fabrics and private bathrooms – offer radio-alarms, TVs and tea-makers.
Amenities in-house movies, fax, laundry service.

| *Rooms* 101 | *Direct dial* Yes | *Confirm by* 6 | *Parking* Difficult |
| *Ensuite bath/shower* 101 | *Room TV* Yes | *Last dinner* 10 | *Room service* 24 hours |

CORK | Jurys Hotel 69% | £B/C

H **Town plan B2** Co. Cork
Western Road
Cork (021) 276622
Telex 76073

Credit Access, Amex, Diners, Visa
Closed 25 & 26 Dec

A modern hotel which has been much extended and refurbished. Public areas include a striking atrium and an elegant foyer with marble floor and chic sofas and armchairs. The comfortable bedrooms are smartly modern, with excellent bathrooms, and there are three luxurious suites. No dogs. *Amenities* garden, indoor & outdoor swimming pool, sauna, solarium, whirlpool bath, gymnasium, tennis, squash, laundry service, coffee shop (7am–11pm). &

| *Rooms* 200 | *Direct dial* Yes | *Confirm by* arrang. | *Parking* Ample |
| *Ensuite bath/shower* 200 | *Room TV* Yes | *Last dinner* 11 | *Room service* 24 hours |

CORK | Lovetts Restaurant | ♛

R **Town plan D3** Co. Cork
Churchyard Lane, off Well
Road, Douglas
Cork (021) 294909

Set L from £10.50 **Set D** £18
About £60 for two
Seats 36 *Parties* 24
Parking Ample
Credit Access, Amex, Diners, Visa

Chef Manuel las Heras has returned, and other developments at this elegant suburban restaurant are a special occasion room and a new lunchtime brasserie. Manuel's a dab hand with fish, and grilled mussels, salmon en papillote and whole black sole are typical items. Meat-eaters are not overlooked, and there's a good selection of Irish cheeses. Wines are also taken seriously – note Nuits St Georges Marchand de Gramont '83, Tignanello '82. ♀ Well-chosen ℮

Lunch 12.30–2.15   *Dinner* 7–10
Closed L Sat, all Sun & 25 Dec

CORK | Silver Springs Hotel |

See under FITZPATRICK'S SILVER SPRINGS HOTEL

CROSSMOLINA | Enniscoe House 64% | £D/E

H **Map 18 B3** Co. Mayo
Castlehill, Nr Ballina
Ballina (096) 31112.
Telex 40855

Credit Access, Amex, Visa
Closed Oct–Mar

There has been a member of the Kellett family in residence here since 1650 and the hotel gives a real feel of Irish country house life. Family portraits adorn the walls, deep armchairs and views over the surrounding parkland create an atmosphere of luxury in the main lounge and the bedrooms are in grand classic style, with half-testers or brass bedsteads.
Amenities garden, game fishing, games room.

| *Rooms* 6 | *Room phone* No | *Confirm by* arrang. | *Parking* Ample |
| *Ensuite bath/shower* 5 | *Room TV* No | *Last dinner* 9 | *Room service* Limited |

**If we recommend meals in a Hotel or Inn,
a separate entry is made for its restaurant.**

DELGANY | Glenview Hotel 61% | £D/E

H **Map 19 D4**
Co. Wicklow
Glen of the Downs
Dublin (01) 862896
Telex 30638
Credit Access, Amex, Visa
Closed 2 days Xmas

Day rooms with picture windows take in the lovely views at this beautifully situated hotel on the slopes of The Sugar Loaf mountain. The bar is cosily traditional, the main lounge more contemporary in style, and there's a second, TV lounge upstairs. Six non-smoking bedrooms feature nice chintzy fabrics and modern bathrooms; remaining accommodation is more basic, with simple fitted units and functional bathrooms. No dogs. *Amenities* garden, laundry service.

| *Rooms* 23 | *Direct dial* Yes | *Confirm by* 6 | *Parking* Ample |
| *Ensuite bath/shower* 23 | *Room TV* Yes | *Last dinner* 9.30 | *Room service* All day |

DINGLE | Doyle's Seafood Bar 🍴

RR Map 19 A5 Co. Kerry
John Street
Dingle (066) 51174

Seafood
About £42 for two
Seats 50
Parties 30
Parking Ample

Credit Access, Amex, Diners, Visa

John and Stella Doyle provide a warm and cheerful welcome at their renowned seafood bar, which they've now developed into a most appealing restaurant with rooms. Seafood is naturally the speciality, the range extending from oysters, smoked salmon and crab mousse with beurre blanc to seafood tartlets with sorrel sauce and hot poached lobster. Note also nettle soup and rack of lamb (about the only meaty concession). Chocolate biscuit cake is a decadent but very good pud.
🍷 Well-chosen 🄯

Lunch 12.30–2.15 *Dinner* 6–9
Closed Sun, late Nov–early Mar

BEDROOMS 8 £E/F
With bath/shower 8

Splendid antique-furnished bedrooms offer first-class overnight accommodation, and there's a stylish lounge.

DUBLIN | Berkeley Court 79% | £A/B

H Town plan E3 Co. Dublin
Lansdowne Road
Dublin (01) 601711
Telex 30554

Rooms 220
Ensuite bath/shower 220
Direct dial Yes
Room TV Yes
Confirm by 6
Last dinner 10.30
Parking Ample
Room service 24 hours

Credit Access, Amex, Diners, Visa

A fine modern hotel, just walkable from the city centre. Pink marble, rich carpeting, antiques and heavy brass lamps set a tone of style and elegance in the foyer, where well-spaced sofas provide plenty of room for relaxation. The bar is handsomely panelled, and there's a pleasant, leafy conservatory grill where breakfast is taken. Bedrooms are uniformly very smart – solid, brass-edged oak furniture, splendidly com-

fortable canopied beds, ample space for armchair and coffee table, good lighting and well-appointed tiled bathrooms. There are ten suites, some with whirlpool baths. No dogs. *Amenities* indoor swimming pool, sauna, hairdressing, in-house movies, secretarial services, fax, laundry service, grill room (7.30am–11.30pm), kiosk. ♿

DUBLIN | Blooms Hotel 62% | £B

H Town plan C2 Co. Dublin
Anglesea Street
Dublin (01) 715622
Telex 31688

Credit Access, Amex, Diners, Visa

Valet parking gives guests their first experience of the excellent, courteous staff at this modern hotel. Room service is good, too – use it for breakfast in preference to the rather dark restaurant. Warm, homely bedrooms include a number with little balconies; bathrooms, though generally quite small, have decent mirror and shelf space. The main bar is a popular drinking rendezvous. No dogs.
Amenities in-house movies, secretarial services, fax, laundry service.

Rooms 86	*Direct dial* Yes	*Confirm by* 6	*Parking* Ample
Ensuite bath/shower 86	*Room TV* Yes	*Last dinner* 10.15	*Room service* 24 hours

DUBLIN | Burlington Hotel 71% | £B

H Town plan D3 Co. Dublin
Upper Leeson Street
Dublin (01) 605222
Telex 93815

Rooms 500
Ensuite bath/shower 500
Direct dial Yes
Room TV Yes
Confirm by 6
Last dinner 11.30
Parking Ample
Room service All day

Credit Access, Amex, Diners, Visa

A well-patronised modern hotel, much used for conferences and functions. The lobby-lounge is not particularly smart, though fresh flowers and some fine antiques help; the main bar with its paddle ceiling fans, Victorian prints and stained glass, is perhaps the pleasantest of the day rooms. Light, spacious bedrooms have brassbound darkwood furniture, an easy chair and coffee table, ample working space and

good lighting. A decent range of toiletries is provided in the neat, practical bathrooms. Our last visit coincided with the Eurovision Song Contest, which might explain the general air of mild chaos. No dogs. *Amenities* hairdressing, in-house movies, secretarial services, fax, laundry service, grill room (6.30am–11.30pm), kiosk. ♿

DUBLIN

Map 19 D4
Town plan opposite

Population 1,003,164

Dublin (from the Erse for 'dark pool'), came into historic prominence when the Norman conquerors in England were invited to help the King of Leinster campaign against the High King of Ireland. The chapter of 'troubles' began. In 1800 the Irish Parliament was absorbed by Westminster, but in 1922 that chapter ended and Dublin is now the bustling capital of the Irish Republic.

Annual Events
Dublin Horse Show *first week of August*
Dublin Millennium Celebrations *to 31st December (1988)*
Dublin Spring Show *May*
Gaelic Football Finals *third Sunday in September*
Hurling Finals *first Sunday in September*

Sights Outside City
Malahide Castle, Hill Abbey of Howth, The Curragh, Bray, Enniskerry Village, Powerscourt House, Vale of Avoca, Glendalough, The Japanese Gardens, Monasterboice, Newgrange

Information Offices
14 Upper O'Connell Street
Telephone Dublin 747733
Telex 25253

Bord Failte Eireann
Baggot Street Bridge
Dublin 2
Telephone Dublin 765871

Fiat Dealers
Rialto Motors Ltd, Herberton Road
Dublin 12. Tel. Dublin 754216
Map reference A3

Sweeney & Forte Ltd
56 Howth Road, Clontarf, Dublin 3
Tel. Dublin 332301

Tractamotors Ltd, 84 Prussia Street
Dublin 7, Tel. Dublin 791722

Autocars Ireland Ltd, Milltown Road
Dublin 6. Tel. Dublin 698577

Finglas Motors Ltd
North Road, Finglas
Dublin 11, Tel. Dublin 342977

Terenure Car Sales
Terenure Road North
Dublin 6. Tel. Dublin 902709

Tractamotors
Blanchardstown
Dublin 15. Tel. Dublin 216622

1 Abbey Theatre **D1**
2 Airport **C1**
3 Bank of Ireland *in old Parliament building* **C1**
4 Botanic Gardens **B1**
5 Castle **C2**
6 Christ Church Cathedral *11th-c Strongbow's tomb* **C2**
7 City Hall *18th-c* **C2**
8 Civic Museum *record of Dublin's history* **C2**
9 Connolly Station **D1**
10 Croke Park *hurling and Gaelic football* **C1**
11 Eblana Theatre **D1**
12 Four Courts *Law Courts* **B1**
13 Gate Theatre **C1**
14 Government Buildings **D2**
15 Heuston Station **A1**
16 Hugh Lane Municipal Gallery of Modern Art **C1**
17 Lansdowne Road Rugby Ground **E3**
18 Leinster House *Dail; National Library; Museum* **D2**
19 Mansion House *Queen Anne period* **D2**
20 Olympia Theatre **C2**
21 Pearse Station **D2**
22 Phoenix Park and Zoo **A1**
23 Pro-Cathedral **C1**
24 Royal Dublin Society Showgrounds **E3**
25 St Audoen's Church *oldest parish church* **B2**
26 St Michan's Church *remarkable vaults* **B1**
27 St Patrick's Cathedral *impressive interior, Swift's tomb* **C2**
28 St Stephen's Green *oasis in city's heart* **C/D2**
29 Tourist Information Centre **C1**
30 Trinity College and Library *Book of Kells* **D2**

Dublin F I A T

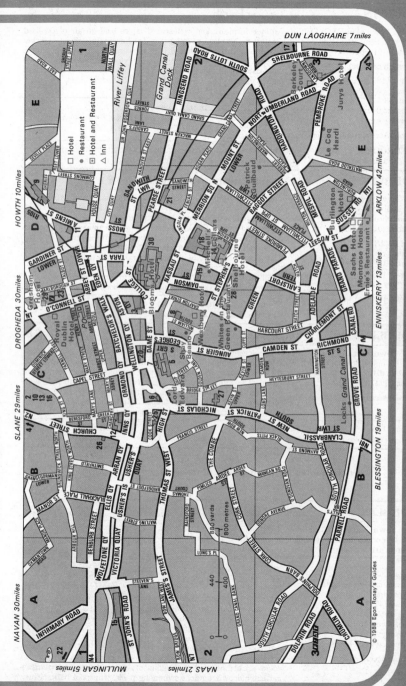

DUBLIN — Le Coq Hardi ♕ ♐

RR Town plan E3 Co. Dublin
35 Pembroke Road
Dublin (01) 689070

French cooking

Set L £13.75
About £85 for two
Seats 48
Parties 20
Parking Ample

Credit Access, Amex, Diners, Visa

Antique furniture and well-spaced tables lend an air of civilised comfort to this pleasant restaurant. The imaginative choice of dishes lays an emphasis on fish and John Howard's competent cooking is classical in concept. Starter might be Wexford mussels with perhaps pot roasted quail to follow. Magnificent cellar of old Bordeaux with many vintages of Château Mouton Rothschild back to 1870. ⌂ Outstanding ♥ Well-chosen ⊜

Lunch 12.30–2.30 *Dinner* 7.30–10.45
Closed L Sat, all Sun, Bank Hols, 2 wks Aug & 1 wk Xmas

BEDROOMS 2 £C/D
With bath/shower 2

There are two luxurious bedrooms with en suite facilities and TVs for overnight guests. No dogs or children.

DUBLIN — Ernie's Restaurant *NEW ENTRY* ♐

R Town plan D3 Co. Dublin
Mulberry Gardens,
Donnybrook
Dublin (01) 693300

Set D £18.50
About £50 for two
Seats 60
Parties 60
Parking Limited

Credit Access, Amex, Diners, Visa

The eponymous owner is Ernie Evans, a talented and experienced chef and a Kerryman of taste and charm. His style is of the old school, with deep, honest flavours, hearty portions and no stinting on the butter and cream. Chicken liver pâté, grilled mussels wrapped in bacon, turbot aux fruits de mer and beef or lamb en croûte show the range, and there are some luscious ice creams among the sweets. The dining room is pretty, with contemporary Irish paintings covering the walls, and service under manager Robert Cahill could not be more delightful. The restaurant is tucked away in a quiet Dublin suburb, so be sure to get directions when making your booking. ⊜

Dinner only 7.15–10.15
Closed Sun, Mon & 2 wks end of Aug

DUBLIN — Gresham Hotel 64% £B

H Town plan C1 Co. Dublin
O'Connell Street, Dublin 2
Dublin (01) 746881
Telex 32473

Credit Access, Amex, Diners, Visa

A fine Regency building which is undergoing refurbishment to restore it to its former handsome self. A fine marble floor graces the foyer and the other public areas include a lively bar and extensive conference rooms. The refurbished bedrooms are in chic modern style with coordinating colours and fabrics, and the elegant suites have antique furniture, smart seating areas, fireplaces and balconies. No dogs. *Amenities* secretarial services, fax, laundry service. ⟨

Rooms 180	*Direct dial* Yes	*Confirm by* 6	*Parking* Ample
Ensuite bath/shower 180	*Room TV* Yes	*Last dinner* 11.15	*Room service* 24 hours

Prices quoted for the Republic of Ireland are in *Irish punts*.

DUBLIN — Jurys Hotel 77% £B

H Town plan E3 Co. Dublin
Pembroke Road, Ballsbridge
Dublin (01) 605000
Telex 93723

Rooms 300
Ensuite bath/shower 300
Direct dial Yes
Room TV Yes
Confirm by 6
Last dinner 10.15
Parking Ample
Room service 24 hours

Credit Access, Amex, Diners, Visa

A distinctive glass-vaulted lobby leads into this low-rise city-centre hotel, where bustling public areas include a choice of two bars – one warmly styled on an Edwardian theme, the other featuring alcove seating, abundant greenery and a soothing waterfall. Nearly half the bedrooms have now been redesigned with up-to-date furnishings and marble-tiled bathrooms; remaining rooms keep their functional light-

wood decor. One floor is designated non-smoking and a further 100 rooms are planned with the building of a new extension. *Amenities* garden, indoor & outdoor swimming pools, whirlpool bath, beauty salon, hairdressing, in-house movies, secretarial services, fax, valeting, laundry service, coffee shop (6am–4.30pm, Sun till 11pm). ⟨

DUBLIN	Locks	♕

R **Town plan C3** Co. Dublin
1 Windsor Terrace,
Portobello
Dublin (01) 543391

Set L from £10.75 **Set D** £16.75
About £58 for two
Seats 50 *Parties* 35
Parking Ample
Credit Access, Amex, Diners, Visa

There's a real buzz about this smart restaurant and it's well worth a visit. Cooking and service remain consistently excellent, and dishes are notable for prime ingredients and honest flavours. Seafood terrine with a Pernod sauce, fritto misto di mare, lamb sweetbreads beurre noisette and medallions of pork fillet with a mild curry sauce show the range. Light, tangy lemon syllabub to finish. ♀ Well-chosen ℮

Lunch 12.30–2 *Dinner* 7.15–11
Closed L Sat, all Sun, Bank Hols & 1 wk Xmas

Any person using our name to obtain free hospitality is a fraud.
Proprietors, please inform the police and us.

DUBLIN	Mitchell's Cellars	⚒

R **Town plan D2** Co. Dublin
21 Kildare Street
Dublin (01) 680367

About £25 for two
Seats 60
Parties 20
Parking Limited

Credit Access, Amex, Diners, Visa

The cellars of the Mitchell family's wine firm houses this popular bistro. Patricia Hogan's daily-changing lunchtime menu is short on items but long on flavour with simple starters such as tomato and orange soup or smoked fish pâté preceding dishes like beef burgundy with rice and salad or baked ham véronique with new potatoes and green beans. Quiches and composite salads are included and there are simple conventional desserts. ℮

Lunch only 12.15–2.30
Closed Sun, Bank Hol wkends, 24 Dec–2 Jan & Sat June–Sept

DUBLIN	Montrose Hotel 63%	£C/D

H **Town plan D3** Co. Dublin
Stillorgan Road
Dublin (01) 693311
Telex 91207

Credit Access, Amex, Diners, Visa

Major refurbishment has revitalised this low, modern hotel on the N11 opposite University College campus. The smart reception area now boasts a marble reception desk and chandeliers, while the large bar has been cleverly divided into contrasting areas. Needed improvements now underway in the bedrooms include attractive furnishings and new light fittings. ***Amenities*** sauna, hairdressing, in-house movies, fax, laundry service, coffee shop (6.30am–11pm).

Rooms 200	*Direct dial* Yes	*Confirm by* 7	*Parking* Ample
Ensuite bath/shower 200	*Room TV* Yes	*Last dinner* 11, Sun 10	*Room service* All day

DUBLIN	Patrick Guilbaud	♕

R **Town plan D2** Co. Dublin
46 James's Place,
Lower Baggot Street
Dublin (01) 601 799

French cooking

Set L £12.15
Set D £18.50
About £70 for two
Seats 50
Parties 80
Parking Limited

Credit Access, Amex, Diners, Visa

Greenery and clever spotlighting create a relaxed, sophisticated atmosphere at this city-centre restaurant, where Patrick Guilbaud is the urbane, welcoming host. Guillaume Lebrun's menus offer modern dishes that are imaginative (occasionally quite elaborate) in concept and appropriately stylish in presentation: succulent dill-marinated salmon with a fresh, light accompaniment of ginger quenelles; chopped pig's trotters in filo pastry with a rich red wine sauce. Simpler dishes such as black pudding with apple purée or lamb cutlets with hazelnuts (part of a six-course tasting menu) are also available, and the impressive trolley of French cheeses is not to be missed. The wine list includes some good bottles, albeit at high prices. ♀ Well-chosen ℮ 🍴

Lunch 12.30–2 *Dinner* 7.30–10.15
Closed L Sat, all Sun & Bank Hols

DUBLIN	Royal Dublin Hotel 60%	£D

H **Town plan C1** Co. Dublin
40 Upper O'Connell Street,
Dublin 1
Dublin (01) 733666
Telex 32568
Credit Access, Amex, Diners, Visa
Closed 1 wk Xmas

There has been a great deal of refurbishment taking place at this centrally located hotel, which is conveniently equipped with its own underground car park. Public areas include a spacious foyer and a pleasant bar. Bright new carpets enliven the corridors and the quiet, well-kept bedrooms have attractive bedspreads and matching curtains. Bathrooms are stylishly tiled. No dogs. ***Amenities*** secretarial services, laundry service, coffee shop (10am–11pm).

Rooms 100	*Direct dial* Yes	*Confirm by* 6	*Parking* Ample
Ensuite bath/shower 100	*Room TV* Yes	*Last dinner* 9.30	*Room service* 24 hours

DUBLIN   Sachs Hotel   59%   £D

H **Town plan D3** Co. Dublin
19 Morehampton Road
Donnybrook
Dublin (01) 680995
Telex 31667

Credit Access, Amex, Diners, Visa

A friendly, down-to-earth hotel with a fresh white facade and cheerful window boxes. Public areas, including a large, welcoming bar and a comfortable reception-lounge, have just been refurbished. Bedrooms, too, are being improved; size and style vary (some nice old furniture) and front rooms are much brighter and sunnier than those at the back. No dogs.
Amenities bistro (10am–5pm & 6pm–11pm).

Rooms 20	*Direct dial* Yes	*Confirm by* arrang.	*Parking* Ample
Ensuite bath/shower 20	*Room TV* Yes	*Last dinner* 10.30	*Room service* 24 hours

DUBLIN   Shay Beano   *NEW ENTRY*

R **Town plan C2** Co Dublin
37 Lower Stephen Street
Dublin (01) 776384

French cooking
Set L £9
Set D £18
About £48 for two
Seats 30
Parking Difficult

Black woodwork, Bauhaus chairs and risqué photographs confer a certain chic on this rather cramped restaurant owned by a patriotic Irishman. Staff, menus and food, however, are strictly French, with fixed-price menus offering well-prepared dishes using quality ingredients in the nouvelle cuisine style. Pluses include real French bread and a tempting display of pâtisserie-style puds. Service tends to be casual. 🍷 Well-chosen ℮

Lunch 12–2.30   *Dinner* 7–10.45
Closed Sun & Bank Hols

DUBLIN   Shelbourne Hotel   78%   £A

H **Town plan D2** Co. Dublin
St Stephen's Green
Dublin (01) 766471
Telex 93653

Rooms 177
Ensuite bath/shower 177
Direct dial Yes
Room TV Yes
Confirm by 6
Last dinner 10.30
Parking Ample
Room service 24 hours

Credit Access, Amex, Diners, Visa

In a prestigious location overlooking St Stephen's Green, this expensively restored 19th-century hotel impresses with the traditional furnishings and decor, high moulded ceilings, marble columns, glittering chandeliers and elegant Georgian features that take the eye in the handsome day rooms. Bedrooms are stylish and well equipped, bathrooms luxurious, but we had some niggles, too, on our last visit  – rather narrow bath, poor ventilation, the telephone system failing twice for long periods. Neither bar nor breakfast room is in pristine decorative order, and the crowds that frequently throng the hotel certainly detract from its distinguished image. *Amenities* beauty salon, hairdressing, laundry service, valeting, fax, secretarial services.

 indicates a **well-chosen** house wine

DUBLIN   The Westbury   76%   £A

H **Town plan C2** Co. Dublin
Off Grafton Street
Dublin (01) 791122
Telex 91091

Rooms 151
Ensuite bath/shower 151
Direct dial Yes
Room TV Yes
Confirm by 6
Last dinner 10.30
Parking Ample
Room service 24 hours

Credit Access, Amex, Diners, Visa

Impressive and luxurious public areas are the hallmark of this city centre hotel. Acres of soft red marble strewn with hand-made Irish rugs, deep, inviting sofas and glittering modern chandeliers impress in the open-plan foyer. Wrought-iron gates lead to the clubby Terrace Bar, while downstairs there's a contrastingly Victorian-style bar complete with carved mahogany and stained-glass windows. Solid  darkwood furniture and canopied beds feature in the spacious bedrooms, all of which have well-equipped bathrooms. Larger Executive rooms and the six handsome suites offer additional extras. No dogs. *Amenities* beauty salon, hairdressing, in-house movies, secretarial services, fax, valeting, coffee shop (10am–11pm), kiosk.

DUBLIN · Whites on the Green   ♛

R Town plan C2 Co. Dublin
119 St Stephen's Green
Dublin (01) 751975

Set L £13.75
Set D £20.75
About £74 for two
Seats 80
Parties 80
Parking Limited

Credit Access, Amex, Diners, Visa

All is stylish sophistication at this fashionable restaurant on St Stephen's Green where chic contemporary decor is a fitting accompaniment to Michael Clifford's modern and imaginative style of cooking. Resounding successes include finely flavoured chicken quenelles with walnut and apple sauce, and tender noisettes of spring lamb with aubergine mousse. Some other dishes are a little too ambitious and fail to live up to expectations, but cooking is never less than enjoyable and presentation is unfailingly pretty. Sweet endings might feature an interesting mango and lime sablé. A fine, rambling wine list: note the old clarets (Fourcas Hosten '49) and a dozen Chablis (Les Preuses '84 from Laroche).   ♍ Well-chosen   ⊖

Lunch 12.30–2.30   *Dinner* 7–10.45
Closed L Sat, all Sun, Bank Hols & 10 days Xmas

DUBLIN AIRPORT · Dublin International Hotel   57%   £C

H Map 18 D3 Co. Dublin
Collinstown
Dublin (01) 379211
Telex 32849

Credit Access, Amex, Diners, Visa
Closed 25 Dec

Soundproofed windows ensure a good night's rest at this modern hotel within the airport complex. Some bedrooms are now rather dated, others have been smartly upgraded; best of all are the 45 executive-style rooms. Public areas include a sunken lobby-lounge and a bar-lounge with evening pianist. No dogs.
Amenities garden, indoor swimming pool, in-house movies, coffee shop (6.30am–10.30pm), 24-hour lounge service, kiosk.   ⅙

Rooms 195	*Direct dial* Yes	*Confirm by* 6	*Parking* Ample
Ensuite bath/shower 195	*Room TV* Yes	*Last dinner* 10.15	*Room service* None

DUN LAOGHAIRE · Digby's   ♙

R Map 19 D4 Co. Dublin
5 Windsor Terrace
Dublin (01) 804600

Set L £9
Set D from £16.50
About £58 for two
Seats 50 *Parties* 54
Parking Ample
Credit Access, Amex, Diners, Visa

Admire the view across the bay while waiting to appreciate part-owner Paul Cathcart's considerable culinary skills. His excellent 4-course meals could start with duck liver salad or moules marinière, with roast pheasant, paupiettes of sole stuffed with prawns, or mallard with a bitter orange sauce as the main course. Choice includes soup or a sorbet, and a simple home-made dessert. Good wines include a Coltassala Castello di Volpaia '81.   ♍ Well-chosen   ⊖

Lunch 12.30–3   *Dinner* 7.30–11, Sat till 10
Closed L Sat, all Tues, Bank Hols & 3 days Xmas

DUN LAOGHAIRE · Restaurant Mirabeau   ♛♛

R Map 19 D4 Co. Dublin
Marine Parade, Sandycove
Dublin (01) 809 873

French cooking
Set L from £10.50
Set D from £18.50
About £74 for two
Seats 35
Parties 40
Parking Ample

Credit Access, Amex, Diners, Visa

Classical French food with thoughtful modern touches is the hallmark of this very chic contemporary restaurant. Michel Flamme's cooking is assured and refined, typified by such dishes as chicken and morels in puff pastry with whiskey sauce, pavé of turbot with moutarde de Meaux and a saffron sauce and breast of duck with honey, thyme and red wine sauce. A recent innovation is an alternative choice of dishes for those watching their weight or cholesterol levels. Delicious sweets include feuilleté de fraises, lime and raspberry bavarois and hazelnut and praline mousse. Exemplary cellar, very strong in fine Bordeaux: Ch Pichon Longueville Lalande '59. ▷ Outstanding   ♍ Well-chosen   ⊖ ⅙

Lunch 12.30–2   *Dinner* 7.30–10
Closed L Sat, Sun & Bank Hols

DUN LAOGHAIRE · Restaurant Na Mara   ♛

R Map 19 D4 Co. Dublin
1 Harbour Road
Dublin (01) 800509

Seafood
Set L £13.90 Set D £19.90
About £55 for two
Seats 70 *Parties* 70
Parking Ample
Credit Access, Amex, Diners, Visa

A former Victorian railway station provides the setting for this stylish seafood restaurant close to the quayside. The cooking is accurate and consistently competent and the seafood is very fresh (there is also provision for meat eaters). Mouthwatering dishes include salmon mousse with lemon sauce, plaited salmon and brill with tomato and ginger sauce and compote of fish in green peppercorn sauce. Good al dente vegetables and pleasant sweets.   ⊖ ⅙

Lunch 1–2.30   *Dinner* 7–10.30
Closed Sun, Mon, 1 wk Easter & 1 wk Xmas

DUNDALK — Ballymascanlon Hotel   59%   £E

H Map 18 D3 Co. Louth
Dundalk (042) 71124
Telex 43735

Credit Access, Amex, Diners, Visa
Closed 24–26 Dec

Extensive gardens surround this friendly, solid old house about three miles out of town on the Carlingford road. Features in the three lounges include a carved marble Adam fireplace and a galleried cupola ceiling, and there's a smart basement bar. Nicest bedrooms are those in the main house. *Amenities* garden, indoor swimming pool, sauna, solarium, keep-fit equipment, tennis, squash, games room, snooker, in-house movies, laundry service.

Rooms 36	*Direct dial* Yes	*Confirm by* arrang.	*Parking* Ample
Ensuite bath/shower 36	*Room TV* Yes	*Last dinner* 9.30	*Room service* 24 hours

DUNDERRY — Dunderry Lodge Restaurant

R Map 18 C3 Co. Meath
Robinstown, Nr Navan
Navan (046) 31671

Set L £10
Set D £16.25
About £50 for two
Seats 36 *Parties* 36
Parking Ample
Credit Access, Amex, Diners, Visa

A sympathetic conversion of an old stone barn and cattle byre has created an unusual and stylish country restaurant. The cooking generally was most enjoyable, and among dishes that pleased on a recent visit were sorrel soup, tagliatelle with mussels, smoked breast of duck with onion confit and wild Irish salmon sauce verte. Good sweets, especially the home-made ice creams. No children under 15. ℗

Lunch 12.30–2   *Dinner* 7.30–9.30
Closed L Sat, all Sun, Mon, Bank Hols, 20 Dec–10 Feb & 23–29 Mar

DUNDRUM — Dundrum House Hotel   66%   £C/D

H Map 19 C5 Co. Tipperary
Nr Cashel
Cashel (062) 71116
Telex 70255

Credit Access, Amex, Diners, Visa
Closed 2 days Xmas

A deer park and trout river are part of the 100 acres of land surrounding this impressive Georgian manor. Both entrance hall and lounge are elegant, lofty rooms, while the bar – in a converted private chapel – boasts stained-glass windows. Good-sized bedrooms, with antique furnishings and attractively coordinated fabrics, all have smartly tiled modern bathrooms. No dogs. *Amenities* garden, tennis, riding, game fishing, snooker, secretarial services.

Rooms 55	*Direct dial* Yes	*Confirm by* arrang.	*Parking* Ample
Ensuite bath/shower 55	*Room TV* No	*Last dinner* 9.30	*Room service* All day

DUNGARVAN — Seanachie

R Map 19 C5 Co. Waterford
Pulla Ring
Dungarvan (058) 46285

About £24 for two
Seats 76
Parties 76
Parking Ample
Credit Access, Amex

Good honest home cooking in an authentically restored thatched house that's full of atmosphere and old-world charm. Open sandwiches, egg mayonnaise, pâté and soup are available throughout opening hours, along with fish pie and hearty Irish stew; at lunchtimes, other hot dishes like chicken mornay or sirloin steak are served. Apple tart and a delicious chocolate roulade figure among the sweets. ℗

Lunch only 12.30–3
Closed Nov–end Mar

**We welcome bona fide complaints and recommendations
on the tear-out pages at the back of the book for readers' comment.
They are followed up by our professional team.**

DUNWORLEY — Dunworley Cottage

R Map 19 B6 Co. Cork
Butlerstown, Bandon
Bandon (023) 40314

Set L & D from £10
About £42 for two
Seats 40
Parties 14
Parking Ample
Credit Access, Amex, Diners, Visa

An old stone cottage with modest decor but a warm and genuine welcome – it's *very* remote, so be sure to ask for directions. Otto Kunze insists on the best fresh ingredients, including eggs from his own hens. His interesting dishes range from mussels gratin, nettle soup, and strongly-smoked Westphalian-style ham to fillet of brill, and succulent pot-roasted kid. End with an authentic apfelstrudel. ♀ Well-chosen ℗

Lunch 1–6 Bank Hols, Sun, Wed–Sat June, July & Aug
Dinner 6.30–10   **Closed** Mon (except Bank Hols), Tues, Jan & Feb

DURRUS — Blair's Cove House ♐

R Map 19 A6 Co. Cork
Nr Bantry
Bantry (027) 61127

Set L £11
About £50 for two
Seats 70
Parties 45
Parking Ample
Credit Access, Diners, Amex, Visa

Set high above a picturesque cove, this restaurant in a converted barn is owned and run by a Belgian couple, Philip and Sabine de Mey. Sabine's cooking is straightforward but extremely enjoyable, featuring top-quality meat and fish – often cooked over an open wood-burning fire. Start with a splendid cold buffet. An intriguing wine list: note the Belgian bottlings of classic French wines. 🍷 Well-chosen ⊖

Lunch Sun only 1–2 *Dinner* 7.30–9
Closed D Sun, Jan & Feb, mid Oct–end Mar

Our inspectors are our full-time employees;
they are professionally trained by us.

ENNIS — Old Ground Hotel 66% £C

H Map 19 B4
Co. Clare
Ennis (065) 28127
Telex 70603

Credit Access, Amex, Diners, Visa

An ivy-clad, characterful hotel, parts of which date back to the 17th century. A handsome desk graces the reception, the comfortable and spacious lounge overlooks the cathedral, and there's a smart cocktail bar and an atmospheric snug. Bedrooms in the old house have solid, traditional furniture and compact practical bathrooms; those in a newer wing have stylish fitted units, brass lamps and tiled, more up-to-date bathrooms. *Amenities* garden, laundry service.

Rooms 60	*Direct dial* Yes	*Confirm by* 6	*Parking* Ample
Ensuite bath/shower 60	*Room TV* Yes	*Last dinner* 9	*Room service* 24 hours

ENNIS — West County Inn Hotel 59% £D/E

H Map 19 B4 Co. Clare
Clare Road
Ennis (065) 28421
Telex 28294

Credit Access, Amex, Diners, Visa

A modern hotel on the Limerick road at the edge of the town. It's popular for conferences and functions, and there are several lively bars where private visitors can socialise. Nearly half the bedrooms have smart, fitted units and brass lamps; the remainder have more utilitarian units and cottage fabrics. No dogs. *Amenities* sauna, keep-fit equipment, snooker, satellite TV, in-house movies, secretarial services, laundry service, coffee shop (7.30am–10.30pm). &

Rooms 110	*Direct dial* Yes	*Confirm by* 6	*Parking* Ample
Ensuite bath/shower 110	*Room TV* Yes	*Last dinner* 9.30	*Room service* All day

---

If we recommend **meals** in a Hotel or Inn,
a separate entry is made for its restaurant.

FERRYCARRIG BRIDGE — Ferrycarrig Hotel 61% *NEW ENTRY* £C/D

H Map 19 D5 Co. Wexford
Nr Wexford
Wexford (053) 22999
Telex 80147

Credit Access, Amex, Diners, Visa

Beautiful views across the Slaney Estuary are enjoyed by all the rooms of this friendly hotel on the N11 not far from Wexford. Major refurbishment has given a facelift to the public rooms, and to bedrooms on the second and fourth floors. These have smart units, extra-long beds, and good tiled bathrooms. Staff are most helpful. *Amenities* garden, tennis, secretarial services, laundry service.

Rooms 38	*Direct dial* Yes	*Confirm by* 6	*Parking* Ample
Ensuite bath/shower 38	*Room TV* Yes	*Last dinner* 9.15	*Room service* 24 hours

GALWAY — Ardilaun House Hotel 64% £D

H Map 19 B4 Co. Galway
Taylors Hill
Galway (091) 21433
Telex 50013

Credit Access, Amex, Diners, Visa
Closed 1 wk Xmas

Gleaming public areas and spotless bedrooms reflect a high standard of housekeeping at this much extended Georgian house. The lounge is formal yet relaxing, and there's a comfortably appointed bar. Solidly furnished bedrooms are well organised to provide good desk/dressing table space, and all are equipped with hairdryers and trouser presses; superior rooms have telephone extensions in their modern tiled bathrooms. *Amenities* garden, secretarial services, fax, laundry service.

Rooms 93	*Direct dial* Yes	*Confirm by* 6	*Parking* Ample
Ensuite bath/shower 93	*Room TV* Yes	*Last dinner* 9.30	*Room service* 24 hours

---

GALWAY   **Corrib Great Southern Hotel**   **63%**   **£C**

H **Map 19 B4** Co. Galway
Dublin Road
Galway (091) 55281
Telex 50044

Credit Access, Amex, Diners, Visa

Holidaymakers and business people alike will find their needs well catered for in this well-designed modern hotel. Public areas include a bright foyer, a summery lounge, a bar and a conference centre. Many bedrooms have been refurbished and equipped with trouser presses and hairdryers; four have been upgraded to luxury status.
Amenities garden, indoor swimming pool, sauna, snooker, satellite TV, in-house movies, secretarial services, fax, laundry service.

Rooms 110	*Direct dial* Yes	*Confirm by* 6	*Parking* Ample
Ensuite bath/shower 110	*Room TV* Yes	*Last dinner* 9	*Room service* 24 hours

---

GALWAY   **Galway Ryan Hotel**   **58%**   **£D**

H **Map 19 B4** Co. Galway
Dublin Road
(091) 53181
Telex 50149

Credit Access, Amex, Diners, Visa
Closed 25 Dec

A basic, no-frills modern hotel which may lack character but offers comfortable and practical accommodation. The public areas include a bright sunken lounge, a small conference room and a pleasant, darkwood-panelled bar. The identical, '60s-style bedrooms are quite spacious and have fitted furniture, well-sprung mattresses and neat, well-equipped en suite bathrooms. No dogs. *Amenities* patio, games room, in-house movies, secretarial services, fax.

Rooms 96	*Direct dial* Yes	*Confirm by* 6	*Parking* Ample
Ensuite bath/shower 96	*Room TV* Yes	*Last dinner* 9.15	*Room service* 24 hours

---

GALWAY   **Great Southern Hotel**   **68%**   **£C**

H **Map 19 B4** Co. Galway
Eyre Square
Galway (091) 64041
Telex 50164

Credit Access, Amex, Diners, Visa
Closed 3 days Xmas

A sturdy Victorian hotel with smart public areas, the two bars drawing locals as well as guests. Pastel walls, dark cane furniture and open fires make for civilised comfort in the reception area and lounge. Bedrooms vary in size, but all have decent dressing table/desk space, armchairs and simple, compact bathrooms. No dogs.
Amenities indoor swimming pool, sauna, solarium, beauty salon, in-house movies, laundry service.

Rooms 120	*Direct dial* Yes	*Confirm by* 6	*Parking* Difficult
Ensuite bath/shower 120	*Room TV* Yes	*Last dinner* 10	*Room service* 24 hours

---

GALWAY   **J. J.'s Malt House**   ⚘

R **Map 19 B4** Co. Galway
High Street
Galway (091) 67866

Set L £8.85 **Set D** £19.03
About £48 for two
Seats 55 *Parties* 60
Parking Ample

Credit Access, Amex, Diners, Visa

A converted malthouse is the setting for this friendly restaurant where the seafood is a particularly good choice. There's a brisk trade from the bar snack menu at lunchtimes, while evenings bring such dishes as moules poulette as a starter with perhaps brill Marsala, turbot in a herb crust or veal florentine to follow. Good brown soda bread and sweets. Booking is advisable. 🍷 Well-chosen ⊖

Lunch 12.30–2.30   *Dinner* 7–10
Closed Sun, Good Fri, 2–3 days Xmas

We publish annually,
so make sure you use the current edition.
It's worth it!

GLEN OF AHERLOW   **Aherlow House Hotel**   **61%**   **£E/F**

H **Map 19 B5** Co. Tipperary
Nr Tipperary
Tipperary (062) 56153

Credit Access, Amex, Diners, Visa

New owners have been busily refurbishing this old hunting lodge, which enjoys a glorious woodland setting overlooking the lovely glen. The spacious main bar, with its timbered ceiling and large open fire, and the chintzy little yellow lounge are most comfortable and inviting. Bright, fresh bedrooms feature traditional white-painted furniture, plus attractive new fabrics and carpeting; decent private bathrooms. No dogs. *Amenities* garden.

Rooms 11	*Direct dial* Yes	*Confirm by* arrang.	*Parking* Ample
Ensuite bath/shower 11	*Room TV* Yes	*Last dinner* 9.30	*Room service* All day

GOREY — Marlfield House — 79% — £B/C

H **Map 19 D5** Co. Wexford
Courtown Road
Gorey (055) 21124
Telex 80757

Rooms 12
Ensuite bath/shower 12
Direct dial Yes
Room TV Yes
Confirm by 5
Last dinner 9.30
Parking Ample
Room service All day

Closed 5 days Xmas & 7–31 Jan

Lovers of peace and tranquillity should look no further than this impeccably kept hotel, built as a dower house around 1850 and set in 35 acres of gardens and woodland. Tireless owner Mary Bowe's superb sense of style is reflected throughout elegant public rooms like the chandelier-hung foyer, antique-filled bar-lounge and the two sumptuously comfortable lounges. Individually decorated bedrooms (some with four-posters or Victorian-style brass beds) offer every modern accessory, including hairdryers, trouser presses and luxurious towels, robes and toiletries in the excellent bathrooms. No children under seven. No dogs. *Amenities* garden, sauna, tennis, croquet, secretarial services, fax, laundry service.

HOWTH — King Sitric

R **Map 19 D4** Co. Dublin
East Pier, Harbour Road
Dublin (01) 326729

Set L £9.50
Set D £17.75
About £62 for two
Seats 65 *Parties* 65
Parking Ample
Credit Access, Amex, Diners, Visa

Top-quality seafood is the mainstay of the menu at King Sitric, whose harbourside setting allows fine views of the bay and the boats. The freshness of the produce is enhanced by simple, unfussy preparation, and favourite dishes include crab mayonnaise, mussels marinière, local grilled soles and lobster. Chocolate marquise is a lovely rich pud, and there are some very good Irish farmhouse cheeses. Friendly, helpful service. Soundly chosen wines. 🍷 Well-chosen 🍂

Lunch 12.30–2.30 *Dinner* 6.30–11
Closed L Sat, all Sun, Bank Hols, 10 days Xmas & Easter

Our inspectors *never* book in the name of Egon Ronay's Guides.
They disclose their identity only if they are considering an establishment
for inclusion in the next edition of the Guide.

KANTURK — Assolas Country House — 67% — £D

HR **Map 19 B5** Co. Cork
Kanturk (029) 50015

Credit Access, Amex, Diners, Visa
Closed end Oct–Easter

The charming Bourke family have occupied their elegant 17th-century manor house in its delightfully sylvan setting for 70 years now and the feel is of being in a private home rather than a hotel. You serve yourself to drinks in the gracious drawing room before sinking into a comfortable armchair and the landing is packed with well-stocked bookcases. Bedrooms in the main house are traditional in style and impeccably maintained; three have been upgraded and given luxury bathrooms with whirlpool baths and bidets. There are also three impressively designed and furnished rooms in an outbuilding. No dogs. *Amenities* garden, whirlpool bath, tennis, croquet, coarse fishing, boating. ⅙

Rooms 9	*Room phone* No	*Confirm by* 6	*Parking* Ample
Ensuite bath/shower 9	*Room TV* No	*Last dinner* 9	*Room service* All day

Restaurant ♔ 🍂

Set D £19
About £54 for two
Seats 24
Parties 20

The finely proportioned period dining room makes a delightful setting in which to enjoy Joe Bourke's excellent meals. His style is imaginative but pleasingly straightforward and the daily-changing menus feature such dishes as oven-baked crab cake with a gratinée of fine herbs and baked fillet of Dunmoreast salmon with lemon and lime beurre blanc. Short, good wine list: Rhône from Jaboulet, Alsace from Trimbach. 🍷 Well-chosen 🍂

Dinner only 7–9
Closed end Oct–Easter

KENMARE   Park Hotel Kenmare   86%   £A

HR Map 19 A6
Co. Kerry
Killarney (064) 41200
Telex 73905

Rooms 50
Ensuite bath/shower 50
Direct dial Yes
Room TV No
Confirm by arrang.
Last dinner 8.45
Parking Ample
Room service 24 hours

Credit Access, Amex, Diners, Visa
Closed 1 Jan–31 Mar

High quality service is the most impressive aspect of this elegant late
Victorian hotel set in immaculate gardens overlooking the Kenmare
Estuary and the mountains of west Cork. Francis Brennan's smartly
turned out staff lace attentiveness with an attractive friendliness that
makes guests feel really welcome. Antiques are much in evidence, in
both the handsome day rooms and the long bedroom corridors. The
bedrooms themselves have their share of antiques and are very
comfortable and well appointed, with fresh flowers and bowls of fruit.
Refurbished bathrooms boast attractive marble tiling. No dogs.
Amenities garden, tennis, 9-hole golf course, croquet, fax, laundry
service. ♿

Park Hotel Kenmare Restaurant   ♛♛

Set L £14
Set D £28.50
About £70 *for two*
Seats 85
Parties 60

A restaurant of exceptional, easy elegance, with superlative service
and a menu that runs from simple grills to more intricate creations.
Raw materials are top quality, especially the fish, and typical dishes
include hot scallop mousse with a creamy nettle sauce and a classic
fillet of beef en croûte served with Madeira sauce and elegant, al dente
vegetables. Desserts are outstanding, and there's a wonderful cellar,
still with some Ch. Montrose '61. ▭ Outstanding ♟ Well-chosen
🕲 ♿

Lunch 1–2   *Dinner* 7–8.45   **Closed** 1 Jan–31 Mar

Changes in data sometimes occur in establishments
after the Guide goes to press.
Prices should be taken as indications rather than firm quotes.

KILCORAN   Kilcoran Lodge Hotel   59%   £E

H Map 19 C5 Co. Tipperary
Cahir
Cahir (052) 41288

Credit Access, Amex, Diners, Visa

Some five miles west of Cahir on the N7, this former hunting lodge
enjoys panoramic views across the Suir Valley to distant mountains.
A welcoming log fire warms the foyer-lounge and there's a pleasant
bar. Simply furnished bedrooms feature attractive floral fabrics and
offer TVs and radio-alarms. A leisure centre is among future plans.
Amenities garden, game fishing, in-house movies, laundry service.

Rooms 23	*Direct dial* Yes	*Confirm by* arrang.	*Parking* Ample
Ensuite bath/shower 20	*Room TV* Yes	*Last dinner* 9.30	*Room service* 24 hours

KILKENNY   Newpark Hotel   62%   £C/D

H Map 19 C5 Co. Kilkenny
Castlecomer Road
Kilkenny (056) 22122
Telex 80080

Credit Access, Amex, Diners, Visa

Set in parkland just north of town, this low-rise modern hotel offers
extensive leisure and conference facilities. Public areas are spacious
and stylish, and bedrooms (including 16 smart new rooms) have up-
to-date units and private bath/shower rooms. No dogs. *Amenities*
garden, indoor swimming pool, sauna, solarium, whirlpool bath,
gymnasium, tennis, in-house movies, secretarial services, fax, laundry
service, coffee shop (12.30pm–11pm), children's play area.

Rooms 60	*Direct dial* Yes	*Confirm by* 6	*Parking* Ample
Ensuite bath/shower 59	*Room TV* Yes	*Last dinner* 10, Sat 10.45	*Room service* 24 hours

KILLARNEY　Aghadoe Heights Hotel　65%　£C

H　**Map 19 A5** Co. Kerry
Aghadoe
Killarney (064) 31766
Telex 73942

Credit Access, Amex, Diners, Visa
Closed 4 wks Xmas

The two main features of this modern hotel are the marvellous lake and mountain views and the very high standards of cleanliness and repair. Good-sized bedrooms are pleasant and practical, with spacious bathrooms and decent accessories. There's plenty of seating in the foyer and split-level bar, and a terrace takes full advantage of the lovely setting. *Amenities* garden, tennis, coarse fishing, satellite TV, laundry service. &

Rooms 60	*Direct dial* Yes	*Confirm by* arrang.	*Parking* Ample
Ensuite bath/shower 60	*Room TV* Yes	*Last dinner* 9.30	*Room service* 24 hours

KILLARNEY　·　Cahernane Hotel　67%　£D

H　**Map 19 A5** Co. Kerry
Muckross Road
Killarney (064) 31895
Telex 73823
Credit Access, Amex, Diners, Visa
Closed end Oct–20 Dec & 6 Jan–Easter

Killarney's lakes and mountains are never very far away at this handsome Victorian mansion – now a comfortable and well-run hotel. Views are especially fine from some of the large, traditional first-floor bedrooms; top-floor rooms are more cottage in character, while those in the extension are smartly contemporary. Day rooms include an elegant lounge and stylish bar. *Amenities* garden, tennis, pitch & putt, game fishing, secretarial services, fax, laundry service.

Rooms 52	*Direct dial* Yes	*Confirm by* 6	*Parking* Ample
Ensuite bath/shower 52	*Room TV* No	*Last dinner* 9.30	*Room service* All day

KILLARNEY　Castlerosse Hotel　60%　£D/E

H　**Map 19 A5**
Co. Kerry
Killarney (064) 31144
Telex 73910

Credit Access, Amex, Diners, Visa
Closed mid Nov–mid Mar

A peaceful rambling hotel delighting in panoramic views of Lough Leane and the Macgillycuddy Reeks, Ireland's highest mountains. Public areas include a smart Scandinavian-style bar-lounge and a bright and airy picture-windowed restaurant. Compact, motel-style bedrooms, with adjacent covered parking spaces, are neat and trim with pine-clad walls, well-designed furniture and practical bathrooms. No dogs. *Amenities* garden, tennis, putting, game fishing, snooker.

Rooms 42	*Direct dial* Yes	*Confirm by* 6	*Parking* Ample
Ensuite bath/shower 42	*Room TV* No	*Last dinner* 9	*Room service* 24 hours

KILLARNEY　Hotel Europe　74%　£C/D

HR　**Map 19 A5** Co. Kerry
Killorglin Road, Fossa
Killarney (064) 31900
Telex 73913

Rooms 180
Ensuite bath/shower 180
Direct dial Yes
Room TV Yes
Confirm by arrang.
Last dinner 9.30
Parking Ample
Room service 24 hours

Credit Access, Amex, Diners, Visa
Closed Nov–mid Mar

A well-run modern hotel in spacious grounds set in the heart of Killarney's beautiful scenery. Much money has been spent in recent years and the public rooms, many with lake views, are in striking, contemporary style with stylish fabrics, the cocktail bar being particularly chic. Many of the bedrooms boast balconies overlooking the lake, and all have well-built fitted units, pleasing decor and excel-

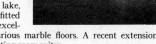

lent bathrooms with luxurious marble floors. A recent extension houses 20 mini bedroom/sitting room suites.
Amenities garden, indoor swimming pool, sauna, solarium, keep-fit equipment, beauty salon, hairdressing, riding, coarse fishing, in-house movies, fax, laundry service, coffee shop (12.30pm–6pm).

Panorama Restaurant

Set D £19
About £55 for two
Seats 650
Parties 650

A spacious, well-named restaurant where you can enjoy the views while you sample Willi Steinbeck's assured cooking. Local produce features strongly and the dishes range from continental style to Irish specialities. Typical dishes are a ragout of turbot, brill and monkfish, goulash soup, Dingle Bay lobster and sirloin steak béarnaise. Vegetables are spot-on and sweets are delicious. Service is smooth and professional. ♟ Well-chosen ⊘ &

Lunch 12–6　*Dinner* 7–9.30
Closed Nov–mid Mar

KILLARNEY   Gaby's   ⚐

R Map 19 A5 Co. Kerry
17 High Street
Killarney (064) 32519

Seafood
About £42 for two
Seats 47
Parking Difficult

Credit Access, Amex, Diners, Visa

Fresh seafood served in a straightforward fashion is the hallmark of this appealing unpretentious restaurant. Geert Maes cooks the pick of the day's catch by the local fishing fleet so the menu varies accordingly, but typical dishes are a delicious seafood soup, black sole in cream, seafood mosaic and Kerry brill fillet in wine sauce. Among the wines note the lovely Australian Chardonnay from the Balgownie estate.
🍷 Well-chosen ℗

Lunch 12.30–2.30   *Dinner* 6–10
Closed L Mon, all Sun & mid Dec–mid Mar

Prices quoted for the Republic of Ireland are in *Irish punts*.

KILLARNEY   Killarney Great Southern Hotel   69%   £B/C

H Map 19 A5 Co. Kerry
Killarney (064) 31262
Telex 73998

Credit Access, Amex, Diners, Visa
Closed early Jan–early Mar

A much-extended Victorian building set in its own extensive grounds next to the railway station. Refurbished public rooms are on the grand scale while bedrooms vary in size and style, the best being very spacious and comfortable. Ten sport rather nice rattan furniture.
Amenities garden, indoor swimming pool, sauna, solarium, keep-fit equipment, beauty salon, hairdressing, tennis, croquet, snooker, satellite TV, secretarial services, fax, laundry service.

Rooms 180	*Direct dial* Yes	*Confirm by* arrang.	*Parking* Ample
Ensuite bath/shower 180	*Room TV* Yes	*Last dinner* 9.30	*Room service* 24 hours

KILLARNEY   Torc Great Southern Hotel   61%   £E

H Map 19 A5 Co. Kerry
Park Road
Killarney (064) 31611
Telex 73807

Credit Access, Amex, Diners, Visa
Closed mid Oct–end Apr

Just half a mile from the town centre, on the Cork road, this low-rise modern hotel enjoys fine views of the Kerry mountains. Public rooms, including an open-plan lobby lounge, are bright and airy. So too are bedrooms, with their light decor, practical white units and neat, well-kept bathrooms.
Amenities garden, indoor swimming pool, sauna, tennis, in-house movies, secretarial services, laundry service, 24-hour lounge service.

Rooms 96	*Direct dial* Yes	*Confirm by* 6	*Parking* Ample
Ensuite bath/shower 96	*Room TV* Yes	*Last dinner* 9	*Room service* All day

---

■ When calling a **Dublin** number from *outside* the Republic, dial **00** *before* the number we print, **e.g.** Berkely Court is **00**01 601711

■ For the rest of the Republic, dial **010-353** then the number we print *less* the initial zero, **e.g.** Park Hotel Kenmare is **010-353** 64 41200.

KILLINEY   Court Hotel   68%   £C

H Map 19 D4 Co. Dublin
Killiney Bay
Dublin (01) 851622
Telex 33244

Credit Access, Amex, Diners, Visa
Closed 25 Dec

A beautiful position overlooking Killiney Bay is just one of the pleasing features of this handsome Victorian hotel. Intricate cornices and ornamental ceilings add to the character of the public areas, which include an attractive panelled cocktail bar and a charming conservatory looking on to the garden, which is ablaze with flowers in the summer and even boasts graceful palm trees thanks to the climate in this sheltered part of the east coast. Bedrooms in the main house have splendid views and fine period furniture; those in the modern but discreet extensions are quiet, comfortable and more contemporary. All have well-equipped bathrooms.
Amenities garden, snooker, secretarial services, laundry service.

Rooms 40	*Direct dial* Yes	*Confirm by* arrang.	*Parking* Ample
Ensuite bath/shower 40	*Room TV* Yes	*Last dinner* 10	*Room service* 24 hours

...**A** little tavern in the Rue Vavin,

Chez Clémence, who makes only one dish,

but a stupendous one: *le cassoulet de Castelnaudry...*

Clémence's cassoulet has been cooking for twenty years.

She replenishes the pot...but it is always the same cassoulet.

The basis remains, and this ancient and precious substance

gives it a taste which one finds in the paintings of old

Venetian masters, in the amber flesh-tints of their women.

ANATOLE FRANCE 1844-1924
HISTOIRE COMIQUE

We may live

without poetry, music and art;

We may live without conscience and live without heart;

We may live without friends, we may live without books,

But civilised man cannot live without cooks.

OWEN MEREDITH 1831-91
LUCILE

Sir Christopher Wren

Said, 'I am going to dine with some men.

If anybody calls

Say I'm designing St Pauls'.

E.C. BENTLEY 1875-1956
BIOGRAPHY FOR BEGINNERS

In carving a partridge

I splashed (Miss Markham) with gravy from head to foot;

and though I saw three distinct brown rills of animal juice

trickling down her cheek, she had the complaisance

to swear that not a drop had reached her.

Such circumstances are the triumph of civilised life.

SYDNEY SMITH 1771-1845

Cited by Pullar in
CONSUMING PASSIONS

KILLINEY   Fitzpatrick's Castle Hotel   71%   £A/B

H **Map 19 D4**
Co. Dublin
Dublin (01) 851533
Telex 30353

Rooms 100
Ensuite bath/shower 100
Direct dial Yes
Room TV Yes
Confirm by arrang.
Last dinner 10
Parking Ample
Room service 24 hours

Credit Access, Amex, Diners, Visa

A turreted castle, built as a private residence in 1741, has had a chequered history which includes housing a renowned smuggling family and, later, an army garrison. The elegant foyer has Louis XIV-style chairs, a Regency fireplace and plenty of fresh flowers; there's a plush cocktail bar and a characterful, exposed brick dungeon bar. Many of the bedrooms have been luxuriously refurbished with co-ordinated colour schemes and fabrics, good quality reproduction furniture and impressive tiled bathrooms; some are extremely comfortable mini-suites. No dogs. *Amenities* garden, indoor swimming pool, sauna, solarium, gymnasium, beauty salon, hairdressing, tennis, squash, satellite TV, secretarial services, laundry service.

**We welcome bona fide complaints and recommendations
on the tear-out pages at the back of the book for readers' comment.
They are followed up by our professional team.**

KINSALE   Actons Hotel   62%   £C/D

H **Map 19 B6** Co. Cork
The Pier
Cork (021) 772135
Telex 75443

Credit Access, Amex, Diners, Visa

Well-kept gardens surround this characterful quayside hotel, created from a row of handsome Georgian houses with attractive slate elevations. The public areas include a comfortable, traditional open-plan lounge and bar, and a new conference and banqueting centre. The majority of the bedrooms have been refurbished and upgraded in a pleasing fashion with fine darkwood reproduction furniture, pretty curtains and extremely smart tiled en suite bathrooms. The remaining bedrooms, more stark with functional '60s furnishings, are due to undergo a similar transformation in the near future. *Amenities* garden, indoor swimming pool, sauna, solarium, in-house movies, secretarial services, fax, laundry service, 24-hour lounge service.

| *Rooms* 57 | *Direct dial* Yes | *Confirm by* 6 | *Parking* Ample |
| *Ensuite bath/shower* 57 | *Room TV* Yes | *Last dinner* 9.30 | *Room service* Limited |

KINSALE   Blue Haven Hotel   £E

I **Map 19 B6** Co. Cork
Pearse Street
Cork (021) 772209

Credit Access, Amex, Diners, Visa

Right in the centre of town, this is an agreeable little inn with pleasant owners and staff. Bedrooms are kept in good order; best are those with private facilities (six showers, one bath). The main day room is a nautically themed bar with an attractive conservatory extension and patio beyond. There's no separate lounge, but the breakfast room is quite appealing. No dogs.

| *Rooms* 10 | *Direct dial* Yes | *Confirm by* 6 | *Parking* Difficult |
| *Ensuite bath/shower* 7 | *Room TV* Yes | *Last dinner* 10 | *Room service* Limited |

KNOCKLOFTY   Knocklofty House Hotel   66%   £D/E

H **Map 19 C5** Co. Tipperary
Nr Clonmel
Clonmel (052) 38222

Credit Access, Visa

Once the home of the Earls of Donoughmore, this substantial Georgian mansion enjoys a superb setting above the river Suir. The galleried library-lounge is particularly handsome, and there's a snug bar with leather wing chairs. Antiques and pleasing fabrics distinguish the spacious bedrooms, all of which have well-kept bathrooms. No dogs. *Amenities* garden, indoor swimming pool, solarium, whirlpool bath, keep-fit equipment, tennis, squash, croquet, clay-pigeon shooting, game fishing.

| *Rooms* 16 | *Room phone* Yes | *Confirm by* arrang. | *Parking* Ample |
| *Ensuite bath/shower* 16 | *Room TV* No | *Last dinner* 9.30 | *Room service* All day |

LETTERFRACK — Rosleague Manor Hotel — 65% — £D

H Map 18 A3 Co. Galway
(095) 41101

Credit Access, Visa
Closed 1 Nov–Easter

A peaceful and attractive Georgian house with a delightful outlook over a wooded bay. The elegant proportions of the day rooms, which include two handsome lounges, are complemented by fine oil paintings, objets d'art and antique pieces, while the individually decorated bedrooms are charming in the extreme, with solid furniture, tasteful colours and lovely views. Bathrooms are modern and practical.
Amenities garden, sauna, tennis, sea & game fishing. &

Rooms 15	*Direct dial* Yes	*Confirm by* arrang.	*Parking* Ample
Ensuite bath/shower 15	*Room TV* No	*Last dinner* 9.30	*Room service* All day

**We publish annually,
so make sure you use the current edition.
It's worth it!**

LIMERICK — Jurys Hotel — 66% — £C/D

H Map 19 B5 Co. Limerick
Ennis Road
Limerick (061) 55266
Telex 28266

Credit Access, Amex, Diners, Visa
Closed 25 Dec

On the banks of the Shannon, this 1960s hotel is notably well kept and efficiently run. The spacious foyer and adjoining coffee shop makes a bright, inviting area with its huge skylight and lush greenery, and there's a handsome bar featuring polished wood and brass. Roomy, freshly painted bedrooms have good-quality modern fittings, pleasant soft furnishings and private bathrooms. No dogs.
Amenities garden, fax, laundry service, coffee shop (7am–11pm).

Rooms 96	*Direct dial* Yes	*Confirm by* 6	*Parking* Ample
Ensuite bath/shower 96	*Room TV* Yes	*Last dinner* 11.15	*Room service* 24 hours

LIMERICK — Limerick Inn Hotel — 66% — £C

H Map 19 B5 Co. Limerick
Ennis Road
Limerick (061) 51544
Telex 70621

Credit Access, Amex, Diners, Visa

Substantial conference and leisure facilities are a popular feature at this modern hotel. There's ample lounge and bar space, and good-sized bedrooms and Executive rooms all have private facilities.
Amenities garden, indoor swimming pool, sauna, solarium, whirlpool bath, gymnasium, beauty salon, tennis, golf practice net, putting, snooker, in-house movies, secretarial services, fax, laundry service, coffee shop (7.30am–11pm), kiosk, children's playground.

Rooms 153	*Direct dial* Yes	*Confirm by* 6	*Parking* Ample
Ensuite bath/shower 153	*Room TV* Yes	*Last dinner* 9.45	*Room service* 24 hours

LIMERICK — New Greenhills Hotel — 60% — £D

H Map 19 B5 Co. Limerick
Ennis Road
Limerick (061) 53033
Telex 70246

Credit Access, Amex, Diners, Visa

Unprepossessing from without, but pleasantly smart inside, this modern, white-painted hotel just outside Limerick is conveniently placed for Shannon airport. The foyer features an attractive autumnal decor, and there's a comfortable residents' lounge and split-level bar. Practical bedrooms with modern units and tweedy fabrics all have TVs, tea-makers and decent bathrooms. No dogs. *Amenities* garden, in-house movies, secretarial services, laundry service.

Rooms 55	*Direct dial* Yes	*Confirm by* arrang.	*Parking* Ample
Ensuite bath/shower 55	*Room TV* Yes	*Last dinner* 9.45	*Room service* 24 hours

LIMERICK — Two Mile Inn Hotel — 60% — £D

H Map 19 B5 Co. Limerick
Ennis Road
Limerick (061) 53122
Telex 70157

Credit Access, Amex, Diners, Visa

Tourists and business people both like the practical comforts offered at this purpose-built former motel, which stands on the road to Shannon Airport. A sunken lobby-lounge provides plenty of seating, and there are two bars. Bedrooms with bold floral decor and fitted furniture have generally spacious bathrooms with good thick towels. Eight rooms are fitted for disabled guests. No dogs. *Amenities* garden, in-house movies, laundry service, 24-hour lounge service. &

Rooms 125	*Direct dial* Yes	*Confirm by* 6	*Parking* Ample
Ensuite bath/shower 125	*Room TV* Yes	*Last dinner* 9.30	*Room service* All day

MALLOW | Longueville House 72% | £C/D

HR **Map 19 B5** Co. Cork
Longueville
Mallow (022) 47156
Telex 75498

Rooms 16
Ensuite bath/shower 16
Direct dial Yes
Room TV No
Confirm by 6
Last dinner 9
Parking Ample
Room service All day

Credit Access, Amex, Diners, Visa
Closed Xmas–early Mar

Michael and June O'Callaghan make guests welcome at their ancestors' fine Georgian mansion home overlooking the ruins of O'Callaghan Castle. Family portraits line elegant public rooms like the splendid entrance hall and drawing room which feature intricately moulded ceilings. The bar is plush and cosy and there's a delightful Victorian conservatory. Appealing bedrooms sport good antique furniture and styl-

ish fabrics; all have well-equipped modern bathrooms. Caring service extends to beds being turned down at night and hot water bottles added. Children under ten by arrangement only. Dogs in kennels only.
Amenities garden, croquet, coarse & game fishing, games room, snooker, secretarial services, laundry service.

Presidents' Restaurant ♛

Set D £21.50
About £60 for two
Seats 40
Parties 10

The O'Callaghans' son has joined the kitchens of this elegant restaurant hung with portraits of Irish presidents. Quality ingredients are carefully handled and often combined in most interesting ways: try, perhaps, provençale vegetables with lamb fillets followed by poached turbot served with spring onions and smoked bacon, or chicken breast stuffed with leeks and blue cheese. Plentiful, garden-fresh vegetables plus tempting sweets and Irish cheeses to finish. ⊘

Lunch 12.45–2 *Dinner* 7–9
Closed Xmas–early Mar

 indicates a **well-chosen** house wine

MAYNOOTH | Moyglare Manor 77% | £B/C

HR **Map 19 C4**
Co. Kildare
Dublin (01) 286351
Telex 90358

Rooms 13
Ensuite bath/shower 13
Direct dial Yes
Room TV No
Confirm by 6
Last dinner 9.45
Parking Ample
Room service All day

Credit Access, Amex, Diners, Visa
Closed Good Fri & 23–26 Dec

Stud farms and race tracks are thick on the ground around this fine Georgian mansion in a parkland setting. Owner Norah Devlin is a keen collector of antiques and objets d'art, and the results are much in evidence in the elegant day rooms, which include various handsome lounges with open fires and a new summery lounge with big windows overlooking the garden. There are flowers everywhere, including

the spacious bedrooms comfortably furnished with antiques, stylish fabrics and quality rugs. Many beds are four-posters or half-testers. Modern bathrooms offer towelling robes and plentiful toiletries. No children under 12. No dogs.
Amenities garden, tennis, secretarial services, laundry service.

Restaurant ♛

Set L from £9.75
Set D from £14.95
About £62 for two
Seats 78
Parties 35

All is elegance at this Georgian dining room with a stylish extension, where Jim Cullinan's enjoyable menus offer well-prepared, flavourful dishes from sole meunière to the more adventurous baked plaice stuffed with shrimps or a brace of stuffed quail with burgundy sauce. Crisp crab croquettes are not to be missed, and there are some delicious puds. Good wine list includes a Tignanello '82 and Bonnes Mares (Drouhin) '78. ♟ Well-chosen ⊘

Lunch 12.45–2.15 *Dinner* 7–9.45
Closed L Sat, all Good Fri & 23–26 Dec

MOYCULLEN   Drimcong House ★   ♛ ⟨

R **Map 19 B4** Co. Galway
Nr Galway
Galway (091) 85115

Lunch Sun only 12.30–2.30
Dinner 7–10.30
Set D £14.95
About £48 for two
Seats 50
Parties 50
Parking Ample

Credit Access, Amex, Diners, Visa
Closed D Sun, all Mon & 25 Dec–
Mar

Ring the front door bell for admission to the Galvins' handsome Queen Anne House run as a restaurant on simple, elegant lines. The short menu is a delight with its imaginative use of seasonal produce from wild garlic (used in a sauce for roast pork) to wild mushrooms (featured in a rich risotto). Gerry's cooking is confidently adventurous, with subtle flavours and superb sauces. Top marks to his succulent lobster baked with fresh asparagus, and to his brandy and praline parfait with its deliciously perfumed sweet geranium sauce. Good wine list includes Nuits St Georges Clos de la Marechal (Faiveley) '82 and Mas de Daumas Gassac '79. ♟ Well-chosen ⊘

Prices quoted for the Republic of Ireland are in *Irish punts*.

NAVAN   Ardboyne Hotel   60%   £E

H **Map 18 C3** Co. Meath
Dublin Road
Navan (046) 23119

Credit Access, Amex, Diners, Visa
Closed 3 days Xmas

On the way out of Navan towards Dublin, the popular Ardboyne provides practical comforts for an overnight stop. It's also a busy conference centre and has a disco that can hold 600. Warm, well-lit bedrooms – well away from the disco – have fitted wooden furniture, armchairs and good hanging space. Breakfast could be better. No dogs. *Amenities* in-house movies, laundry service, coffee shop (8am–10pm).

Rooms 27	*Direct dial* Yes	*Confirm by* 6	*Parking* Ample
Ensuite bath/shower 27	*Room TV* Yes	*Last dinner* 10	*Room service* 24 hours

NEWBAWN   Cedar Lodge Hotel   62%   £D/E

H **Map 19 C5** Co. Wexford
Carrigbyrne, Nr New Ross
Waterford (051) 28386

Credit Access, Visa
Closed 3 weeks Jan

An attractive modern hotel on the N25 beneath the slopes of Carrigbyrne Forest. Extensive refurbishment has recently taken place and standards of repair and cleanliness are highly commendable. Exposed brick walls, an open fire and a cedar ceiling make for a pleasing lounge bar, while the foyer boasts good leather button-back chairs. Bedrooms have simple wooden units, cedar ceilings and neatly tiled bathrooms. *Amenities* garden, in-house movies. ♿

Rooms 13	*Room phone* Yes	*Confirm by* arrang.	*Parking* Ample
Ensuite bath/shower 13	*Room TV* Yes	*Last dinner* 9	*Room service* All day

NEWBRIDGE   Hotel Keadeen   71%   £D/E

H **Map 19 C4** Co. Kildare
Ballymany
Newbridge (045) 31666
Telex 60672

Rooms 37
Ensuite bath/shower 37
Direct dial Yes
Room TV Yes
Confirm by 6
Last dinner 10.30
Parking Ample
Room service 24 hours

Credit Access, Amex, Diners, Visa
Closed 2 days Xmas

Set back from the N7 just south of the town, not far from Curragh racecourse, this well-kept hotel stands in its own landscaped gardens. Comfortable public areas, like the welcoming foyer, the cosy lounge with its chintzy settees and the plush bar, are smartly modern in style. Bedrooms have been attractively refurbished, many with new beds, and all now feature stylish English fabrics with matching

bedcovers and curtains. All of the spacious, fully-tiled bathrooms now have tubs with good showers above and many offer bidets and telephone extensions. Extensive and well-appointed function facilities are also available. No dogs.
Amenities garden, in-house movies, fax, laundry service.

NEWMARKET-ON-FERGUS   Clare Inn   70%   £C/D

H Map 19 B4
Co. Clare
Limerick (061) 71161
Telex 72085

Rooms 106
Ensuite bath/shower 106
Direct dial Yes
Room TV Yes
Confirm by arrang.
Last dinner 9
Parking Ample
Room service 24 hours

Credit Access, Amex, Diners, Visa
Closed Jan–Mar

Now under new ownership and management (and no longer bearing any connection with the Dromoland Castle next door), this low-rise modern hotel enjoys splendid views of the Shannon estuary from its hilltop position. Spacious public areas include a pleasant foyer-lounge with ample seating and writing desks, a simply appointed bar carpeted in tartan overlooking the golf course, plus numerous conference suites. Comfortably furnished bedrooms are also on the generous side and have attractive coordinated fabrics, TVs, telephones and part-tiled private bathrooms with showers over small tubs. No dogs.
Amenities garden, 18-hole golf course, secretarial services, laundry service, kiosk.

NEWMARKET-ON-FERGUS   Dromoland Castle   78%   £A

H Map 19 B4
Co. Clare
Limerick (061) 71144
Telex 70654

Rooms 75
Ensuite bath/shower 75
Direct dial Yes
Room TV Yes
Confirm by arrang.
Last dinner 10.30
Parking Ample
Room service 24 hours

Credit Access, Amex, Diners, Visa

Now under new management and undergoing major refurbishment, this imposing greystone castle stands amid delightful parkland complete with a lake and golf course. Two full suits of armour flank the doors to the new entrance hall, while elegant public rooms, freshly gilded plaster friezes, ornately framed oil paintings and inviting chesterfields abound. Many bedrooms have been enlarged and now include 15 extremely spacious suites. All rooms boast good-quality mahogany furniture plus stylish wall coverings and fabrics; well-kept private bathrooms throughout. No dogs. *Amenities* garden, tennis, 18-hole golf course, croquet, clay-pigeon shooting, game fishing, bicycles, snooker, secretarial services, fax, laundry service.

If we recommend meals in a Hotel or Inn, a separate entry is made for its restaurant.

NEWPORT   Newport House   65%   £E

HR Map 18 A3 Co. Mayo
Newport (098) 41222
Telex 53740

Credit Amex, Diners, Visa
Closed end Sept–mid Mar

In the skilful hands of Kieran and Thelma Thompson, Newport House combines the charm of a fisherman's haunt with the elegance of a country house. No expense is being spared in restoring the gracious public rooms. Individually decorated bedrooms are warm and comfortable. Modern bathrooms, some with showers only, are well equipped. *Amenities* garden, croquet, sea, coarse & game fishing, games room, billiards, snooker, secretarial services, laundry service.

Rooms 20	*Direct dial* Yes	*Confirm by* arrang.	*Parking* Ample
Ensuite bath/shower 18	*Room TV* No	*Last dinner* 9.30	*Room service* 24 hours

Restaurant

Set D £20
About £55 for two
Seats 40

Home-smoked salmon is an experience not to be missed at this stylish restaurant. Enjoy it with home-made brown bread as a prelude, perhaps, to a delicately flavoured tomato soup. We enjoyed escalope of salmon with a superb sorrel sauce, followed by a faultless crème brûlée. The Irish farmhouse cheeses are excellent. Fine wine list with a powerful showing of château-bottled clarets; note too the excellent range of Chablis from Raveneau. 🍷 Well-chosen ☺

Lunch by arrang. only   *Dinner* 7.30–9.30
Closed end Sept–mid Mar

OUGHTERARD   Connemara Gateway Hotel   64%   £D

H Map 18 B3
Co. Galway
Galway (091) 82328
Telex 50905

Credit Access, Amex, Diners, Visa
Closed all Dec & Jan

A modern hotel that continues to thrive under keen private ownership. Behind a rather nondescript exterior, day rooms full of character and charm come as a pleasant surprise: note the rustic-style bar decorated with original sketches of local folk, and the quiet, comfortable lounge. Bedrooms feature attractive beds made from Connemara wood; best rooms, in a new wing, also sport brass fittings and tweedy fabrics. Three suites, again in the new wing, overlook the splendidly rugged landscape. All rooms have radios and tea-makers.
Amenities garden, outdoor swimming pool, tennis, croquet, snooker, in-house movies, secretarial services, laundry service, children's playground.

Rooms 62	*Direct dial* Yes	*Confirm by* 6	*Parking* Ample
Ensuite bath/shower 62	*Room TV* Yes	*Last dinner* 9	*Room service* All day

We publish annually,
so make sure you use the current edition.
It's worth it!

OUGHTERARD   Currarevagh House   66%   £D/E

HR Map 18 B3 Co. Galway
Galway (091) 82313

Closed Oct–Easter

June and Harry Hodgson provide a warm, house party atmosphere for guests at their civilised Victorian country mansion set in leafy gardens beside Lough Corrib. Old-fashioned charm pervades the delightful, homely drawing room; this extends to the thoughtfully tended bedrooms (some with lake views) furnished with handsome antiques. Modern bathrooms and excellent breakfasts. *Amenities* garden, tennis, croquet, coarse & game fishing, mooring, hotel boats.

Rooms 15	*Room phone* No	*Confirm by* 3	*Parking* Ample
Ensuite bath/shower 15	*Room TV* No	*Last dinner* 8	*Room service* All day

Restaurant   ⅌

Set D £14.50
About £40 for two
Seats 30
Parties 20

Guests respond eagerly to the eight o'clock gong that summons them to sit down to June Hodgson's daily-changing five-course dinner. She uses quality ingredients to produce good, traditional dishes with honest flavours, such as well-made soups, plain roasts, simply prepared vegetables and real old fashioned puddings. We enjoyed the delicious roast lamb and magnificent baked Alsaka. Good choice of farmhouse Irish cheese. Wine list includes good vintage ports. ☯

Dinner only at 8
Closed Oct–Easter

Prices quoted for the Republic of Ireland are in *Irish punts*.

OUGHTERARD   Sweeney's Oughterard House   59%   £C/D

H Map 18 B3 Co. Galway
Galway (091) 82207

Credit Access, Amex, Diners, Visa
Closed 4 days Xmas

The Higgins family have owned this creeper-clad hotel for 75 years now and their personal touch shows in the large collection of antique pieces and paintings to be found in the public areas, which include a bar and two lounges. Bedrooms vary in size, the best rooms being furnished with antiques while the smaller ones have lightwood fitted units. Bathrooms vary accordingly but all are adequate.
Amenities garden.

Rooms 20	*Direct dial* Yes	*Confirm by* arrang.	*Parking* Ample
Ensuite bath/shower 20	*Room TV* Some	*Last dinner* 8.30	*Room service* All day

PARKNASILLA | Parknasilla Great Southern Hotel 75% | £B

H Map 19 A6 Co. Kerry
Killarney (064) 45122
Telex 73899

Rooms 59
Ensuite bath/shower 59
Direct dial Yes
Room TV Yes
Confirm by 6
Last dinner 8.30
Parking Ample
Room service 24 hours

Credit Access, Amex, Diners, Visa
Closed end Oct–23 Dec & 2 Jan–
Etr

A handsome Victorian hotel with a stunning wooded setting overlooking Kenmare Bay. Public rooms are spacious, elegant and comfortable; open fires glow a welcome in the entrance hall, lounge and cocktail bar, and when the sun shines the ample terrace is a favoured spot. Two rooms commemorate Shaw, who was a frequent visitor and wrote *St Joan* here. Furniture in the bedrooms is of good, solid quality and Superior rooms are particularly appealing, with stylish drapes, new carpets and period-style easy chairs – sofas in the bigger rooms. Smart, friendly staff. No dogs. *Amenities* garden, indoor swimming pool, sauna, solarium, tennis, 9-hole golf course, games room, sea & game fishing, mooring, snooker, satellite TV, laundry service, helipad.

POULAPHOUCA | Tulfarris 70% *NEW ENTRY* | £B/C

H Map 19 C4 Co Wicklow
Blessington
Naas (045) 64574

Rooms 21
Ensuite bath/shower 21
Direct dial Yes
Room TV Yes
Confirm by 6
Last dinner 10
Parking Ample
Room service All day

Credit Access, Amex, Diners, Visa

New owners have created a comfortable and stylish hotel from a late-Georgian house overlooking Poulaphouca Lake to the front and sheltered by the Wicklow mountains to the rear. Marble fireplaces, chandeliers and sweeping drapes grace the two elegantly proportioned lounges, and there's a cheerful bar with brightly upholstered rattan seating and an open fire. Spacious bedrooms, with views of the lake or garden courtyard, combine handsome darkwood furnishings with attractive fabrics. All offer remote-control TVs, direct dial telephones, radio-alarms and excellent bathrooms equipped with lavish towels. *Amenities* garden, 9-hole golf course, putting, croquet, game fishing, snooker, secretarial services, fax, laundry service. &

PROSPEROUS | Curryhills House Hotel 55% | £E

H Map 19 C4 Co. Kildare
Nr Naas
Naas (045) 68150

Credit Access, Amex, Diners, Visa
Closed 1 wk Xmas

Homely comforts are provided for overnight guests at this converted Georgian farmhouse. Bedrooms in a new wing are plain but well kept, and all have tea-makers and smartly tiled modern bathrooms. Turf fires add to the lived-in feel of the lounges (one with TV), and there's a spacious, convivial bar where traditional Irish music is a feature of Friday nights. *Amenities* garden. &

Rooms 12	*Direct dial* Yes	*Confirm by* arrang.	*Parking* Ample
Ensuite bath/shower 12	*Room TV* No	*Last dinner* 11	*Room service* All day

★ For a *discount* on next year's guide, see **An Offer for Answers**. ★

RATHMULLAN | Rathmullan House 62% | £D/E

H Map 18 C1 Co. Donegal
Nr Letterkenny
Letterkenny (074) 58188

Credit Access, Amex, Diners, Visa
Closed end Oct–Easter

A position amid 20 acres of well-tended lawns on the banks of Lough Swilly with views across to Inch Island makes a superb setting in which to enjoy hospitable accommodation. Public areas are spacious and comfortable. Bedrooms vary from basic, budget family rooms to larger, more modern ones, some with splendid bathrooms (and one with Victorian tub complete with gold taps). No dogs. *Amenities* garden, tennis, croquet, sea fishing.

Rooms 19	*Room phone* No	*Confirm by* arrang.	*Parking* Ample
Ensuite bath/shower 16	*Room TV* No	*Last dinner* 8.30	*Room service* Limited

RATHNEW   Tinakilly House Hotel   70%   £C/D

HR **Map 19 D4** Co. Wicklow
Wicklow (0404) 69274
Telex 80412

Rooms 14
Ensuite bath/shower 14
Direct dial Yes
Room TV Yes
Confirm by arrang.
Last dinner 8.30
Parking Ample
Room service All day

Credit Access, Amex, Diners, Visa
Closed 3 days Xmas & all Jan

Built by the commander of Brunel's Great Eastern steamship, this handsome Victorian house, in seven acres of gardens, is today a welcoming and hospitable hotel. Most impressive of the lofty public rooms is the splendid entrance hall with its galleried landing, marble fireplace and antique furnishings. The air of gracious living extends to the comfortably elegant bar and library lounge. Bedrooms blend

Victorian charm with modern comforts, including smart bathrooms; the larger rooms have whirlpool baths and one has its grand original fittings. Beds are either four-posters or half-testers, and extras include magazines and hairdryers. No children under seven. No dogs. *Amenities* garden, tennis, croquet, secretarial services, laundry service.

Restaurant   *NEW ENTRY*

Set L £14
Set D £23.65
About £60 for two
Seats 70
Parties 40

Top quality local produce skilfully prepared makes for an enjoyable meal in a lofty Victorian setting. The fixed-price menu offers such delights as a feuilleté of sweetbreads with wild mushrooms, lovely plump scallops in a beurre blanc, as well as Wicklow lamb, breast of pigeon, and brill in a lettuce and lime sauce. The home-baked bread is particularly good. Nice desserts or cheese for afters. ❷

Lunch 1–2   *Dinner* 7.30–8.30
Closed 3 days Xmas & all Jan

**Our inspectors *never* book in the name of Egon Ronay's Guides.
They disclose their identity only if they are considering an establishment
for inclusion in the next edition of the Guide.**

RENVYLE   Renvyle House Hotel   64%   £D

H **Map 18 A3** Co. Galway
Clifden (095) 43511
Telex 50896

Credit Access, Amex, Diners, Visa
Closed 6 Jan–Feb & mid Nov–
mid Dec

A warm welcome is guaranteed at this comfortable hotel. Peat fires, parquet flooring and a natural beech staircase add character to the pleasant lounge/reception; other public rooms include a leafy conservatory and a book-lined library/snooker room. Some bedrooms are simply furnished, but the majority are spacious and modern with more luxurious facilities. Sloping ceilings and dormer windows add appeal to the attic rooms, while eight family rooms have balconies. *Amenities* garden, outdoor swimming pool, sauna, solarium, keep-fit equipment, tennis, 9-hole golf course, putting, bowling green, croquet, riding, shooting, sea, coarse & game fishing, boating, in-house movies, laundry service, children's playground.

Rooms 70	*Direct dial* Yes	*Confirm by* arrang.	*Parking* Ample
Ensuite bath/shower 70	*Room TV* Some	*Last dinner* 9	*Room service* All day

RIVERSTOWN   Coopershill   58%   £D/E

H **Map 18 B2** Co. Sligo
Sligo (071) 65108

Credit Access, Amex, Visa
Closed end Oct–end Mar

Coopershill is a lovely old house, built in 1774 and standing in 500 acres of woods and farmland. There's a relaxing, family feel to the day rooms, with antiques and cheerful fires in evidence. Spacious bedrooms, with individual heating controls, are supplied with tea-makers, hairdryers and books; one room has a four-poster, two others half-testers. *Amenities* garden, coarse & game fishing, laundry service.

Rooms 6	*Room phone* No	*Confirm by* arrang.	*Parking* Ample
Ensuite bath/shower 4	*Room TV* No	*Last dinner* 8.30	*Room service* Limited

ROSSES POINT — Reveries ♛ ⌕

R **Map 18 B2**
Co. Sligo
Sligo (071) 77371

Set D £17.85
About £50 for two
Seats 48
Parties 18
Parking Ample
Credit Access, Visa

Sophisticated decor, Rosenthal porcelain and fine views from the picture windows give this restaurant an air of luxury which is complemented by the imaginative and competent cooking of Paula Brennan. Local produce includes fresh fish, home-grown vegetables and wonderful Irish cheeses. Start with cassolette of mussels topped with pastry and move on to wild Irish salmon or fricassee of chicken with ginger and lemon on pilau rice. Excellent sweets. ☺

Dinner only 7.30–10
Closed Sun, Mon, 2 wks Nov & 4 days Xmas

Changes in data sometimes occur in establishments
after the Guide goes to press.
Prices should be taken as indications rather than firm quotes.

ROSSLARE — Casey's Cedars Hotel 62% £E

H **Map 19 D5** Co. Wexford
Strand Road
Wexford (053) 32124
Telex 80237

Credit Amex, Diners
Closed Jan

A white-painted hotel rebuilt by its family owners in 1980. Decent-size bedrooms have darkwood furniture and tiled bathrooms with shower over the tubs. The main public area is a vast bar in red plush with a dance floor and regular entertainment. There's also a very well-furnished lounge. Some aspects of service and housekeeping could be improved. No dogs.
Amenities garden, sauna, solarium, keep-fit equipment.

Rooms 34	Direct dial Yes	Confirm by arrang.	Parking Ample
Ensuite bath/shower 34	Room TV Yes	Last dinner 10	Room service All day

ROSSLARE — Kelly's Strand Hotel 72% £E

H **Map 19 D5** Co. Wexford
Strand Road
Wexford (053) 32114
Telex 80111

Rooms 89
Ensuite bath/shower 89
Direct dial Yes
Room TV Yes
Confirm by arrang.
Last dinner 9.15
Parking Ample
Room service 24 hours

Closed early Dec–late Feb

Outstanding leisure facilities, high standards of housekeeping and friendly, efficient service make this popular, beach-side hotel a splendid choice for family holidays. Extensive public areas include numerous smart, comfortable lounges and bars enhanced by a fine collection of Irish contemporary art. Bright, fresh bedrooms have good tiled bath or shower rooms complete with good toiletries and bath-

robes. Book well ahead. Courtesy transport. No dogs. *Amenities* garden, indoor and outdoor swimming pools, sauna, solarium, whirlpool bath, gymnasium, beauty salon, hairdressing, tennis, squash, badminton, croquet, bicycles, games room, snooker, in-house movies, laundry service, laundry room, fax, creche, childrens' play area. &

ROSSNOWLAGH — Sand House Hotel 68% £D

H **Map 18 B2** Co. Donegal
Bundoran (072) 51777
Telex 40460

Credit Access, Amex, Diners, Visa
Closed Oct–Easter

A solid, comfortable seaside hotel run by the Britton family and their staff on good old-fashioned principles of service. A spacious Victorian-style reception-lounge sets the tone for the day rooms, which include various other lounges and several cosy bars (one with a sea theme and its own entrance from the beach). Stylish antiques are much in evidence. Bedrooms vary in size, decor and furnishings, but all are pleasantly light and the majority enjoy sea views. Excellent modern bathrooms. Housekeeping throughout is of a good standard.
Amenities garden, tennis, croquet, sea & game fishing, board sailing, canoeing, games room.

Rooms 40	Direct dial Yes	Confirm by 5	Parking Ample
Ensuite bath/shower 40	Room TV No	Last dinner 9	Room service All day

SCOTSHOUSE | Hilton Park 64% | £D

H Map 18 C3 Co. Monaghan
Nr Clones
Monaghan (047) 56007

Credit Amex
Closed Oct–Mar

A porticoed mansion set in 600 acres overlooking hills, woodland and a pretty lake. Johnny and Lucy Madden run it as a family home and guests will soon discover that a very friendly, informal atmosphere prevails. First-floor day rooms include a splendid drawing room with a cheerful log fire, lived-in leather arm chairs, oil paintings and fine antiques. Books are in plentiful supply, and there's a cosy little TV room. Large bedrooms also feature antiques, and some rooms have four-poster beds. Central heating keeps things cosy, and there are lovely parkland views. Super breakfasts. No children under 12. No dogs. *Amenities* garden, 9-hole golf course, croquet, shooting, coarse fishing, rowing boat.

Rooms 5	*Room phone* No	*Confirm by* arrang.	*Parking* Ample
Ensuite bath/shower 2	*Room TV* No	*Dinner at* 8	*Room service* None

SHANAGARRY | Ballymaloe House 63% | £C/D

HR Map 19 C6 Co. Cork
Nr Midleton
Cork (021) 652531
Telex 75208

Credit Access, Amex, Diners, Visa

Delightful parkland dotted with sheep surrounds this creeper-clad country house. The Allens run it with charm and efficiency, maintaining a relaxed, homely feel in the day rooms which include a gracefully proportioned lounge. Bedrooms vary in style, some traditional with antique furniture and huge bathrooms while others, located in a converted stable block, are more modern. No dogs. *Amenities* garden, outdoor swimming pool, tennis, croquet, laundry service.

Rooms 30	*Direct dial* Yes	*Confirm by* arrang.	*Parking* Ample
Ensuite bath/shower 30	*Room TV* No	*Last dinner* 9.30	*Room service* All day

Restaurant

Set L from £11
Set D £21
About £56 *for two*
Seats 80
Parties 25

Contemporary Irish paintings line the walls of the four rooms that form the dining area. The cooking is French in influence, while many of the ingredients – lamb, vegetables, herbs – come from the Allens' own land. Start perhaps with an excellent pâté, then move on to Ballycotton salmon with hollandaise and buttered cucumber. Simple sweets from the trolley to finish. Splendid choice of clarets, with nine '70s and 16 '75s.

Lunch at 1   *Dinner* 7–9.30
Closed 3 days Xmas

SHANNON | Shannon International Hotel 61% | £C/D

H Map 19 B5 Co. Clare
Shannon Airport
Shannon (061) 61122
Telex 72072

Credit Access, Amex, Diners, Visa
Closed 1 Nov–1 Apr

A modern, no-frills hotel close to the airport, the Shannon is well geared to the needs of air travellers. Luggage is transported free between hotel and air terminal and flight information is on display in the foyer. The pleasant, comfortable lounge overlooks the estuary. The bedrooms are spacious and extremely practical and excellent bathrooms have first-rate shower units. No dogs. *Amenities* garden, in-house movies, secretarial services, laundry service. &

Rooms 120	*Direct dial* Yes	*Confirm by* 6	*Parking* Ample
Ensuite bath/shower 120	*Room TV* Yes	*Last dinner* 8.45	*Room service* 24 hours

 indicates a **well-chosen** house wine

SLIGO | Sligo Park Hotel 55% | £D/E

H Map 18 B2 Co. Sligo
Pearse Road
Sligo (071) 60291
Telex 40397

Credit Access, Amex, Diners, Visa

A modern hotel on the Dublin road offering clean, spacious and practical accommodation. Green and brown are the colours used in the uniform bedrooms with neatly designed bathrooms. A new leisure centre is to be added to the day rooms, which include a large cane-furnished bar with picture windows looking out over well-kept grounds. *Amenities* garden, in-house movies, secretarial services, fax, laundry service.

Rooms 62	*Direct dial* Yes	*Confirm by* 6	*Parking* Ample
Ensuite bath/shower 62	*Room TV* Yes	*Last dinner* 9.15	*Room service* 24 hours

SPIDDAL — Bridge House Hotel — £E/F

Map 19 B4
Co. Galway
Galway (091) 83118

Credit Access, Amex, Diners, Visa
Closed 1 wk Xmas

Modest comforts in a spotlessly kept inn that's easily found on the main road through Spiddal. Reception has plenty of seating space, but the nicest day room is a large pine-panelled bar with access to the garden. Bedrooms are very basic in their appointments (no phone or television – but there's a little TV lounge) and three of the private bathrooms are shower/WC only. No dogs.
Amenities garden, laundry service, coffee shop (noon–10pm).

Rooms 14	*Room phone* No	*Confirm by* 7	*Parking* Ample
Ensuite bath/shower 8	*Room TV* No	*Last dinner* 10	*Room service* All day

Prices quoted for the Republic of Ireland are in *Irish punts*.

WATERFORD — Ardree Hotel 59% — £C/D

Map 19 C5 Co. Waterford
Ferrybank
Waterford (051) 32111
Telex 80684

Credit Access, Amex, Diners, Visa
Closed 25 & 26 Dec

A functional modern hotel with views of the quayside, the river Suir and the town beyond. The bar and foyer are designed for large numbers of visitors, and bedrooms and bathrooms are straightforward and practical. Staff are pleasant, but housekeeping and maintenance are not strong points. A leisure centre is due to open as we publish. No dogs.
Amenities garden, tennis, in-house movies.

Rooms 100	*Direct dial* Yes	*Confirm by* 6	*Parking* Ample
Ensuite bath/shower 100	*Room TV* Yes	*Last dinner* 9.15	*Room service* 24 hours

WATERFORD — Granville Hotel 69% — £D/E

Map 19 C5 Co. Waterford
Waterford (051) 55111
Telex 80188

Credit Access, Amex, Diners, Visa
Closed 25 & 26 Dec

Standards of accommodation are high at this well-run quayside hotel. The central hall is graced by a chandelier, grandfather clock and marble fireplace, while period-style easy chairs offer comfort in the small lounge. Bedrooms have undergone major refurbishment and the best ones boast good quality Regency-style furniture and stylish fabrics. Good-sized bathrooms have smart tiling. No dogs. *Amenities* satellite TV, laundry service, coffee shop (12.30pm–10.30pm).

Rooms 66	*Direct dial* Yes	*Confirm by* arrang.	*Parking* Limited
Ensuite bath/shower 66	*Room TV* Yes	*Last dinner* 9.30	*Room service* 24 hours

WATERFORD — Tower Hotel 57% — £D

Map 19 C5 Co. Waterford
The Mall
Waterford (051) 75801
Telex 80699

Credit Access, Amex, Diners, Visa
Closed 2 days Xmas

On the quayside at the eastern end of town, the Tower is a modern hotel offering modest comforts for an overnight stop. Bedrooms are straightforward, the best having been refurnished with decent lightwood units; all rooms have serviceable tiled bathrooms with showers over the tubs. Nicest of the day rooms is the mahogany-panelled bar – much more attractive than the lobby with its rather tatty banquettes.

Rooms 80	*Direct dial* Yes	*Confirm by* 7	*Parking* Limited
Ensuite bath/shower 80	*Room TV* Yes	*Last dinner* 10	*Room service* 24 hours

WATERFORD — Waterford Castle *NEW ENTRY* — £A

Map 19 C5 The Island
Ballinakill
Waterford (051) 78203

Rooms 20
Ensuite bath/shower 20
Direct dial Yes
Room TV Yes
Confirm by arrang.
Last dinner 10.30
Parking Ample
Room service 24 hours

Credit Access, Amex, Diners, Visa

A chain ferry provides the only access to this splendid island castle, long the Fitzgerald family seat. It has been acquired by entrepreneur Edward Kearns who has converted it with considerable style and flair. A specially made carpet echoing the coat of arms above the massive fireplace in the hall sets the tone for sumptuous public areas and beautifully furnished bedrooms with antiques or fine reproduction pieces have elaborately decorated old-style bathrooms. As it was on the point of opening when we visited, we are unable to grade it for 1989. No dogs.
Amenities garden, indoor swimming pool, tennis, riding, shooting, clay-pigeon shooting, sea, coarse and game fishing, bicycles, fax, laundry service.

WATERVILLE — Huntsman ᶐ

RR Map 19 A6
Co. Kerry
Waterville (0667) 4124

Set L £12
Set D £17.50
About £50 for two
Seats 80
Parties 100
Parking Ample

Credit Access, Amex, Diners, Visa

Super-fresh seafood is the great attraction of Raymond and Deirdre Hunt's unpretentious, appealing restaurant with panoramic marine views. Oysters, mussels, jumbo prawns and sole are handled with loving care, while meat-eaters can console themselves with steak chasseur or noisettes of Kerry lamb. Vegetables too get respectful treatment – even the sauté potatoes pass muster – while other pluses include excellent bread, well-kept Irish cheeses, and warm-hearted service. ☺

Lunch 12–3   *Dinner* 6–10
Closed Nov–May

BEDROOMS 6   £F
With bath/shower 2

Accommodation comprises prettily decorated twin rooms or self-catering two-bedroom apartments with TVs. No dogs.

WATERVILLE — Waterville Lake Hotel   62%   £C/D

H Map 19 A6 Co. Kerry
Waterville (0667) 4133
Telex 73806

Credit Access, Amex, Diners, Visa
Closed mid Oct–mid April

There is a colonial look to this spacious modern hotel overlooking Lough Currane. Day rooms include a vast reception area with comfortable seating and a large first-floor lounge and bar. Many of the bedrooms have been upgraded, with new furniture, carpets and accessories. There are several suites. No dogs. *Amenities* garden, indoor swimming pool, sauna, solarium, whirlpool bath, tennis, golf course, coarse & game fishing, snooker, fax, laundry service.

Rooms 80	*Direct dial* Yes	*Confirm by* arrang.	*Parking* Ample
Ensuite bath/shower 80	*Room TV* Yes	*Last dinner* 9.30	*Room service* 24 hours

---

■ When calling a **Dublin** number
from *outside* the Republic, dial
00 *before* the number we print,
e.g. Berkely Court is
0001 601711

■ For the rest of the Republic,
dial **010-353** then the number
we print *less* the initial zero,
e.g. Park Hotel Kenmare is
010-353 64 41200.

WEXFORD — White's Hotel   59%   £E

H Map 19 D5 Co. Wexford
George Street
Wexford (053) 22311
Telex 80630

Credit Access, Amex, Diners, Visa
Closed 25 Dec

Owned by the same family since 1880, this friendly town-centre hotel boasts a smart new conservatory-style entrance. An open fire warms the spacious foyer, and there's a plushly comfortable bar-lounge plus a quarry-tiled coffee shop. Practical bedrooms in the original building and modern five-storey block all offer simple furniture and pleasing fabrics.
Amenities in-house movies, coffee shop (8am–9.30pm).

Rooms 74	*Direct dial* Yes	*Confirm by* arrang.	*Parking* Ample
Ensuite bath/shower 74	*Room TV* Yes	*Last dinner* 9.45	*Room service* 24 hours

---

Prices quoted for the Republic of Ireland are in *Irish punts*.

WICKLOW — Old Rectory   60%   £D/E

HR Map 19 D4
Co. Wicklow
Wicklow (0404) 67048

Credit Access, Amex, Diners, Visa
Closed end Oct–Easter

Paul and Linda Saunders run their nice old Victorian rectory on the edge of town in a personal, friendly style. A welcoming fire blazes in the marble fireplace of the pleasant lounge, furnished with period pieces, while the tastefully decorated bedrooms also have some pleasing antiques. Thoughtful touches include magazines and mineral water, and the well-kept bathrooms offer good toiletries and towels. No dogs. *Amenities* garden.

Rooms 6	*Room phone* Yes	*Confirm by* arrang.	*Parking* Ample
Ensuite bath/shower 5	*Room TV* No	*Last dinner* 7.30, Fri & Sat 9	*Room service* None
			see over

Restaurant *NEW ENTRY* ♀

Set D £18.50
About £45 for two
Seats 12
Parties 12

The great attraction of this lofty dining room – surprisingly furnished in modern style – is Linda Saunders' excellent cooking. Interesting and adventurous dishes range from lobster Malibu – lobster and fresh pineapple tossed in coconut liqueur – to turkey breast flambéed in whisky with apricots and cream. Other successes included delicious country soup, tender spiced beef, and a very pretty strawberry roulade. Friendly service by husband Paul.

Dinner 7.30, Fri & Sat 9
Closed End Oct to Easter

YOUGHAL Aherne's Seafood Restaurant ♀

R **Map 19 C6** Co. Cork
163 North Main Street
Youghal (024) 92424

Set L £7.95 **Set D** £13.50
About £45 for two
Seats 60 *Parties* 60
Parking Ample

Credit Access, Amex, Diners, Visa

It's seafood almost all the way at the Fitzgibbons' popular restaurant where oysters, mussels and lobsters share a tank. Huge local prawns are highly prized, and Dover sole meunière, Blackwater salmon and sea bass baked in orange juice and wine are other delights. A decent cellar includes very good house wines. Bar snacks are served between 11.30am and 10.30pm. No children under ten. ♀ Well-chosen ℮

Lunch 12.30–2.15 *Dinner* 6.30–10, Sun 6.30–9.30
Closed L Sun, all Mon (except July & Aug), Good Fri & 4 days Xmas

Opening doors to the World of books

Book Tokens can be bought and exchanged at most bookshops

AN OFFER FOR ANSWERS

A DISCOUNT ON THE NEXT GUIDE

■ Readers' answers to questionnaires included in the Guide prove invaluable to us in planning future editions, either through their reactions to the contents of the current Guide, or through the tastes and inclinations indicated. Please send this tear-out page to us *after you have used the Guide for some time*, addressing the envelope to:

Egon Ronay's Guides
City Wall House
Basing View
Basingstoke
Hampshire RG21 2AP

■ As a token of thanks for your help, we will enable respondents to obtain the 1990 Guide post free from us at a 33⅓% discount off the retail price. We will send you an order form before publication, but answering the questionnaire imposes no obligation to purchase.
All answers will be treated in confidence.

This offer closes 30 June 1989.
Open to UK residents only.

---

1 Are You

Male? ☐   Under 21? ☐   31–45? ☐   over 65? ☐
Female? ☐   21–30? ☐   46–65? ☐

---

2 Your occupation

. . . .

---

3 Do you have any previous editions of this Guide?

1986 ☐   1987 ☐   1988 ☐

---

4 Do you refer to this Guide

Four times a week? ☐   Once a week? ☐
Three times a week? ☐   Once a fortnight? ☐
Twice a week? ☐   Once a month? ☐

---

5 How many people, apart from yourself, are likely to consult this Guide (including those in your home and place of work)?

. . . .

---

6 Are you likely to use the 'Bargain Break' Section?

Yes ☐   No ☐

---

7 Do you have our 'Just a Bite' Guide?

1987 ☐   1988 ☐   1989 ☐

893

8 Do you have our Pub Guide?

1987 ☐   1988 ☐   1989 ☐

9 How many times have you travelled overseas in the past year?

Business ☐   Pleasure ☐

10 How many nights have you spent in hotels during the past year?

Business ☐   Pleasure ☐

11 Do you occupy more than one home?

Yes ☐   No ☐

Do you own the house you live in?

Yes ☐   No ☐

12 Your car

type... year........

13 What is your daily newspaper?

....

14 Which of the following credit cards do you use?

Access ☐   Diners ☐
American Express ☐   Visa ☐

15 What fields would you like us to survey or what improvements do you suggest?

....
....
....

■ Please *print* your name and address here if you would like us to send you a pre-publication order form for the 1990 Hotel & Restaurant Guide.

Name ....

Address ....

....

....

Proposed coverage to mid 1989

The coverage area shown on this map indicates where, in most circumstances, it should be possible to make and receive calls on the Cellnet System using a vehicle mounted telephone (cellphone).

The coverage for hand-held portables is generally less wide, particularly in rural areas.

Coverage may be affected by atmospheric conditions, topographical features, or by system engineering and maintenance requirements.

The introduction of new cells may be subject to delays in obtaining planning permission, owner's consent detailed radio survey work etc.

For further information see the Cellnet section pages 24-30.

○ Proposed Coverage mid 1989

Cellnet
THE CELLPHONE NETWORK

France

Maps

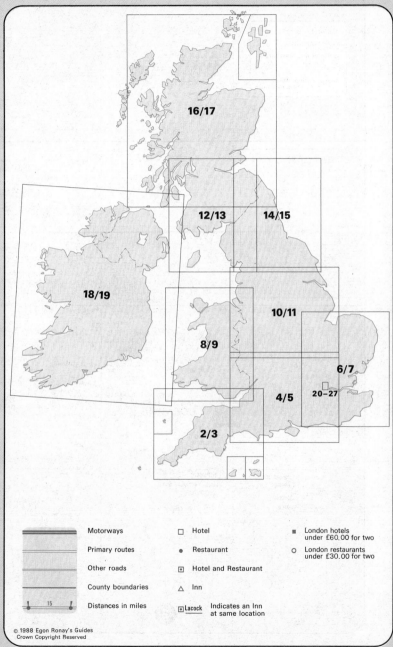

Motorways	□ Hotel	■ London hotels under £60.00 for two
Primary routes	● Restaurant	○ London restaurants under £30.00 for two
Other roads	▣ Hotel and Restaurant	
County boundaries	△ Inn	
Distances in miles	▣ Lacock Indicates an Inn at same location	

© 1988 Egon Ronay's Guides
Crown Copyright Reserved

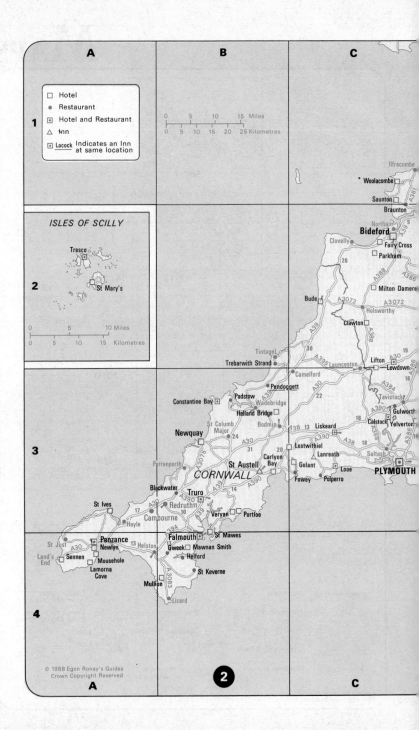

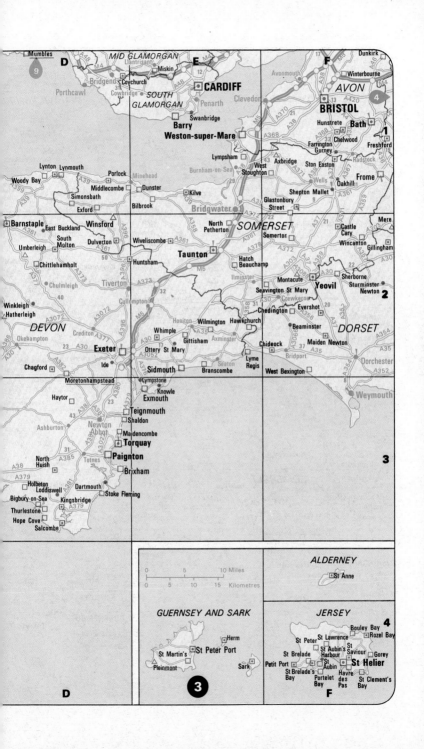

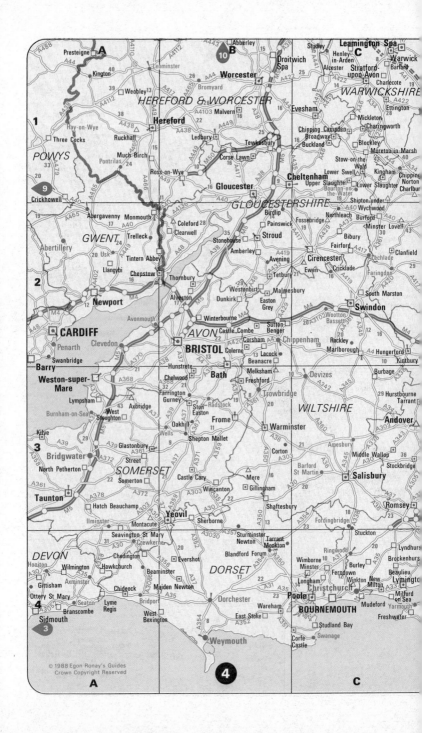

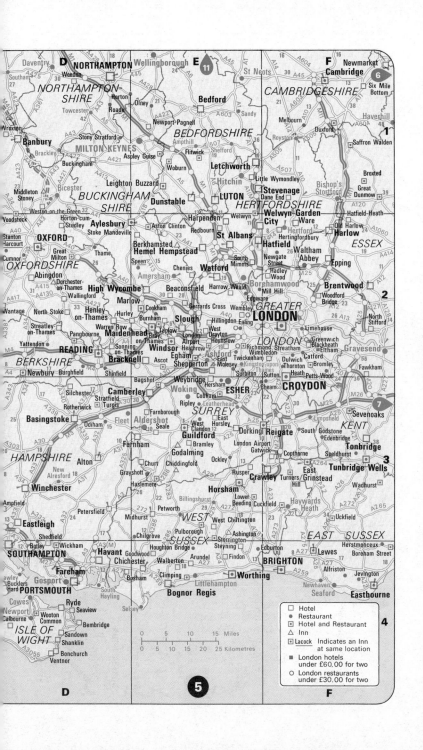

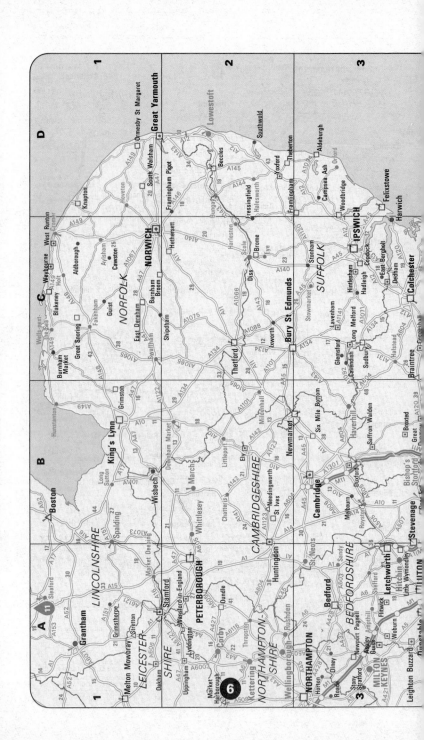

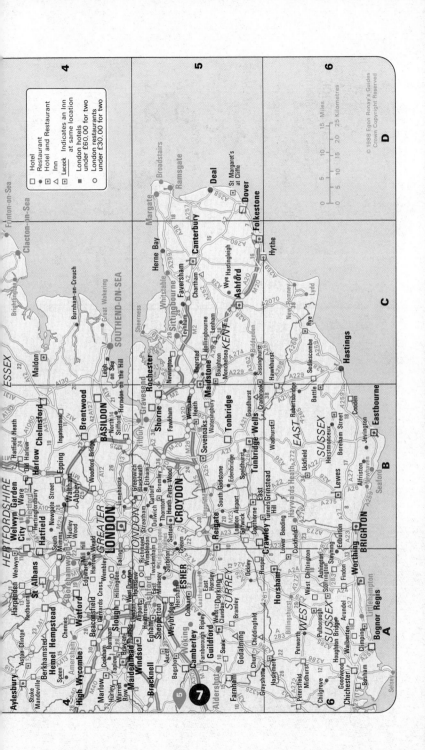

Hotel
Restaurant
Hotel and Restaurant
Inn
Lacock Indicates an Inn
at same location

■ London hotels
under £60.00 for two
○ London restaurants
under £30.00 for two

© 1988 Egon Ronay's Guides
Crown Copyright Reserved

0   5   10   15 Miles
0 5 10 .15 20 25 Kilometres

4
5
6
D
C
B
A

7
⑤
④

HERTFORDSHIRE
ESSEX
GREATER LONDON
LONDON
SOUTHEND-ON-SEA
SURREY
WEST SUSSEX
EAST SUSSEX
KENT

Frinton-on-Sea
Clacton-on-Sea
Brightlingsea
Maldon
Burnham-on-Crouch
Great Wakering
Leigh on Sea
Horndon on the Hill
Broadstairs
Ramsgate
Margate
Deal
St. Margaret's at Cliffe
Dover
Folkestone
Hythe
Herne Bay
Whitstable
Faversham
Canterbury
Chartham
Wye Hastingleigh
Ashford
Sittingbourne
Teynham
Rochester
Gravesend
Sheerness
Hollingbourne
Lenham
Bearsted
Maidstone
Boughton Monchelsea
Biddenden
Sissinghurst
Hawkhurst
Cranbrook
Goudhurst
Tonbridge
Tunbridge Wells
Edenbridge
Wadhurst
New Romney
Lydd
Rye
Sedlescombe
Battle
Hastings
Robertsbridge
Cooden
Eastbourne
Herstmonceux
Boreham Street
Jevington
Alfriston
Newhaven
Seaford
Lewes
Uckfield
Haywards Heath
BRIGHTON
Worthing
Littlehampton
Bognor Regis
Arundel
Walberton
Climping
Chichester
Bosham
Selsey
Goodwood
Midhurst
Petworth
Pulborough
Houghton Bridge
Billingshurst
West Chiltington
Ashington
Steyning
Findon
Storrington
Lower Beeding
Handcross
Horsham
Rusper
Crawley
Gatwick
London Airport
East Grinstead
Turners Hill
Copthorne
Reigate
Redhill
CROYDON
South Godstone
Godstone
Oxted
Speldhurst
Petersfield
Chilgrove
Haslemere
Grayshott
Churt
Chiddingfold
Godalming
Seale
Guildford
Bramley
Clandon
Dorking
Leatherhead
East Horsley
Cobham
ESHER
Epsom
Sutton
Carshalton
Thornton Heath
Purley
Beckenham
Bromley
Petts Wood
Orpington
Catford
Dulwich
Streatham
Dartford
Greenwich
Woolwich
Eltham
Sidcup
Shorne
Fawkham
Stone
Wrotham
Heath
Wateringbury
West Malling
Sevenoaks
Newington
Farnham
Aldershot
Camberley
Bagshot
Ascot
Bracknell
Windsor
Cookham
Burnham
Taplow
Maidenhead
Bray
Warren Row
Hurley
Marlow
High Wycombe
Amersham
Chenies
Speen
Stoke Mandeville
Aston Clinton
Aylesbury
Berkhamsted
Hemel Hempstead
Harpenden
Redbourn
St. Albans
Watford
Beaconsfield
Gerrards Cross
Hillingdon
West Drayton
Slough
Heathrow Airport
Hounslow
Richmond
Kingston
Twickenham
Wembley
Ealing
Edgware
Mill Hill
Hadley Wood
South Mimms
Hatfield
Welwyn
Welwyn Garden City
Hertford
Hertingfordbury
Ware
Hatfield Heath
Harlow
Old Harlow
Newgate Street
Epping
Waltham Abbey
Woodford Bridge
Loughton
Brentwood
Ingatestone
BASILDON
Chelmsford
Stifford
Weybridge
Shepperton
Hersham
Walton
Molesey
Egham
Woking
Ripley
Farnborough
Chelsfield

A41 A413 A40 M40 A404 M4 A308 A30 M3 A31 A3 A287 A325 A286 A283 A29 A27 A259 A280 A24 A264 A272 A281 A261 A285 A286 A22 A26 A23 A25 M25 A21 M20 A2 A20 A229 A228 A227 A262 A274 A249 A257 A258 A256 A260 A259 A20 A2070 M2 A299 A28 A251 M23 A217 A22 A25 A3 A232 A23 A30 A316 A406 A41 A13 A127 A130 A414 A120 M11 A11 A10 A1000 A414 A131 A12 A127

KENT
EAST SUSSEX
WEST SUSSEX

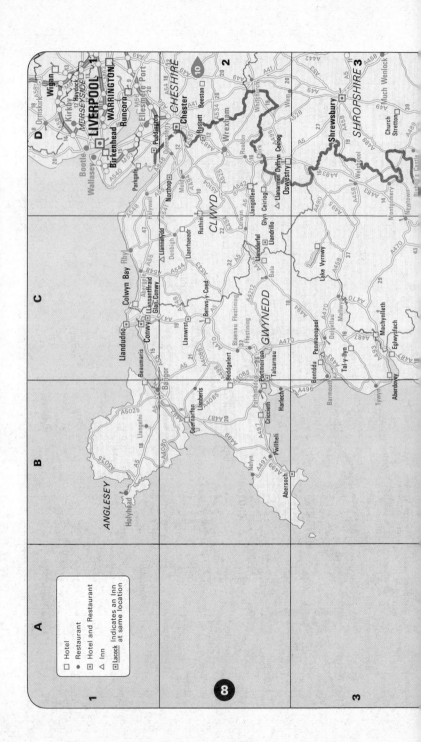

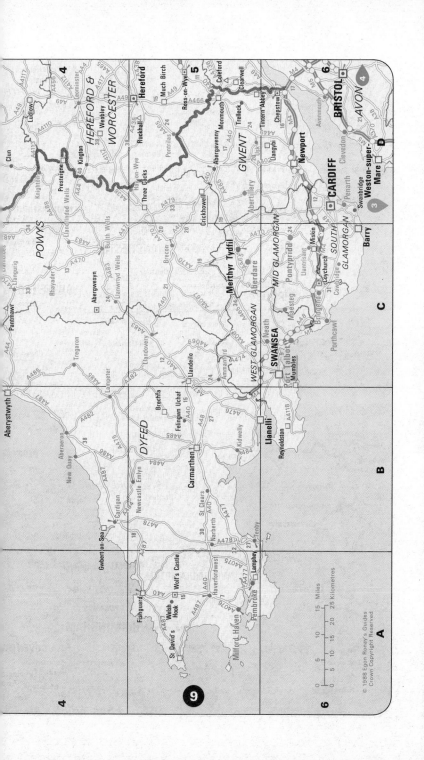

© 1988 Egon Ronay's Guides
Crown Copyright Reserved

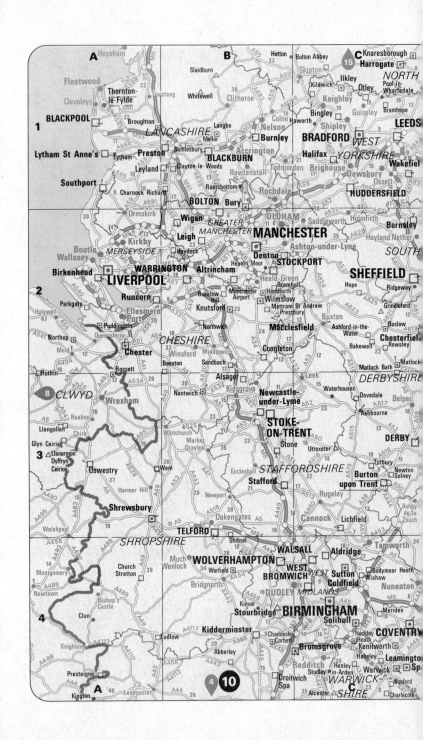

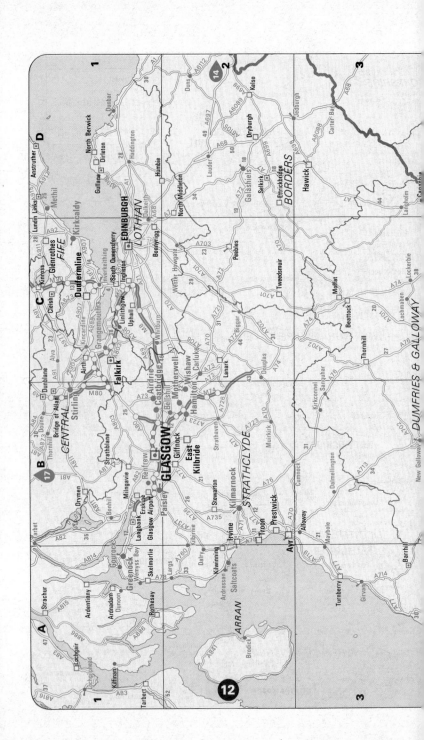

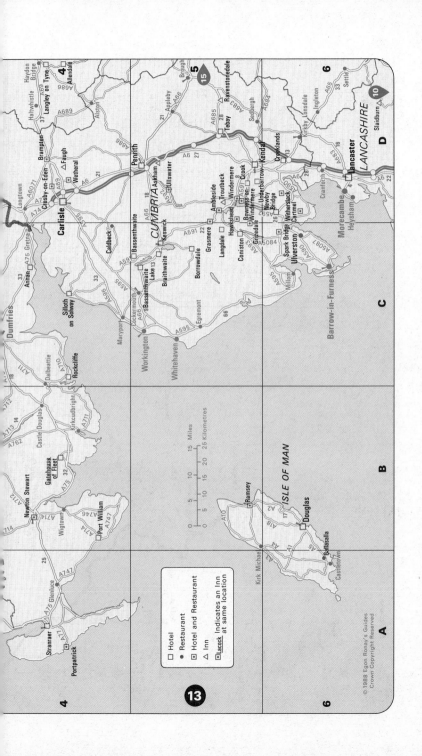

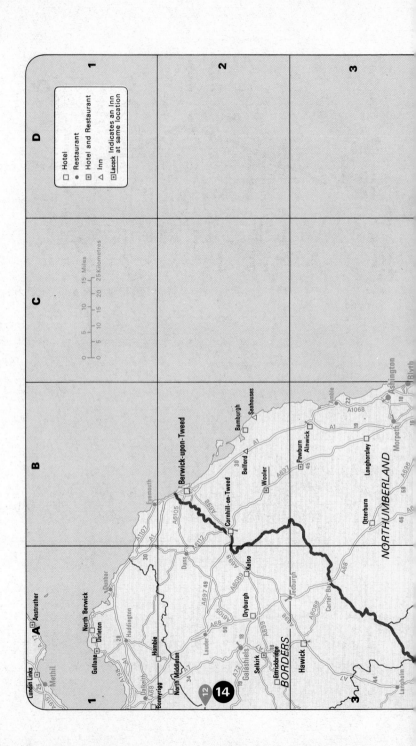

12
14

Legend:
□ Hotel
● Restaurant
⊡ Hotel and Restaurant
△ Inn
Lacock Indicates an Inn at same location

0 5 10 15 Miles
0 5 10 15 20 25 Kilometres

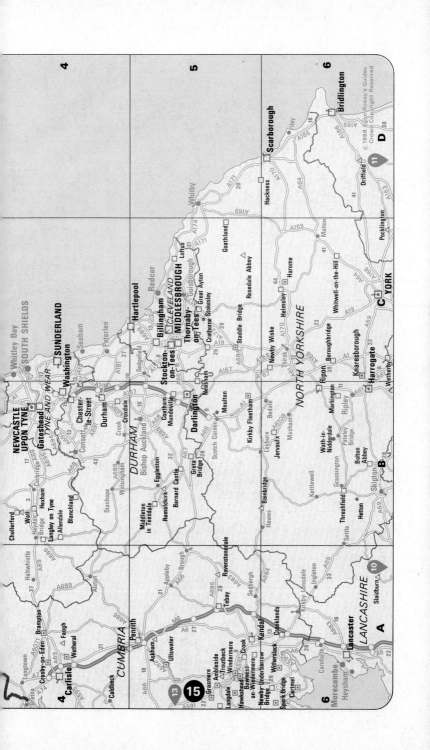

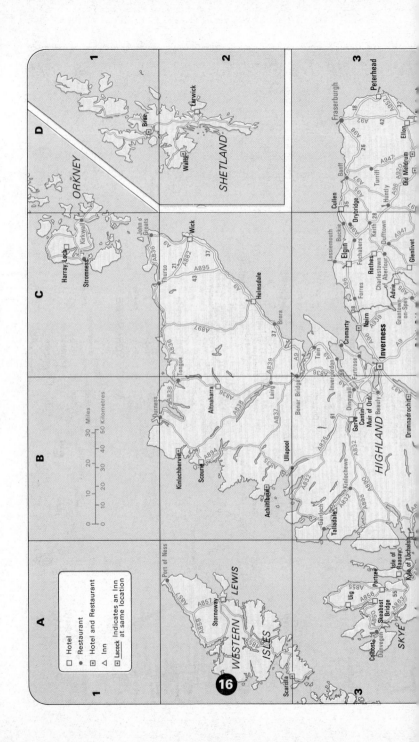

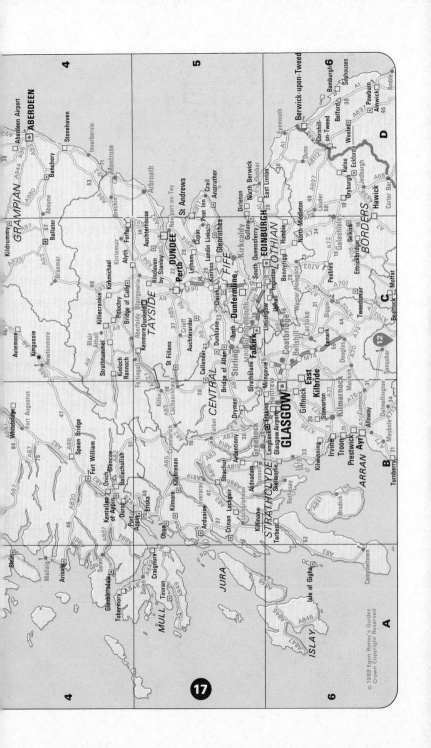

17

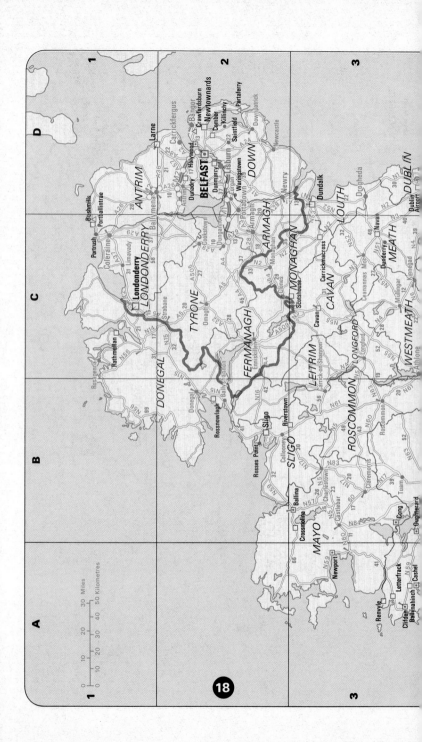

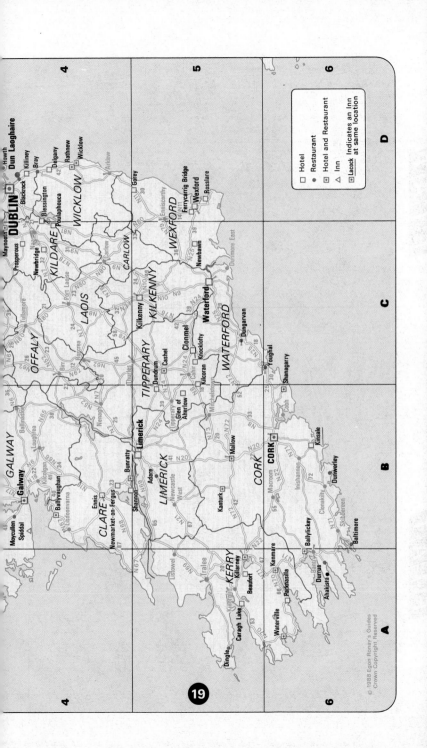

Hotel

Restaurant

Hotel and Restaurant

△ Inn

Lacock Indicates an Inn
at same location

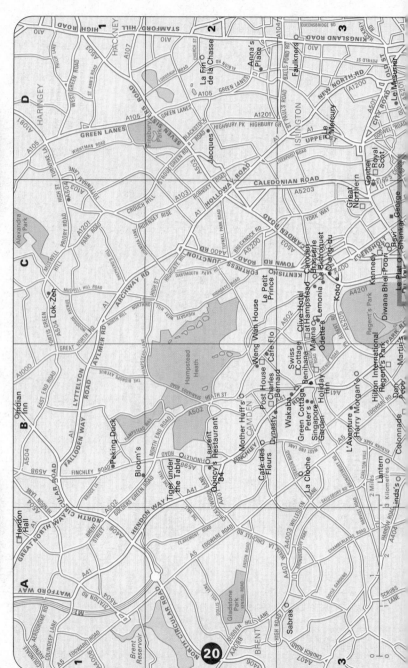

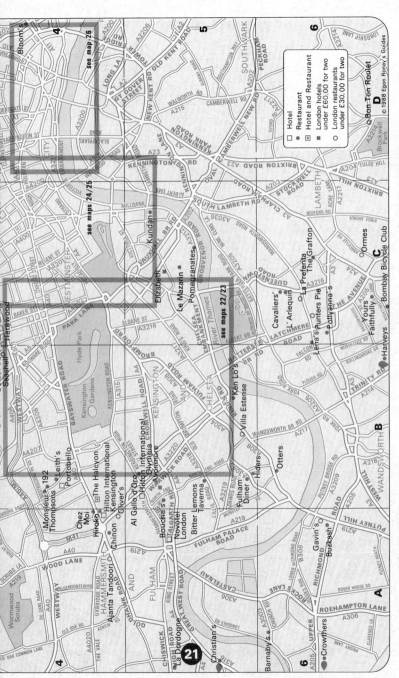

Hotel □
Restaurant ●
Hotel and Restaurant ◖
London hotels ■
under £60.00 for two
London restaurants ○
under £30.00 for two

F/I/A/T See pages 158-161 for list of dealers in London

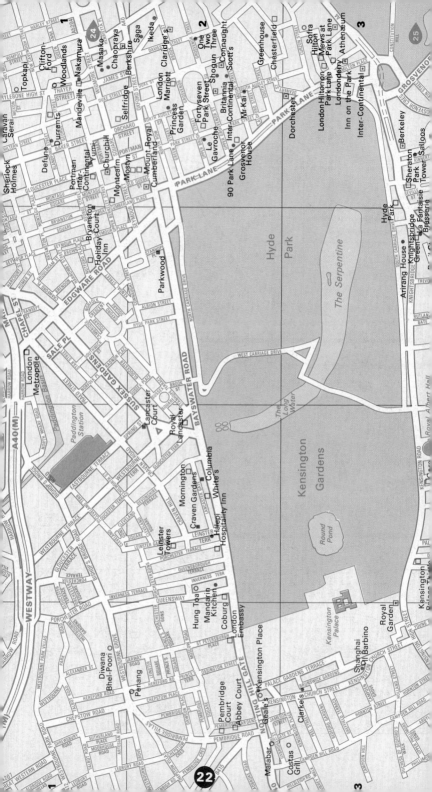

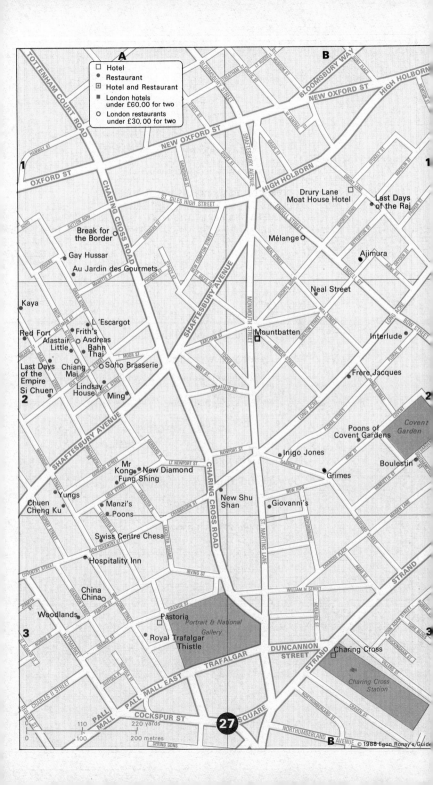

Gastronomy...

the intelligent knowledge of whatever

concerns man's nourishment.

BRILLAT-SAVARIN 1755-1826
PHYSIOLOGIE DU GOÛT

' **C**uisine ' means that

Things taste just like what they are!

CURNONSKY 1872-1956
' To Melanie Rouat '

Strange to say

how a good dinner and feasting

reconciles everybody.

SAMUEL PEPYS 1633-1703
DIARY

READERS' COMMENTS

■ Please use this sheet to recommend hotels or restaurants of **really outstanding quality.** Your complaints about any of the Guide's entries will be treated seriously and passed on to our inspectorate, but we would like to remind you always to take up your complaint with the management at the time.

■ Please post to **Egon Ronay's Guides,** City Wall House, Basing View, Basingstoke, Hampshire RG21 2AP

Please use an up to date Guide. We publish annually. (1989)

Your recommendation or complaint

Name and address of establishment

Your name (block letters)

Address (block letters)

N.B. We regret that owing to the enormous volume of readers' communications received each year, we will be unable to acknowledge these forms, but they will certainly be seriously considered.

READERS' COMMENTS

■ Please use this sheet to recommend hotels or restaurants of **really outstanding quality.** Your complaints about any of the Guide's entries will be treated seriously and passed on to our inspectorate, but we would like to remind you always to take up your complaint with the management at the time.

■ Please post to **Egon Ronay's Guides,** City Wall House, Basing View, Basingstoke, Hampshire RG21 2AP

Please use an up to date Guide. We publish annually. (1989)

Your recommendation or complaint

Name and address of establishment

Your name (block letters)

Address (block letters)

N.B. We regret that owing to the enormous volume of readers' communications received each year, we will be unable to acknowledge these forms, but they will certainly be seriously considered.

READERS' COMMENTS

- Please use this sheet to recommend hotels or restaurants of **really outstanding quality.** Your complaints about any of the Guide's entries will be treated seriously and passed on to our inspectorate, but we would like to remind you always to take up your complaint with the management at the time.

- Please post to **Egon Ronay's Guides,** City Wall House, Basing View, Basingstoke, Hampshire RG21 2AP

Please use an up to date Guide. We publish annually. (1989)

Your recommendation or complaint

Name and address of establishment

Your name (block letters)

Address (block letters)

N.B. We regret that owing to the enormous volume of readers' communications received each year, we will be unable to acknowledge these forms, but they will certainly be seriously considered.

READERS' COMMENTS

■ Please use this sheet to recommend hotels or restaurants of **really outstanding quality.** Your complaints about any of the Guide's entries will be treated seriously and passed on to our inspectorate, but we would like to remind you always to take up your complaint with the management at the time.

■ Please post to **Egon Ronay's Guides,** City Wall House, Basing View, Basingstoke, Hampshire RG21 2AP

Please use an up to date Guide. We publish annually. (1989)

Your recommendation or complaint

Name and address of establishment

Your name (block letters)

Address (block letters)

N.B. We regret that owing to the enormous volume of readers' communications received each year, we will be unable to acknowledge these forms, but they will certainly be seriously considered.